Index of Selected Applications

Mathematical Applications for the Management, Life, and Social Sciences

11th Edition

Ronald J. Harshbarger | James J. Reynolds

CENGAGE
Learning·

Australia • Brazil • Japan • Korea • Mexico • Singapore • Spain • United Kingdom • United States

Mathematical Applications for the Management, Life, and Social Sciences

Mathematical Applications for the Management, Life, and Social Sciences, 11th Edition
Ronald J. Harshbarger | James J. Reynolds

© 2016, 2013, 2009 Cengage Learning. All rights reserved.

For product information and technology assistance, contact us at
Cengage Learning Customer & Sales Support, 1-800-354-9706

For permission to use material from this text or product,
submit all requests online at **cengage.com/permissions**
Further permissions questions can be emailed to
permissionrequest@cengage.com

This book contains select works from existing Cengage Learning resources and was produced by Cengage Learning Custom Solutions for collegiate use. As such, those adopting and/or contributing to this work are responsible for editorial content accuracy, continuity and completeness.

Compilation © 2015 Cengage Learning

ISBN: 978-1-305-74713-5

WCN: 01-100-101

Cengage Learning
20 Channel Center Street
Boston, MA 02210
USA

Cengage Learning is a leading provider of customized learning solutions with office locations around the globe, including Singapore, the United Kingdom, Australia, Mexico, Brazil, and Japan. Locate your local office at:
www.international.cengage.com/region.

Cengage Learning products are represented in Canada by Nelson Education, Ltd.

For your lifelong learning solutions, visit **www.cengage.com/custom.**

Visit our corporate website at **www.cengage.com.**

Contents

Preface

To paraphrase English mathematician, philosopher, and educator Alfred North Whitehead, the purpose of education is not to fill a vessel but to kindle a fire. In particular, Whitehead encouraged students to be creative and imaginative in their learning and to continually form ideas into new and more exciting combinations. This desirable goal is not always an easy one to realize in mathematics with students whose primary interests are in areas other than mathematics. The purpose of this text, then, is to present mathematical skills and concepts and to apply them to ideas that are important to students in the management, life, and social sciences. We hope that this look at the relevance of mathematical ideas to a broad range of fields will help inspire the imaginative thinking and excitement for learning that Whitehead spoke of. The applications included allow students to view mathematics in a practical setting relevant to their intended careers. Almost every chapter of this book includes a section or two devoted to the applications of mathematical topics, and every section contains a number of application examples and problems. An index of these applications on the front and back inside covers demonstrates the wide variety used in examples and exercises. Although intended for students who have completed two years of high school algebra or its equivalent, this text begins with a brief review of algebra that, if covered, will aid in preparing students for the work ahead.

Pedagogical Features

In this new edition, we have incorporated many suggestions that reflect the needs and wishes of our users, including effective pedagogical features from previous editions.

Intuitive Viewpoint.   The book is written from an intuitive viewpoint, with emphasis on concepts and problem solving rather than on mathematical theory. Yet each topic is carefully developed and explained, and examples illustrate the techniques involved.

Flexibility.   At different colleges and universities, the coverage and sequencing of topics may vary according to the purpose of the course and the nature of the student audience. To accommodate alternate approaches, the text has a great deal of flexibility in the order in which topics may be presented and the degree to which they may be emphasized.

Applications.   We have found that integrating applied topics into the discussions and exercises helps provide motivation within the sections and demonstrates the relevance of each topic. Numerous real-life application examples and exercises represent the applicability of the mathematics, and each application problem is identified so the instructor or student can select applications that are of special interest. In addition, we have found that offering separate lessons on applied topics such as cost, revenue, and profit functions brings the preceding mathematical discussions into clear, concise focus and provides a thread of continuity as mathematical sophistication increases. There are 10 such sections throughout the book and two application-focused chapters: Chapter 4, devoted to linear programming, and Chapter 6, devoted to financial applications. Of the more than 5500 exercises in the book, more than 2000 are applied.

Chapter Warm-ups.   With the exception of Chapter 0, a Warm-up appears at the beginning of each chapter and invites students to test themselves on the skills needed for that chapter. The Warm-up sections present many prerequisite problem types that are keyed to the appropriate sections in the upcoming chapter where those skills are needed. Students who have difficulty with any particular skill are directed to specific sections of the text for review. Instructors may also find the Warm-ups useful in creating a course syllabus that includes an appropriate scope and sequence of topics.

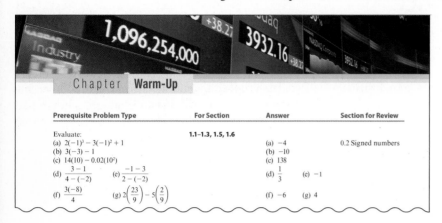

Prerequisite Problem Type	For Section	Answer	Section for Review
Evaluate:	1.1–1.3, 1.5, 1.6		
(a) $2(-1)^3 - 3(-1)^2 + 1$		(a) -4	0.2 Signed numbers
(b) $3(-3) - 1$		(b) -10	
(c) $14(10) - 0.02(10^2)$		(c) 138	
(d) $\dfrac{3-1}{4-(-2)}$ (e) $\dfrac{-1-3}{2-(-2)}$		(d) $\dfrac{1}{3}$ (e) -1	
(f) $\dfrac{3(-8)}{4}$ (g) $2\left(\dfrac{23}{9}\right) - 5\left(\dfrac{2}{9}\right)$		(f) -6 (g) 4	

Application Previews and Associated Examples.   Each section begins with an Application Preview that establishes the context and direction for the concepts that will be presented. Each of these Previews motivates the mathematics in the section and references a completely worked Application Preview Example appearing later in the section.

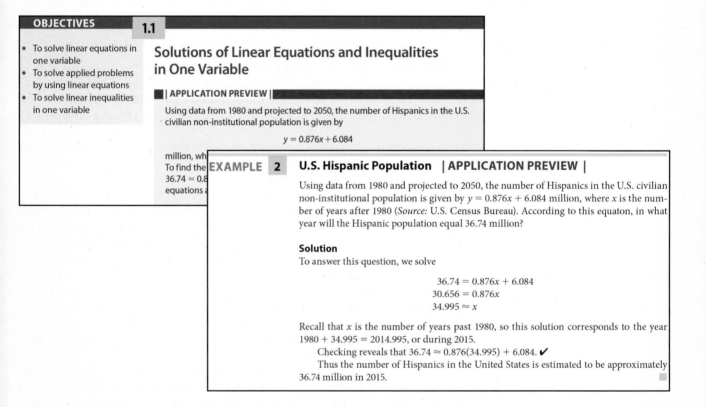

OBJECTIVES

- To solve linear equations in one variable
- To solve applied problems by using linear equations
- To solve linear inequalities in one variable

1.1

Solutions of Linear Equations and Inequalities in One Variable

| APPLICATION PREVIEW |

Using data from 1980 and projected to 2050, the number of Hispanics in the U.S. civilian non-institutional population is given by

$$y = 0.876x + 6.084$$

EXAMPLE   2   U.S. Hispanic Population | APPLICATION PREVIEW |

Using data from 1980 and projected to 2050, the number of Hispanics in the U.S. civilian non-institutional population is given by $y = 0.876x + 6.084$ million, where x is the number of years after 1980 (*Source:* U.S. Census Bureau). According to this equaton, in what year will the Hispanic population equal 36.74 million?

Solution

To answer this question, we solve

$$36.74 = 0.876x + 6.084$$
$$30.656 = 0.876x$$
$$34.995 \approx x$$

Recall that x is the number of years past 1980, so this solution corresponds to the year $1980 + 34.995 = 2014.995$, or during 2015.

Checking reveals that $36.74 \approx 0.876(34.995) + 6.084$. ✔

Thus the number of Hispanics in the United States is estimated to be approximately 36.74 million in 2015.

Comprehensive Exercise Sets.   The overall variety and grading of drill and application exercises offer problems for different skill levels, and there are enough challenging problems to stimulate students in thoughtful investigations. Many exercise sets contain critical-thinking and thought-provoking multistep problems that extend students' knowledge and skills.

Extended Applications and Group Projects.   Starting with Chapter 1, each chapter ends with at least two case studies, which further illustrate how mathematics can be used in business and personal decision making. In addition, many applications are cumulative in that solutions require students to combine the mathematical concepts and techniques they learned in some of the preceding chapters.

Extended Applications & Group Projects

I. Hospital Administration

Southwest Hospital has an operating room used only for eye surgery. The annual cost of rent, heat, and electricity for the operating room and its equipment is $360,000, and the annual salaries of the people who staff this room total $540,000.

Each surgery performed requires the use of $760 worth of medical supplies and drugs. To promote goodwill, every patient receives a bouquet of flowers the day after surgery. In addition, one-quarter of the patients require dark glasses, which the hospital provides

Graphical, Numerical, and Symbolic Methods.   A large number of real data modeling applications are included in the examples and exercises throughout the text and are denoted by the header *Modeling.* Many sections include problems with functions that are modeled from real data, and some problems ask students to model functions from the data given. These problems are solved by using one or more graphical, numerical, or symbolic methods.

 Graphing Calculators and Excel.   Instructors differ on how they use technology in their course. The icon on the left denotes the many examples, applications, Technology Notes, Calculator Notes, and Spreadsheet Notes throughout the text where technology use is featured or appropriate. Many of these notes reference detailed step-by-step instructions in Appendix A (Graphing Calculator Guide) and Appendix B (Excel Guide) and in the Online Guide for Excel. Discussions of the use of technology are placed in subsections and examples in many sections so they can be emphasized or de-emphasized at the option of the instructor.

The discussions of graphing calculator technology highlight its most common features and uses, such as graphing, window setting, Trace, Zoom, Solver, tables, finding points of intersection, numerical derivatives, numerical integration, matrices, solving inequalities, and modeling (curve fitting). While technology never replaces the mathematics, it does supplement and extend the mathematics by providing opportunities for generalization and alternative ways of understanding, doing, and checking. Some exercises that are better worked with the use of technology—including graphing calculators and Excel—are highlighted with the technology icon. Of course, many additional exercises can benefit from the use of technology, at the option of the instructor. Technology can be used to graph functions and to discuss the generalizations, applications, and implications of problems being studied.

Excel is useful in solving problems involving linear equations; systems of equations; quadratic equations; matrices; linear programming; output comparisons of $f(x), f'(x)$, and $f''(x)$; and maxima and minima of functions subject to constraints. Excel is also a useful problem-solving tool when studying the mathematics of finance in Chapter 6.

Checkpoints.   The Checkpoints ask questions and pose problems within each section's discussion, allowing students to check their understanding of the skills and concepts under discussion before they proceed. Answers to these Checkpoints appear before the section exercises. Complete solutions are available on the textbook's companion web site (www.cengagebrain.com).

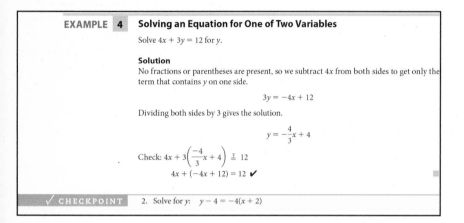

EXAMPLE 4   **Solving an Equation for One of Two Variables**

Solve $4x + 3y = 12$ for y.

Solution
No fractions or parentheses are present, so we subtract $4x$ from both sides to get only the term that contains y on one side.

$$3y = -4x + 12$$

Dividing both sides by 3 gives the solution.

$$y = -\frac{4}{3}x + 4$$

Check: $4x + 3\left(\dfrac{-4}{3}x + 4\right) \overset{?}{=} 12$

$4x + (-4x + 12) = 12$ ✔

✓ CHECKPOINT   2. Solve for y: $y - 4 = -4(x + 2)$

✓ CHECKPOINT   1. (a) $x = 0$ (b) $x = -63$ (c) $x = -12$
ANSWERS   2. $y = -4x - 4$ 3. $y \le 3$ 4. $y < \dfrac{1}{2}$ 5. $y \le -\dfrac{1}{7}$

Objective Lists.   Every section begins with a brief list of objectives that outline the goals of that section for the student.

OBJECTIVES
• To solve linear equations in one variable
• To solve applied problems by using linear equations
• To solve linear inequalities in one variable

1.1

Solutions of Linear Equations and Inequalities in One Variable

■ | APPLICATION PREVIEW | ■
Using data from 1980 and projected to 2050, the number of Hispanics in the U.S.

Procedure/Example and Property/Example Tables.   Appearing throughout the text, these tables aid student understanding by giving step-by-step descriptions of important procedures and properties with illustrative examples worked out beside them.

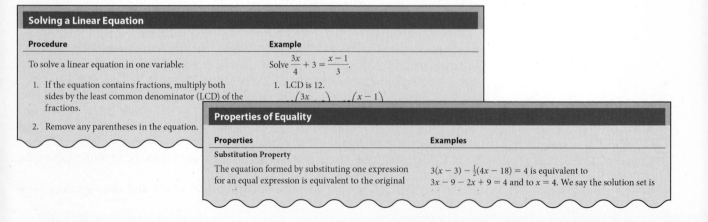

Solving a Linear Equation

Procedure	Example
To solve a linear equation in one variable:	Solve $\dfrac{3x}{4} + 3 = \dfrac{x-1}{3}$.
1. If the equation contains fractions, multiply both sides by the least common denominator (LCD) of the fractions.	1. LCD is 12.
2. Remove any parentheses in the equation.	

Properties of Equality

Properties	Examples
Substitution Property	
The equation formed by substituting one expression for an equal expression is equivalent to the original	$3(x - 3) - \frac{1}{2}(4x - 18) = 4$ is equivalent to $3x - 9 - 2x + 9 = 4$ and to $x = 4$. We say the solution set is

Boxed Information.   All important information is boxed for easy reference, and key terms are highlighted in boldface.

Key Terms and Formulas.   At the end of each chapter, just before the Chapter Review Exercises, there is a section-by-section listing of that chapter's key terms and formulas, including their page references. This provides a well-organized core from which a student can build a review, both to consult while working the Review Exercises and to identify quickly any section needing additional study.

Chapter 1 **Summary & Review**

KEY TERMS AND FORMULAS

Section 1.1

Equation; variable; solution (p. 53)
Identities; conditional equations (p. 53)
Properties of equality (p. 53)
Solving a linear equation (p. 54)
Aligning the data (p. 54)

Fractional equation (p. 55)
Linear equation in two variables (p. 56)
Linear inequalities (p. 57)
  Properties
  Solutions

Section 1.2

Relation (p. 63)
Function (p. 64)

Graph (p. 65)
Function notation (p. 66)

Review Exercises and Chapter Tests.   At the end of each chapter, a set of Review Exercises offers students extra practice on topics in that chapter. These reviews cover each chapter's topics in their section order, with section references, so that students get a thorough, structured review and can readily find a section for further review if difficulties occur. A Chapter Test follows each set of Review Exercises. All Chapter Tests provide a mixture of problems that do not directly mirror the order of topics found within the chapter. This organization of the Chapter Test ensures that students have a firm grasp of material in the chapter. All answers to both the Review Exercises and Chapter Tests appear in the Answers section.

Changes in the Eleventh Edition

In the eleventh Edition, we continue to offer a text characterized by complete and accurate pedagogy, mathematical precision, excellent exercise sets, numerous and varied applications, and student-friendly exposition. The most significant changes to this edition are as follows.

■ Most of the real-data application examples, exercises, and Group Projects that are data based have been updated or replaced. This includes new real-data projects in Chapters 5, 9, and 11.
■ The Checkpoints were redesigned and relocated to enhance their effectiveness. In addition, new Checkpoints were added as needed. Checkpoint answers appear before the section exercises. Complete solutions are available on the textbook's companion web site (www.cengagebrain.com).
■ While full graphing calculator and Excel details remain in the Appendices, more details, including specific steps and screen shots, were integrated in the text.
■ The Chapter Summary and Key Terms were redesigned, with page references included to improve their effectiveness.
■ Section references were added to the Chapter Reviews to help Instructors assign review problems and to help students focus their review. The Chapter Tests do not contain section references in order to provide a comprehensive review in anticipation of testing.
■ Specific steps for solving financial problems with graphing calculators and Excel have been added to Chapter 6 and retained in the Appendices. Because of the ease of solving financial problems with technology, the financial tables were removed from the Appendices.
■ Additional applications relating to environmental issues and demographics were added.

- A discussion of significant digits was added to the modeling introduction in Chapter 2, and significant digits were integrated in modeling discussions throughout the text.
- Example solutions were made more effective and student-friendly by adding steps where needed and removing excessive detail where possible.
- Example redundancies were removed.
- Several Application Previews were streamlined to more quickly and effectively engage students.
- Exposition was streamlined wherever appropriate.

Chapter-Specific Changes

Chapter 0:

- The discussion of Properties of Real Numbers was improved.
- Formula evaluation discussion and an example were added.
- The discussion of polynomial multiplication was unified.

Chapter 1:

- Exercises involving writing equations of lines from their graphs were added.

Chapter 2:

- The discussion of polynomial functions was expanded; examples and exercises including the y-intercept were added.
- More specific instructions were added to the modeling procedures.
- Significant digits were defined, and rules for their use were discussed.
- The modeling examples and exercises were reorganized to improve grading and variety. All real-data applications involving dates were replaced or updated.

Chapter 4:

- The exercises throughout the chapter were reorganized to improve grading and eliminate redundancy.
- The Application Previews in Sections 4.1 and 4.2 were streamlined.
- The discussion and the example introducing graphical methods for solving linear programming problems were simplified.
- The introduction to the simplex method for solving linear programming problems in Section 4.3 was rewritten to shorten and simplify it while retaining the applied context of constraints and slack variables.
- The applied exercises in Section 4.5 were categorized to help instructors assign problems.

Chapter 5:

- Discussion and an example of solving logarithmic equations were added.
- A new Group Project was added.

Chapter 6:

- The use of graphing calculators and Excel in the solution of financial applications was strengthened and now includes specific steps and screen shots in the text as well as in the Appendix. The financial tables were removed from the Appendix.
- The exercises in Sections 6.3, 6.4, and 6.5 and the Chapter 6 Review that require multiple financial ideas for their solution were isolated and labeled as *Combined Applications*.
- Redundant examples and exercises were removed to streamline the discussion.
- The balance between exercises involving ordinary annuities and annuities due in Sections 6.3 and 6.4 was improved in both the labeled and the miscellaneous exercises.

- The discussion of bond pricing was improved by clarifying the exposition and adding a figure.
- A discussion of loan refinancing and an accompanying example and exercises were added.

Chapter 7:

- A new Group Project that uses Bayes' formula was added.

Chapter 8:

- The introduction to the normal distribution was streamlined and clarified.
- Discussion and exercises involving finding intervals or threshold values in a normal distribution satisfying given probability conditions and using inverse normal calculations were added.

Chapter 9:

- The Warm-up was improved, and piecewise functions were added.
- Definitions and exposition were streamlined and clarified where appropriate.
- The number of examples and exercises involving derivative calculations with variables other than x and y was increased.
- An additional real-data Group Project was added.

Chapter 10:

- Details were added to the solution steps in applied max-min examples.
- An example to illustrate all possible cases for horizontal asymptotes of rational functions was added.

Chapter 11:

- The drill exercises in the Chapter Review were rebalanced to improve grading and variety.
- A new real-data modeling Group Project was added.

Chapter 12:

- The drill exercises were improved and expanded.

Chapter 14:

- The exposition in the Test for Maximum and Minimum box as well as in examples and exercises was improved.
- The notation in the development of linear regression formulas was clarified.

Resources for the Student

Student Solutions Manual (978-1-305-10806-6)
This manual provides complete worked-out solutions to all odd-numbered exercises in the text, giving you a chance to check your answers and ensure you took the correct steps to arrive at an answer.

Enhanced WebAssign
www.webassign.net
Printed Access Card: 9781285857589
Instant Access Code: 9781285857619
Enhanced WebAssign combines exceptional mathematics content with the most powerful online homework solution, WebAssign. Enhanced WebAssign engages you with

immediate feedback, rich tutorial content, and an interactive, fully customizable eBook, Cengage YouBook, helping you to develop a deeper conceptual understanding of the subject matter. *Enhanced WebAssign for Mathematical Applications now includes Quick Prep content to review key precalculus content, available as a CoursePack of prebuilt assignments to assign at the beginning of the course or where needed most.*

CengageBrain.com

To access additional course materials and companion resources, please visit www.cengage brain.com. At the CengageBrain.com home page, search for the ISBN of your title (from the back cover of your book) using the search box at the top of the page. This will take you to the product page where free companion resources can be found.

Resources for the Instructor

Instructor Companion Site

Everything you need for your course in one place! This collection of book-specific lecture and class tools is available online via www.cengage.com/login. Access and download PowerPoint presentations, images, the instructor's manual, and more.

Complete Solutions Manual

The Complete Solutions Manual provides worked-out solutions of all exercises in the text. In addition, it contains the solutions of the special features in the text, such as *Extended Applications and Group Projects.* This manual can be found on the Instructor Companion Site.

Cengage Learning Testing Powered by Cognero® (978-1-305-11234-6)

This flexible, online system allows you to author, edit, and manage test bank content, create multiple test versions in an instant, and deliver tests from your LMS, your classroom, or wherever you want. This is available online via www.cengage.com/login.

Enhanced WebAssign®
www.webassign.net
Printed Access Card: 9781285857589
Instant Access Code: 9781285857619

Enhanced WebAssign combines exceptional mathematics content with the most powerful online homework solution, WebAssign. Enhanced WebAssign engages students with immediate feedback, rich tutorial content, and an interactive, fully customizable eBook, Cengage YouBook, helping students to develop a deeper conceptual understanding of their subject matter. Enhanced WebAssign for Mathematical Applications now includes Quick Prep content to review key precalculus content, available as a CoursePack of prebuilt assignments to assign at the beginning of the course or where needed most.

Cengage YouBook

YouBook is an interactive and customizable eBook! Containing all the content from Harshbarger/Reynolds' *Mathematical Applications for the Management, Life, and Social Sciences,* YouBook features a text edit tool that allows instructors to modify the textbook narrative as needed. With YouBook, you can quickly reorder entire sections and chapters or hide any content you don't teach to create an eBook that perfectly matches your syllabus. You can further customize the text by publishing web links. Additional media assets include: video clips, highlighting, notes, and more! YouBook is available in Enhanced WebAssign.

Acknowledgments

We would like to thank the many people who helped us at various stages of revising this text. The encouragement, criticism, contributions, and suggestions that were offered were invaluable to us. We are deeply grateful to Edwin Herman for his skillful and thorough accuracy checking of the entire text and answer section.

For their reviews of draft manuscript and the many helpful comments that were offered, we would like to thank

Rebecca Baranowski	*Estrella Mountain Community College*
Kay Geving	*Belmont University*
Brian Gillspie	*Kirkwood Community College*
Caleb Grisham	*National Park Community College*
Thomas Hagedorn	*The College of New Jersey*
Sheyleah Harris-Plant	*South Plains College*
Mark Hopkins	*Oakland Community College*
Allen Moody	*National Park Community College*
Mark Riggs	*Abilene Christian University*
Frank Rodriguez	*Lone Star College-University Park*
Stephanie Swindle	*Community College of Allegheny County*
Zia Khwaja	*California State University, Los Angeles & Rio Hondo College*

Ronald J. Harshbarger
James J. Reynolds

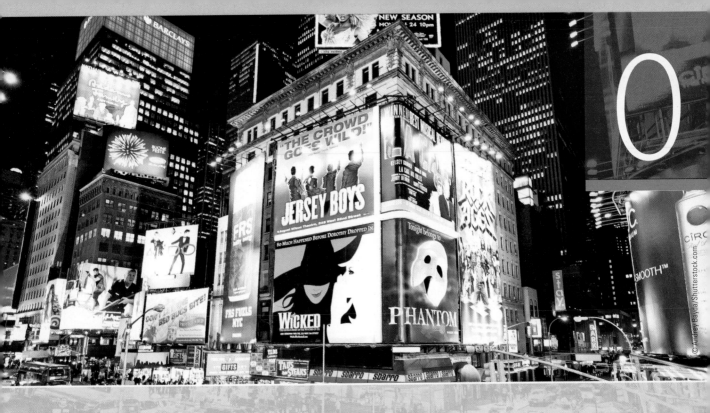
© Andrey Bayda/Shutterstock.com

Algebraic Concepts

This chapter provides a brief review of the algebraic concepts that will be used throughout the text. You may be familiar with these topics, but it may be helpful to spend some time reviewing them. In addition, each chapter after this one opens with a warm-up page that identifies prerequisite skills needed for that chapter. If algebraic skills are required, the warm-up cites their coverage in this chapter. Thus you will find that this chapter is a useful reference as you study later chapters.

The topics and some representative applications studied in this chapter include the following.

0.1

Sets

A **set** is a well-defined collection of objects. We may talk about a set of books, a set of dishes, a set of students, or a set of individuals with a certain blood type. There are two ways to tell what a given set contains. One way is by listing the **elements** (or **members**) of the set, in any order and usually between braces. We may say that a set A contains 1, 2, 3, and 4 by writing $A = \{1, 2, 3, 4\}$. To say that 4 is an element of set A, we write $4 \in A$. Similarly, we write $5 \notin A$ to denote that 5 is not an element of set A.

If all the elements of the set can be listed, the set is said to be a **finite set.** $A = \{1, 2, 3, 4\}$ and $B = \{x, y, z\}$ are examples of finite sets. When we do not wish to list all the elements of a finite set, we can use three dots to indicate the unlisted elements of the set. For example, the set of even integers from 8 to 8952, inclusive, could be written as

$$\{8, 10, 12, 14, \ldots, 8952\}$$

Since we cannot list all the elements of an **infinite set**, we use the three dots to indicate that the list continues. For example, $N = \{1, 2, 3, 4, \ldots\}$ is an infinite set. This set N is called the set of **natural numbers.**

Another way to specify the elements of a given set is by description. For example, we may write $D = \{x: x \text{ is a Ford automobile}\}$ to describe the set of all Ford automobiles. Furthermore, $F = \{y: y \text{ is an odd natural number}\}$ is read "F is the set of all y such that y is an odd natural number."

EXAMPLE 1   **Describing Sets**

Write the following sets in two ways.
(a) The set A of natural numbers less than 6
(b) The set B of natural numbers greater than 10
(c) The set C containing only 3

Solution
(a) $A = \{1, 2, 3, 4, 5\}$ or $A = \{x: x \text{ is a natural number less than 6}\}$
(b) $B = \{11, 12, 13, 14, \ldots\}$ or $B = \{x: x \text{ is a natural number greater than 10}\}$
(c) $C = \{3\}$ or $C = \{x: x = 3\}$

A set that contains no elements is called the **empty set** or the **null set,** and it is denoted by $\varnothing$ or by $\{ \ \}$. The set of living veterans of the War of 1812 is empty because there are no living veterans of that war. Thus

$$\{x: x \text{ is a living veteran of the War of 1812}\} = \varnothing$$

Special relations that may exist between two sets are defined as follows.

Relations between Sets

Definition	Example
1. Sets X and Y are **equal** if they contain the same elements.	1. If $X = \{1, 2, 3, 4\}$ and $Y = \{4, 3, 2, 1\}$, then $X = Y$.
2. A is called a **subset** of B, which is written $A \subseteq B$ if every element of A is an element of B. The empty set is a subset of every set. Each set A is a subset of itself.	2. If $A = \{1, 2, c, f\}$ and $B = \{1, 2, 3, a, b, c, f\}$, then $A \subseteq B$. Also, $\varnothing \subseteq A, \varnothing \subseteq B, A \subseteq A$, and $B \subseteq B$.
3. If C and D have no elements in common, they are called **disjoint.**	3. If $C = \{1, 2, a, b\}$ and $D = \{3, e, 5, c\}$, then C and D are disjoint.

In the discussion of particular sets, the assumption is always made that the sets under discussion are all subsets of some larger set, called the **universal set** U. The choice of the universal set depends on the problem under consideration. For example, in discussing the set of all students and the set of all female students, we may use the set of all humans as the universal set.

We may use **Venn diagrams** to illustrate the various relationships among sets. A rectangle represents the universal set, and closed figures inside the rectangle represent the sets under consideration. Figures 0.1–0.3 show such Venn diagrams.

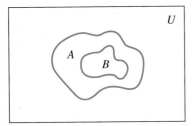

Figure 0.1
B is a subset of A; $B \subseteq A$.

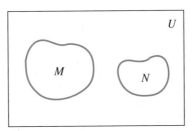

Figure 0.2
M and N are disjoint.

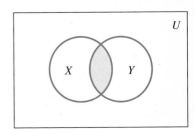

Figure 0.3
X and Y are not disjoint.

✓ CHECKPOINT

Let $A = \{2, 3, 5, 7, 11\}$, $B = \{2, 4, 6, 8, 10\}$, and $C = \{6, 10, 14, 18, 22\}$. Use these sets to answer the following.

1. (a) Of which sets is 6 an element?
   (b) Of which sets is $\{2\}$ a subset?
2. Which of the following are true?
   (a) $2 \in A$
   (b) $\{2\} \in B$
   (c) $2 \in C$
   (d) $5 \notin A$
   (e) $5 \notin B$
3. Which pair of A, B, and C is disjoint?
4. Which of $\varnothing$, A, B, and C are subsets of
   (a) the set P of all prime numbers?
   (b) the set M of all multiples of 2?
5. Which of A, B, and C is equal to $D = \{x\colon x = 4n + 2$ for natural numbers $1 \le n \le 5\}$?

Set Operations   The set containing the members that are common to two sets is said to be the **intersection** of the two sets.

Set Intersection

The intersection of A and B, written $A \cap B$, is defined by

$$A \cap B = \{x\colon x \in A \text{ and } x \in B\}$$

EXAMPLE 2   **Set Intersection**

(a) If $A = \{2, 3, 4, 5\}$ and $B = \{3, 5, 7, 9, 11\}$, find $A \cap B$.
(b) Which of A, B, and $A \cap B$ is a subset of A?

Solution

(a) $A \cap B = \{3, 5\}$ because 3 and 5 are the common elements of A and B. Figure 0.4 shows the sets and their intersection.
(b) $A \cap B$ and A are subsets of A.

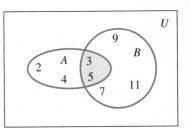

Figure 0.4

The **union** of two sets is the set that contains all members of the two sets.

Set Union	The union of A and B, written $A \cup B$, is defined by
	$$A \cup B = \{x: x \in A \text{ or } x \in B \text{ (or both)}\}^*$$

EXAMPLE 3   **Set Union**

If $X = \{a, b, c, f\}$ and $Y = \{e, f, a, b\}$, find $X \cup Y$.

Solution
$X \cup Y = \{a, b, c, e, f\}$

We can illustrate the intersection and union of two sets by the use of Venn diagrams. The shaded region in Figure 0.5 represents $A \cap B$, the intersection of A and B, and the shaded region in Figure 0.6—which consists of all parts of both circles—represents $A \cup B$.

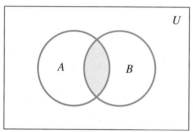

Figure 0.5
Intersection of A and B.

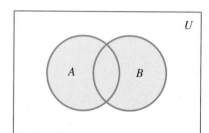

Figure 0.6
Union of A and B.

EXAMPLE 4   **Set Intersection and Union**

Let $A = \{x: x \text{ is a natural number less than 6}\}$ and $B = \{1, 3, 5, 7, 9, 11\}$.
(a) Find $A \cap B$.
(b) Find $A \cup B$.

Solution
Note that $A = \{1, 2, 3, 4, 5\}$.
(a) $A \cap B = \{1, 3, 5\}$
(b) $A \cup B = \{1, 2, 3, 4, 5, 7, 9, 11\}$

All elements of the universal set that are not contained in a set A form a set called the **complement** of A.

Set Complement	The complement of A, written A', is defined by
	$$A' = \{x: x \in U \text{ and } x \notin A\}$$

We can use a Venn diagram to illustrate the complement of a set. The shaded region of Figure 0.7 represents A', and the *unshaded* region of Figure 0.5 represents $(A \cap B)'$.

---

* In mathematics, the word *or* means "one or the other or both."

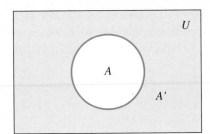

Figure 0.7

EXAMPLE 5   Operations with Sets

If U is the set of natural numbers less than 10, $A = \{1, 3, 6\}$, and $B = \{1, 6, 8, 9\}$, find the following.

(a) A'
(b) B'
(c) $(A \cap B)'$
(d) $A' \cup B'$

Solution

(a) $U = \{1, 2, 3, 4, 5, 6, 7, 8, 9\}$ so $A' = \{2, 4, 5, 7, 8, 9\}$
(b) $B' = \{2, 3, 4, 5, 7\}$
(c) $A \cap B = \{1, 6\}$ so $(A \cap B)' = \{2, 3, 4, 5, 7, 8, 9\}$
(d) $A' \cup B' = \{2, 4, 5, 7, 8, 9\} \cup \{2, 3, 4, 5, 7\} = \{2, 3, 4, 5, 7, 8, 9\}$

✓ CHECKPOINT

Given the sets $U = \{1, 2, 3, 4, 5, 6, 7, 8, 9, 10\}$, $A = \{1, 3, 5, 7, 9\}$, $B = \{2, 3, 5, 7\}$, and $C = \{4, 5, 6, 7, 8, 9, 10\}$, find the following.

6. $A \cup B$
7. $B \cap C$
8. A'

EXAMPLE 6   Stocks

Suppose an investment advisor monitored several stocks for clients and on a certain day categorized 23 stocks according to whether

- their closing price on the previous day was less than $50/share (set C)
- their price-to-earnings ratio was less than 20 (set P)
- their dividend per share was at least $1.50 (set D).

Of these 23 stocks,

16 belonged to set P	10 belonged to both C and P
12 belonged to set C	7 belonged to both D and P
8 belonged to set D	2 belonged to all three sets.
3 belonged to both C and D	

(a) How many stocks had closing prices of less than $50 per share or price-to-earnings ratios of less than 20?
(b) How many stocks had none of the characteristics of set C, P, or D?
(c) How many stocks had only dividends per share of at least $1.50?

Solution

We use a Venn diagram to organize the information. Note that the Venn diagram for three sets has eight separate regions (see Figure 0.8(a) on the next page). To assign numbers from our data, we must begin with some information that refers to a single region, namely that two stocks belonged to all three sets (see Figure 0.8(b)). Because the region common to all three sets is also common to any pair, we can next use the information about stocks that belonged to two of the sets (see Figure 0.8(c)). Finally, we can complete the Venn diagram (see Figure 0.8(d)).

(a) We need to add the numbers in the separate regions that lie within $C \cup P$. That is, 18 stocks closed under $50 per share or had price-to-earnings ratios of less than 20.

(b) There are 5 stocks outside the three sets C, D, and P.

(c) Those stocks that had only dividends of at least $1.50 per share are inside D but outside both C and P. There are no such stocks. ▪

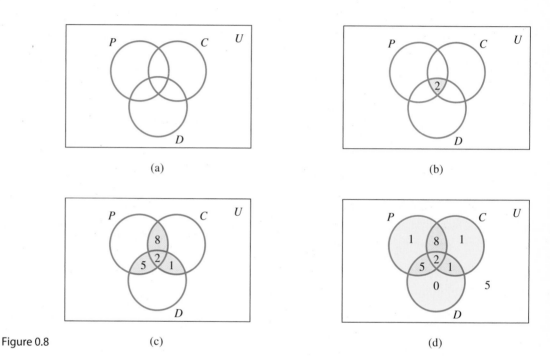

(a)   (b)

Figure 0.8   (c)   (d)

✓ **CHECKPOINT**
ANSWERS

1. (a) B and C
    (b) A and B
2. (a) True
    (b) False
    (c) False
    (d) False
    (e) True
3. A and C
4. (a) $\varnothing$ and A
    (b) $\varnothing$, B, and C
5. $C = D$
6. $\{1, 2, 3, 5, 7, 9\}$
7. $\{5, 7\}$
8. $\{2, 4, 6, 8, 10\}$

| EXERCISES | 0.1

In Problems 1–4, use ∈ or ∉ to indicate whether the given object is an element of the given set in the following problems.
1. 12 $\{1, 2, 3, 4, \ldots\}$
2. 5 $\{x: x$ is a natural number greater than 5$\}$
3. 6 $\{x: x$ is a natural number less than 6$\}$
4. 3 $\varnothing$

In Problems 5–8, write the following sets a second way.
5. $\{x: x$ is a natural number less than 8$\}$
6. $\{x: x$ is a natural number greater than 6, less than 10$\}$
7. $\{3, 4, 5, 6, 7\}$
8. $\{7, 8, 9, 10, \ldots\}$

In Problems 9 and 10, which of $\varnothing$, A, and B are subsets of B?
9. $A = \{1, 2, 3, 4\}$ and $B = \{1, 2, 3, 4, 5, 6\}$
10. $A = \{a, b, c, d\}$ and $B = \{c, d, a, b\}$?
11. Is $A \subseteq B$ if $A = \{a, b, c, d\}$ and $B = \{a, b, d\}$?
12. Is $A \subseteq B$ if $A = \{6, 8, 10, 12\}$ and $B = \{6, 8, 10, 14, 18\}$?

In Problems 13–16, use $\subseteq$ notation to indicate which set is a subset of the other.
13. $C = \{a, b, 1, 2, 3\}$ and $D = \{a, b, 1\}$
14. $E = \{x, y, a, b\}$, $F = \{x, 1, a, y, b, 2\}$
15. $A = \{6, 8, 7, 4\}$, $B = \{8, 7, 6, 4\}$
16. $D = \{a, e, 1, 3, c\}$, $F = \{e, a, c, 1, 3\}$

In Problems 17–20, indicate whether the two sets are equal.
17. $A = \{a, b, \pi, \sqrt{3}\}$, $B = \{a, \pi, \sqrt{3}, b\}$
18. $A = \{x, g, a, b\}$, $D = \{x, a, b, y\}$
19. $D = \{x: x$ is a natural number less than 4$\}$, $E = \{1, 2, 3, 4\}$
20. $F = \{x: x$ is a natural number greater than 6$\}$, $G = \{7, 8, 9, \ldots\}$
21. From the following list of sets, indicate which pairs of sets are disjoint.

$$A = \{1, 2, 3, 4\}$$
$$B = \{x: x \text{ is a natural number greater than 4}\}$$
$$C = \{4, 5, 6, \ldots\}$$
$$D = \{1, 2, 3\}$$

22. If A and B are disjoint sets, what does $A \cap B$ equal?

In Problems 23–26, find $A \cap B$.
23. $A = \{2, 3, 4, 5, 6\}$ and $B = \{4, 6, 8, 10, 12\}$
24. $A = \{a, b, c, d, e\}$ and $B = \{a, d, e, f, g, h\}$
25. $A = \varnothing$ and $B = \{x, y, a, b\}$
26. $A = \{x: x$ is a natural number less than 4$\}$ and $B = \{3, 4, 5, 6\}$

In Problems 27–30, find $A \cup B$.
27. $A = \{1, 2, 4, 5\}$ and $B = \{2, 3, 4, 5\}$
28. $A = \{a, e, i, o, u\}$ and $B = \{a, b, c, d\}$
29. $A = \varnothing$ and $B = \{1, 2, 3, 4\}$
30. $A = \{x: x$ is a natural number greater than 5$\}$ and $B = \{x: x$ is a natural number less than 5$\}$

In Problems 31–42, let

$$A = \{1, 3, 5, 8, 7, 2\}$$
$$B = \{4, 3, 8, 10\}$$
$$C = \{2, 4, 6, 8, 10\}$$

and U be the universal set of natural numbers less than 11. Find the following.
31. A'
32. B'
33. $A \cap B'$
34. $A' \cap B'$
35. $(A \cup B)'$
36. $(A \cap B)'$
37. $A' \cup B'$
38. $(A' \cup B)'$
39. $(A \cap B') \cup C'$
40. $A \cap (B' \cup C')$
41. $(A \cap B')' \cap C$
42. $A \cap (B \cup C)$

The difference of two sets, $A - B$, is defined as the set containing all elements of A except those in B. That is, $A - B = A \cap B'$. Find $A - B$ for each pair of sets in Problems 43–46 if $U = \{1, 2, 3, 4, 5, 6, 7, 8, 9\}$.
43. $A = \{1, 3, 7, 9\}$ and $B = \{3, 5, 8, 9\}$
44. $A = \{1, 2, 3, 6, 9\}$ and $B = \{1, 4, 5, 6, 7\}$
45. $A = \{2, 1, 5\}$ and $B = \{1, 2, 3, 4, 5, 6\}$
46. $A = \{1, 2, 3, 4, 5\}$ and $B = \{7, 8, 9\}$

APPLICATIONS

47. *Dow Jones Industrial Average* The following table shows information about yearly lows, highs, and percentage changes for the years 2000 to 2012. Let L be the set of years where the low was greater than 8000. Let H be the set of years where the high was greater than 11,000. Let C be the years when the percentage change (from low to high) exceeded 35%.
    (a) List the elements of L, H, and C.
    (b) Is any of L, H, or C a subset of one of the others (besides itself)?
    (c) Write a verbal description of C'.
    (d) Find $H' \cup C'$ and describe it in words.
    (e) Find $L' \cap C$ and describe it in words.

Dow Jones Industrial Average

Year	Low	High	% Change
2012	12,101.46	13,610.15	12.5
2011	10,655.30	12,810.54	20.2
2010	9686.48	11,585.33	19.6
2009	6547.05	10,092.19	54.1
2008	7552.29	13,056.72	72.9
2007	12,050.41	14,164.53	17.5
2006	10,667.39	12,510.57	17.3
2005	10,012.36	10,940.50	9.3
2004	9749.99	10,854.54	11.3
2003	7524.06	10,453.92	38.9
2002	7286.27	10,635.65	46.0
2001	8235.94	11,332.92	37.6
2000	9796.03	11,722.98	19.7

Source: Dow Jones & Company

48. *Job growth* The number of jobs in 2000, the number projected in 2025, and the projected annual growth rate for jobs in some cities are shown in the following table. Consider the following sets.

$A =$ set of cities with at least 2,000,000 jobs in 2000 or projected in 2025

$B =$ set of cities with at least 1,500,000 jobs in 2000

$C =$ set of cities with projected annual growth rate of at least 2.5%

   (a) List A, B, and C (using the letters to represent the cities).
   (b) Is any of A, B, or C a subset of the other?
   (c) Find $A \cap C$ and describe the set in words.
   (d) Give a verbal description of B'.

Cities	Jobs in 2000 (thousands)	Projected Jobs in 2025 (thousands)	Annual Rates of Increase (%)
O (Orlando)	1098	2207	2.83
M (Myrtle Beach)	133	256	2.64
L (Atlanta)	2715	4893	2.38
P (Phoenix)	1953	3675	2.56
B (Boulder)	233	420	2.38

Source: Based on data from NPA Data Services, Inc.

Carbon emission controls **Suppose that the following table summarizes the opinions of various groups on the issue of carbon emission controls. Use this table for Problems 49 and 50.**

	Whites		Nonwhites		
Opinion	Rep.	Dem.	Rep.	Dem.	Total
Favor	100	250	30	200	580
Oppose	250	150	10	10	420
Total	350	400	40	210	1000

49. Identify the number of individuals in each of the following sets.
   (a) Republicans and those who favor carbon emission controls
   (b) Republicans or those who favor carbon emission controls
   (c) White Republicans or those who oppose carbon emission controls

50. Identify the number of individuals in each of the following sets.
   (a) Whites and those who oppose carbon emission controls
   (b) Whites or those who oppose carbon emission controls
   (c) Nonwhite Democrats and those who favor carbon emission controls

51. *Languages* A survey of 100 aides at the United Nations revealed that 65 could speak English, 60 could speak French, and 40 could speak both English and French.
   (a) Draw a Venn diagram representing the 100 aides. Use E to represent English-speaking aides and F to represent French-speaking aides.
   (b) How many aides are in $E \cap F$?
   (c) How many aides are in $E \cup F$?
   (d) How many aides are in $E \cap F'$?

52. *Advertising* Suppose that a survey of 100 advertisers in *U.S. News, These Times,* and *World* found the following.

   14 advertised in all three
   30 advertised in *These Times* and *U.S. News*
   26 advertised in *World* and *U.S. News*
   27 advertised in *World* and *These Times*
   60 advertised in *These Times*
   52 advertised in *U.S. News*
   50 advertised in *World*

   (a) Draw a Venn diagram representing the 100 advertisers.
   (b) How many advertised in none of these publications?
   (c) How many advertised only in *These Times*?
   (d) How many advertised in *U.S. News* or *These Times*?

53. *College enrollments* Records at a small college show the following about the enrollments of 100 first-year students in mathematics, fine arts, and economics.

   38 take math
   42 take fine arts
   20 take economics
   4 take economics and fine arts
   15 take math and economics
   9 take math and fine arts
   12 take math and economics but not fine arts

(a) How many take none of these three courses?
(b) How many take math or economics?
(c) How many take exactly one of these three courses?

54. *Survey analysis* In a survey of the dining preferences of 110 dormitory students at the end of the spring semester, the following facts were discovered about Adam's Lunch (AL), Pizza Tower (PT), and the Dining Hall (DH).

> 30 liked AL but not PT
> 21 liked AL only
> 63 liked AL
> 58 liked PT
> 27 liked DH
> 25 liked PT and AL but not DH
> 18 liked PT and DH

(a) How many liked PT or DH?
(b) How many liked all three?
(c) How many liked only DH?

55. *Blood types* Blood types are determined by the presence or absence of three antigens: A antigen, B antigen, and an antigen called the Rh factor. The resulting blood types are classified as follows:

> *type A* if the A antigen is present
> *type B* if the B antigen is present
> *type AB* if both the A and B antigens are present
> *type O* if neither the A nor the B antigen is present

These types are further classified as *Rh-positive* if the Rh-factor antigen is present and *Rh-negative* otherwise.

(a) Draw a Venn diagram that illustrates this classification scheme.
(b) Identify the blood type determined by each region of the Venn diagram (such as A^+ to indicate type A, Rh-positive).
(c) Use a library or another source to find what percentage of the U.S. population has each blood type.

0.2

The Real Numbers

In this text we use the set of **real numbers** as the universal set. We can represent the real numbers along a line called the **real number line.** This number line is a picture, or graph, of the real numbers. Each point on the real number line corresponds to exactly one real number, and each real number can be located at exactly one point on the real number line. Thus, two real numbers are said to be equal whenever they are represented by the same point on the real number line. The equation $a = b$ (a equals b) means that the symbols a and b represent the same real number. Thus, $3 + 4 = 7$ means that $3 + 4$ and 7 represent the same number. Table 0.1 lists special subsets of the real numbers.

▮| TABLE 0.1 |▮

SUBSETS OF THE SET OF REAL NUMBERS

	Description	Example (some elements shown)
Natural numbers	$\{1, 2, 3, \ldots\}$ The counting numbers.	
Integers	$\{\ldots, -2, -1, 0, 1, 2, \ldots\}$ The natural numbers, 0, and the negatives of the natural numbers.	
Rational numbers	All numbers that can be written as the ratio of two integers, a/b, with $b \neq 0$. These numbers have decimal representations that either terminate or repeat.	
Irrational numbers	Those real numbers that *cannot* be written as the ratio of two integers. Irrational numbers have decimal representations that neither terminate nor repeat.	
Real numbers	The set containing all rational and irrational numbers (the entire number line).	

The following properties of the real numbers are fundamental to the study of algebra.

Properties of the Real Numbers

Let a, b, and c denote real numbers.

1. The **Commutative Properties** for addition and multiplication.
$$a + b = b + a \qquad ab = ba$$

2. The **Associative Properties** for addition and multiplication.
$$(a + b) + c = a + (b + c) \qquad (ab)c = a(bc)$$

3. The **Additive Identity** is 0.
$$a + 0 = 0 + a = a$$

4. The **Multiplicative Identity** is 1.
$$a \cdot 1 = 1 \cdot a = a$$

5. Each real number a has an **Additive Inverse**, denoted by $-a$.
$$a + (-a) = -a + a = 0$$

6. The **Multiplicative Inverse** of the nonzero real number a is $1/a$, called the **reciprocal of a** and denoted by a^{-1}. (Note that $a^{-1} = 1/a$.)
$$a \cdot a^{-1} = a^{-1} \cdot a = 1$$

7. The **Distributive Law** for multiplication over addition.
$$a(b + c) = ab + ac \qquad (a + b)c = ac + bc$$

Note that there is a difference between a negative number and the negative of a number. For example, -5 is a negative number, but its negative is $-(-5) = 5$. Note also that Property 5 provides the means to subtract by defining $a - b = a + (-b)$ and Property 6 provides a means to divide by defining $a \div b = a \cdot (1/b)$. The number 0 has no multiplicative inverse, so division by 0 is undefined.

Inequalities and Intervals   We say that a is less than b (written $a < b$) if the point representing a is to the left of the point representing b on the real number line. For example, $4 < 7$ because 4 is to the left of 7 on the real number line. We may also say that 7 is greater than 4 (written $7 > 4$). We indicate that the number x is less than or equal to another number y by writing $x \le y$. We also indicate that p is greater than or equal to 4 by writing $p \ge 4$.

EXAMPLE 1   Inequalities

Use $<$ or $>$ notation to write the following.
(a)   6 is greater than 5.   (b)   10 is less than 15.
(c)   3 is to the left of 8 on the real number line.   (d) x is at most 12.

Solution
(a) $6 > 5$ (b) $10 < 15$ (c) $3 < 8$
(d)   "x is at most 12" means it must be less than or equal to 12. Thus, $x \le 12$.

The subset of the real numbers consisting of all real numbers x that lie between a and b, excluding a and b, can be denoted by the *double inequality* $a < x < b$ or by the **open interval** (a, b). It is called an open interval because neither of the endpoints is included in the interval. The **closed interval** $[a, b]$ represents the set of all real numbers x satisfying $a \le x \le b$. Intervals containing one endpoint, such as $(a, b]$ and $[a, b)$, are called **half-open intervals.**

We can use $[a, \infty)$ to represent the inequality $x \geq a$ and $(-\infty, a)$ to represent $x < a$. In each of these cases, the symbols ∞ and $-\infty$ are not real numbers but represent the fact that x increases without bound (∞) or decreases without bound ($-\infty$). Table 0.2 summarizes the three types of intervals.

■| TABLE 0.2 |

INTERVALS

Type of Interval	Inequality Notation	Interval Notation	Graph
Open interval	$x > a$	(a, ∞)	
	$x < b$	$(-\infty, b)$	
	$a < x < b$	(a, b)	
Half-open interval	$x \geq a$	$[a, \infty)$	
	$x \leq b$	$(-\infty, b]$	
	$a \leq x < b$	$[a, b)$	
	$a < x \leq b$	$(a, b]$	
Closed interval	$a \leq x \leq b$	$[a, b]$	

Note that the interval $(-\infty, \infty)$, representing $-\infty < x < \infty$, is an open interval containing all real numbers; that is, the entire real number line.

✓ CHECKPOINT

1. Decide which of the following are undefined.
   (a) $\dfrac{4}{0}$
   (b) $\dfrac{0}{4}$
   (c) $\dfrac{4}{4}$
   (d) $\dfrac{4-4}{4-4}$

2. For parts (a)–(d), write the inequality corresponding to the given interval and sketch its graph on a real number line.
   (a) $(1, 3)$
   (b) $(0, 3]$
   (c) $[-1, \infty)$
   (d) $(-\infty, 2)$

3. Express the following inequalities in interval notation and name the type of interval.
   (a) $3 \leq x \leq 6$
   (b) $-6 \leq x < 4$

Absolute Value   Sometimes we are interested in the *distance* a number is from the origin (0) of the real number line, without regard to direction. The distance a number a is from 0 on the number line is the **absolute value** of a, denoted $|a|$. The absolute value of any nonzero number is positive, and the absolute value of 0 is 0.

EXAMPLE 2   **Absolute Value**

Evaluate the following.
(a) $|-4|$
(b) $|+2|$
(c) $|0|$
(d) $|-5 - |-3||$

Solution
(a) $|-4| = +4 = 4$
(b) $|+2| = +2 = 2$
(c) $|0| = 0$
(d) $|-5 - |-3|| = |-5 - 3| = |-8| = 8$

Note that if a is a nonnegative number, then |a| = a, but if a is negative, then |a| is the positive number (−a). Thus

Absolute Value	$$|a| = \begin{cases} a & \text{if } a \geq 0 \\ -a & \text{if } a < 0 \end{cases}$$

In performing computations with real numbers, it is important to remember the following rules for computations.

Operations with Real (Signed) Numbers

Procedure

1. (a) To add two real numbers with the same sign, add their absolute values and affix their common sign.
   (b) To add two real numbers with unlike signs, find the difference of their absolute values and affix the sign of the number with the larger absolute value.

2. To subtract one real number from another, change the sign of the number being subtracted and proceed as in addition.

3. (a) The product of two real numbers with like signs is positive.

   (b) The product of two real numbers with unlike signs is negative.

4. (a) The quotient of two real numbers with like signs is positive.
   (b) The quotient of two real numbers with unlike signs is negative.

Example

1. (a) $(5) + (6) = 11$
   $$\left(-\frac{1}{6}\right) + \left(-\frac{2}{6}\right) = -\frac{3}{6} = -\frac{1}{2}$$
   (b) $(5) + (-3) = 2$
   $$\left(-\frac{11}{7}\right) + (1) = -\frac{4}{7}$$

2. $(-9) - (-8) = (-9) + (8) = -1$
   $16 - (8) = 16 + (-8) = 8$

3. (a) $(-3)(-4) = 12$
   $$\left(\frac{3}{4}\right)(4) = 3$$

   (b) $5(-3) = -15$
   $(-3)(4) = -12$

4. (a) $(-14) \div (-2) = 7$
   $36/4 = 9$
   (b) $(-28)/4 = -7$
   $45 \div (-5) = -9$

When two or more operations with real numbers are indicated in an evaluation, it is important that everyone agree on the order in which the operations are performed so that a unique result is guaranteed. The following **order of operations** is universally accepted.

Order of Operations

1. Perform operations within parentheses, or other symbols of grouping.
2. Find indicated powers ($2^3 = 2 \cdot 2 \cdot 2 = 8$).
3. Perform multiplications and divisions from left to right.
4. Perform additions and subtractions from left to right.

EXAMPLE 3   Order of Operations

Evaluate the following.
(a) $-4 + 3$
(b) $4 + 3(-2)$
(c) $-4^2 + 3$
(d) $[2(3 - 4)]^2 + 3$
(e) $6 \div 2(2 + 1)$

Solution

(a) -1

(b) $4 + (-6) = -2$

(c) Note that with -4^2 the power 2 is applied only to 4, not to -4 (which would be written $(-4)^2$). Thus $-4^2 + 3 = -(4^2) + 3 = -16 + 3 = -13$

(d) $[2(-1)]^2 + 3 = [-2]^2 + 3 = 4 + 3 = 7$

(e) $6 \div 2(3) = (6 \div 2)(3) = 3 \cdot 3 = 9$

✓ CHECKPOINT

True or false:

4. $-(-5)^2 = 25$

5. $|4 - 6| = |4| - |6|$

6. $9 - 2(2)(-10) = 7(2)(-10) = -140$

Often we use letters to represent real numbers, such as in the formula for the area of a circle, $A = \pi r^2$. Formula evaluations also use the order of operations.

EXAMPLE   4

Average Annual Wage

By using Social Security Administration data for the years from 2011 and projected to 2021, the U.S. average annual wage W (in dollars) can be approximated with the formula

$$W = 48t^2 + 1000(1.8t + 41)$$

where t is the number of years past 2010. Use the formula to approximate the U.S. average annual wage in 2020.

Solution

Note that 2020 is 10 years past 2010, so we use $t = 10$. Substituting $t = 10$ into the formula for W and using the order of operations give

$$W = 48(10^2) + 1000(1.8(10) + 41)$$
$$= 48(100) + 1000(18 + 41) = 4800 + 1000(59)$$
$$= 4800 + 59,000 = \$63,800$$

We will assume that you have a scientific or graphing calculator. Discussions of some of the capabilities of graphing calculators and graphing utilities will be found throughout the text.

Most scientific and graphing calculators use standard algebraic order when evaluating arithmetic expressions. Working outward from inner parentheses, calculations are performed from left to right. Powers and roots are evaluated first, followed by multiplications and divisions, and then additions and subtractions.

✓ CHECKPOINT
ANSWERS

1. Parts (a) and (d) are undefined because a denominator of zero means division by zero. Parts (b) and (c) are defined and their values are 0 and 1 respectively.

2. (a) $1 < x < 3$

    (b) $0 < x \le 3$

    (c) $-1 \le x < \infty$ or $x \ge -1$

    (d) $-\infty < x < 2$ or $x < 2$

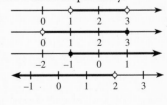

3. (a) [3, 6]; closed interval

    (b) $[-6, 4)$; half-open interval

4. False; $-(-5)^2 = -25$.

5. False; $|4 - 6| = |-2| = 2$ and $|4| - |6| = 4 - 6 = -2$.

6. False; $9 - (2)(2)(-10) = 49$.

| EXERCISES | 0.2

In Problems 1–2, indicate whether the given expression is one or more of the following types of numbers: rational, irrational, integer, natural. If the expression is meaningless, so state.

1. (a) $\dfrac{-\pi}{10}$

   (b) -9

   (c) $\dfrac{9}{3}$

   (d) $\dfrac{4}{0}$

2. (a) $\dfrac{0}{6}$

   (b) -1.2916

   (c) 1.414

   (d) $\dfrac{9}{6}$

Which property of real numbers is illustrated in each part of Problems 3 and 4?

3. (a) $8 + 6 = 6 + 8$

   (b) $5(3 + 7) = 5(3) + 5(7)$

   (c) $6(4 \cdot 5) = (6 \cdot 4)(5)$

   (d) $-15 + 0 = -15$

4. (a) $-e \cdot 1 = -e$

   (b) $4 + (-4) = 0$

   (c) $\left(\dfrac{3}{2}\right)\left(\dfrac{2}{3}\right) = 1$

   (d) $(12)\left(\dfrac{3}{4}\right) = \left(\dfrac{3}{4}\right)(12)$

Insert the proper sign $<, =$, or $>$ to replace $\square$ in Problems 5–12.

5. $-6 \;\square\; 0$

6. $2 \;\square\; -20$

7. $-14 \;\square\; -3$

8. $\pi \;\square\; 3.14$

9. $0.333 \;\square\; \dfrac{1}{3}$

10. $\dfrac{1}{3} + \dfrac{1}{2} \;\square\; \dfrac{5}{6}$

11. $|-3| + |5| \;\square\; |-3 + 5|$

12. $|-9 - 3| \;\square\; |-9| + |3|$

In Problems 13–24, evaluate each expression.

13. $-3^2 + 10 \cdot 2$

14. $(-3)^2 + 10 \cdot 2$

15. $\dfrac{4 + 2^2}{2}$

16. $\dfrac{(4 + 2)^2}{2}$

17. $\dfrac{16 - (-4)}{8 - (-2)}$

18. $\dfrac{(-5)(-3) - (-2)(3)}{-9 + 2}$

19. $\dfrac{|5 - 2| - |-7|}{|5 - 2|}$

20. $\dfrac{|3 - |4 - 11\||}{-|5^2 - 3^2|}$

21. $\dfrac{(-3)^2 - 2 \cdot 3 + 6}{4 - 2^2 + 3}$

22. $\dfrac{6^2 - 4(-3)(-2)}{6 - 6^2 \div 4}$

23. $\dfrac{-4^2 + 5 - 2 \cdot 3}{5 - 4^2}$

24. $\dfrac{3 - 2(5 - 2)}{(-2)^2 - 2^2 + 3}$

25. What part of the real number line corresponds to the interval $(-\infty, \infty)$?

26. Write the interval corresponding to $x \geq 0$.

In Problems 27–30, express each inequality or graph using interval notation, and name the type of interval.

27. $1 < x \leq 3$

28. $-4 \leq x \leq 3$

29.

30.

In Problems 31–34, write an inequality that describes each interval or graph.

31. $[-3, 5)$

32. $(-2, \infty)$

33.

34.

In Problems 35–42, graph the subset of the real numbers that is represented by each of the following and write your answer in interval notation.

35. $(-\infty, 4) \cap (-3, \infty)$

36. $[-4, 17) \cap [-20, 10]$

37. $x > 4$ and $x \geq 0$

38. $x < 10$ and $x < -1$

39. $[0, \infty) \cup [-1, 5]$

40. $(-\infty, 4) \cup (0, 2)$

41. $x > 7$ or $x < 0$

42. $x > 4$ and $x < 0$

In Problems 43–48, use your calculator to evaluate each of the following. List all the digits on your display in the answer.

43. $\dfrac{-1}{25916.8}$

44. $\dfrac{51.412}{127.01}$

45. $(3.679)^7$

46. $(1.28)^{10}$

47. $\dfrac{2500}{(1.1)^6 - 1}$

48. $100\left[\dfrac{(1.05)^{12} - 1}{0.05}\right]$

APPLICATIONS

49. *Take-home pay* A sales clerk's take-home pay is found by subtracting all taxes and retirement contributions from gross pay (which consists of salary plus commission). Given the following information, complete parts (a)–(c).

Salary = \$300.00   Commission = \$788.91
Retirement = 5% of gross pay
Taxes: State = 5% of gross pay
             Local = 1% of gross pay
             Federal withholding =
                 25% of (gross pay less retirement)
             Federal social security and Medicare =
                 7.65% of gross pay
(a) Find the gross pay.
(b) Find the amount of federal withholding.
(c) Find the take-home pay.

50. *Public health expenditures* The expenditures E for government public health activities (in billions of dollars) can be approximated by

$$E = 5.03t^2 + 100t + 1380$$

where t is the number of years past 2000 (*Source: Centers for Medicare and Medicaid Services*).
(a) What t-value represents the year 2010?
(b) Actual expenditures for 2010 were \$2879 billion. What does the formula give as the 2010 approximation?
(c) Estimate the expenditures for 2015.

51. *Worldwide Internet users* Using data from 2002 projected through 2016, the number of worldwide users of the Internet, in billions, can be approximated quite accurately either by

(1) $y = 0.207t - 0.000370$ or by
(2) $y = 0.00454t^2 + 0.126t + 0.271$

with t equal to the number of years past 2000 (*Source: dailytech.com*).
(a) Which of the equations is more accurate for 2013, when the number was 2.70 billion?
(b) Use both formulas to estimate the number of users in 2018.

52. *Health statistics* From data adapted from the National Center for Health Statistics, the height H in inches and age A in years for boys between 4 and 16 years of age are related according to

$$H = 2.31A + 31.26$$

To account for normal variability among boys, normal height for a given age is $\pm 5\%$ of the height obtained from the equation.
(a) Find the normal height range for a boy who is 10.5 years old, and write it as an inequality.
(b) Find the normal height range for a boy who is 5.75 years old, and write it as an inequality.

53. *Income taxes* Use the following federal tax table for a single person claiming one personal exemption.

Taxable Income *I*	Tax Due *T*
0–8375	10% I
8376–34,000	$837.50 + 15\%(I - 8375)$
34,001–82,400	$4681.25 + 25\%(I - 34{,}000)$
82,401–171,850	$16{,}781.25 + 28\%(I - 82{,}400)$
171,851–373,650	$41{,}827.25 + 33\%(I - 171{,}850)$
Over 373,650	$108{,}421.25 + 35\%(I - 373{,}650)$

Source: Internal Revenue Service

(a) Write the last three taxable income ranges as inequalities.
(b) If an individual has a taxable income of \$34,000, calculate the tax due. Repeat this calculation for a taxable income of \$82,400.
(c) Write an interval that represents the amount of tax due for a taxable income between \$34,000 and \$82,400.

0.3

Integral Exponents

If \$1000 is placed in a 5-year savings certificate that pays an interest rate of 10% per year, compounded annually, then the amount returned after 5 years is given by

$$1000(1.1)^5$$

The 5 in this expression is an *exponent*. Exponents provide an easier way to denote certain multiplications. For example,

$$(1.1)^5 = (1.1)(1.1)(1.1)(1.1)(1.1)$$

An understanding of the properties of exponents is fundamental to the algebra needed to study functions and solve equations. Furthermore, the definition of exponential and logarithmic functions and many of the techniques in calculus also require an understanding of the properties of exponents.

For any real number a,

$$a^2 = a \cdot a, \quad a^3 = a \cdot a \cdot a, \quad \text{and} \quad a^n = a \cdot a \cdot a \cdot \ldots \cdot a \quad (n \text{ factors})$$

for any positive integer n. The positive integer n is called the **exponent,** the number a is called the **base,** and a^n is read "a to the nth power."

Note that $4a^n$ means $4(a^n)$, which is different from $(4a)^n$. The 4 is the coefficient of a^n in $4a^n$. Note also that $-a^n$ is not equivalent to $(-a)^n$ when n is even. For example, $-3^4 = -81$, but $(-3)^4 = 81$.

Some of the rules of exponents follow.

Positive Integer Exponents

For any real numbers a and b and positive integers m and n,

1. $a^m \cdot a^n = a^{m+n}$

2. For $a \neq 0$, $\dfrac{a^m}{a^n} = \begin{cases} a^{m-n} & \text{if } m > n \\ 1 & \text{if } m = n \\ 1/a^{n-m} & \text{if } m < n \end{cases}$

3. $(ab)^m = a^m b^m$

4. $\left(\dfrac{a}{b}\right)^m = \dfrac{a^m}{b^m} \quad (b \neq 0)$

5. $(a^m)^n = a^{mn}$

EXAMPLE   1   Positive Integer Exponents

Use rules of positive integer exponents to rewrite the following. Assume all denominators are nonzero.

(a) $\dfrac{5^6}{5^4}$

(b) $\dfrac{x^2}{x^5}$

(c) $\left(\dfrac{x}{y}\right)^4$

(d) $(3x^2y^3)^4$

(e) $3^3 \cdot 3^2$

Solution

(a) $\dfrac{5^6}{5^4} = 5^{6-4} = 5^2$

(b) $\dfrac{x^2}{x^5} = \dfrac{1}{x^{5-2}} = \dfrac{1}{x^3}$

(c) $\left(\dfrac{x}{y}\right)^4 = \dfrac{x^4}{y^4}$

(d) $(3x^2y^3)^4 = 3^4(x^2)^4(y^3)^4 = 81x^8y^{12}$

(e) $3^3 \cdot 3^2 = 3^{3+2} = 3^5$

For certain calculus operations, use of negative exponents is necessary in order to write problems in the proper form. We can extend the rules for positive integer exponents to all integers by defining a^0 and a^{-n}. Clearly $a^m \cdot a^0$ should equal $a^{m+0} = a^m$, and it will if $a^0 = 1$.

Zero Exponent

For any nonzero real number a, we define $a^0 = 1$. We leave 0^0 undefined.

In Section 0.2, we defined a^{-1} as $1/a$ for $a \neq 0$, so we define a^{-n} as $(a^{-1})^n$.

Negative Exponents

$$a^{-n} = (a^{-1})^n = \left(\frac{1}{a}\right)^n = \frac{1}{a^n} \qquad (a \neq 0)$$

$$\left(\frac{a}{b}\right)^{-n} = \left[\left(\frac{a}{b}\right)^{-1}\right]^n = \left(\frac{b}{a}\right)^n \qquad (a \neq 0, \ b \neq 0)$$

EXAMPLE 2   **Negative and Zero Exponents**

Write the following without exponents.
(a) $6 \cdot 3^0$
(b) 6^{-2}
(c) $\left(\frac{1}{3}\right)^{-1}$
(d) $-\left(\frac{2}{3}\right)^{-4}$
(e) $(-4)^{-2}$

Solution
(a) $6 \cdot 3^0 = 6 \cdot 1 = 6$

(b) $6^{-2} = \frac{1}{6^2} = \frac{1}{36}$

(c) $\left(\frac{1}{3}\right)^{-1} = \frac{3}{1} = 3$

(d) $-\left(\frac{2}{3}\right)^{-4} = -\left(\frac{3}{2}\right)^4 = \frac{-81}{16}$

(e) $(-4)^{-2} = \frac{1}{(-4)^2} = \frac{1}{16}$

As we'll see in the chapter on the mathematics of finance (Chapter 6), negative exponents arise in financial calculations when we have a future goal for an investment and want to know how much to invest now. For example, if money can be invested at 9%, compounded annually, then the amount we must invest now (which is called the present value) in order to have $10,000 in the account after 7 years is given by $10,000(1.09)^{-7}$. Calculations such as this are often done directly with a calculator.

Using the definitions of zero and negative exponents enables us to extend the rules of exponents to all integers and to express them more simply.

Rules of Exponents

For real numbers a and b and *integers* m and n,

1. $a^m \cdot a^n = a^{m+n}$
2. $a^m/a^n = a^{m-n}$ $(a \neq 0)$
3. $(ab)^m = a^m b^m$
4. $(a^m)^n = a^{mn}$
5. $(a/b)^m = a^m/b^m$ $(a, b \neq 0)$
6. $a^0 = 1$ $(a \neq 0)$
7. $a^{-n} = 1/a^n$ $(a \neq 0)$
8. $(a/b)^{-n} = (b/a)^n$ $(a, b \neq 0)$

Throughout the remainder of the text, we will assume all variable expressions are defined.

EXAMPLE 3   Using Rules of Exponents

Use the rules of exponents and the definitions of a^0 and a^{-n} to simplify the following with positive exponents.

(a) $2(x^2)^{-2}$ (b) $x^{-2} \cdot x^{-5}$

(c) $\dfrac{x^{-8}}{x^{-4}}$ (d) $\left(\dfrac{2x^3}{3x^{-5}}\right)^{-2}$

Solution

(a) $2(x^2)^{-2} = 2x^{-4} = 2\left(\dfrac{1}{x^4}\right) = \dfrac{2}{x^4}$

(b) $x^{-2} \cdot x^{-5} = x^{-2-5} = x^{-7} = \dfrac{1}{x^7}$

(c) $\dfrac{x^{-8}}{x^{-4}} = x^{-8-(-4)} = x^{-4} = \dfrac{1}{x^4}$

(d) $\left(\dfrac{2x^3}{3x^{-5}}\right)^{-2} = \left(\dfrac{2x^8}{3}\right)^{-2} = \left(\dfrac{3}{2x^8}\right)^2 = \dfrac{9}{4x^{16}}$

✓ CHECKPOINT

1. Complete the following.

(a) $x^3 \cdot x^8 = x^?$ (b) $x \cdot x^4 \cdot x^{-3} = x^?$

(c) $\dfrac{1}{x^4} = x^?$ (d) $x^{24} \div x^{-3} = x^?$

(e) $(x^4)^2 = x^?$ (f) $(2x^4y)^3 = ?$

2. True or false:

(a) $3x^{-2} = \dfrac{1}{9x^2}$ (b) $-x^{-4} = \dfrac{-1}{x^4}$ (c) $x^{-3} = -x^3$

3. Evaluate the following, if possible. For any that are undefined, so state. Assume $x > 0$.

(a) 0^4 (b) 0^0 (c) x^0 (d) 0^x (e) 0^{-4} (f) -5^{-2}

EXAMPLE 4   Rewriting a Quotient

Write $(x^2y)/(9wz^3)$ with all factors in the numerator.

Solution

$$\dfrac{x^2y}{9wz^3} = x^2y\left(\dfrac{1}{9wz^3}\right) = x^2y\left(\dfrac{1}{9}\right)\left(\dfrac{1}{w}\right)\left(\dfrac{1}{z^3}\right) = x^2y \cdot 9^{-1}w^{-1}z^{-3}$$

$$= 9^{-1}x^2yw^{-1}z^{-3}$$

EXAMPLE 5   Rewriting with Positive Exponents

Simplify the following so all exponents are positive.

(a) $(2^3x^{-4}y^5)^{-2}$

(b) $\dfrac{2x^4(x^2y)^0}{(4x^{-2}y)^2}$

Solution

(a) $(2^3x^{-4}y^5)^{-2} = 2^{-6}x^8y^{-10} = \dfrac{1}{2^6} \cdot x^8 \cdot \dfrac{1}{y^{10}} = \dfrac{x^8}{64y^{10}}$

(b) $\dfrac{2x^4(x^2y)^0}{(4x^{-2}y)^2} = \dfrac{2x^4 \cdot 1}{4^2x^{-4}y^2} = \dfrac{2}{4^2} \cdot \dfrac{x^4}{x^{-4}} \cdot \dfrac{1}{y^2} = \dfrac{2}{16} \cdot \dfrac{x^8}{1} \cdot \dfrac{1}{y^2} = \dfrac{x^8}{8y^2}$

1. (a) x^{11} (b) x^2
    (c) x^{-4} (d) x^{27}
    (e) x^8 (f) $8x^{12}y^3$

2. (a) False; $3x^{-2} = \dfrac{3}{x^2}$

    (b) True.

    (c) False; $x^{-3} = \dfrac{1}{x^3}$

3. (a) $0^4 = 0$ (b) 0^0 is undefined.
    (c) $x^0 = 1$ since $x \neq 0$ (d) $0^x = 0$ because $x > 0$

    (e) 0^{-4} would be $\dfrac{1}{0^4}$, which is undefined.

    (f) $\dfrac{-1}{25}$

| EXERCISES | 0.3

Evaluate in Problems 1–8. Write all answers without using exponents.

1. $(-4)^4$ 2. -5^3
3. -2^6 4. $(-2)^5$
5. 3^{-2} 6. 6^{-1}
7. $-\left(\dfrac{3}{2}\right)^2$ 8. $\left(\dfrac{2}{3}\right)^3$

In Problems 9–12, use a calculator to evaluate the indicated powers.

9. 1.2^4 10. $(-3.7)^3$
11. $(1.5)^{-5}$ 12. $(-0.8)^{-9}$

In Problems 13–22, simplify the expressions with all exponents positive.

13. $6^5 \cdot 6^3$ 14. $8^4 \cdot 8^2 \cdot 8$
15. $\dfrac{10^8}{10^9}$ 16. $\dfrac{7^8}{7^3}$
17. $\dfrac{9^4 \cdot 9^{-7}}{9^{-3}}$ 18. $\dfrac{5^4}{(5^{-2} \cdot 5^3)}$
19. $(3^3)^3$ 20. $(2^{-3})^{-2}$
21. $\left(\dfrac{2}{3}\right)^{-2}$ 22. $\left(\dfrac{-2}{5}\right)^{-4}$

In Problems 23–26, rewrite the expression with positive exponents ($x, y, z \neq 0$).

23. $-x^{-3}$ 24. x^{-4}
25. $xy^{-2}z^0$ 26. $4^{-1}x^0y^{-2}$

In Problems 27–40, use the rules of exponents to simplify so that only positive exponents remain.

27. $x^3 \cdot x^4$ 28. $a^5 \cdot a$ 29. $x^{-5} \cdot x^3$
30. $y^{-5} \cdot y^{-2}$ 31. $\dfrac{x^8}{x^4}$ 32. $\dfrac{a^5}{a^{-1}}$
33. $\dfrac{y^5}{y^{-7}}$ 34. $\dfrac{y^{-3}}{y^{-4}}$ 35. $(x^4)^3$

36. $(y^3)^{-2}$ 37. $(xy)^2$ 38. $(2m)^3$
39. $\left(\dfrac{2}{x^5}\right)^4$ 40. $\left(\dfrac{8}{a^3}\right)^3$

In Problems 41–52, compute and simplify so that only positive exponents remain.

41. $(2x^{-2}y)^{-4}$ 42. $(-32x^5)^{-3}$
43. $(-8a^{-3}b^2)(2a^5b^{-4})$ 44. $(-3m^2y^{-1})(2m^{-3}y^{-1})$
45. $(2x^{-2}) \div (x^{-1}y^2)$ 46. $(-8a^{-3}b^2c) \div (2a^5b^4)$
47. $\left(\dfrac{x^3}{y^{-2}}\right)^{-3}$ 48. $\left(\dfrac{x^{-2}}{y}\right)^{-3}$
49. $\left(\dfrac{a^{-2}b^{-1}c^{-4}}{a^4b^{-3}c^0}\right)^{-3}$ 50. $\left(\dfrac{4x^{-1}y^{-40}}{2^{-2}x^4y^{-10}}\right)^{-2}$

51. (a) $\dfrac{2x^{-2}}{(2x)^2}$ (b) $\dfrac{(2x)^{-2}}{(2x)^2}$
     (c) $\dfrac{2x^{-2}}{2x^2}$ (d) $\dfrac{2x^{-2}}{(2x)^{-2}}$

52. (a) $\dfrac{2^{-1}x^{-2}}{(2x)^2}$ (b) $\dfrac{2^{-1}x^{-2}}{2x^2}$
     (c) $\dfrac{(2x^{-2})^{-1}}{(2x)^{-2}}$ (d) $\dfrac{(2x^{-2})^{-1}}{2x^2}$

In many applications it is necessary to write expressions in the form cx^n where c is a constant and n is an integer. In Problems 53–60, write the expressions in this form.

53. $\dfrac{1}{x}$ 54. $\dfrac{1}{x^2}$
55. $(2x)^3$ 56. $(3x)^2$
57. $\dfrac{1}{4x^2}$ 58. $\dfrac{3}{2x^4}$
59. $\left(\dfrac{-x}{2}\right)^3$ 60. $\left(\dfrac{-x}{3}\right)^2$

APPLICATIONS

Compound interest **If P is invested for n years at rate i (as a decimal), compounded annually, the future value that accrues is given by $S = P(1 + i)^n$, and the interest earned is $I = S - P$. In Problems 61–64, find S and I for the given P, n, and i.**

61. $1200 for 5 years at 12%
62. $1800 for 7 years at 10%
63. $5000 for 6 years at 11.5%
64. $800 for 20 years at 10.5%

Present value **If an investment has a goal (future value) of S after n years, invested at interest rate i (as a decimal), compounded annually, then the present value P that must be invested is given by $P = S(1 + i)^{-n}$. In Problems 65 and 66, find P for the given S, n, and i.**

65. $15,000 after 6 years at 11.5%
66. $80,000 after 20 years at 10.5%
67. *Personal income* For selected years from 1960 to 2018, total U.S. personal income I (in billions of dollars) can be approximated by the formula

$$I = 492.4(1.070)^t$$

where t is the number of years past 1960.
   (a) What t-values correspond to the years 1980, 2000, and 2008?
   (b) The actual total personal incomes (in billions of dollars) for selected years were as follows.

1980	2000	2008
2308	8430	12,101

   What does the formula estimate for these years?
   (c) What does the formula estimate for the total personal income in 2018?
68. *China's shale gas* For the years 2013 through 2020, the estimated annual production of shale-natural gas in China, in billions of cubic feet, can be approximated by the formula

$$y = 0.012(1.75)^t$$

where t is the number of years past 2010 (*Source:* Sanford C. Bernstein).
   (a) What t-value corresponds to 2019?
   (b) According to the formula, what is the production in 2019?
   (c) What is the production in 2022 if this formula remains accurate?
69. *Endangered species* The total number of endangered species y can be approximated by the formula

$$y = \frac{1095}{1 + 10.12(1.212)^{-t}}$$

where t is the number of years past 1980 (*Source:* U.S. Fish and Wildlife Service).

(a) The actual numbers of endangered species for selected years were as follows.

1990	2003	2012
442	987	1086

For each of these years, find the number of endangered species predicted by the formula. Round your answer to the nearest integer.
(b) Given that there were 1037 endangered species in 2007, how many more species does the formula estimate will be added to the endangered list in the next 13 years, by 2020?
(c) Why do you think the answer to (b) is smaller than the number of species added during the 13-year period from 1990 to 2003?
(d) Why is it reasonable for a formula such as this to have an upper limit that cannot be exceeded? Use large t-values in the formula to discover this formula's upper limit.
70. *U.S. population, ages 20–64* By using Social Security Administration data for selected years from 1950 and projected to 2050, the U.S. population, ages 20–64, P (in millions) can be approximated by the equation

$$P = \frac{249.6}{1 + 1.915(1.028)^{-t}}$$

where t is the number of years past 1950.
(a) Some of the Social Security Administration data for this population (in millions) are as follows.

1980	2000	2020
134.0	169.8	198.2

For each of these years, use the equation to find the predicted U.S. population, ages 20–64.
(b) From 2000 to 2020, this population group is predicted to change by 28.4 million individuals. Find the population change predicted by the equation for 2025 to 2045. Is this greater or less than 2000–2020?
(c) Why is it reasonable for a formula such as this to have an upper limit that cannot be exceeded? Use large t-values to discover this formula's upper limit.
71. *Health care expenditures* The national health care expenditure H (in billions of dollars) can be modeled (that is, accurately approximated) by the formula

$$H = 738.1(1.065)^t$$

where t is the number of years past 1990 (*Source:* U.S. Department of Health and Human Services).
(a) What t-value corresponds to 2000?
(b) Approximate the national health care expenditure in 2000.
(c) Approximate the national health care expenditure in 2010.
(d) Estimate the national health care expenditure in 2018.

0.4

Radicals and Rational Exponents

Roots   A process closely linked to raising numbers to powers is that of extracting roots. From geometry we know that if an edge of a cube has a length of x units, its volume is x^3 cubic units. Reversing this process, we determine that if the volume of a cube is V cubic units, the length of an edge is the cube root of V, which is denoted

$$\sqrt[3]{V} \text{ units}$$

When we seek the **cube root** of a number such as 8 (written $\sqrt[3]{8}$), we are looking for a real number whose cube equals 8. Because $2^3 = 8$, we know that $\sqrt[3]{8} = 2$. Similarly, $\sqrt[3]{-27} = -3$ because $(-3)^3 = -27$. The expression $\sqrt[n]{a}$ is called a **radical,** where $\sqrt{}$ is the **radical sign,** n is the **index,** and a is the **radicand.** When no index is indicated, the index is assumed to be 2 and the expression is called a **square root;** thus $\sqrt{4}$ is the square root of 4 and represents the positive number whose square is 4.

Only one real number satisfies $\sqrt[n]{a}$ for a real number a and an odd number n; we call that number the **principal nth root** or, more simply, the **nth root.**

For an even index n, there are two possible cases:

1. If a is negative, there is no real number equal to $\sqrt[n]{a}$. For example, there are no real numbers that equal $\sqrt{-4}$ or $\sqrt[4]{-16}$ because there is no real number b such that $b^2 = -4$ or $b^4 = -16$. In this case, we say $\sqrt[n]{a}$ is not a real number.
2. If a is positive, there are two real numbers whose nth power equals a. For example, $3^2 = 9$ and $(-3)^2 = 9$. In order to have a unique nth root, we define the (principal) nth root, $\sqrt[n]{a}$, as the *positive* number b that satisfies $b^n = a$.

We summarize this discussion as follows.

---

nth Root of a

The **(principal) nth root** of a real number is defined as

$$\sqrt[n]{a} = b \quad \text{only if} \quad a = b^n$$

subject to the following conditions:

	$a = 0$	$a > 0$	$a < 0$
n even	$\sqrt[n]{a} = 0$	$\sqrt[n]{a} > 0$	$\sqrt[n]{a}$ not real
n odd	$\sqrt[n]{a} = 0$	$\sqrt[n]{a} > 0$	$\sqrt[n]{a} < 0$

When we are asked for the root of a number, we give the principal root.

EXAMPLE 1   **Roots**

Find the roots, if they are real numbers.
(a) $\sqrt[6]{64}$ (b) $-\sqrt{16}$ (c) $\sqrt[3]{-8}$ (d) $\sqrt{-16}$

Solution
(a) $\sqrt[6]{64} = 2$ because $2^6 = 64$ (b) $-\sqrt{16} = -\left(\sqrt{16}\right) = -4$ (c) $\sqrt[3]{-8} = -2$
(d) $\sqrt{-16}$ is not a real number because an even root of a negative number is not real. ∎

Fractional Exponents   In order to perform evaluations on a calculator or to perform calculus operations, it is sometimes necessary to rewrite radicals in exponential form with fractional exponents.

We have stated that for $a \geq 0$ and $b \geq 0$,

$$\sqrt{a} = b \text{ only if } a = b^2$$

This means that $\left(\sqrt{a}\right)^2 = b^2 = a$, or $\left(\sqrt{a}\right)^2 = a$. In order to extend the properties of exponents to rational exponents, it is necessary to define

$$a^{1/2} = \sqrt{a} \text{ so that } \left(a^{1/2}\right)^2 = a$$

Exponent 1/n

For a positive integer n, we define

$$a^{1/n} = \sqrt[n]{a} \quad \text{if} \quad \sqrt[n]{a} \text{ exists}$$

Thus $\left(a^{1/n}\right)^n = a^{(1/n)\cdot n} = a$.

Because we wish the properties established for integer exponents to extend to rational exponents, we make the following definitions.

Rational Exponents

For positive integer n and any integer m (with $a \neq 0$ when $m \leq 0$, with m/n in lowest terms, and with a nonnegative when n is even):

1. $a^{m/n} = (a^{1/n})^m = (\sqrt[n]{a})^m$
2. $a^{m/n} = (a^m)^{1/n} = \sqrt[n]{a^m}$

Throughout the remaining discussion, we assume all expressions are real.

EXAMPLE 2   **Radical Form**

Write the following in radical form and simplify.
(a) $16^{3/4}$ (b) $y^{-3/2}$ (c) $(6m)^{2/3}$

Solution
(a) $16^{3/4} = \sqrt[4]{16^3} = (\sqrt[4]{16})^3 = (2)^3 = 8$

(b) $y^{-3/2} = \dfrac{1}{y^{3/2}} = \dfrac{1}{\sqrt{y^3}}$

(c) $(6m)^{2/3} = \sqrt[3]{(6m)^2} = \sqrt[3]{36m^2}$

EXAMPLE 3   **Fractional Exponents**

Write the following without radical signs.

(a) $\sqrt{x^3}$ (b) $\dfrac{1}{\sqrt[3]{b^2}}$ (c) $\sqrt[3]{(ab)^3}$

Solution

(a) $\sqrt{x^3} = x^{3/2}$ (b) $\dfrac{1}{\sqrt[3]{b^2}} = \dfrac{1}{b^{2/3}} = b^{-2/3}$ (c) $\sqrt[3]{(ab)^3} = (ab)^{3/3} = ab$

Our definition of $a^{m/n}$ guarantees that the rules for exponents will apply to fractional exponents. Thus we can perform operations with fractional exponents as we did with integer exponents.

EXAMPLE 4   **Operations with Fractional Exponents**

Simplify the following expressions.
(a) $a^{1/2} \cdot a^{1/6}$
(b) $a^{3/4}/a^{1/3}$
(c) $(a^3 b)^{2/3}$
(d) $(a^{3/2})^{1/2}$
(e) $a^{-1/2} \cdot a^{-3/2}$

Solution

(a) $a^{1/2} \cdot a^{1/6} = a^{1/2+1/6} = a^{3/6+1/6} = a^{4/6} = a^{2/3}$

(b) $a^{3/4}/a^{1/3} = a^{3/4-1/3} = a^{9/12-4/12} = a^{5/12}$

(c) $(a^3 b)^{2/3} = (a^3)^{2/3} b^{2/3} = a^2 b^{2/3}$

(d) $(a^{3/2})^{1/2} = a^{(3/2)(1/2)} = a^{3/4}$

(e) $a^{-1/2} \cdot a^{-3/2} = a^{-1/2-3/2} = a^{-2} = 1/a^2$

✓ CHECKPOINT

1. Which of the following are *not* real numbers?

   (a) $\sqrt[3]{-64}$ (b) $\sqrt{-64}$ (c) $\sqrt{0}$ (d) $\sqrt[4]{1}$ (e) $\sqrt[5]{-1}$ (f) $\sqrt[8]{-1}$

2. (a) Write as radicals: $x^{1/3}, x^{2/5}, x^{-3/2}$

   (b) Write with fractional exponents: $\sqrt[4]{x^3} = x^?,\ \dfrac{1}{\sqrt{x}} = \dfrac{1}{x^?} = x^?$

3. Evaluate the following.

   (a) $8^{2/3}$ (b) $(-8)^{2/3}$ (c) $8^{-2/3}$ (d) $-8^{-2/3}$ (e) $\sqrt[15]{71}$

4. Complete the following.

   (a) $x \cdot x^{1/3} \cdot x^3 = x^?$ (b) $x^2 \div x^{1/2} = x^?$ (c) $(x^{-2/3})^{-3} = x^?$

   (d) $x^{-3/2} \cdot x^{1/2} = x^?$ (e) $x^{-3/2} \cdot x = x^?$ (f) $\left(\dfrac{x^4}{y^2}\right)^{3/2} = ?$

5. True or false:

   (a) $\dfrac{8x^{2/3}}{x^{-1/3}} = 4x$ (b) $(16x^8 y)^{3/4} = 12x^6 y^{3/4}$

   (c) $\left(\dfrac{x^2}{y^3}\right)^{-1/3} = \left(\dfrac{y^3}{x^2}\right)^{1/3} = \dfrac{y}{x^{2/3}}$

Operations with Radicals

We can perform operations with radicals by first rewriting in exponential form, performing the operations with exponents, and then converting the answer back to radical form. Another option is to apply directly the following rules for operations with radicals.

Rules for Radicals	Example
Given that $\sqrt[n]{a}$ and $\sqrt[n]{b}$ are real,*	
1. $\sqrt[n]{a^n} = (\sqrt[n]{a})^n = a$	1. $\sqrt[5]{6^5} = (\sqrt[5]{6})^5 = 6$
2. $\sqrt[n]{a} \cdot \sqrt[n]{b} = \sqrt[n]{ab}$	2. $\sqrt[3]{2}\sqrt[3]{4} = \sqrt[3]{8} = \sqrt[3]{2^3} = 2$
3. $\dfrac{\sqrt[n]{a}}{\sqrt[n]{b}} = \sqrt[n]{\dfrac{a}{b}}\ \ (b \neq 0)$	3. $\dfrac{\sqrt{18}}{\sqrt{2}} = \sqrt{\dfrac{18}{2}} = \sqrt{9} = 3$

*Note that this means $a \geq 0$ and $b \geq 0$ if n is even.

Let us consider Rule 1 for radicals more carefully. Note that if n is even and $a < 0$, then $\sqrt[n]{a}$ is not real, and Rule 1 does not apply. For example, $\sqrt{-2}$ is not a real number, and

$$\sqrt{(-2)^2} \neq -2 \text{ because } \sqrt{(-2)^2} = \sqrt{4} = 2, \text{ which is not } -2$$

We can generalize this observation as follows: If $a < 0$, then $\sqrt{a^2} = -a > 0$, so

$$\sqrt{a^2} = \begin{cases} a & \text{if } a \geq 0 \\ -a & \text{if } a < 0 \end{cases}$$

This means

$$\sqrt{a^2} = |a|$$

We can use the rules for radicals to simplify radical expressions. In general, a radical expression $\sqrt[n]{x}$ is considered simplified if x has no nth powers as factors.

EXAMPLE 5   **Simplifying Radicals**

Simplify the following radicals; assume the expressions are real numbers.

(a) $\sqrt[3]{8^3}$ (b) $\left[\sqrt[7]{(3x^2 + 4)^3}\right]^7$ (c) $\sqrt{x^2}$

(d) $\sqrt{48x^5y^6}$ $(y \geq 0)$ (e) $\sqrt[3]{72a^3b^4}$

Solution

(a) $\sqrt[3]{8^3} = 8$ by Rule 1

(b) $\left[\sqrt[7]{(3x^2 + 4)^3}\right]^7 = (3x^2 + 4)^3$ by Rule 1

(c) $\sqrt{x^2} = |x|$ by the previous discussion

(d) To simplify $\sqrt{48x^5y^6}$, we first factor $48x^5y^6$ into perfect-square factors and other factors. Then we apply Rule 2.

$$\sqrt{48x^5y^6} = \sqrt{16 \cdot 3 \cdot x^4xy^6} = \sqrt{16}\sqrt{x^4}\sqrt{y^6}\sqrt{3x} = 4x^2y^3\sqrt{3x}$$

(e) We factor $72a^3b^4$ into factors that are perfect cubes and other factors. Then we apply Rule 2.

$$\sqrt[3]{72a^3b^4} = \sqrt[3]{8 \cdot 9a^3b^3b} = \sqrt[3]{8} \cdot \sqrt[3]{a^3} \cdot \sqrt[3]{b^3} \cdot \sqrt[3]{9b} = 2ab\sqrt[3]{9b}$$

Rule 2 for radicals also provides a procedure for multiplying two roots with the same index.

EXAMPLE 6   **Multiplying Radicals**

Multiply the following and simplify, assuming nonnegative variables.

(a) $\sqrt[3]{2xy} \cdot \sqrt[3]{4x^2y}$ (b) $\sqrt{8xy^3z} \cdot \sqrt{4x^2y^3z^2}$

Solution

(a) $\sqrt[3]{2xy} \cdot \sqrt[3]{4x^2y} = \sqrt[3]{2xy \cdot 4x^2y} = \sqrt[3]{8x^3y^2} = \sqrt[3]{8} \cdot \sqrt[3]{x^3} \cdot \sqrt[3]{y^2} = 2x\sqrt[3]{y^2}$

(b) $\sqrt{8xy^3z} \cdot \sqrt{4x^2y^3z^2} = \sqrt{32x^3y^6z^3} = \sqrt{16x^2y^6z^2} \cdot \sqrt{2xz} = 4xy^3z\sqrt{2xz}$

Rule 3 for radicals ($\sqrt[n]{a}/\sqrt[n]{b} = \sqrt[n]{a/b}$) indicates how to find the quotient of two roots with the same index.

EXAMPLE 7   **Dividing Radicals**

Find the quotients and simplify, assuming nonnegative variables.

(a) $\dfrac{\sqrt[3]{32}}{\sqrt[3]{4}}$ (b) $\dfrac{\sqrt{16a^3x}}{\sqrt{2ax}}$

Solution

(a) $\dfrac{\sqrt[3]{32}}{\sqrt[3]{4}} = \sqrt[3]{\dfrac{32}{4}} = \sqrt[3]{8} = 2$

(b) $\dfrac{\sqrt{16a^3x}}{\sqrt{2ax}} = \sqrt{\dfrac{16a^3x}{2ax}} = \sqrt{8a^2} = 2a\sqrt{2}$

Rationalizing   Occasionally, we wish to express a fraction containing radicals in an equivalent form that contains no radicals in the denominator. This is accomplished by multiplying the numerator *and* the denominator by the expression that will remove the radical from the denominator. This process is called **rationalizing the denominator.**

EXAMPLE 8   Rationalizing Denominators

Express the following with no radicals in the denominator. (Rationalize each denominator.)

(a) $\dfrac{15}{\sqrt{x}}$ (b) $\dfrac{2x}{\sqrt{18xy}}$ $(x, y > 0)$ (c) $\dfrac{3x}{\sqrt[3]{2x^2}}$ $(x \neq 0)$

Solution

(a) We wish to create a perfect square under the radical in the denominator.

$$\frac{15}{\sqrt{x}} \cdot \frac{\sqrt{x}}{\sqrt{x}} = \frac{15\sqrt{x}}{x}$$

(b) $\dfrac{2x}{\sqrt{18xy}} \cdot \dfrac{\sqrt{2xy}}{\sqrt{2xy}} = \dfrac{2x\sqrt{2xy}}{\sqrt{36x^2y^2}} = \dfrac{2x\sqrt{2xy}}{6xy} = \dfrac{\sqrt{2xy}}{3y}$

(c) We wish to create a perfect cube under the radical in the denominator.

$$\frac{3x}{\sqrt[3]{2x^2}} \cdot \frac{\sqrt[3]{4x}}{\sqrt[3]{4x}} = \frac{3x\sqrt[3]{4x}}{\sqrt[3]{8x^3}} = \frac{3x\sqrt[3]{4x}}{2x} = \frac{3\sqrt[3]{4x}}{2}$$

---

6. Simplify:
   (a) $\sqrt[3]{24x^3y}$
   (b) $\sqrt{12xy^2} \cdot \sqrt{3x^2y}$
   (c) $\dfrac{\sqrt{24x^4y^3}}{\sqrt{3y^2}}$

7. Rationalize the denominator of $\dfrac{x}{\sqrt{5x}}$ if $x \neq 0$.

It is also sometimes useful, especially in calculus, to *rationalize the numerator* of a fraction. For example, in the following expression we can rationalize the numerator by multiplying the numerator and denominator by $\sqrt[3]{2x}$, which creates a perfect cube under the radical:

$$\frac{\sqrt[3]{4x^2}}{3x} = \frac{\sqrt[3]{4x^2}}{3x} \cdot \frac{\sqrt[3]{2x}}{\sqrt[3]{2x}} = \frac{\sqrt[3]{8x^3}}{3x\sqrt[3]{2x}} = \frac{2x}{3x\sqrt[3]{2x}} = \frac{2}{3\sqrt[3]{2x}}$$

---

1. Part (b) $\sqrt{-64}$ and part (f) $\sqrt[8]{-1}$ are not real numbers.

2. (a) $\sqrt[3]{x}$; $\sqrt[5]{x^2}$; $\dfrac{1}{\sqrt{x^3}}$

   (b) $x^{3/4}$; $\dfrac{1}{x^{1/2}} = x^{-1/2}$

3. (a) 4   (b) 4   (c) $\dfrac{1}{4}$

   (d) $-\dfrac{1}{4}$ (e) ≈ 1.32867

4. (a) $x^{13/3}$ (b) $x^{3/2}$ (c) x^2

   (d) x^{-1} (e) $x^{-1/2}$ (f) $\dfrac{x^6}{y^3}$

5. (a) False; $8x$
   (b) False; $8x^6y^{3/4}$
   (c) True.

6. (a) $2x\sqrt[3]{3y}$
   (b) $6xy\sqrt{xy}$
   (c) $2x^2\sqrt{2y}$

7. $\dfrac{\sqrt{5x}}{5}$

| EXERCISES | 0.4

Unless stated otherwise, assume all variables are nonnegative and all denominators are nonzero.

In Problems 1–8, find the powers and roots, if they are real numbers.

1. (a) $\sqrt{256/9}$ (b) $\sqrt{1.44}$
2. (a) $\sqrt[5]{-32^3}$ (b) $\sqrt[4]{-16^5}$
3. (a) $16^{3/4}$ (b) $(-16)^{-3/2}$
4. (a) $-27^{-1/3}$ (b) $32^{3/5}$
5. $\left(\dfrac{8}{27}\right)^{-2/3}$ 6. $\left(\dfrac{4}{9}\right)^{3/2}$
7. (a) $64^{2/3}$ (b) $(-64)^{-2/3}$
8. (a) $64^{-2/3}$ (b) $-64^{2/3}$

In Problems 9 and 10, rewrite each radical with a fractional exponent, and then approximate the value with a calculator.

9. $\sqrt[9]{(6.12)^4}$ 10. $\sqrt[12]{4.96}$

In Problems 11–14, replace each radical with a fractional exponent. Do not simplify.

11. $\sqrt{m^3}$ 12. $\sqrt[3]{x^5}$ 13. $\sqrt[4]{m^2n^5}$ 14. $\sqrt[5]{x^3}$

In Problems 15–20, write in radical form. Do not simplify.

15. $2x^{1/2}$ 16. $12x^{1/4}$
17. $x^{7/6}$ 18. $y^{11/5}$
19. $-(1/4)x^{-5/4}$ 20. $-x^{-5/3}$

In Problems 21–34, simplify each expression so that only positive exponents remain.

21. $y^{1/4} \cdot y^{1/2}$ 22. $x^{2/3} \cdot x^{1/5}$ 23. $z^{3/4} \cdot z^4$
24. $x^{-2/3} \cdot x^2$ 25. $y^{-3/2} \cdot y^{-1}$ 26. $z^{-2} \cdot z^{5/3}$
27. $\dfrac{x^{1/3}}{x^{-2/3}}$ 28. $\dfrac{x^{-1/2}}{x^{-3/2}}$ 29. $\dfrac{y^{-5/2}}{y^{-2/5}}$
30. $\dfrac{x^{4/9}}{x^{1/12}}$ 31. $(x^{2/3})^{3/4}$ 32. $(x^{4/5})^3$
33. $(x^{-1/2})^2$ 34. $(x^{-2/3})^{-2/5}$

In Problems 35–40, simplify each expression.

35. $\sqrt{64x^4}$ 36. $\sqrt[3]{-64x^6y^3}$
37. $\sqrt{128x^4y^5}$ 38. $\sqrt[3]{54x^5x^8}$
39. $\sqrt[3]{40x^8y^5}$ 40. $\sqrt{32x^5y}$

In Problems 41–48, perform the indicated operations and simplify.

41. $\sqrt{12x^3y} \cdot \sqrt{3x^2y}$ 42. $\sqrt[3]{16x^2y} \cdot \sqrt[3]{3x^2y}$
43. $\sqrt{63x^5y^3} \cdot \sqrt{28x^2y}$ 44. $\sqrt{10xz^{10}} \cdot \sqrt{30x^{17}z}$
45. $\dfrac{\sqrt{12x^3y^{12}}}{\sqrt{27xy^2}}$ 46. $\dfrac{\sqrt{250xy^7z^4}}{\sqrt{18x^{17}y^2}}$
47. $\dfrac{\sqrt[4]{32a^9b^5}}{\sqrt[4]{162a^{17}}}$ 48. $\dfrac{\sqrt[3]{-16x^3y^4}}{\sqrt[3]{128y^2}}$

In Problems 49–52, determine a value for x that makes each statement true.

49. $(A^9)^x = A$ 50. $(B^{20})^x = B$
51. $(\sqrt[5]{R})^x = R$ 52. $(\sqrt{T^3})^x = T$

In Problems 53–58, rationalize each denominator and then simplify.

53. $\sqrt{2/3}$ 54. $\sqrt{5/8}$ 55. $\dfrac{\sqrt{m^2x}}{\sqrt{mx^2}}$
56. $\dfrac{5x^3w}{\sqrt{4xw^2}}$ 57. $\dfrac{\sqrt[3]{m^2x}}{\sqrt[3]{mx^5}}$ 58. $\dfrac{\sqrt[4]{mx^3}}{\sqrt[4]{y^2z^5}}$

In calculus it is frequently important to write an expression in the form cx^n, where c is a constant and n is a rational number. **In Problems 59–62, write each expression in this form.**

59. $\dfrac{-2}{3\sqrt[3]{x^2}}$ 60. $\dfrac{-2}{3\sqrt[4]{x^3}}$ 61. $3x\sqrt{x}$ 62. $\sqrt{x} \cdot \sqrt[3]{x}$

In calculus problems, the answers are frequently expected to be in a form with a radical instead of a fractional exponent. **In Problems 63–66, write each expression with radicals.**

63. $\dfrac{3}{2}x^{1/2}$ 64. $\dfrac{4}{3}x^{1/3}$
65. $\dfrac{1}{2}x^{-1/2}$ 66. $\dfrac{-1}{2}x^{-3/2}$

APPLICATIONS

67. *Richter scale* The Richter scale reading for an earthquake measures its intensity (as a multiple of some minimum intensity used for comparison). The intensity I corresponding to a Richter scale reading R is given by

$$I = 10^R$$

   (a) A quake measuring 8.5 on the Richter scale would be severe. Express the intensity of such a quake in exponential form and in radical form.
   (b) Find the intensity of a quake measuring 9.0.
   (c) The San Francisco quake that occurred during the 1989 World Series measured 6.9, and the March 2011 quake that devastated Sendai, Japan, measured 9.0. Calculate the ratio of these intensities (larger to smaller).

68. *Sound intensity* The intensity of sound I (as a multiple of the average minimum threshold of hearing intensity) is related to the decibel level D (or loudness of sound) according to

$$I = 10^{D/10}$$

   (a) Express $10^{D/10}$ using radical notation.
   (b) The background noise level of a relatively quiet room has a decibel reading of 32. Find the intensity I_1 of this noise level.

(c) A decibel reading of 140 is at the threshold of pain. If I_2 is the intensity of this threshold and I_1 is the intensity found in part (b), express the ratio I_2/I_1 as a power of 10. Then approximate this ratio.

69. *Investment* If $1000 is invested at $r\%$ compounded annually, the future value S of the account after two and a half years is given by

$$S = 1000\left(1 + \frac{r}{100}\right)^{5/2}$$

(a) Express this equation with radical notation.
(b) Find the value of this account if the interest rate is 6.6% compounded annually.

70. *Life span* Life expectancy in the United States can be approximated with the equation

$$L = 29x^{0.21}$$

where x is the number of years that the birth year is past 1900 (*Source:* National Center for Health Statistics).
(a) Express this equation with radical notation.
(b) Use the equation to estimate the life expectancy for a person born in 2015.

71. *Population* The population P of India (in billions) for 2000–2050 can be approximated by the equation

$$P = 0.924t^{0.13}$$

where $t > 0$ is the number of years past 2000 (*Source:* United Nations).
(a) Express this equation with radical notation.
(b) Does this equation predict a greater increase from 2005 to 2010 or from 2045 to 2050? What might explain this difference?

72. *Transportation* The percent p of paved roads and streets in the United States can be approximated with the equation

$$p = 14.32t^{0.38}$$

where t is the number of years past 1950 (*Source:* U.S. Department of Transportation).
(a) Express this equation with radical notation.
(b) Does this equation estimate a greater percent change during the decade from 1970 to 1980 or

during the decade from 2000 to 2010? What might explain this?
(c) When can you be certain this equation is no longer valid?

Half-life **In Problems 73 and 74, use the fact that the quantity of a radioactive substance after t years is given by $q = q_0(2^{-t/k})$, where q_0 is the original amount of radioactive material and k is its half-life (the number of years it takes for half the radioactive substance to decay).**

73. The half-life of strontium-90 is 25 years. Find the amount of strontium-90 remaining after 10 years if $q_0 = 98$ kg.

74. The half-life of carbon-14 is 5730 years. Find the amount of carbon-14 remaining after 10,000 years if $q_0 = 40.0$ g.

75. *Population growth* Suppose the formula for the growth of the population of a city for the next 10 years is given by

$$P = P_0(2.5)^{ht}$$

where P_0 is the population of the city at the present time and P is the population t years from now. If $h = 0.03$ and $P_0 = 30,000$, find P when $t = 10$.

76. *Advertising and sales* Suppose it has been determined that the sales at Ewing Gallery decline after the end of an advertising campaign, with daily sales given by

$$S = 2000(2^{-0.1x})$$

where S is in dollars and x is the number of days after the campaign ends. What are the daily sales 10 days after the end of the campaign?

77. *Company growth* The growth of a company can be described by the equation

$$N = 500(0.02)^{0.7t}$$

where t is the number of years the company has been in existence and N is the number of employees.
(a) What is the number of employees when $t = 0$? (This is the number of employees the company has when it starts.)
(b) What is the number of employees when $t = 5$?

0.5

Operations with Algebraic Expressions

In algebra we are usually dealing with combinations of real numbers (such as 3, 6/7, and $-\sqrt{2}$) and letters (such as x, a, and m). Unless otherwise specified, the letters are symbols used to represent real numbers and are sometimes called **variables.** An expression obtained by performing additions, subtractions, multiplications, divisions, or extractions of roots with one or more real numbers or variables is called an **algebraic expression.**

Unless otherwise specified, the variables represent all real numbers for which the algebraic expression is a real number. Examples of algebraic expressions include

$$3x + 2y, \quad \frac{x^3y + y}{x - 1}, \quad \text{and} \quad \sqrt{x - 3}$$

Note that the variable x cannot be negative in $\sqrt{x - 3}$ and that $(x^3y + y)/(x - 1)$ is not a real number when $x = 1$, because division by 0 is undefined.

Any product of a real number (called the **coefficient**) and one or more variables to powers is called a **term**. The sum of a finite number of terms with nonnegative integer powers on the variables is called a **polynomial**. If a polynomial contains only one variable x, then it is called a polynomial in x.

Polynomial in *x*	The general form of a **polynomial in *x*** is $$a_nx^n + a_{n-1}x^{n-1} + \cdots + a_1x + a_0$$ where each coefficient a_i is a real number for $i = 0, 1, 2, \ldots, n$. If $a_n \neq 0$, the **degree** of the polynomial is n, and a_n is called the **leading coefficient**. The term a_0 is called the **constant term**.

Thus $4x^3 - 2x - 3$ is a third-degree polynomial in x with leading coefficient 4 and constant term -3. If a term has two or more variables, the degree of the term is the sum of the exponents of the variables. The degree of a constant term is zero. Thus the degree of $4x^2y$ is $2 + 1 = 3$, the degree of $6xy$ is $1 + 1 = 2$, and the degree of 3 is 0. The **degree of a polynomial** containing one or more variables is the degree of the term in the polynomial having the highest degree. Therefore, $2xy - 4x + 6$ is a second-degree polynomial.

A polynomial containing two terms is called a **binomial**, and a polynomial containing three terms is called a **trinomial.** A single-term polynomial is a **monomial.**

Because polynomials represent real numbers, the properties of real numbers can be used to add, subtract, multiply, divide, and simplify polynomials. For example, we can use the Distributive Law to add $3x$ and $2x$.

$$3x + 2x = (3 + 2)x = 5x$$

Similarly, $9xy - 3xy = (9 - 3)xy = 6xy$.

Terms with exactly the same variable factors are called **like terms.** We can add or subtract like terms by adding or subtracting the coefficients of the variables. Subtraction of polynomials uses the Distributive Law to remove the parentheses.

EXAMPLE 1   Combining Polynomials

Compute (a) $(4xy + 3x) + (5xy - 2x)$ and (b) $(3x^2 + 4xy + 5y^2 + 1) - (6x^2 - 2xy + 4)$.

Solution
(a) $(4xy + 3x) + (5xy - 2x) = 4xy + 3x + 5xy - 2x = 9xy + x$
(b) Removing the parentheses yields

$$3x^2 + 4xy + 5y^2 + 1 - 6x^2 + 2xy - 4 = -3x^2 + 6xy + 5y^2 - 3$$

Using the rules of exponents and the Commutative and Associative Laws for multiplication, we can multiply and divide monomials, as the following example shows.

EXAMPLE 2   Products and Quotients

Perform the indicated operations.
(a) $(8xy^3)(2x^3y)(-3xy^2)$ (b) $-15x^2y^3 \div (3xy^5)$

Solution

(a) $8 \cdot 2 \cdot (-3) \cdot x \cdot x^3 \cdot x \cdot y^3 \cdot y \cdot y^2 = -48x^5y^6$

(b) $\dfrac{-15x^2y^3}{3xy^5} = -\dfrac{15}{3} \cdot \dfrac{x^2}{x} \cdot \dfrac{y^3}{y^5} = -5 \cdot x \cdot \dfrac{1}{y^2} = -\dfrac{5x}{y^2}$

    Symbols of grouping are used in algebra in the same way as they are used in the arithmetic of real numbers. Recall that when an expression has two or more symbols of grouping, we begin with the innermost and work outward.

EXAMPLE 3　　**Symbols of Grouping**

Simplify $3x^2 - [2x - (3x^2 - 2x)]$.

Solution

$$3x^2 - [2x - (3x^2 - 2x)] = 3x^2 - [2x - 3x^2 + 2x]$$
$$= 3x^2 - [4x - 3x^2]$$
$$= 3x^2 - 4x + 3x^2 = 6x^2 - 4x$$

    We can use the Distributive Law to multiply a polynomial by a monomial. For example,

$$x(2x + 3) = x \cdot 2x + x \cdot 3 = 2x^2 + 3x \quad \text{and} \quad 5(x + y + 2) = 5x + 5y + 10$$

EXAMPLE 4　　**Using the Distributive Law**

Find the following products.

(a) $-4ab(3a^2b + 4ab^2 - 1)$ (b) $(4a + 5b + c)ac$

Solution

(a) $-4ab(3a^2b + 4ab^2 - 1) = -4ab(3a^2b) + (-4ab)(4ab^2) + (-4ab)(-1)$
$$= -12a^3b^2 - 16a^2b^3 + 4ab$$

(b) $(4a + 5b + c)ac = 4a \cdot ac + 5b \cdot ac + c \cdot ac = 4a^2c + 5abc + ac^2$

    The Distributive Law can be used to multiply two polynomials. Consider the product of two binomials $(a + b)(c + d)$. If we first treat the sum $(a + b)$ as a single quantity, then two successive applications of the Distributive Law give

$$(a + b)(c + d) = (a + b) \cdot c + (a + b) \cdot d = ac + bc + ad + bd$$

Thus we see that the product can be found by multiplying $(a + b)$ by c, multiplying $(a + b)$ by d, and then adding the products.

EXAMPLE 5　　**The Product of Two Polynomials**

Find the following products.

(a) $(x + 2)(x + 5)$ (b) $(4x^2 + 3xy + 4x)(2x - 3y)$

Solution

Notice that each part uses two successive applications of the Distributive Law.

(a) $(x + 2)(x + 5) = (x + 2)(x) + (x + 2)(5) = x^2 + 2x + 5x + 10 = x^2 + 7x + 10$

(b) $(4x^2 + 3xy + 4x)(2x - 3y) = (4x^2 + 3xy + 4x)(2x) + (4x^2 + 3xy + 4x)(-3y)$
$$= 8x^3 + 6x^2y + 8x^2 - 12x^2y - 9xy^2 - 12xy$$
$$= 8x^3 - 6x^2y + 8x^2 - 9xy^2 - 12xy$$

Note in Example 5(a) that the product of two binomials has a special structure. We can obtain these products by finding the products of the First terms, Outside terms, Inside terms, and Last terms, and then adding the results. This is called the FOIL method of multiplying two binomials.

EXAMPLE 6 Products of Binomials

Multiply the following.
(a) $(x - 4)(x + 3)$
(b) $(3x + 2)(2x + 5)$

Solution

$$\overset{\text{First}}{}\ \ \overset{\text{Outside}}{}\ \ \overset{\text{Inside}}{}\ \ \ \overset{\text{Last}}{}$$

(a) $(x - 4)(x + 3) = (x^2) + (3x) + (-4x) + (-12) = x^2 - x - 12$
(b) $(3x + 2)(2x + 5) = (6x^2) + (15x) + (4x) + (10) = 6x^2 + 19x + 10$ ∎

While all binomial products can be found with the Distributive Law (or FOIL), some products have special forms worth remembering.

Special Products

1. $(x + a)^2 = x^2 + 2ax + a^2$ binomial squared
2. $(x - a)^2 = x^2 - 2ax + a^2$ binomial squared
3. $(x + a)(x - a) = x^2 - a^2$ difference of two squares
4. $(x + a)^3 = x^3 + 3ax^2 + 3a^2x + a^3$ binomial cubed
5. $(x - a)^3 = x^3 - 3ax^2 + 3a^2x - a^3$ binomial cubed

EXAMPLE 7 Special Products

Multiply the following.
(a) $(x + 5)^2$ (b) $(3x - 4y)^2$
(c) $(x - 2)(x + 2)$ (d) $(x^2 - y^3)^2$
(e) $(x + 4)^3$

Solution
(a) $(x + 5)^2 = x^2 + 2(5)x + 25 = x^2 + 10x + 25$
(b) $(3x - 4y)^2 = (3x)^2 - 2(3x)(4y) + (4y)^2 = 9x^2 - 24xy + 16y^2$
(c) $(x - 2)(x + 2) = x^2 - 4$
(d) $(x^2 - y^3)^2 = (x^2)^2 - 2(x^2)(y^3) + (y^3)^2 = x^4 - 2x^2y^3 + y^6$
(e) $(x + 4)^3 = x^3 + 3(4)(x^2) + 3(4^2)(x) + 4^3 = x^3 + 12x^2 + 48x + 64$ ∎

✓ CHECKPOINT
1. Remove parentheses and combine like terms: $9x - 5x(x + 2) + 4x^2$
2. Find the following products.
   (a) $(2x + 1)(4x^2 - 2x + 1)$ (b) $(x + 3)^2$
   (c) $(3x + 2)(x - 5)$ (d) $(1 - 4x)(1 + 4x)$

The techniques used to perform operations on polynomials and to simplify polynomials also apply to other algebraic expressions.

EXAMPLE 8 Operations with Algebraic Expressions

Perform the indicated operations.
(a) $3\sqrt{3} + 4x\sqrt{y} - 5\sqrt{3} - 11x\sqrt{y} - (\sqrt{3} - x\sqrt{y})$
(b) $x^{3/2}(x^{1/2} - x^{-1/2})$
(c) $(x^{1/2} - x^{1/3})^2$
(d) $(\sqrt{x} + 2)(\sqrt{x} - 2)$

Solution

(a) We remove parentheses and then combine the terms containing $\sqrt{3}$ and the terms containing $x\sqrt{y}$.

$$(3 - 5 - 1)\sqrt{3} + (4 - 11 + 1)x\sqrt{y} = -3\sqrt{3} - 6x\sqrt{y}$$

(b) $x^{3/2}(x^{1/2} - x^{-1/2}) = x^{3/2} \cdot x^{1/2} - x^{3/2} \cdot x^{-1/2} = x^2 - x$

(c) $(x^{1/2} - x^{1/3})^2 = (x^{1/2})^2 - 2x^{1/2}x^{1/3} + (x^{1/3})^2 = x - 2x^{5/6} + x^{2/3}$

(d) $(\sqrt{x} + 2)(\sqrt{x} - 2) = (\sqrt{x})^2 - (2)^2 = x - 4$

In later chapters we will need to write problems in a simplified form so that we can perform certain operations on them. We can often use division of one polynomial by another to obtain the simplification, as shown in the following procedure.

Division of Polynomials

Procedure	Example
To divide one polynomial by another:	Divide $4x^3 + 4x^2 + 5$ by $2x^2 + 1$.
1. Write both polynomials in descending powers of a variable. Include missing terms with coefficient 0 in the dividend.	1. $2x^2 + 1\overline{)4x^3 + 4x^2 + 0x + 5}$

2. (a) Divide the highest-power term of the divisor into the highest-power term of the dividend, and write this partial quotient above the dividend. Multiply the partial quotient times the divisor, write the product under the dividend, and subtract, getting a new dividend.

(b) Repeat until the degree of the new dividend is less than the degree of the divisor. Any remainder is written over the divisor and added to the quotient.

2. (a)
$$\begin{array}{r} 2x \phantom{{}+ 4x^2 + 0x + 5} \\ 2x^2 + 1\overline{)4x^3 + 4x^2 + 0x + 5} \\ \underline{4x^3 \phantom{{}+ 4x^2} + 2x \phantom{{}+ 5}} \\ 4x^2 - 2x + 5 \end{array}$$

(b)
$$\begin{array}{r} 2x + 2 \phantom{{}+ 0x + 5} \\ 2x^2 + 1\overline{)4x^3 + 4x^2 + 0x + 5} \\ \underline{4x^2 \phantom{{}+ 0x} + 2x \phantom{{}+ 5}} \\ 4x^2 - 2x + 5 \\ \underline{4x^2 \phantom{{}- 2x} + 2} \\ -2x + 3 \end{array}$$

Degree $(-2x + 3) <$ degree $(2x^2 + 1)$

Quotient: $2x + 2 + \dfrac{-2x + 3}{2x^2 + 1}$

EXAMPLE 9 **Division of Polynomials**

Divide $(4x^3 - 13x - 22)$ by $(x - 3)$, $x \neq 3$.

Solution

$$\begin{array}{r} 4x^2 + 12x + 23 \\ x - 3\overline{)4x^3 + 0x^2 - 13x - 22} \\ \underline{4x^3 - 12x^2 } \\ 12x^2 - 13x - 22 \\ \underline{12x^2 - 36x } \\ 23x - 22 \\ \underline{23x - 69} \\ 47 \end{array}$$

Insert $0x^2$ so that each power of x is present.

The quotient is $4x^2 + 12x + 23$, with remainder 47, or

$$4x^2 + 12x + 23 + \frac{47}{x - 3}$$

✓ CHECKPOINT   3. Use long division to find $(x^3 + 2x + 7) \div (x - 4)$.

✓ CHECKPOINT
ANSWERS

1. $-x^2 - x$
2. (a) $8x^3 + 1$
   (b) $x^2 + 6x + 9$
   (c) $3x^2 - 13x - 10$
   (d) $1 - 16x^2$
3. $x^2 + 4x + 18 + \dfrac{79}{x - 4}$

| EXERCISES | 0.5

For each polynomial in Problems 1–4, (a) give the degree of the polynomial, (b) give the coefficient (numerical) of the highest-degree term, (c) give the constant term, and (d) decide whether it is a polynomial of one or several variables.

1. $10 - 3x - x^2$
2. $5x^4 - 2x^9 + 7$
3. $7x^2y - 14xy^3z$
4. $2x^5 + 7x^2y^3 - 5y^6$

The expressions in Problems 5 and 6 are polynomials with the form $a_nx^n + a_{n-1}x^{n-1} + \cdots + a_1x + a_0$, where n is a positive integer. Complete the following.

5. For $2x^5 - 3x^2 - 5$,
   (a) $2 = a_?$
   (b) $a_3 = ?$
   (c) $-3 = a_?$
   (d) $a_0 = ?$
6. For $5x^3 - 4x - 17$,
   (a) $a_3 = ?$
   (b) $a_1 = ?$
   (c) $a_2 = ?$
   (d) $-17 = a_?$

In Problems 7–12, evaluate each algebraic expression at the indicated values of the variables.

7. $4x - x^2$ at $x = -2$
8. $10 - 6(4 - x)^2$ at $x = -1$
9. $10xy - 4(x - y)^2$ at $x = 5$ and $y = -2$
10. $3x^2 - 4y^2 - 2xy$ at $x = 3$ and $y = -4$
11. $\dfrac{2x - y}{x^2 - 2y}$ at $x = -5$ and $y = -3$
12. $\dfrac{16y}{1 - y}$ at $y = -3$
13. Evaluate $1.98T - 1.09(1 - H)(T - 58) - 56.8$ when $T = 74.7$ and $H = 0.80$.
14. Evaluate $R\left[\dfrac{0.083i}{1 - (1 + 0.083i)^{-n}}\right]$ when $R = 100,000$, $i = 0.07$, and $n = 360$.

In Problems 15–22, simplify by combining like terms.

15. $(16pq - 7p^2) + (5pq + 5p^2)$
16. $(3x^3 + 4x^2y^2) + (3x^2y^2 - 7x^3)$
17. $(4m^2 - 3n^2 + 5) - (3m^2 + 4n^2 + 8)$
18. $(4rs - 2r^2s - 11rs^2) - (11rs^2 - 2rs + 4r^2s)$
19. $-[8 - 4(q + 5) + q]$
20. $x^3 + [3x - (x^3 - 3x)]$
21. $x^2 - [x - (x^2 - 1) + 1 - (1 - x^2)] + x$
22. $y^3 - [y^2 - (y^3 + y^2)] - [y^3 + (1 - y^2)]$

In Problems 23–58, perform the indicated operations and simplify.

23. $(5x^3)(7x^2)$
24. $(-3x^2y)(2xy^3)(4x^2y^2)$
25. $(39r^3s^2) \div (13r^2s)$
26. $(-15m^3n) \div (5mn^4)$
27. $ax^2(2x^2 + ax + ab)$
28. $-3(3 - x^2)$
29. $(3y + 4)(2y - 3)$
30. $(4x - 1)(x - 3)$
31. $6(1 - 2x^2)(2 - x^2)$
32. $2(x^3 + 3)(2x^3 - 5)$
33. $(4x + 3)^2$
34. $(2y + 5)^2$
35. $(0.1 - 4x)(0.1 + 4x)$
36. $(x^3y^3 - 0.3)^2$
37. $9(2x + 1)(2x - 1)$
38. $3(5y + 2)(5y - 2)$
39. $\left(x^2 - \dfrac{1}{2}\right)^2$
40. $\left(\dfrac{2}{3} + x\right)\left(\dfrac{2}{3} - x\right)$
41. $(0.1x - 2)(x + 0.05)$
42. $(6.2x + 4.1)(6.2x - 4.1)$
43. $(x - 2)(x^2 + 2x + 4)$
44. $(a + b)(a^2 - ab + b^2)$
45. $(x^3 + 5x)(x^5 - 2x^3 + 5)$
46. $(x^3 - 1)(x^7 - 2x^4 - 5x^2 + 5)$
47. $(18m^2n + 6m^3n + 12m^4n^2) \div (6m^2n)$
48. $(16x^2 + 4xy^2 + 8x) \div (4xy)$
49. $(24x^8y^4 + 15x^5y - 6x^7y) \div (9x^5y^2)$
50. $(27x^2y^2 - 18xy + 9xy^2) \div (6xy)$
51. $(x + 1)^3$
52. $(x - 3)^3$
53. $(2x - 3)^3$
54. $(3x + 4)^3$
55. $(x^3 + x - 1) \div (x + 2)$
56. $(x^5 + 5x - 7) \div (x + 1)$
57. $(x^4 + 3x^3 - x + 1) \div (x^2 + 1)$
58. $(x^3 + 5x^2 - 6) \div (x^2 - 2)$

In Problems 59 and 60, simplify each expression.

59. (a) $(3x - 2)^2 - 3x - 2(3x - 2) + 5$
    (b) $(3x - 2)^2 - (3x - 2)(3x - 2) + 5$
60. (a) $(2x - 3)(3x + 2) - (5x - 2)(x - 3)$
    (b) $2x - 3(3x + 2) - 5x - 2(x - 3)$

In Problems 61–68, perform the indicated operations with expressions involving fractional exponents and radicals and then simplify.

61. $x^{1/2}(x^{1/2} + 2x^{3/2})$
62. $x^{-2/3}(x^{5/3} - x^{-1/3})$
63. $(x^{1/2} + 1)(x^{1/2} - 2)$
64. $(x^{1/3} - x^{1/2})(4x^{2/3} - 3x^{3/2})$
65. $(\sqrt{x} + 3)(\sqrt{x} - 3)$
66. $(x^{1/5} + x^{1/2})(x^{1/5} - x^{1/2})$
67. $(2x + 1)^{1/2}[(2x + 1)^{3/2} - (2x + 1)^{-1/2}]$
68. $(4x - 3)^{-5/3}[(4x - 3)^{8/3} + 3(4x - 3)^{5/3}]$

APPLICATIONS

69. *Revenue* A company sells its product for $55 per unit. Write an expression for the amount of money received (revenue) from the sale of x units of the product.

70. *Profit* Suppose a company's revenue R (in dollars) from the sale of x units of its product is given by

$$R = 215x$$

Suppose further that the total costs C (in dollars) of producing those x units is given by

$$C = 65x + 15{,}000$$

(a) If profit is revenue minus cost, find an expression for the profit from the production and sale of x units.

(b) Find the profit received if 1000 units are sold.

71. *Rental* A rental truck costs $49.95 for a day plus 49¢ per mile.

(a) If x is the number of miles driven, write an expression for the total cost of renting the truck for a day.

(b) Find the total cost of the rental if it was driven 132 miles.

72. *Cell phones* Cell Pro makes cell phones and has weekly costs of $1500 for rent, utilities, and equipment plus labor and material costs of $18.50 for each phone it makes.

(a) If x represents the number of phones produced and sold, write an expression for Cell Pro's weekly total cost.

(b) If Cell Pro sells the phones to dealers for $45.50 each, write an expression for the weekly total revenue for the phones.

(c) Cell Pro's weekly profit is the total revenue minus the total cost. Write an expression for Cell Pro's weekly profit.

73. *Investments* Suppose that you have $4000 to invest, and you invest x dollars at 10% and the remainder at 8%. Write expressions in x that represent

(a) the amount invested at 8%,

(b) the interest earned on the x dollars at 10%,

(c) the interest earned on the money invested at 8%,

(d) the total interest earned.

74. *Medications* Suppose that a nurse needs 10 cc (cubic centimeters) of a 15.5% solution (that is, a solution that is 15.5% ingredient) of a certain medication, which must be obtained by mixing x cc of a 20% solution and y cc of a 5% solution. Write expressions involving x for

(a) y, the amount of 5% solution,

(b) the amount of ingredient in the x cc of 20% solution,

(c) the amount of ingredient in the 5% solution,

(d) the total amount of ingredient in the mixture.

75. *Package design* The volume of a rectangular box is given by $V = (\text{length})(\text{width})(\text{height})$. If a rectangular piece of cardboard that is 10 in. by 15 in. has a square with sides of length x cut from each corner (see Figure 0.9), and if the sides are folded up along the dotted lines to form a box, what expression of x would represent the volume?

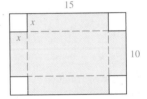

Figure 0.9

0.6

Factoring

Common Factors We can factor monomial factors out of a polynomial by using the Distributive Law in reverse; $ab + ac = a(b + c)$ is an example showing that a is a monomial factor of the polynomial $ab + ac$. But it is also a statement of the Distributive Law (with the sides of the equation interchanged). In order to factor out a monomial factor, it must be a factor of each term of the polynomial, so it is frequently called a **common monomial factor.**

EXAMPLE 1 **Monomial Factor**

Factor $-3x^2t - 3x + 9xt^2$.

Solution

1. We can factor out $3x$ and obtain

$$-3x^2t - 3x + 9xt^2 = 3x \cdot (-xt) + 3x \cdot (-1) + 3x \cdot 3t^2 = 3x(-xt - 1 + 3t^2)$$

2.   Or we can factor out $-3x$ (factoring out the negative will make the first term of the polynomial positive) and obtain

$$-3x^2t - 3x + 9xt^2 = -3x(xt + 1 - 3t^2)$$

We can use this procedure to factor out common factors that are not monomials. For example, we can factor $(a + b)$ out of the polynomial $2x(a + b) - 3y(a + b)$ and get $(a + b)(2x - 3y)$. The following example demonstrates the **factoring by grouping** technique.

EXAMPLE 2   **Factoring by Grouping**

Factor $5x - 5y + bx - by$.

Solution
We can factor this polynomial by the use of grouping. The grouping is done so that common factors (frequently binomial factors) can be removed. We see that we can factor 5 from the first two terms and b from the last two, which gives

$$5(x - y) + b(x - y)$$

This gives us two terms with the common factor $x - y$, so we get

$$(x - y)(5 + b)$$

Factoring Trinomials   We can use the formula for multiplying two binomials to factor certain trinomials. The formula

$$(x + a)(x + b) = x^2 + (a + b)x + ab$$

can be used to factor trinomials such as $x^2 - 7x + 6$.

EXAMPLE 3   **Factoring a Trinomial**

Factor $x^2 - 7x + 6$.

Solution
If this trinomial can be factored into an expression of the form

$$(x + a)(x + b)$$

then we need to find a and b such that

$$x^2 - 7x + 6 = x^2 + (a + b)x + ab$$

That is, we need to find a and b such that $a + b = -7$ and $ab = 6$. The two numbers whose sum is -7 and whose product is 6 are -1 and -6. Thus

$$x^2 - 7x + 6 = (x - 1)(x - 6)$$

A similar method can be used to factor trinomials such as $9x^2 - 31x + 12$. However, finding the proper factors for this type of trinomial may involve a fair amount of trial and error, because we must find factors a, b, c, and d such that

$$(ax + b)(cx + d) = acx^2 + (ad + bc)x + bd$$

Therefore, we can use another technique to factor more complicated trinomials, such as $9x^2 - 31x + 12$. This procedure for factoring second-degree trinomials follows.

Factoring a Trinomial

Procedure	Example
To factor a trinomial into the product of its binomial factors:	Factor $9x^2 - 31x + 12$.
1. Form the product of the second-degree term and the constant term.	1. $9x^2 \cdot 12 = 108x^2$
2. Determine whether there are any factors of the product of Step 1 that will sum to the middle term of the trinomial. (If the answer is no, the trinomial will not factor into two binomials.)	2. The factors $-27x$ and $-4x$ give a sum of $-31x$.
3. Use the sum of these two factors to replace the middle term of the trinomial.	3. $9x^2 - 31x + 12 = 9x^2 - 27x - 4x + 12$
4. Factor this four-term expression by grouping.	4. $9x^2 - 31x + 12 = (9x^2 - 27x) + (-4x + 12)$ $= 9x(x - 3) - 4(x - 3)$ $= (x - 3)(9x - 4)$

In the example just completed, note that writing the middle term $(-31x)$ as $-4x - 27x$ rather than as $-27x - 4x$ (as we did) will also result in the correct factorization. (Try it.)

EXAMPLE 4 Factoring a Trinomial

Factor $9x^2 - 9x - 10$.

Solution

The product of the second-degree term and the constant is $-90x^2$. Factors of $-90x^2$ that sum to $-9x$ are $-15x$ and $6x$. Thus

$$9x^2 - 9x - 10 = 9x^2 - 15x + 6x - 10$$
$$= (9x^2 - 15x) + (6x - 10)$$
$$= 3x(3x - 5) + 2(3x - 5) = (3x - 5)(3x + 2)$$

We can check this factorization by multiplying.

$$(3x - 5)(3x + 2) = 9x^2 + 6x - 15x - 10$$
$$= 9x^2 - 9x - 10$$

Some special products that make factoring easier are as follows.

Special Factorizations

The perfect-square trinomials:

$$x^2 + 2ax + a^2 = (x + a)^2$$
$$x^2 - 2ax + a^2 = (x - a)^2$$

The difference of two squares:

$$x^2 - a^2 = (x + a)(x - a)$$

EXAMPLE 5 Special Factorizations

(a) Factor $25x^2 - 36y^2$.
(b) Factor $4x^2 + 12x + 9$.

Solution

(a) The binomial $25x^2 - 36y^2$ is the difference of two squares, so we get

$$25x^2 - 36y^2 = (5x - 6y)(5x + 6y)$$

These two factors are called binomial **conjugates** because they differ in only one sign.

(b) Although we can use the technique we have learned to factor trinomials, the factors come quickly if we recognize that this trinomial is a perfect square. It has two square terms, and the remaining term ($12x$) is twice the product of the square roots of the squares ($12x = 2 \cdot 2x \cdot 3$). Thus

$$4x^2 + 12x + 9 = (2x + 3)^2$$

Most of the polynomials we have factored have been second-degree polynomials, or **quadratic polynomials.** Some polynomials that are not quadratic are in a form that can be factored in the same manner as quadratics. For example, the polynomial $x^4 + 4x^2 + 4$ can be written as $a^2 + 4a + 4$, where $a = x^2$.

EXAMPLE 6   **Polynomials in Quadratic Form**

Factor (a) $x^4 + 4x^2 + 4$ and (b) $x^4 - 16$.

Solution

(a) The trinomial is in the form of a perfect square, so letting $a = x^2$ will give us

$$x^4 + 4x^2 + 4 = a^2 + 4a + 4 = (a + 2)^2$$

Thus

$$x^4 + 4x^2 + 4 = (x^2 + 2)^2$$

(b) The binomial $x^4 - 16$ can be treated as the difference of two squares, $(x^2)^2 - 4^2$, so

$$x^4 - 16 = (x^2 - 4)(x^2 + 4)$$

But $x^2 - 4$ can be factored into $(x - 2)(x + 2)$, so

$$x^4 - 16 = (x - 2)(x + 2)(x^2 + 4)$$

✓ CHECKPOINT

1. Factor the following.
   (a) $8x^3 - 12x$ (b) $3x(x^2 + 5) - 5(x^2 + 5)$ (c) $x^2 - 10x - 24$
   (d) $x^2 - 5x + 6$ (e) $4x^2 - 20x + 25$ (f) $100 - 49x^2$
2. Consider $10x^2 - 17x - 20$ and observe that $(10x^2)(-20) = -200x^2$.
   (a) Find two expressions whose product is $-200x^2$ and whose sum is $-17x$.
   (b) Replace $-17x$ in $10x^2 - 17x - 20$ with the two expressions in (a).
   (c) Factor (b) by grouping.
3. True or false:
   (a) $4x^2 + 9 = (2x + 3)^2$ (b) $x^2 + x - 12 = (x - 4)(x + 3)$
   (c) $5x^5 - 20x^3 = 5x^3(x^2 - 4) = 5x^3(x + 2)(x - 2)$

A polynomial is said to be factored completely if all possible factorizations have been completed. For example, $(2x - 4)(x + 3)$ is not factored completely because a 2 can still be factored out of $2x - 4$. The following guidelines are used to factor polynomials completely.

Guidelines for Factoring Completely

Look for: Common monomial factors first.
Then for: Difference of two squares (if the expression is a binomial).
Then for: Trinomial squares.
Then for: Other methods of factoring trinomials.
Then for: Factoring by grouping (for 4-term polynomials).

EXAMPLE **7**   **Factoring Completely**

Factor completely (a) $12x^2 - 36x + 27$ and (b) $16x^2 - 64y^2$.

Solution

(a) $12x - 36x + 27 = 3(4x^2 - 12x + 9)$ Monomial
$$= 3(2x - 3)^2$$ Perfect Square

(b) $16x^2 - 64y^2 = 16(x^2 - 4y^2)$
$$= 16(x + 2y)(x - 2y)$$

Factoring the difference of two squares immediately would give $(4x + 8y)(4x - 8y)$, which is not factored completely (because we could still factor 4 from $4x + 8y$ and 4 from $4x - 8y$).

✓ CHECKPOINT
ANSWERS

1. (a) $4x(2x^2 - 3)$
    (b) $(x^2 + 5)(3x - 5)$
    (c) $(x - 12)(x + 2)$
    (d) $(x - 3)(x - 2)$
    (e) $(2x - 5)^2$
    (f) $(10 + 7x)(10 - 7x)$
2. (a) $(-25x)(+8x) = -200x^2$ and $-25x + 8x = -17x$
    (b) $10x^2 - 25x + 8x - 20$
    (c) $(2x - 5)(5x + 4)$
3. (a)   False; $4x^2 + 9$ cannot be factored. In fact, sums of squares cannot be factored.
    (b)   False; $(x + 4)(x - 3)$
    (c)   True.

| EXERCISES | 0.6

In Problems 1–4, factor out the common monomial factor.

1. $9ab - 12a^2b + 18b^2$
2. $8a^2b - 160x + 4bx^2$
3. $4x^2 + 8xy^2 + 2xy^3$
4. $12y^3z + 4yz^2 - 8y^2z^3$

In Problems 5–8, factor by grouping.

5. $7x^3 - 14x^2 + 2x - 4$
6. $5y - 20 - x^2y + 4x^2$
7. $6x - 6m + xy - my$
8. $x^3 - x^2 - 5x + 5$

Factor each expression in Problems 9–20 as a product of binomials.

9. $x^2 + 8x + 12$
10. $x^2 - 2x - 8$
11. $x^2 - 15x - 16$
12. $x^2 - 21x + 20$
13. $7x^2 - 10x - 8$
14. $12x^2 + 11x + 2$
15. $x^2 - 10x + 25$
16. $4y^2 + 12y + 9$
17. $49a^2 - 144b^2$
18. $16x^2 - 25y^2$

19. (a) $9x^2 + 21x - 8$ (b) $9x^2 + 22x + 8$
20. (a) $10x^2 - 99x - 63$ (b) $10x^2 - 27x - 63$
    (c) $10x^2 + 61x - 63$ (d) $10x^2 + 9x - 63$

In Problems 21–46, factor completely.

21. $4x^2 - x$
22. $2x^5 + 18x^3$
23. $x^3 + 4x^2 - 5x - 20$
24. $x^3 - 2x^2 - 3x + 6$
25. $x^2 - x - 6$
26. $x^2 + 6x + 8$
27. $2x^2 - 8x - 42$
28. $3x^2 - 21x + 36$
29. $2x^3 - 8x^2 + 8x$
30. $x^3 + 16x^2 + 64x$
31. $2x^2 + x - 6$
32. $2x^2 + 13x + 6$
33. $3x^2 + 3x - 36$
34. $4x^2 - 8x - 60$
35. $2x^3 - 8x$
36. $16z^2 - 81w^2$
37. $10x^2 + 19x + 6$
38. $6x^2 + 67x - 35$
39. $9 - 47x + 10x^2$
40. $10x^2 + 21x - 10$

41. $y^4 - 16x^4$ 42. $x^8 - 81$
43. $x^4 - 8x^2 + 16$ 44. $81 - 18x^2 + x^4$
45. $4x^4 - 5x^2 + 1$ 46. $x^4 - 3x^2 - 4$

In Problems 47–50, determine the missing factor.
47. $x^{3/2} + x^{1/2} = x^{1/2}(?)$ 48. $2x^{1/4} + 4x^{3/4} = 2x^{1/4}(?)$
49. $x^{-3} + x^{-2} = x^{-3}(?)$ 50. $x^{-1} - x = x^{-1}(?)$

Use the following factorization formulas involving cubes to factor each expression in Problems 51–58.

Factorizations with Cubes

Perfect cube
$$a^3 + 3a^2b + 3ab^2 + b^3 = (a + b)^3$$
Perfect cube
$$a^3 - 3a^2b + 3ab^2 - b^3 = (a - b)^3$$
Difference of two cubes
$$a^3 - b^3 = (a - b)(a^2 + ab + b^2)$$
Sum of two cubes
$$a^3 + b^3 = (a + b)(a^2 - ab + b^2)$$

---

51. $x^3 + 3x^2 + 3x + 1$ 52. $x^3 + 6x^2 + 12x + 8$
53. $x^3 - 12x^2 + 48x - 64$ 54. $y^3 - 9y^2 + 27y - 27$
55. $x^3 - 64$ 56. $8x^3 - 1$
57. $27 + 8x^3$ 58. $a^3 + 216$

APPLICATIONS

59. *Simple interest* The future value of a simple-interest investment of P dollars at an annual interest rate r for t years is given by the expression $P + Prt$. Factor this expression.

60. *Reaction to medication* When medicine is administered, the reaction (measured in change of blood pressure or temperature) can be modeled by (that is, described by)
$$R = \frac{cm^2}{2} - \frac{m^3}{3}$$
where c is a positive constant and m is the amount of medicine absorbed into the blood.* Factor the expression for the reaction.

*Source: R. M. Thrall et al., *Some Mathematical Models in Biology*, U.S. Department of Commerce, 1967.

61. *Sensitivity to medication* From the formula for reaction to medication given in Problem 60, an expression for sensitivity S can be obtained, where
$$S = cm - m^2$$
Factor this expression for sensitivity.

62. *Volume* Squares of side x are cut from four corners of an 8-by-8-inch piece of cardboard and an open-top box is formed (see Figure 0.10). The volume of the box is given by $64x - 32x^2 + 4x^3$. Factor this expression.

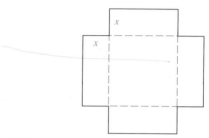

Figure 0.10

63. *Consumer expenditure* The consumer expenditure for a commodity is the product of its market price, p, and the number of units demanded. Suppose that for a certain commodity, the consumer expenditure is given by
$$10{,}000p - 100p^2$$
(a) Factor this in order to find an expression for the number of units demanded.
(b) Use (a) to find the number of units demanded when the market price is $38.

64. *Power in a circuit* Factor the following expression for the maximum power in a certain electrical circuit.
$$(R + r)^2 - 2r(R + r)$$

65. *Revenue* Revenue R from the sale of x units of a product is found by multiplying the price by the number of items sold.
(a) Factor the right side of $R = 300x - x^2$.
(b) What is the expression for the price of the item?

66. *Poiseuille's law* The expression for the speed of blood through an artery of radius r at a distance x from the artery wall is given by $r^2 - (r - x)^2$. Factor and simplify this expression.

0.7

Algebraic Fractions

Evaluating certain limits and graphing rational functions require an understanding of algebraic fractions. The fraction $6/8$ can be reduced to $3/4$ by dividing both the numerator and the denominator by 2. In the same manner, we can reduce the algebraic fraction

$$\frac{(x + 2)(x + 1)}{(x + 1)(x + 3)} \quad \text{to} \quad \frac{x + 2}{x + 3}$$

by dividing both the numerator and the denominator by $x + 1$, if $x \neq -1$.

| **Simplifying Fractions** | We *simplify* algebraic fractions by factoring the numerator and denominator and then dividing both the numerator and the denominator by any common factors.* |

EXAMPLE 1 Simplifying a Fraction

Simplify $\dfrac{3x^2 - 14x + 8}{x^2 - 16}$ if $x^2 \neq 16$.

Solution

$$\frac{3x^2 - 14x + 8}{x^2 - 16} = \frac{(3x - 2)(x - 4)}{(x - 4)(x + 4)}$$

$$= \frac{(3x - 2)\cancel{(x-4)}}{\cancel{(x-4)}(x + 4)} = \frac{3x - 2}{x + 4}$$

Products of Fractions

We can multiply fractions by writing the product as the product of the numerators divided by the product of the denominators and then reducing. For example,

$$\frac{4}{5} \cdot \frac{10}{12} \cdot \frac{2}{5} = \frac{80}{300} = \frac{4}{15}$$

We can also find the product by reducing the fractions before we multiply. For instance, in the example above, we can divide the first numerator and the second denominator by 4 and divide the second numerator and the first denominator by 5, which yields

$$\frac{4}{5} \cdot \frac{10}{12} \cdot \frac{2}{5} = \frac{\overset{1}{\cancel{4}}}{\underset{1}{\cancel{5}}} \cdot \frac{\overset{2}{\cancel{10}}}{\underset{3}{\cancel{12}}} \cdot \frac{2}{5} = \frac{1}{1} \cdot \frac{2}{3} \cdot \frac{2}{5} = \frac{4}{15}$$

| **Product of Fractions** | We *multiply* algebraic fractions by writing the product of the numerators divided by the product of the denominators, and then reduce to lowest terms. We may also reduce prior to finding the product. |

EXAMPLE 2 Multiplying Fractions

Multiply:

(a) $\dfrac{4x^2}{5y} \cdot \dfrac{10x}{y^2} \cdot \dfrac{y}{8x^2}$ (b) $\dfrac{-4x + 8}{3x + 6} \cdot \dfrac{2x + 4}{4x + 12}$

Solution

(a) $\dfrac{4x^2}{5y} \cdot \dfrac{10x}{y^2} \cdot \dfrac{y}{8x^2} = \dfrac{\overset{1}{\cancel{4x^2}}}{\underset{1\cdot1}{\cancel{5y}}} \cdot \dfrac{\overset{2}{\cancel{10x}}}{y^2} \cdot \dfrac{\overset{1}{\cancel{y}}}{\underset{2}{\cancel{8x^2}}} = \dfrac{1}{1} \cdot \dfrac{\overset{}{2x}}{y^2} \cdot \dfrac{1}{\underset{1}{2}} = \dfrac{x}{y^2}$

(b) $\dfrac{-4x + 8}{3x + 6} \cdot \dfrac{2x + 4}{4x + 12} = \dfrac{-4(x - 2)}{3(x + 2)} \cdot \dfrac{2(x + 2)}{4(x + 3)}$ Factor the numerators and denominators

$$= \frac{\overset{-1}{\cancel{-4}}(x - 2)}{3\cancel{(x+2)}} \cdot \frac{2\cancel{(x+2)}}{\underset{1}{\cancel{4}}(x + 3)} = \frac{-2(x - 2)}{3(x + 3)}$$

*We assume that all fractions are defined.

Quotients of Fractions In arithmetic we learned to divide one fraction by another by inverting the divisor and multiplying. The same rule applies to division of algebraic fractions.

EXAMPLE 3 Dividing Fractions

(a) Divide $\dfrac{a^2b}{c}$ by $\dfrac{ab}{c^2}$.

(b) Find $\dfrac{6x^2-6}{x^2+3x+2} \div \dfrac{x-1}{x^2+4x+4}$.

Solution

(a) $\dfrac{a^2b}{c} \div \dfrac{ab}{c^2} = \dfrac{a^2b}{c} \cdot \dfrac{c^2}{ab} = \dfrac{\overset{a\cdot1}{a^2b}}{\underset{1}{c}} \cdot \dfrac{\overset{c}{c^2}}{\underset{1\cdot1}{ab}} = \dfrac{ac}{1} = ac$

(b) $\dfrac{6x^2-6}{x^2+3x+2} \div \dfrac{x-1}{x^2+4x+4} = \dfrac{6x^2-6}{x^2+3x+2} \cdot \dfrac{x^2+4x+4}{x-1}$

$= \dfrac{6(x-1)(x+1)}{(x+2)(x+1)} \cdot \dfrac{(x+2)(x+2)}{x-1}$

$= 6(x+2)$

✓ CHECKPOINT

1. Simplify: $\dfrac{2x^2-4x}{2x}$

2. Multiply: $\dfrac{x^2}{x^2-9} \cdot \dfrac{x+3}{3x}$

3. Divide: $\dfrac{5x^2(x-1)}{2(x+1)} \div \dfrac{10x^2}{(x+1)(x-1)}$

Adding and Subtracting Fractions Recall from arithmetic that we can add or subtract two fractions when the denominators are the same. If the denominators are not the same, we can write the equivalents of each of the fractions with a common denominator—usually the least common denominator (LCD). For algebraic fractions, the **least common denominator** is the lowest-degree variable expression into which all denominators will divide. If the denominators are polynomials, then the LCD is the lowest-degree polynomial into which all denominators will divide. We can find the least common denominator as follows.

Finding the Least Common Denominator

Procedure	Example
To find the least common denominator of a set of fractions:	Find the LCD of $\dfrac{1}{x^2-x}, \dfrac{1}{x^2-1}, \dfrac{1}{x^2}$.
1. Completely factor each denominator.	1. The factored denominators are $x(x-1)$, $(x+1)(x-1)$, and $x\cdot x$.
2. Identify the different factors that appear.	2. The different factors are x, $x-1$, and $x+1$.
3. The LCD is the product of these different factors, with each factor used the maximum number of times it occurs in any one denominator.	3. x occurs a maximum of twice in one denominator, $x-1$ occurs once, and $x+1$ occurs once. Thus the LCD is $x\cdot x(x-1)(x+1) = x^2(x-1)(x+1)$.

The procedure for combining (adding or subtracting) two or more fractions follows.

Combining Fractions

Procedure	Example
To combine fractions:	Combine $\dfrac{y-3}{y-5}+\dfrac{y-23}{y^2-y-20}$.
1. Find the LCD of the fractions.	1. $y^2-y-20=(y-5)(y+4)$, so the LCD is $(y-5)(y+4)$.
2. Write the equivalent of each fraction with the LCD as its denominator.	2. The sum is $\dfrac{(y-3)(y+4)}{(y-5)(y+4)}+\dfrac{y-23}{(y-5)(y+y)}$.
3. Add or subtract, as indicated, by combining like terms in the numerator over the LCD.	3. $=\dfrac{y^2+y-12+y-23}{(y-5)(y+4)}$ $=\dfrac{y^2+2y-35}{(y-5)(y+4)}$
4. Reduce the fraction, if possible.	4. $=\dfrac{(y+7)(y-5)}{(y-5)(y+4)}=\dfrac{y+7}{y+4}$, if $y\neq5$.

EXAMPLE 4   Combining Fractions

Combine:

(a) $\dfrac{3x}{a^2}+\dfrac{4}{ax}$ (b) $\dfrac{y-3}{(y-5)^2}-\dfrac{y-2}{y^2-4y-5}$

Solution

(a) 1. The LCD is a^2x.

2. $\dfrac{3x}{a^2}+\dfrac{4}{ax}=\dfrac{3x}{a^2}\cdot\dfrac{x}{x}+\dfrac{4}{ax}\cdot\dfrac{a}{a}=\dfrac{3x^2}{a^2x}+\dfrac{4a}{a^2x}$

3. $\dfrac{3x^2}{a^2x}+\dfrac{4a}{a^2x}=\dfrac{3x^2+4a}{a^2x}$

4. The sum is in lowest terms.

(b) Since $y^2-4y-5=(y-5)(y+1)$, the LCD is $(y-5)^2(y+1)$.

Writing the equivalent fractions and then combining them, we get

$\dfrac{y-3}{(y-5)^2}-\dfrac{y-2}{(y-5)(y+1)}=\dfrac{(y-3)(y+1)}{(y-5)^2(y+1)}-\dfrac{(y-2)(y-5)}{(y-5)(y+1)(y-5)}$

$=\dfrac{(y^2-2y-3)-(y^2-7y+10)}{(y-5)^2(y+1)}$

$=\dfrac{y^2-2y-3-y^2+7y-10}{(y-5)^2(y+1)}$

$=\dfrac{5y-13}{(y-5)^2(y+1)}$

Complex Fractions   A fractional expression that contains one or more fractions in its numerator or denominator is called a **complex fraction**. An example of a complex fraction is

$$\dfrac{\dfrac{1}{3}+\dfrac{4}{x}}{3-\dfrac{1}{xy}}$$

We can simplify fractions of this type using the property $\dfrac{a}{b} = \dfrac{ac}{bc}$, with c equal to the LCD of *all* the fractions contained in the numerator and denominator of the complex fraction.

For example, all fractions contained in the preceding complex fraction have LCD $3xy$. We simplify this complex fraction by multiplying the numerator and denominator as follows:

$$\frac{\dfrac{1}{3} + \dfrac{4}{x}}{3 - \dfrac{1}{xy}} = \frac{3xy\left(\dfrac{1}{3} + \dfrac{4}{x}\right)}{3xy\left(3 - \dfrac{1}{xy}\right)} = \frac{3xy\left(\dfrac{1}{3}\right) + 3xy\left(\dfrac{4}{x}\right)}{3xy(3) - 3xy\left(\dfrac{1}{xy}\right)} = \frac{xy + 12y}{9xy - 3}$$

EXAMPLE 5 | **Complex Fractions**

Simplify $\dfrac{x^{-3} + x^2 y^{-3}}{(xy)^{-2}}$ so that only positive exponents remain.

Solution

$$\frac{x^{-3} + x^2 y^{-3}}{(xy)^{-2}} = \frac{\dfrac{1}{x^3} + \dfrac{x^2}{y^3}}{\dfrac{1}{(xy)^2}} \qquad \text{LCD} = x^3 y^3$$

$$= \frac{x^3 y^3\left(\dfrac{1}{x^3} + \dfrac{x^2}{y^3}\right)}{x^3 y^3\left(\dfrac{1}{x^2 y^2}\right)} = \frac{x^3 y^3\left(\dfrac{1}{x^3}\right) + x^3 y^3\left(\dfrac{x^2}{y^3}\right)}{x^3 y^3\left(\dfrac{1}{x^2 y^2}\right)} = \frac{y^3 + x^5}{xy}$$

✓ CHECKPOINT

4. Combine the following fractions.

(a) $\dfrac{5x - 1}{2x - 5} - \dfrac{x + 9}{2x - 5}$ (b) $\dfrac{x + 1}{x} + \dfrac{x}{x - 1}$

5. Simplify $\dfrac{\dfrac{y}{x} - 1}{\dfrac{y}{x} - \dfrac{x}{y}}$.

Rationalizing Denominators

We can simplify algebraic fractions whose denominators contain sums and differences that involve square roots by rationalizing the denominators. Using the fact that $(x + y)(x - y) = x^2 - y^2$, we multiply the numerator and denominator of an algebraic fraction of this type by the conjugate of the denominator to simplify the fraction.

EXAMPLE 6 | **Rationalizing Denominators**

Rationalize the denominators.

(a) $\dfrac{1}{\sqrt{x} - 2}$ (b) $\dfrac{3 + \sqrt{x}}{\sqrt{x} + \sqrt{5}}$

Solution

Multiplying $\sqrt{x} - 2$ by $\sqrt{x} + 2$, its conjugate, gives the difference of two squares and removes the radical from the denominator in (a). We also use the conjugate in (b).

(a) $\dfrac{1}{\sqrt{x} - 2} \cdot \dfrac{\sqrt{x} + 2}{\sqrt{x} + 2} = \dfrac{\sqrt{x} + 2}{(\sqrt{x})^2 - (2)^2} = \dfrac{\sqrt{x} + 2}{x - 4}$

(b) $\dfrac{3 + \sqrt{x}}{\sqrt{x} + \sqrt{5}} \cdot \dfrac{\sqrt{x} - \sqrt{5}}{\sqrt{x} - \sqrt{5}} = \dfrac{3\sqrt{x} - 3\sqrt{5} + x - \sqrt{5x}}{x - 5}$

✓ CHECKPOINT

6. Rationalize the denominator: $\dfrac{\sqrt{x}}{\sqrt{x}-3}$.

✓ CHECKPOINT
ANSWERS

1. $x-2$

2. $\dfrac{x}{3x-9}$

3. $\dfrac{(x-1)^2}{4}$

4. (a) 2

    (b) $\dfrac{2x^2-1}{x(x-1)}$

5. $\dfrac{y}{y+x}$

6. $\dfrac{x+3\sqrt{x}}{x-9}$

| EXERCISES | 0.7

In Problems 1–6 simplify each fraction.

1. $\dfrac{18x^3y^3}{9x^3z}$

2. $\dfrac{15a^4b^5}{30a^3b}$

3. $\dfrac{x-3y}{3x-9y}$

4. $\dfrac{x^2-6x+8}{x^2-16}$

5. $\dfrac{x^2-2x+1}{x^2-4x+3}$

6. $\dfrac{x^2-5x+6}{9-x^2}$

In Problems 7–34, perform the indicated operations and simplify.

7. $\dfrac{6x^3}{8y^3}\cdot\dfrac{16x}{9y^2}\cdot\dfrac{15y^4}{x^3}$

8. $\dfrac{25ac^2}{15a^2c}\cdot\dfrac{4ad^4}{15abc^3}$

9. $\dfrac{8x-16}{x-3}\cdot\dfrac{4x-12}{3x-6}$

10. $(x^2-4)\cdot\dfrac{2x-3}{x+2}$

11. $\dfrac{x^2+7x+12}{3x^2+13x+4}\cdot(9x+3)$

12. $\dfrac{4x+4}{x-4}\cdot\dfrac{x^2-6x+8}{8x^2+8x}$

13. $\dfrac{x^2-x-2}{2x^2-8}\cdot\dfrac{18-2x^2}{x^2-5x+4}\cdot\dfrac{x^2-2x-8}{x^2-6x+9}$

14. $\dfrac{x^2-5x-6}{x^2-5x+4}\cdot\dfrac{x^2-x-12}{x^3-6x^2}\cdot\dfrac{x-x^3}{x^2-2x+1}$

15. $\dfrac{15ac^2}{7bd}\div\dfrac{4a}{14b^2d}$

16. $\dfrac{16}{x-2}\div\dfrac{4}{3x-6}$

17. $\dfrac{y^2-2y+1}{7y^2-7y}\div\dfrac{y^2-4y+3}{35y^2}$

18. $\dfrac{6x^2}{4x^2y-12xy}\div\dfrac{3x^2+12x}{x^2+x-12}$

19. $(x^2-x-6)\div\dfrac{9-x^2}{x^2-3x}$

20. $\dfrac{2x^2+7x+3}{4x^2-1}\div(x+3)$

21. $\dfrac{2x}{x^2-x-2}-\dfrac{x+2}{x^2-x-2}$

22. $\dfrac{4}{9-x^2}-\dfrac{x+1}{9-x^2}$

23. $\dfrac{a}{a-2}-\dfrac{a-2}{a}$

24. $x-\dfrac{2}{x-1}$

25. $\dfrac{x}{x+1}-x+1$

26. $\dfrac{x-1}{x+1}-\dfrac{2}{x^2+x}$

27. $\dfrac{4a}{3x+6}+\dfrac{5a^2}{4x+8}$

28. $\dfrac{b-1}{b^2+2b}+\dfrac{b}{3b+6}$

29. $\dfrac{3x-1}{2x-4}+\dfrac{4x}{3x-6}-\dfrac{x-4}{5x-10}$

30. $\dfrac{2x+1}{4x-2}+\dfrac{5}{2x}-\dfrac{x+4}{2x^2-x}$

31. $\dfrac{x}{x^2-4}+\dfrac{4}{x^2-x-2}-\dfrac{x-2}{x^2+3x+2}$

32. $\dfrac{3x^2}{x^2-4}+\dfrac{2}{x^2-4x+4}-3$

33. $\dfrac{-x^3+x}{\sqrt{3-x^2}}+2x\sqrt{3-x^2}$

34. $\dfrac{3x^2(x+1)}{\sqrt{x^3+1}}+\sqrt{x^3+1}$

In Problems 35–42, simplify each complex fraction.

35. $\dfrac{3-\dfrac{2}{3}}{14}$

36. $\dfrac{4}{\dfrac{1}{4}+\dfrac{1}{4}}$

37. $\dfrac{x+y}{\dfrac{1}{x}+\dfrac{1}{y}}$

38. $\dfrac{\dfrac{5}{2y}+\dfrac{3}{y}}{\dfrac{1}{4}+\dfrac{1}{3y}}$

39. $\dfrac{2-\dfrac{1}{x}}{2x-\dfrac{3x}{x+1}}$

40. $\dfrac{1-\dfrac{2}{x-2}}{x-6+\dfrac{10}{x+1}}$

41. $\dfrac{\sqrt{a}-\dfrac{b}{\sqrt{a}}}{a-b}$

42. $\dfrac{\sqrt{x-1}+\dfrac{1}{\sqrt{x-1}}}{x}$

In Problems 43–46, rewrite each of the following so that only positive exponents remain and simplify.

43. (a) $(2^{-2}-3^{-1})^{-1}$ (b) $(2^{-1}+3^{-1})^2$

44. (a) $(3^2+4^2)^{-1/2}$ (b) $(2^2+3^2)^{-1}$

45. $\dfrac{2a^{-1}-b^{-2}}{(ab^2)^{-1}}$

46. $\dfrac{x^{-2}+xy^{-2}}{(x^2y)^{-2}}$

In Problems 47 and 48, rationalize the denominator of each fraction and simplify.

47. $\dfrac{1-\sqrt{x}}{1+\sqrt{x}}$

48. $\dfrac{x-3}{x-\sqrt{3}}$

In Problems 49 and 50, rationalize the numerator of each fraction and simplify.

49. $\dfrac{\sqrt{x+h}-\sqrt{x}}{h}$

50. $\dfrac{\sqrt{9+2h}-3}{h}$

APPLICATIONS

51. *Time study* Workers A, B, and C can complete a job in a, b, and c hours, respectively. Working together, they can complete

$$\frac{1}{a}+\frac{1}{b}+\frac{1}{c}$$

of the job in 1 hour. Add these fractions over a common denominator to obtain an expression for what they can do in 1 hour, working together.

52. *Focal length* Two thin lenses with focal lengths p and q and separated by a distance d have their combined focal length given by the reciprocal of

$$\frac{1}{p}+\frac{1}{q}-\frac{d}{pq}$$

(a) Combine these fractions.
(b) Use the reciprocal of your answer in (a) to find the combined focal length.

Average cost **A company's average cost per unit when x units are produced is defined to be**

$$\textbf{Average cost}=\frac{\textbf{Total cost}}{x}$$

Use this equation in Problems 53 and 54.

53. Suppose a company's average costs are given by

$$\text{Average cost}=\frac{4000}{x}+55+0.1x$$

(a) Express the average-cost formula as a single fraction.
(b) Write the expression that gives the company's total costs.

54. Suppose a company's average costs are given by

$$\text{Average cost}=\frac{40{,}500}{x}+190+0.2x$$

(a) Express the average-cost formula as a single fraction.
(b) Write the expression that gives the company's total costs.

55. *Advertising and sales* Suppose that a company's daily sales volume attributed to an advertising campaign is given by

$$\text{Sales volume}=1+\frac{3}{t+3}-\frac{18}{(t+3)^2}$$

where t is the number of days since the campaign started. Express the sales volume as a single fraction.

56. *Annuity* The formula for the future value of an annuity due involves the expression

$$\frac{(1+i)^{n+1}-1}{i}-1$$

Write this expression over a common denominator and factor the numerator to simplify.

Chapter 0 **Summary & Review**

KEY TERMS AND FORMULAS

Section 0.1

Sets and set membership (p. 2)
Natural numbers (p. 2)
$\quad N = \{1, 2, 3, 4 \ldots\}$
Empty set (p. 2)
$\quad \varnothing$
Set equality (p. 2)
Subset (p. 2)
$\quad A \subseteq B$
Disjoint sets (p. 2)
$\quad A \cap B = \varnothing$

Universal set (p. 3)
$\quad U$
Venn diagrams (p. 3)
Set intersection (p. 3)
$\quad A \cap B$
Set union (p. 4)
$\quad A \cup B$
Set complement (p. 4)
$\quad A'$

Section 0.2

Real numbers (p. 9)
$\quad$ Subsets
Real number line (p. 9)
Properties of real numbers (p. 10)
Inequalities (p. 10)
Intervals and interval notation (p. 10)

Closed interval
$\quad a \leq x \leq b$ or $[a, b]$
Open interval
$\quad a < x < b$ or (a, b)
Absolute value (p. 11)
Order of operations (p. 12)

Section 0.3

Exponent and base (p. 16)
$\quad a^n$ has base a, exponent n
Zero exponent (p. 17)
$\quad a^0 = 1, a \neq 0$

Negative exponent (p. 17)
$$a^{-n} = \frac{1}{a^n}$$
Rules of exponents (p. 17)

Section 0.4

Radical $\sqrt[n]{a}$ (p. 21)
$\quad$ radicand $= a$; index $= n$
Principal nth root (p. 21)
$\quad \sqrt[n]{a} = b$ only if $b^n = a$ and $a \geq 0$ and $b \geq 0$ when n is even

Fractional exponents (p. 21)
$\quad a^{1/n} = \sqrt[n]{a}$
$\quad a^{m/n} = \sqrt[n]{a^m} = \left(\sqrt[n]{a}\right)^m$
Properties of radicals (p. 23)
Rationalizing the denominator (p. 24)

Section 0.5

Variable (p. 27)
Algebraic expression (p. 27)
Coefficient (p. 28)
Term (p. 28)
Polynomial in x (p. 28)
$\quad a_n x^n + \cdots + a_1 x + a_0$
Degree (p. 28)
Constant term (p. 28)
Binomial (p. 28)

Trinomial (p. 28)
Monomial (p. 28)
Like terms (p. 28)
Distributive Law (p. 29)
$\quad a(b + c) = ab + ac$
Polynomial products (p. 29)
Special binomial products (p. 30)
Division of polynomials (p. 31)

Section 0.6

Factor (p. 33)
Common factor (p. 33)
Factoring by grouping (p. 34)
Factoring trinomials (p. 35)
Special factorizations (p. 35)
$\quad$ Perfect squares
$\quad\quad a^2 + 2ab + b^2 = (a + b)^2$
$\quad\quad a^2 - 2ab + b^2 = (a - b)^2$

Difference of squares
$\quad a^2 - b^2 = (a + b)(a - b)$
Conjugates (p. 35)
$\quad a + b; a - b$
Quadratic polynomials (p. 36)
$\quad ax^2 + bx + c$
Factoring completely (p. 37)

Section 0.7

REVIEW EXERCISES

Section 0.1

1. Is $A \subseteq B$ if $A = \{1, 2, 5, 7\}$ and
   $B = \{x: x \text{ is a positive integer}, x \le 8\}$?
2. Is it true that $3 \in \{x: x > 3\}$?
3. Are $A = \{1, 2, 3, 4\}$ and $B = \{x: x \le 1\}$ disjoint?

In Problems 4–7, use sets $U = \{1, 2, 3, 4, 5, 6, 7, 8, 9, 10\}$, $A = \{1, 2, 3, 9\}$, and $B = \{1, 3, 5, 6, 7, 8, 10\}$ to find the elements of the sets described.

4. $A \cup B'$
5. $A' \cap B$
6. $(A' \cap B)'$
7. Does $(A' \cup B')' = A \cap B$?

Section 0.2

8. State the property of the real numbers that is illustrated in each case.
   (a) $6 + \dfrac{1}{3} = \dfrac{1}{3} + 6$ (b) $2(3 \cdot 4) = (2 \cdot 3)4$
   (c) $\dfrac{1}{3}(6 + 9) = 2 + 3$

9. Indicate whether each given expression is one or more of the following: rational, irrational, integer, natural, or undefined.
   (a) π (b) $0/6$ (c) $6/0$

10. Insert the proper sign ($<$, $=$, or $>$) to replace each $\square$.
    (a) $\pi \; \square \; 3.14$ (b) $-100 \; \square \; 0.1$ (c) $-3 \; \square -12$

For Problems 11–18, evaluate each expression.

11. $|5 - 11|$
12. $44 \div 2 \cdot 11 - 10^2$
13. $(-3)^2 - (-1)^3$
14. $\dfrac{(3)(2)(15) - (5)(8)}{(4)(10)}$
15. $2 - [3 - (2 - |-3|)] + 11$
16. $-4^2 - (-4)^2 + 3$
17. $\dfrac{4 + 3^2}{4}$
18. $\dfrac{(-2.91)^5}{\sqrt{3.29^5}}$

19. Write each inequality in interval notation, name the type of interval, and graph it on a real number line.
    (a) $0 \le x \le 5$
    (b) $x \ge -3$ and $x < 7$
    (c) $(-4, \infty) \cap (-\infty, 0)$

20. Write an inequality that represents each of the following.
    (a) $(-1, 16)$ (b) $[-12, 8]$
    (c)

Section 0.3

21. Evaluate the following without a calculator.
    (a) $\left(\dfrac{3}{8}\right)^0$ (b) $2^3 \cdot 2^{-5}$
    (c) $\dfrac{4^9}{4^3}$ (d) $\left(\dfrac{1}{7}\right)^3 \left(\dfrac{1}{7}\right)^{-4}$

22. Rewrite each of the following with positive exponents. Assume all variables are nonzero.
    (a) $x^5 \cdot x^{-7}$ (b) x^8/x^{-2} (c) $(x^3)^3$
    (d) $(y^4)^{-2}$ (e) $(-y^{-3})^{-2}$

For Problems 23–28, simplify each expression so that only positive exponents remain. Assume all variables are nonzero.

23. $\dfrac{-(2xy^2)^{-2}}{(3x^{-2}y^{-3})^2}$
24. $\left(\dfrac{2}{3}x^2y^{-4}\right)^{-2}$
25. $\left(\dfrac{x^{-2}}{2y^{-1}}\right)^2$
26. $\dfrac{(-x^4y^{-2}z^2)^0}{-(x^4y^{-2}z^2)^{-2}}$
27. $\left(\dfrac{x^{-3}y^4z^{-2}}{3x^{-2}y^{-3}z^{-3}}\right)^{-1}$
28. $\left(\dfrac{x}{2y}\right)\left(\dfrac{y}{x^2}\right)^{-2}$

Section 0.4

29. Find the following roots.
    (a) $-\sqrt[3]{-64}$ (b) $\sqrt{4/49}$ (c) $\sqrt[7]{1.9487171}$
30. Write each of the following with an exponent and with the variable in the numerator.
    (a) $\sqrt{x}$ (b) $\sqrt[3]{x^2}$ (c) $1/\sqrt[4]{x}$
31. Write each of the following in radical form.
    (a) $x^{3/7}$ (b) $x^{-1/2}$ (c) $-x^{3/2}$
32. Rationalize each of the following denominators and simplify.
    (a) $\dfrac{5xy}{\sqrt{2x}}$ (b) $\dfrac{y}{x\sqrt[3]{xy^2}}$

In Problems 33–38, simplify so that only positive exponents remain. Assume all variables are positive.

33. $x^{1/2} \cdot x^{1/3}$
34. $y^{-3/4}/y^{-7/4}$
35. $x^4 \cdot x^{1/4}$
36. $1/(x^{-4/3} \cdot x^{-7/3})$
37. $(x^{4/5})^{1/2}$
38. $(x^{1/2}y^2)^4$

In Problems 39–44, simplify each expression. Assume all variables are positive.

39. $\sqrt{12x^3y^5}$
40. $\sqrt{1250x^6y^9}$
41. $\sqrt[3]{24x^4y^4} \cdot \sqrt[3]{45x^4y^{10}}$
42. $\sqrt{16a^2b^3} \cdot \sqrt{8a^3b^5}$

43. $\dfrac{\sqrt{52x^3y^6}}{\sqrt{13xy^4}}$

44. $\dfrac{\sqrt{32x^4y^3}}{\sqrt{6xy^{10}}}$

Section 0.5

In Problems 45–62, perform the indicated operations and simplify.

45. $(3x + 5) - (4x + 7)$
46. $x(1 - x) + x[x - (2 + x)]$
47. $(3x^3 - 4xy - 3) + (5xy + x^3 + 4y - 1)$
48. $(4xy^3)(6x^4y^2)$ 49. $(3x - 4)(x - 1)$
50. $(3x - 1)(x + 2)$ 51. $(4x + 1)(x - 2)$
52. $(3x - 7)(2x + 1)$ 53. $(2x - 3)^2$
54. $(4x + 3)(4x - 3)$ 55. $(2x^2 + 1)(x^2 + x - 3)$
56. $(2x - 1)^3$ 57. $(x - y)(x^2 + xy + y^2)$
58. $\dfrac{4x^2y - 3x^3y^3 - 6x^4y^2}{2x^2y^2}$
59. $(3x^4 + 2x^3 - x + 4) \div (x^2 + 1)$
60. $(x^4 - 4x^3 + 5x^2 + x) \div (x - 3)$
61. $x^{4/3}(x^{2/3} - x^{-1/3})$
62. $(\sqrt{x} + \sqrt{a - x})(\sqrt{x} - \sqrt{a - x})$

Section 0.6

In Problems 63–73, factor each expression completely.

63. $2x^4 - x^3$ 64. $4(x^2 + 1)^2 - 2(x^2 + 1)^3$
65. $4x^2 - 4x + 1$ 66. $16 - 9x^2$
67. $2x^4 - 8x^2$ 68. $x^2 - 4x - 21$
69. $3x^2 - x - 2$ 70. $x^2 - 5x + 6$
71. $x^2 - 10x - 24$ 72. $12x^2 - 23x - 24$
73. $16x^4 - 72x^2 + 81$
74. Factor as indicated: $x^{-2/3} + x^{-4/3} = x^{-4/3}(?)$

Section 0.7

75. Simplify each of the following.

   (a) $\dfrac{2x}{2x + 4}$ (b) $\dfrac{4x^2y^3 - 6x^3y^4}{2x^2y^2 - 3xy^3}$

In Problems 76–82, perform the indicated operations and simplify.

76. $\dfrac{x^2 - 4x}{x^2 + 4} \cdot \dfrac{x^4 - 16}{x^4 - 16x^2}$

77. $\dfrac{x^2 + 6x + 9}{x^2 - 7x + 12} \div \dfrac{x^2 + 4x + 3}{x^2 - 3x - 4}$

78. $\dfrac{x^4 - 2x^3}{3x^2 - x - 2} \div \dfrac{x^3 - 4x}{9x^2 - 4}$

79. $1 + \dfrac{3}{2x} - \dfrac{1}{6x^2}$

80. $\dfrac{1}{x - 2} - \dfrac{x - 2}{4}$

81. $\dfrac{x + 2}{x^2 - x} - \dfrac{x^2 + 4}{x^2 - 2x + 1} + 1$

82. $\dfrac{x - 1}{x^2 - x - 2} - \dfrac{x}{x^2 - 2x - 3} + \dfrac{1}{x - 2}$

In Problems 83 and 84, simplify each complex fraction.

83. $\dfrac{x - 1 - \dfrac{x - 1}{x}}{\dfrac{1}{x - 1} + 1}$ 84. $\dfrac{x^{-2} - x^{-1}}{x^{-2} + x^{-1}}$

85. Rationalize the denominator of $\dfrac{3x - 3}{\sqrt{x} - 1}$ and simplify.

86. Rationalize the numerator of $\dfrac{\sqrt{x} - \sqrt{x - 4}}{2}$ and simplify.

APPLICATIONS

Section 0.1

87. *Job effectiveness factors* In an attempt to determine some off-the-job factors that might be indicators of on-the-job effectiveness, a company made a study of 200 of its employees. It was interested in whether the employees had been recognized for superior work by their supervisors within the past year, whether they were involved in community activities, and whether they followed a regular exercise plan. The company found the following.

    30 answered "yes" to all three
    50 were recognized and they exercised
    52 were recognized and were involved in the community
    77 were recognized
    37 were involved in the community but did not exercise
    95 were recognized or were involved in the community
    95 answered "no" to all three

    (a) Draw a Venn diagram that represents this information.
    (b) How many exercised only?
    (c) How many exercised or were involved in the community?

Section 0.2

88. *Health insurance coverage* The percent of the U.S. population covered by an employment-based health insurance plan can be approximated by the expression

$$-0.75x + 63.8$$

   where x is the number of years past 2000 (*Source:* U.S. Census Bureau). Use this expression to estimate the percent covered by such a plan in the year 2015.

89. *Poiseuille's law* The expression for the speed of blood through an artery of radius r at a distance x from the artery wall is given by $r^2 - (r - x)^2$. Evaluate this expression when $r = 5$ and $x = 2$.

Section 0.3

90. *Future value* If an individual makes monthly deposits of $100 in an account that earns 9% compounded monthly, then the future value S of the account after n months is given by the formula

$$S = \$100\left[\frac{(1.0075)^n - 1}{0.0075}\right]$$

   (a) Find the future value after 36 months (3 years).
   (b) Find the future value after 20 years.

91. *Health insurance cost* The per capita net cost C (in dollars) of private health insurance coverage in the United States from 2009 and projected to 2021 can be approximated by the formula

$$C = 31.9t + 310$$

   where t is the number of years past 2005 (*Source:* Centers for Medicare and Medicaid Services).
   (a) To estimate these per capita costs for 2021, what t-value must be used?
   (b) Estimate the per capita net cost of private heath insurance coverage in 2021.
   (c) What does part (b) mean for a family of 4 in 2021?

92. *Severe weather ice makers* Thunderstorms severe enough to produce hail develop when an upper-level low (a pool of cold air high in the atmosphere) moves through a region where there is warm, moist air at the surface. These storms create an updraft that draws the moist air into subfreezing air above 10,000 feet. The strength of the updraft, as measured by its speed s (in mph), affects the diameter of the hail h (in inches) according to

$$h = 0.000595s^{1.922} \quad \text{or equivalently} \quad s = 47.7h^{0.519}$$

   (*Source:* National Weather Service).
   (a) What size hail is produced by an updraft of 50 mph?
   (b) When a storm produces softball-sized hail (about 4.5 inches in diameter), how fast is the updraft?

Sections 0.3 and 0.7

93. *Loan payment* Suppose you borrow $10,000 for n months to buy a car at an interest rate of 7.8% compounded monthly. The size of each month's payment R is given by the formula

$$R = 10,000\left[\frac{0.0065}{1 - (1.0065)^{-n}}\right]$$

   (a) Rewrite the expression on the right-hand side of this formula as a fraction with only positive exponents.
   (b) Find the monthly payment for a 48-month loan. Use both the original formula and your result from (a). (Both formulas should give the same payment.)

Section 0.4

94. *Environment* Suppose that in a study of water birds, the relationship between the number of acres of wetlands A and the number of species of birds S found in the wetlands area was given by

$$S = kA^{1/3}$$

   where k is a constant.
   (a) Express this formula using radical notation.
   (b) If the area is expanded by a factor of 2.25 from 20,000 acres to 45,000 acres, find the expected increase in the number of species (as a multiple of the number of species on the 20,000 acres).

Section 0.5

95. *Profit* Suppose that the total cost of producing and selling x units of a product is $300 + 4x$ and the total revenue from the sale of x units is $30x - 0.001x^2$. Find the difference of these expressions (total revenue minus total cost) to find the profit from the production and sale of x units of the product.

96. *Business loss* Suppose that a commercial building costs $1,450,000. After it is placed into service, it loses 0.25% of its original value in each of the x months it is in service. Write an expression for the value of the building after x months.

Section 0.6

97. *Revenue* The revenue for a boat tour is $600 - 13x - 0.5x^2$, where x is the number of passengers above the minimum of 50. This expression will factor into two binomials, with one representing the total number of passengers. Factor this expression.

Section 0.7

98. *Pollution: cost-benefit* Suppose that the cost C (in dollars) of removing $p\%$ of the pollution from the waste water of a manufacturing process is given by

$$C = \frac{1,200,000}{100 - p} - 12,000$$

   (a) Express the right-hand side of this formula as a single fraction.
   (b) Find the cost if $p = 0$. Write a sentence that explains the meaning of what you found.
   (c) Find the cost of removing 98% of the pollution.
   (d) What happens to this formula when $p = 100$? Explain why you think this happens.

99. *Average cost* The average cost of producing a product is given by the expression

$$1200 + 56x + \frac{8000}{x}$$

   Write this expression with all terms over a common denominator.

EXAMPLE 2   **U.S. Hispanic Population | APPLICATION PREVIEW |**

Using data from 1980 and projected to 2050, the number of Hispanics in the U.S. civilian non-institutional population is given by $y = 0.876x + 6.084$ million, where x is the number of years after 1980 (*Source:* U.S. Census Bureau). According to this equaton, in what year will the Hispanic population equal 36.74 million?

Solution
To answer this question, we solve

$$36.74 = 0.876x + 6.084$$
$$30.656 = 0.876x$$
$$34.995 \approx x$$

Recall that x is the number of years past 1980, so this solution corresponds to the year $1980 + 34.995 = 2014.995$, or during 2015.
Checking reveals that $36.74 \approx 0.876(34.995) + 6.084$. ✔
Thus the number of Hispanics in the United States is estimated to be approximately 36.74 million in 2015.

Fractional Equations   A **fractional equation** is an equation that contains a variable in a denominator. It is solved by first multiplying both sides of the equation by the least common denominator (LCD) of the fractions in the equation. Some fractional equations lead to linear equations. Note that the solution to any fractional equation *must* be checked in the original equation, because multiplying both sides of a fractional equation by a variable expression may result in an equation that is not equivalent to the original equation. If a solution to the fraction-free linear equation makes a denominator of the original equation equal to zero, that value cannot be a solution to the original equation. Some fractional equations have no solutions.

EXAMPLE 3   **Solving Fractional Equations**

Solve for x: (a) $\dfrac{3x}{2x + 10} = 1 + \dfrac{1}{x + 5}$ (b) $\dfrac{2x - 1}{x - 3} = 4 + \dfrac{5}{x - 3}$

Solution
(a) Multiply each term on both sides by the LCD, $2x + 10$. Then simplify and solve.

$$(2x + 10)\left(\frac{3x}{2x + 10}\right) = (2x + 10)(1) + (2x + 10)\left(\frac{1}{x + 5}\right)$$
$$3x = (2x + 10) + 2 \quad \text{gives} \quad x = 12$$

Check: $\dfrac{3(12)}{2(12) + 10} \overset{?}{=} 1 + \dfrac{1}{12 + 5}$ gives $\dfrac{36}{34} = \dfrac{18}{17}$ ✔

(b) Multiply each term on both sides by the LCD, $x - 3$. Then simplify.

$$(x - 3)\left(\frac{2x - 1}{x - 3}\right) = (x - 3)(4) + (x - 3)\left(\frac{5}{x - 3}\right)$$
$$2x - 1 = (4x - 12) + 5 \quad \text{or} \quad 2x - 1 = 4x - 7$$

Add $(-4x) + 1$ to both sides.

$$-2x = -6 \quad \text{gives} \quad x = 3$$

The value $x = 3$ gives undefined expressions in the original equation because the denominators equal 0 when $x = 3$. Hence the equation has no solution.

✓ CHECKPOINT

1. Solve the following for x.

   (a) $4(x - 3) = 10x - 12$ (b) $\dfrac{5(x - 3)}{6} - x = 1 - \dfrac{x}{9}$

   (c) $\dfrac{x}{3x - 6} = 2 - \dfrac{2x}{x - 2}$

Linear Equations in Two Variables   The steps used to solve linear equations in one variable can also be used to solve linear equations in more than one variable for one of the variables in terms of the other. Solving an equation such as the one in the following example is important when using a graphing utility.

EXAMPLE 4   Solving an Equation for One of Two Variables

Solve $4x + 3y = 12$ for y.

Solution
No fractions or parentheses are present, so we subtract $4x$ from both sides to get only the term that contains y on one side.

$$3y = -4x + 12$$

Dividing both sides by 3 gives the solution.

$$y = -\frac{4}{3}x + 4$$

Check: $4x + 3\left(\dfrac{-4}{3}x + 4\right) \overset{?}{=} 12$

$4x + (-4x + 12) = 12$ ✔

✓ CHECKPOINT

2. Solve for y: $y - 4 = -4(x + 2)$

EXAMPLE 5   Profit

Suppose that the relationship between a firm's profit P and the number x of items sold can be described by the equation

$$5x - 4P = 1200$$

(a) How many units must be produced and sold for the firm to make a profit of $150?
(b) Solve this equation for P in terms of x.
(c) Find the profit when 240 units are sold.

Solution
(a) $5x - 4(150) = 1200$
        $5x - 600 = 1200$
             $5x = 1800$
              $x = 360$ units

   Check: $5(360) - 4(150) = 1800 - 600 = 1200$ ✔

(b) $5x - 4P = 1200$
         $5x - 1200 = 4P$
   $P = \dfrac{5x}{4} - \dfrac{1200}{4} = \dfrac{5x}{4} - 300$

(c) $P = \dfrac{5x}{4} - 300$

   $P = \dfrac{5(240)}{4} - 300 = 0$

Because $P = 0$ when $x = 240$, we know that profit is $0 when 240 units are sold, and we say that the firm **breaks even** when 240 units are sold. ◼

Stated Problems   With an applied problem, it is frequently necessary to convert the problem from its stated form into one or more equations from which the problem's solution can be found. The following guidelines may be useful in solving stated problems.

Guidelines for Solving Stated Problems

1. Read the problem carefully to determine what you are to find. Use variables to represent the quantities to be found.
2. Reread the problem and use your variables to translate given information into algebraic expressions. Often, drawing a figure is helpful.
3. Use the algebraic expressions and the problem statement to formulate an equation (or equations).
4. Solve the equation(s).
5. Check the solution in the problem, not just in your equation or equations. The answer should satisfy the conditions.

EXAMPLE   6   **Investment Mix**

Jill Ball has $90,000 to invest. She has chosen one relatively safe investment fund that has an annual yield of 10% and another, riskier one that has a 15% annual yield. How much should she invest in each fund if she would like to earn $10,000 in one year from her investments?

Solution

1. We want to find the amount of each investment, so we begin as follows:

   Let $x =$ the amount invested at 10%, then
   $90,000 - x =$ the amount invested at 15% (becuse the two investments total $90,000)

2. If P is the amount of an investment and r is the annual rate of yield (expressed as a decimal), then the annual earnings $I = Pr$. Using this relationship, we can summarize the information about these two investments in a table.

	P	r	I
10% investment	x	0.10	0.10x
15% investment	$90,000 - x$	0.15	0.15(90,000 $- x$)
Total investment	90,000		10,000

3. The column under I shows that the sum of the earnings is

   $$0.10x + 0.15(90,000 - x) = 10,000$$

4. We solve this as follows.

   $$0.10x + 13,500 - 0.15x = 10,000$$
   $$-0.05x = -3500 \quad \text{or} \quad x = 70,000$$

   Thus the amount invested at 10% is $70,000, and the amount invested at 15% is $90,000 - 70,000 = 20,000$.

5. To check, we return to the problem and note that 10% of $70,000 plus 15% of $20,000 gives a yield of $7000 + $3000 = $10,000. ✔ ◼

Linear Inequalities   An **inequality** is a statement that one quantity is greater than (or less than) another quantity. The inequality $3x - 2 > 2x + 1$ is a first-degree (linear) inequality that states that the left side is greater than the right side. Certain values of the variable will satisfy the inequality. These values form the solution set of the inequality.

For example, $x = 4$ is in the solution set of $3x - 2 > 2x + 1$ because $3 \cdot 4 - 2 > 2 \cdot 4 + 1$. On the other hand, $x = 2$ is not in the solution set because $3 \cdot 2 - 2 \not> 2 \cdot 2 + 1$. *Solving* an inequality means finding its solution set, and two inequalities are *equivalent* if they have the same solution set. As with equations, we find the solutions to inequalities by finding equivalent inequalities from which the solutions can be easily seen. We use the following properties to reduce an inequality to a simple equivalent inequality.

Properties of Inequalities

Properties	Examples
Substitution Property	
The inequality formed by substituting one expression for an equal expression is equivalent to the original inequality.	$5x - 4x < 6$ $x < 6$ The solution set is $\{x\colon x < 6\}$.
Addition Property	
The inequality formed by adding the same quantity to both sides of an inequality is equivalent to original inequality.	$2x - 4 > x + 6$ $2x - 4 + 4 > x + 6 + 4$ $2x > x + 10$ $2x + (-x) > x + 10 + (-x)$ $x > 10$
Multiplication Property I	
The inequality formed by multiplying both sides of an inequality by the same *positive* quantity is equivalent to the original inequality.	$\dfrac{x}{2} > 8 \qquad\qquad 3x < 6$ $\dfrac{x}{2}(2) > 8(2) \qquad 3x\left(\dfrac{1}{3}\right) < 6\left(\dfrac{1}{3}\right)$ $x > 16 \qquad\qquad x < 2$
Multiplication Property II	
The inequality formed by multiplying both sides of an inequality by the same *negative* number and *reversing* the direction of the inequality symbol is equivalent to the original inequality.	$-x < 6 \qquad\qquad -3x > -27$ $-x(-1) > 6(-1) \qquad -3x\left(-\dfrac{1}{3}\right) < -27\left(-\dfrac{1}{3}\right)$ $x > -6 \qquad\qquad x < 9$

For some inequalities, several operations are required to find their solution sets. In this case, the order in which the operations are performed is the same as that used in solving linear equations.

EXAMPLE 7   Solving an Inequality

Solve the inequality $2(x - 4) < \dfrac{x - 3}{3}$.

Solution

$$2(x - 4) < \frac{x - 3}{3}$$

$6(x - 4) < x - 3 \qquad$ Multiply both sides by the LCD, 3.

$6x - 24 < x - 3 \qquad$ Remove parentheses.

$5x < 21 \qquad$ Subtract x from and add 24 to both sides.

$x < \dfrac{21}{5} \qquad$ Multiply both sides by $\dfrac{1}{5}$.

Check: If we want to check that this solution is a reasonable one, we can substitute the integer values around 21/5 into the original inequality. Note that $x = 4$ satisfies the inequality because

$$2[(4) - 4] < \frac{(4) - 3}{3}$$

but that $x = 5$ does not because

$$2[(5) - 4] \not< \frac{(5) - 3}{3}$$

Thus the solution $x < 21/5$ is reasonable. ✔

We may also solve inequalities of the form $a \leq b$. This means "a is less than b or a equals b."

EXAMPLE 8   **Solving an Inequality**

Solve the inequality $3x - 2 \leq 7$ and graph the solution.

Solution
This inequality states that $3x - 2 = 7$ or $3x - 2 < 7$. By solving in the usual manner, we get $3x \leq 9$, or $x \leq 3$. Then $x = 3$ is the solution to $3x - 2 = 7$ and $x < 3$ is the solution to $3x - 2 < 7$, so the solution set for $3x - 2 \leq 7$ is $\{x: x \leq 3\}$.
    The graph of the solution set includes the point $x = 3$ and all points $x < 3$ (see Figure 1.1).

Figure 1.1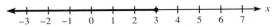

✓ CHECKPOINT   Solve the following inequalities for y.

3. $3y - 7 \leq 5 - y$ 4. $2y + 6 > 4y + 5$ 5. $4 - 3y \geq 4y + 5$

EXAMPLE 9   **Normal Height for a Given Age**

For boys between 4 and 16 years of age, height and age are linearly related. That relation can be expressed as

$$H = 2.31A + 31.26$$

where H is height in inches and A is age in years. To account for natural variation among individuals, normal is considered to be any measure falling within ±5% of the height obtained from the equation.* Write as an inequality the range of normal heights for a boy who is 9 years old.

Solution
For a 9-year-old boy, the height from the formula is $H = 2.31(9) + 31.26 = 52.05$ inches. To be considered of normal height, H would have to be within ±5% of 52.05 inches. That is, the boy's height H is considered normal if $H \geq 52.05 - (0.05)(52.05)$ and $H \leq 52.05 + (0.05)(52.05)$. We can express this range of normal heights by the compound inequality

$$52.05 - (0.05)(52.05) \leq H \leq 52.05 + (0.05)(52.05)$$

or

$$49.45 \leq H \leq 54.65$$

*Adapted from data from the National Center for Health Statistics

| EXERCISES | 1.1

In Problems 1–14, solve each equation.

1. $4x - 7 = 8x + 2$
2. $3x + 22 = 7x + 2$
3. $x + 8 = 8(x + 1)$
4. $x + x + x = x$
5. $-\dfrac{3}{4}x = 24$
6. $-\dfrac{1}{6}x = 12$
7. $2(x - 7) = 5(x + 3) - x$
8. $3(x - 4) = 4 - 2(x + 2)$
9. $8 - 2(3x + 9) - 6x = 50$
10. $10x + 6 - 2(1 - 5x) = 9$
11. $\dfrac{5x}{2} - 4 = \dfrac{2x - 7}{6}$
12. $\dfrac{2x}{3} - 1 = \dfrac{x - 2}{2}$
13. $x + \dfrac{1}{3} = 2\left(x - \dfrac{2}{3}\right) - 6x$
14. $\dfrac{3x}{4} - \dfrac{1}{3} = 1 - \dfrac{2}{3}\left(x - \dfrac{1}{6}\right)$

In Problems 15–20, solve each fractional equation. Check your answers in the original equations.

15. $\dfrac{33 - x}{5x} = 2$
16. $\dfrac{3x + 3}{x - 3} = 7$
17. $\dfrac{2x}{2x + 5} = \dfrac{2}{3} - \dfrac{5}{4x + 10}$
18. $\dfrac{3}{x} + \dfrac{1}{4} = \dfrac{2}{3} + \dfrac{1}{x}$
19. $\dfrac{2x}{x - 1} + \dfrac{1}{3} = \dfrac{5}{6} + \dfrac{2}{x - 1}$
20. $\dfrac{2x}{x - 3} = 4 + \dfrac{6}{x - 3}$

In Problems 21–24, use a calculator to solve each equation. Round your answer to three decimal places.

21. $3.259x - 8.638 = -3.8(8.625x + 4.917)$
22. $3.319(14.1x - 5) = 9.95 - 4.6x$
23. $0.000316x + 9.18 = 2.1(3.1 - 0.0029x) - 4.68$
24. $3.814x = 2.916(4.2 - 0.06x) + 5.3$

In Problems 25–28, solve for y in terms of x.

25. $3x - 4y = 15$
26. $3x - 5y = 25$
27. $9x + \dfrac{3}{2}y = 11$
28. $\dfrac{3x}{2} + 5y = \dfrac{1}{3}$
29. Solve $S = P + Prt$ for t.
30. Solve $\dfrac{y - b}{x - a} = m$ for y.

In Problems 31–36, solve each inequality.

31. $3(x - 1) < 2x - 1$
32. $2(x + 1) > x - 1$
33. $1 - 2x > 9$
34. $17 - x < -4$
35. $\dfrac{3(x - 1)}{2} \le x - 2$
36. $\dfrac{x - 1}{2} + 1 > x + 1$

In Problems 37–42, solve each inequality and graph the solution.

37. $2(x - 1) - 3 > 4x + 1$
38. $7x + 4 \le 2(x - 1)$
39. $\dfrac{-3x}{2} > 3 - x$
40. $\dfrac{-2x}{5} \le -10 - x$
41. $\dfrac{3x}{4} - \dfrac{1}{6} < x - \dfrac{2(x - 1)}{3}$
42. $\dfrac{4x}{3} - 3 > \dfrac{1}{2} + \dfrac{5x}{12}$

APPLICATIONS

43. *Depreciation* A \$648,000 property is depreciated for tax purposes by its owner with the straight-line depreciation method. The value of the building, y, after x months of use is given by $y = 648,000 - 1800x$ dollars. After how many months will the value of the building be \$387,000?

44. *Depreciation* When an \$810,000 building is depreciated for tax purposes (by the straight-line method), its value, y, after x months of use is given by $y = 810,000 - 2250x$. How many months will it be before the building is fully depreciated (that is, its value is \$0)? How many years is this?

45. *Credit card debt* High interest rates make it difficult for people to pay off credit card debt in a reasonable period of time. The interest I (in dollars) paid on a \$10,000 debt over 3 years when the interest rate is $r\%$ can be approximated by the equation

$$\dfrac{I}{175.393} + 0.663 = r$$

(*Source:* Consumer Federation of America). If the credit card interest rate is 19.8%, find the amount of interest paid during the 3 years.

46. *Seawater pressure* In seawater, the pressure p is related to the depth d according to

$$33p - 18d = 495$$

where d is in feet and p is in pounds per square inch.
(a) Solve this equation for p in terms of d.
(b) The *Titanic* was discovered at a depth of 12,460 ft. Find the pressure at this depth.

47. *Break-even* Burnem, Inc. manufactures blank CDs and sells them to a distributor in packs of 500 CDs. Burnem's total cost and total revenue (in dollars) for x packs of 500 CDs are given by

Total cost $= 2x + 7920$ and   Total revenue $= 20x$

How many packs of 500 CDs must Burnem sell to break even?

48. *Break-even* Dish Systems manufactures satellite systems and has its monthly profit P in dollars related to the number of satellite systems, x, by

$$4P = 81x - 29{,}970$$

Find the number of systems that Dish Systems needs to produce and sell in order to break even.

49. *Profit* In its second year of operation, a local Internet provider's profits were $170,500. If this amount was 576% of the company's first-year profits, find the first-year profits (to the nearest hundred dollars).

50. *Sales tax* The total price of a used car (including 6% sales tax) is $21,041. How much of this is tax?

51. *Internet access* The percent P of the U.S. population with Internet access is given by

$$25P - 34t = 1378$$

where t is the number of years past 1990 (*Source: Digital Future Report, USC Annenberg*).
   (a) What percent of the U.S. population had Internet access in 2010?
   (b) In what year will 90% have Internet access?

52. *Out-of-pocket health care expenses* Data and projections from the Centers for Medicare and Medicaid Services from 2000 to 2018 indicate that the annual per capita out-of-pocket expenses for health care can be approximated by

$$y = 30.65x + 667.43 \quad \text{(dollars)}$$

where x is the number of years past 2000. When are the per capita out-of-pocket expenses for health care predicted to be $1280.43?

53. *Course grades* To earn an A in a course, a student must get at least a 90 average on four tests and a final exam, with the final exam weighted twice that of any one test. If the four test scores are 93, 69, 89, and 97, what is the lowest score the student can earn on the final exam and still get an A in the course?

54. *Course grades* Suppose a professor counts the final exam as being equal to each of the other tests in her course, and she will also change the lowest test score to match the final exam score if the final exam score is higher. If a student's four test scores are 83, 67, 52, and 90, what is the lowest score the student can earn on the final exam and still obtain at least an 80 average for the course?

55. *Investment mix* A retired woman has $120,000 to invest. She has chosen one relatively safe investment fund that has an annual yield of 9% and another, riskier fund that has a 13% annual yield. How much should she invest in each fund if she would like to earn $12,000 per year from her investments?

56. *Investment yields* One safe investment pays 10% per year, and a riskier investment pays 18% per year. A woman who has $145,600 to invest wants to have an income of $20,000 per year from her investments. How much should she invest at each rate?

57. *Salary increases* A woman making $2000 per month has her salary reduced by 10% because of sluggish sales. One year later, after a dramatic improvement in sales, she is given a 20% raise over her reduced salary. Find her salary after the raise. What percent change is this from the $2000 per month?

58. *Wildlife management* In wildlife management, the capture-mark-recapture technique is used to estimate the populations of fish or birds in an area or to measure the infestation of insects such as Japanese beetles. Suppose 100 individuals of the species being studied are caught, marked, and released, and one week later 100 more are caught. To estimate the total number of individuals, the following relationship is used:

$$\frac{\text{Total marked found in 2nd capture}}{\text{Total in 2nd capture}} = \frac{\text{Total number marked}}{\text{Total population}}$$

   (a) If in the second capture of 100, it is found that 3 are marked, what is the total population?
   (b) Suppose that 1000 beetles are captured, marked, and released. Suppose further that in the second capture of 1000, it is found that 63 are marked. What is the population estimate?

59. *Profit* For a certain product, the revenue is given by $R = 40x$ and the cost is given by $C = 20x + 1600$. To obtain a profit, the revenue must be greater than the cost. For what values of x will there be a profit? Graph the solution.

60. *Car rental* Thrift rents a compact car for $33 per day, and General rents a similar car for $20 per day plus an initial fee of $78. For how many days would it be cheaper to rent from General? Graph the solution.

61. *Purchasing* Sean can spend at most $900 for a camera and some memory sticks. He plans to buy the camera for $695 and sticks for $5.75 each. Write an inequality that could be used to find the number of sticks (x) that he could buy. How many sticks could he buy?

62. *Taxes* In Sweetwater, Arizona, water bills are taxed on the basis of the amount of the monthly bill in order to encourage conservation. If the bill is more than $0 but less than $60, the tax is 2% of the bill; if the bill is $60 or more but less than $80, the tax is 4% of the bill; and if the bill is $80 or more, the tax is 6% of the bill. Write the inequalities that represent the amounts of tax owed in these three cases.

63. **Obesity** Severely obese persons (BMI > 40) are at serious health risk, and their number is increasing. Using data from 1990 and projected to 2030 the percent of severely obese U.S. adults can be approximated by

$$S = 0.264t - 2.57$$

with t equal to the number of years past 1980 (*Source:* American Journal of Preventive Medicine).
   (a) What t-value represents 2018?
   (b) What value of t gives $S = 10$?
   (c) In what year does the equation predict that at least 10% of U.S. adults will be severely obese?

64. **Federal income tax per capita** Using data from 2010 and projected to 2018, the federal income tax per capita can be approximated by the equation

$$y = 486.48t + 3486.84$$

where t is the number of years past 2010 and y is in dollars (*Source:* usgovernmentrevenue.com).
   (a) What t-value corresponds to 2018?
   (b) Find the approximate federal income tax per capita in 2018.
   (c) If the equation applies after 2018, in what year is the federal income tax per capita expected to exceed $10,000?

65. **Heat index** During a particular summer, Dallas, Texas, endured 29 consecutive days on which the temperature was at least 110°F. On many of those days, the combination of heat and humidity made it feel even hotter than it was. When the temperature is 100°F, the apparent temperature A (or heat index) depends on the humidity h (expressed as a decimal) according to

$$A = 90.2 + 41.3h*$$

* *Source:* Bosch, W., and C. G. Cobb, "Temperature-Humidity Indices," UMAP Unit 691, *The UMAP Journal,* 10(3), Fall 1989, 237–256.

   (a) For what humidity levels is the apparent temperature at least 110°F? (Note that this answer will be a closed interval. Why?)
   (b) For what humidity levels is the apparent temperature less than 100°F?

66. **Wind chill** The combination of cold temperatures and wind speed determine what is called wind chill. The wind chill is a temperature that is the still-air equivalent of the combination of cold and wind. When the wind speed is 25 mph, the wind chill WC depends on the temperature t (in degrees Fahrenheit) according to

$$WC = 1.337t - 24.094$$

For what temperatures does it feel at least 30°F colder than the air temperature? That is, find t such that $WC \leq t - 30$.

MCHUMOR.COM by T. McCracken

"I swear it wasn't this cold before they invented the wind chill factor."

©T. McCracken/mchumor.com

- To determine whether a relation is a function
- To state the domains and ranges of certain functions
- To use function notation
- To perform operations with functions
- To find the composite of two functions

Functions

■ | APPLICATION PREVIEW |

The number of personal income tax returns filed electronically has increased in recent years. The number of returns filed electronically T (in millions) can be described by the equation

$$T = 6.35x + 4.65$$

where x is the number of years past 1995 (*Source:* Internal Revenue Service). In this equation, T depends uniquely on x, so we say that T is a function of x. Understanding the mathematical meaning of the phrase *function of* and learning to interpret and apply such relationships are the goals of this section. (The function here will be discussed in Example 4.)

Relations and Functions

A **relation** is defined by a set of **ordered pairs** of real numbers. These ordered pairs may be determined from a table, a graph, an equation, or an inequality. For example, the solutions to the equation $y = 4x - 3$ are pairs of numbers (one for x and one for y), so $y = 4x - 3$ expresses a relation between x and y. We write the ordered pairs in this relation in the form (x, y) so that the first number is the x-value and the second is the y-value. Because we cannot list all of the ordered pairs that define this relation, we use the equation to give its definition. Similarly, the inequality $R \leq 5x$ expresses a relation between the two variables x and R.

Relation	A **relation** is defined by a set of ordered pairs or by a rule that determines how the ordered pairs are found. The relation may also be defined by a table, a graph, an equation, or an inequality.

| TABLE 1.1 |

FEDERAL INCOME TAX

Income	Rate
$0–$8375	10%
$8376–$34,000	15%
$34,001–$82,400	25%
$82,401–$171,850	28%
$171,851–$373,650	33%
Over $373,650	35%

Source: Internal Revenue Service

For example, the set of ordered pairs

$$\{(1, 3), (1, 6), (2, 6), (3, 9), (3, 12), (4, 12)\}$$

expresses a relation between the set of first components, $\{1, 2, 3, 4\}$, and the set of second components, $\{3, 6, 9, 12\}$. The set of first components is called the **domain** of the relation, and the set of second components is called the **range** of the relation. Figure 1.2(a) uses arrows to indicate how the inputs from the domain (the first components) are associated with the outputs in the range (the second components). Figure 1.2(b) shows another example of a relation. Because relations can also be defined by tables and graphs, Table 1.1 and Figure 1.3 are examples of relations.

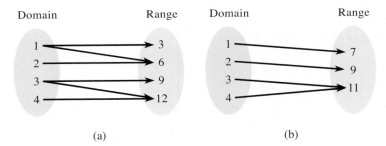

Figure 1.2

(a)   (b)

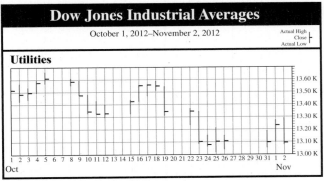

Figure 1.3   *Source:* Based on data from Yahoo Finance

An equation frequently expresses how the second component (the output) is obtained from the first component (the input). For example, the equation

$$y = 4x - 3$$

expresses how the output y results from the input x. This equation expresses a special relation between x and y called a **function** because each input x results in exactly one output y.

Definition of a Function

> A **function** is a relation between two sets such that to each element of the domain (input) there corresponds exactly one element of the range (output). A function may be defined by a set of ordered pairs, a table, a graph, or an equation.

When a function is defined, the variable that represents the numbers in the domain (input) is called the **independent variable** of the function, and the variable that represents the numbers in the range (output) is called the **dependent variable** (because its values depend on the values of the independent variable). For example, in the function $y = 4x - 3$, x is the independent variable and y is the dependent variable.

We can also apply this idea to a relation defined by a table or a graph. In Figure 1.2(b) on the previous page, because each input in the domain corresponds to exactly one output in the range, the relation is a function. Similarly, the data given in Table 1.1 on the previous page (the tax brackets for U.S. income tax for single wage earners) represents the tax rate as a function of the income. Note in Table 1.1 that even though many different amounts of taxable income have the same tax rate, each amount of taxable income (input) corresponds to exactly one tax rate (output). On the other hand, the relation defined in Figure 1.3 on the previous page is not a function because the graph representing the Dow Jones Industrial Average shows that for each day there are at least three different values—the actual high, the actual low, and the close. This particular figure also has historical interest because it shows a break in the graph when the New York Stock Exchange closed in the wake of Hurricane Sandy.

EXAMPLE 1   Functions

Does $y^2 = 2x$ express y as a function of x?

Solution

No, because some values of x are associated with more than one value of y. In fact, there are two y-values for each $x > 0$. For example, if $x = 8$, then $y = 4$ or $y = -4$. The equation $y^2 = 2x$ expresses a relation between x and y, but y is not a function of x. ∎

Graphs of Functions

It is possible to picture geometrically the relations and functions that we have been discussing by sketching their graphs on a rectangular coordinate system. We construct a rectangular coordinate system by drawing two real number lines (called **coordinate axes**) that are perpendicular to each other and intersect at their origins (called the **origin** of the system).

The ordered pair (a, b) represents the point P that is located a units along the x-axis and b units along the y-axis (see Figure 1.4). Similarly, any point has a unique ordered pair that describes it.

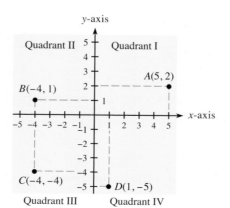

Figure 1.4

The values a and b in the ordered pair associated with the point P are called the **rectangular** (or **Cartesian**) **coordinates** of the point, where a is the **x-coordinate** (or **abscissa**), and b is the **y-coordinate** (or **ordinate**). The ordered pairs (a, b) and (c, d) are equal if and only if $a = c$ and $b = d$.

The **graph** of an equation that defines a function (or relation) is the picture that results when we plot the points whose coordinates (x, y) satisfy the equation. To sketch the graph, we plot enough points to suggest the shape of the graph and draw a smooth curve through the points. This is called the **point-plotting method** of sketching a graph.

EXAMPLE 2

Graphing a Function

Graph the function $y = 3x^2$.

Solution

We choose some values of x and find the corresponding values of y. Placing these in a table, we have points to plot. When we have enough to determine the shape of the graph, we connect the points to complete the graph. The table and graph are shown in Figure 1.5.

x	y
-2	12
-1	3
0	0
1	3
2	12

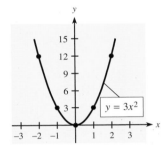

Figure 1.5

We can determine whether a relation is a function by inspecting its graph. If the relation is a function, then no one input (x-value) has two different outputs (y-values). This means that no two points on the graph will have the same first coordinate (component). Thus no two points of the graph will lie on the same vertical line.

Vertical-Line Test

If no vertical line exists that intersects the graph at more than one point, then the graph is that of a function.

Performing this test on the graph of $y = 3x^2$ (Figure 1.6(a)), we easily see that this equation describes a function. The graph of $y^2 = 2x$ is shown in Figure 1.6(b), and we can see that the vertical-line test confirms that this is not a function (see Example 1). For example, a vertical line at $x = 2$ intersects the curve at $(2, 2)$ and $(2, -2)$.

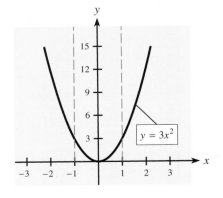

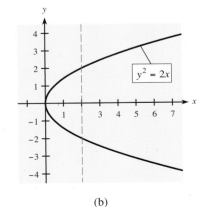

Figure 1.6   (a)   (b)

Function Notation   We can use function notation to indicate that y is a function of x. The function is denoted by f, and we write $y = f(x)$. This is read "y is a function of x" or "y equals f of x." For specific values of x, $f(x)$ represents the values of the function (that is, outputs, or y-values) at those x-values. Thus if $y = f(x) = 3x^2 + 2x + 1$

then $f(2) = 3(2)^2 + 2(2) + 1 = 17$ so $y = 17$ when $x = 2$
and $f(-3) = 3(-3)^2 + 2(-3) + 1 = 22$ so $y = 22$ when $x = -3$

Figure 1.7 shows the function notation $f(x)$ as (a) an operator on x and (b) a y-coordinate for a given x-value.

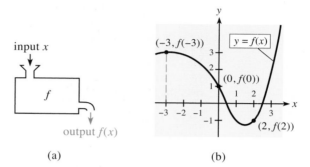

Figure 1.7   (a)   (b)

Letters other than f may also be used to denote functions. For example, $y = g(x)$ or $y = h(x)$ may be used.

EXAMPLE 3   Evaluating Functions

If $f(x) = 2x^3 - 3x^2 + 1$, find the following.
(a) $f(3)$ (b) $f(-1)$ (c) $f(-a)$

Solution
(a) $f(3) = 2(3)^3 - 3(3)^2 + 1 = 2(27) - 3(9) + 1 = 28$
(b) $f(-1) = 2(-1)^3 - 3(-1)^2 + 1 = 2(-1) - 3(1) + 1 = -4$
(c) $f(-a) = 2(-a)^3 - 3(-a)^2 + 1 = -2a^3 - 3a^2 + 1$

When a function fits a set of data exactly or approximately, we say that the function **models** the data. The model includes descriptions of all involved variables.

EXAMPLE 4   Electronic Income Tax Returns | APPLICATION PREVIEW |

The number of personal income tax returns filed electronically T (in millions) can be modeled by the function

$$T(x) = 6.35x + 4.65$$

where x is the number of years after 1995 (*Source:* Internal Revenue Service).

(a) Find $T(20)$.
(b) Write a sentence that explains the meaning of the result in part (a).

Solution
(a) $T(20) = 6.35(20) + 4.65 = 131.65$
(b) The statement $T(20) = 131.65$ means that in $1995 + 20 = 2015$, approximately 131.65 million personal income tax returns were filed electronically.

EXAMPLE 5   **Mortgage Payment**

| TABLE 1.2 |

r(%)	f(r)
2.6	12
5.2	15
6.3	17
7.4	20
9	30

Table 1.2 shows the approximate number of years that it will take a couple to pay off a $100,000 mortgage at several different interest rates if they pay $800 per month. If r denotes the rate and $f(r)$ denotes the number of years:

(a) What is $f(6.3)$ and what does it mean?
(b) If $f(r) = 30$, what is r?
(c) Does $2 \cdot f(2.6) = f(2 \cdot 2.6)$?

Solution
(a) $f(6.3) = 17$. This means that with a 6.3% interest rate, a couple can pay off the $100,000 mortgage in 17 years by paying $800 per month.
(b) The table indicates that $f(9) = 30$, so $r = 9$.
(c) $2 \cdot f(2.6) = 2 \cdot 12 = 24$ and $f(2 \cdot 2.6) = f(5.2) = 15$, so $2 \cdot f(2.6) \neq f(2 \cdot 2.6)$.

If we have points $(x, f(x))$ and $(x + h, f(x + h))$ on the graph of $y = f(x)$, evaluations like the one in the following example (called difference quotients) arise in measuring rates of change of functions.

EXAMPLE 6   **Function Notation**

Given $f(x) = x^2 - 3x + 8$, find $\dfrac{f(x + h) - f(x)}{h}$ and simplify (if $h \neq 0$).

Solution
We find $f(x + h)$ by replacing each x in $f(x)$ with the expression $x + h$.

$$\frac{f(x + h) - f(x)}{h} = \frac{[(x + h)^2 - 3(x + h) + 8] - [x^2 - 3x + 8]}{h}$$

$$= \frac{[(x^2 + 2xh + h^2) - 3x - 3h + 8] - x^2 + 3x - 8}{h}$$

$$= \frac{x^2 + 2xh + h^2 - 3x - 3h + 8 - x^2 + 3x - 8}{h}$$

$$= \frac{2xh + h^2 - 3h}{h} = \frac{h(2x + h - 3)}{h} = 2x + h - 3$$

Domains and Ranges   We will limit our discussion in this text to **real functions,** which are functions whose domains and ranges contain only real numbers. If the domain and range of a function are not specified, it is assumed that the domain consists of all real inputs (x-values) that result in real outputs (y-values), making the range a subset of the real numbers.

For the types of functions we are now studying, if the domain is unspecified, it will include all real numbers except

1. values that result in a denominator of 0, and
2. values that result in an even root of a negative number.

EXAMPLE 7   **Domain and Range**

Find the domain of each of the following functions; find the range for the functions in parts (a) and (b).

(a) $y = 4x^2$ (b) $y = \sqrt{4 - x}$ (c) $y = 1 + \dfrac{1}{x - 2}$

Solution

(a) There are no restrictions on the numbers substituted for x, so the domain consists of all real numbers. Because the square of any real number is nonnegative, $4x^2$ must be nonnegative. Thus the range is $y \geq 0$. The graph shown in Figure 1.8(a) illustrates our conclusions about the domain and range.

(b) We note the restriction that $4 - x$ cannot be negative. Thus the domain consists of only numbers less than or equal to 4. That is, the domain is the set of real numbers satisfying $x \leq 4$. Because $\sqrt{4 - x}$ is always nonnegative, the range is all $y \geq 0$. Figure 1.8(b) shows the graph of $y = \sqrt{4 - x}$. Note that the graph is located only where $x \leq 4$ and on or above the x-axis (where $y \geq 0$).

(c) $y = 1 + \dfrac{1}{x - 2}$ is undefined at $x = 2$ because $\dfrac{1}{0}$ is undefined. Hence, the domain consists of all real numbers except 2. Figure 1.8(c) shows the graph of $y = 1 + \dfrac{1}{x - 2}$.

The break where $x = 2$ indicates that $x = 2$ is not part of the domain.

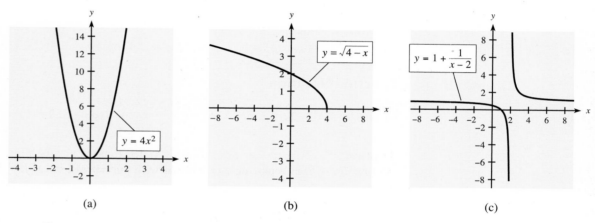

(a)   (b)   (c)

Figure 1.8

✓ **CHECKPOINT**

1. If $y = f(x)$, the independent variable is _____ and the dependent variable is _____.

2. If $(1, 3)$ is on the graph of $y = f(x)$, then $f(1) = $?

3. If $f(x) = 1 - x^3$, find $f(-2)$.

4. If $f(x) = 2x^2$, find $f(x + h)$.

5. If $f(x) = \dfrac{1}{x + 1}$, what is the domain of $f(x)$?

Operations with Functions   We can form new functions by performing algebraic operations with two or more functions. We define new functions that are the sum, difference, product, and quotient of two functions as follows.

Operations with Functions	Let f and g be functions of x, and define the following.
	Sum $\qquad\qquad (f + g)(x) = f(x) + g(x)$
	Difference $\quad\ (f - g)(x) = f(x) - g(x)$
	Product $\qquad\ (f \cdot g)(x) = f(x) \cdot g(x)$
	Quotient $\qquad \left(\dfrac{f}{g}\right)(x) = \dfrac{f(x)}{g(x)} \quad$ if $\ g(x) \neq 0$

EXAMPLE 8   Operations with Functions

If $f(x) = 3x + 2$ and $g(x) = x^2 - 3$, find the following functions.

(a) $(f + g)(x)$ (b) $(f - g)(x)$ (c) $(f \cdot g)(x)$ (d) $\left(\dfrac{f}{g}\right)(x)$

Solution

(a) $(f + g)(x) = f(x) + g(x) = (3x + 2) + (x^2 - 3) = x^2 + 3x - 1$

(b) $(f - g)(x) = f(x) - g(x) = (3x + 2) - (x^2 - 3) = -x^2 + 3x + 5$

(c) $(f \cdot g)(x) = f(x) \cdot g(x) = (3x + 2)(x^2 - 3) = 3x^3 + 2x^2 - 9x - 6$

(d) $\left(\dfrac{f}{g}\right)(x) = \dfrac{f(x)}{g(x)} = \dfrac{3x + 2}{x^2 - 3}$, if $x^2 - 3 \neq 0$

We now consider a new way to combine two functions. Just as we can substitute a number for the independent variable in a function, we can substitute a second function for the variable. This creates a new function called a **composite function.**

Composite Functions

Let f and g be functions. Then the **composite functions** g of f (denoted $g \circ f$) and f of g (denoted $f \circ g$) are defined as follows:

$$(g \circ f)(x) = g(f(x))$$
$$(f \circ g)(x) = f(g(x))$$

Note that the domain of $g \circ f$ is the subset of the domain of f for which $g \circ f$ is defined. Similarly, the domain of $f \circ g$ is the subset of the domain of g for which $f \circ g$ is defined.

EXAMPLE 9   Composite Functions

If $f(x) = 2x^3 + 1$ and $g(x) = x^2$, find the following.

(a) $(g \circ f)(x)$ (b) $(f \circ g)(x)$

Solution

(a) $(g \circ f)(x) = g(f(x))$
$= g(2x^3 + 1)$
$= (2x^3 + 1)^2 = 4x^6 + 4x^3 + 1$

(b) $(f \circ g)(x) = f(g(x))$
$= f(x^2)$
$= 2(x^2)^3 + 1$
$= 2x^6 + 1$

Figure 1.9 illustrates both composite functions found above.

$(g \circ f)(x)$ $\qquad$ $(f \circ g)(x)$

$f(x) = 2x^3 + 1$ $\qquad$ $g(x) = x^2$

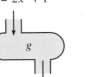

Figure 1.9

$g(f(x)) = (2x^3 + 1)^2$ $\qquad$ $f(g(x)) = 2(x^2)^3 + 1$

$(g \circ f)(x) = 4x^6 + 4x^3 + 1$ $\qquad$ $(f \circ g)(x) = 2x^6 + 1$

✓ CHECKPOINT

6. If $f(x) = 1 - 2x$ and $g(x) = 3x^2$, find the following.
    (a) $(g - f)(x)$ (b) $(f \cdot g)(x)$ (c) $(f \circ g)(x)$ (d) $(g \circ f)(x)$
    (e) $(f \circ f)(x) = f(f(x))$

✓ CHECKPOINT
ANSWERS

1. Independent variable is x; dependent variable is y.
2. $f(1) = 3$
3. $f(-2) = 9$
4. $f(x + h) = 2(x^2 + 2xh + h^2)$
5. All real numbers except $x = -1$; $f(x)$ is undefined when $x = -1$.
6. (a) $(g - f)(x) = 3x^2 + 2x - 1$
    (b) $(f \cdot g)(x) = 3x^2 - 6x^3$
    (c) $(f \circ g)(x) = 1 - 6x^2$
    (d) $(g \circ f)(x) = 3(1 - 2x)^2$
    (e) $(f \circ f)(x) = 4x - 1$

| EXERCISES | 1.2

In Problems 1 and 2, use the values in the following table.

x	-7	-1	0	3	4.2	9	11	14	18	22
y	0	0	1	5	9	11	35	22	22	60

1. (a) Explain why the table defines y as a function of x.
    (b) State the domain and range of this function.
    (c) If the table expresses $y = f(x)$, find $f(0)$ and $f(11)$.
2. (a) If the function defined by the table is denoted by f, so that $y = f(x)$, is $f(9)$ an input or an output of f?
    (b) Does the table describe x as a function of y? Explain.

In Problems 3 and 4, are the relations defined by the tables functions? Explain why or why not and give the domain and range.

3.
x	1	2	3	8	9
y	-4	-4	5	16	5

4.
x	-1	0	1	3	1
y	0	2	4	6	9

In Problems 5–8, determine whether each graph represents y as a function of x. Explain your answer.

5.
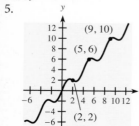

6.
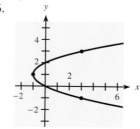

7.

8.
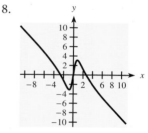

In Problems 9–12, determine if the equation represents y as a function of x.

9. $y = 3x^3$
10. $y = 6x^2$
11. $y^2 = 3x$
12. $y^2 = 10x^2$
13. If $R(x) = 8x - 10$, find the following.
    (a) $R(0)$ (b) $R(2)$ (c) $R(-3)$ (d) $R(1.6)$
14. If $f(x) = 17 - 6x$, find the following.
    (a) $f(-3)$ (b) $f(1)$ (c) $f(10)$ (d) $f(\frac{2}{3})$
15. If $C(x) = 4x^2 - 3$, find the following.
    (a) $C(0)$ (b) $C(-1)$ (c) $C(-2)$ (d) $C(-\frac{3}{2})$
16. If $h(x) = 3x^2 - 2x$, find the following.
    (a) $h(3)$ (b) $h(-3)$ (c) $h(2)$ (d) $h(\frac{1}{6})$
17. If $h(x) = x - 2(4 - x)^3$, find the following.
    (a) $h(-1)$ (b) $h(0)$ (c) $h(6)$ (d) $h(2.5)$
18. If $R(x) = 100x - x^3$, find the following.
    (a) $R(1)$ (b) $R(10)$ (c) $R(2)$ (d) $R(-10)$
19. If $f(x) = x^3 - 4/x$, find the following.
    (a) $f(-\frac{1}{2})$ (b) $f(2)$ (c) $f(-2)$
20. If $C(x) = (x^2 - 1)/x$, find the following.
    (a) $C(1)$ (b) $C(\frac{1}{2})$ (c) $C(-2)$
21. Let $f(x) = 1 + x + x^2$ and $h \neq 0$.
    (a) Is $f(2 + 1) = f(2) + f(1)$?
    (b) Find $f(x + h)$.
    (c) Does $f(x + h) = f(x) + f(h)$?

(d) Does $f(x + h) = f(x) + h$?

(e) Find $\dfrac{f(x + h) - f(x)}{h}$ and simplify.

22. Let $f(x) = 3x^2 - 6x$ and $h \neq 0$.
(a) Is $f(3 + 2) = f(3) + 2$?
(b) Find $f(x + h)$.
(c) Does $f(x + h) = f(x) + h$?
(d) Does $f(x + h) = f(x) + f(h)$?
(e) Find $\dfrac{f(x + h) - f(x)}{h}$ and simplify.

23. If $f(x) = x - 2x^2$ and $h \neq 0$, find the following and simplify.
(a) $f(x + h)$
(b) $\dfrac{f(x + h) - f(x)}{h}$

24. If $f(x) = 2x^2 - x + 3$ and $h \neq 0$, find the following and simplify.
(a) $f(x + h)$
(b) $\dfrac{f(x + h) - f(x)}{h}$

25. If $y = f(x)$ has the graph in Problem 5, find the following.
(a) $f(9)$
(b) $f(5)$

26. Suppose $y = g(x)$ has the graph in Problem 8.
(a) Find $g(0)$.
(b) How many x-values in the domain of this function satisfy $g(x) = 0$?

27. The graph of $y = x^2 - 4x$ is shown below.

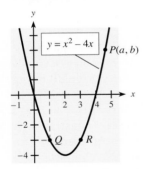

(a) What are the coordinates of the point Q? Do they satisfy the equation?
(b) What are the coordinates of R? Do they satisfy the equation?
(c) If the coordinates of the point P on the graph are (a, b), how are a and b related?
(d) What are the x-values of the points on the graph whose y-coordinates are 0? Are these x-values solutions to the equation $x^2 - 4x = 0$?

28. The graph of $y = 2x^2$ is shown below.

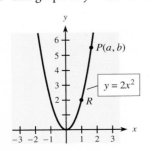

(a) Does the point $(1, 1)$ lie on the graph? Do the coordinates satisfy the equation?
(b) What are the coordinates of point R? Do they satisfy the equation?
(c) If the point P, with coordinates (a, b), is on the graph, how are a and b related?
(d) What is the x-value of the point whose y-coordinate is 0? Does this value of x satisfy the equation $0 = 2x^2$?

State the domain and range of each of the functions in Problems 29–32.

29. $y = x^2 + 4$
30. $y = x^2 - 1$
31. $y = \sqrt{x + 4}$
32. $y = \sqrt{x^2 + 1}$

In Problems 33–36, a function and its graph are given. In each problem, find the domain.

33. $f(x) = \dfrac{\sqrt{x - 1}}{x - 2}$

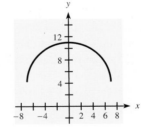

34. $f(x) = \dfrac{x + 1}{\sqrt{x + 3}}$

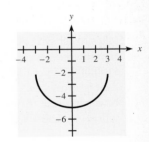

35. $f(x) = 4 + \sqrt{49 - x^2}$

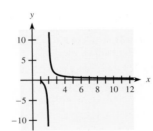

36. $f(x) = -2 - \sqrt{9 - x^2}$

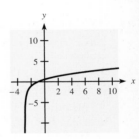

For $f(x)$ and $g(x)$ given in Problems 37–40, find
(a) $(f + g)(x)$
(b) $(f - g)(x)$
(c) $(f \cdot g)(x)$
(d) $(f/g)(x)$

37. $f(x) = 3x$ $g(x) = x^3$
38. $f(x) = \sqrt{x}$ $g(x) = 1/x$
39. $f(x) = \sqrt{2x}$ $g(x) = x^2$
40. $f(x) = (x - 1)^2$ $g(x) = 1 - 2x$

For $f(x)$ and $g(x)$ given in Problems 41–44, find
  (a) $(f \circ g)(x)$
  (b) $(g \circ f)(x)$
  (c) $f(f(x))$
  (d) $f^2(x)=(f \cdot f)(x)$
41. $f(x) = (x - 1)^3 \qquad g(x) = 1 - 2x$
42. $f(x) = 3x \qquad g(x) = x^3 - 1$
43. $f(x) = 2\sqrt{x} \qquad g(x) = x^4 + 5$
44. $f(x) = \dfrac{1}{x^3} \qquad g(x) = 4x + 1$

APPLICATIONS

45. **Mortgage** A couple seeking to buy a home decides that a monthly payment of $800 fits their budget. The amount they can borrow, A, is a function of the time t, in years, it will take to repay the debt. If we denote this function by $A = f(t)$, then the following table defines the function.

t	A	t	A
5	40,000	20	103,000
10	69,000	25	113,000
15	89,000	30	120,000

Source: Comprehensive Mortgage Payment Tables, Publication No. 492, Financial Publishing Co., Boston

  (a) Find $f(20)$ and write a sentence that explains its meaning.
  (b) Does $f(5 + 5) = f(5) + f(5)$? Explain.
  (c) If the couple is looking at a house that requires them to finance $89,000, how long must they make payments? Write this correspondence in the form $A = f(t)$.

46. **Debt refinancing** When a debt is refinanced, sometimes the term of the loan (that is, the time it takes to repay the debt) is shortened. Suppose the current interest rate is 7%, and a couple's current debt is $100,000. The monthly payment R of the refinanced debt is a function of the term of the loan, t, in years. If we represent this function by $R = f(t)$, then the following table defines the function.

t	R	t	R
5	1980.12	15	898.83
10	1161.09	20	775.30
12	1028.39	25	706.78

Source: Comprehensive Mortgage Payment Tables, Publication No. 492, Financial Publishing Co., Boston

  (a) If they refinance for 20 years, what is the monthly payment? Write this correspondence in the form $R = f(t)$.

  (b) Find $f(10)$ and write a sentence that explains its meaning.
  (c) Is $f(5 + 5) = f(5) + f(5)$? Explain.
47. **Social Security benefits** The figure below gives the monthly Social Security benefits for persons whose benefit would be $1000 at a full retirement age of 66 as a function of the age these beneficiaries start receiving benefits. The figure shows the benefits, $y = f(x)$, as a function of x, for $62 \le x \le 70$.
  (a) Find $f(64)$ and $f(67)$.
  (b) Find $f(68)$ and give its meaning.
  (c) Find $f(66) - f(62)$ and gives its meaning.

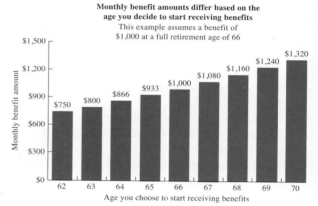

Source: Social Security Administration

48. **Dow Jones Industrial Average** The graph shows the Dow Jones Industrial Average on a particularly tumultuous day soon after the U.S. credit rating was downgraded from AAA to AA + in 2011. If t represents the number of hours after 9:30 A.M., then the graph defines the Dow Jones Industrial Average D as a function of time t. If we represent this function by $D = f(t)$, use the graph to complete the following.
  (a) Find $f(0)$ and $f(6.5)$.
  (b) Find the domain and range for $D = f(t)$ as defined by the graph.
  (c) About how many t-values satisfy $f(t) = 11{,}000$? Estimate one such t-value.

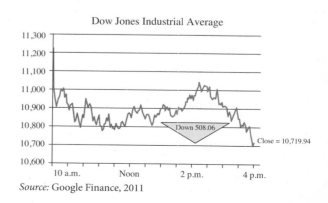

Source: Google Finance, 2011

49. *Population dynamics* As the U.S. population diversifies, the number of White, non-Hispanic individuals (the traditional "White majority") accounts for a smaller percent of the total. The following figure shows data from 1980 and projected to 2050 concerning the numbers of White, non-Hispanics and others (non-Whites or Hispanics) in the U.S. civilian non-institutional population age 16 and older. Let $y = W(t)$ be the function that represents the number of White non-Hispanics and $y = O(t)$ be the function that represents the number of others, where t is the number of years past 1900. Use the figure to complete the following.
    (a) Estimate $W(100)$ and $O(140)$.
    (b) Find $W(120)$ and explain its meaning.
    (c) Find $O(90)$ and explain its meaning.
    (d) Find $(W - O)(120)$ and explain its meaning.
    (e) Find $(W + O)(150)$ and explain its meaning.
    (f) Which of $(W - O)(100)$ and $(W - O)(140)$ is greater? Explain.

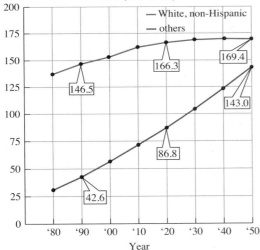

Civilian non-institutional population: 16 years and older (in millions)

Source: U.S. Census Bureau

50. *Women in the workforce* The number (in millions) of women in the workforce, given as a function f of the year for selected years from 1920 and projected to 2016, is shown in the figure.
    (a) How many women were in the labor force in 1970?
    (b) Estimate $f(1930)$ and write a sentence that explains its meaning.
    (c) Estimate $f(2005) - f(1990)$ and explain its meaning.

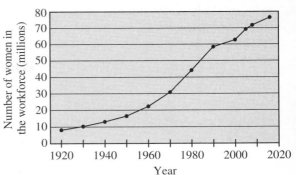

Source: U.S. Bureau of Labor Statistics

51. *Temperature measurement* The equation

$$C = \frac{5}{9}F - \frac{160}{9}$$

gives the relation between temperature readings in Celsius and Fahrenheit.
    (a) Is C a function of F?
    (b) What is the mathematical domain of this function?
    (c) If we consider this equation as relating temperatures of water in its liquid state, what are the domain and range?
    (d) What is C when $F = 40°$?

52. *Profit* The profit from the production and sale of a product is $P(x) = 47x - 0.01x^2 - 8000$, where x represents the number of units produced and sold. Give
    (a) the profit from the production and sale of 2000 units
    (b) the value of $P(5000)$
    (c) the meaning of $P(5000)$.

53. *Cost* The total cost of producing a product is given by

$$C(x) = 300x + 0.1x^2 + 1200$$

where x represents the number of units produced. Give
    (a) the total cost of producing 10 units
    (b) the value of $C(100)$
    (c) the meaning of $C(100)$.

54. *Test reliability* If a test that has reliability r is lengthened by a factor n ($n \geq 1$), the reliability R of the new test is given by

$$R(n) = \frac{nr}{1 + (n - 1)r} \qquad 0 < r \leq 1$$

If the reliability is $r = 0.6$, the equation becomes

$$R(n) = \frac{0.6n}{0.4 + 0.6n}$$

    (a) Find $R(1)$.
    (b) Find $R(2)$; that is, find R when the test length is doubled.
    (c) What percent improvement is there in the reliability when the test length is doubled?

55. **Pollution** Suppose that the cost C (in dollars) of removing p percent of the particulate pollution from the smokestacks of an industrial plant is given by

$$C(p) = \frac{7300p}{100 - p}$$

(a) Find the domain of this function.
In parts (b)–(e), find the functional values and explain what each means.
(b) $C(45)$ (c) $C(90)$
(d) $C(99)$ (e) $C(99.6)$

56. **Shipping restrictions** If a box with a square cross section is to be sent by a delivery service, there are restrictions on its size such that its volume is given by $V = x^2(108 - 4x)$, where x is the length of each side of the cross section (in inches).
(a) Is V a function of x?
(b) If $V = V(x)$, find $V(10)$ and $V(20)$.
(c) What restrictions must be placed on x (the domain) so that the problem makes physical sense?

57. **Profit** Suppose that the profit from the production and sale of x units of a product is given by

$$P(x) = 180x - \frac{x^2}{100} - 200$$

In addition, suppose that for a certain month the number of units produced on day t of the month is

$$x = q(t) = 1000 + 10t$$

(a) Find $(P \circ q)(t)$ to express the profit as a function of the day of the month.
(b) Find the number of units produced, and the profit, on the fifteenth day of the month.

58. **Fish species growth** For many species of fish, the weight W is a function of the length L that can be expressed by

$$W = W(L) = kL^3 \qquad k = \text{constant}$$

Suppose that for a particular species $k = 0.02$, that for this species the length (in centimeters) is a function of the number of years t the fish has been alive, and that this function is given by

$$L = L(t) = 50 - \frac{(t - 20)^2}{10} \qquad 0 \le t \le 20$$

Find $(W \circ L)(t)$ in order to express W as a function of the age t of the fish.

59. **Revenue and advertising** Suppose that a company's revenue $R = f(C)$ is a function f of the number of customers C. Suppose also that the amount spent on advertising A affects the number of customers so that $C = g(A)$ is a function g of A.
(a) Is $f \circ g$ defined? Explain.
(b) Is $g \circ f$ defined? Explain.
(c) For the functions in parts (a) and (b) that are defined, identify the input (independent variable) and the output (dependent variable) and explain what the function means.

60. **Manufacturing** Two of the processes (functions) used by a manufacturer of factory-built homes are sanding (denote this as function s) and painting (denote this as function p). Write a sentence of explanation for each of the following functional expressions involving s and p applied to a door.
(a) $s(\text{door})$ (b) $p(\text{door})$ (c) $(p \circ s)(\text{door})$
(d) $(s \circ p)(\text{door})$ (e) $(p \circ p)(\text{door})$

61. **Fencing a lot** A farmer wishes to fence the perimeter of a rectangular lot with an area of 1600 square feet. If the lot is x feet long, express the number of feet L of fence needed as a function of x.

62. **Cost** A shipping crate has a square base with sides of length x feet, and it is half as tall as it is wide. If the material for the bottom and sides of the box costs \$2.00 per square foot and the material for the top costs \$1.50 per square foot, express the total cost of material for the box as a function of x.

63. **Revenue** An agency charges \$100 per person for a trip to a concert if 30 people travel in a group. But for each person above the 30, the amount charged each traveler will be reduced by \$2.00. If x represents the number of people above the 30, write the agency's revenue R as a function of x.

64. **Revenue** A company handles an apartment building with 50 units. Experience has shown that if the rent for each of the units is \$720 per month, all of the units will be filled, but one unit will become vacant for each \$20 increase in the monthly rate. If x represents the number of \$20 increases, write the revenue R from the building as a function of x.

OBJECTIVES

1.3

- To find the intercepts of graphs
- To graph linear functions
- To find the slope of a line from its graph and from its equation
- To find the rate of change of a linear function
- To graph a line, given its slope and y-intercept or its slope and one point on the line
- To write the equation of a line, given information about its graph

Linear Functions

| APPLICATION PREVIEW |

The population of U.S. males, y (in thousands), projected from 2015 to 2060 can be modeled by

$$y = 1125.9x + 142{,}690$$

where x is the number of years past 2000 (*Source:* U.S. Census Bureau). What does this function tell us about the population of U.S. males during this period? (See Example 7.) In this section, we find the rates of change of linear functions and the slopes and intercepts of graphs of linear functions.

The function in the Application Preview is an example of a special function, called the **linear function,** defined as follows.

Linear Function

A **linear function** is a function of the form

$$y = f(x) = ax + b$$

where a and b are constants.

As in Section 1.1 with linear equations, a linear function is also called a first-degree function, and the graph of such a function is a straight line.

Intercepts

The point(s) where a graph intersects the x-axis are called the x-intercept points, and the x-coordinates of these points are the **x-intercepts.** Similarly, the points where a graph intersects the y-axis are the y-intercept points, and the y-coordinates of these points are the **y-intercepts.** Because any point on the x-axis has y-coordinate 0 and any point on the y-axis has x-coordinate 0, we find intercepts as follows.

Intercepts

(a) To find the **y-intercept(s)** of the graph of an equation, set $x = 0$ in the equation and solve for y. *Note:* A function of x has at most one y-intercept.
(b) To find the **x-intercept(s),** set $y = 0$ and solve for x.

Because the graph of a linear function is a line, only two points are necessary to determine its graph. It is frequently possible to use intercepts to graph a linear function.

EXAMPLE   1

Intercepts and Graphing

Find the intercepts and graph the following.
(a) $3x + y = 9$ (b) $x = 4y$

Solution

(a) To find the y-intercept, we set $x = 0$ and solve for y:
     $3(0) + y = 9$ gives $y = 9$, so the y-intercept is 9.
     To find the x-intercept, we set $y = 0$ and solve for x:
     $3x + 0 = 9$ gives $x = 3$, so the x-intercept is 3.
     Using the intercepts gives the graph, shown in Figure 1.10.

(b) Letting $x = 0$ gives $y = 0$, and letting $y = 0$ gives $x = 0$, so the only intercept of the graph of $x = 4y$ is at the point (0, 0). A second point is needed to graph the line. Hence, if we let $y = 1$ in $x = 4y$, we get $x = 4$ and have a second point (4, 1) on the graph. It is wise to plot a third point as a check. The graph is shown in Figure 1.11.

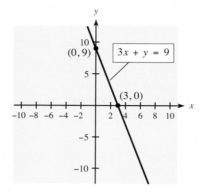

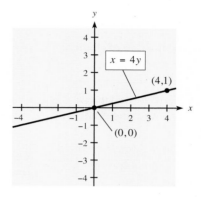

Figures 1.10 & 1.11

Note that the equation graphed in Figure 1.10 can be rewritten as

$$y = 9 - 3x \quad \text{or} \quad f(x) = 9 - 3x$$

We see in Figure 1.10 that the x-intercept (3, 0) is the point where the function value is zero. The x-coordinate of such a point is called a **zero of the function.** Thus we see that the *x-intercepts of a function are the same as its zeros.*

EXAMPLE 2   Depreciation

A business property is purchased for $122,880 and depreciated over a period of 10 years. Its value y is related to the number of months of service x by the equation

$$4096x + 4y = 491{,}520$$

Find the x-intercept and the y-intercept and use them to sketch the graph of the equation.

Solution

$$x\text{-intercept: } y = 0 \quad \text{gives} \quad 4096x = 491{,}520$$
$$x = 120$$

Thus 120 is the x-intercept.

$$y\text{-intercept: } x = 0 \quad \text{gives} \quad 4y = 491{,}520$$
$$y = 122{,}880$$

Thus 122,880 is the y-intercept. The graph is shown in Figure 1.12 on the next page. Note that the units on the x- and y-axes are different. The y-intercept corresponds to the value of the property 0 months after purchase—that is, the purchase price. The x-intercept corresponds to the number of months that have passed before the value is 0; that is, the property is fully depreciated after 120 months, or 10 years. Note that only positive values for x and y make sense in this application, so only the Quadrant I portion of the graph is shown.

Despite the ease of using intercepts to graph linear equations, this method is not always the best. For example, vertical lines, horizontal lines, or lines that pass through the origin may have a single intercept, and if a line has both intercepts very close to the origin, using the intercepts may lead to an inaccurate graph.

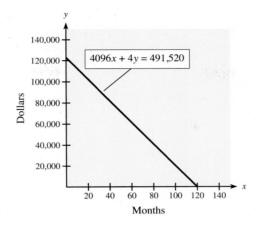

Figure 1.12

Rate of Change; Slope of a Line

Note that in Figure 1.12, as the graph moves from the y-intercept point $(0, 122{,}880)$ to the x-intercept point $(120, 0)$, the y-value on the line changes $-122{,}880$ units (from $122{,}880$ to 0), whereas the x-value changes 120 units (from 0 to 120). Thus the **rate of change** of the value of the business property is

$$\frac{-122{,}880}{120} = -1024 \text{ dollars per month}$$

This means that each month the value of the property changes by -1024 dollars, or the value decreases by \$1024 per month. This **rate of change** of a linear function is called the **slope** of the line that is its graph (see Figure 1.12). For the graph of a linear function, the ratio of the change in y to the corresponding change in x measures the slope of the line. For any nonvertical line, the slope can be found by using any two points on the line, as follows.

Slope of a Line

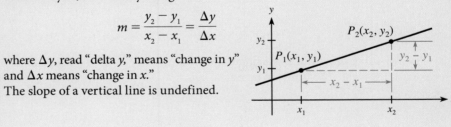

If a nonvertical line passes through the points $P_1(x_1, y_1)$ and $P_2(x_2, y_2)$, its **slope,** denoted by m, is found by using

$$m = \frac{y_2 - y_1}{x_2 - x_1} = \frac{\Delta y}{\Delta x}$$

where Δy, read "delta y," means "change in y" and Δx means "change in x."
The slope of a vertical line is undefined.

Note that for a given line, the slope is the same regardless of which two points are used in the calculation; this is because corresponding sides of similar triangles are in proportion.

EXAMPLE 3   Slopes

Find the slope of
(a)   line ℓ_1, passing through $(-2, 1)$ and $(4, 3)$
(b)   line ℓ_2, passing through $(3, 0)$ and $(4, -3)$

Solution

(a) $m = \dfrac{3 - 1}{4 - (-2)} = \dfrac{2}{6} = \dfrac{1}{3}$ or, equivalently, $m = \dfrac{1 - 3}{-2 - 4} = \dfrac{-2}{-6} = \dfrac{1}{3}$

This means that a point 3 units to the right and 1 unit up from any point on the line is also on the line. Line ℓ_1 is shown in Figure 1.13.

(b) $m = \dfrac{0 - (-3)}{3 - 4} = \dfrac{3}{-1} = -3$

This means that a point 1 unit to the right and 3 units down from any point on the line is also on the line. Line ℓ_2 is also shown in Figure 1.13.

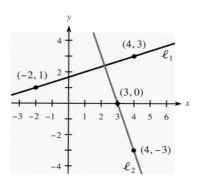

Figure 1.13

From the previous discussion, we see that the slope describes the direction of a line as follows.

Orientation of a Line and Its Slope

1. The slope is *positive* if the line slopes upward toward the right. The function is increasing.

$$m = \frac{\Delta y}{\Delta x} > 0$$

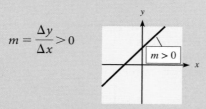

2. The slope is *negative* if the line slopes downward toward the right. The function is decreasing.

$$m = \frac{\Delta y}{\Delta x} < 0$$

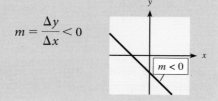

3. The slope of a *horizontal line* is 0, because $\Delta y = 0$. The function is constant.

$$m = \frac{\Delta y}{\Delta x} = 0$$

4. The slope of a *vertical line* is *undefined*, because $\Delta x = 0$.

$$m = \frac{\Delta y}{\Delta x} \text{ is undefined.}$$

Two distinct nonvertical lines that have the same slope are parallel, and conversely, two nonvertical parallel lines have the same slope.

Parallel Lines | Two distinct nonvertical lines are *parallel* if and only if their slopes are *equal*.

In general, two lines are perpendicular if they intersect at right angles. However, the appearance of this perpendicularity relationship can be obscured when we graph lines, unless the axes have the same scale. Note that the lines ℓ_1 and ℓ_2 in Figure 1.13 appear to be perpendicular. However, the same lines graphed with different scales on the axes will not look perpendicular. To avoid being misled by graphs with different scales, we use slopes to tell us when lines are perpendicular. Note that the slope of ℓ_1, $\frac{1}{3}$, is the negative reciprocal of the slope of ℓ_2, -3. In fact, as with lines ℓ_1 and ℓ_2, any two nonvertical lines that are perpendicular have slopes that are negative reciprocals of each other.

Slopes of Perpendicular Lines	A line ℓ_1 with slope m, where $m \neq 0$, is *perpendicular* to line ℓ_2 if and only if the slope of ℓ_2 is $-1/m$. (The slopes are *negative reciprocals*.)

Because the slope of a vertical line is undefined, we cannot use slope in discussing parallel and perpendicular relations that involve vertical lines. Two vertical lines are parallel, and any horizontal line is perpendicular to any vertical line.

✓ CHECKPOINT

1. Find the slope of the line through $(4, 6)$ and $(28, -6)$.
2. If a line has slope $m = 0$, then the line is _____. If a line has an undefined slope, then the line is _____.
3. Suppose that line 1 has slope $m_1 = 5$ and line 2 has slope m_2.
   (a)   If line 1 is perpendicular to line 2, find m_2.
   (b)   If line 1 is parallel to line 2, find m_2.

Writing Equations of Lines   If the slope of a line is m, then the slope between a fixed point (x_1, y_1) and any other point (x, y) on the line is also m. That is,

$$m = \frac{y - y_1}{x - x_1}$$

Solving for $y - y_1$ gives the point-slope form of the equation of a line.

Point-Slope Form	The equation of the line passing through the point (x_1, y_1) and with slope m can be written in the **point-slope form** $$y - y_1 = m(x - x_1)$$

EXAMPLE   4   **Equations of Lines**

Write the equation for each line that passes through $(1, -2)$ and has

(a)   slope $\frac{2}{3}$ (b)   undefined slope   (c)   point $(2, 3)$ also on the line

Solution
(a)   Here $m = \frac{2}{3}$, $x_1 = 1$, and $y_1 = -2$. An equation of the line is

$$y - (-2) = \frac{2}{3}(x - 1)$$

$$y + 2 = \frac{2}{3}x - \frac{2}{3}$$

$$y = \frac{2}{3}x - \frac{8}{3}$$

This equation also may be written in **general form** as $2x - 3y - 8 = 0$. Figure 1.14 shows the graph of this line; the point $(1, -2)$ and the slope are highlighted.

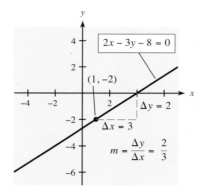

Figure 1.14

(b) Because m is undefined, we cannot use the point-slope form. This line is vertical, so every point on it has x-coordinate 1. Thus the equation is $x = 1$. Note that $x = 1$ is not a function.

(c) First use $(1, -2)$ and $(2, 3)$ to find the slope.

$$m = \frac{3 - (-2)}{2 - 1} = 5$$

Using $m = 5$ and the point $(1, -2)$ (the other point could also be used) gives

$$y - (-2) = 5(x - 1) \quad \text{or} \quad y = 5x - 7$$

The graph of $x = 1$ (from Example 4(b)) is a vertical line, as shown in Figure 1.15(a); the graph of $y = 1$ has slope 0, and its graph is a horizontal line, as shown in Figure 1.15(b).

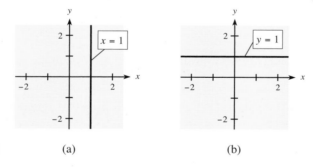

Figure 1.15   (a)   (b)

In general, **vertical lines** have undefined slope and the equation form $x = a$, where a is the x-coordinate of each point on the line. **Horizontal lines** have $m = 0$ and the equation form $y = b$, where b is the y-coordinate of each point on the line.

EXAMPLE 5   Pricing

U.S. Census Bureau data indicate that the average price p of digital television sets can be expressed as a linear function of the number of sets sold N (in thousands). In addition, as N increased by 1000, p dropped by \$10.40, and when 6485 (thousand) sets were sold, the average price per set was \$504.39. Write the equation of the line determined by this information.

Solution
We see that price p is a function of the number of sets N (in thousands), so the slope is given by

$$m = \frac{\text{change in } p}{\text{change in } N} = \frac{-10.40}{1000} = -0.0104$$

A point on the line is $(N_1, p_1) = (6485, 504.39)$. We use the point-slope form adapted to the variables N and p.

$$p - p_1 = m(N - N_1)$$
$$p - 504.39 = -0.0104(N - 6485)$$
$$p - 504.39 = -0.0104N + 67.444$$
$$p = -0.0104N + 571.834$$

The point-slope form, with the y-intercept point $(0, b)$, can be used to derive a special form for the equation of a line, called the **slope-intercept form**.

$$y - b = m(x - 0)$$
$$y = mx + b$$

Slope-Intercept Form

The **slope-intercept form** of the equation of a line with slope m and y-intercept b is

$$y = mx + b$$

Note that if a linear equation has the form $y = mx + b$, then the coefficient of x is the slope and the constant term is the y-intercept.

EXAMPLE 6   Writing an Equation of a Line

Write the slope-intercept form of the equation of the line with slope $\frac{1}{2}$ and y-intercept -3.

Solution
Substituting $m = \frac{1}{2}$ and $b = -3$ in the equation $y = mx + b$ gives $y = \frac{1}{2}x + (-3)$, or $y = \frac{1}{2}x - 3$.

EXAMPLE 7   Population of U.S. Males | APPLICATION PREVIEW |

The population of U.S. males, y (in thousands), projected from 2015 to 2060 can be modeled by

$$y = 1125.9x + 142{,}690$$

where x is the number of years after 2000 (*Source:* U.S. Census Bureau).
(a)   Find the slope and the y-intercept of the graph of this function.
(b)   What does the y-intercept tell us about the population of U.S. males?
(c)   Interpret the slope as a rate of change.

Solution
(a)   The slope is $m = 1125.9$ and the y-intercept is $b = 142{,}690$.
(b)   Because x is the number of years after 2000, $x = 0$ represents 2000 and the y-intercept tells us that there were approximately 142,690,000 males in the United States in 2000.
(c)   The slope is 1125.9, which tells us that the population of U.S. males is predicted to increase at a rate of approximately 1,125,900 per year during this period.

When a linear equation does not appear in slope-intercept form (and does not have the form $x = a$), it can be put into slope-intercept form by solving the equation for y.

EXAMPLE 8   Slope-Intercept Form

(a)   Find the slope and y-intercept of the line whose equation is $x + 2y = 8$.
(b)   Use this information to graph the equation.

Solution

(a) To put the equation in slope-intercept form, we must solve it for y.

$$2y = -x + 8 \quad \text{or} \quad y = -\frac{1}{2}x + 4$$

Thus the slope is $-\frac{1}{2}$ and the y-intercept is 4.

(b) First we plot the y-intercept point $(0, 4)$. Because the slope is $-\frac{1}{2} = \frac{-1}{2}$, moving 2 units to the right and down 1 unit from $(0, 4)$ gives the point $(2, 3)$ on the line. A third point (for a check) is plotted at $(4, 2)$. The graph is shown in Figure 1.16. ■

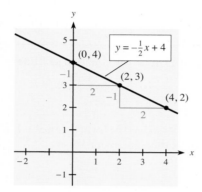

Figure 1.16

It is also possible to graph a straight line if we know its slope and any point on the line; we simply plot the point that is given and then use the slope to plot other points. The following summarizes the forms of equations of lines.

Forms of Linear Equations	General form: $ax + by + c = 0$ Point-slope form: $y - y_1 = m(x - x_1)$ Slope-intercept form: $y = mx + b$ Vertical line: $x = a$ Horizontal line: $y = b$

✓ **CHECKPOINT**

4. Write the equation of the line that has slope $-\frac{3}{4}$ and passes through $(4, -6)$.
5. What are the slope and y-intercept of the graph of $x = -4y + 1$?

✓ **CHECKPOINT ANSWERS**

1. $m = -\dfrac{1}{2}$

2. If $m = 0$, then the line is horizontal. If m is undefined, then the line is vertical.

3. (a) $m_2 = -\dfrac{1}{5}$ (b) $m_2 = 5$

4. $y = -\frac{3}{4}x - 3$.

5. $m = -\frac{1}{4}$; y-intercept is $\frac{1}{4}$.

| EXERCISES | 1.3

In Problems 1–4, find the intercepts and graph the functions.

1. $3x + 4y = 12$
2. $6x - 5y = 90$
3. $5x - 8y = 60$
4. $2x - y + 17 = 0$

In Problems 5–10, find the slope of the line passing through the given pair of points.

5. $(22, 11)$ and $(15, -17)$
6. $(-6, -12)$ and $(-18, -24)$

7. $(3, -1)$ and $(-1, 1)$
8. $(-5, 6)$ and $(1, -3)$
9. $(3, 2)$ and $(-1, 2)$
10. $(-4, 2)$ and $(-4, -2)$
11. If a line is horizontal, then its slope is _____.
12. If a line is vertical, then its slope is _____.
13. What is the rate of change of the function whose graph is a line passing through $(3, 2)$ and $(-1, 2)$?
14. What is the rate of change of the function whose graph is a line passing through $(11, -5)$ and $(-9, -4)$?

In Problems 15 and 16, for each given graph, determine whether each line has a slope that is positive, negative, 0, or undefined.

15.

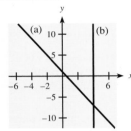

16.

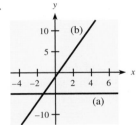

In Problems 17–24, find the slope and y-intercept and then graph each equation.

17. $y = \dfrac{7}{3}x - \dfrac{1}{4}$

18. $y = \dfrac{4}{3}x + \dfrac{1}{2}$

19. $y = 3$

20. $y = -2$

21. $x = -8$

22. $x = -1/2$

23. $2x + 3y = 6$

24. $3x - 2y = 18$

In Problems 25–28, write the slope-intercept form of the equation of the line that has the given slope and y-intercept. Then graph the line.

25. Slope $\frac{1}{2}$ and y-intercept -3
26. Slope 4 and y-intercept 2
27. Slope -2 and y-intercept $\frac{1}{2}$
28. Slope $-\frac{2}{3}$ and y-intercept -1

In Problems 29–34, write the equation of the line that passes through the given point and has the given slope. Then graph the line.

29. $(2, 0)$ with slope -5

30. $(1, 1)$ with slope $-\frac{1}{3}$

31. $(-1, 4)$ with slope $-\frac{3}{4}$

32. $(3, -1)$ with slope 1

33. $(-1, 1)$ with undefined slope
34. $(1, 1)$ with 0 slope

In Problems 35–40, write the equation of each line described or shown.

35. Through $(3, 2)$ and $(-1, -6)$
36. Through $(-4, 2)$ and $(2, 4)$
37. Through $(7, 3)$ and $(-6, 2)$
38. Through $(10, 2)$ and $(8, 7)$

39.

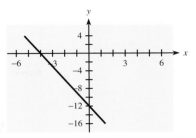

40.

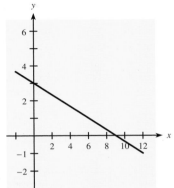

In Problems 41–44, determine whether the following pairs of equations represent parallel lines, perpendicular lines, or neither of these.

41. $3x + 2y = 6$; $2x - 3y = 6$
42. $5x - 2y = 8$; $10x - 4y = 8$
43. $6x - 4y = 12$; $3x - 2y = 6$
44. $5x + 4y = 7$; $y = \dfrac{4}{5}x + 7$

45. Write the equation of the line passing through $(-2, -7)$ that is parallel to $3x + 5y = 11$.
46. Write the equation of the line passing through $(6, -4)$ that is parallel to $4x - 5y = 6$.
47. Write the equation of the line passing through $(3, 1)$ that is perpendicular to $5x - 6y = 4$.
48. Write the equation of the line passing through $(-2, -8)$ that is perpendicular to $x = 4y + 3$.

APPLICATIONS

49. *Depreciation* A \$360,000 building is depreciated by its owner. The value y of the building after x months of use is $y = 360{,}000 - 1500x$.
    (a) Graph this function for $x \geq 0$.
    (b) How long is it until the building is completely depreciated (its value is zero)?
    (c) The point $(60, 270{,}000)$ lies on the graph. Explain what this means.

50. *U.S population* Using Social Security Administration data for selected years from 1950 and projected to 2050, the U.S. population (in millions) can be described by

$$p(t) = 2.53t + 162.2$$

where t is the number of years past 1950.

(a) Find $p(0)$ and explain its meaning.

(b) Find the slope and explain its meaning.

(c) Graph this function for $t \geq 0$.

51. *Internet users* The percent of the U.S. population with Internet service can be described by

$$y = 1.36x + 55.98$$

where x is the number of years past 1990 (*Source: Jupiter Media Metrix*).

(a) Find the slope and y-intercept of this equation.

(b) What interpretation could be given to the slope?

(c) Graph the function.

52. *Cigarette use* The percent p of high school students who occasionally smoke cigarettes can be described by

$$p = 38.56 - 1.53t$$

where t is the number of years past 1995 (*Source: National Institute on Drug Abuse*).

(a) Find the slope and p-intercept of this equation.

(b) Write a sentence that interprets the meaning of the slope as a rate of change.

(c) Write a sentence that interprets the meaning of the p-intercept.

53. *World forest area* When x is the number of years past 1990, the world forest area (that is, natural forest or planted stands) as a percent of land area is given by

$$F(x) = -0.065x + 31.39$$

(*Source: The World Bank, Food and Agriculture Organization*)

(a) Find the slope and F-intercept for this linear function.

(b) Write a sentence that interprets the F-intercept.

(c) Find the annual rate of change of world forest area as a percent of land area, and write a sentence that explains its meaning.

54. *Temperature–humidity models* Two models for measuring the effects of high temperature and humidity are the Summer Simmer Index and the Apparent Temperature.* For an outside temperature of 100°F, these indices relate the relative humidity, H (expressed as a decimal), to the perceived temperature as follows.

Summer Simmer: $S = 141.1 - 45.78(1 - H)$
Apparent Temperature: $A = 91.2 + 41.3H$

(a) For each index, find the point that corresponds to a relative humidity of 40%.

(b) For each point in part (a), write a sentence that explains its meaning.

(c) Graph both equations for $0 \leq H \leq 1$.

55. *Earnings and gender* According to the U.S. Census Bureau, the relation between the average annual earnings of males and females with various levels

of educational attainment can be modeled by the function

$$F = 0.78M - 1.316$$

where M and F represent the average annual earnings (in thousands of dollars) of males and females, respectively.

(a) Viewing F as a function of M, what is the slope of the graph of this function?

(b) Interpret the slope as a rate of change.

(c) When the average annual earnings for males reach $60,000, what does the equation predict for the average annual earnings for females?

56. *Gross domestic product* The U.S. gross domestic product (GDP), y, for the years from 2011 and projected to 2021 is given by

$$y = 977.8x + 13,643.2$$

where x is the number of years past 1990 and y is in billions of dollars (*Source: Social Security Administration*).

(a) What is the slope of the graph of this function?

(b) Interpret the slope as a rate of change.

57. *Residential electric costs* An electric utility company determines the monthly bill for a residential customer by adding an energy charge of 8.38 cents per kilowatt-hour to its base charge of $16.37 per month. Write an equation for the monthly charge y in terms of x, the number of kilowatt-hours used.

58. *Residential heating costs* Residential customers who heat their homes with natural gas have their monthly bills calculated by adding a base service charge of $9.19 per month and an energy charge of 91.91 cents per hundred cubic feet. Write an equation for the monthly charge y in terms of x, the number of hundreds of cubic feet used.

59. *Civilian workforce* The size of the U.S. civilian workforce for the years from 1950 and projected to 2050 can be approximated by a linear equation determined by the line connecting the points (1950, 62.2) and (2050, 191.8), where the x-coordinate is the year and the y-coordinate is the number in the civilian workforce (in millions) in year x (*Source: U.S. Bureau of Labour Statistics*).

(a) Write the equation of the line connecting the two points.

(b) Interpret the slope of this line as a rate of change.

60. *Pension plans* According to *USA Today* Research, most pensions for state legislators are based on the product of the legislator's years of service, compensation, and a multiplier (usually between 1% and 5%). When the multiplier is 2.5%, a state legislator's pension would be calculated with a formula like the following:
  "2.5% of average final compensation multiplied by the years of credited service"

Let p represent annual retirement pension, y years of service, and c average final compensation.

(a) For someone with average final compensation of $80,000, write the linear equation that gives p in terms of y.

*Bosch, W., and C. G. Cobb, "Temperature-Humidity Indices," UMAP Unit 691, *The UMAP Journal,* 10(3), Fall 1989, 237–256.

(b) For someone intending to retire after 30 years, write the linear equation that gives p in terms of c.

61. **Consumer price index** The projected consumer price index (CPI) for the years 2020 to 2050 can be approximated by a linear equation determined by the line connecting (2020, 120.56) and (2050, 276.05), where the x-coordinate is the year and the y-coordinate is the price consumers pay in year x for goods that cost $100 in 2012 (*Source:* Social Security Administration).
    (a) Write the equation of the line connecting these two points to find a linear model for these data.
    (b) Interpret the slope of this line as a rate of change.

62. **Drinking and driving** The following table gives the number of drinks and the resulting blood alcohol percent for a 180-pound man legally considered driving under the influence (DUI).

Number of Drinks	5	6	7	8	9	10
Blood Alcohol Percent	0.11	0.13	0.15	0.17	0.19	0.21

Source: Pennsylvania Liquor Control Board

   (a) Is the average rate of change of the blood alcohol percent with respect to the number of drinks a constant?
   (b) Use the rate of change and one point determined by a number of drinks and the resulting blood alcohol percent to write the equation of a linear model for these data.
   (c) Verify that the values in the table fit the model.

63. **Pollution effects** It has been estimated that a certain stream can support 85,000 fish if it is pollution-free. It has further been estimated that for each ton of pollutants in the stream, 1700 fewer fish can be supported. Assuming the relationship is linear, write the equation that gives the population of fish p in terms of the tons of pollutants x.

64. **Age–sleep relationship** Each day, a young person should sleep 8 hours plus $\frac{1}{4}$ hour for each year that the

person is under 18 years of age. Assuming the relation is linear, write the equation relating hours of sleep y and age x.

65. **Insulation R-values** The R-value of insulation is a measure of its ability to resist heat transfer. For fiberglass insulation, $3\frac{1}{2}$ inches is rated at R-11 and 6 inches is rated at R-19. Assuming this relationship is linear, write the equation that gives the R-value of fiberglass insulation as a function of its thickness t (in inches).

66. **Depreciation** Suppose the cost of a business property is $960,000 and a company wants to use a straight-line depreciation schedule for a period of 240 months. If y is the value of this property after x months, write the equation of this depreciation schedule.

67. **Cholesterol and coronary heart disease risk** The Seven Countries Study, conducted by Ancel Keys, was a long-term study of the relationship of cholesterol to coronary heart disease (CHD) mortality in men. The relationship was approximated by the line shown in the accompanying figure. The line passes through the points (200, 25) and (250, 49), which means there were 25 CHD deaths per 1000 among men with 200 mg/dl (milligrams per deciliter) of cholesterol and 49 CHD deaths per 1000 among men with 250 mg/dl of cholesterol. Using x to represent the cholesterol and y to represent CHD deaths, write the equation that represents this relationship.

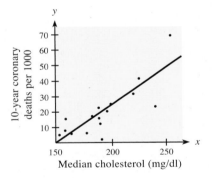

OBJECTIVES   1.4

- To use a graphing utility to graph equations in the standard viewing window
- To use a graphing utility and a specified range to graph equations
- To use a graphing utility to evaluate functions, to find intercepts, and to find zeros of a function
- To solve linear equations with a graphing utility

Graphs and Graphing Utilities

■ | APPLICATION PREVIEW | ■

Suppose that for a certain city the cost C of obtaining drinking water with p percent impurities (by volume) is given by

$$C = \frac{120{,}000}{p} - 1200$$

where $0 < p \le 100$. A graph of this equation would illustrate how the purity of water is related to the cost of obtaining it. Because this equation is not linear, graphing it would require many more than two points. Such a graph could be efficiently obtained with a graphing utility. (See Example 1.)

In Section 1.3, "Linear Functions," we saw that a linear equation could easily be graphed by plotting points because only two points are required. When we want the graph of an equation that is not linear, we can still use point plotting, but we must have enough points to sketch an accurate graph.

Some computer software and all graphing calculators have **graphing utilities** (also called *graphics utilities*) that can be used to generate an accurate graph. All graphing utilities use the point-plotting method to plot scores of points quickly and thereby graph an equation.

The computer monitor or calculator screen consists of a fine grid that looks like a piece of graph paper. In this grid, each tiny area is called a pixel. Essentially, a pixel corresponds to a point on a piece of graph paper, and as a graphing utility plots points, the pixels corresponding to the points are lighted and then connected, revealing the graph. The graph is shown in a viewing window or viewing rectangle. The values that define the viewing window of Texas Instruments calculators can be set individually or by using ZOOM keys. The important values are

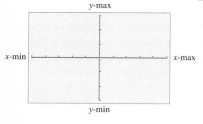

x-min:	the smallest value on the x-axis (the leftmost x-value in the window)
x-max:	the largest value on the x-axis (the rightmost x-value in the window)
y-min:	the smallest value on the y-axis (the lowest y-value in the window)
y-max:	the largest value on the y-axis (the highest y-value in the window)

Most graphing utilities have a *standard viewing window* that gives a window with x-values and y-values between -10 and 10.

$$x\text{-min: } -10 \qquad\qquad y\text{-min: } -10$$
$$x\text{-max: } 10 \qquad\qquad y\text{-max: } 10$$

To graph $y = \frac{1}{3}x^3 - x^2 - 3x + 2$ with the standard viewing window:

1. Under the Y = menu, enter the right side of the equation in Y1.
2. Under ZOOM, press 6:Z standard.

The resulting graph is shown in Figure 1.17.

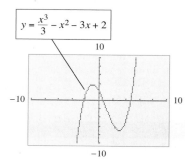

$$y = \frac{x^3}{3} - x^2 - 3x + 2$$

Figure 1.17

Calculator Note With a graphing calculator, as with a graph plotted by hand, the appearance of the graph is determined by the part of the graph we are viewing, and the standard window does not always give a **complete graph**. (A complete graph shows the important parts of the graph and suggests the unseen parts.) The steps for graphing a function with a graphing calculator are shown in Appendix A, Section 1.4.

EXAMPLE 1   Water Purity | APPLICATION PREVIEW |

For a certain city, the cost C of obtaining drinking water with p percent impurities (by volume) is given by

$$C = \frac{120{,}000}{p} - 1200$$

The equation for C requires that $p \neq 0$, and because p is the percent impurities, we know that $0 < p \leq 100$. Use the restriction on p and a graphing calculator to obtain an accurate graph of the equation.

Solution

To use a graphing calculator, we identify C with y and p with x. Thus we enter

$$y = \frac{120{,}000}{x} - 1200$$

Because $0 < p \leq 100$, we set the x-range to *include* these values, with the realization that only the portion of the graph above these values applies to our equation and that $p = 0$ (that is, $x = 0$) is excluded from the domain because it makes the denominator 0. With this x-range we can determine a y-, or C-, range from the equation or by tracing; see Figure 1.18(a). We see that when p is near 0 (the value excluded from the domain), the C-coordinates of the points are very large, indicating that water free of impurities is very costly. However, Figure 1.18(a) does not accurately show what happens for large p-values. Figure 1.18(b) shows another view of the equation with the C-range (that is, the y-range) from -500 to 3500. We see the p-intercept is $p = 100$, which indicates that water containing 100% impurities costs nothing ($C = 0$). Note that $p > 100$ has no meaning. Why? ■

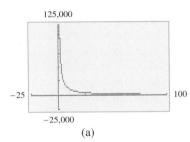
(a)

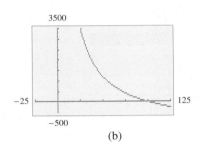
(b)

Figure 1.18

Two views of $C = \dfrac{120{,}000}{p} - 1200$

✓ CHECKPOINT

Use a graphing calculator and the standard viewing window to graph the following.

1. $y = -x^2/4$

2. $y = \dfrac{4(x + 1)^2}{x^2 + 1}$

We can evaluate a function $y = f(x)$ with a graphing calculator by using TABLE to find the function values corresponding to values of the independent variable. We can also use TRACE to evaluate or approximate function values.

EXAMPLE 2 Women in the Workforce

The number y (in millions) of women in the workforce is modeled by the function

$$y = -0.005x^2 + 1.38x + 0.07$$

where x is the number of years past 1940 (*Source:* Bureau of Labor Statistics).

(a) Graph this function from $x = 0$ to $x = 85$.
(b) Find the value of y when $x = 60$. Explain what this means.
(c) Use the model to estimate the number of women in the workforce in 2015.

Solution

(a) Enter the equation and set the window with x-min $= 0$ and x-max $= 85$. Using TRACE for x-values between 0 and 85 helps determine that y-values between

0 and 85 give a complete graph. These values are entered in the screen under WINDOW (see Figure 1.19(a)). The graph is shown in Figure 1.19(b).

(b) By using TRACE or TABLE, we can find $f(60) = 64.87$ (see Figure 1.19(c) and Figure 1.19(d)). This means that there were approximately 64.87 million, or 64,870,000, women in the workforce in $1940 + 60 = 2000$.

(c) The year 2015 corresponds to $x = 75$ and $f(75) = 75.445$ (see Figure 1.19(d)). Thus in 2015, approximately 75,445,000 women are estimated to be in the workforce. ▪

```
WINDOW
Xmin=0
Xmax=85
Xsc1=10
Ymin=0
Ymax=85
Ysc1=10
Xres=1
```

(a)

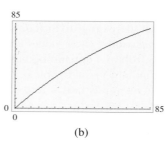

(b)

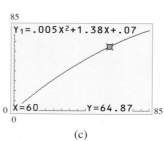

(c)

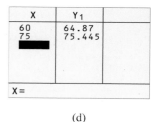

X	Y₁	
60	64.87	
75	75.445	
■■■		

X =

(d)

Figure 1.19

Spreadsheet Note

■| TABLE 1.3 |■

	A	B
1	x	$f(x) = 6x - 3$
2	−5	−33
3	−2	−15
4	−1	−9
5	0	−3
6	1	3
7	3	15
8	5	27

Representing quantities or their interrelationships algebraically is one of the keys to using spreadsheets. Each cell in a spreadsheet has an address based on its row and column. For example, cell B3 in Table 1.3 is the second column and the third row.

The cells can contain numbers or formulas that use numbers and cell addresses. These cell addresses act like variables in an algebraic expression. We can use "fill down" or "fill across" to find the ouputs of a function for given inputs. Table 1.3 shows a spreadsheet for the function $f(x) = 6x - 3$ for the input set $\{-5, -2, -1, 0, 1, 3, 5\}$, with these inputs listed as entries in the first column (column A). If −5 is in cell A2, then $f(-5)$ can be found in cell B2 by typing $= 6*A2 - 3$ in cell B2. By using the fill-down capability, we can obtain all the function values shown in column B.

We can graph the function with inputs in column A and outputs in column B of Table 1.3 by highlighting the two columns and selecting the XY (scatter) chart type with the smooth curve option (see Figure 1.20) See Appendix B, Section 1.4 and the online Excel Guide for details on graphing functions. ▪

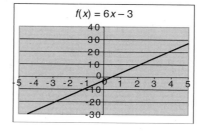

Figure 1.20

Graphical Solutions of Equations

We can use graphing utilities to find the x-intercepts of graphs of functions. Recall that an x-intercept is also a zero of the function. Thus if an equation is written in the form $0 = f(x)$, an x-intercept of $y = f(x)$ is a solution of the equation. This method of solving an equation is called the **x-intercept method.**

> ### Solving an Equation Using the x-Intercept Method with a Graphing Calculator
>
> 1. Rewrite the equation to be solved with 0 (and nothing else) on one side of the equation.
> 2. Enter the nonzero side of the equation found in the previous step in the equation editor of your graphing calculator, and graph the equation in an appropriate viewing window. Be certain that you can see the graph cross the horizontal axis.

3. Find or approximate the *x*-intercept by inspection with TRACE or by using the graphical solver that is often called ZERO or ROOT. The *x*-intercept is the value of *x* that makes the equation equal to zero, so it is the solution to the equation. The value of *x* found by this method is often displayed as a decimal approximation of the exact solution rather than as the exact solution.

4. Verify the solution in the original equation.

See the following example and Appendix A, Section 1.4, for more details for using the *x*-intercept solution method with a graphing calculator.

EXAMPLE 3   ## Solving an Equation with a Graphing Calculator

Graphically solve $5x + \dfrac{1}{2} = 7x - 8$ for *x*.

Solution

To solve this equation, we rewrite the equation with 0 on one side.

$$0 = 7x - 8 - \left(5x + \frac{1}{2}\right)$$

Graphing $y = 7x - 8 - (5x + \frac{1}{2})$ and finding the *x*-intercept gives *x* approximately equal to $4.25 = \frac{17}{4}$ (see Figure 1.21). Checking $x = \frac{17}{4}$ in the original equation, or solving the equation analytically, shows that $x = \frac{17}{4}$ is the exact solution.

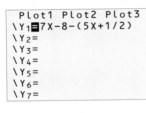

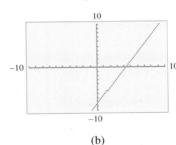

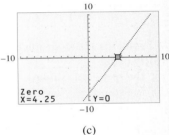

Figure 1.21   (a)   (b)   (c)

Spreadsheet Note

We can use Excel to solve the equation $0 = 5x - 8$ by finding the value of *x* that makes $f(x) = 5x - 8$ equal to 0—that is, by finding the zero of $f(x) = 5x - 8$. To find the zero of $f(x)$ with Excel, we enter the formula for $f(x)$ in the worksheet and use Goal Seek. Under the goal set menu, setting cell B2 to the value 0 and choosing A2 as the changing cell gives $x = 1.6$, which is the solution to the equation.

	A	B
1	x	$f(x) = 5x - 8$
2	1	= 5*A2 − 8

	A	B
1	x	$f(x) = 5x - 8$
2	1.6	0

1.

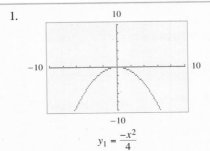

$$y_1 = \frac{-x^2}{4}$$

2.

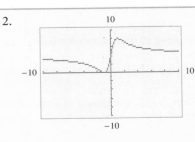

$$y_1 = (4(x + 1)^2)/(x^2 + 1)$$

| EXERCISES | 1.4

In Problems 1–8, use a graphing utility with the standard viewing window to graph each function.

1. $y = x^2 + 4x + 1$
2. $y = 4 - 3x - x^2$
3. $y = x^3 - 3x$
4. $y = x^3 - 6x^2$
5. $y = 0.1x^3 - 0.3x^2 - 2.4x + 3$
6. $y = \frac{1}{4}x^4 - \frac{1}{3}x^3 - 3x^2 + 8$
7. $y = \frac{12x}{x^2 + 1}$
8. $y = \frac{8}{x^2 + 1}$

In Problems 9 and 10, use a graphing utility with the specified window to graph each equation.

9. $y = x^3 - 12x - 1$
   x-min $= -5$, x-max $= 5$;
   y-min $= -20$, y-max $= 20$
10. $y = x^4 - 4x^3 + 6$
    x-min $= -4$, x-max $= 6$;
    y-min $= -40$, y-max $= 10$

In Problems 11 and 12, show the correct way to enter each function in a calculator.

11. $y = \frac{3x + 7}{x^2 + 4}$
12. $y = x^2 - \frac{4}{x - 1}$

In Problems 13–16, graph each equation with a graphing utility using
(a) the specified window.
(b) the standard viewing window (for comparison).

13. $y = 0.01x^3 + 0.3x^2 - 72x + 150$
    x-min $= -100$, x-max $= 80$;
    y-min $= -2000$, y-max $= 4000$
14. $y = -0.0001x^3 + 0.0015x^2 + 0.6x + 7$
    x-min $= -100$, x-max $= 100$;
    y-min $= -50$, y-max $= 50$
15. $y = \frac{x + 15}{x^2 + 400}$
    x-min $= -200$, x-max $= 200$;
    y-min $= -0.02$, y-max $= 0.06$
16. $y = \frac{x - 80}{x^2 + 1700}$
    x-min $= -200$, x-max $= 400$;
    y-min $= -0.06$, y-max $= 0.01$

In Problems 17 and 18, (a) algebraically find the x- and y-intercepts of the graph and (b) graph each equation with a graphing utility, using a window that includes the intercepts.

17. $y = 0.001x - 0.03$
18. $y = 50,000 - 100x$

In Problems 19–22, the graph of a function is shown in the standard viewing window. Experiment with the viewing window to obtain a complete graph.

19. $y = -0.15(x - 10.2)^2 + 10$

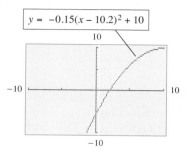

20. $y = x^2 - x - 42$

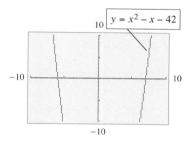

21. $y = \frac{x^3 + 19x^2 - 62x - 840}{20}$

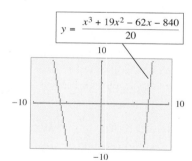

22. $y = \frac{-x^3 + 33x^2 + 120x}{20}$

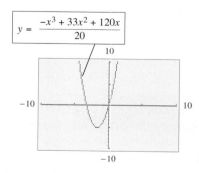

In Problems 23–28, graph the equations in the standard viewing window on a graphing utility. Identify any linear functions.

23. $4x - y = 8$
24. $5x + y = 8$

25. $4x^2 + 2y = 5$ 26. $6x^2 + 3y = 8$
27. $x^2 - 2y - 6 = 0$ 28. $3x^2 - 4y = 8$

In Problems 29 and 30, use VALUE or TABLE to evaluate the function.

29. If $f(x) = x^3 - 3x^2 + 2$, find $f(-2)$ and $f(3/4)$.

30. If $f(x) = \dfrac{x^2 - 2x}{x - 1}$, find $f(3)$ and $f(-4)$.

In Problems 31–34, graph each function using a window that gives a complete graph.

31. $y = \dfrac{12x^2 - 12}{x^2 + 1}$ 32. $y = \dfrac{9x^3}{4x^4 + 9}$

33. $y = \dfrac{x^2 - x - 6}{x^2 + 5x + 6}$ 34. $y = \dfrac{x^2 - 4}{x^2 - 9}$

In Problems 35–38, use the x-intercept method to find one solution of each equation.

35. $0 = 6x - 21$ 36. $12x + 28 = 0$
37. $10 = x^2 - 3x$ 38. $6x^2 + 4x = 4$

In Problems 39 and 40, use a graphing utility to (a) approximate two x-intercepts of the graph of the function (to four decimal places) and (b) give the approximate zeros of the function.

39. $y = x^2 - 7x - 9$ 40. $y = 2x^2 - 4x - 11$

APPLICATIONS

41. *Earnings and gender* With U.S. Census Bureau data, the model that relates the average annual earnings (in thousands of dollars) of females, F, and males, M, with various levels of educational attainment was found to be

$$F = 0.78M - 1.316$$

   (a) Use a graphing calculator to graph this equation for the range M-min $= 0$, M-max $= 70$; F-min $= 0$, F-max $= 60$.
   (b) The point (50, 37.684) lies on the graph of this equation. Explain its meaning.
   (c) Find the average annual female earnings that correspond to male earnings of $62,500.

42. *Women in the workforce* By using U.S. Bureau of Labor Statistics data from 1950 and projected to 2050, the number of women in the workforce (in millions) can be described by $W = 0.79x + 20.86$, where x equals the number of years past 1950.
   (a) Use a graphing calculator to graph this equation with x-min $= 0$ to x-max $= 100$ and with W-min $= 0$ to W-max $= 100$.
   (b) The point (86, 88.8) lies on the graph of this equation. Explain its meaning.
   (c) Find the projected number of women in the workforce in 2040 according to this model.

43. *Consumer expenditure* Suppose that the consumer expenditure E (in dollars) depends

on the market price p per unit (in dollars) according to

$$E = 10,000p - 100p^2$$

   (a) Graph this equation with a graphing calculator and the window p-min $= -50$, p-max $= 150$; E-min $= -50,000$, E-max $= 300,000$.
   (b) Because E represents consumer expenditure, only values of $E \geq 0$ have meaning. For what p-values is $E \geq 0$?

44. *Rectilinear motion* The height above ground (in feet) of a ball thrown vertically into the air is given by

$$S = 112t - 16t^2$$

   where t is the time in seconds since the ball was thrown.
   (a) Graph this equation with a graphing calculator and the window t-min $= -2$, t-max $= 10$; S-min $= -20$, S-max $= 250$.
   (b) Estimate the time at which the ball is at its highest point, and estimate the height of the ball at that time.

45. *Advertising impact* An advertising agency has found that when it promotes a new product in a city of 350,000 people, the rate of change R of the number of people who are aware of the product is related to the number of people x who are aware of it and is given by

$$R = 28,000 - 0.08x$$

   where $x \geq 0$ and $R \geq 0$.
   (a) Use the intercepts to determine a window, and then graph the equation for $x \geq 0$.
   (b) Is the rate of change increasing or decreasing? Explain why your answer makes sense in the context of the problem.

46. *Learning rate* In a study using 50 foreign-language vocabulary words, the learning rate L (in words per minute) was found to depend on the number of words already learned, x, according to the equation

$$L = 20 - 0.4x$$

   (a) Use the intercepts to determine a window, and then graph the equation for $x \geq 0$.
   (b) Is the learning rate increasing or decreasing? Explain why your answer makes sense in the context of the problem.

47. *Elderly men in the workforce* Using data from 1920 and projected to 2030, the percent P of men 65 years of age or older in the labor force can be modeled by

$$P = 0.000078x^3 - 0.0107x^2 - 0.182x + 64.68$$

   where x is the number of years past 1900 (*Source:* U.S. Census Bureau).
   (a) What x-min and x-max should you use to view this graph for values representing 1900 to 2030?

(b) If P-min $= 0$, use a table to determine a value for P-max that would show a complete graph of the model.

(c) Graph this equation.

(d) Write a sentence that describes the percent of men 65 years of age or older in the workforce.

48. ***Cell phone users*** Using data from 2010 and projected to 2016, the number of millions of U.S. cell phone users can be described by

$$y = -0.187x^2 + 5.71x + 232$$

where x is the number of years past 2010 (*Source:* emarketer.com).

(a) Use a table to determine a viewing window that shows a complete graph of this model for the years from 2010 to 2016. State the window used.

(b) Graph this equation.

(c) For years beyond 2016, does this graph increase or decrease? (Look at this graph in a window that includes several of these years.) Explain why this means the model eventually will not accurately describe the relationship between the number of cell phone users and the year.

49. ***Environment*** The Millcreek watershed area was heavily strip mined for coal. Because of the resulting pollution, the streams cannot support fish. Suppose the cost C of obtaining stream water that contains p percent of the current pollution levels is given by

$$C = \frac{285{,}000}{p} - 2850$$

where $0 < p \le 100$.

(a) Use the restriction on p and determine a range for C so that a graphing utility can be used to obtain an accurate graph. Then graph the equation.

(b) Describe what happens to the cost as p takes on values near 0.

(c) The point $(1, 282{,}150)$ lies on the graph of this equation. Explain its meaning.

(d) Explain the meaning of the p-intercept.

50. ***Pollution*** Suppose the cost C of removing p percent of the particulate pollution from the exhaust gases at an industrial site is given by

$$C = \frac{8100p}{100 - p}$$

where $0 \le p < 100$.

(a) Use the restriction on p and experiment with a C-range to obtain an accurate graph of the equation with a graphing utility.

(b) Describe what happens to C as p gets close to 100.

(c) The point $(98, 396{,}900)$ lies on the graph of this equation. Explain the meaning of the coordinates.

(d) Explain the meaning of the p-intercept.

51. ***Tax burden*** The dollars per capita of federal tax burden T can be described by

$$T = 2.11x^3 - 93.01x^2 + 1373.9x + 394$$

where x is the number of years past 1990 (*Source:* Internal Revenue Service).

(a) Graph this function for values of x that correspond to the years 1990 to 2018.

(b) Is the graph increasing or decreasing over these years? What does this tell us about the per capita federal tax burden?

52. ***Carbon dioxide emissions*** By using U.S. Department of Energy data from 2010 and projected to 2032, the millions of metric tons of carbon dioxide emissions from biomass energy combustion, y, in the United States can be described by

$$y = -0.022x^3 + 0.86x^2 + 9.9x + 340$$

where x is the number of years past 2010.

(a) Graph this function for values of x that represent the years from 2010 to 2035.

(b) Does the graph in part (a) show carbon dioxide emissions increase or decrease over this time period?

(c) Use the equation to find the change in carbon dioxide emissions from 2010 to 2011 and from 2029 to 2030.

OBJECTIVES

1.5

- To solve systems of linear equations in two variables by graphing
- To solve systems of linear equations by substitution
- To solve systems of linear equations by elimination
- To solve systems of three linear equations in three variables

Solutions of Systems of Linear Equations

■ | APPLICATION PREVIEW | ■

Suppose that a person has $200,000 invested, part at 9% and part at 8%, and that the yearly income from the two investments is $17,200. If x represents the amount invested at 9% and y represents the amount invested at 8%, then to find how much is invested at each rate we must find the values of x and y that satisfy both

$$x + y = 200{,}000 \quad \text{and} \quad 0.09x + 0.08y = 17{,}200$$

See Example 3 for the solution to this system of equations. Methods of solving systems of linear equations are discussed in this section.

Graphical Solution

In the previous sections, we graphed linear equations in two variables and observed that the graphs are straight lines. Each point on the graph represents an ordered pair of values (x, y) that satisfies the equation, so a point of intersection of two (or more) lines represents a solution to both (or all) the equations of those lines.

The equations are referred to as a **system of equations,** and the ordered pairs (x, y) that satisfy all the equations in the system are the **solutions** (or **simultaneous solutions**) of the system. Finding the solution to a system of equations is called **solving the system** or **solving simultaneously**.

We can use graphing to find the solution of a system of equations.

EXAMPLE 1 | **Graphical Solution of a System**

Use graphing to find the solution of the system

$$\begin{cases} 4x + 3y = 11 \\ 2x - 5y = -1 \end{cases}$$

Solution

The graphs of the two equations intersect at the point $(2, 1)$. (See Figure 1.22.) The solution of the system is $x = 2$, $y = 1$. Note that these values satisfy both equations. ∎

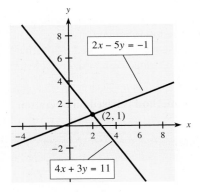

Figure 1.22

Two distinct nonparallel lines: one solution

If the graphs of two equations are parallel lines, they have no point in common, and thus the system has no solution. Such a system of equations is called **inconsistent.** For example,

$$\begin{cases} 4x + 3y = 4 \\ 8x + 6y = 18 \end{cases}$$

is an **inconsistent system** (see Figure 1.23(a) on the next page).

It is also possible that two equations describe the same line. When this happens, the equations are equivalent, and values that satisfy either equation are solutions of the system. For example,

$$\begin{cases} 4x + 3y = 4 \\ 8x + 6y = 8 \end{cases}$$

is called a **dependent system** because all points that satisfy one equation also satisfy the other (see Figure 1.23(b) on the next page).

Figures 1.22, 1.23(a), and 1.23(b) represent the three possibilities that can occur when we are solving a system of two linear equations in two variables.

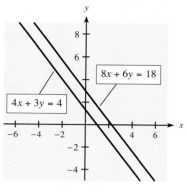

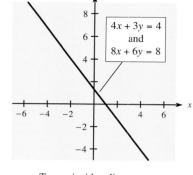

Two parallel lines: no solution	Two coincident lines: infinitely many solutions

Figure 1.23   (a)   (b)

Solution by Substitution

Graphical solution methods may yield only approximate solutions to some systems. To find exact solutions we can use algebraic methods, which are based on the fact that equivalent systems result when any of the following operations is performed.

Equivalent Systems

Equivalent systems result when

1. One expression is replaced by an equivalent expression.
2. Two equations are interchanged.
3. A multiple of one equation is added to another equation.
4. An equation is multiplied by a nonzero constant.

The **substitution method** is based on operation (1).

Substitution Method for Solving Systems

Procedure	Example
To solve a system of two equations in two variables by substitution:	Solve the system $\begin{cases} 2x + 3y = 4 & (1) \\ x - 2y = 3 & (2) \end{cases}$
1. Solve one of the equations for either one of the variables in terms of the other.	1. Solve Equation (2) for x: $x = 2y + 3$.
2. Substitute this expression into the other equation to give one equation in one unknown.	2. Substitute $2y + 3$ for x in Equation (1). $2(2y + 3) + 3y = 4$.
3. Solve this linear equation for the unknown.	3. $4y + 6 + 3y = 4$ $$7y = -2 \Rightarrow y = -\frac{2}{7}$$
4. Substitute this solution into the equation in Step 1 or into one of the original equations to solve for the other variable.	4. $x = 2\left(-\frac{2}{7}\right) + 3 \Rightarrow x = \frac{17}{7}$
5. Check the solution by substituting for x and y in both original equations.	5. $2\left(\frac{17}{7}\right) + 3\left(-\frac{2}{7}\right) = 4 \checkmark$ $$\frac{17}{7} - 2\left(-\frac{2}{7}\right) = 3 \checkmark$$

EXAMPLE 2   **Solution by Substitution**

Solve the system

$$\begin{cases} 4x + 5y = 18 & (1) \\ 3x - 9y = -12 & (2) \end{cases}$$

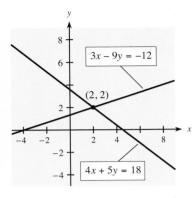

Figure 1.24

Solution

1. $x = \dfrac{9y - 12}{3} = 3y - 4$ Solve for x in equation (2).

2. $4(3y - 4) + 5y = 18$ Substitute for x in equation (1).

3. $12y - 16 + 5y = 18$ Solve for y.

$$17y = 34$$
$$y = 2$$

4. $x = 3(2) - 4$ Use $y = 2$ to find x.

$$x = 2$$

5. $4(2) + 5(2) = 18$ and $3(2) - 9(2) = -12$ ✔   Check.

Thus the solution is $x = 2$, $y = 2$. This means that when the two equations are graphed simultaneously, their point of intersection is $(2, 2)$. See Figure 1.24.

Solution by Elimination   We can also eliminate one of the variables in a system by the **elimination method,** which uses addition or subtraction of equations.

Elimination Method for Solving Systems

Procedure	Example
To solve a system of two equations in two variables by the elimination method:	Solve the system $\begin{cases} 2x - 5y = 4 & (1) \\ x + 2y = 3 & (2) \end{cases}$
1. If necessary, multiply one or both equations by a nonzero number that will make the coefficients of one of the variables identical, except perhaps for signs.	1. Multiply equation (2) by -2. $$2x - 5y = 4$$ $$-2x - 4y = -6$$
2. Add or subtract the equations to eliminate one of the variables.	2. Add the equations: $0x - 9y = -2$
3. Solve for the variable in the resulting equation.	3. $y = \dfrac{2}{9}$
4. Substitute the solution into one of the original equations and solve for the other variable.	4. $2x - 5\left(\dfrac{2}{9}\right) = 4$ $$2x = 4 + \dfrac{10}{9} = \dfrac{36}{9} + \dfrac{10}{9}$$ $$2x = \dfrac{46}{9} \quad \text{so} \quad x = \dfrac{23}{9}$$
5. Check the solutions in both original equations.	5. $2\left(\dfrac{23}{9}\right) - 5\left(\dfrac{2}{9}\right) = 4$ ✔ $$\dfrac{23}{9} + 2\left(\dfrac{2}{9}\right) = 3 ✔$$

EXAMPLE 3   **Investment Mix** | APPLICATION PREVIEW |

A person has $200,000 invested, part at 9% and part at 8%. If the total yearly income from the two investments is $17,200, how much is invested at 9% and how much at 8%?

Solution

Let x represent the amount invested at 9% and y represent the amount invested at 8%. Note that this means $x + y$ is the total investment.

$$x + y = 200{,}000 \quad (1)$$

and $0.09x + 0.08y$ is the total income earned.

$$0.09x + 0.08y = 17{,}200 \quad (2)$$

We solve these equations as follows:

$$
\begin{array}{ll}
-8x - 8y = -1{,}600{,}000 & (3) \qquad \text{Multiply equation (1) by } -8. \\
\underline{9x + 8y = 1{,}720{,}000} & (4) \qquad \text{Multiply equation (2) by 100.} \\
x = \phantom{-1{,}}120{,}000 & \qquad \text{Add.}
\end{array}
$$

We find y by using $x = 120{,}000$ in equation (1).

$$120{,}000 + y = 200{,}000 \quad \text{gives} \quad y = 80{,}000$$

Thus $120,000 is invested at 9%, and $80,000 is invested at 8%.
As a check, we note that equation (1) is satisfied and

$$0.09(120{,}000) + 0.08(80{,}000) = 10{,}800 + 6400 = 17{,}200 \; \checkmark$$

EXAMPLE 4   **Solution by Elimination**

Solve the systems:

(a) $\begin{cases} 4x + 3y = 4 \\ 8x + 6y = 18 \end{cases}$
 (b) $\begin{cases} 4x + 3y = 4 \\ 8x + 6y = 8 \end{cases}$

Solution

(a) $\begin{cases} 4x + 3y = 4 \\ 8x + 6y = 18 \end{cases}$

Multiply by -2 to get:	$-8x - 6y = -8$
Leave as is, which gives:	$\underline{8x + 6y = 18}$
Add the equations to get:	$0x + 0y = 10$
	$0 = 10$

The system is solved when $0 = 10$. This is impossible, so there are no solutions of the system. The equations are inconsistent. Their graphs are parallel lines; see Figure 1.23(a) earlier in this section.

(b) $\begin{cases} 4x + 3y = 4 \\ 8x + 6y = 8 \end{cases}$

Multiply by -2 to get:	$-8x - 6y = -8$
Leave as is, which gives:	$\underline{8x + 6y = 8}$
Add the equations to get:	$0x + 0y = 0$
	$0 = 0$

This is an identity, so the two equations share infinitely many solutions. The equations are dependent. Their graphs coincide, and each point on this graph represents a solution of the system; see Figure 1.23(b) earlier in this section.

EXAMPLE 5   **Medicine Concentrations**

A nurse has two solutions that contain different concentrations of a certain medication. One is a 12.5% concentration and the other is a 5% concentration. How many cubic centimeters of each should she mix to obtain 20 cubic centimeters of an 8% concentration?

Solution

Let x equal the cubic centimeters of the 12.5% solution, and let y equal the cubic centimeters of the 5% solution. The total amount of substance is

$$x + y = 20 \qquad (1)$$

and the total amount of medication is

$$0.125x + 0.05y = (0.08)(20) = 1.6 \qquad (2)$$

Solving this pair of equations simultaneously gives

$50x + 50y = 1000$	Multiply Equation (1) by 50.
$\underline{-125x - 50y = -1600}$	Multiply Equation (2) by 1000.
$-75x = -600$	Add.

$$x = 8$$
$$8 + y = 20, \text{ so } y = 12$$

Thus 8 cubic centimeters of a 12.5% concentration and 12 cubic centimeters of a 5% concentration yield 20 cubic centimeters of an 8% concentration.
Checking, we see that $8 + 12 = 20$ and

$$0.125(8) + 0.05(12) = 1 + 0.6 = 1.6 \checkmark$$

✓ CHECKPOINT

1. Solve by substitution: $\begin{cases} 3x - 4y = -24 \\ x + y = -1 \end{cases}$

2. Solve by elimination: $\begin{cases} 2x + 3y = 5 \\ 3x + 5y = -25 \end{cases}$

3. In Problems 1 and 2, the solution method is given.
   (a) In each case, explain why you think that method is appropriate.
   (b) In each case, would the other method work as well? Explain.

Calculator Note Solutions of systems of equations, if they exist, can be found by using INTERSECT. To use this method:

1. Solve both equations for y and enter each in the Y = menu.
2. Graph both equations in a window that contains their point of intersection.
3. Choose CALC (2nd TRACE) and 5:intersect; follow the prompts to find the point of intersection.

INTERSECT will give the point of intersection exactly or approximately to a large number of significant digits. Figure 1.25 shows a system and its solution, $x = 2$, $y = 3$. Details of solving systems of linear equations are shown in Appendix A, Section 1.5.

$$\begin{cases} 3x + 2y = 12 \\ 4x - 3y = -1 \end{cases}$$

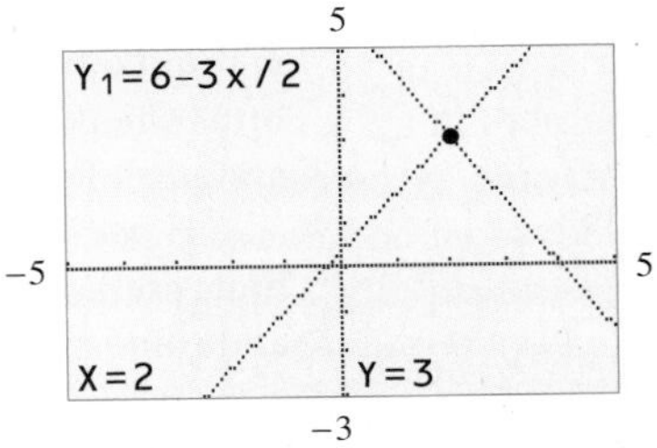

Figure 1.25

Spreadsheet Note We can use Excel to solve the system of equations in Figure 1.25.

1. Solve both equations for y.
2. Enter an input in A2 and the formulas for the two equations in B2 and C2.
3. In the *Goal Seek* menu, set D2 to 0 and select A2 as the changing cell.
4. Click OK to get the x-value of the solution in A2 and y-value in both B2 and C2.

The following spreadsheets show the input formulas and the solution ($x = 2$, $y = 3$) for the system. Details of the solution method are shown in Appendix B, Section 1.5.

	A	B	C	D
1	x	= 6 − 1.5x	= 1/3 + 4x/3	= y1 − y2
2	1	= 6 − 1.5*A2	= 1/3 + 4*A2/3	= B1 − C2

	A	B	C	D
1	x	= 6 − 1.5x	= 1/3 + 4x/3	= y1 − y2
2	2	3	3	0

EXAMPLE 6 — Workforce Participation

With data from the U.S. Bureau of Labor Statistics for selected years from 1950 and projected to 2050, the number of men M and of women W in the workforce (both in millions) can be described by the functions

$$M(t) = 0.591t + 37.3 \quad \text{and} \quad W(t) = 0.786t + 13.1$$

where t is the number of years past 1940. Graphically find the year these functions redict there will be equal numbers of men and women in the U.S. workforce.

Solution

Entering the two functions in a graphing calculator and setting the window with x-min = 0, x-max = 200, y-min = 0, and y-max = 200 give the graph in Figure 1.26(a). Using INTERSECT (see Figure 1.26(b)) gives a point of intersection at approximately $x = 124.1$ and $y = 110.6$. Thus, approximately 124.1 years after 1940 (in 2065), there will be equal numbers of men and women in the U.S. workforce, about 110.6 million of each.

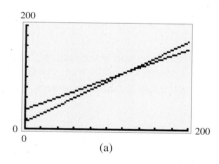

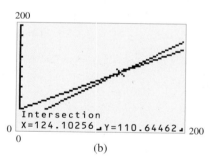

Figure 1.26

(a)   (b)

Solving a system of equations by graphing, whether by hand or with a graphing utility, is limited by two factors. (1) It may be difficult to determine a viewing window that contains the point of intersection, and (2) the solution may be only approximate. With *some* systems of equations, the only practical method may be graphical approximation.

However, systems of *linear* equations can be consistently and accurately solved with algebraic methods. Computer algebra systems, some software packages (including spreadsheets), and some graphing calculators have the capability of solving systems of linear equations.

Three Equations in Three Variables

If a, b, c, and d represent constants, then

$$ax + by + cz = d$$

is a first-degree (linear) equation in three variables. When equations of this form are graphed in a three-dimensional coordinate system, their graphs are planes. Two different planes may intersect in a line (like two walls) or may not intersect at all (like a floor and ceiling). Three different planes may intersect in a single point (as when two walls meet the ceiling), may intersect in a line (as in a paddle wheel), or may not have a common intersection. (See Figures 1.27, 1.28, and 1.29.) Thus three linear equations in three variables may have a unique solution, infinitely many solutions, or no solution. For example, the solution of the system

$$\begin{cases} 3x + 2y + z = 6 \\ x - y - z = 0 \\ x + y - z = 4 \end{cases}$$

is $x = 1$, $y = 2$, $z = -1$, because these three values satisfy all three equations, and these are the only values that satisfy them. In this section, we will discuss only systems of three linear equations in three variables that have unique solutions. Additional systems will be discussed in Section 3.3, "Gauss-Jordan Elimination: Solving Systems of Equations."

We can solve three equations in three variables using a systematic procedure called the **left-to-right elimination method.**

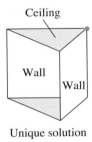

Ceiling

Wall

Wall

Unique solution

Figure 1.27

Infinitely many
solutions

Figure 1.28

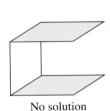

No solution

Figure 1.29

Left-to-Right Elimination Method

Procedure	Example
To solve a system of three equations in three variables by the left-to-right elimination method:	Solve: $\begin{cases} 2x + 4y + 5z = 4 \\ x - 2y - 3z = 5 \\ x + 3y + 4z = 1 \end{cases}$

1. If necessary, interchange two equations or use multiplication to make the coefficient of the first variable in equation (1) a factor of the other first variable coefficients.

   1. Interchange the first two equations.
   $$\begin{aligned} x - 2y - 3z &= 5 && (1) \\ 2x + 4y + 5z &= 4 && (2) \\ x + 3y + 4z &= 1 && (3) \end{aligned}$$

2. Add multiples of the first equation to each of the following equations so that the coefficients of the first variable in the second and third equations become zero.

   2. Add $(-2) \times$ equation (1) to equation (2) and add $(-1) \times$ equation (1) to equation (3).
   $$\begin{aligned} x - 2y - 3z &= 5 && (1) \\ 0x + 8y + 11z &= -6 && (2) \\ 0x + 5y + 7z &= -4 && (3) \end{aligned}$$

3. Add a multiple of the second equation to the third equation so that the coefficient of the second variable in the third equation becomes zero.

   3. Add $\left(-\frac{5}{8}\right) \times$ equation (2) to equation (3).
   $$\begin{aligned} x - 2y - 3z &= 5 && (1) \\ 8y + 11z &= -6 && (2) \\ 0y + \frac{1}{8}z &= -\frac{2}{8} && (3) \end{aligned}$$

4. Solve the third equation and *back substitute* from the bottom to find the remaining variables.

   4. $z = -2$ from equation (3)
   $y = \frac{1}{8}(-6 - 11z) = 2$ from equation (2)
   $x = 5 + 2y + 3z = 3$ from equation (1)
   so $x = 3$, $y = 2$, $z = -2$

EXAMPLE 7   Left-to-Right Elimination

Solve: $\begin{cases} x + 2y + 3z = 6 & (1) \\ 2x + 3y + 2z = 6 & (2) \\ -x + y + z = 4 & (3) \end{cases}$

Solution

Using equation (1) to eliminate x from the other equations gives the equivalent system

$\begin{cases} x + 2y + 3z = 6 & (1) \\ {-y - 4z = -6} & (2) \quad \text{$(-2)\times$ equation (1) added to equation (2)} \\ {3y + 4z = 10} & (3) \quad \text{Equation (1) added to equation (3)} \end{cases}$

Using equation (2) to eliminate y from equation (3) gives

$\begin{cases} x + 2y + 3z = 6 & (1) \\ {-y - 4z = -6} & (2) \\ {-8z = -8} & (3) \quad \text{$(3)\times$ equation (2) added to equation (3)} \end{cases}$

In a system of equations such as this, the first variable appearing in each equation is called the **lead variable.** Solving for each lead variable gives

$$x = 6 - 2y - 3z$$
$$y = 6 - 4z$$
$$z = 1$$

Using **back substitution** from the bottom gives

$$z = 1$$
$$y = 6 - 4 = 2$$
$$x = 6 - 4 - 3 = -1$$

Hence the solution is $x = -1$, $y = 2$, $z = 1$.

Although other methods for solving systems of equations in three variables may be useful, the left-to-right elimination method is important because it is systematic and can easily be extended to larger systems and to systems solved with matrices. (See Section 3.3, "Gauss-Jordan Elimination: Solving Systems of Equations.")

✓ CHECKPOINT   4. Use left-to-right elimination to solve.

$\begin{cases} x - y - z = 0 & (1) \\ y - 2z = -18 & (2) \\ x + y + z = 6 & (3) \end{cases}$

✓ CHECKPOINT ANSWERS

1. $x = -4$, $y = 3$
2. $x = 100$, $y = -65$
3. (a) Substitution works well in Problem 1 because it is easy to solve for x (or for y). Substitution would not work well in Problem 2 because solving for x (or for y) would introduce fractions.
    (b) Elimination would work well in Problem 1 if we multiplied the first equation by 4. As stated in (a), substitution would not be as easy in Problem 2.
4. $x = 3$, $y = -4$, $z = 7$

| EXERCISES | 1.5

In Problems 1–4, decide whether the system of equations in each problem has one solution, no solution, or an infinite number of solutions. If the system has one solution, estimate it.

1.

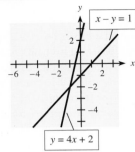

2.

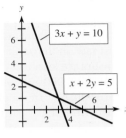

3.

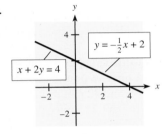

4.

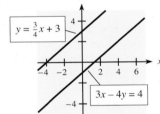

In Problems 5–8, solve the systems of equations by using graphing.

5. $\begin{cases} 4x - 2y = 4 \\ x - 2y = -2 \end{cases}$ 6. $\begin{cases} x - y = -2 \\ 2x + y = -1 \end{cases}$

7. $\begin{cases} 3x - y = 10 \\ 6x - 2y = 5 \end{cases}$ 8. $\begin{cases} 2x - y = 3 \\ 4x - 2y = 6 \end{cases}$

In Problems 9–12, solve the systems of equations by substitution.

9. $\begin{cases} 3x - 2y = 6 \\ 4y = 8 \end{cases}$ 10. $\begin{cases} 3x = 6 \\ 4x - 3y = 5 \end{cases}$

11. $\begin{cases} 2x - y = 2 \\ 3x + 4y = 6 \end{cases}$ 12. $\begin{cases} 4x - y = 3 \\ 2x + 3y = 19 \end{cases}$

In Problems 13–24, solve each system by elimination or by any convenient method.

13. $\begin{cases} 7x + 2y = 26 \\ 3x - 4y = 16 \end{cases}$ 14. $\begin{cases} 2x + 5y = 24 \\ -6x + 2y = 30 \end{cases}$

15. $\begin{cases} 3x + 4y = 1 \\ 2x - 3y = 12 \end{cases}$ 16. $\begin{cases} 5x - 2y = 4 \\ 2x - 3y = 5 \end{cases}$

17. $\begin{cases} -4x + 3y = -5 \\ 3x - 2y = 4 \end{cases}$ 18. $\begin{cases} x + 2y = 3 \\ 3x + 6y = 6 \end{cases}$

19. $\begin{cases} 0.2x - 0.3y = 4 \\ 2.3x - y = 1.2 \end{cases}$ 20. $\begin{cases} 0.5x + y = 3 \\ 0.3x + 0.2y = 6 \end{cases}$

21. $\begin{cases} \frac{5}{2}x - \frac{7}{2}y = -1 \\ 8x + 3y = 11 \end{cases}$ 22. $\begin{cases} x - \frac{1}{2}y = 1 \\ \frac{2}{3}x - \frac{1}{3}y = 1 \end{cases}$

23. $\begin{cases} 4x + 6y = 4 \\ 2x + 3y = 2 \end{cases}$ 24. $\begin{cases} 6x - 4y = 16 \\ 9x - 6y = 24 \end{cases}$

 Use a graphing calculator or Excel to find the solution of each system of equations in Problems 25–28.

25. $\begin{cases} y = 8 - \dfrac{3x}{2} \\ y = \dfrac{3x}{4} - 1 \end{cases}$ 26. $\begin{cases} y = 9 - \dfrac{2x}{3} \\ y = 5 + \dfrac{2x}{3} \end{cases}$

27. $\begin{cases} 5x + 3y = -2 \\ 3x + 7y = 4 \end{cases}$ 28. $\begin{cases} 4x - 5y = -3 \\ 2x - 7y = -6 \end{cases}$

Use the left-to-right elimination method to solve the systems in Problems 29–34.

29. $\begin{cases} x + 2y + z = 2 \\ -y + 3z = 8 \\ 2z = 10 \end{cases}$ 30. $\begin{cases} x - 2y + 2z = -10 \\ y + 4z = -10 \\ -3z = 9 \end{cases}$

31. $\begin{cases} x - y - 8z = 0 \\ y + 4z = 8 \\ 3y + 14z = 22 \end{cases}$ 32. $\begin{cases} x + 3y - 8z = 20 \\ y - 3z = 11 \\ 2y + 7z = -4 \end{cases}$

33. $\begin{cases} x + 4y - 2z = 9 \\ x + 5y + 2z = -2 \\ x + 4y - 28z = 22 \end{cases}$ 34. $\begin{cases} x - 3y - z = 0 \\ x - 2y + z = 8 \\ 2x - 6y + z = 6 \end{cases}$

APPLICATIONS

35. *Temperatures and traveling* When U.S. citizens travel abroad, they need some understanding of Celsius temperature readings—does one need mittens if the temperature will be 20° C? A quick conversion formula often used by tour guides to give a rough Fahrenheit equivalent for a Celsius reading is

$$F = 2C + 30 \qquad \text{Tourist formula}$$

The exact conversion formula relating these readings is

$$F = 1.8C + 32 \qquad \text{Scientific formula}$$

(a) At what temperatures, Fahrenheit and Celsius, do these formulas agree?

(b) As the Celsius temperature rises above the reading found in part (a), does the tourist formula over-estimate or underestimate the actual Fahrenheit temperature? How can you tell this from the two given formulas?

36. *Population distribution* Using U.S. Census Bureau data (and projections to 2050), the percent of the U.S. population that is Black $B(x)$ and Hispanic $H(x)$ can be described by

$$B(x) = 0.057x + 12.3 \quad \text{and} \quad H(x) = 0.224x + 9.01$$

where x is the number of years past 1990.

(a) In what year were the percents of these groups equal? What was the percent of each?

(b) Do these models indicate there are more Blacks or more Hispanics in 2012?

37. *Pricing* A concert promoter needs to make $42,000 from the sale of 1800 tickets. The promoter charges $20 for some tickets and $30 for the others. Let x represent the number of $20 tickets and y represent the number of $30 tickets.

(a) Write an equation that states that the sum of the tickets sold is 1800.

(b) How much money is received from the sale of $20 tickets?

(c) How much money is received from the sale of $30 tickets?

(d) Write an equation that states that the total amount received from the sale is $42,000.

(e) Solve the equations simultaneously to find how many tickets of each type must be sold to yield the $42,000.

38. *Rental income* A woman has $500,000 invested in two rental properties. One yields an annual return of 10% on her investment, and the other returns 12% per year on her investment. Her total annual return from the two investments is $53,000. Let x represent the amount of the 10% investment and y represent the amount of the 12% investment.

(a) Write an equation that states that the sum of the investments is $500,000.

(b) What is the annual return on the 10% investment?

(c) What is the annual return on the 12% investment?

(d) Write an equation that states that the sum of the annual returns is $53,000.

(e) Solve these two equations simultaneously to find how much is invested in each property.

39. *Investment yields* One safe investment pays 10% per year, and a riskier investment pays 18% per year. A woman who has $145,600 to invest would like to have an income of $20,000 per year from her investments. How much should she invest at each rate?

40. *Loans* A bank lent $237,000 to a company for the development of two products. If the loan for product

A was for $69,000 more than that for product B, how much was lent for each product?

41. *Rental income* A woman has $470,000 invested in two rental properties. One yields 10% on the invest-ment, and the other yields 12%. Her total income from them is $51,000. How much is her income from each property?

42. *Loans* Mr. Jackson borrowed money from his bank and on his life insurance to start a business. His inter-est rate on the bank loan was 10%, and his rate on the insurance loan was 12%. If the total amount borrowed was $100,000 and his total yearly interest payment was $10,900, how much did he borrow from the bank?

43. *Nutrition* Each ounce of substance A supplies 5% of the nutrition a patient needs. Substance B supplies 12% of the required nutrition per ounce. If diges-tive restrictions require that the ratio of substance A to substance B be 3/5, how many ounces of each should be in the diet to provide 100% of the required nutrition?

44. *Nutrition* A glass of skim milk supplies 0.1 mg of iron and 8.5 g of protein. A quarter pound of lean red meat provides 3.4 mg of iron and 22 g of protein. If a person on a special diet is to have 7.15 mg of iron and 73.75 g of protein, how many glasses of skim milk and how many quarter-pound servings of meat would provide this?

45. *Bacterial growth* Bacteria of species A and species B are kept in a single test tube, where they are fed two nutrients. Each day the test tube is supplied with 10,600 units of the first nutrient and 19,650 units of the second nutrient. Each bacterium of species A requires 2 units of the first nutrient and 3 units of the second, and each bacterium of species B requires 1 unit of the first nutrient and 4 units of the second. What populations of each species can coexist in the test tube so that all the nutrients are consumed each day?

46. *Botany* A biologist has a 40% solution and a 10% solution of the same plant nutrient. How many cubic centimeters of each solution should be mixed to obtain 25 cc of a 28% solution?

47. *Medications* A nurse has two solutions that contain different concentrations of a certain medication. One is a 20% concentration and the other is a 5% concen-tration. How many cubic centimeters of each should he mix to obtain 10 cc of a 15.5% solution?

48. *Medications* Medication A is given every 4 hours and medication B is given twice each day. The total intake of the two medications is restricted to 50.6 mg per day, for a certain patient. If the ratio of the dosage of A to the dosage of B is 5 to 8, find the dosage for each administration of each medication.

49. *Pricing* A concert promoter needs to take in $760,000 on the sale of 16,000 tickets. If the promoter charges $40 for some tickets and $60 for others, how many of each type must be sold to yield the $760,000?

50. *Pricing* A nut wholesaler sells a mix of peanuts and cashews. He charges $2.80 per pound for peanuts and $5.30 per pound for cashews. If the mix is to sell for $3.30 per pound, how many pounds each of peanuts and cashews should be used to make 100 pounds of the mix?

51. *Nutrient solutions* How many cubic centimeters of a 20% solution of a nutrient must be added to 100 cc of a 2% solution of the same nutrient to make a 10% solution of the nutrient?

52. *Mixtures* How many gallons of washer fluid that is 13.5% antifreeze must a manufacturer add to 200 gallons of washer fluid that is 11% antifreeze to yield washer fluid that is 13% antifreeze?

Application Problems 53–56 require systems of equations in three variables.

53. *Nutrition* Each ounce of substance A supplies 5% of the nutrition a patient needs. Substance B supplies 15% of the required nutrition per ounce, and substance C supplies 12% of the required nutrition per ounce. If digestive restrictions require that substances A and C be given in equal amounts, and the amount of substance B be one-fifth of either of these other amounts, find the number of ounces of each substance that should be in the meal to provide 100% of the required nutrition.

54. *Dietary requirements* A glass of skim milk supplies 0.1 mg of iron, 8.5 g of protein, and 1 g of carbohydrates. A quarter pound of lean red meat provides 3.4 mg of iron, 22 g of protein, and 20 g of carbohydrates. Two slices of whole grain bread supply 2.2 mg of iron, 10 g of protein, and 12 g of carbohydrates. If a person on a special diet must have 10.5 mg of iron, 94.5 g of protein, and 61 g of carbohydrates, how many glasses of skim milk, how many quarter-pound servings of meat, and how many two-slice servings of whole grain bread will supply this?

55. *Social services* A social agency is charged with providing services to three types of clients: A, B, and C. A total of 500 clients are to be served, with $150,000 available for counseling and $100,000 available for emergency food and shelter. Type A clients require an average of $200 for counseling and $300 for emergencies, type B clients require an average of $500 for counseling and $200 for emergencies, and type C clients require an average of $300 for counseling and $100 for emergencies. How many of each type of client can be served?

56. *Social services* If funding for counseling is cut to $135,000 and funding for emergency food and shelter is cut to $90,000, only 450 clients can be served. How many of each type can be served in this case? (See Problem 55.)

Applications of Functions in Business and Economics

| APPLICATION PREVIEW |

Suppose a firm manufactures MP3 players and sells them for $50 each, with costs incurred in the production and sale equal to $200,000 plus $10 for each unit produced and sold. Forming the total cost, total revenue, and profit as functions of the quantity x that is produced and sold (see Example 1) is called the theory of the firm. We will also discuss market analysis, in which supply and demand are found as functions of price, and market equilibrium is found.

Total Cost, Total Revenue, and Profit

The **profit** a firm makes on its product is the difference between the amount it receives from sales (its revenue) and its cost. If x units are produced and sold, we can write

$$P(x) = R(x) - C(x)$$

where

$P(x)$ = profit from sale of x units

$R(x)$ = total revenue from sale of x units

$C(x)$ = total cost of production and sale of x units*

*The symbols generally used in economics for total cost, total revenue, and profit are TC, TR, and π, respectively. In order to avoid confusion, especially with the use of π as a variable, we do not use these symbols.

In general, **revenue** is found by using the equation

$$\text{Revenue} = (\text{price per unit})(\text{number of units})$$

The **cost** is composed of two parts: fixed costs and variable costs. **Fixed costs** (*FC*), such as depreciation, rent, utilities, and so on, remain constant regardless of the number of units produced. **Variable costs** (*VC*) are those directly related to the number of units produced. Thus the cost is found by using the equation

$$\text{Cost} = \text{variable costs} + \text{fixed costs}$$

EXAMPLE **1** **Cost, Revenue, and Profit** | APPLICATION PREVIEW |

Suppose a firm manufactures MP3 players and sells them for $50 each. The costs incurred in the production and sale of the MP3 players are $200,000 plus $10 for each player produced and sold. Write the profit function for the production and sale of *x* players.

Solution
The total revenue for *x* MP3 players is $50x$, so the total revenue function is $R(x) = 50x$. The fixed costs are $200,000, so the total cost for *x* players is $10x + 200,000$. Hence, $C(x) = 10x + 200,000$. The profit function is given by $P(x) = R(x) - C(x)$. Thus,

$$P(x) = 50x - (10x + 200,000)$$
$$P(x) = 40x - 200,000$$

Figure 1.30 shows the graphs of $R(x)$, $C(x)$, and $P(x)$.

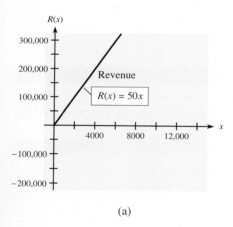
(a)

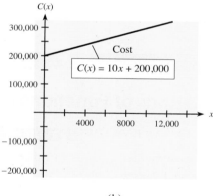
(b)

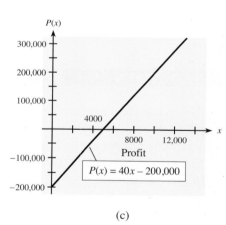
(c)

Figure 1.30

By observing the intercepts on the graphs in Figure 1.30, we note the following.

Revenue:	0 units produce 0 revenue; $R(0) = 0$.
Cost:	0 units' costs equal fixed costs = $200,000; $C(0) = FC = 200,000$.
Profit:	0 units yield a loss equal to fixed costs = $200,000;$
	$P(0) = -FC = -200,000$.
	5000 units result in a profit of $0 (no loss or gain); $P(5000) = 0$.

Marginals In Example 1, both the total revenue function and the total cost function are linear, so their difference, the profit function, is also linear. The slope of the profit function represents the rate of change in profit with respect to the number of units produced and sold. This is called the **marginal profit** ($\overline{MP}$) for the product. Thus the marginal profit for the MP3 players in Example 1 is $40. Similarly, the **marginal cost** ($\overline{MC}$) for this product is

$10 (the slope of the cost function), and the **marginal revenue** $(\overline{MR})$ is $50 (the slope of the revenue function).

EXAMPLE 2   Marginal Cost

Suppose that the cost (in dollars) for a product is $C = 21.75x + 4890$. What is the marginal cost for this product, and what does it mean?

Solution
The equation has the form $C = mx + b$, so the slope is 21.75. Thus the marginal cost is $\overline{MC} = 21.75$ dollars per unit.

Because the marginal cost is the slope of the cost line, production of each additional unit will cost $21.75 more, at any level of production.

Note that when total cost functions are linear, the marginal cost is the same as the variable cost per unit. This is not the case if the functions are not linear, as we shall see later.

✓ CHECKPOINT

1. Suppose that when a company produces its product, fixed costs are $12,500 and variable cost per item is $75.
   (a) Write the total cost function if x represents the number of units.
   (b) Are fixed costs equal to $C(0)$?
2. Suppose the company in Problem 1 sells its product for $175 per item.
   (a) Write the total revenue function.
   (b) Find $R(100)$ and give its meaning.
3. (a) Give the formula for profit in terms of revenue and cost.
   (b) Find the profit function for the company in Problems 1 and 2.

Break-Even Analysis   We can solve the equations for total revenue and total cost simultaneously to find the point where cost and revenue are equal. This point is called the **break-even point.** Graphically, the break-even point is the point of intersection of the graphs of the total revenue function and the total cost function.

EXAMPLE 3   Break-Even

A manufacturer sells a product for $10 per unit. The manufacturer's variable costs are $2.50 per unit and the total cost of 100 units is $1450. How many units must the manufacturer produce each month to break even?

Solution
The total revenue for x units of the product is $10x$, so the equation for total revenue is $R = R(x) = 10x$. The equation for total cost is

$$C - 1450 = 2.50(x - 100) \qquad \text{or} \qquad C = C(x) = 2.50x + 1200$$

To find the break-even point, solve the two equations simultaneously ($R = C$ at the break-even point). By substitution,

$$10x = 2.50x + 1200$$
$$7.5x = 1200 \qquad \text{so} \qquad x = 160$$

Thus the manufacturer will break even if 160 units are produced per month. The manufacturer will make a profit if more than 160 units are produced. Figure 1.31 shows that for $x < 160$, $R(x) < C(x)$ (resulting in a loss) and that for $x > 160$, $R(x) > C(x)$ (resulting in a profit).

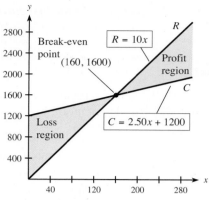

Figure 1.31

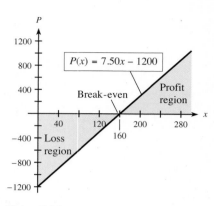

Figure 1.32

The profit function for Example 3 is given by

$$P(x) = R(x) - C(x) = 10x - (2.50x + 1200) \quad \text{or} \quad P(x) = 7.50x - 1200$$

We can find the point where the profit is zero (the break-even point) by setting $P(x) = 0$ and solving for x.

$$0 = 7.50x - 1200 \Rightarrow 1200 = 7.50x \Rightarrow x = 160$$

Note that this is the same break-even quantity that we found by solving the total revenue and total cost equations simultaneously (see Figure 1.32).

✓ **CHECKPOINT**   4. Identify two ways in which break-even can be found.

Supply, Demand, and Market Equilibrium

Economists and managers also use points of intersection to determine market equilibrium. **Market equilibrium** occurs when the quantity of a commodity demanded is equal to the quantity supplied.

Demand by consumers for a commodity is related to the price of the commodity. The **law of demand** states that the quantity demanded will increase as price decreases and that the quantity demanded will decrease as price increases. The **law of supply** states that the quantity supplied for sale will increase as the price of a product increases. Note that although quantity demanded and quantity supplied are both functions of price p, economists traditionally graph these with price on the vertical axis. We will follow this tradition (see Figure 1.33).

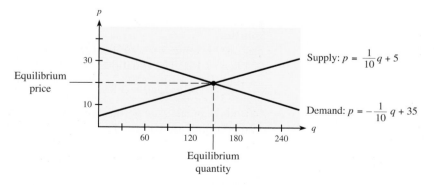

Figure 1.33

If the supply and demand curves for a commodity are graphed on the same coordinate system, with the same units, market equilibrium occurs at the point where the curves intersect. The price at that point is the **equilibrium price,** and the quantity at that point is the **equilibrium quantity.**

For the supply and demand functions shown in Figure 1.33, we see that the curves intersect at the point (150, 20). This means that when the price is $20, consumers are willing to purchase the same number of units (150) that producers are willing to supply.

In general, the equilibrium price and the equilibrium quantity must both be positive for the market equilibrium to have meaning.

EXAMPLE 4 Market Equilibrium

Find the market equilibrium point for the following supply and demand functions.

$$\text{Demand:} \quad p = -3q + 36$$
$$\text{Supply:} \quad p = 4q + 1$$

Solution

At market equilibrium, the demand price equals the supply price. Thus,

$$-3q + 36 = 4q + 1$$
$$35 = 7q$$
$$q = 5$$
$$p = 21$$

The equilibrium point is (5, 21).

Checking, we see that

$$21 = -3(5) + 36 \ \checkmark \qquad \text{and} \qquad 21 = 4(5) + 1 \ \checkmark$$

Spreadsheet Note We can use Goal Seek with Excel to find the market equilibrium for given supply and demand functions, as we did to find solutions of systems in Section 1.5. The following spreadsheets show the Excel setup and solution for the market equilibrium problem of Example 4.

	A	B	C	D
1	q	p: demand	p: supply	demand − supply
2	1	= −3*A2 + 36	= 4*A2 + 1	= B2 − C2

	A	B	C	D
1	q	p: demand	p: supply	demand − supply
2	5	21	21	0

EXAMPLE 5 Market Equilibrium

A group of wholesalers will buy 50 dryers per month if the price is $200 and 30 per month if the price is $300. The manufacturer is willing to supply 20 if the price is $210 and 30 if the price is $230. Assuming that the resulting supply and demand functions are linear, find the equilibrium point for the market.

Solution

Representing price by p and quantity by q, we can write the equations for the supply and demand functions as follows.

Demand function:

$$m = \frac{300 - 200}{30 - 50} = -5$$
$$p - 200 = -5(q - 50)$$
$$p = -5q + 450$$

Supply function:

$$m = \frac{230 - 210}{30 - 20} = 2$$
$$p - 230 = 2(q - 30)$$
$$p = 2q + 170$$

Because the prices are equal at market equilibrium, we have

$$-5q + 450 = 2q + 170$$
$$280 = 7q$$
$$q = 40$$
$$p = 250$$

The equilibrium point is (40, 250). See Figure 1.34 for the graphs of these functions.   ■

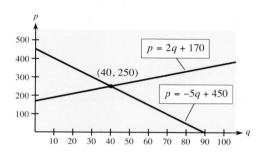

Figure 1.34

✓ **CHECKPOINT**

5. (a) Does a typical linear demand function have positive slope or negative slope? Why?
    (b) Does a typical linear supply function have positive slope or negative slope? Why?
6. (a) What do we call the point of intersection of a supply function and a demand function?
    (b) If supply is given by $p = 0.1q + 20$ and demand is given by $p = 130 - 0.1q$, find the market equilibrium point.

Supply and Demand with Taxation

Suppose a supplier is taxed K per unit sold, and the tax is passed on to the consumer by adding K to the selling price of the product. If the original supply function $p = f(q)$ gives the supply price per unit, then passing the tax on gives a new supply function, $p = f(q) + K$. Because the value of the product is not changed by the tax, the demand function is unchanged. Figure 1.35 shows the effect that this has on market equilibrium.

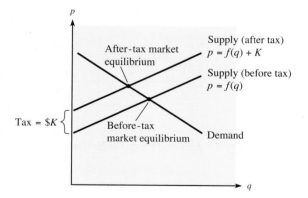

Figure 1.35

Note that the new market equilibrium point is the point of intersection of the original demand function and the new (after-tax) supply function.

EXAMPLE 6 **Taxation**

In Example 5 the supply and demand functions for dryers were given as follows.

$$\text{Supply:}\quad p = 2q + 170$$
$$\text{Demand:}\quad p = -5q + 450$$

The equilibrium point was $q = 40$, $p = \$250$. If the wholesaler is taxed $14 per unit sold, what is the new equilibrium point?

Solution

The \$14 tax per unit is passed on by the wholesaler, so the new supply function is

$$p = 2q + 170 + 14$$

and the demand function is unchanged. Thus we solve the system

$$\begin{cases} p = 2q + 184 \\ p = -5q + 450 \end{cases}$$

$$2q + 184 = -5q + 450$$

$$7q = 266$$

Thus $q = 38$ so $p = 2(38) + 184 = 260$.
The new equilibrium point is $q = 38$, $p = \$260$.
Checking, we see that

$$260 = 2(38) + 184 \checkmark \qquad \text{and} \qquad 260 = -5(38) + 450 \checkmark$$

✓ **CHECKPOINT**
ANSWERS

1. (a) $C(x) = 75x + 12{,}500$
   (b) Yes. $C(0) = 12{,}500 = $ Fixed costs.
2. (a) $R(x) = 175x$
   (b) $R(100) = 17{,}500$; revenue is \$17,500 when 100 units are sold.
3. (a) Profit = Revenue − Cost or $P(x) = R(x) - C(x)$
   (b) $P(x) = 100x - 12{,}500$
4. Break-even occurs where $R(x) = C(x)$ or where $P(x) = 0$.
5. (a) Negative slope, because demand falls as price increases.
   (b) Positive slope, because supply increases as price increases.
6. (a) Market equilibrium
   (b) $q = 550$, $p = 75$

| EXERCISES | 1.6

TOTAL COST, TOTAL REVENUE, AND PROFIT

1. Suppose a calculator manufacturer has the total cost function $C(x) = 34x + 6800$ and the total revenue function $R(x) = 68x$.
   (a) What is the equation of the profit function for the calculator?
   (b) What is the profit on 3000 units?
2. Suppose a stereo receiver manufacturer has the total cost function $C(x) = 210x + 3300$ and the total revenue function $R(x) = 430x$.
   (a) What is the equation of the profit function for this commodity?
   (b) What is the profit on 500 items?
3. Suppose a ceiling fan manufacturer has the total cost function $C(x) = 43x + 1850$ and the total revenue function $R(x) = 80x$.
   (a) What is the equation of the profit function for this commodity?
   (b) What is the profit on 30 units? Interpret your result.
   (c) How many fans must be sold to avoid losing money?

4. Suppose a computer manufacturer has the total cost function $C(x) = 85x + 3300$ and the total revenue function $R(x) = 385x$.
   (a) What is the equation of the profit function for this commodity?
   (b) What is the profit on 351 items?
   (c) How many items must be sold to avoid losing money?
5. A linear cost function is $C(x) = 5x + 250$.
   (a) What are the slope and the C-intercept?
   (b) What is the marginal cost, and what does it mean?
   (c) How are your answers to parts (a) and (b) related?
   (d) What is the cost of producing *one more* item if 50 are currently being produced? What is it if 100 are currently being produced?
6. A linear cost function is $C(x) = 27.55x + 5180$.
   (a) What are the slope and the C-intercept?
   (b) What is the marginal cost, and what does it mean?
   (c) How are your answers to parts (a) and (b) related?
   (d) What is the cost of producing *one more* item if 50 are currently being produced? What is it if 100 are currently being produced?

7. A linear revenue function is $R = 27x$.
   (a) What is the slope?
   (b) What is the marginal revenue, and what does it mean?
   (c) What is the revenue received from selling *one more* item if 50 are currently being sold? If 100 are being sold?

8. A linear revenue function is $R = 38.95x$.
   (a) What is the slope?
   (b) What is the marginal revenue, and what does it mean?
   (c) What is the revenue received from selling *one more* item if 50 are currently being sold? If 100 are being sold?

9. Let $C(x) = 5x + 250$ and $R(x) = 27x$.
   (a) Write the profit function $P(x)$.
   (b) What is the slope of the profit function?
   (c) What is the marginal profit?
   (d) Interpret the marginal profit.

10. Given $C(x) = 21.95x + 1400$ and $R(x) = 20x$, find the profit function.
    (a) What is the marginal profit, and what does it mean?
    (b) What should a firm with these cost, revenue, and profit functions do? (*Hint:* Graph the profit function and see where it goes.)

11. A company charting its profits notices that the relationship between the number of units sold, x, and the profit, P, is linear. If 200 units sold results in $3100 profit and 250 units sold results in $6000 profit, write the profit function for this company. Find the marginal profit.

12. Suppose that the total cost function for an MP3 player is linear, that the marginal cost is $54, and that the total cost for 50 players is $8700. Write the equation of this cost function and then graph it.

13. Extreme Protection, Inc. manufactures helmets for skiing and snow boarding. The fixed costs for one model of helmet are $6600 per month. Materials and labor for each helmet of this model are $35, and the company sells this helmet to dealers for $60 each.
    (a) For this helmet, write the function for monthly total costs.
    (b) Write the function for total revenue.
    (c) Write the function for profit.
    (d) Find $C(200)$, $R(200)$, and $P(200)$ and interpret each answer.
    (e) Find $C(300)$, $R(300)$, and $P(300)$ and interpret each answer.
    (f) Find the marginal profit and write a sentence that explains its meaning.

14. A manufacturer of DVD players has monthly fixed costs of $9800 and variable costs of $65 per unit for one particular model. The company sells this model to dealers for $100 each.
    (a) For this model DVD player, write the function for monthly total costs.
    (b) Write the function for total revenue.

   (c) Write the function for profit.
   (d) Find $C(250)$, $R(250)$, and $P(250)$ and interpret each answer.
   (e) Find $C(400)$, $R(400)$, and $P(400)$ and interpret each answer.
   (f) Find the marginal profit and write a sentence that explains its meaning.

BREAK-EVEN ANALYSIS

15. The figure shows graphs of the total cost function and the total revenue function for a commodity.

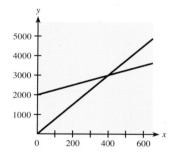

   (a) Label each function correctly.
   (b) Determine the fixed costs.
   (c) Locate the break-even point and determine the number of units sold to break even.
   (d) Estimate the marginal cost and marginal revenue.

16. A manufacturer of shower-surrounds has a revenue function of

$$R(x) = 81.50x$$

   and a cost function of

$$C(x) = 63x + 1850$$

   Find the number of units that must be sold to break even.

17. A jewelry maker incurs costs for a necklace according to

$$C(x) = 35x + 1650$$

   If the revenue function for the necklaces is

$$R(x) = 85x$$

   how many necklaces must be sold to break even?

18. A small business recaps and sells tires. If a set of four tires has the revenue function

$$R(x) = 89x$$

   and the cost function

$$C(x) = 1400 + 75x$$

   find the number of sets of recaps that must be sold to break even.

19. A manufacturer sells belts for $12 per unit. The fixed costs are $1600 per month, and the variable cost per unit is $8.
    (a) Write the equations of the revenue and cost functions.
    (b) Find the break-even point.

20. A manufacturer sells watches for $50 per unit. The fixed cost related to this product are $10,000 per month, and the variable cost per unit is $30.
    (a) Write the equations of the revenue and cost functions.
    (b) How many watches must be sold to break even?
21. (a) Write the profit function for Problem 19.
    (b) Set profit equal to zero and solve for x. Compare this x-value with the break-even point from Problem 19(b).
22. (a) Write the profit function for Problem 20.
    (b) Set profit equal to zero and solve for x. Compare this x-value with the break-even point from Problem 20(b).
23. Electronic equipment manufacturer Dynamo Electric, Inc. makes several types of surge protectors. Their base model surge protector has monthly fixed costs of $1045. This particular model wholesales for $10 each and costs $4.50 per unit to manufacture.
    (a) Write the function for Dynamo's monthly total costs.
    (b) Write the function for Dynamo's monthly total revenue.
    (c) Write the function for Dynamo's monthly profit.
    (d) Find the number of this type of surge protector that Dynamo must produce and sell each month to break even.
24. Financial Paper, Inc. is a printer of checks and forms for financial institutions. For individual accounts, boxes of 200 checks cost $0.80 per box to print and package and sell for $4.95 each. Financial Paper's monthly fixed costs for printing and packaging these checks for individuals are $1245.
    (a) Write the function for Financial Paper's monthly total costs.
    (b) Write the function for Financial Paper's monthly total revenue.
    (c) Write the function for Financial Paper's monthly profit.
    (d) Find the number of orders for boxes of checks for individual accounts that Financial Paper must receive and fill each month to break even.
25. A company manufactures and sells bookcases. The selling price is $54.90 per bookcase. The total cost function is linear, and costs amount to $50,000 for 2000 bookcases and $32,120 for 800 bookcases.
    (a) Write the equation for revenue.
    (b) Write the equation for total costs.
    (c) Find the break-even quantity.
26. A company distributes college logo sweatshirts and sells them for $50 each. The total cost function is linear, and the total cost for 100 sweatshirts is $4360, whereas the total cost for 250 sweatshirts is $7060.
    (a) Write the equation for the revenue function.
    (b) Write the equation for the total cost function.
    (c) Find the break-even quantity.

In Problems 27 and 28, *some* of the graphs of total revenue (R), total cost (C), variable cost (VC), fixed cost (FC), and profit (P) are shown as functions of the number of units, x.
    (a) Correctly label the graphs shown.
    (b) Carefully sketch and label the graphs of the other functions. Explain your method.

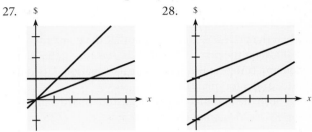

27.   28.

SUPPLY, DEMAND, AND MARKET EQUILIBRIUM

29. As the price of a commodity increases, what happens to demand?
30. As the price of a commodity increases, what happens to supply?

The graphs of the demand function and supply function for a certain product, are given below. Use these graphs to answer the questions in Problems 31 and 32.

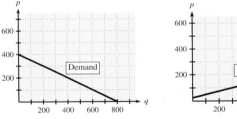
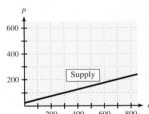

31. (a) How many units q are *demanded* when the price p is $100?
    (b) How many units q are *supplied* when the price p is $100?
    (c) Will there be a market surplus (more supplied) or shortage (more demanded) when $p = $100?
32. (a) How many units q are *demanded* when the price p is $200?
    (b) How many units q are *supplied* when the price p is $200?
    (c) Will there be a market surplus or shortage when the price p is $200?
33. If the demand for a pair of shoes is given by $2p + 5q = 200$ and the supply function for it is $p - 2q = 10$, compare the quantity demanded and the quantity supplied when the price is $60. Will there be a surplus or shortfall at this price?
34. If the demand function and supply function for Z-brand phones are $p + 2q = 100$ and $35p - 20q = 350$, respectively, compare the quantity demanded and the quantity supplied when $p = 14$. Are there surplus phones or not enough to meet demand?

35. Suppose a certain outlet chain selling appliances has found that for one brand of stereo system, the monthly demand is 240 when the price is $900. However, when the price is $850, the monthly demand is 315. Assuming that the demand function for this system is linear, write the equation for the demand function. Use p for price and q for quantity.

36. Suppose a certain home improvements outlet knows that the monthly demand for framing studs is 2500 when the price is $4.00 each but that the demand is 3500 when the price is $3.60 each. Assuming that the demand function is linear, write its equation. Use p for price and q for quantity.

37. Suppose the manufacturer of a custom board game will supply 10,000 games if the wholesale price is $15 each but will supply only 5000 if the price is $10 each. Assuming that the supply function is linear, write its equation. Use p for price and q for quantity.

38. Suppose a mining company will supply 100,000 tons of ore per month if the price is $30 per ton but will supply only 80,000 tons per month if the price is $25 per ton. Assuming that the supply function is linear, write its equation.

Complete Problems 39–43 by using the accompanying figure, which shows a supply function and a demand function.

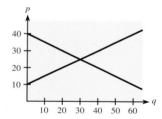

39. (a) Label each function as "demand" or "supply."
    (b) Label the equilibrium point and determine the price and quantity at which market equilibrium occurs.
40. (a) If the price is $30, what quantity is demanded?
    (b) If the price is $30, what quantity is supplied?
    (c) Is there a surplus or shortage when the price is $30? How many units is this surplus or shortage?
41. (a) If the price is $20, what quantity is supplied?
    (b) If the price is $20, what quantity is demanded?
    (c) Is there a surplus or a shortage when the price is $20? How many units is this surplus or shortage?
42. Will a price above the equilibrium price result in a market surplus or shortage?
43. Will a price below the equilibrium price result in a market surplus or shortage?
44. Find the market equilibrium point for the following demand and supply functions.

$$\text{Demand: } p = -2q + 320$$
$$\text{Supply: } \quad p = 8q + 2$$

45. Find the market equilibrium point for the following demand and supply functions.

$$\text{Demand: } \quad 2p = -q + 56$$
$$\text{Supply: } \quad 3p - q = 34$$

46. Find the equilibrium point for the following supply and demand functions.

$$\text{Demand: } p = 480 - 3q$$
$$\text{Supply: } \quad p = 17q + 80$$

47. Find the equilibrium point for the following supply and demand functions.

$$\text{Demand: } p = -4q + 220$$
$$\text{Supply: } \quad p = 15q + 30$$

48. Retailers will buy 45 cordless phones from a wholesaler if the price is $10 each but only 20 if the price is $60. The wholesaler will supply 35 phones at $30 each and 70 at $50 each. Assuming the supply and demand functions are linear, find the market equilibrium point.

49. A group of retailers will buy 80 televisions from a wholesaler if the price is $350 and 120 if the price is $300. The wholesaler is willing to supply 60 if the price is $280 and 140 if the price is $370. Assuming the resulting supply and demand functions are linear, find the equilibrium point for the market.

50. A shoe store owner will buy 10 pairs of a certain shoe if the price is $75 per pair and 30 pairs if the price is $25. The supplier of the shoes is willing to provide 35 pairs if the price is $80 per pair but only 5 pairs if the price is $20. Assuming the supply and demand functions for the shoes are linear, find the market equilibrium point.

Problems 51–58 involve market equilibrium after taxation.
Use the following figure to answer Problems 51 and 52.

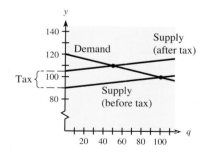

51. (a) What is the amount of the tax?
    (b) What are the original equilibrium price and quantity?
    (c) What are the new equilibrium price and quantity?
    (d) Does the supplier suffer from the tax even though it is passed on?

52. (a) If the tax is doubled, how many units will be sold?
    (b) Can a government lose money by increasing taxes?
53. If a $38 tax is placed on each unit of the product of Problem 47, what are the new equilibrium price and quantity?
54. If a $56 tax is placed on each unit of the product of Problem 46, what is the new equilibrium point?
55. Suppose that a certain product has the following demand and supply functions.

$$\text{Demand: } p = -0.05q + 65$$
$$\text{Supply: } \quad p = 0.05q + 10$$

If a $5 tax per item is levied on the supplier and this tax is passed on to the consumer, find the market equilibrium point after the tax.
56. Suppose that a certain product has the following demand and supply functions.

$$\text{Demand: } p = -8q + 2800$$
$$\text{Supply: } \quad p = 3q + 35$$

If a $15 tax per item is levied on the supplier, who passes it on to the consumer as a price increase, find the market equilibrium point after the tax.
57. Suppose that in a certain market the demand function for a product is given by $60p + q = 2100$ and the supply function is given by $120p - q = 540$. Then a tax of $0.50 per item is levied on the supplier, who passes it on to the consumer as a price increase. Find the equilibrium price and quantity after the tax is levied.
58. Suppose that in a certain market the demand function for a product is given by $10p + q = 2300$ and the supply function is given by $45p - q = 360$. If the government levies a tax of $2 per item on the supplier, who passes the tax on to the consumer as a price increase, find the equilibrium price and quantity after the tax is levied.

Chapter 1 Summary & Review

KEY TERMS AND FORMULAS

Section 1.1

Equation; variable; solution (p. 53)
Identities; conditional equations (p. 53)
Properties of equality (p. 53)
Solving a linear equation (p. 54)
Aligning the data (p. 54)

Fractional equation (p. 55)
Linear equation in two variables (p. 56)
Linear inequalities (p. 57)
    Properties
    Solutions

Section 1.2

Relation (p. 63)
Function (p. 64)
    Vertical-line test
    Domain, range
Coordinate system (p. 64)
    Ordered pair, origin, x-axis, y-axis

Graph (p. 65)
Function notation (p. 66)
Operations with functions (p. 68)
Composite functions (p. 69)
    $(f \circ g)(x) = f(g(x))$

Section 1.3

Linear function (p. 75)
    $y = ax + b$
Intercepts (p. 75)
    x-intercept (zero of a function)
        where $y = 0$
    y-intercept
        where $x = 0$
Slope of a line (p. 77)
    Rate of change
    $m = \dfrac{y_2 - y_1}{x_2 - x_1}$

Parallel lines (p. 78)
    $m_1 = m_2$
Perpendicular lines (p. 79)
    $m_2 = -1/m_1$
Point-slope form (p. 79)
    $y - y_1 = m(x - x_1)$
Vertical line (p. 80)
    $x = a$
Horizontal line (p. 80)
    $y = b$
Slope-intercept form (p. 81)
    $y = mx + b$

Section 1.4

Graphing utilities (p. 86)
Standard viewing window (p. 86)

Complete graph (p. 86)
Evaluating functions (p. 88)

REVIEW EXERCISES

Section 1.1

Solve the equations in Problems 1–6.

1. $3x - 8 = 23$

2. $2x - 8 = 3x + 5$

3. $\dfrac{6x + 3}{6} = \dfrac{5(x - 2)}{9}$

4. $2x + \dfrac{1}{2} = \dfrac{x}{2} + \dfrac{1}{3}$

5. $\dfrac{6}{3x - 5} = \dfrac{6}{2x + 3}$

6. $\dfrac{2x + 5}{x + 7} = \dfrac{1}{3} + \dfrac{x - 11}{2x + 14}$

7. Solve for y: $3(y - 2) = -2(x + 5)$

In Problems 8–10, solve the inequality and graph the solution.

8. $3x - 9 \le 4(3 - x)$

9. $2x/5 \le x + 4$

10. $5x + 1 \ge \dfrac{2}{3}(x - 6)$

Section 1.2

11. If $p = 3q^3$, is p a function of q?
12. If $y^2 = 9x$, is y a function of x?
13. If $R = \sqrt[3]{x} + 4$, is R a function of x?
14. What are the domain and range of the function $y = \sqrt{9 - x}$?
15. If $f(x) = x^2 + 4x + 5$, find the following.

   (a) $f(-3)$ (b) $f(4)$ (c) $f\left(\dfrac{1}{2}\right)$

16. If $g(x) = x^2 + 1/x$, find the following.

   (a) $g(-1)$ (b) $g\left(\dfrac{1}{2}\right)$ (c) $g(0.1)$

17. If $f(x) = 9x - x^2$, find $\dfrac{f(x + h) - f(x)}{h}$ and simplify.

In Problems 18 and 19, determine whether each graph represents y as a function of x.

18.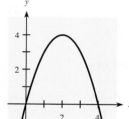

19.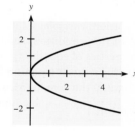

20. For the function f graphed in Exercise 18, what is $f(2)$?
21. For the function f graphed in Exercise 18, for what values of x does $f(x) = 0$?
22. The following table defines y as a function of x, denoted $y = f(x)$.

x	-2	-1	0	1	3	4
y	8	2	-3	4	2	7

Use the table to complete the following.
   (a) Identify the domain and range of $y = f(x)$.
   (b) Find $f(4)$.
   (c) Find all x-values for which $f(x) = 2$.
   (d) Graph $y = f(x)$.
   (e) Does the table define x as a function of y? Explain.

23. If $f(x) = 3x + 5$ and $g(x) = x^2$, find
   (a) $(f + g)(x)$ (b) $(f/g)(x)$
   (c) $f(g(x))$ (d) $(f \circ f)(x)$

Section 1.3

In Problems 24–26, find the intercepts and graph.
24. $5x + 2y = 10$ 25. $6x + 5y = 9$ 26. $x = -2$

In Problems 27 and 28, find the slope of the line that passes through each pair of points.
27. $(2, -1)$ and $(-1, -4)$
28. $(-3.8, -7.16)$ and $(-3.8, 1.16)$

In Problems 29 and 30, find the slope and y-intercept of each line.

29. $2x + 5y = 10$

30. $x = -\dfrac{3}{4}y + \dfrac{3}{2}$

In Problems 31–37, write the equation of each line described.
31. Slope 4 and y-intercept 2
32. Slope $-\frac{1}{2}$ and y-intercept 3
33. Through $(-2, 1)$ with slope $\frac{2}{5}$
34. Through $(-2, 7)$ and $(6, -4)$
35. Through $(-1, 8)$ and $(-1, -1)$
36. Through $(1, 6)$ and parallel to $y = 4x - 6$
37. Through $(-1, 2)$ and perpendicular to $3x + 4y = 12$

Section 1.4

In Problems 38 and 39, graph each equation with a graphing calculator and the standard viewing window.

38. $x^2 + y - 2x - 3 = 0$ 39. $y = \dfrac{x^3 - 27x + 54}{15}$

In Problems 40 and 41, use a graphing calculator and
(a) **graph each equation in the viewing window given.**
(b) **graph each equation in the standard viewing window.**
(c) **explain how the two views differ and why.**
40. $y = (x + 6)(x - 3)(x - 15)$ with x-min $= -15$, x-max $= 25$; y-min $= -700$, y-max $= 500$
41. $y = x^2 - x - 42$ with x-min $= -15$, x-max $= 15$; y-min $= -50$, y-max $= 50$

42. What is the domain of $y = \dfrac{\sqrt{x + 3}}{x}$? Check with a graphing utility.

43. Use a graphing utility and the x-intercept method to approximate the solution of $7x - 2 = 0$.

Section 1.5

In Problems 44–50, solve each system of equations.

44. $\begin{cases} 4x - 2y = 6 \\ 3x + 3y = 9 \end{cases}$

45. $\begin{cases} 2x + y = 19 \\ x - 2y = 12 \end{cases}$

46. $\begin{cases} 3x + 2y = 5 \\ 2x - 3y = 12 \end{cases}$

47. $\begin{cases} 6x + 3y = 1 \\ y = -2x + 1 \end{cases}$

48. $\begin{cases} 4x - 3y = 253 \\ 13x + 2y = -12 \end{cases}$

49. $\begin{cases} x + 2y + 3z = 5 \\ y + 11z = 21 \\ 5y + 9z = 13 \end{cases}$

50. $\begin{cases} x + y - z = 12 \\ 2y - 3z = -7 \\ 3x + 3y - 7z = 0 \end{cases}$

APPLICATIONS

Section 1.1

51. *Life expectancy at age 65* By using Social Security Administration data for selected years from 1950 and projected to 2050, the additional years of life expectancy at age 65 can be described by
$$y = 0.077x + 13.8$$
where x equals the number of years past 1950.
  (a) To what year does $x = 70$ correspond?
  (b) What is the predicted additional years of life expectancy of a 65-year-old in 2050?
  (c) In what year does the function predict the life expectancy to be 20 years after age 65?

52. *Course grades* In a certain course, grades are based on three tests worth 100 points each, three quizzes worth 50 points each, and a final exam worth 200 points. A student has test grades of 91, 82, and 88, and quiz grades of 50, 42, and 42. What is the lowest percent the student can get on the final and still earn an A (90% or more of the total points) in the course?

53. *Cost analysis* The owner of a small construction business needs a new truck. He can buy a diesel truck for $58,000 and it will cost him $0.76 per mile to operate. He can buy a gas engine truck for $53,200, and it will cost him $0.88 per mile to operate. Find the number of miles he must drive before the costs are equal. If he normally keeps a truck for 7 years, which is the better buy?

Section 1.2

54. *Heart disease risk* The Multiple Risk Factor Intervention Trial (MRFIT) used data from 356,222 men aged 35 to 57 to investigate the relationship between serum cholesterol and coronary heart disease (CHD) risk. The following figure shows the graph of the relationship of CHD risk and cholesterol, where a risk of 1 is assigned to 200 mg/dl of serum cholesterol and where the CHD risk is 4 times as high when serum cholesterol is 300 mg/dl.

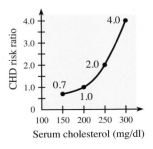

(a) Does this graph indicate that the CHD risk is a function of the serum cholesterol?
(b) Is the relationship a linear function?
(c) If CHD risk is a function f of serum cholesterol, what is $f(300)$?

55. *Mortgage loans* When a couple purchases a home, one of the first questions they face deals with the relationship between the amount borrowed and the monthly payment. In particular, if a bank offers 25-year loans at 7% interest, then the data in the following table would apply.

Amount Borrowed	Monthly Payment
$40,000	$282.72
50,000	353.39
60,000	424.07
70,000	494.75
80,000	565.44
90,000	636.11
100,000	706.78

Source: Comprehensive Mortgage Payment Tables, Publication No. 492, Financial Publishing Co., Boston

Assume that the monthly payment P is a function of the amount borrowed A (in thousands) and is denoted by $P = f(A)$, and answer the following.
(a) Find $f(80)$.
(b) Write a sentence that explains the meaning of $f(70) = 494.75$.

56. *Profit* Suppose that the profit from the production and sale of x units of a product is given by

$$P(x) = 330x - 0.05x^2 - 5000$$

In addition, suppose that for a certain month, the number of units produced on day t of the month is

$$x = q(t) = 100 + 10t$$

(a) Find $(P \circ q)(t)$ to express the profit as a function of the day of the month.
(b) Find the number of units produced, and the profit, on the fifteenth day of the month.

57. *Fish species growth* For many species of fish, the weight W is a function of the length L that can be expressed by

$$W = W(L) = kL^3 \qquad k = \text{constant}$$

Suppose that for a particular species $k = 0.03$ and that for this species, the length (in centimeters) is a function of the number of years t the fish has been alive and that this function is given by

$$L = L(t) = 65 - 0.1(t - 25)^2 \qquad 0 \le t \le 25$$

Find $(W \circ L)(t)$ in order to express W as a function of the age t of the fish.

Section 1.3

58. *Distance to a thunderstorm* The distance d (in miles) to a thunderstorm is given by

$$d = \frac{t}{4.8}$$

where t is the number of seconds that elapse between seeing the lightning and hearing the thunder.
(a) Graph this function for $0 \le t \le 20$.
(b) The point (9.6, 2) satisfies the equation. Explain its meaning.

59. *Body-heat loss* Body-heat loss due to convection depends on a number of factors. If H_c is body-heat loss due to convection, A_c is the exposed surface area of the body, $T_s - T_a$ is skin temperature minus air temperature, and K_c is the convection coefficient (determined by air velocity and so on), then we have

$$H_c = K_c A_c (T_s - T_a)$$

When $K_c = 1$, $A_c = 1$, and $T_s = 90$, the equation is

$$H_c = 90 - T_a$$

Sketch the graph.

60. *Profit* A company charting its profits notices that the relationship between the number of units sold, x, and the profit, P, is linear.
(a) If 200 units sold results in $3100 profit and 250 units sold results in $6000 profit, write the profit function for this company.
(b) Interpret the slope from part (a) as a rate of change.

61. *Health care costs* The average annual cost per consumer for health care can be modeled by

$$A = 427x + 4541$$

where x is the number of years from 2000 and projected to 2018 (*Source*: U.S. Census Bureau and U.S. Centers for Medicare and Medicaid Services).
(a) Is A a linear function of x?
(b) Find the slope and A-intercept of this function.
(c) Write a sentence that interprets the A-intercept.
(d) Write a sentence that interprets the slope of this function as a rate of change.

62. *Temperature* Write the equation of the linear relationship between temperature in Celsius (C) and Fahrenheit (F) if water freezes at 0°C and 32°F and boils at 100°C and 212°F.

Section 1.4

63. *Photosynthesis* The amount y of photosynthesis that takes place in a certain plant depends on the intensity x of the light present, according to

$$y = 120x^2 - 20x^3 \qquad \text{for } x \ge 0$$

(a) Graph this function with a graphing utility. (Use y-min $= -100$ and y-max $= 700$.)

(b) The model is valid only when $f(x) \geq 0$ (that is, on or above the x-axis). For what x-values is this true?

64. **Flow rates of water** The speed at which water travels in a pipe can be measured by directing the flow through an elbow and measuring the height to which it spurts out the top. If the elbow height is 10 cm, the equation relating the height h (in centimeters) of the water above the elbow and its velocity v (in centimeters per second) is given by

$$v^2 = 1960(h + 10)$$

(a) Solve this equation for h and graph the result, using the velocity as the independent variable.

(b) If the velocity is 210 cm/sec, what is the height of the water above the elbow?

Section 1.5

65. **Investment mix** A retired couple have $150,000 to invest and want to earn $15,000 per year in interest. The safer investment yields 9.5%, but they can supplement their earnings by investing some of their money at 11%. How much should they invest at each rate to earn $15,000 per year?

66. **Botany** A botanist has a 20% solution and a 70% solution of an insecticide. How much of each must be used to make 4.0 liters of a 35% solution?

Section 1.6

67. **Supply and demand** A certain product has supply and demand functions $p = 4q + 5$ and $p = -2q + 81$, respectively.

(a) If the price is $53, how many units are supplied and how many are demanded?

(b) Does this give a shortfall or a surplus?

(c) Is the price likely to increase from $53 or decrease from it?

68. **Market analysis** Of the equations $p + 6q = 420$ and $p = 6q + 60$, one is the supply function for a product and one is the demand function for that product.

(a) Graph these equations on the same set of axes.

(b) Label the supply function and the demand function.

(c) Find the market equilibrium point.

69. **Cost, revenue, and profit** The total cost and total revenue for a certain product are given by

$$C(x) = 38.80x + 4500$$
$$R(x) = 61.30x$$

(a) Find the marginal cost.

(b) Find the marginal revenue.

(c) Find the marginal profit.

(d) Find the number of units required to break even.

70. **Cost, revenue, and profit** A certain commodity has the following costs for a period.

Fixed cost:	$1500
Variable cost per unit:	$22

The commodity is sold for $52 per unit.

(a) What is the total cost function?

(b) What is the total revenue function?

(c) What is the profit function?

(d) What is the marginal cost?

(e) What is the marginal revenue?

(f) What is the marginal profit?

(g) What is the break-even quantity?

71. **Market analysis** The supply function and the demand function for a product are linear and are determined by the tables that follow.

(a) Write an equation for the supply function and one for the demand function.

(b) Find the quantity and price that give market equilibrium.

Supply Function		Demand Function	
Price ($)	Quantity	Price ($)	Quantity
100	125	100	355
200	150	200	330
400	200	400	280

72. **Market analysis** Suppose that for a certain product the supply and demand functions prior to any taxation are

$$\text{Supply:} \quad p = \frac{q}{10} + 8$$

$$\text{Demand:} \quad 10p + q = 1500$$

If a tax of $2 per item is levied on the supplier and is passed on to the consumer as a price increase, find the market equilibrium after the tax is levied.

Chapter 1 **TEST**

In Problems 1–4, solve the equations.

1. $10 - 2(2x - 9) - 4(6 + x) = 52$

2. $4x - 3 = \dfrac{x}{2} + 6$

3. $\dfrac{3}{x} + 4 = \dfrac{4x}{x + 1}$

4. $\dfrac{3x - 1}{4x - 9} = \dfrac{5}{7}$

5. For $f(x) = 7 + 5x - 2x^2$, find and simplify $\dfrac{f(x + h) - f(x)}{h}$.

6. Solve $1 + \dfrac{2}{3}x \le 3x + 22$ and graph the solution.

In Problems 7 and 8, find the intercepts and graph the functions.

7. $5x - 6y = 30$ 8. $7x + 5y = 21$

9. Consider the function $f(x) = \sqrt{4x + 16}$.
    (a) Find the domain and range.
    (b) Find $f(3)$.
    (c) Find the y-coordinate on the graph of $y = f(x)$ when $x = 5$.

10. Write the equation of the line passing through $(-1, 2)$ and $(3, -4)$. Write your answer in slope-intercept form.

11. Find the slope and the y-intercept of the graph of $5x + 4y = 15$.

12. Write the equation of the line through $(-3, -1)$ that
    (a) has undefined slope
    (b) is perpendicular to $x = 4y - 8$.

13. Which of the following relations [(a), (b), (c)] are functions? Explain.
    (a) y

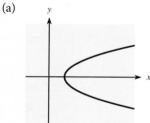

    (b) $\begin{array}{cc} x & y \\ 1 & 3 \\ -1 & 3 \\ 4 & 2 \end{array}$ (c) $y = \pm\sqrt{x^2 - 1}$

14. Graph $y = x^2 - 12x$
    (a) in the standard window and
    (b) in x-min $= -10$, x-max $= 30$; y-min $= -40$, y-max $= 40$.

15. Solve the system
$$\begin{cases} 3x + 2y = -2 \\ 4x + 5y = 2 \end{cases}$$

16. Given $f(x) = 5x^2 - 3x$ and $g(x) = x + 1$, find
    (a) $(fg)(x)$
    (b) $g(g(x))$
    (c) $(f \circ g)(x)$

17. Using U.S. Bureau of Labor Statistics data for selected years from 1950 and projected to 2050, the number

of men in the U.S. workforce (in millions) can be approximated by

$$M = 0.59x + 43.2$$

where x equals the number of years past 1950.
    (a) Use a graphing calculator to graph this equation with x-min $= 0$ to x-max $= 100$ and with y-min $= 0$ to y-max $= 100$
    (b) The point $(80, 90.4)$ lies on the graph of this equation. Explain its meaning.
    (c) Find the projected number of men in the U.S. workforce in 2050 according to this model.

18. The total cost function for a product is $C(x) = 30x + 1200$, and the total revenue is $R(x) = 38x$, where x is the number of units produced and sold.
    (a) Find the marginal cost.
    (b) Find the profit function.
    (c) Find the number of units that gives the break-even point.
    (d) Find the marginal profit and explain what it means.

19. The selling price for each item of a product is $50, and the total cost is given by $C(x) = 10x + 18,000$, where x is the number of items.
    (a) Write the revenue function.
    (b) Find $C(100)$ and write a sentence that explains its meaning.
    (c) Find the number of units that gives the break-even point.

20. The supply function for a product is $p = 5q + 1500$ and the demand function is $p = -3q + 3100$. Find the quantity and price that give market equilibrium.

21. A building is depreciated by its owner, with the value y of the building after x months given by $y = 720,000 - 2000x$.
    (a) Find the y-intercept of the graph of this function, and explain what it means.
    (b) Find the slope of the graph and tell what it means.

22. An airline has 360 seats on a plane for one of its flights. If 90% of the people making reservations actually buy a ticket, how many reservations should the airline accept to be confident that it will sell 360 tickets?

23. Amanda plans to invest $20,000, part of it at a 9% interest rate and part of it in a safer fund that pays 6%. How much should be invested in each fund to yield an annual return of $1560?

I. Hospital Administration

Southwest Hospital has an operating room used only for eye surgery. The annual cost of rent, heat, and electricity for the operating room and its equipment is $360,000, and the annual salaries of the people who staff this room total $540,000.

Each surgery performed requires the use of $760 worth of medical supplies and drugs. To promote goodwill, every patient receives a bouquet of flowers the day after surgery. In addition, one-quarter of the patients require dark glasses, which the hospital provides free of charge. It costs the hospital $30 for each bouquet of flowers and $40 for each pair of glasses.

The hospital receives a payment of $2000 for each eye operation performed.

1. Identify the revenue per case and the annual fixed and variable costs for running the operating room.
2. How many eye operations must the hospital perform each year in order to break even?
3. Southwest Hospital currently averages 70 eye operations per month. One of the nurses has just learned about a machine that would reduce by $100 per patient the amount of medical supplies needed. It can be leased for $100,000 annually. Keeping in mind the financial cost and benefits, advise the hospital on whether it should lease this machine.
4. An advertising agency has proposed to the hospital's president that she spend $20,000 per month on television and radio advertising to persuade people that Southwest Hospital is the best place to have any eye surgery performed. Advertising account executives estimate that such publicity would increase business by 40 operations per month. If they are correct and if this increase is not big enough to affect fixed costs, what impact would this advertising have on the hospital's profits?
5. In case the advertising agency is being overly optimistic, how many extra operations per month are needed to cover the cost of the proposed ads?
6. If the ad campaign is approved and subsequently meets its projections, should the hospital review its decision about the machine discussed in Question 3?

II. Fundraising

At most colleges and universities, student organizations conduct fundraising activities, such as selling T-shirts or candy. If a club or organization decided to sell coupons for submarine sandwiches, it would want to find the best deal, based on the amount the club thought it could sell and how much profit it would make. In this project, you'll try to discover the best deal for this type of fundraiser conducted in your area.

1. Contact at least two different sub shops in your area from among local sub shops, a national chain, or a regional or national convenience store chain. From each contact, find the details of selling sub sandwich coupons as a fundraiser. In particular, determine the following for each sub shop, and present your findings in a chart.
   (a) The selling price for each coupon and its value to the coupon holder, including any expiration date
   (b) Your cost for each coupon sold and for each one returned
   (c) The total number of coupons provided
   (d) The duration of the sale
2. For each sub shop, determine a club's total revenue and total costs as linear functions of the number of coupons sold.
3. Form the profit function for each sub shop, and graph the profit functions together. For each function, determine the break-even point. Find the marginal profit for each function, and interpret its meaning.
4. The shop with the best deal will be the one whose coupons will provide the maximum profit for a club.
   (a) For each shop, determine a sales estimate that is based on location, local popularity, and customer value.
   (b) Use each estimate from part (a) with that shop's profit function to determine which shop gives the maximum profit.

Fully explain and support your claims; make and justify a recommendation.

2

Quadratic and Other Special Functions

In Chapter 1 we discussed functions in general and linear functions in particular. In this chapter we will discuss quadratic functions and their applications, and we will also discuss other types of functions, including identity, constant, power, absolute value, piecewise defined, and reciprocal functions. Graphs of polynomial and rational functions will also be introduced; they will be studied in detail in Chapter 10. We will pay particular attention to quadratic equations and to quadratic functions, and we will see that cost, revenue, profit, supply, and demand are sometimes modeled by quadratic functions. We also include, in a section on modeling, the creation of functions that approximately fit real data points.

The topics and some representative applications discussed in this chapter follow.

Prerequisite Problem Type	For Section	Answer	Section for Review
Find $b^2 - 4ac$ if (a) $a = 1, b = 2, c = -2$ (b) $a = -2, b = 3, c = -1$ (c) $a = -3, b = -3, c = -2$	**2.1–2.3**	(a) 12 (b) 1 (c) -15	0.2 Signed numbers
(a) Factor $6x^2 - x - 2$. (b) Factor $6x^2 - 9x$.	**2.1–2.3**	(a) $(3x-2)(2x + 1)$ (b) $3x(2x-3)$	0.6 Factoring
Is $\dfrac{1 + \sqrt{-3}}{2}$ a real number?	**2.1**	No	0.4 Radicals
(a) Find the y-intercept of $y = x^2 - 6x + 8$. (b) Find the x-intercept of $y = 2x - 3$.	**2.2** **2.3**	(a) 8 (b) $\frac{3}{2}$	1.3 x- and y-intercepts
If $f(x) = -x^2 + 4x$, find $f(2)$. Find the domain of $$f(x) = \dfrac{12x + 8}{3x - 9}$$	**2.2–2.4**	4 All $x \neq 3$	1.2 Functions
Assume revenue is $R(x) = 500x - 2x^2$ and cost is $C(x) = 3600 + 100x + 2x^2$. (a) Find the profit function $P(x)$. (b) Find $P(50)$.	**2.3**	(a) $P(x) =$ $-3600 + 400x - 4x^2$ (b) $P(50) = 6400$	1.6 Cost, revenue, and profit

OBJECTIVES

2.1

- To solve quadratic equations with factoring methods
- To solve quadratic equations with the quadratic formula

Quadratic Equations

■ | APPLICATION PREVIEW |■

With fewer workers, future income from payroll taxes used to fund Social Security benefits won't keep pace with scheduled benefits. By using Social Security Administration data (adjusted for inflation to 2012 dollars), the Social Security Trust Fund balance B, in trillion of 2012 dollars can be approximated by the function

$$B = -0.0046t^2 - 0.033t + 6.05$$

where t is the number of years past the year 2000. For planning purposes, it is important to know when the trust fund balance will be 0. That is, for what t-value does

$$0 = -0.0046t^2 - 0.033t + 6.05$$

(See Example 7 for the solution.)
　In this section, we learn how to solve equations of this type, using factoring methods and using the quadratic formula.

Factoring Methods　A **quadratic equation** in one variable is an equation of second degree that can be written in the *general form*

$$ax^2 + bx + c = 0 \quad (a \neq 0)$$

where a, b, and c represent constants. For example, the equations

$$3x^2 + 4x + 1 = 0 \quad \text{and} \quad 2x^2 + 1 = x^2 - x$$

are quadratic equations; the first of these is in general form, and the second can easily be rewritten in general form.
　When we solve quadratic equations, we will be interested only in real number solutions and will consider two methods of solution: factoring and the quadratic formula. We will discuss solving quadratic equations by factoring first. (For a review of factoring, see Section 0.6, "Factoring.")
　Solution by factoring is based on the following property of the real numbers.

Zero Product Property　For real numbers a and b, $ab = 0$ if and only if $a = 0$ or $b = 0$ or both.

Hence, to solve by factoring, we must first write the equation with zero on one side.

EXAMPLE　1　**Solving Quadratic Equations**

Solve: (a) $6x^2 + 3x = 4x + 2$　(b) $6x^2 = 9x$

Solution
(a)
$$6x^2 + 3x = 4x + 2$$
$$6x^2 - x - 2 = 0 \quad \text{Proper form for factoring}$$
$$(3x - 2)(2x + 1) = 0 \quad \text{Factored}$$
$$3x - 2 = 0 \quad \text{or} \quad 2x + 1 = 0 \quad \text{Factors equal to zero}$$
$$3x = 2 \qquad\qquad 2x = -1$$
$$x = \frac{2}{3} \qquad\qquad x = -\frac{1}{2} \quad \text{Solutions}$$

We now check that these values are, in fact, solutions to our original equation.

$$6\left(\frac{2}{3}\right)^2 + 3\left(\frac{2}{3}\right) \overset{?}{=} 4\left(\frac{2}{3}\right) + 2 \qquad 6\left(-\frac{1}{2}\right)^2 + 3\left(-\frac{1}{2}\right) \overset{?}{=} 4\left(-\frac{1}{2}\right) + 2$$

$$\frac{14}{3} = \frac{14}{3} \checkmark \qquad\qquad\qquad 0 = 0 \checkmark$$

(b)
$$6x^2 = 9x$$
$$6x^2 - 9x = 0$$
$$3x(2x - 3) = 0$$

$$3x = 0 \quad \text{or} \quad 2x - 3 = 0$$
$$x = 0 \qquad\qquad 2x = 3$$
$$x = \frac{3}{2}$$

Check: $6(0)^2 = 9(0)$ ✔ $\qquad 6\left(\frac{3}{2}\right)^2 = 9\left(\frac{3}{2}\right)$ ✔

Thus the solutions are $x = 0$ and $x = \frac{3}{2}$.

Note that in Example 1(b) it is tempting to divide both sides of the equation by x, but this is incorrect because it results in the loss of the solution $x = 0$. Never divide both sides of an equation by an expression containing the variable.

EXAMPLE 2 Solving by Factoring

Solve: (a) $(y - 3)(y + 2) = -4$ $\qquad$ (b) $\dfrac{x + 1}{3x + 6} = \dfrac{3}{x} + \dfrac{2x + 6}{x(3x + 6)}$

Solution

(a) Note that the left side of the equation is factored, but the right member is not 0. Therefore, we must multiply the factors before we can rewrite the equation in general form.

$$(y - 3)(y + 2) = -4$$
$$y^2 - y - 6 = -4$$
$$y^2 - y - 2 = 0$$
$$(y - 2)(y + 1) = 0$$
$$y - 2 = 0 \quad \text{or} \quad y + 1 = 0$$
$$y = 2 \quad\Big|\quad y = -1$$

Check: $(2 - 3)(2 + 2) = -4$ ✔ $\qquad (-1 - 3)(-1 + 2) = -4$ ✔

(b) The LCD of all fractions is $x(3x + 6)$. Multiplying both sides of the equation by this LCD gives a quadratic equation that is equivalent to the original equation for $x \neq 0$ and $x \neq -2$. (The original equation is undefined for these values.)

$$\frac{x + 1}{3x + 6} = \frac{3}{x} + \frac{2x + 6}{x(3x + 6)}$$

$$x(3x + 6)\frac{x + 1}{3x + 6} = x(3x + 6)\left(\frac{3}{x} + \frac{2x + 6}{x(3x + 6)}\right) \qquad \text{Multiply both sides by } x(3x + 6).$$

$$x(x + 1) = 3(3x + 6) + (2x + 6)$$
$$x^2 + x = 9x + 18 + 2x + 6$$
$$x^2 - 10x - 24 = 0$$
$$(x - 12)(x + 2) = 0$$
$$x - 12 = 0 \text{ or } x + 2 = 0$$
$$x = 12 \text{ or } x = -2$$

Checking $x = 12$ and $x = -2$ in the original equation, we see that $x = -2$ makes the denominator equal to zero. Hence the only solution is $x = 12$. ✔

1. The factoring method for solving a quadratic equation is based on the _____ product property. Hence, in order for us to solve a quadratic equation by factoring, one side of the equation must equal _____.
2. Solve the following equations by factoring.
   (a) $x^2 - 19x = 20$ (b) $2x^2 = 6x$

EXAMPLE 3   ## Falling Object

A tennis ball is thrown into a swimming pool from the top of a tall hotel. The height of the ball from the pool is modeled by $D(t) = -16t^2 - 4t + 300$ feet, where t is the time, in seconds, after the ball was thrown. How long after the ball was thrown was it 144 feet above the pool?

Both Shutterstock.com

Solution
To find the number of seconds until the ball is 144 feet above the pool, we solve the following equation for t.

$$144 = -16t^2 - 4t + 300$$
$$0 = -16t^2 - 4t + 156 \quad \text{Subtract 144 from both sides.}$$
$$0 = 4t^2 + t - 39 \quad \text{Divide both sides by } (-4).$$
$$0 = (t - 3)(4t + 13)$$
$$t - 3 = 0 \text{ or } 4t + 13 = 0$$
$$4t = -13$$
$$t = 3 \quad | \quad t = -13/4$$

This indicates that the ball will be 144 feet above the pool 3 seconds after it is thrown. The negative value for t has no meaning in this application.

The Quadratic Formula   Factoring does not lend itself easily to solving quadratic equations such as

$$x^2 - 5 = 0$$

However, we can solve this equation by writing

$$x^2 = 5$$
$$x = \pm\sqrt{5}$$

In general, we can solve quadratic equations of the form $x^2 = C$ (no x-term) by taking the square root of both sides.

Square Root Property   The solution of $x^2 = C$ is

$$x = \pm\sqrt{C}$$

This property also can be used to solve equations such as those in the following example.

| EXAMPLE 4 | **Square Root Method** |

Solve the following equations.
(a) $4x^2 = 5$ (b) $(3x - 4)^2 = 9$

Solution
We can use the square root property for both parts.
(a) $4x^2 = 5$ is equivalent to $x^2 = \frac{5}{4}$. Thus

$$x = \pm\sqrt{\frac{5}{4}} = \pm\frac{\sqrt{5}}{\sqrt{4}} = \pm\frac{\sqrt{5}}{2}$$

(b) $(3x - 4)^2 = 9$ is equivalent to $3x - 4 = \pm\sqrt{9} = \pm 3$. Thus

$3x - 4 = 3$	$3x - 4 = -3$
$3x = 7$	$3x = 1$
$x = \dfrac{7}{3}$	$x = \dfrac{1}{3}$

The solution of the general quadratic equation $ax^2 + bx + c = 0$, where $a \neq 0$, is called the **quadratic formula**. It can be derived by using the square root property, as follows:

$$ax^2 + bx + c = 0 \qquad \text{Standard form}$$
$$ax^2 + bx = -c \qquad \text{Subtract } c \text{ from both sides.}$$
$$x^2 + \frac{b}{a}x = -\frac{c}{a} \qquad \text{Divide both sides by } a.$$

We would like to make the left side of the last equation a perfect square of the form $(x + k)^2 = x^2 + 2kx + k^2$. If we let $2k = b/a$, then $k = b/(2a)$ and $k^2 = b^2/(4a^2)$. Hence we continue as follows:

$$x^2 + \frac{b}{a}x + \frac{b^2}{4a^2} = \frac{b^2}{4a^2} - \frac{c}{a} \qquad \text{Add } \frac{b^2}{4a^2} \text{ to both sides.}$$

$$\left(x + \frac{b}{2a}\right)^2 = \frac{b^2 - 4ac}{4a^2} \qquad \text{Simplify.}$$

$$x + \frac{b}{2a} = \pm\sqrt{\frac{b^2 - 4ac}{4a^2}} \qquad \text{Square root property}$$

$$x = \frac{-b}{2a} \pm \frac{\sqrt{b^2 - 4ac}}{2|a|} \qquad \text{Solve for } x.$$

Because $\pm 2|a|$ represents the same numbers as $\pm 2a$, we obtain the following.

Quadratic Formula

If $ax^2 + bx + c = 0$, where $a \neq 0$, then

$$x = \frac{-b \pm \sqrt{b^2 - 4ac}}{2a}$$

We may use the quadratic formula to solve all quadratic equations, but especially those in which factorization is difficult or impossible to see. The proper identification of values for a, b, and c to be substituted into the formula requires that the equation be in general form.

EXAMPLE   5   **Quadratic Formula**

Use the quadratic formula to solve $2x^2 - 3x - 6 = 0$ for x.

Solution
The equation is already in general form, with $a = 2$, $b = -3$, and $c = -6$. Hence

$$x = \frac{-b \pm \sqrt{b^2 - 4ac}}{2a} = \frac{-(-3) \pm \sqrt{(-3)^2 - 4(2)(-6)}}{2(2)}$$

$$= \frac{3 \pm \sqrt{9 + 48}}{4} = \frac{3 \pm \sqrt{57}}{4}$$

Thus the solutions are

$$x = \frac{3 + \sqrt{57}}{4} \quad \text{and} \quad x = \frac{3 - \sqrt{57}}{4}$$

EXAMPLE   6   **Nonreal Solution**

Using the quadratic formula, find the (real) solutions to $x^2 = x - 1$.

Solution
We must rewrite the equation in general form before we can determine the values of a, b, and c. We write $x^2 = x - 1$ as $x^2 - x + 1 = 0$. Note that $a = 1$, $b = -1$, and $c = 1$.

$$x = \frac{-(-1) \pm \sqrt{(-1)^2 - 4(1)(1)}}{2(1)} = \frac{1 \pm \sqrt{1 - 4}}{2} = \frac{1 \pm \sqrt{-3}}{2}$$

Because $\sqrt{-3}$ is not a real number, the values of x are not real. Hence there are no real solutions to the given equation.

In Example 6 there were no real solutions to the quadratic equation because the radicand of the quadratic formula was negative. In general, when solving a quadratic equation, we can use the sign of the radicand, $b^2 - 4ac$, in the quadratic formula to determine how many real solutions there are. Thus we refer to $b^2 - 4ac$ as the **quadratic discriminant.**

Quadratic Discriminant

Given $ax^2 + bx + c = 0$ and $a \neq 0$,

If $b^2 - 4ac > 0$, the equation has two distinct real solutions.
If $b^2 - 4ac = 0$, the equation has exactly one real solution.
If $b^2 - 4ac < 0$, the equation has no real solutions.

The quadratic formula is especially useful when the coefficients of a quadratic equation are decimal values that make factorization impractical. This occurs in many applied problems.

EXAMPLE   7   **Social Security Trust Fund** | APPLICATION PREVIEW |

The Social Security Trust Fund balance B, in trillions of inflation-adjusted 2012 dollars, can be described by the function

$$B = -0.0046t^2 - 0.033t + 6.05$$

where t is the number of years past the year 2000 (*Source:* Social Security Administration). For planning purposes, it is important to know when the trust fund balance will be 0. To find when this occurs, solve

$$0 = -0.0046t^2 - 0.033t + 6.05$$

Solution

We solve the equation with the quadratic formula using

$$a = -0.0046, \quad b = -0.033, \quad c = 6.05$$

Thus

$$t = \frac{-b \pm \sqrt{b^2 - 4ac}}{2a}$$

$$= \frac{-(-0.033) \pm \sqrt{(-0.033)^2 - 4(-0.0046)(6.05)}}{2(-0.0046)}$$

$$= \frac{0.033 \pm \sqrt{0.112409}}{-0.0092} \approx \frac{0.033 \pm 0.3353}{-0.0092}$$

We are interested only in the positive solution, so

$$t \approx \frac{0.033 - 0.3353}{-0.0092} \approx 32.86$$

Therefore, the trust fund balance is projected to reach zero about 32.86 years past 2000, during the year 2033.

✓ **CHECKPOINT**

3. The statement of the quadratic formula says that if _____ and $a \neq 0$, then $x =$ _____.
4. Solve $2x^2 - 5x = 9$ using the quadratic formula.

Calculator Note

We can use graphing calculators to determine (or approximate) the solutions of quadratic equations. The solutions can be found by using commands (such as ZERO or SOLVER) or programs. TRACE can be used to approximate where the graph of the function $y = f(x)$ intersects the x-axis. This **x-intercept** is also the value of x that makes the function zero, so it is called a **zero of the function.** Because this value of x makes $f(x) = 0$, it is also a **solution** (or **root**) of the equation $0 = f(x)$. The steps for solving an equation of the form $f(x) = 0$ with a graphing calculator are:

1. Graph Y1 $= f(x)$ on a window that shows all possible x-intercepts. (Quadratic functions frequently have two x-intercepts.)
2. Under the CALC (2nd TRACE) menu, select 2:zero and follow the prompts to find each x-intercept, whose x-value is a solution.

For example, we can find the solutions of the equation $0 = -7x^2 + 16x - 4$ by graphing $y = -7x^2 + 16x - 4$, as in Figures 2.1(a) and 2.1(b). The graphs show $y = 0$ when $x = 2$ and when $x = 0.2857$ (approximately).

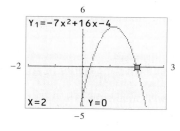
(a)

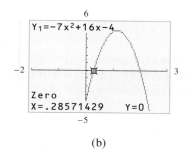
(b)

Figure 2.1

Solving $f(x) = 0$ algebraically gives solutions $x = 2$ and $x = \frac{2}{7} \approx 0.2857$. These values agree with those found graphically. See Appendix A, Section 2.1, for further details.

Spreadsheet Note To solve $f(x) = ax^2 + bx + c = 0$ with Excel if it has two solutions:

1. Graph $y = f(x)$ to find x-values close to the x-intercepts, and enter those values in Column A.
2. Use the *Goal Seek* menu, selecting a cell in column B containing a value at or near 0, setting it to 0, and entering the changing cell in column A that corresponds to the cell in column B.
3. Click OK, and an exact or approximate solution appears in Column A.
4. Repeat the process with a second function value at or near 0 to find a second solution.

For example, to solve the equation $0 = -7x^2 + 16x - 4$, we use its graph to find x-values close to the x-intercepts (use 2 and 0). The following screens illustrate how Excel works to solve the equation $0 = -7x^2 + 16x - 4$. The first screen shows how we input the formula with values near 0 and 2, and the second screen shows the approximate solutions (in column A). The solutions are $x = 0$ and $x \approx 0.2857$. See Appendix B, Section 2.1, for details.

	A	B
1	x	$-7x^2 + 16x - 4$
2	2	= $-7{*}A2^2 + 16{*}A2 - 4$
3	0	= $-7{*}A3^2 + 16{*}A3 - 4$

	A	B
1	x	$-7x^2 + 16x - 4$
2	2	0
3	0.285688	-0.00032

✓ CHECKPOINT ANSWERS

1. Zero; zero
2. (a) $x = 20$; $x = -1$
   (b) $x = 0$; $x = 3$
3. If $ax^2 + bx + c = 0$ and $a \neq 0$, then
$$x = \frac{-b \pm \sqrt{b^2 - 4ac}}{2a}$$
4. $x = \dfrac{5 + \sqrt{97}}{4} \approx 3.712$ or $x = \dfrac{5 - \sqrt{97}}{4} \approx -1.212$.

| EXERCISES | 2.1

In Problems 1–4, write the equations in general form.
1. $2x^2 + 3 = x^2 - 2x + 4$
2. $x^2 - 2x + 5 = 2 - 2x^2$
3. $(y + 1)(y + 2) = 4$
4. $(z - 1)(z - 3) = 1$

In Problems 5–12, solve each equation by factoring.
5. $x^2 - 4x = 12$
6. $x^2 = 11x - 10$
7. $9 - 4x^2 = 0$
8. $25x^2 - 16 = 0$
9. $x = x^2$
10. $t^2 - 4t = 3t^2$
11. $4t^2 - 4t + 1 = 0$
12. $49z^2 + 14z + 1 = 0$

In Problems 13–16, solve each equation by using the quadratic formula. Give real answers (a) exactly and (b) rounded to two decimal places.
13. $x^2 - 4x = 4$
14. $x^2 + 7 = 6x$
15. $2w^2 + w + 1 = 0$
16. $z^2 + 2z + 4 = 0$

In Problems 17–22, find the exact real solutions to each equation, if they exist.
17. $y^2 = 7$
18. $z^2 = 12$
19. $5x^2 = 80$
20. $3x^2 = 75$
21. $(x + 4)^2 = 25$
22. $(x + 1)^2 = 2$

In Problems 23–32, use any method to find the exact real solutions, if they exist.
23. $x^2 + 5x = 21 + x$
24. $x^2 + 17x = 8x - 14$
25. $\dfrac{w^2}{8} - \dfrac{w}{2} - 4 = 0$
26. $\dfrac{y^2}{2} - \dfrac{11}{6}y + 1 = 0$
27. $16z^2 + 16z - 21 = 0$
28. $10y^2 - y - 65 = 0$
29. $(x - 1)(x + 5) = 7$
30. $(x - 3)(1 - x) = 1$
31. $5x^2 = 2x + 6$
32. $3x^2 = -6x - 2$

In Problems 33–38, solve each equation by using a graphing utility.
33. $21x + 70 = 7x^2$
34. $3x^2 + 6 = 11x$
35. $300 - 2x - 0.01x^2 = 0$
36. $-9.6 + 2x - 0.1x^2 = 0$
37. $25.6x^2 - 16.1x - 1.1 = 0$
38. $6.8z^2 - 4.9z - 2.6 = 0$

In Problems 39–42, multiply both sides of the equation by the LCD and solve the resulting quadratic equation.
39. $x + \dfrac{8}{x} = 9$
40. $\dfrac{x}{x - 2} - 1 = \dfrac{3}{x + 1}$

41. $\dfrac{x}{x-1} = 2x + \dfrac{1}{x-1}$ 42. $\dfrac{5}{z+4} - \dfrac{3}{z-2} = 4$

In Problems 43 and 44, solve using quadratic methods.

43. $(x+8)^2 + 3(x+8) + 2 = 0$

44. $(s-2)^2 - 5(s-2) - 24 = 0$

APPLICATIONS

45. *Profit* If the profit from the sale of x units of a product is $P = 90x - 200 - x^2$, what level(s) of production will yield a profit of $1200?

46. *Profit* If the profit from the sale of x units of a product is $P = 16x - 0.1x^2 - 100$, what level(s) of production will yield a profit of $180?

47. *Profit* Suppose the profit from the sale of x units of a product is $P = 6400x - 18x^2 - 400$.
    (a) What level(s) of production will yield a profit of $61,800?
    (b) Can a profit of more than $61,800 be made?

48. *Profit* Suppose the profit from the sale of x units of a product is $P = 50x - 300 - 0.01x^2$.
    (a) What level(s) of production will yield a profit of $250?
    (b) Can a profit of more than $250 be made?

49. *Flight of a ball* If a ball is thrown upward at 96 feet per second from the top of a building that is 100 feet high, the height of the ball is given by

$$S = 100 + 96t - 16t^2 \text{ feet}$$

where t is the number of seconds after the ball is thrown. How long after it is thrown is the height 100 feet?

50. *Flight of a ball* A tennis ball is thrown into the air from the top of a hotel that is 350 feet above the ground. The height of the ball from the ground is given by

$$D(t) = -16t^2 + 10t + 350 \text{ feet}$$

where t is the time, in seconds, after the ball is thrown. How long after the ball is thrown does it hit the ground?

51. *Wind and pollution* The amount of airborne particulate pollution p from a power plant depends on the wind speed s, among other things, with the relationship between p and s approximated by

$$p = 25 - 0.01s^2$$

    (a) Find the value(s) of s that will make $p = 0$.
    (b) What value of s from part (a) makes sense in the context of this application? What does $p = 0$ mean in this application?

52. *Drug sensitivity* The sensitivity S to a drug is related to the dosage size by

$$S = 100x - x^2$$

where x is the dosage size in milliliters.
    (a) What dosage(s) will yield 0 sensitivity?
    (b) Explain what your answer in part (a) might mean.

53. *Corvette acceleration* The time t, in seconds, that it takes a Corvette to accelerate to x mph can be described by

$$t = 0.001(0.732x^2 + 15.417x + 607.738)$$

(*Source: Motor Trend*). How fast is the Corvette going after 8.99 seconds? Give your answer to the nearest tenth.

54. *Social Security trust fund* Social Security benefits are paid from a trust fund. As mentioned in the Application Preview, the trust fund balance, B, in trillions of 2012 dollars, t years past the year 2000 is described by

$$B = -0.0046t^2 - 0.033t + 6.05$$

(*Source: Social Security Administration*). Find in what year the trust fund balance is projected to be $5 trillion in the red—that is, when $B = -5$.

55. *Marijuana use* For the years from 2001 to 2012, the percent p of high school seniors who have tried marijuana can be considered as a function of time t according to

$$p = f(t) = 0.17t^2 - 2.61t + 52.64$$

where t is the number of years past 2000 (*Source: National Institute on Drug Abuse*). In what year after 2000 is the percent predicted to reach 55%, if this function remains valid?

56. *Projectile motion* Two projectiles are shot into the air over a lake. The paths of the projectiles are given by
    (a) $y = -0.0013x^2 + x + 10$ and
    (b) $y = -\dfrac{x^2}{81} + \dfrac{4}{3}x + 10$

    where y is the height and x is the horizontal distance traveled (both in feet). Determine which projectile travels farther by substituting $y = 0$ in each equation and finding x.

57. *Percent profit* The Ace Jewelry Store sold a necklace for $144. If the percent profit (based on cost) equals the cost of the necklace to the store, how much did the store pay for it? Use

$$P = \left(\dfrac{C}{100}\right) \cdot C$$

where P is profit and C is cost.

58. *Tourism spending* The global spending on travel and tourism (in billions of dollars) can be described by the equation

$$y = 0.787x^2 - 11.0x + 290$$

where x equals the number of years past 1990 (*Source: World Tourism Organization*). Find the year after 1990 in which spending is projected to reach $1000 billion.

59. *National health care* Using data from 2006 and with projections to 2021, total annual expenditures

for national health care (in billions of dollars) can be described by

$$E = 7.94x^2 + 33.2x + 2190$$

where x is the number of years past 2005 (*Source*: U.S. Centers for Medicare and Medicaid Services). If the pattern indicated by this equation remains valid, when does the model predict these expenditures will reach $5 trillion (that is, $5000 billion)?

60. *Velocity of blood* Because of friction from the walls of an artery, the velocity of a blood corpuscle in an artery is greatest at the center of the artery and decreases as the distance r from the center increases. The velocity of the blood in the artery can be modeled by the function

$$v = k(R^2 - r^2)$$

where R is the radius of the artery and k is a constant that is determined by the pressure, the viscosity of the blood, and the length of the artery. In the case where $k = 2$ and $R = 0.1$ centimeters, the velocity is $v = 2(0.01 - r^2)$ centimeters per second.
(a) What distance r would give a velocity of 0.02 cm/sec?
(b) What distance r would give a velocity of 0.015 cm/sec?

(c) What distance r would give a velocity of 0 cm/sec? Where is the blood corpuscle?

61. *Body-heat loss* The model for body-heat loss depends on the coefficient of convection K, which depends on wind speed v according to the equation

$$K^2 = 16v + 4$$

where v is in miles per hour. Find the positive coefficient of convection when the wind speed is
(a) 20 mph
(b) 60 mph
(c) What is the change in K for a change in speed from 20 mph to 60 mph?

62. *Depth of a fissure* A fissure in the earth appeared after an earthquake. To measure its vertical depth, a stone was dropped into it, and the sound of the stone's impact was heard 3.9 seconds later. The distance (in feet) the stone fell is given by $s = 16t_1^2$, and the distance (in feet) the sound traveled is given by $s = 1090t_2$. In these equations, the distances traveled by the sound and the stone are the same, but their times are not. Using the fact that the total time is 3.9 seconds, find the depth of the fissure.

2.2

Quadratic Functions: Parabolas

| APPLICATION PREVIEW |

Because additional equipment, raw materials, and labor may cause variable costs of some products to increase dramatically as more units are produced, total cost functions are not always linear functions. For example, suppose that the total cost of producing a product is given by the equation

$$C = C(x) = 300x + 0.1x^2 + 1200$$

where x represents the number of units produced. That is, the cost of this product is represented by a second-degree function, or a quadratic function. We can find the cost of producing 10 units by evaluating

$$C(10) = 300(10) + 0.1(10)^2 + 1200 = 4210$$

If the revenue function for this product is

$$R = R(x) = 600x$$

then the profit is also a quadratic function:

$$P = R - C = 600x - (300x + 0.1x^2 + 1200)$$
$$P = -0.1x^2 + 300x - 1200$$

We can use this function to find how many units give maximum profit and what that profit is. (See Example 2.) In this section we will describe ways to find the maximum point or minimum point for a quadratic function.

Parabolas   In Chapter 1, we studied functions of the form $y = ax + b$, called linear (or first-degree) functions. We now turn our attention to **quadratic** (or second-degree) **functions.** The general equation of a quadratic function has the form

$$y = f(x) = ax^2 + bx + c$$

where a, b, and c are real numbers and $a \neq 0$.

The graph of a quadratic function,

$$y = ax^2 + bx + c \qquad (a \neq 0)$$

has a distinctive shape called a **parabola.**

The basic function $y = x^2$ and a variation of it, $y = -\frac{1}{2}x^2$ are parabolas whose graphs are shown in Figure 2.2.

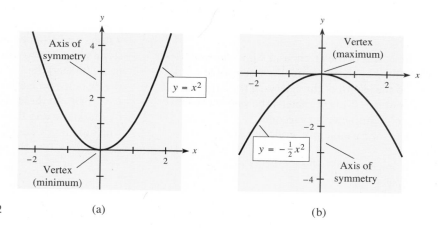

Figure 2.2   (a)   (b)

Vertex of a Parabola   As these examples illustrate, the graph of $y = ax^2$ is a parabola that opens upward if $a > 0$ and downward if $a < 0$. The **vertex,** where the parabola turns, is a **minimum point** if $a > 0$ and a **maximum point** if $a < 0$. The vertical line through the vertex of a parabola is called the **axis of symmetry** because one half of the graph is a reflection of the other half through this line.

The graph of $y = (x - 2)^2 - 1$ is the graph of $y = x^2$ shifted to a new location that is 2 units to the right and 1 unit down; its vertex is shifted from $(0, 0)$ to $(2, -1)$ and its axis of symmetry is shifted 2 units to the right. (See Figure 2.3(a).) The graph of $y = -\frac{1}{2}(x + 1)^2 + 2$ is the graph of $y = -\frac{1}{2}x^2$ shifted 1 unit to the left and 2 units up, with its vertex at $(-1, 2)$. (See Figure 2.3(b).)

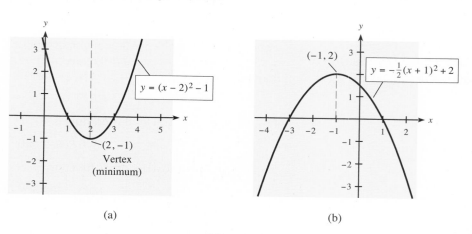

Figure 2.3   (a)   (b)

We can find the x-coordinate of the vertex of the graph of $y = ax^2 + bx + c$ by using the fact that the axis of symmetry of a parabola passes through the vertex. Regardless of the location of the vertex of $y = ax^2 + bx + c$ or the direction it opens, the y-intercept of the graph of $y = ax^2 + bx + c$ is $(0, c)$ and if $b \neq 0$, then there is another point on the graph with y-coordinate c. See Figure 2.4.

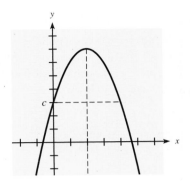

Figure 2.4

The x-coordinates of the points on this graph with y-coordinate c satisfy

$$c = ax^2 + bx + c$$

Solving this equation gives

$$0 = ax^2 + bx$$
$$0 = x(ax + b)$$
$$x = 0 \quad \text{or} \quad x = \frac{-b}{a}$$

The x-coordinate of the vertex is on the axis of symmetry, which is halfway from $x = 0$ to $x = \dfrac{-b}{a}$, at $x = \dfrac{-b}{2a}$. Thus we have the following.

Vertex of a Parabola

The quadratic function $y = f(x) = ax^2 + bx + c$ has its **vertex** at

$$\left(\frac{-b}{2a}, \ f\left(\frac{-b}{2a}\right) \right)$$

The optimum value (either maximum or minimum) of the function occurs at $x = \dfrac{-b}{2a}$ and is $y = f\left(\dfrac{-b}{2a}\right)$. See Figure 2.5.

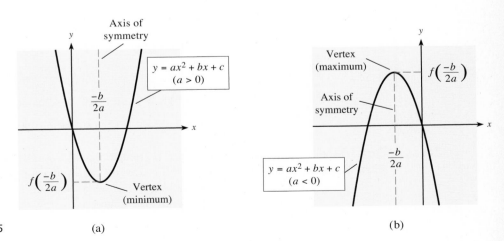

Figure 2.5   (a)   (b)

If we know the location of the vertex and the direction in which the parabola opens, we need very few other points to make a good sketch.

EXAMPLE 1 | Vertex and Graph of a Parabola

Find the vertex and sketch the graph of

$$f(x) = 2x^2 - 4x + 4$$

Solution

Because $a = 2 > 0$, the graph of $f(x)$ opens upward and the vertex is the minimum point. We can calculate its coordinates as follows:

$$x = \frac{-b}{2a} = \frac{-(-4)}{2(2)} = 1$$
$$y = f(1) = 2$$

Thus the vertex is $(1, 2)$. Using x-values on either side of the vertex to plot additional points enables us to sketch the graph accurately. (See Figure 2.6.) $\int$ ∎

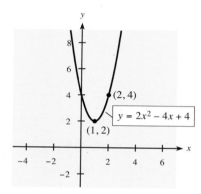

Figure 2.6

We can also use the coordinates of the vertex to find maximum or minimum values without a graph.

EXAMPLE 2 | Profit Maximization | APPLICATION PREVIEW |

For the profit function

$$P(x) = -0.1x^2 + 300x - 1200$$

find the number of units that give maximum profit and find the maximum profit.

Solution

$P(x)$ is a quadratic function with $a < 0$. Thus the graph of $y = P(x)$ is a parabola that opens downward, so the vertex is a maximum point. The coordinates of the vertex are

$$x = \frac{-b}{2a} = \frac{-300}{2(-0.1)} = 1500$$
$$P = P(1500) = -0.1(1500)^2 + 300(1500) - 1200 = 223{,}800$$

Therefore, the maximum profit is \$223,800 when 1500 units are sold.   ∎

Zeros of Quadratic Functions   As we noted in Chapter 1, "Linear Equations and Functions," the x-intercepts of the graph of a function $y = f(x)$ are the values of x for which $f(x) = 0$, called the **zeros** of the function. As we saw in the previous section, the zeros of the quadratic function $y = f(x) = ax^2 + bx + c$ are the solutions of the quadratic equation $ax^2 + bx + c = 0$, which are given by the quadratic formula

$$x = \frac{-b \pm \sqrt{b^2 - 4ac}}{2a}$$

The information that is useful in graphing quadratic functions is summarized as follows.

Graphs of Quadratic Functions

Form: $y = f(x) = ax^2 + bx + c$
Graph: parabola

$\quad$ $a > 0$ parabola opens upward; vertex is a minimum point
$\quad$ $a < 0$ parabola opens downward; vertex is a maximum point

Coordinates of vertex: $x = \dfrac{-b}{2a}$, $\quad y = f\left(\dfrac{-b}{2a}\right)$

Axis of symmetry equation: $x = \dfrac{-b}{2a}$

x-intercepts or zeros (if real*):

$$x = \frac{-b + \sqrt{b^2 - 4ac}}{2a},$$

$$x = \frac{-b - \sqrt{b^2 - 4ac}}{2a}$$

y-intercept: Let $x = 0$; then $y = c$.

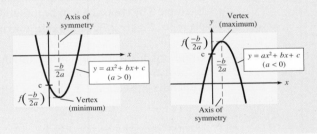

EXAMPLE 3 **Graph of a Quadratic Function**

For the function $y = 4x - x^2$, determine whether its vertex is a maximum point or a minimum point and find the coordinates of this point, find the zeros, if any exist, find the y-intercept, and sketch the graph.

Solution
The proper form is $y = -x^2 + 4x + 0$, so $a = -1$, $b = 4$, $c = 0$. Because $a < 0$, the parabola opens downward, and the vertex is the highest (maximum) point.

$\quad$ The vertex occurs at $x = \dfrac{-b}{2a} = \dfrac{-4}{2(-1)} = 2$.

The y-coordinate of the vertex is $f(2) = -(2)^2 + 4(2) = 4$.
The zeros of the function are solutions to

$$-x^2 + 4x = 0$$
$$x(-x + 4) = 0$$
$$\text{so } x = 0 \text{ or } x = 4$$

$\quad$ The y-intercept is $c = 0$ (at the origin).

The graph of this function can be found by drawing a parabola with these points (see Figure 2.7(a)).

---

*If the zeros are not real, the graph does not cross the x-axis.

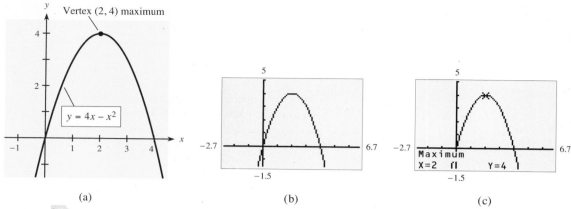

Figure 2.7   (a)   (b)   (c)

Calculator Note We can graph the function $y = 4x - x^2$, discussed in Example 3, and other quadratic functions with a graphing calculator by using the same methods as those for linear functions. Knowing the shape of a quadratic function is useful in setting a window that gives a complete graph. Figure 2.7(b) shows a graphing calculator graph of the function.

In Example 3, we used the vertex and x-intercepts to sketch the graph of a quadratic function. On the other hand, we can use a graphing calculator to graph a quadratic function and to find its vertex. For example, we can find the vertex of the quadratic function in Example 3 by choosing maximum under the CALC (2nd TRACE) menu and following the prompts. Figure 2.7(c) shows the maximum point (vertex) of the graph of $y = 4x - x^2$. ■

Spreadsheet Note Graphing quadratic (and other polynomial) functions with Excel requires the same steps as those for graphing linear functions. See Figure 2.8 for an Excel graph of $y = 4x - x^2$ and Appendix B, Section 2.2, and the Online Excel Guide for procedural details. ■

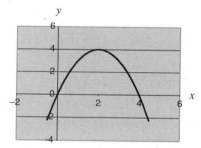

Figure 2.8

Example 3 showed how to find to find x-intercepts of a quadratic function $y = f(x)$ by solving $f(x) = 0$. Conversely, we can use the x-intercepts of $y = f(x)$, if they exist, to find or approximate the solutions of $f(x) = 0$. Exact integer solutions found in this way can also be used to determine factors of $f(x)$.

EXAMPLE 4   Graph Comparison

Figure 2.9 shows the graphs of two different quadratic functions. Use the figure to answer the following.

(a) Determine the vertex of each function.

(b) Determine the real solutions of $f_1(x) = 0$ and $f_2(x) = 0$.

(c) One of the graphs in Figure 2.9 is the graph of $y = 7 + 6x - x^2$, and one is the graph of $y = x^2 - 6x + 10$. Determine which is which, and why.

Solution

(a) For $y = f_1(x)$, the vertex is the maximum point, at $(3, 16)$.
     For $y = f_2(x)$, the vertex is the minimum point, at $(3, 1)$.

(b) For $y = f_1(x)$, the real solutions of $f_1(x) = 0$ are the zeros, or x-intercepts, at $x = -1$ and $x = 7$. For $y = f_2(x)$, the graph has no x-intercepts, so $f_2(x) = 0$ has no real solutions.

(c) Because the graph of $y = f_1(x)$ opens downward, the coefficient of x^2 must be negative. Hence Figure 2.9(a) shows the graph of $y = f_1(x) = 7 + 6x - x^2$. Similarly, the coefficient of x^2 in $y = f_2(x)$ must be positive, so Figure 2.9(b) shows the graph of $y = f_2(x) = x^2 - 6x + 10$. Note also that for each function the y-intercept is $f(0) = c$. Thus, the constants in the functions are $c = 7$ for $f_1(x)$ and $c = 10$ for $f_2(x)$.

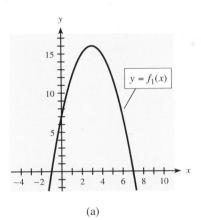

$y = f_1(x)$

$y = f_2(x)$

Figure 2.9   (a)   (b)

✓ CHECKPOINT

1. Name the graph of a quadratic function.
2. (a) What is the x-coordinate of the vertex of $y = ax^2 + bx + c$?
   (b) For $y = 12x - \frac{1}{2}x^2$, what is the x-coordinate of the vertex? What is the y-coordinate of the vertex?
3. (a) How can you tell whether the vertex of $f(x) = ax^2 + bx + c$ is a maximum point or a minimum point?
   (b) In part 2(b), is the vertex a maximum point or a minimum point?
4. The zeros of a function correspond to what feature of its graph?
5. What is the y-intercept of $y = ax^2 + bx + c$?

EXAMPLE 5   **Maximizing Revenue**

Ace Cruises offers a sunset cruise to a group of 50 people for a price of $30 per person, but it reduces the price per person by $0.50 for each additional person above the 50.

(a) Does reducing the price per person to get more people in the group give the cruise company more revenue?
(b) How many people will provide maximum revenue for the cruise company?

Solution

(a) The revenue to the company if 50 people are in the group and each pays $30 is $50(\$30) = \$1500$. The following table shows the revenue for the addition of people to the group. The table shows that as the group size begins to increase past 50 people, the revenue also increases. However, it also shows that increasing the group size too much (to 70 people) reduces revenue.

Increase in Group Size	Number of People	Decrease in Price	New Price ($)	Revenue ($)
0	50	0	30	50(30) = 1500
1	51	0.50(1)	29.50	51(29.50) = 1504.50
2	52	0.50(2) = 1	29	52(29) = 1508
3	53	0.50(3) = 1.50	28.50	53(28.50) = 1510.50
⋮	⋮	⋮	⋮	⋮
20	70	0.50(20) = 10	20	70(20) = 1400
⋮	⋮	⋮	⋮	⋮
x	$50 + x$	$0.50(x)$	$30 - 0.50x$	$(50 + x)(30 - 0.50x)$

(b) The last entry in the table shows the revenue for an increase of x people in the group.

$$R(x) = (50 + x)(30 - 0.50x) = 1500 + 5x - 0.50x^2$$

In expanded form we see that $a = -0.50, b = 5$, and $c = 1500$. Thus, the vertex of the graph of this function is $x = \dfrac{-b}{2a} = \dfrac{-5}{2(-0.50)} = 5, R(5) = 1512.50$.

This means that the revenue will be maximized at \$1512.50 when $50 + 5 = 55$ people are in the group, with each paying $30 - 0.50(5) = 27.50$ dollars. ◼

Average Rate of Change   Because the graph of a quadratic function is not a line, the rate of change of the function is not constant. We can, however, find the **average rate of change** of a function between two input values if we know how much the function output values change between the two input values.

Average Rate of Change

The **average rate of change** of $f(x)$ with respect to x over the interval from $x = a$ to $x = b$ (where $a < b$) is calculated as

$$\text{Average rate of change} = \frac{\text{change of } f(x)}{\text{corresponding change in } x\text{-values}} = \frac{f(b) - f(a)}{b - a}$$

The average rate of change is also the slope of the segment (or secant line) joining the points $(a, f(a))$ and $(b, f(b))$.

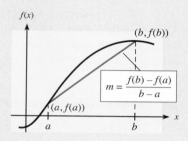

EXAMPLE   6   **Average Rate of Change of Revenue**

We found that the revenue for the cruise in Example 5 was defined by the quadratic function

$$R(x) = 1500 + 5x - 0.50x^2$$

where x is the increase in the group size beyond 50 people. What is the average rate of change of revenue per person if the group increases from 50 to 55 persons?

Solution

The average rate of change of revenue from 50 to 55 persons is the average rate of change of the function from $x = 0$ to $x = 5$.

$$\frac{R(5) - R(0)}{5 - 0} = \frac{1512.50 - 1500}{5} = 2.50 \text{ dollars per person}$$

This average rate of change is also the slope of the **secant line** connecting the points $(0, 1500)$ and $(5, 1512.50)$ on the graph of the function (see Figure 2.10). ◼

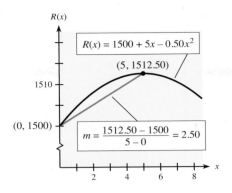

Figure 2.10

 CHECKPOINT ANSWERS

1. Parabola
2. (a) $x = \dfrac{-b}{2a}$
   (b) $x = 12$; $y = 72$
3. (a) Maximum point if $a < 0$; minimum point if $a > 0$.
   (b) $(12, 72)$ is a maximum point.
4. The x-intercepts
5. y-intercept $= c$

| EXERCISES | 2.2

In Problems 1–6, (a) find the vertex of the graph of the equation, (b) determine if the vertex is a maximum or minimum point, (c) determine what value of x gives the optimal value of the function, and (d) determine the optimal (maximum or minimum) value of the function.

1. $y = \dfrac{1}{2}x^2 + x$ 	 2. $y = x^2 - 2x$

3. $y = 8 + 2x - x^2$ 	 4. $y = 6 - 4x - 2x^2$

5. $f(x) = 6x - x^2$ 	 6. $f(x) = x^2 + 2x - 3$

In Problems 7–12, determine whether each function's vertex is a maximum point or a minimum point and find the coordinates of this point. Find the zeros, if any exist, and the y-intercept. Then sketch the graph of the function.

7. $y = x - \dfrac{1}{4}x^2$ 	 8. $y = -2x^2 + 18x$

9. $y = x^2 + 4x + 4$ 	 10. $y = x^2 - 6x + 9$

11. $\dfrac{1}{2}x^2 + x - y = 3$ 	 12. $x^2 + x + 2y = 5$

For each function in Problems 13–16, (a) tell how the graph of $y = x^2$ is shifted, and (b) graph the function.

13. $y = (x - 3)^2 + 1$
14. $y = (x - 10)^2 + 1$
15. $y = (x + 2)^2 - 2$
16. $y = (x + 12)^2 - 8$

 In Problems 17–20, graph each function with a graphing utility. Use the graph to find the vertex and zeros. Check your results algebraically.

17. $y = \dfrac{1}{2}x^2 - x - \dfrac{15}{2}$ 	 18. $y = 0.1(x^2 + 4x - 32)$

19. $y = \dfrac{1}{4}x^2 + 3x + 12$ 	 20. $y = x^2 - 2x + 5$

In Problems 21 and 22, find the average rate of change of the function between the given values of x.

21. $y = -5x - x^2$ between $x = -1$ and $x = 1$.
22. $y = 8 + 3x + 0.5x^2$ between $x = 2$ and $x = 4$.

 In Problems 23–26, find the vertex and zeros and use them to determine a range for a graphing utility that includes these values; graph the function with that range.

23. $y = 63 + 0.2x - 0.01x^2$
24. $y = 0.2x^2 + 16x + 140$
25. $y = 0.0001x^2 - 0.01$
26. $y = 0.01x - 0.001x^2$

In Problems 27 and 28, (a) find the vertex of each function $f(x)$. Use the vertex to set the window in which to graph $y = f(x)$ and then (b) graphically approximate the solutions to $f(x) = 0$.

27. $f(x) = 8x^2 - 16x - 16$ 	 28. $f(x) = 3x^2 - 18x + 16$

In Problems 29 and 30, complete the following.
(a) Use the graph of $y = f(x)$ to find an integer solution to $f(x) = 0$.
(b) Use the solution from (a) to find a factor of $f(x)$.
(c) Factor $f(x)$.
(d) Solve $f(x) = 0$.

29. $f(x) = 3x^2 - 8x + 4$ 30. $f(x) = 5x^2 - 2x - 7$

APPLICATIONS

31. **Profit** The daily profit from the sale of a product is given by $P = 16x - 0.1x^2 - 100$ dollars.
   (a) What level of production maximizes profit?
   (b) What is the maximum possible profit?

32. **Profit** The daily profit from the sale of x units of a product is $P = 80x - 0.4x^2 - 200$ dollars.
   (a) What level of production maximizes profit?
   (b) What is the maximum possible profit?

33. **Crop yield** The yield in bushels from a grove of orange trees is given by $Y = x(800 - x)$, where x is the number of orange trees per acre. How many trees will maximize the yield?

34. **Stimulus-response** One of the early results in psychology relating the magnitude of a stimulus x to the magnitude of a response y is expressed by the equation

$$y = kx^2$$

where k is an experimental constant. Sketch this graph for $k = 1$, $k = 2$, and $k = 4$.

35. **Drug sensitivity** The sensitivity S to a drug is related to the dosage x (in milligrams) by

$$S = 1000x - x^2$$

Sketch the graph of this function and determine what dosage gives maximum sensitivity. Use the graph to determine the maximum sensitivity.

36. **Maximizing an enclosed area** If 100 feet of fence is used to enclose a rectangular yard, then the resulting area is given by

$$A = x(50 - x)$$

where x feet is the width of the rectangle and $50 - x$ feet is the length. Graph this equation and determine the length and width that give maximum area.

37. **Photosynthesis** The rate of photosynthesis R for a certain plant depends on the intensity of light x, in lumens, according to

$$R = 270x - 90x^2$$

Sketch the graph of this function, and determine the intensity that gives the maximum rate.

38. **Projectiles** A ball thrown vertically into the air has its height above ground given by

$$s = 112t - 16t^2$$

where t is in seconds and s is in feet. Find the maximum height of the ball.

39. **Projectiles** Two projectiles are shot into the air from the same location. The paths of the projectiles are parabolas and are given by
   (a) $y = -0.0013x^2 + x + 10$ and
   (b) $y = \dfrac{-x^2}{81} + \dfrac{4}{3}x + 10$

   where x is the horizontal distance and y is the vertical distance, both in feet. Determine which projectile goes higher by locating the vertex of each parabola.

40. **Flow rates of water** The speed at which water travels in a pipe can be measured by directing the flow through an elbow and measuring the height to which it spurts out the top. If the elbow height is 10 cm, the equation relating the height h (in centimeters) of the water above the elbow and its velocity v (in centimeters per second) is given by

$$v^2 = 1960(h + 10)$$

Solve this equation for h and graph the result, using the velocity as the independent variable.

41. **Cost** The following figure shows the graph of a total cost function, with x equal to the number of units produced.
   (a) Is the average rate of change of cost greater from $x = a$ to $x = b$ or from $x = b$ to $x = c$? Explain.
   (b) Would the number of units d need to satisfy $d < b$ or $d > b$ for the average rate of change of cost from $x = a$ to $x = d$ to be greater than that from $x = a$ to $x = b$? Explain.

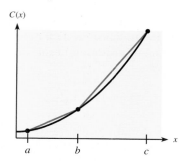

42. **Revenue** The following figure shows the graph of a total revenue function, with x equal to the number of units sold.
   (a) Is the average rate of change of revenue negative from $x = a$ to $x = b$ or from $x = b$ to $x = c$? Explain.
   (b) Would the number of units d need to satisfy $d < b$ or $d > b$ for the average rate of change of revenue from $x = a$ to $x = d$ to be greater than that from $x = a$ to $x = b$? Explain.

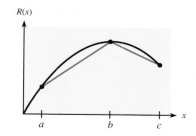

43. *Apartment rental* The owner of an apartment building can rent all 50 apartments if she charges $600 per month, but she rents one fewer apartment for each $20 increase in monthly rent.
    (a) Construct a table that gives the revenue generated if she charges $600, $620, and $640.
    (b) Does her revenue from the rental of the apartments increase or decrease as she increases the rent from $600 to $640?
    (c) Write an equation that gives the revenue from rental of the apartments if she makes x increases of $20 in the rent.
    (d) Find the rent she should charge to maximize her revenue.

44. *Revenue* The owner of a skating rink rents the rink for parties at $600 if 50 or fewer skaters attend, so that the cost per person is $12 if 50 attend. For each 5 skaters above 50, she reduces the price per skater by $0.50.
    (a) Construct a table that gives the revenue generated if 50, 60, and 70 skaters attend.
    (b) Does the owner's revenue from the rental of the rink increase or decrease as the number of skaters increases from 50 to 70?
    (c) Write the equation that describes the revenue for parties with x more than 50 skaters.
    (d) Find the number of skaters that will maximize the revenue.

45. *Pension resources* The Pension Benefit Guaranty Corporation is the agency that insures pensions. The figure shows one study's projection for the agency's total resources, initially rising (from taking over the assets of failing plans) but then falling (as more workers retire and payouts increase).
    (a) What kind of function might be used to model the agency's total resources?
    (b) If a function of the form $f(x) = ax^2 + bx + c$ were used to model these total resources, would $f(x)$ have $a > 0$ or $a < 0$? Explain.
    (c) If the model from part (b) used x as the number of years past 2004, explain why the model would have $b > 0$ and $c > 0$.

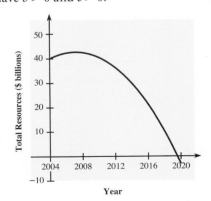

46. *Projectile motion* When a stone is thrown upward, it follows a parabolic path given by a form of the equation
$$y = ax^2 + bx + c$$
If $y = 0$ represents ground level, find the equation of a stone that is thrown from ground level at $x = 0$ and lands on the ground 40 units away if the stone reaches a maximum height of 40 units. (*Hint:* Find the coordinates of the vertex of the parabola and two other points.)

47. *Health care costs per capita* Rising health care costs are a growing concern for everyone in the United States. With U.S. Centers for Medicare and Medicaid Services data from 2006 and projected to 2021, U.S. per capita health care costs can be described by
$$y = 20.61x^2 - 116.4x + 7406$$
where x is the number of years past 2000. Use this equation to find, to the nearest dollar, the average rate of change of U.S. per capita health care costs from 2010 to 2015 and from 2015 to 2020.

48. *Women in the workforce* Using U.S. Census Bureau data for selected years from 1970 and projected to 2040, the percent of the total workforce that is female is given by
$$p(t) = -0.0036t^2 + 0.38t + 38.62$$
where t is the number of years past 1970.
    (a) Graph the function $y = p(t)$.
    (b) From the equation, identify the maximum point on the graph of $y = p(t)$.
    (c) In what year is the percent of women workers projected to be at its maximum, according to this model?

E-commerce Online sales, which make up about 5% of total retail sales in the United States, are expected to top $400 billion by 2017. Using data from 2000 and projected to 2017, the revenue, in billions of dollars, can be described by
$$y = 1.230x^2 - 22.87x + 142.9$$
where x is the number of years past 1990. Use this function in Problems 49–50 (*Sources:* U.S. Census Bureau, Forrester Research, Inc.).
49. Graph the function for $x = 0$ to $x = 27$.
50. The data starts in 2000, at $x = 10$, and the function may not apply before then. The graph has a minimum point; where is this point?

OBJECTIVES

2.3

- To find break-even points by using quadratic cost and revenue functions
- To maximize quadratic revenue and profit functions
- To graph quadratic supply and demand functions
- To find market equilibrium by using quadratic supply and demand functions

Business Applications Using Quadratics

| APPLICATION PREVIEW |

Suppose that the supply function for a product is given by $2p - q - 38 = 0$ and the demand function is given by $p(q + 4) = 400$. Finding the market equilibrium involves solving a quadratic equation (see Example 3).

In this section, we graph quadratic supply and demand functions and find market equilibrium by solving supply and demand functions simultaneously using quadratic methods. We will also discuss quadratic revenue, cost, and profit functions, including break-even points and profit maximization.

Break-Even Points   When we know the functions for total costs, $C(x)$, and total revenue, $R(x)$, we can find the break-even point by finding the quantity x that makes $C(x) = R(x)$.

For example, if $C(x) = 360 + 40x + 0.1x^2$ and $R(x) = 60x$, then setting $C(x) = R(x)$ we have

$$360 + 40x + 0.1x^2 = 60x$$
$$0.1x^2 - 20x + 360 = 0$$
$$x^2 - 200x + 3600 = 0$$
$$(x - 20)(x - 180) = 0$$
$$x = 20 \quad \text{or} \quad x = 180$$

Thus $C(x) = R(x)$ at $x = 20$ and at $x = 180$. If 20 items are produced and sold, $C(x)$ and $R(x)$ are both \$1200; if 180 items are sold, $C(x)$ and $R(x)$ are both \$10,800. Thus there are two break-even points. (See Figure 2.11.)

In a **monopoly market**, the revenue of a company is restricted by the demand for the product. In this case, the relationship between the price p of the product and the number of units sold x is described by the demand function $p = f(x)$, and the total revenue function for the product is given by

$$R = px = [f(x)]x$$

If, for example, the demand for a product is given by $p = 300 - x$, where x is the number of units sold and p is the price, then the revenue function for this product is the quadratic function

$$R = px = (300 - x)x = 300x - x^2$$

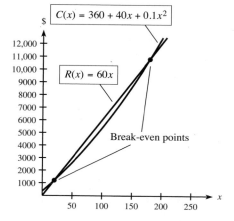

Figure 2.11

EXAMPLE   1   **Break-Even Point**

Suppose that in a monopoly market the total cost per week of producing a high-tech product is given by $C = 3600 + 100x + 2x^2$. Suppose further that the weekly demand function for this product is $p = 500 - 2x$. Find the number of units that will give the break-even point for the product.

Solution

The total cost function is $C(x) = 3600 + 100x + 2x^2$, and the total revenue function is $R(x) = px = (500 - 2x)x = 500x - 2x^2$.

Setting $C(x) = R(x)$ and solving for x gives

$$3600 + 100x + 2x^2 = 500x - 2x^2$$
$$4x^2 - 400x + 3600 = 0$$
$$x^2 - 100x + 900 = 0$$
$$(x - 90)(x - 10) = 0$$
$$x = 90 \quad \text{or} \quad x = 10$$

Does this mean the firm will break even at 10 units and at 90 units? Yes. Figure 2.12 shows the graphs of $C(x)$ and $R(x)$. From the graph we can observe that the firm makes a profit after $x = 10$ until $x = 90$, because $R(x) > C(x)$ in that interval. At $x = 90$, the profit is 0, and the firm loses money if it produces more than 90 units per week.

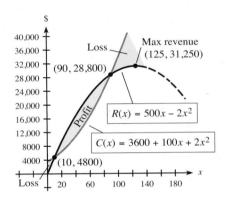

Figure 2.12

✓ CHECKPOINT

1. The point of intersection of the revenue function and the cost function is called _____.
2. If $C(x) = 120x + 15,000$ and $R(x) = 370x - x^2$, finding the break-even points requires solution of what equation? Find the break-even points.

Revenue and Profit Maximization

Note that for Example 1, the revenue function

$$R(x) = (500 - 2x)x = 500x - 2x^2$$

is a parabola that opens downward. Thus the vertex is the point at which revenue is maximum. We can locate this vertex by using the methods discussed in the previous section.

$$\text{Vertex: } x = \frac{-b}{2a} = \frac{-500}{2(-2)} = \frac{500}{4} = 125 \text{ (units)}$$

It is interesting to note that when $x = 125$, the firm achieves its maximum revenue of

$$R(125) = 500(125) - 2(125)^2 = 31,250 \text{ (dollars)}$$

but the costs when $x = 125$ are

$$C(125) = 3600 + 100(125) + 2(125)^2 = 47,350 \text{ (dollars)}$$

which results in a loss. This illustrates that maximizing revenue is not a good goal. We should seek to maximize profit. Figure 2.12 shows that maximum profit will occur where the distance between the revenue and cost curves (that is, $R(x) - C(x)$) is largest. This appears to be near $x = 50$, which is midway between the x-values of the break-even points. This is verified in the next example.

EXAMPLE 2   Profit Maximization

For the total cost function $C(x) = 3600 + 100x + 2x^2$ and the total revenue function $R(x) = 500x - 2x^2$ (from Example 1), find the number of units that maximizes profit and find the maximum profit.

Solution

Using Profit = Revenue − Cost, we can determine the profit function:

$$P(x) = (500x - 2x^2) - (3600 + 100x + 2x^2) = -3600 + 400x - 4x^2$$

This profit function is a parabola with $a = -4$, $b = 400$, and $c = -3600$. Because $a < 0$, the graph opens downward, so the vertex will be the maximum point.

$$\text{Vertex: } x = \frac{-b}{2a} = \frac{-400}{2(-4)} = \frac{-400}{-8} = 50$$

Furthermore, when $x = 50$, we have

$$P(50) = -3600 + 400(50) - 4(50)^2 = 6400 \text{ (dollars)}$$

Thus, when 50 items are produced and sold, a maximum profit of $6400 is made (see Figure 2.13).

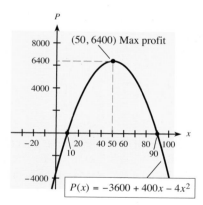

Figure 2.13

Figure 2.13 shows that the break-even points are at $x = 10$ and $x = 90$ and that the maximum profit occurs at the x-value midway between these x-values. This is reasonable because the graph of the profit function is a parabola, and the x-value of any parabola's vertex occurs midway between its x-intercepts.

It is important to note that the procedures for finding maximum revenue and profit in these examples depend on the fact that these functions are parabolas. For more general functions, procedures for finding maximum or minimum values are discussed in Chapter 10, "Applications of Derivatives."

Supply, Demand, and Market Equilibrium

The first-quadrant parts of parabolas or other quadratic equations are frequently used to represent supply and demand functions. For example, the first-quadrant part of $p = q^2 + q + 2$ (Figure 2.14(a)) may represent a supply curve, whereas the first-quadrant part of $q^2 + 2q + 6p - 23 = 0$ (Figure 2.14(b)) may represent a demand curve.

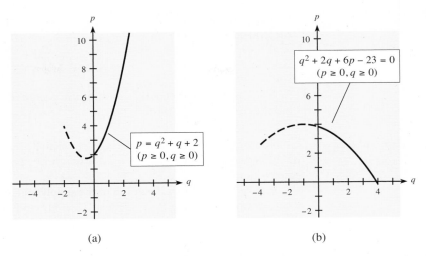

Figure 2.14   (a)   (b)

When quadratic equations are used to represent supply or demand curves, we can solve their equations simultaneously to find the market equilibrium as we did with linear supply and demand functions. As in Section 1.5, we can solve two equations in two variables by eliminating one variable and obtaining an equation in the other variable. When the functions are quadratic, the substitution method of solution is perhaps the best, and the resulting equation in one unknown will usually be quadratic.

| EXAMPLE | 3 | **Market Equilibrium | APPLICATION PREVIEW |** |

If the demand function for a commodity is given by $p(q + 4) = 400$ and the supply function is given by $2p - q - 38 = 0$, find the market equilibrium.

Solution
Solving the supply equation $2p - q - 38 = 0$ for p gives $p = \frac{1}{2}q + 19$. Substituting for p in $p(q + 4) = 400$ gives

$$\left(\frac{1}{2}q + 19\right)(q + 4) = 400$$

$$\frac{1}{2}q^2 + 21q + 76 = 400$$

$$\frac{1}{2}q^2 + 21q - 324 = 0$$

Multiplying both sides of the equation by 2 yields $q^2 + 42q - 648 = 0$. Factoring gives

$$(q - 12)(q + 54) = 0$$
$$q = 12 \quad \text{or} \quad q = -54$$

Thus the market equilibrium occurs when 12 items are sold, at a price of $p = \frac{1}{2}(12) + 19 = \$25$ each. The graphs of the demand and supply functions are shown in Figure 2.15.

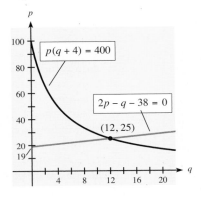

Figure 2.15

✓ **CHECKPOINT**

3. The point of intersection of the supply and demand functions is called _____.

4. If the demand and supply functions for a product are

$$p + \frac{1}{10}q^2 = 1000 \quad \text{and} \quad p = \frac{1}{10}q + 10$$

respectively, finding the market equilibrium point requires solution of what equation? Find the market equilibrium.

Calculator Note   Graphing calculators also can be used to sketch these graphs. The INTERSECT command in the CALC menu can be used to determine points of intersection that give market equilibrium.

Figure 2.16(a) shows the graph of the supply and demand functions for the commodity in Example 3. Using the INTERSECT command gives the same market equilibrium point determined in Example 3 (see Figure 2.16(b)).

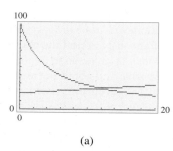

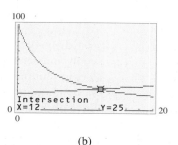

Figure 2.16   (a)   (b)

✓ **CHECKPOINT**
ANSWERS

1. The break-even point
2. Solve $120x + 15,000 = 370x - x^2$. Break-even points are at 100 units and 150 units.
3. The market equilibrium point or market equilibrium
4. Solve $-\frac{1}{10}q^2 + 1000 = \frac{1}{10}q + 10$. Market equilibrium occurs when $q = 99$ and $p = 19.90$.

| EXERCISES | 2.3

BREAK-EVEN POINTS AND MAXIMIZATION

1. The total costs for a company are given by

$$C(x) = 2000 + 40x + x^2$$

   and the total revenues are given by

$$R(x) = 130x$$

   Find the break-even points.

2. If a firm has the following cost and revenue functions, find the break-even points.

$$C(x) = 3600 + 25x + \frac{1}{2}x^2,$$

$$R(x) = \left(175 - \frac{1}{2}x\right)x$$

3. If a company has total costs $C(x) = 15,000 + 35x + 0.1x^2$ and total revenues given by $R(x) = 385x - 0.9x^2$, find the break-even points.

4. If total costs are $C(x) = 1600 + 1500x$ and total revenues are $R(x) = 1600x - x^2$, find the break-even points.

5. Given that $P(x) = 11.5x - 0.1x^2 - 150$ and that production is restricted to fewer than 75 units, find the break-even points.

6. If the profit function for a firm is given by $P(x) = -1100 + 120x - x^2$ and limitations on space require that production is less than 100 units, find the break-even points.

7. Find the maximum revenue for the revenue function $R(x) = 385x - 0.9x^2$.

8. Find the maximum revenue for the revenue function $R(x) = 1600x - x^2$.

9. If, in a monopoly market, the demand for a product is $p = 175 - 0.50x$ and the revenue function is $R = px$, where x is the number of units sold, what price will maximize revenue?

10. If, in a monopoly market, the demand for a product is $p = 1600 - x$ and the revenue is $R = px$, where x is the number of units sold, what price will maximize revenue?

11. The profit function for a certain commodity is $P(x) = 110x - x^2 - 1000$. Find the level of production that yields maximum profit, and find the maximum profit.

Basic Functions   The special linear function

$$y = f(x) = x$$

is called the **identity function** (see Figure 2.17(a) on the next page), and a linear function defined by

$$y = f(x) = C \qquad C \text{ a constant}$$

is called a **constant function.** Figure 2.17(b) shows the graph of the constant function $y = f(x) = 2$. (Note that the slope of the graph of any constant function is 0.)

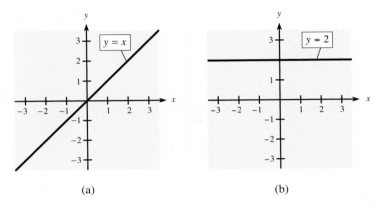

Figure 2.17   (a)   (b)

The functions of the form $y = ax^b$, where $b > 0$, are called **power functions.** Examples of power functions include $y = x^2$, $y = x^3$, $y = \sqrt{x} = x^{1/2}$, and $y = \sqrt[3]{x} = x^{1/3}$. (See Figure 2.18(a)–(d).) The functions $y = \sqrt{x}$ and $y = \sqrt[3]{x}$ are also called **root functions,** and $y = x^2$ and $y = x^3$ are also called basic **polynomial functions.**

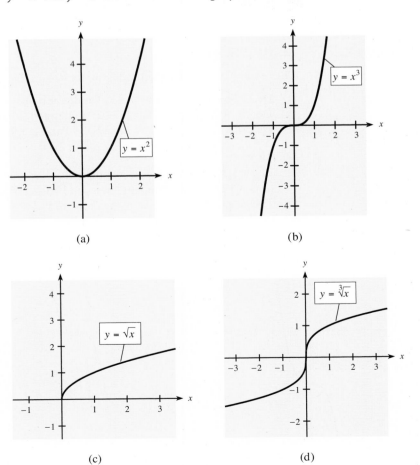

Figure 2.18   (c)   (d)

The general shape for the power function $y = ax^b$, where $a > 0$ and $b > 0$, depends on the value of b. Figure 2.19 shows the first-quadrant portions of typical graphs of $y = x^b$ for different values of b. Note how the direction in which the graph bends differs for $b > 1$ and for $0 < b < 1$. Getting accurate graphs of these functions requires plotting a number of points by hand or with a graphing utility. Our goal at this stage is to recognize the basic shapes of certain functions.

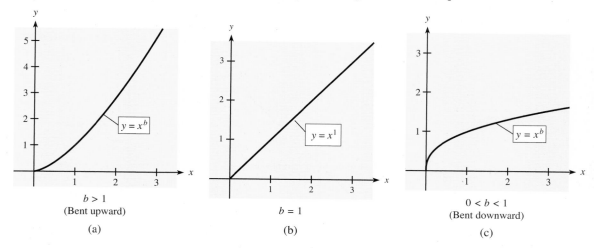

Figure 2.19

(a) $b > 1$ (Bent upward)

(b) $b = 1$

(c) $0 < b < 1$ (Bent downward)

Shifts

In Section 2.2, "Quadratic Functions: Parabolas," we noted that the graph of $y = (x - h)^2 + k$ is a parabola that is shifted h units in the x-direction and k units in the y-direction. These shifts also apply to other functions.

Shifts of Graphs	The graph of $y = f(x - h) + k$ is the graph of $y = f(x)$ shifted h units in the x-direction and k units in the y-direction.

EXAMPLE 1 Shifted Graph

The graph of $y = x^3$ is shown in Figure 2.18(b) on the preceding page.

(a) Describe the graph of $y = x^3 - 3$ and graph this function.
(b) Describe the graph of $y = (x - 2)^3$ and graph this function.
(c) Describe the graph of $y = (x - 2)^3 - 3$ and graph this function.

Solution

(a) The graph of $y = x^3 - 3$ is the graph of $y = x^3$ shifted -3 units in the y-direction (down 3 units). The graph is shown in Figure 2.20(a).
(b) The graph of $y = (x - 2)^3$ is the graph of $y = x^3$ shifted 2 units in the x-direction (to the right 2 units). The graph is shown in Figure 2.20(b).
(c) The graph of $y = (x - 2)^3 - 3$ is the graph of $y = x^3$ shifted to the right 2 units and down 3 units. The graph is shown in Figure 2.20(c).

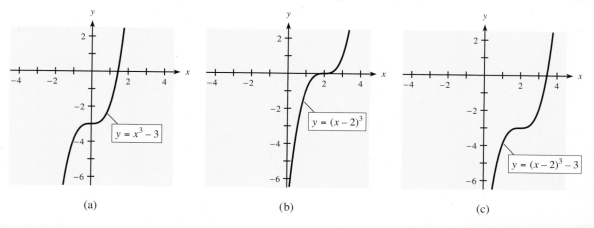

Figure 2.20

(a)

(b)

(c)

Polynomial Functions

A **polynomial function of degree** n has the form

$$y = a_n x^n + a_{n-1} x^{n-1} + \cdots + a_1 x + a_0$$

where $a_n \neq 0$, and n is an integer, $n \geq 0$.

A **linear function** is a polynomial function of degree 1, and a **quadratic function** is a polynomial function of degree 2.

Accurate graphing of a polynomial function of degree greater than 2 may require the methods of calculus; we will investigate these methods in Chapter 10, "Applications of Derivatives." For now, we will observe some characteristics of the graphs of polynomial functions of degrees 2, 3, and 4; these are summarized in Table 2.1. Using this information and point plotting or using a graphing utility yields the graphs of these functions.

| TABLE 2.1 |

GRAPHS OF SOME POLYNOMIALS

	Degree 2	Degree 3	Degree 4
Turning points	1	0 or 2	1 or 3
x-intercepts	0, 1, or 2	1, 2, or 3	0, 1, 2, 3, or 4
Possible shapes			

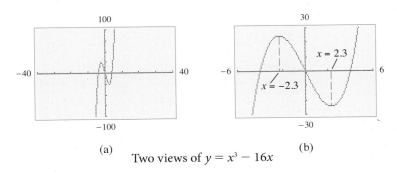

Calculator Note   The function $y = x^3 - 16x$ is a third-degree (cubic) polynomial function, so it has one of the four shapes shown in the "Degree 3" column in Table 2.1. Details of graphing this function are shown in Appendix A, Section 2.4 (see Figure 2.21).

Figure 2.21   Two views of $y = x^3 - 16x$

EXAMPLE 2   Quartic Polynomial

Graph $y = x^4 - 2x^2$.

Solution

This is a degree 4 (quartic) polynomial function. Thus it has one or three turning points and has one of the six shapes in the "Degree 4" column of Table 2.1. We begin by graphing this function with a large viewing window to obtain the graph in Figure 2.22(a). Figure 2.22(b) shows the same graph with a smaller viewing window, near $x = 0$. We now see that the graph has shape (f) from Table 2.1, with turning points at $x = -1$, $x = 0$, and $x = 1$.

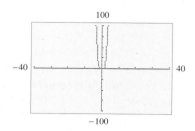

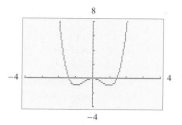

Figure 2.22 (a) Two views of $y = x^4 - 2x^2$ (b)

Spreadsheet Note It is also possible to graph additional polynomial functions with Excel, by using the same methods as those for graphing linear and quadratic function. See Appendix B, Section 2.4, and the Online Excel Guide. ◼

✓ CHECKPOINT

1. All constant functions (such as $f(x) = 8$) have graphs that are _____.
2. Which of the following are polynomial functions?
   (a) $f(x) = x^3 - x + 4$
   (b) $f(x) = \dfrac{x + 1}{4x}$
   (c) $f(x) = 1 + \sqrt{x}$
   (d) $g(x) = \dfrac{1 + \sqrt{x}}{1 + x + \sqrt{x}}$
   (e) $h(x) = 5x$
3. A third-degree polynomial can have at most _____ turning points.

Rational Functions

The function $f(x) = \dfrac{1}{x}$ is a special function called a **reciprocal function.** A table of sample values and the graph of $y = \dfrac{1}{x}$ are shown in Figure 2.23. Because division by 0 is not possible, $x = 0$ is not in the domain of the function.

x	y
−3	−0.33
−2	−0.5
−1	−1
−0.1	−10
−0.04	−25
−0.001	−1000
3	0.33
2	0.5
1	1
0.1	10
0.04	25
0.001	1000

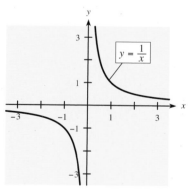

Figure 2.23

The reciprocal function $y = \dfrac{1}{x}$ is also a special **rational function,** defined below.

Rational Function

A **rational function** is a function of the form

$$y = \frac{f(x)}{g(x)} \quad \text{with } g(x) \neq 0$$

where $f(x)$ and $g(x)$ are both polynomials. Its domain is the set of all real numbers for which $g(x) \neq 0$.

Asymptotes   The table of values and the graph in Figure 2.23 show that $|y|$ gets very large as x approaches 0, and that y is undefined at $x = 0$. In this case, we call the line $x = 0$ (that is, the y-axis) a **vertical asymptote.** On the graphs of polynomial functions, the turning points are usually the features of greatest interest. However, on graphs of rational functions, vertical asymptotes frequently are the most interesting features.

Rational functions sometimes have **horizontal asymptotes** as well as vertical asymptotes. Whenever the values of y approach some finite number b as $|x|$ becomes very large, we say that there is a horizontal asymptote at $y = b$.

Note that the graph of $y = \frac{1}{x}$ appears to get close to the x-axis as $|x|$ becomes large. Testing values of x for which $|x|$ is large, we see that y is close to 0. Thus, we say that the line $y = 0$ (or the x-axis) is a horizontal asymptote for the graph of $y = \frac{1}{x}$. The graph in the following example has both a vertical and a horizontal asymptote.

EXAMPLE 3   **Rational Function**

(a) Use values of x from -5 to 5 to develop a table of function values for the graph of

$$y = \frac{12x + 8}{3x - 9}$$

(b) Sketch the graph.

Solution

(a) Because $3x - 9 = 0$ when $x = 3$, it follows that $x = 3$ is not in the domain of this function. The values in the table indicate that the graph is approaching a vertical asymptote at $x = 3$.

x	-5	-4	-3	-2	-1	0	1
y	2.17	1.90	1.56	1.07	0.33	-0.89	-3.33

2	2.5	2.9	3.1	3.5	4	5
-10.7	-25.33	-142.67	150.67	33.33	18.67	11.33

To see if the function has a horizontal asymptote, we calculate y as $|x|$ becomes larger.

x	$-10{,}000$	-1000	1000	$10{,}000$
y	3.999	3.99	4.01	4.001

This table indicates that the graph is approaching $y = 4$ as $|x|$ increases, so we have a horizontal asymptote at $y = 4$.

(b) Using the information about vertical and horizontal asymptotes and plotting these points give the graph in Figure 2.24(a).

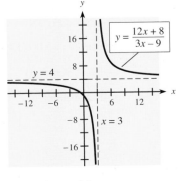

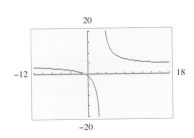

Figure 2.24   (a)   (b)

Calculator Note   When a graphing calculator is used to graph a rational function, breaks in the graph will be visible if the window is chosen carefully. For example, Figure 2.24(b) shows the graph of $y = \dfrac{12x + 8}{3x - 9}$ on a graphing calculator with the window $[-12, 18]$ by $[-20, 20]$.

Note that a window centered at the x-value of the vertical asymptote ($x = 3$) shows the break. For details, see Appendix A, Section 2.4.   ◼

Spreadsheet Note   When graphing a function that has a break at $x = a$ with Excel, we must leave the cell corresponding to $f(a)$ blank so that Excel will not connect the values. See Appendix B, Section 2.4, and the Online Excel Guide for details.   ◼

A general procedure for finding vertical and horizontal asymptotes of rational functions follows (see proof in Chapter 9).

Asymptotes

Vertical Asymptote

The graph of the rational function $y = \dfrac{f(x)}{g(x)}$ has a vertical asymptote at $x = c$ if $g(c) = 0$ and $f(c) \neq 0$.

Horizontal Asymptote

Consider the rational function $y = \dfrac{f(x)}{g(x)} = \dfrac{a_n x^n + \cdots + a_1 x + a_0}{b_m x^m + \cdots + b_1 x + b_0}$.

1. If $n < m$ (that is, if the degree of the numerator is less than that of the denominator), a horizontal asymptote occurs at $y = 0$ (the x-axis).
2. If $n = m$ (that is, if the degree of the numerator equals that of the denominator), a horizontal asymptote occurs at $y = \dfrac{a_n}{b_m}$ (the ratio of the leading coefficients).
3. If $n > m$ (that is, if the degree of the numerator is greater than that of the denominator), there is no horizontal asymptote.

Recall that the graph of the function $y = \dfrac{12x + 8}{3x - 9}$ (shown in Figure 2.24 on the previous page) has a vertical asymptote at $x = 3$, and that $x = 3$ makes the denominator 0 but does not make the numerator 0. Observe also that this graph has a horizontal asymptote at $y = 4$, and that the degree of the numerator is the same as that of the denominator with the ratio of the leading coefficients equal to $12/3 = 4$.

Determining the vertical and/or horizontal asymptotes of a rational function, if any exist, is very useful in determining a window for graphing. A rational function may or may not have turning points. The graph of the rational function in the following example has a vertical asymptote and a turning point.

EXAMPLE   4   Total Costs and Average Costs | APPLICATION PREVIEW |

Suppose the total cost function for x units of a product is given by

$$C(x) = 900 + 3x + x^2$$

Graph the average cost function for this product, and determine the minimum average cost.

Solution

The average cost per unit is

$$\overline{C}(x) = \frac{C(x)}{x} = \frac{900 + 3x + x^2}{x} \qquad \text{or} \qquad \overline{C}(x) = \frac{900}{x} + 3 + x$$

Because x represents the number of units produced, $x \geq 0$. Because $x = 0$ cannot be in the domain of the function, we choose a window with $x \geq 0$. Figure 2.25 shows the graph of $\overline{C}(x)$. The graph appears to have a minimum near $x = 30$. By plotting points or using MINIMUM on a graphing utility, we can verify that the minimum point occurs at $x = 30$ and $\overline{C} = 63$. Thus the minimum average cost is \$63 per unit when 30 units are produced. ∎

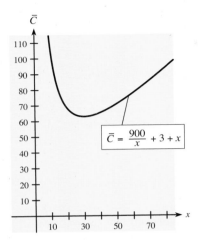

$$\overline{C} = \frac{900}{x} + 3 + x$$

Figure 2.25

✓ **CHECKPOINT**

4. Given $f(x) = \dfrac{3x}{x - 4}$, decide whether the following are true or false.

   (a) $f(x)$ has a vertical asymptote at $x = 4$.

   (b) $f(x)$ has a horizontal asymptote at $x = 3$.

Piecewise Defined Functions

Another special function comes from the definition of $|x|$. The **absolute value function** can be written as

$$f(x) = |x| \quad \text{or} \quad f(x) = \begin{cases} x & \text{if } x \geq 0 \\ -x & \text{if } x < 0 \end{cases}$$

Note that restrictions on the domain of the absolute value function specify different formulas for different parts of the domain. To graph $f(x) = |x|$, we graph the portion of the line $y = x$ for $x \geq 0$ (see Figure 2.26(a)) and the portion of the line $y = -x$ for $x < 0$ (see Figure 2.26(b)). When we put these pieces on the same graph (Figure 2.26(c)), they give us the graph of $f(x) = |x|$. Because the absolute value function is defined by two equations, we say it is a **piecewise defined function.**

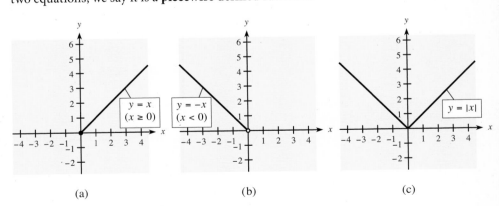

Figure 2.26   (a)   (b)   (c)

It is possible for the selling price S of a product to be defined as a piecewise function of the cost C of the product. For example, the selling price might be defined by two different equations on two different intervals, as follows:

$$S = f(C) = \begin{cases} 3C & \text{if } 0 \leq C \leq 20 \\ 1.5C + 30 & \text{if } C > 20 \end{cases}$$

Each C-value corresponds to only one piece of the formula for $S = f(C)$, so each C-value results in exactly one S-value, and therefore S is a function of C.

Note that the selling price of a product that costs \$15 uses the top formula and is $f(15) = 3(15) = 45$ (dollars) and that the selling price of a product that costs \$25 uses the bottom formula and is $f(25) = 1.5(25) + 30 = 67.50$ (dollars). Each of the two pieces of the graph of this function is a line and is easily graphed. It remains only to graph each in the proper interval. The graph is shown in Figure 2.27(a).

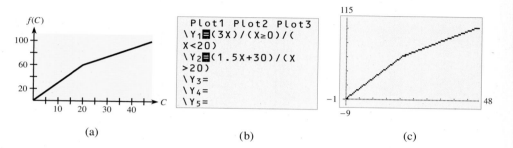

Figure 2.27

(a)   (b)   (c)

Calculator Note   Graphing calculators can be used to graph piecewise defined functions by entering each piece as a separate equation, along with the interval over which it is defined. Figure 2.27(b) shows how the selling price function graphed in Figure 2.27(a) could be entered on a graphing calculator, using x to represent C and Figure 2.27(c) shows the graph. Details of graphing piecewise defined functions with a graphing calculator are shown in Appendix A, Section 2.4. ■

EXAMPLE 5   Residential Electrical Costs

The 2012 monthly charge in dollars for x kilowatt hours (kWh) of electricity used by a residential customer of Excelsior Electric Membership Corporation during the months of November through June is given by the function

$$C(x) = \begin{cases} 10 + 0.094x & \text{if } 0 \le x \le 100 \\ 19.40 + 0.075(x - 100) & \text{if } 100 < x \le 500 \\ 49.40 + 0.05(x - 500) & \text{if } x > 500 \end{cases}$$

(a) What is the monthly charge if 1100 kWh of electricity are consumed in a month?
(b) What is the monthly charge if 450 kWh are consumed in a month?

Solution
(a) We need to find $C(1100)$. Because $1100 > 500$, we use the third formula line.

$$C(1100) = 49.40 + 0.05(1100 - 500) = \$79.40$$

(b) We evaluate $C(450)$ by using the second formula line for $C(x)$.

$$C(450) = 19.40 + 0.075(450 - 100) = \$45.65$$

✓ CHECKPOINT

5. If $f(x) = \begin{cases} 5 & \text{if } x \le 0 \\ 2x & \text{if } 0 < x < 5, \text{ find the following.} \\ x + 6 & \text{if } x \ge 5 \end{cases}$

(a) $f(-5)$ (b) $f(4)$ (c) $f(20)$

✓ CHECKPOINT ANSWERS

1. Horizontal lines
2. Polynomial functions are (a) and (e).
3. Two
4. (a) True.   (b) False; $y = 3$.
5. (a) $f(-5) = 5$ (b) $f(4) = 8$ (c) $f(20) = 26$

| EXERCISES | 2.4

In Problems 1–12, match each of the functions with one of the graphs labeled (a)–(l) shown following these functions. Recognizing special features of certain types of functions and plotting points for the functions will be helpful.

1. $f(x) = -3$

2. $y = \sqrt{x}$

3. $y = \sqrt[3]{x}$

4. $y = (\sqrt{x})^5$

5. $y = (x + 4)^3 + 1$

6. $y = \dfrac{1}{x}$

7. $y = |x|$

8. $y = |x - 2|$

9. $f(x) = \begin{cases} x^2 & \text{if } x \le 2 \\ 4 & \text{if } x > 2 \end{cases}$

10. $f(x) = \begin{cases} 2 & \text{if } x < 0 \\ x^3 & \text{if } x \ge 0 \end{cases}$

11. $y = \begin{cases} -x & \text{if } x < -1 \\ 1 & \text{if } -1 \le x \le 1 \\ x & \text{if } x > 1 \end{cases}$

12. $y = \sqrt{x - 2}$

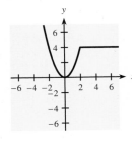

(a)

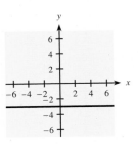

(b)

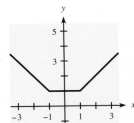

(c)

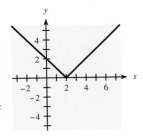

(d)

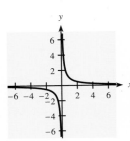

(e)

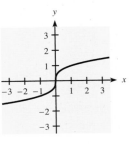

(f)

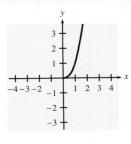

(g)

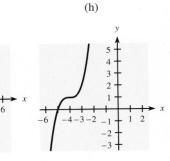

(h)

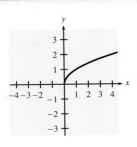

(i)

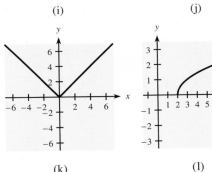

(j)

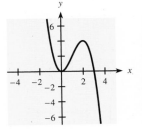

(k)

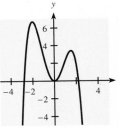

(l)

In Problems 13 and 14, decide whether each function whose graph is shown is the graph of a cubic (third-degree) or quartic (fourth-degree) function.

13.

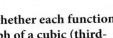

(a)

(b)

14.

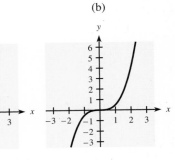

(a)

(b)

In Problems 15–22, match each equation with the correct graph among those labeled (a)–(h) by recognizing shapes and features of polynomial and rational functions. Use a graphing utility to confirm your choice.

15. $y = x^3 - x$

16. $y = (x - 3)^2(x + 1)$

17. $y = 16x^2 - x^4$

18. $y = x^4 - 3x^2 - 4$

19. $y = x^2 + 7x$

20. $y = 7x - x^2$

21. $y = \dfrac{x - 3}{x + 1}$

22. $y = \dfrac{1 - 3x}{2x + 5}$

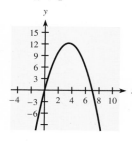

(a)

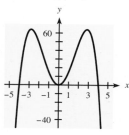

(b)

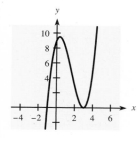

(c)

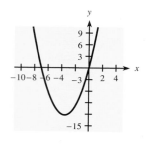

(d)

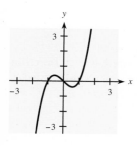

(e)

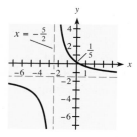

(f)

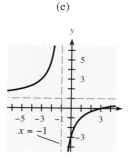

(g)

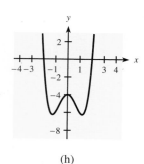

(h)

In Problems 23–28, graph the function.

23. $y = (x + 1)(x - 3)(x - 1)$

24. $y = x^3 - 8x^2 + 19x - 12$

25. $y = \dfrac{1 - 2x}{x}$

26. $y = \dfrac{x}{x - 1}$

27. $y = \begin{cases} x^3 + 2 & \text{if } x < 1 \\ \sqrt{x - 1} & \text{if } x \geq 1 \end{cases}$

28. $y = \begin{cases} x^2 & \text{if } x < 2 \\ 4 - x & \text{if } x \geq 2 \end{cases}$

29. If $F(x) = \dfrac{x^2 - 1}{x}$, find the following.

   (a) $F(-\frac{1}{3})$ (b) $F(10)$

   (c) $F(0.001)$ (d) Is $F(0)$ defined?

30. If $H(x) = |x - 1|$, find the following.

   (a) $H(-1)$ (b) $H(1)$

   (c) $H(0)$ (d) Does $H(-x) = H(x)$?

31. If $f(x) = x^{3/2}$, find the following.

   (a) $f(16)$ (b) $f(1)$ (c) $f(100)$ (d) $f(0.09)$

32. If $k(x) = \begin{cases} 4 - 2x & \text{if } x < 0 \\ |x - 4| & \text{if } 0 < x < 4, \end{cases}$

   find the following.

   (a) $k(-0.1)$ (b) $k(0.1)$ (c) $k(3.9)$ (d) $k(4.1)$

33. If $k(x) = \begin{cases} 2 & \text{if } x < 0 \\ x + 4 & \text{if } 0 \leq x < 1, \\ 1 - x & \text{if } x \geq 1 \end{cases}$

   find the following.

   (a) $k(-5)$ (b) $k(0)$ (c) $k(1)$ (d) $k(-0.001)$

34. If $g(x) = \begin{cases} 0.5x + 4 & \text{if } x < 0 \\ 4 - x & \text{if } 0 \leq x < 4, \\ 0 & \text{if } x > 4 \end{cases}$

   find the following.

   (a) $g(-4)$ (b) $g(1)$ (c) $g(7)$ (d) $g(3.9)$

In Problems 35–40, (a) graph each function with a graphing utility; (b) classify each function as a polynomial function, a rational function, or a piecewise defined function; (c) identify any asymptotes; and (d) use the graphs to locate turning points.

35. $f(x) = 1.6x^2 - 0.1x^4$

36. $f(x) = \dfrac{x^4 - 4x^3}{3}$

37. $f(x) = \dfrac{2x + 4}{x + 1}$

38. $f(x) = \dfrac{x - 3}{x + 2}$

39. $f(x) = \begin{cases} -x & \text{if } x < 0 \\ 5x & \text{if } x \geq 0 \end{cases}$

40. $f(x) = \begin{cases} 2x - 1 & \text{if } x < 1 \\ -x & \text{if } x \geq 1 \end{cases}$

APPLICATIONS

41. *Postal restrictions* If a box with a square cross section is to be sent by the postal service, there are restrictions on its size such that its volume is limited by $V = x^2(108 - 4x)$, where x is the length of each side of the cross section (in inches).

   (a) If $V = V(x)$, find $V(10)$ and $V(20)$.

   (b) What restrictions must be placed on x (the domain) so that the problem makes physical sense?

42. **Fixed costs** Fixed costs FC are business costs that remain constant regardless of the number of units produced. Some items that might contribute to fixed costs are rent and utilities.

$$FC = 2000$$

is an equation indicating that a business has fixed costs of $2000. Graph $FC = 2000$ by putting x (the number of units produced) on the horizontal axis. (Note that FC does not mean the product of F and C.)

43. **Tourism spending** Global spending on travel and tourism (in billions of dollars) can be modeled by

$$f(x) = 15.875x^{1.18}$$

where x is the number of years after 1980 (*Source: World Almanac*).
  (a) Does the graph of this function bend upward or bend downward?
  (b) Graph this function for the years 1980–2020.
  (c) Use the model to find when global spending is predicted to reach $1,150,000,000,000.

44. **Allometric relationships** For fiddler crabs, data gathered by Thompson show that the relationship between the weight C of the claw and the weight W of the body is given by

$$C = 0.11W^{1.54}$$

where W and C are in grams (*Source:* d'Arcy Thompson, *On Growth and Form*, Cambridge University Press, 1961).
  (a) Does the graph of this function bend upward or bend downward?
  (b) Graph this function.
  (c) Use this function to compute the weight of a claw if the weight of the crab's body is 10 grams.

45. **Pollution** Suppose that the cost C (in dollars) of removing p percent of the particulate pollution from the smokestacks of an industrial plant is given by

$$C(p) = \frac{7300p}{100 - p}$$

  (a) Is $C(p)$ undefined at any p-value? If so, what value?
  (b) What is the domain of $C(p)$ as given by the equation?
  (c) What is the domain of $C(p)$ in the context of the application?
  (d) What happens to the cost as the percent of pollution removed approaches 100%?

46. **Average cost** If the weekly total cost of producing 27″ Toshiba television sets is given by $C(x) = 50,000 + 105x$, where x is the number of sets produced per week, then the average cost per unit is given by

$$\overline{C}(x) = \frac{50,000 + 105x}{x}$$

  (a) What is the average cost per set if 3000 sets are sold?

(b) Graph this function.
(c) Does the average cost per set continue to fall as the number of sets produced increases?

47. **Area** If 100 feet of fence is to be used to enclose a rectangular yard, then the resulting area of the fenced yard is given by

$$A = x(50 - x)$$

where x is the width of the rectangle.
  (a) If $A = A(x)$, find $A(2)$ and $A(30)$.
  (b) What restrictions must be placed on x (the domain) so that the problem makes physical sense?

48. **Water usage** The monthly charge for water in a small town is given by

$$f(x) = \begin{cases} 58 & \text{if } 0 \le x \le 20 \\ 58 + 0.4(x - 20) & \text{if } x > 20 \end{cases}$$

where x is water usage in hundreds of gallons and $f(x)$ is in dollars. Find the monthly charge for each of the following usages: (a) 30 gallons, (b) 3000 gallons, and (c) 4000 gallons. (d) Graph the function for $0 \le x \le 100$.

49. **Gross domestic product** By using data for selected years from 1950 and projected to 2040, the gross domestic product (GDP), in billions of dollars, of the United States is modeled by

$$y = \begin{cases} 5.59x^2 - 93.5x + 633 & \text{for } 0 \le x \le 55 \\ 6.56x^2 - 519x + 20,900 & \text{for } 55 < x \le 90 \end{cases}$$

where x is the number of years past 1950 (*Sources:* Bureau of Economic Analysis; U.S. Energy Information Administration).
  (a) Graph the function for $0 \le x \le 90$.
  (b) What does the model estimate the GDP was in 2000?
  (c) What does the model predict the GDP to be in 2025?

50. **Commercial electrical usage** The monthly charge (in dollars) for x kilowatt hours (kWh) of electricity used by a commercial customer is given by the following function.

$$C(x) = \begin{cases} 7.52 + 0.1079x & \text{if } 0 \le x \le 5 \\ 19.22 + 0.1079x & \text{if } 5 < x \le 750 \\ 20.795 + 0.1058x & \text{if } 750 < x \le 1500 \\ 131.345 + 0.0321x & \text{if } x > 1500 \end{cases}$$

Find the monthly charges for the following usages.
  (a) 5 kWh   (b) 6 kWh   (c) 3000 kWh

51. **First-class postage** The postage charged for first-class mail is a function of its weight. The U.S. Postal Service uses the following table to describe the rates.

Weight Increment	Rate ($)
First ounce or fraction of an ounce	0.49
Each additional ounce or fraction	0.21

Source: United States Postal Service

(a) Convert this table to a piecewise defined function that represents postage for letters weighing between 0 and 4 ounces, using x as the weight in ounces and P as the postage in cents.

(b) Find $P(1.2)$ and explain what it means.

(c) Give the domain and range of P as it is defined above.

(d) Find the postage for a 2-ounce letter and for a 2.01-ounce letter.

52. *Income tax* In a given year the U.S. federal income tax owed by a married couple filing jointly can be found from the following table (*Source:* Internal Revenue Service, Form 1040 Instructions).

Filing Status: Married Filing Jointly

If taxable income is between	Tax due is	Of the amount over
$0 − $16,750	$0.00 + 10.0%	$0
$16,750 − $68,000	$1,675.00 + 15.0%	$16,750
$68,000 − $137,300	$9,362.50 + 25.0%	$68,000
$137,300 − $209,250	$26,687.50 + 28.0%	$137,300
$209,250 − $373,650	$46,833.50 + 33.0%	$209,250
$373,650 − Up	$101,085.50 + 35.0%	$373,650

(a) For incomes up to $137,300, write the piecewise defined function T with input x that models the federal tax dollars due as a function of x, the taxable income dollars earned.

(b) Use the function to find $T(70,000)$.

(c) Find the tax due on a taxable income of $50,000.

(d) A friend tells Jack Waddell not to earn any money over $68,000 because it would raise his tax rate to 25% on all of his taxable income. Test this statement by finding the tax due on $68,000 and $68,000 + $1. What do you conclude?

53. *Demand* The demand function for a product is given by

$$p = \frac{200}{2 + 0.1x}$$

where x is the number of units and p is the price in dollars.

(a) Graph this demand function for $0 \le x \le 250$, with x on the horizontal axis.

(b) Does the demand ever reach 0?

54. *Mob behavior* In studying lynchings between 1899 and 1946, psychologist Brian Mullin found that the size of a lynch mob relative to the number of victims predicted the level of brutality. He developed a formula for the other-total ratio (y) that predicts the level of self-attentiveness of people in a crowd of size x with 1 victim.

$$y = \frac{1}{x + 1}$$

The lower the value of y, the more likely an individual is to be influenced by "mob psychology." Graph this function; use positive integers as its domain.

55. *Production costs* A manufacturer estimates that the cost of a production run for a product is

$$C(x) = 30(x - 1) + \frac{3000}{x + 10}$$

where x is the number of machines used.

(a) Graph this total cost function for values of $x \ge 0$.

(b) Interpret any turning points.

(c) Interpret the y-intercept.

- To graph data points in a scatter plot
- To determine the function type that will best model data
- To use a graphing utility to create an equation that models the data
- To graph the data points and model on the same graph

Modeling; Fitting Curves to Data with Graphing Utilities

| APPLICATION PREVIEW |

When the plot of a set of data points looks like a line, we can use a technique called linear regression (or the least-squares method) to find the equation of the line that is the best fit for the data points. The resulting equation (model) describes the data and gives a formula to plan for the future. We can use technology to fit linear and other functions to sets of data.

For selected years from 1995 and projected to 2018, the data in Table 2.2 show the amount of tax paid per capita (per person). In this section we develop a model for these data (see Example 3).

Linear Regression

We saw in Section 1.3, "Linear Functions," that it is possible to write the equation of a straight line if we have two points on the line. Business firms frequently like to treat demand functions as linear, even when they are not exactly linear. They do this because linear functions are much easier to handle than other functions. If a firm has more than two points describing the demand for its product, it is likely that all the points will not lie on the same straight line. However, by using a technique called **linear regression,** the firm can determine the "best line" that fits these points.

Suppose we have the points shown in Figure 2.28, and we seek the line that is the "best fit" for the points.

| TABLE 2.2 |

Year	Federal Tax per Capita
1995	$5110
2000	7177
2005	7228
2010	7005
2013	8559
2015	10,335
2018	12,029

Source: usgovernmentrevenue.com

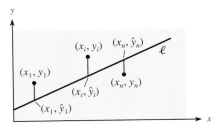

Figure 2.28

The formulas that give the best-fitting line for given data are developed in Chapter 14, "Functions of Two or More Variables," but graphing calculators, computer programs, and spreadsheets have built-in formulas or programs that give the equation of the best-fitting line for a set of data.

Modeling

Creating an equation, or **mathematical model,** for a set of data is a complex process that involves careful analysis of the data in accordance with a number of guidelines. Our approach to creating a model is much simplified and relies on a knowledge of the appearance of linear, quadratic, power, cubic, and quartic functions and the capabilities of computers and graphing calculators. We should note that the equations the computers and calculators provide are based on sophisticated formulas that are derived using calculus of several variables. These formulas provide the best fit for the data using the function type we choose, but we should keep the following limitations in mind.

1. The computer/calculator will give the best fit for whatever type of function we choose (even if the selected function is a bad fit for the points), so we must choose a function type carefully. To choose a function type, compare the plot of the data with the graphs of the functions discussed earlier in this chapter. The model will not fit the data if we choose a function type whose graph does not match the shape of the plotted data.
2. Some sets of data have no pattern, so they cannot be modeled by functions. Other data sets cannot be modeled by the functions we have studied.
3. Modeling provides a formula that relates the data. Even though a model may accurately fit a data set, it may not be a good predictor for values outside the data set.

To find a function that models a set of data, the first step is to plot the data and determine the shape of the curve that would best fit the data points. The plot of the data points is called a **scatter plot.** The scatter plot's shape determines the type of function that will be the best model for the data.

EXAMPLE 1   Curve Fitting

Graphs of three scatter plots are shown in Figure 2.29(a–c). Determine what type of function is your choice as the best-fitting curve for each scatter plot. If it is a polynomial function, state the degree.

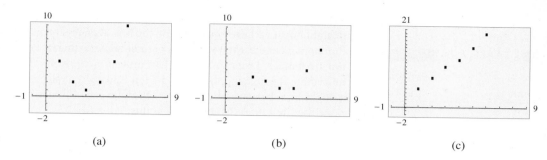

Figure 2.29   (a)   (b)   (c)

Solution

(a) It appears that a parabola will fit the data points in Figure 2.29(a), so the data points can be modeled by a second-degree (quadratic) function.

(b) The two "turns" in the scatter plot in Figure 2.29(b) suggest that it could be modeled by a cubic function.

(c) The data points in Figure 2.29(c) appear to lie (approximately) along a line, so the data can be modeled by a linear function.

After the type of function that gives the best fit for the data is chosen, a graphing utility or spreadsheet can be used to develop the best-fitting equation for the function chosen. The following steps are used with a Texas Instruments calculator to create a scatter plot of data and to find an equation that models the data.

Modeling Data with a Graphing Calculator

1. Enter the inputs (x-values) into list L1 under STAT, EDIT. Similarly enter the outputs (y-values) into list L2 under STAT, EDIT.

2. Turn on PLOT1 in the Y = menu. Then press ZOOM and 9:ZoomStat to show a scatter plot of the data.

3. Press STAT, move to CALC, and select the function type that matches the scatter plot.

4. Press VARS, move to Y-VARS and press ENTER twice to select Y1. Press ENTER again to get the equation on the screen and stored as Y1 under Y =.

5. To see how well the function models the data, press GRAPH to see the graph of the function and the data points on the same set of axes. If the graph of the equation does not fit the data points well, another type of function may model the data better.

6. After the model for a data set has been found, it can be rounded for reporting purposes. However, use the unrounded model in graphing and in calculations, unless otherwise instructed. Numerical answers found using a model should be rounded in a way that agrees with the context of the problem and with no more accuracy than the original output data.

The following example illustrates modeling data with a graphing calculator.

EXAMPLE 2   World Population

The table below gives the world population, in billions, for selected years from 2000 and projected to 2050.

(a) Use a graphing calculator to create a scatter plot of the data, with x equal to the number of years after 2000.

(b) Use the graphing calculator to create an equation that models the data.

(c) Graph the function and the data on the same set of axes to see how well the function models (fits) the data.

Year	2000	2010	2020	2030	2040	2050
Population (billions)	6.08	6.82	7.52	8.18	8.72	9.19

Source: U.S. Census Bureau, International Data Base

Solution

(a) When we use x as the number of years past 2000 (so $x = 0$ in 2000) and use y to represent the world population, in billions, then the points representing this function are

$$(0, 6.08), (10, 6.82), (20, 7.52), (30, 8.18), (40, 8.72), (50, 9.19)$$

The scatter plot of these points is developed in Appendix A, Section 2.5, and shown in Figure 2.30(a).

(b) It appears that a line would fit close to the points in Figure 2.30(a). The points do not fit perfectly on a line because the population does not increase by exactly the same amount each year. The steps used to create the linear function that models these data are shown on page 162 and in Appendix A, Section 2.5. The line that is the best fit for the points is

$$y = 0.0626x + 6.19$$

(c) Figure 2.30(b) shows the graph of the function and the data on the same set of axes. Note that not all points lie on the graph of the function, even though this is the line that is the best fit for the data.

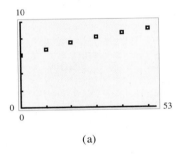

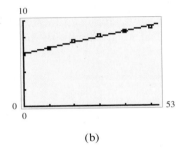

Figure 2.30   (a)   (b)

Notice in Example 2 that the population data all had 3 digits of accuracy (called 3 significant digits) and our reported model used this same accuracy. In general, **significant digits** are those from the first nonzero digit on the left to the last digit *after* the decimal point, if there is a decimal point. If there is no decimal point, any zeros to the right of the nonzero digits are not significant. Thus, 0.0126, 73,800, and 10.0 all have 3 significant digits.

EXAMPLE 3   **Federal Tax per Capita | APPLICATION PREVIEW |**

The following table gives the amount of federal tax paid per capita (per person) for selected years from 1995 and projected to 2018.

(a) Create a scatter plot of these data, with $x = 0$ representing 1990.
(b) Find a cubic model that fits the data points.
(c) Graph the function and the scatter plot on the same axes.
(d) Use the model to predict the per capita tax for 2020.

Year	Federal Tax per Capita	Year	Federal Tax per Capita
1995	$5110	2013	$8559
2000	7177	2015	10,335
2005	7228	2018	12,029
2010	7005		

Source: usgovernmentrevenue.com

Solution

(a) The scatter plot is shown in Figure 2.31(a). The "turns" in the graph indicate that a cubic function would be a good fit for the data.

(b) Figure 2.3(b) shows the cubic regression. The rounded model that is the best fit for the data is

$$y = 2.114x^3 - 93.01x^2 + 1374x + 393.8$$

(c) The graph of the (unrounded) function and the scatter plot are shown in Figure 2.31(c).
(d) For 2020 we use $x = 30$; the corresponding y-value (shown in Figure 2.31(d)) predicts $14,982 as the tax per capita in 2020. The graph's upward turn indicates an increase in future tax per capita, which is likely with the current government debt.

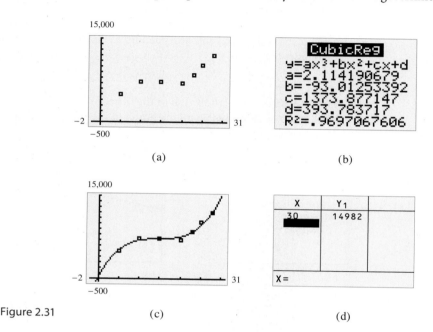

Figure 2.31

(a)   (b)   (c)   (d)

✓ **CHECKPOINT**   The following table gives the Social Security Trust Fund balance (in billions of dollars) for selected years from 2000 and projected to 2030.

(1) Make a scatter plot of the data with x as the number of years past 1995.
(2) Find a model for the data. Graph the model and the data on the same axes.

Year	2000	2005	2010	2015	2020	2025	2030
Balance	1049.4	1858.7	2609.0	2682.6	2440.5	1866.5	777.3

Source: Social Security Administration

If it is not obvious what model will best fit a given set of data, several models can be developed and compared graphically with the data.

EXAMPLE 4 Expected Life Span

The expected life span of people in the United States depends on their year of birth.

Year	Life Span (years)	Year	Life Span (years)	Year	Life Span (years)	Year	Life Span (years)
1920	54.1	1960	69.7	1985	74.7	2005	77.9
1930	59.7	1970	70.8	1990	75.4	2010	78.1
1940	62.9	1975	72.6	1995	75.8	2015	78.9
1950	68.2	1980	73.7	2000	77.0	2020	79.5

Source: National Center for Health Statistics

(a) Create linear and quadratic models that give life span as a function of birth year with $x = 0$ representing 1900 and, by visual inspection, decide which model gives the better fit.

(b) Use both models to estimate the life span of a person born in the year 2000.

(c) Which model's estimation for the life span in 2015 seems better?

Solution

(a) The scatter plot for the data is shown in Figure 2.32(a). It appears that a linear function could be used to model the data. The linear equation that is the best fit for the data is

$$y = 0.233x + 53.7$$

The graph in Figure 2.32(b) shows how well the unrounded linear model fits the data points. The quadratic function that is the best fit for the data is

$$y = -0.00186x^2 + 0.498x + 46.0$$

The graph of this unrounded model is shown in Figure 2.32(c).

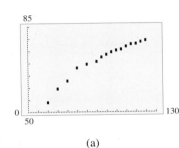
(a)

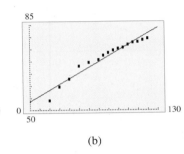
(b)

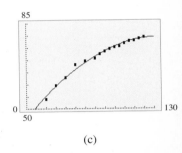
(c)

Figure 2.32

| TABLE 2.3 |

X	Y_1	Y_2
90	74.648	75.72
100	76.975	77.161
110	79.302	78.23
115	80.465	78.625

X =

The quadratic model appears to fit the data points better than the linear model. A table can be used to compare the models (see Table 2.3 with y_1 giving values from the linear model and y_2 giving values from the quadratic model).

(b) We can estimate the life span of people born in the year 2000 with either model by evaluating the unrounded functions at $x = 100$. The x-values in Table 2.3 represent the years 1990, 2000, 2010, and 2015. From the linear model the expected life span in 2000 is 77.0, and from the quadratic model the expected life span is 77.2.

(c) Looking at Table 2.3 and at Figures 2.32(b) and (c), we see that the linear model may be giving optimistic values in 2015, when $x = 115$, so the quadratic model may be better in the years after 2010.

Spreadsheet Note

Excel can also be used to model data. Doing so involves using *Chart Wizard* to plot the data points, clicking on the scatter plot and selecting *Add Trendline*, choosing the appropriate function type (with the degree if *polynomial* is selected), and checking the *Display equation on chart* box. See Example 5, Appendix B, Section 2.5, and the Online Excel Guide for details.

EXAMPLE 5   Corvette Acceleration

The following table shows the times that it takes a Corvette to reach speeds from 0 mph to 100 mph, in increments of 10 mph after 30 mph.

Time (sec)	Speed (mph)	Time (sec)	Speed (mph)
1.7	30	5.5	70
2.4	40	7.0	80
3.5	50	8.5	90
4.3	60	10.2	100

(a) Use a power function with Excel to model the data, and graph the points and the function to see how well the function fits the points.
(b) What does the model indicate the speed is 5 seconds after the car starts to move?
(c) Use the model to determine the number of seconds until the Corvette reaches 110 mph.

Solution

(a) Using x as the time and y as the speed, the scatter plot is shown in Figure 2.33(a). (See Appendix B, Section 2.5 for details of finding the model.) The Excel model found using the power function $y = ax^b$ (graphed in Figure 2.33(b)) is

$$y = 21.875x^{0.6663}$$

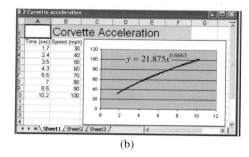

Figure 2.33   (a)   (b)

(b) Using $x = 5$ in this equation gives 64 mph as the speed of the Corvette.
(c) Excel Goal Seek (discussed in Section 2.1) using $y = 21.875x^{0.6663}$ set equal to 110 gives $x = 11.3$, so the time required to reach 110 mph is 11.3 seconds.

✓ **CHECKPOINT ANSWERS**

(1) The first data point is plotted as (5, 1049.4). Figure 2.34(a) shows the scatter plot.
(2) Use a quadratic function; a rounded model is $y = 7.974x^2 + 312.0x - 356.0$. Figure 2.34(b) shows a graph of the unrounded model and the data.

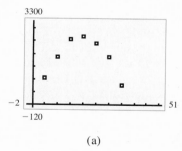
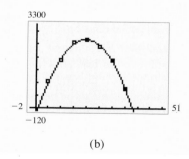

Figure 2.34   (a)   (b)

| EXERCISES | 2.5

In Problems 1–8, determine whether the scatter plot should be modeled by a linear, power, quadratic, cubic, or quartic function.

1.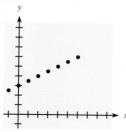

2.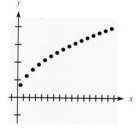

3.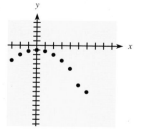

4.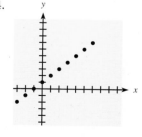

5.

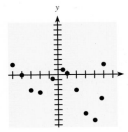

6.

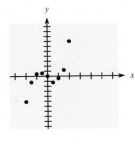

7.

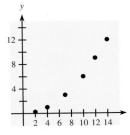

8.

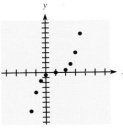

15. power

x	y
1	2
2	2.8284
3	3.4641
4	4
5	4.4721
6	4.899

16. power

x	y
1	3
2	8.4853
3	15.588
4	24
5	33.541
6	44.091

In Problems 17–24, (a) plot the given points, (b) determine what type of function best models the data, and (c) find the equation that is the best fit for the data.

17.

x	y
−1	−8
0	−3
1	2
2	7
3	12
4	17
5	22

18.

x	y
−1	−2
0	2
1	6
2	10
3	14
4	18
5	22

In Problems 9–16, find the equation of the function of the specified type that is the best fit for the given data. Plot the data and the equation.

9. linear

x	y
−2	−7
−1	−5
0	−3
1	−1
2	1
3	3
4	5

10. linear

x	y
−1	−5.5
0	−4
1	−2.5
2	−1
3	0.5
4	2
5	3.5

19.

x	y
−1	2
0	0
1	2
2	3.1748
3	4.1602
4	5.0397
5	5.848

20.

x	y
0.01	0.3
1	3
2	4.2426
3	5.1962
4	6
5	6.7082
6	7.3485

11. quadratic

x	y
−2	7
−1	−0.5
0	−4
1	−3.5
2	1
3	9.5
4	22

12. quadratic

x	y
−4	−8
−3	−4
−2	−2
−1	−2
0	−4
1	−8
2	−14

21.

x	y
−2	19
−1	8
0	1
1	−2
2	−1
3	4
4	13

22.

x	y
−4	37
−3	19
−2	7
−1	1
0	1
1	7
2	19

13. cubic

x	y
−4	−72
−3	−31
−2	−10
−1	−3
0	−4
1	−7
2	−6

14. cubic

x	y
−3	−22
−2	−6
−1	−2
0	−4
1	−6
2	−2
3	14

23.

x	y
−3	−11
−2	3
−1	5
0	1
1	−3
2	−1
3	13

24.

x	y
−3	−54
−2	−14
−1	0
0	0
1	−2
2	6
3	36

APPLICATIONS

25. Population of females under 18 The following table gives the projected population, in thousands, of U.S. females under the age of 18.

Year	Population (1000s)	Year	Population (1000s)
2020	37,222	2045	41,067
2025	38,201	2050	41,963
2030	39,244	2055	42,855
2035	39,809	2060	43,610
2040	40,352		

Source: U.S. Census Bureau

(a) Create a linear function that models the projected population *y*, in thousands, as a function of the number of years past 2010.
(b) What is the projected population of females under age 18 in 2037, according to this model?
(c) When will this population reach 45,000,000, according to this model?

26. CO_2 emissions The following table gives the millions of metric tons of carbon dioxide emissions in the United States for selected years from 2010 and projected to 2032.
(a) Create a linear function that models these data, with *x* as the number of years past 2010 and *y* as the millions of metric tons of carbon dioxide emissions.
(b) Find the model's estimate for the 2024 data point.
(c) Find and interpret the slope of the linear model.

Year	2010	2012	2014	2016	2018	2020
CO_2 Emissions	338.5	364.5	396.1	425.8	453.1	498.4

Year	2022	2024	2026	2028	2030	2032
CO_2 Emissions	556.2	590.9	629.7	663.1	701.1	743.7

Source: U.S. Department of Energy

27. Disposable income Disposable income is the amount left after taxes have been paid and is one measure of the health of the economy. The following table gives the total U.S disposable income (in billions of 2005 dollars) for selected years from 2010 and projected to 2040.
(a) Use *x* as the number of years past 2010 and write the equation of the function that is the best fit for these data.
(b) What does the model predict for the disposable income in 2027?
(c) Interpret the slope of the model found in part (a).

28. Diabetes As the following table shows, projections indicate that the percent of U.S. adults with diabetes could dramatically increase.

Year	Percent	Year	Percent	Year	Percent
2010	15.7	2025	24.2	2040	31.4
2015	18.9	2030	27.2	2045	32.1
2020	21.1	2035	29.0	2050	34.3

Source: Centers for Disease Control and Prevention

(a) Find a linear model that fits the data in the table, with *x* = 0 in 2000.
(b) Use the model to predict the percent of U.S. adults with diabetes in 2018.
(c) In what year does this model predict the percent of U.S. adults with diabetes will reach 25%?

29. Wind chill The table gives the wind chill temperature when the outside temperature is 20°F.

Wind (mph)	Wind Chill (°F)	Wind (mph)	Wind Chill (°F)
5	13	35	0
10	9	40	−1
15	6	45	−2
20	4	50	−3
25	3	55	−3
30	1	60	−4

Source: National Weather Service

(a) Use *x* as the wind speed and create a quadratic model for these data.
(b) At what wind speed does the model predict that the wind chill temperature will be lowest?
(c) Do you think the model found in part (a) is valid for *x* > 60? Explain.

30. Developing economies The developing economies' share of the global gross domestic product (GDP) from 2003 and projected to 2017 is shown in the following table.
(a) Find the quadratic function that best models the developing economies' share of the global GDP as a function of the number of years after 2000.
(b) Use technology to find the maximum share of GDP that the developing economies can achieve, according to this model.

Year	2010	2015	2020	2025	2030	2035	2040
Income (billions)	$10,017	$11,120	$12,655	$14,259	$15,948	$17,752	$19,785

Source: U.S. Energy Information Administration

Year	Share (% of GDP)	Year	Share (% of GDP)
2003	20	2011	35
2004	22	2012	38
2005	23	2013	39
2006	27	2014	40
2007	28	2015	41
2008	31	2016	42
2009	31	2017	43
2010	33		

Source: International Monetary Fund

31. **Gross domestic product** The table gives the gross domestic product (GDP), in billions of dollars, of the United States for selected years from 2000 and projected to 2070.
    (a) Create a scatter plot of the data, with y representing GDP in billions of dollars and x representing the number of years past 2000.
    (b) Find the quadratic function that best fits the data.
    (c) Find the cubic function that best fits the data.
    (d) Graph each of these functions on the same axes as the data points, and visually determine which model is the better fit for the data.

Year	GDP	Year	GDP
2000	9143	2040	79,680
2005	12,145	2045	103,444
2010	16,174	2050	133,925
2015	21,270	2055	173,175
2020	27,683	2060	224,044
2025	35,919	2065	290,042
2030	46,765	2070	375,219
2035	61,100		

Source: Social Security Administration

32. **Alzheimer's disease** As the baby boom generation ages and the proportion of the U.S. population over age 65 increases, the number of Americans with Alzheimer's disease and other dementia is projected to grow each year. The table below gives the millions of U.S. citizens age 65 and older with Alzheimer's from 2000 and projected to 2050.
    (a) Find the quadratic function that models the data, with x equal to the number of years past 2000 and y equal to the number of millions of Americans with Alzheimer's.
    (b) Find the cubic function that models the data, with x equal to the number of years past 2000 and y equal to the number of millions of Americans with Alzheimer's.
    (c) Graph each model and the data on the same axes.
    (d) Determine if one model is a better visual fit to the data.

Year	2000	2010	2020	2030	2040	2050
Millions	4.5	5.1	5.7	7.7	11.0	13.2

Source: Alzheimer's Association

33. **Crude oil** The following table gives the U.S. crude oil production, in billions of barrels, for selected years from 2010 and projected to 2030.
    (a) Find the linear function that models the data, with x equal to the number of years past 2010 and y equal to the number of billions of barrels of crude oil.
    (b) Find the quadratic function that models the data, with x and y as in part (a).
    (c) Graph each model and the data on the same axes.
    (d) Determine if one model is a better visual fit to the data.

Year	2010	2012	2014	2016	2018	2020
Billions of Barrels	1.94	2.00	2.10	2.10	2.16	2.24

Year	2022	2024	2026	2028	2030
Billions of Barrels	2.24	2.21	2.26	2.27	2.26

Source: U.S. Department of Energy

34. **Energy use** Energy use per dollar of GDP indexed to 1980 means that energy use for any year is viewed as a percent of the use per dollar of GDP in 1980. The following data show the energy use per dollar of GDP, as a percent, for selected years from 1985 and projected to 2035.
    (a) Find a linear function that models these data, with x equal to the number of years past 1980 and y equal to the energy use per dollar of GDP, as a percent.
    (b) Find a cubic function that models these data, with x equal to the number of years past 1980 and y equal to the energy use per dollar of GDP, as a percent.
    (c) Graph each model and the data on the same axes.
    (d) Which model indicates that the percent of energy use may increase after 2035?

Energy Use per Dollar of GDP

Year	1985	1990	1995	2000	2005	2010
Percent	83	79	75	67	60	56

Year	2015	2020	2025	2030	2035
Percent	51	45	41	37	34

Source: U.S. Department of Energy

35. **Income by age** The median income for workers ages 20 to 62 is shown in the following table.
    (a) Use a scatter plot of the data with x equal to the age and y equal to the median income in dollars to decide what type of function is the best model for these data. Explain your choice.
    (b) Find the best model for the data.

(c) Graph the function on the same axes as the scatter plot.

(d) At what age does the model estimate the median income to be $56,520?

Median Age	Median Income ($)	Median Age	Median Income ($)
20	25,404	47	54,260
27	37,896	52	54,405
32	45,770	57	56,427
37	50,740	62	59,222
42	51,613		

Source: U.S. Census Bureau

36. *National health care* The table shows the national expenditures for health care in the United States for selected years, with projections to 2020.

Year	National Expenditures for Health Care (billions)
1960	$28
1970	75
1980	254
1990	714
1995	1017
2000	1353
2005	1981
2010	2954
2015	3308
2020	4487

Source: U.S. Centers for Medicare and Medicaid Services

(a) Use a scatter plot with x as the number of years past 1950 and y as the total expenditures for health care (in billions) to identify what type (or types) of function(s) would make a good model for these data.

(b) Find a power model and a quadratic model for the data.

(c) Which model from part (b) more accurately approximates the data point for 2020?

(d) Use the quadratic model to predict the 2025 expenditures for national health care.

37. *E-commerce* The following table gives the online sales, in billions of dollars, from 2000 and projected to 2017.

(a) Find the power function that models these data, with x as the number of years past 1990.

(b) Graph the data and the function on the same axes.

(c) What does the model predict the online sales revenue to be in 2020?

Year	Sales (billions)	Year	Sales (billions)
2000	$28	2009	$134
2001	34	2010	171
2002	44	2011	202
2003	56	2012	226
2004	70	2013	259
2005	87	2014	297
2006	106	2015	339
2007	126	2016	386
2008	132	2017	434

Sources: U.S. Census Bureau; Forrester Research, Inc.

38. *U.S. population* The table gives the U.S. population, in millions, for selected years from 1950 and projected to 2050.

Year	1950	1960	1970	1980	1990	2000
Population (millions)	160.1	190.2	214.8	235.1	259.6	287.9

Year	2010	2015	2020	2030	2040	2050
Population (millions)	315.2	328.4	342.9	369.5	390.8	409.1

Source: Social Security Administration

(a) Create a scatter plot for the data in the table. Use x as the number of years past 1950.

(b) Use the scatter plot to identify and determine at least two function types that could be used to model these data.

(c) Which model more accurately approximates the data point for the year 2040?

(d) Use the linear model to determine when the U.S. population is predicted to reach 425 million.

Chapter 2 Summary & Review

KEY TERMS AND FORMULAS

Section 2.1

Quadratic equation (p. 123)

$$ax^2 + bx + c = 0 \ (a \neq 0)$$

Square root property (p. 125)

$$x^2 = C \Rightarrow x = \pm\sqrt{C}$$

Quadratic formula (p. 126)

$$x = \frac{-b \pm \sqrt{b^2 - 4ac}}{2a}$$

Quadratic discriminant (p. 127)

$$b^2 - 4ac$$

Section 2.2

Quadratic function; parabola (pp. 132, 135)
$$y = f(x) = ax^2 + bx + c$$
Vertex of a parabola (p. 132)
$$(-b/2a, f(-b/2a))$$
  Maximum point if $a < 0$
  Minimum point if $a > 0$

Axis of symmetry (p. 132)
$$x = -b/2a$$
Zeros of a quadratic function (p. 134)
Average rates of change (p. 143)
$$\frac{f(b) - f(a)}{b - a}$$

Section 2.3

Cost, revenue, and profit functions (p. 142)
$$P(x) = R(x) - C(x)$$
Break-even points (p. 142)
$$R(x) = C(x) \text{ or } P(x) = 0$$

Revenue and profit maximization (p. 143)
Supply function (p. 144)
Demand function (p. 144)
Market equilibrium (p. 144)

Section 2.4

Basic functions (p. 149)
  $f(x) = ax + b$ (linear)
  $f(x) = C, \quad C = $ constant
  $f(x) = ax^b$ (power)
  $f(x) = x$ (identity)
  $f(x) = x^2, f(x) = x^3, f(x) = 1/x$
Shifts of graphs (p. 150)
  $f(x - h)$ shifts $f(x)$ h units horizontally
  $f(x) + k$ shifts $f(x)$ k units vertically
Polynomial function of degree n (p. 151)
  $f(x) = a_n x^n + a_{n-1} x^{n-1} + \cdots + a_1 x + a_0$
  $a_n \neq 0, n \geq 0, n$ an integer

Rational function (p. 152)
  $f(x) = p(x)/q(x)$, where $p(x)$ and $q(x)$
  are polynomials
Vertical asymptote (p. 154)
Horizontal asymptote (p. 154)
Absolute value function (p. 155)
$$f(x) = |x| = \begin{cases} x & \text{if } x \geq 0 \\ -x & \text{if } x < 0 \end{cases}$$
Piecewise defined functions (p. 155)

Section 2.5

Mathematical models (p. 161)
Scatter plots (p. 161)

Significant digits (p. 163)
Modeling data with a graphing calculator (p. 166)

REVIEW EXERCISES

Section 2.1

In Problems 1–10, find the real solutions to each quadratic equation.

1. $3x^2 + 10x = 5x$
2. $4x - 3x^2 = 0$
3. $x^2 + 5x + 6 = 0$
4. $11 - 10x - 2x^2 = 0$
5. $(x - 1)(x + 3) = -8$
6. $4x^2 = 3$
7. $20x^2 + 3x = 20 - 15x^2$
8. $8x^2 + 8x = 1 - 8x^2$
9. $7 = 2.07x - 0.02x^2$
10. $46.3x - 117 - 0.5x^2 = 0$

In Problems 11–14, solve each equation by using a graphing utility to find the zeros of the function. Solve the equation algebraically to check your results.

11. $4z^2 + 25 = 0$
12. $z(z + 6) = 27$
13. $3x^2 - 18x - 48 = 0$
14. $3x^2 - 6x - 9 = 0$
15. Solve $x^2 + ax + b = 0$ for x.
16. Solve $xr^2 - 4ar - x^2c = 0$ for r.

In Problems 17 and 18, approximate the real solutions to each quadratic equation to two decimal places.

17. $23.1 - 14.1x - 0.002x^2 = 0$
18. $1.03x^2 + 2.02x - 1.015 = 0$

Section 2.2

For each function in Problems 19–24, find the vertex and determine if it is a maximum or minimum point, find the zeros if they exist, and sketch the graph.

19. $y = \frac{1}{2}x^2 + 2x$
20. $y = 4 - \frac{1}{4}x^2$
21. $y = 6 + x - x^2$
22. $y = x^2 - 4x + 5$
23. $y = x^2 + 6x + 9$
24. $y = 12x - 9 - 4x^2$

In Problems 25–30, use a graphing utility to graph each function. Use the vertex and zeros to determine an appropriate window. Be sure to label the maximum or minimum point.

25. $y = \frac{1}{3}x^2 - 3$
26. $y = \frac{1}{2}x^2 + 2$
27. $y = x^2 + 2x + 5$
28. $y = -10 + 7x - x^2$
29. $y = 20x - 0.1x^2$
30. $y = 50 - 1.5x + 0.01x^2$

31. Find the average rate of change of $f(x) = 100x - x^2$ from $x = 30$ to $x = 50$.

32. Find the average rate of change of
$$f(x) = x^2 - 30x + 22$$
over the interval [10, 50].

In Problems 33–36, a graph is given. Use the graph to
(a) locate the vertex,
(b) determine the zeros, and
(c) match the graph with one of the equations A, B, C, or D.

A. $y = 7x - \frac{1}{2}x^2$
B. $y = \frac{1}{2}x^2 - x - 4$
C. $y = 8 - 2x - x^2$
D. $y = 49 - x^2$

33.

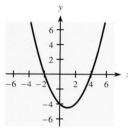

34.

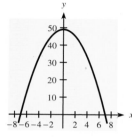

35.

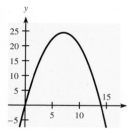

36.

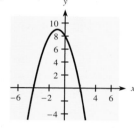

Section 2.4

37. Sketch a graph of each of the following basic functions.
   (a) $f(x) = x^2$ (b) $f(x) = 1/x$ (c) $f(x) = x^{1/4}$

38. If $f(x) = \begin{cases} -x^2 & \text{if } x \le 0 \\ 1/x & \text{if } x > 0 \end{cases}$, find the following.

   (a) $f(0)$ (b) $f(0.0001)$
   (c) $f(-5)$ (d) $f(10)$

39. If $f(x) = \begin{cases} x & \text{if } x \le 1 \\ 3x - 2 & \text{if } x > 1 \end{cases}$, find the following.

   (a) $f(-2)$ (b) $f(0)$ (c) $f(1)$ (d) $f(2)$

In Problems 40 and 41, graph each function.

40. $f(x) = \begin{cases} x & \text{if } x \le 1 \\ 3x - 2 & \text{if } x > 1 \end{cases}$

41. (a) $f(x) = (x - 2)^2$ (b) $f(x) = (x + 1)^3$

In Problems 42 and 43, use a graphing utility to graph each function. Find any turning points.

42. $y = x^3 + 3x^2 - 9x$
43. $y = x^3 - 9x$

In Problems 44 and 45, graph each function. Find and identify any asymptotes.

44. $y = \dfrac{1}{x - 2}$

45. $y = \dfrac{2x - 1}{x + 3}$

Section 2.5

46. *Modeling* Consider the data given in the table.
   (a) Make a scatter plot.
   (b) Fit a linear function to the data.
   (c) Try other function types and find one that fits better than a linear function.

x	0	4	8	12	16	20	24
y	153	151	147	140	128	115	102

47. *Modeling* Consider the data given in the table.
   (a) Make a scatter plot.
   (b) Fit a linear function to the data.
   (c) Try other function types and find one that fits better than a linear function.

x	3	5	10	15	20	25	30
y	35	45	60	70	80	87	95

APPLICATIONS

Section 2.1

48. *Physics* A ball is thrown into the air from a height of 96 ft above the ground, and its height is given by $S = 96 + 32t - 16t^2$, where t is the time in seconds.
   (a) Find the values of t that make $S = 0$.
   (b) Do both of the values of t have meaning for this application?
   (c) When will the ball strike the ground?

49. *Profit* The profit for a product is given by $P(x) = 82x - 0.10x^2 - 1600$, where x is the number of units produced and sold. Break-even points will occur at values of x where $P(x) = 0$. How many units will give a break-even point for the product?

Section 2.2

50. *Manufacturing employment* By using U.S. Energy Information Administration data from 2012 and projected to 2040, the total U.S. employment in manufacturing, E in millions, can be modeled by

$$E(t) = -0.0052t^2 + 0.080t + 12$$

where t is the number of years past 2010.
   (a) In what year does the model predict that manufacturing employment will be at its maximum, and what is that maximum?
   (b) When does the model predict that manufacturing employment will be 11.5 million?

51. *Maximum area* A rectangular lot is to be fenced in and then divided down the middle to create two identical fenced lots (see the figure). If 1200 ft of fence is to be used, the area of each lot is given by

$$A = x\left(\frac{1200 - 3x}{4}\right)$$

(a) Find the *x*-value that maximizes this area.
(b) Find the maximum area.

Section 2.3

52. *Supply* Graph the first-quadrant portion of the supply function

$$p = 2q^2 + 4q + 6$$

53. *Demand* Graph the first-quadrant portion of the demand function

$$p = 18 - 3q - q^2$$

54. *Market equilibrium*
   (a) Suppose the supply function for a product is $p = 0.1q^2 + 1$ and the demand function is $p = 85 - 0.2q - 0.1q^2$. Sketch the first-quadrant portion of the graph of each function. Use the same set of axes for both and label the market equilibrium point.
   (b) Use algebraic methods to find the equilibrium price and quantity.

55. *Market equilibrium* The supply function for a product is given by $p = q^2 + 300$, and the demand is given by $p + q = 410$. Find the equilibrium quantity and price.

56. *Market equilibrium* If the demand function for a commodity is given by the equation $p^2 + 5q = 200$ and the supply function is given by $40 - p^2 + 3q = 0$, find the equilibrium quantity and price.

57. *Break-even points* If total costs for a product are given by $C(x) = 1760 + 8x + 0.6x^2$ and total revenues are given by $R(x) = 100x - 0.4x^2$, find the break-even quantities.

58. *Break-even points* If total costs for a commodity are given by $C(x) = 900 + 25x$ and total revenues are given by $R(x) = 100x - x^2$, find the break-even quantities.

59. *Maximizing revenue and profit* Find the maximum revenue and maximum profit for the functions described in Problem 58.

60. *Break-even and profit maximization* Given total profit $P(x) = 1.3x - 0.01x^2 - 30$, find maximum profit and the break-even quantities and sketch the graph.

61. *Maximum profit* Given $C(x) = 360 + 10x + 0.2x^2$ and $R(x) = 50x - 0.2x^2$, find the level of production that gives maximum profit and find the maximum profit.

62. *Break-even and profit maximization* A certain company has fixed costs of $15,000 for its product and variable costs given by $140 + 0.04x$ dollars per unit, where *x* is the total number of units. The selling price of the product is given by $300 - 0.06x$ dollars per unit.
   (a) Formulate the functions for total cost and total revenue.

(b) Find the break-even quantities.
(c) Find the level of sales that maximizes revenue.
(d) Form the profit function and find the level of production and sales that maximizes profit.
(e) Find the profit (or loss) at the production levels found in parts (c) and (d).

Section 2.4

63. *Diabetes* The rise of adult diabetes in the United States is a growing concern for health professionals. Using Centers for Disease Control and Prevention data for selected years from 2010 and projected to 2050, the percent of U.S. adults with diabetes can be modeled by the function

$$D(t) = 4.95t^{0.495}$$

where *t* is the number of years past 2000.
   (a) What type of function is this?
   (b) What does the function predict as the percent of U.S. adults with diabetes in the year 2020?
   (c) Find $D(25)$ and write a sentence that explains its meaning.

64. *Photosynthesis* The amount *y* of photosynthesis that takes place in a certain plant depends on the intensity *x* of the light present, according to

$$y = 120x^2 - 20x^3 \quad \text{for } x \geq 0$$

   (a) Graph this function with a graphing utility. (Use *y*-min $= -100$ and *y*-max $= 700$.)
   (b) The model is valid only when $f(x) \geq 0$ (that is, on or above the *x*-axis). For what *x*-values is this true?

65. *Cost-benefit* Suppose the cost *C*, in dollars, of eliminating *p* percent of the pollution from the emissions of a factory is given by

$$C(p) = \frac{4800p}{100 - p}$$

   (a) What type of function is this?
   (b) Given that *p* represents the percent of pollution removed, what is the domain of $C(p)$?
   (c) Find $C(0)$ and interpret its meaning.
   (d) Find the cost of removing 99% of the pollution.

66. *Municipal water costs* The Borough Municipal Authority of Beaver, Pennsylvania, used the following function to determine charges for water.

$$C(x) = \begin{cases} 2.557x & \text{if } 0 \leq x \leq 100 \\ 255.70 + 2.04(x - 100) & \text{if } 100 < x \leq 1000 \\ 2091.07 + 1.689(x - 1000) & \text{if } x > 1000 \end{cases}$$

where $C(x)$ is the cost in dollars for *x* thousand gallons of water.
   (a) Find the monthly charge for 12,000 gallons of water.
   (b) Find the monthly charge for 825,000 gallons of water.

Section 2.5

67. *Modeling (Subaru WRX)* The table shows the times that it takes a Subaru WRX to accelerate from 0 mph to speeds of 30 mph, 40 mph, etc., up to 90 mph, in increments of 10 mph.

Time (sec)	Speed (mph)	Time (sec)	Speed (mph)
1.6	30	7.8	70
2.7	40	10.2	80
4.0	50	12.9	90
5.6	60		

Source: Motor Trend

(a) Represent the times by x and the speeds by y, and name at least 2 function types that would be reasonable choices to model these data.

(b) Find the power function model for the data.

(c) Graph the points and the function to see how well the function fits the points.

(d) What does the model indicate the speed is 5 seconds after the car starts to move?

(e) According to the model, in how many seconds will the car reach 79.3 mph?

68. *Average annual wage* The tables below give Social Security Administration data for the U.S. average annual wage from 2011 and projected to 2021 and for selected years from 2012 and projected to 2050.

(a) Make a scatter plot of each of these data sets with x as the number of years past 2010.

(b) Decide which one function type could be used as a model for both data sets and find the two models. Let $a(x)$ be the model for the data to 2021 and $A(x)$ be the one for data to 2050. Report both models with 4 significant digit coefficients.

(c) How well do the reported models agree for the data points for 2020 and for 2050?

(d) When does each reported model predict the average annual wage will reach $150,000?

Data to 2021 (in dollars)

Year	2011	2012	2013	2014
Wage	43,009	44,644	46,496	48,595
Year	2015	2016	2017	2018
Wage	50,893	53,317	55,989	58,698
Year	2019	2020	2021	
Wage	61,179	63,676	66,161	

Data to 2050 (in thousands of dollars)

Year	2012	2014	2016	2018
Wage	44.6	48.6	53.3	58.7
Year	2020	2025	2030	2035
Wage	63.7	76.8	93.2	113.2
Year	2040	2045	2050	
Wage	137.6	167.1	202.5	

69. *Obesity* Obesity (BMI $\geq$ 30) is a serious problem in the United States and is expected to get worse. Being overweight increases the risk of diabetes, heart disease, and many other ailments, but the severely obese (BMI $\geq$ 40) are most at risk and the most expensive to treat. The percent of Americans who are obese and severely obese from 1990 and projected to 2030 are shown in the table below.

(a) Find the linear function, $O(x)$, that models obesity, with x equal to the number of years past 1980 and y the percent of obese Americans. Report the model as $y = O(x)$ with 3 significant digit coefficients.

(b) Find the linear function, $S(x)$, that models severe obesity, with x equal to the number of years past 1980 and y the percent of severely obese Americans. Report the model as $y = S(x)$ with 3 significant digit coefficients.

(c) Let $F(x) = \dfrac{S(x)}{O(x)}$. What is the mathematical name for this type of function, and what does it measure in terms of these data?

(d) Find the horizontal asymptote for $F(x)$, and tell what it means in terms of these data.

Year	1990	2000	2010	2015	2020	2025	2030
% Obese	12.7	22.1	30.9	34.5	37.4	39.9	42.2
% Severely Obese	0.8	2.2	4.9	6.4	7.9	9.5	11.1

Source: American Journal of Preventive Medicine, 42, June 2012: 563–570, ajpmonline.org

70. *U.S. population demographics* The makeup of various groups within the U.S. population may reshape the electorate in ways that could change political representation and policies. The following table shows U.S. Department of Labor data from 1980 and projected to 2050 for the civilian non-institutional population age 16 and older, in millions, according to those who are White non-Hispanic and others (non-White or Hispanic).

(a) With x as the number of years past 1970, use a scatter plot to determine which single function type could be used to model each set of data, and find a model for each set. Let $W(x)$ be the function for the population of White non-Hispanic and $O(x)$ be the function for the non-Whites or Hispanics. Report both models with 3 significant digit coefficients.

(b) If these models remain valid, use them to determine the year in which these population segments are predicted to be equal.

Year	1980	1990	2000	2010	2015
White non-Hispanic	136.8	146.5	153.1	162.1	164.6
Others	30.9	42.6	56.6	71.6	79.0

Year	2020	2030	2040	2050
White non-Hispanic	166.3	168.8	169.7	169.4
Others	86.8	104.2	123.1	143.0

Source: U.S. Department of Labor

Chapter 2 TEST

1. Sketch a graph of each of the following functions.
   (a) $f(x) = x^4$
   (b) $g(x) = |x|$
   (c) $h(x) = -1$
   (d) $k(x) = \sqrt{x}$

2. The following figures show graphs of the power function $y = x^b$. Which is the graph for $b > 1$? Which is the graph for $0 < b < 1$?

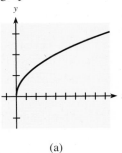
(a)

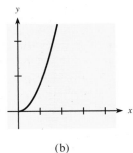
(b)

3. If $f(x) = ax^2 + bx + c$ and $a < 0$, sketch the shape of the graph of $y = f(x)$.

4. Graph:
   (a) $f(x) = (x + 1)^2 - 1$
   (b) $f(x) = (x - 2)^3 + 1$

5. Which of the following three graphs is the graph of $f(x) = x^3 - 4x^2$? Explain your choice.

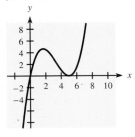
(a)

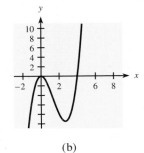
(b)

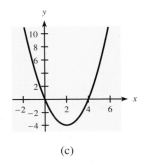
(c)

6. Let $f(x) = \begin{cases} 8x + 1/x & \text{if } x < 0 \\ 4 & \text{if } 0 \le x \le 2 \\ 6 - x & \text{if } x > 2 \end{cases}$

   Find the following:
   (a) the y-coordinate of the point on the graph of $y = f(x)$ where $x = 16$
   (b) $f(-2)$
   (c) $f(13)$

7. Sketch the graph of $g(x) = \begin{cases} x^2 & \text{if } x \le 1 \\ 4 - x & \text{if } x > 1 \end{cases}$

8. Find the vertex and zeros, if they exist, and sketch the graph of $f(x) = 21 - 4x - x^2$.

9. Solve $3x^2 + 2 = 7x$.

10. Solve $2x^2 + 6x = 9$.

11. Solve $\dfrac{1}{x} + 2x = \dfrac{1}{3} + \dfrac{x + 1}{x}$

12. Which of the following three graphs is that of
$$g(x) = \frac{3x - 12}{x + 2}?$$ Explain your choice.

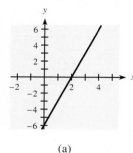

(a)

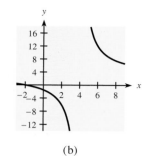

(b)

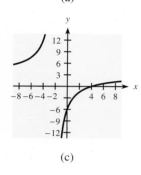

(c)

13. Find the horizontal and vertical asymptotes of the graph of

$$f(x) = \frac{8}{2x - 10}$$

14. Find the average rate of change of

$$P(x) = 92x - x^2 - 1760$$

over the interval from $x = 10$ to $x = 40$.

15. Choose the type of function that models each of the following graphs.

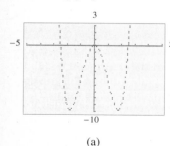

(a)

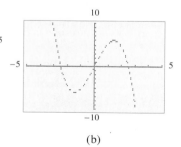

(b)

16. *Modeling*
   (a) Make a scatter plot, then develop a model, for the following data.
   (b) What does the model predict for $x = 40$?
   (c) When does the model predict $f(x) = 0$?

x	0	2	4	6	8	10	12	14	16	18	20
y	20.1	19.2	18.8	17.5	17.0	15.8	16	14.9	13.8	13.7	13.0

17. Suppose the supply and demand functions for a product are given by $6p - q = 180$ and $(p + 20)q = 30,000$, respectively. Find the equilibrium price and quantity.

18. Suppose a company's total cost for a product is given by $C(x) = 15,000 + 35x + 0.1x^2$ and the total revenue for the product is given by $R(x) = 285x - 0.9x^2$, where x is the number of units produced and sold.
   (a) Find the profit function.
   (b) Determine the number of units at which the profit for the product is maximized, and find the maximum possible profit.
   (c) Find the break-even point(s) for the product.

19. The wind chill expresses the combined effects of low temperatures and wind speeds as a single temperature reading. When the outside temperature is 0°F, the wind chill, WC, is a function of the wind speed s (in mph) and is approximated by the following function.[*]

$$WC = f(s) = \begin{cases} 0 & \text{if } 0 \leq s \leq 1.13 \\ 36.23 - 35.50\sqrt[6]{s} & \text{if } 1.13 < s < 55 \\ -33 & \text{if } s \geq 55 \end{cases}$$

   (a) Find $f(15)$ and write a sentence that explains its meaning.
   (b) Find the wind chill when the wind speed is 48 mph.

20. The table gives the annual per capita out-of-pocket expenses (to the nearest dollar) for health care in the United States for selected years from 2000 and projected to 2021.

Year	2000	2002	2004	2006	2008	2010
Expenses	$684	$733	$802	$912	$967	$971

Year	2012	2014	2016	2018	2020	2021
Expenses	$995	$996	$1046	$1154	$1267	$1325

Source: U.S. Centers for Medicare and Medicaid Services

   (a) Plot the data, with x representing the number of years after 2000 and y representing the expenses.
   (b) Find a linear and a cubic function model for the data.
   (c) Use both models to estimate the per capita expenses in 2021 (to the nearest dollar). Comment on how well the models approximate the projected data value.
   (d) What happens to the two models for years past 2021?

*Source: National Weather Service

I. Body Mass Index (Modeling)

Obesity is a risk factor for the development of several medical problems, including high blood pressure, high cholesterol, heart disease, and diabetes. Of course, whether a person is considered obese depends not only on weight but also on height. One way of comparing weights that accounts for height is the *body mass index (BMI)*. The table below gives the BMI for a variety of heights and weights for people. Medical professionals generally agree that a BMI of 30 or greater increases the risk of developing medical problems associated with obesity.

Describe how to assist a group of people in using this information. Some things you would want to include in your description follow.

A. How a person uses the table to determine his or her BMI.
B. How a person determines the weight that will put him or her at medical risk.
C. How a person whose weight or height is not in the table can determine whether his or her BMI is 30 or higher. To address this particular issue, develop a formula to find the weight that would give a BMI of 30 for a person of a given height, including how you would:
1. Pick the points from the table that correspond to a BMI of 30 and create a table of these heights and weights. Change the units of height measurement to simplify the data.
2. Determine what type of model seems to be the best fit for the data.
3. Create a model for the data.
4. Test the model with existing data.
5. Explain how to use the model to test for obesity. In particular, use the model to find the obesity threshold for someone who is 5 feet tall and someone who is 6 feet 2 inches tall (heights that are not in the table).
6. Use the Internet to find the definition of BMI, and, if necessary, convert it to a formula that uses inches and pounds.
7. Make a table for heights from 61 inches to 73 inches that compares the threshold weights for a BMI of 30 from your model, from the definition of BMI, and from the table.

Body Mass Index for Specified Height (ft/in.) and Weight (lb)														
Height/Weight	120	130	140	150	160	170	180	190	200	210	220	230	240	250
5'1"	23	25	27	28	30	32	34	36	38	40	42	44	45	47
5'2"	22	24	26	27	29	31	33	35	37	38	40	42	44	46
5'3"	21	23	25	27	28	30	32	34	36	37	39	41	43	44
5'4"	21	22	24	26	28	29	31	33	34	36	38	40	41	43
5'5"	20	22	23	25	27	28	30	32	33	35	37	38	40	42
5'6"	19	21	23	24	26	27	29	31	32	34	36	37	39	40
5'7"	19	20	23	24	25	27	28	30	31	33	35	36	38	39
5'8"	18	20	21	23	24	26	27	29	30	32	34	35	37	38
5'9"	18	19	21	22	24	25	27	28	30	31	33	34	36	37
5'10"	17	19	20	22	23	24	25	27	28	29	31	33	35	36
5'11"	17	18	20	21	22	24	25	27	28	29	31	32	34	35
6'0"	16	18	19	20	22	23	24	26	27	29	30	31	33	34
6'1"	16	17	19	20	21	22	24	25	26	28	29	30	32	33

Source: Roche Pharmaceuticals

II. Operating Leverage and Business Risk

Once you have determined the break-even point for your product, you can use it to examine the effects of increasing or decreasing the role of fixed costs in your operating structure. The extent to which a business uses fixed costs (compared to variable costs) in its operations is referred to as **operating leverage.** The greater the use of operating leverage (fixed costs, often associated with fixed assets), the larger the increase in profit as sales rise, and the larger the increase in loss as sales fall (*Source:* **www.toolkit.cch.com/ text/P06_7540.asp**). The higher the break-even quantity for your product, the greater your **business risk.** To see how operating leverage is related to business risk, complete the following.

1. If x is the number of units of a product that is sold and the price is p per unit, write the function that gives the revenue R for the product.
2. (a) If the fixed cost for production of this product is $10,000 and the variable cost is $100 per unit, find the function that gives the total cost C for the product.
    (b) What type of function is this?
3. Write an equation containing only the variables p and x that describes when the break-even point occurs.
4. (a) Solve the equation from Question 3 for x, so that x is written as a function of p.
    (b) What type of function is this?
    (c) What is the domain of this function?
    (d) What is the domain of this function in the context of this application?
5. (a) Graph the function from Question 4 for the domain of the problem.
    (b) Does the function increase or decrease as p increases?
6. Suppose that the company has a monopoly for this product so that it can set the price as it chooses. What are the benefit and the danger to the company of pricing its product at $1100 per unit?
7. If the company has a monopoly for this product so that it can set the price, what are the benefit and the danger to the company of pricing its product at $101 per unit?
8. Suppose the company currently is labor-intensive, so that the monthly fixed cost is $10,000 and the variable cost is $100 per unit, but installing modern equipment will reduce the variable cost to $50 per unit while increasing the monthly fixed cost to $30,000. Also suppose the selling price per unit is $P = \$200$.
    (a) Which of these operations will have the highest operating leverage? Explain.
    (b) Which of these operations will have the highest business risk? Explain.
    (c) What is the relation between high operating leverage and risk? Discuss the benefit and danger of the second operating plan to justify your answer.

Exponential and Logarithmic Functions

In this chapter we study exponential and logarithmic functions, which provide models for many applications that at first seem remote and unrelated. In our study of these functions, we will examine their descriptions, their properties, their graphs, and the special inverse relationship between these two functions. We will see how exponential and logarithmic functions are applied to some of the concerns of social scientists, business managers, and life scientists.

The chapter topics and some representative applications include the following.

SECTIONS

5.1 Exponential Functions
Graphs
Modeling

5.2 Logarithmic Functions and Their Properties
Graphs and modeling
Properties
Change of base

5.3 Equations and Applications with Exponential and Logarithmic Functions
Solving exponential equations
Solving logarithmic equations
Growth and decay
Gompertz curves and logistic functions

APPLICATIONS

Investments, purchasing power and inflation

Doubling time, market share, life expectancy, Richter scale

Sales decay, demand, organizational growth, computer tablet sales

Prerequisite Problem Type	For Section	Answer	Section for Review
Write the following with positive exponents: (a) x^{-3} (b) $\dfrac{1}{x^{-2}}$ (c) $\sqrt{x}$	**5.1–5.3**	(a) $\dfrac{1}{x^3}$ (b) x^2 (c) $x^{1/2}$	0.3, 0.4 Exponents and radicals
Simplify: (a) 2^0 (b) $x^0 (x \neq 0)$ (c) $49^{1/2}$ (d) 10^{-2}	**5.1–5.3**	(a) 1 (b) 1 (c) 7 (d) $\dfrac{1}{100}$	0.3, 0.4 Exponents
Answer true or false: (a $\left(\dfrac{1}{2}\right)^x = 2^{-x}$ (b) $\sqrt{50} = 50^{1/2}$ (c) If $8 = 2^y$, then $y = 4$. (d) If $x^3 = 8$, then $x = 2$.	**5.1–5.2**	(a) True (b) True (c) False; $y = 3$ (d) True	0.3, 0.4 Exponents and radicals
(a) If $f(x) = 2^{-2x}$, what is $f(-2)$? (b) If $f(x) = 2^{-2x}$, what is $f(1)$? (c) If $f(t) = (1 + 0.02)^t$, what is $f(0)$? (d) If $f(t) = 100(0.03)^{0.02t}$, what is $f(0)$? (e) If $f(x) = \dfrac{9.46}{1 + 53.08e^{-1.28x}}$, what is $f(5)$?	**5.1–5.3**	(a) 16 (b) $\dfrac{1}{4}$ (c) 1 (d) 3 (e) ≈ 8.693	1.2 Function notation

OBJECTIVES

- To graph exponential functions
- To evaluate exponential functions
- To model with exponential functions

5.1

Exponential Functions

| APPLICATION PREVIEW |

If $10,000 is invested at 6%, compounded monthly, then the future value S of the investment after x years is given by the exponential function

$$S = 10{,}000(1.005)^{12x}$$

(We will find the future value of the investment after 5 years in Example 2.)

In this section we will evaluate and graph exponential functions, and we will model data with exponential functions.

Exponential Functions and Graphs

Suppose a culture of bacteria has the characteristic that each minute, every microorganism splits into two new organisms. We can describe the number of bacteria in the culture as a function of time. That is, if we begin the culture with one microorganism, we know that after 1 minute we will have two organisms, after 2 minutes, 4, and so on. Table 5.1 gives a few of the values that describe this growth. If x represents the number of minutes that have passed and y represents the number of organisms, the points (x, y) lie on the graph of the function with equation

$$y = 2^x$$

The equation $y = 2^x$ is an example of a special group of functions called **exponential functions**, defined as follows.

| TABLE 5.1 |

Minutes Passed	Number of Organisms
0	1
1	2
2	4
3	8
4	16

Exponential Functions

If a is a real number with $a > 0$ and $a \neq 1$, then the function

$$f(x) = a^x$$

is an **exponential function** with base a.

A table of some values satisfying $y = 2^x$ and the graph of this function are given in Figure 5.1. This function is said to model the growth of the number of organisms in the previous discussion, even though some points on the graph do not correspond to a time and a number of organisms. For example, time x could not be negative, and the number of organisms y could not be fractional.

x	$y = 2^x$
-3	$2^{-3} = \frac{1}{8}$
-2	$2^{-2} = \frac{1}{4}$
-1	$2^{-1} = \frac{1}{2}$
0	$2^0 = 1$
1	$2^1 = 2$
2	$2^2 = 4$
3	$2^3 = 8$

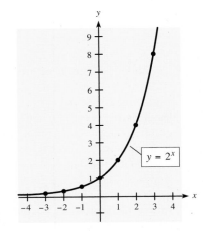

Figure 5.1

We defined rational powers of x in terms of radicals in Chapter 0, so 2^x makes sense for any rational power x. It can also be shown that the laws of exponents apply for irrational numbers. We will assume that if we graphed $y = 2^x$ for irrational values of x, those points would lie on the curve in Figure 5.1. Thus, in general, we can graph an exponential function by plotting easily calculated points, such as those in the table in Figure 5.1, and drawing a smooth curve through the points.

EXAMPLE 1 **Graphing an Exponential Function**

Graph $y = 10^x$.

Solution

A table of values and the graph are given in Figure 5.2.

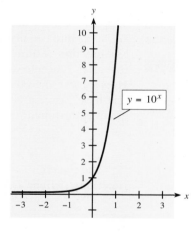

x	y
-3	$10^{-3} = 1/1000$
-2	$10^{-2} = 1/100$
-1	$10^{-1} = 1/10$
0	$10^0 = 1$
1	$10^1 = 10$
2	$10^2 = 100$
3	$10^3 = 1000$

Figure 5.2

Calculator Note   We also could have used a graphing calculator to graph $y = 2^x$ and $y = 10^x$. Figure 5.3 shows graphs of $f(x) = 1.5^x$, $f(x) = 4^x$, and $f(x) = 20^x$ that were obtained using a graphing calculator. Note the viewing window for each graph in the figure. See Appendix A, Section 5.1, for details.

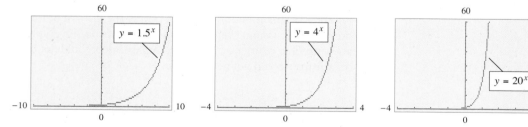

Figure 5.3

Note that the three graphs in Figure 5.3 and the graphs of $y = 2^x$ and $y = 10^x$ are similar. The graphs of $y = 2^x$ and $y = 10^x$ clearly approach, but do not touch, the negative x-axis. However, the graphs in Figure 5.3 appear as if they might eventually merge with the negative x-axis. By adjusting the viewing window, however, we would see that these graphs also approach, but do not touch, the negative x-axis. That is, the negative x-axis is an asymptote for these functions.

In fact, the shapes of the graphs of functions of the form $y = f(x) = a^x$, with $a > 1$, are similar to those in Figures 5.1, 5.2, and 5.3. Exponential functions of this type, and more generally of the form $f(x) = C(a^x)$, where $C > 0$ and $a > 1$, are called **exponential growth functions** because they are used to model growth in diverse applications. Their graphs have the basic shape shown in the following box.

Graphs of Exponential Growth Functions

Function: $y = f(x) = C(a^x)$ $(C > 0, a > 1)$
y-intercept: $(0, C)$
Graph shape:

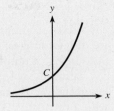

Domain: All real numbers;   Range: $y > 0$.
Asymptote: The x-axis (negative half)

One exponential growth model concerns money invested at compound interest. Often we seek to evaluate rather than graph these functions.

EXAMPLE   2   **Future Value of an Investment | APPLICATION PREVIEW |**

If $10,000 is invested at 6%, compounded monthly, then the future value of the investment S after x years is given by

$$S = 10{,}000(1.005)^{12x}$$

Find the future value of the investment after (a) 5 years and (b) 30 years.

Solution

These future values can be found with a calculator.

(a) $S = 10{,}000(1.005)^{12(5)} = 10{,}000(1.005)^{60} = \$13{,}488.50$ (nearest cent)
(b) $S = 10{,}000(1.005)^{12(30)} = 10{,}000(1.005)^{360} = \$60{,}225.75$ (nearest cent)

Note that the amount after 30 years is significantly more than the amount after 5 years, a result consistent with exponential growth models.

1. Can any value of x give a negative value for y if $y = a^x$ and $a > 1$?
2. If $a > 1$, what asymptote does the graph of $y = a^x$ approach?
3. Given $y = f(x) = 2.5^x$. Find $f(x)$ for $x = -2, -1, 0, 1,$ and 2. Then graph $y = f(x)$.

A special function that occurs frequently in economics and biology is $y = e^x$, where e is a fixed irrational number (approximately 2.71828 …). We will see how e arises when we discuss interest that is compounded continuously, and we will formally define e in Section 9.2, "Continuous Functions; Limits at Infinity."

Because $e > 1$, the graph of $y = e^x$ will have the same basic shape as other growth exponentials. We can calculate the y-coordinate for points on the graph of this function with a calculator. A table of some values (with y-values rounded to two decimal places) and the graph are shown in Figure 5.4.

x	$y = e^x$
-2	0.14
-1	0.37
0	1.00
1	2.72
2	7.39

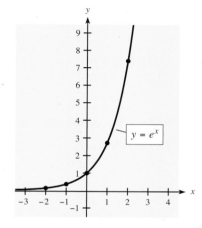

Figure 5.4

Exponentials whose bases are between 0 and 1, such as $y = \left(\frac{1}{2}\right)^x$, have graphs different from those of the exponentials just discussed. Using the properties of exponents, we have

$$y = \left(\frac{1}{2}\right)^x = (2^{-1})^x = 2^{-x}$$

By using this technique, all exponentials of the form $y = b^x$, where $0 < b < 1$, can be rewritten in the form $y = a^{-x}$, where $a = \frac{1}{b} > 1$. Thus, graphs of equations of the form $y = a^{-x}$, where $a > 1$, and of the form $y = b^x$, where $0 < b < 1$, will have the same shape.

EXAMPLE 3   Graphing an Exponential Function

Graph $y = 2^{-x}$.

Solution

A table of values and the graph are given in Figure 5.5.

x	$y = 2^{-x}$
-3	$2^3 = 8$
-2	$2^2 = 4$
-1	$2^1 = 2$
0	$2^0 = 1$
1	$2^{-1} = \frac{1}{2}$
2	$2^{-2} = \frac{1}{4}$
3	$2^{-3} = \frac{1}{8}$

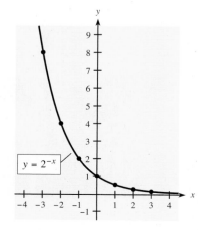

Figure 5.5

EXAMPLE   4   **Graphing an Exponential Function with Base *e***

Graph $y = e^{-2x}$.

Solution

Using a calculator to find the values of powers of *e* (to 2 decimal places), we get the graph shown in Figure 5.6.

x	$y = e^{-2x}$
-3	$e^6 = 403.43$
-2	$e^4 = 54.60$
-1	$e^2 = 7.39$
0	$e^0 = 1.00$
1	$e^{-2} = 0.14$
2	$e^{-4} = 0.02$

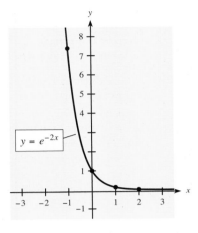

Figure 5.6

We can also use a graphing utility to graph exponential functions such as those in Examples 3 and 4. Additional examples of functions of this type would yield graphs with the same shape. **Exponential decay functions** have the form $y = a^{-x}$, where $a > 1$, or, more generally, the form $y = C(a^{-x})$, where $C > 0$ and $a > 1$. They model decay for various phenomena, and their graphs have the characteristics and shape shown in the following box.

Graphs of Exponential Decay Functions

Function: $y = f(x) = C(a^{-x})$ $(C > 0, a > 1)$ or
$y = f(x) = C(b^x)$ $(C > 0, 0 < b < 1)$

y-intercept: $(0, C)$

Graph shape:

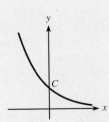

Domain: All real numbers;   Range: $y > 0$.

Asymptote: The x-axis (positive half)

Exponential decay functions can be used to describe various physical phenomena, such as the number of atoms of a radioactive element (radioactive decay), the lingering effect of an advertising campaign on new sales after the campaign ends, and the effect of inflation on the purchasing power of a fixed income.

EXAMPLE 5   Purchasing Power and Inflation

The purchasing power P of a fixed income of $30,000 per year (such as a pension) after t years of 4% inflation can be modeled by

$$P = 30,000(1.04)^{-t}$$

Find the purchasing power after (a) 5 years and (b) 20 years.

Solution
We can use a calculator to answer both parts.

(a) $P = 30,000(1.04)^{-5} \approx \$24,657.81$
(b) $P = 30,000(1.04)^{-20} \approx \$13,691.61$

Note that the impact of inflation over time significantly erodes purchasing power and provides some insight into the plight of elderly people who live on fixed incomes. ■

Exponential functions with base e often arise in natural ways. As we will see in Section 6.2, the growth of money that is compounded continuously is given by $S = Pe^{rt}$, where P is the original principal, r is the annual interest rate, and t is the time in years. Certain populations (of insects, for example) grow exponentially, and the number of individuals can be closely approximated by the equation $y = P_0 e^{ht}$, where P_0 is the original population size, h is a constant that depends on the type of population, and y is the population size at any instant t. Also, the amount y of a radioactive substance is modeled by the exponential decay equation $y = y_0 e^{-kt}$, where y_0 is the original amount and k is a constant that depends on the radioactive substance.

✓ CHECKPOINT

4.   True or false: The graph of $y = \left(\dfrac{1}{a}\right)^x$, with $a > 1$, is the same as the graph of $y = a^{-x}$.

5.   True or false: The graph of $y = a^{-x}$, with $a > 1$, approaches the positive x-axis as an asymptote.

6.   True or false: The graph of $y = 2^{-x}$ is the graph of $y = 2^x$ reflected about the y-axis.

Calculator Note   As with other functions, exponential functions can be graphed with graphing calculators. Because the outputs of exponential functions grow very rapidly, it is sometimes hard to find an appropriate window in which to show the graph. One way to find appropriate values of y-min and y-max when x-min and x-max are given is to use TABLE to find values of y for selected values of x. See Appendix A, Section 5.1, for details.

Figure 5.7(a) shows a table of values of $y = 1000e^{0.12x}$ that correspond to certain values of x, and Figure 5.7(b) shows the graph of this function in a window that uses the table values to set y-max $= 3500$, and y-min $= 0$. ■

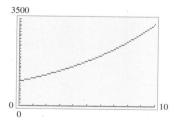

X	Y₁
0	1000
1	1127.5
2	1271.2
4	1616.1
6	2054.4
8	2611.7
10	3320.1

Y₁⊟1000e^(.12X)

Figure 5.7

Graphing calculators also allow us to investigate variations of the growth and decay exponentials. For example, we can examine the similarities and differences between the graphs of $y = f(x) = a^x$ and those of $y = mf(x)$, $y = f(kx)$, $y = f(x + h)$, and $y = f(x) + C$ for constants m, k, h, and C. Figure 5.8 shows graphs of $y = f(x) = e^x$ and $y = mf(x) = me^x$ for $m = -6$ and 2.

From the graphs, we see that when $m > 0$, the shape of the graph is still that of a growth exponential. When $m < 0$, the shape is that of a growth exponential turned upside down, or reflected through the x-axis (making the range $y < 0$). In all cases, the asymptote is unchanged and is the negative x-axis. In each case, the y-intercept is $(0, m)$.

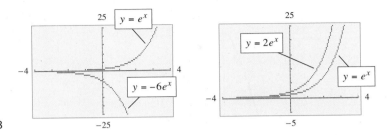

Figure 5.8

Similarly, for $a > 1$ the graphs of $y = a^{-x}$ and $y = ma^{-x}$ give graphs of exponential decay functions if $m > 0$ and give graphs of exponential decay functions turned upside down if $m < 0$. Figure 5.9(a) shows the graph of $y = 2^{-x}$, and Figure 5.9(b) shows the graph of $y = -3(2^{-x})$.

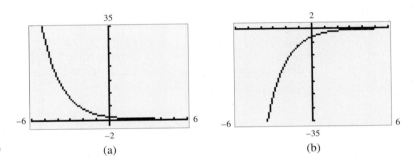

Figure 5.9   (a)   (b)

Spreadsheet Note Exponential functions can also be graphed with Excel. Figure 5.10 shows the outputs of $y = 4(1.06^x)$ for some values of x, using the formula $=4*(1.06)\wedge(\text{number})$ and the graph of the function. To graph $y = e^x$ with Excel, use the formula "$= \exp(\text{number})$." See Appendix B, Section 5.1, for details.

x	$y = f(x)$
-4	3.168375
-2	3.559986
0	4
2	4.4944
4	5.049908
6	5.674076
8	6.375392
10	7.163391
12	8.048786
14	9.043616
16	10.16141
18	11.41736
20	12.82854
22	14.41415
24	16.19574

Figure 5.10

There are other important exponential functions that use base e but whose graphs are different from those we have discussed. For example, the standard normal probability curve (often referred to as a bell-shaped curve) is the graph of an exponential function with base e (see Figure 5.11). Later in this chapter we will study other exponential functions that model growth but whose graphs are also different from those discussed previously.

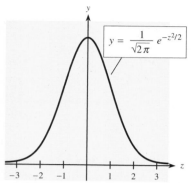

$$y = \frac{1}{\sqrt{2\pi}}\, e^{-z^2/2}$$

Figure 5.11   Standard normal probability curve

Modeling with Exponential Functions

Many types of data can be modeled using an exponential growth function. Figure 5.12(a) shows a graph of amounts of carbon in the atmosphere due to emissions from the burning of fossil fuels. With curve-fitting tools available with some computer software or on graphing calculators, we can develop an equation that models, or approximates, these data. The model and its graph are shown in Figure 5.12(b).

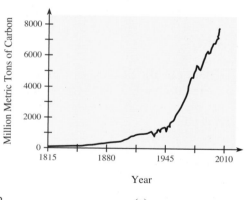

Year

(a)

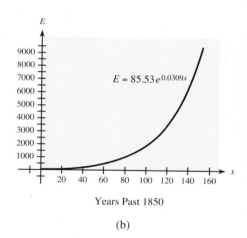

$$E = 85.53\, e^{0.0309x}$$

Years Past 1850

(b)

Figure 5.12

Source: http://cdiac.ornl.gov/

Calculator Note   The model in Figure 5.12(b) is an exponential growth function. As we have noted, functions of this type have the general form $y = C(a^x)$ with $a > 1$, and exponential decay functions have the general form $y = C(a^{-x})$ with $a > 1$ [or $y = C(b^x)$ with $0 < b < 1$]. When technology is applied to model exponentials (either growth or decay), the calculator form of the model is $y = a*b\wedge x$. The calculator automatically uses $b > 1$ for a growth model and $0 < b < 1$ for a decay. The details of modeling exponential functions with a graphing calculator are shown in Example 6 and Appendix A, Section 5.1.

EXAMPLE   6   Purchasing Power

Historically, prices for goods and services rise, resulting in the erosion of the purchasing power of $1.00. Table 5.2 gives the purchasing power of a 2012 dollar for selected years from 2012 and projected to 2050. With the 2012 dollar as a reference, the 2016 purchasing power of 0.921 can be interpreted as meaning that in 2016 a dollar will purchase 92.1% of the goods and services that could be purchased for $1.00 in 2012.

(a) Use these data, with $x = 0$ in 2010, to find an exponential function that models the decay of the purchasing power of a 2012 dollar.

(b) What does the model predict as the purchasing power of $1.00 in 2028?

(c) When will the purchasing power fall below $0.25?

■| **TABLE 5.2** |■■■■■■■■■■■■■■■■■■■■■■■■■■■■■■■■■■■■

Year	Purchasing power of $1.00	Year	Purchasing power of $1.00
2012	1.00	2030	0.629
2014	0.962	2035	0.548
2016	0.921	2040	0.477
2018	0.877	2045	0.416
2020	0.829	2050	0.362
2025	0.722		

Source: Social Security Administration

Solution

(a) From a scatter plot of the points, with $x = 0$ in 2010, it appears that an exponential decay model is appropriate (see Figure 5.13(a)). Using the function of the form $a*b{\wedge}x$, the data can be modeled by the equation $y = 1.078(0.9732^x)$. Figure 5.13(b) shows how the graph of this equation fits the data.

To write this equation with a base greater than 1, we can write 0.9732 as $(1/0.9732)^{-1} \approx 1.028^{-1}$. Thus the model could also be written as

$$y = 1.078(1.028^{-x})$$

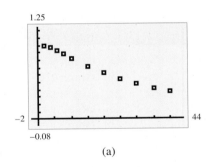

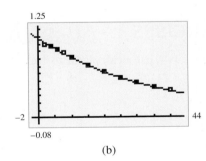

Figure 5.13   (a)   (b)

(b) Recall that we use an unrounded model in our calculations and graphs, unless otherwise instructed. We use $x = 18$ for the year 2028 and evaluate the function. This gives a 2028 purchasing power of about $0.66.

(c) Evaluation from the graph or a table shows that the purchasing power falls below $0.25 when $x \approx 53.8$, or in the year 2064, if the model remains valid.

Spreadsheet Note   A spreadsheet also can be used to create a scatter plot of the data in Table 5.2 and to develop an exponential model. Figure 5.14(a) on the next page shows an Excel scatter plot of the Table 5.2 data, and Figure 5.14(b) shows the scatter plot with Excel's base e exponential model, which is

$$y = 1.078e^{-0.02714x}$$

Procedural details for using Excel are in Appendix B, Section 5.1, and in the Online Excel Guide.

Note that the model $y = 1.078(1.028^{-x})$ found with a graphing calculator in Example 6 is equivalent to $y = 1.078e^{-0.02714x}$ because $e^{-0.02714x} = (e^{0.02714})^{-x} \approx (1.028)^{-x}$.

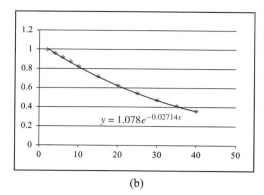

Figure 5.14 (a) (b)

1. No, all values of y are positive.
2. The left side of the x-axis ($y = 0$)
3. The table shows the values of $f(x)$ and the points to plot. The figure shows the graph of $y = 2.5^x$.

x	$y = f(x)$
-2	0.16
-1	0.4
0	1
1	2.5
2	6.25

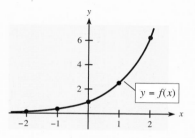

4. True   5. True   6. True

| EXERCISES | 5.1

In Problems 1–4, use a calculator to evaluate each expression.

1. (a) $10^{0.5}$
   (b) $5^{-2.7}$
2. (a) $10^{3.6}$
   (b) $8^{-2.6}$
3. (a) $3^{1/3}$
   (b) e^2
4. (a) $2^{11/6}$
   (b) e^{-3}

In Problems 5–16, graph each function.

5. $y = 4^x$
6. $y = 8^x$
7. $y = 2(3^x)$
8. $y = 3(2^x)$
9. $y = \left(\dfrac{4}{5}\right)^x$
10. $y = \left(\dfrac{2}{3}\right)^x$
11. $y = 5^{-x}$
12. $y = 3^{x-1}$
13. $y = 2e^x$
14. $y = 3^{-x}$
15. $y = 3^{-2x}$
16. $y = 5e^{-x}$

17. (a) Find $a > 1$ to express $y = 3\left(\frac{2}{5}\right)^x$ in the form $y = 3(a^{-x})$.
    (b) Are these functions growth exponentials or decay exponentials? Explain.
    (c) Check your result by graphing both functions.
18. (a) Find $a > 1$ to express $y = 8\left(\frac{5}{7}\right)^x$ in the form $y = 8(a^{-x})$.
    (b) Are these functions growth exponentials or decay exponentials? Explain.
    (c) Check your result by graphing both functions.

19. (a) Graph $y = 2(1.5)^{-x}$.
    (b) Graph $2\left(\frac{2}{3}\right)^x$.
    (c) Algebraically show why these graphs are identical.
20. (a) Graph $y = 2.5(3.25)^{-x}$.
    (b) Graph $y = 2.5\left(\frac{4}{13}\right)^x$.
    (c) Algebraically show why these graphs are identical.
21. Given that $y = \left(\dfrac{4}{5}\right)^x$, write an equivalent equation in the form $y = b^{-x}$, with $b > 1$.
22. Given that $y = 2.5^{-x}$, write an equivalent equation in the form $y = b^x$, with $0 < b < 1$.

In Problems 23–26, use a graphing utility to graph the functions.

23. Given $f(x) = e^{-x}$. Graph $y = f(x)$ and $y = f(kx) = e^{-kx}$ for each k, where $k = 0.1, 0.5, 2,$ and 5. Explain the effect that different values of k have on the graphs.
24. Given $f(x) = 2^{-x}$. Graph $y = f(x)$ and $y = mf(x) = m(2^{-x})$ for each m, where $m = -7, -2, 3,$ and 8. Explain the effect that different values of m have on the graphs.
25. Given $f(x) = 4^x$. Graph $y = f(x)$ and $y = f(x) + C = 4^x + C$ for each C, where $C = -5, -2, 3,$ and 6. Explain the effect that C has on the graphs.

26. Given $f(x) = 3^x$. Graph $y = f(x)$ and $y = f(x - h) = 3^{x-h}$ for each h, where $h = 4, 1, -2$, and -5. Explain the effect that h has on the graphs.

For Problems 27 and 28, let $f(x) = c(1 + e^{-ax})$ with $a > 0$. Use a graphing utility to graph the functions.

27. (a) Fix $a = 1$ and graph $y = f(x) = c(1 + e^{-x})$ for $c = 10, 50$, and 100.
    (b) What effect does c have on the graphs?
28. (a) Fix $c = 50$ and graph $y = f(x) = 50(1 + e^{-ax})$ for $a = 0.1, 1$, and 10.
    (b) What effect does a have on the graphs?

APPLICATIONS

29. *Compound interest* If $1000 is invested for x years at 8%, compounded quarterly, the future value that will result is

$$S = 1000(1.02)^{4x}$$

What amount will result in 8 years?

30. *Compound interest* If $3200 is invested for x years at 8%, compounded quarterly, the interest earned is

$$I = 3200(1.02)^{4x} - 3200$$

What interest is earned in 5 years?

31. *Compound interest* We will show in the next chapter that if P is invested for n years at 10% compounded continuously, the future value of the investment is given by

$$S = Pe^{0.1n}$$

Use $P = 1000$ and graph this function for $0 \le n \le 20$.

32. *Compound interest* If $1000 is invested for x years at 10%, compounded continuously, the future value that results is

$$S = 1000e^{0.10x}$$

What amount will result in 5 years?

33. *Drug in the bloodstream* The percent concentration y of a certain drug in the bloodstream at any time t in minutes is given by the equation

$$y = 100(1 - e^{-0.462t})$$

Graph this equation for $0 \le t \le 10$. Write a sentence that interprets the graph.

34. *Bacterial growth* A single bacterium splits into two bacteria every half hour, so the number of bacteria in a culture quadruples every hour. Thus the equation by which a colony of 10 bacteria multiplies in t hours is given by

$$y = 10(4^t)$$

Graph this equation for $0 \le t \le 8$.

35. *Product reliability* A statistical study shows that the fraction of television sets of a certain brand that are still in service after x years is given by $f(x) = e^{-0.15x}$. Graph this equation for $0 \le x \le 10$. Write a sentence that interprets the graph.

36. *National health care expenditures* With U.S. Department of Health and Human Services data since 2000 and projected to 2018, the total public expenditures for health care H can be modeled by

$$H = 624e^{0.07t}$$

where t is the number of years after 2000 and H is in billions of dollars. Graph this equation with a graphing utility to show the graph through the year 2020.

Population growth **Use the following information to answer Problems 37–40. World population can be considered as growing according to the equation**

$$N = N_0(1 + r)^t$$

where N_0 is the number of individuals at time $t = 0$, r is the yearly rate of growth, and t is the number of years.

37. Sketch the graph for $t = 0$ to $t = 10$ when the growth rate is 2% and N_0 is 4.1 billion.
38. Sketch the graph for $t = 0$ to $t = 10$ when the growth rate is 3% and N_0 is 4.1 billion.
39. Repeat Problem 37 when the growth rate is 5%.
40. Repeat Problem 38 when the growth rate is 7%.
41. *Personal consumption* With data from the U.S. Bureau of Labor Statistics for selected years from 1988 and projected to 2018, the billions of dollars spent for personal consumption in the United States can be modeled by

$$P = 2969e^{0.051t}$$

where t is the number of years past 1985.
    (a) Is this model one of exponential growth or exponential decay? Explain.
    (b) Graph this equation with a graphing utility to show the graph from 1985 through the year 2020.

42. *Advertising and sales* Suppose that sales are related to advertising expenditures according to one of the following two models, where S_1 and S_n are sales and x is advertising, all in millions of dollars.

$$S_1 = 30 + 20x - 0.4x^2$$
$$S_n = 24.58 + 325.18(1 - e^{-x/14})$$

    (a) Graph both of these functions on the same set of axes. Use a graphing utility.
    (b) Do these two functions give approximately the same sales per million dollars of advertising for $0 \le x \le 20$?
    (c) How do these functions differ for $x > 20$? Which more realistically represents the relationship between sales and advertising expenditures after $20 million is spent on advertising? Why?

43. Modeling *Carbon dioxide emissions* The following table gives the millions of metric tons of carbon dioxide (CO_2) emissions from biomass energy combustion in the United Sates for selected years from 2010 and projected to 2032.

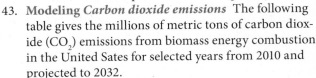

(a) Create a scatter plot of the data with x equal to the number of years past 2010 and y equal to the millions of metric tons of carbon dioxide.
(b) Find an exponential function that models the data.
(c) Graph the data and the model on the same axes and comment on the fit of the model to the data.

Year	CO$_2$ emissions	Year	CO$_2$ emissions
2010	338.5	2022	556.2
2012	364.5	2024	590.9
2014	396.1	2026	629.7
2016	425.8	2028	663.1
2018	453.1	2030	701.1
2020	498.4	2032	743.7

Source: U.S. Department of Energy

44. **Modeling *National debt*** The following table gives the U.S. national debt for selected years from 1900 to 2013.
(a) Using a function of the form $y = a*b\^x$, with $x = 0$ in 1900 and y equal to the national debt in billions, model the data.
(b) Use the model to predict the debt in 2018.
(c) Predict when the debt will be $51 trillion ($51,000 billion).

Year	U.S. Debt ($billions)	Year	U.S. Debt ($billions)
1900	1	1990	3233
1910	1	1996	5225
1920	24	2000	5674
1930	16	2005	7933
1940	43	2009	11,957
1945	259	2010	13,529
1955	273	2011	15,476
1965	314	2012	16,067
1975	533	2013	16,856
1985	1823		

Source: U.S. Treasury

45. **Modeling *Personal income*** Total personal income in the United States (in billions of dollars) for selected years from 1960 and projected to 2018 follows.

Year	1960	1970	1980	1990	2000	2008	2018
Personal Income	411.5	838.8	2307.9	4878.6	8429.7	12,100.7	19,129.6

Source: Bureau of Economic Analysis, U.S. Department of Commerce

(a) These data can be modeled by an exponential function. Write the equation of this function, with x as the number of years past 1960.
(b) Does the model overestimate or underestimate the projected total personal income in 2018?
(c) In what year does the model predict the total personal income will reach $30 trillion?

46. **Modeling *Energy use*** Energy use per dollar of GDP indexed to 1980 means that energy use for any year is viewed as a percent of the use per dollar of GDP in 1980. The following data show the energy use per dollar of GDP, as a percent, for selected years from 1985 and projected to 2035.
(a) Create a scatter plot of these data, with x equal to the number of years past 1980 and y equal to the energy use per dollar of GDP, as a percent.
(b) Find an exponential function that models these data, with x and y as in part (a).
(c) Graph the model and the data on the same axes.
(d) What does this model predict the energy use per dollar of GDP will be in 2040?

Energy Use per Dollar of GDP

Year	Percent	Year	Percent
1985	83	2015	51
1990	79	2020	45
1995	75	2025	41
2000	67	2030	37
2005	60	2035	34
2010	56		

Source: U.S. Department of Energy

47. **Modeling *Consumer price index*** The table below gives the U.S. consumer price index (CPI) for selected years from 2012 and projected to 2050. With the reference year as 2012, a 2020 CPI $= 120.56$ means goods and services that cost $100.00 in 2012 are expected to cost $120.56 in 2020.
(a) Find the exponential function that is the best fit for the data, with x as the number of years past 2010 and y as the CPI in dollars.
(b) Graph the model and the data on the same axes.
(c) Use the model to predict the CPI in 2038.
(d) According to the model, in what year will the CPI pass $250?

Year	CPI	Year	CPI
2012	100.00	2030	158.90
2014	104.00	2035	182.43
2016	108.58	2040	209.44
2018	114.09	2045	240.45
2020	120.56	2050	276.05
2025	138.41		

Source: Social Security Administration

48. **Modeling *Compound interest*** The following table gives the value of an investment, after intervals ranging from 0 to 7 years, of $20,000 invested at 10%, compounded annually.
(a) Develop an exponential model for these data, accurate to four decimal places, with x in years and y in dollars.

(b) Use the model to find the amount to which $20,000 will grow in 30 years if it is invested at 10%, compounded annually.

Year	Amount Investment Grows To
0	20,000
1	22,000
2	24,200
3	26,620
4	29,282
5	32,210.20
6	35,431.22
7	38,974.34

49. **Modeling *Alzheimer's disease*** As the baby boom generation ages and the proportion of the U.S population over age 65 increases, the number of Americans with Alzheimer's disease and other dementia is projected to grow each year. The table below gives the millions of U.S. citizens age 65 and older with Alzheimer's from 2000 and projected to 2050.

(a) Find the exponential function that models the data, with x equal to the number of years past 2000 and y equal to the millions of Americans with Alzheimer's.

(b) Is the model in part (a) an exponential growth or exponential decay function?

(c) Graph the model and the data on the same axes.

(d) How many Americans are projected to have Alzheimer's in 2060?

Year	2000	2010	2020	2030	2040	2050
Millions	4.5	5.1	5.7	7.7	11.0	13.2

Source: Alzheimer's Association

OBJECTIVES

- To use and apply the definition of logarithmic functions
- To graph logarithmic functions
- To model logarithmic functions
- To use properties of logarithmic functions
- To use the change-of-base formula

5.2

Logarithmic Functions and Their Properties

❚ | APPLICATION PREVIEW |

If P dollars is invested at an annual rate r, compounded continuously, then the future value of the investment after t years is given by

$$S = Pe^{rt}$$

A common question with investments such as this is "How long will it be before the investment doubles?" That is, when does $S = 2P$? (See Example 3.) The answer to this question gives an important formula, called a "doubling-time" formula. This requires the use of logarithmic functions.

Logarithmic Functions and Graphs

Before the development and easy availability of calculators and computers, certain arithmetic computations, such as $(1.37)^{13}$ and $\sqrt[16]{3.09}$, were difficult to perform. The computations could be performed relatively easily using **logarithms,** which were developed in the 17th century by John Napier, or by using a slide rule, which is based on logarithms. The use of logarithms as a computing technique has all but disappeared today, but the study of **logarithmic functions** is still very important because of the many applications of these functions.

For example, let us again consider the culture of bacteria described at the beginning of the previous section. If we know that the culture is begun with one microorganism and that each minute every microorganism present splits into two new ones, then we can find the number of minutes it takes until there are 1024 organisms by solving

$$1024 = 2^y$$

The solution of this equation may be written in the form

$$y = \log_2 1024$$

which is read "y equals the logarithm of 1024 to the base 2."

In general, we may express the equation $x = a^y$ ($a > 0, a \neq 1$) in the form $y = f(x)$ by defining a **logarithmic function.**

Logarithmic Function

For $a > 0$ and $a \neq 1$, the **logarithmic function**

$$y = \log_a x \quad \text{(logarithmic form)}$$

has domain $x > 0$, base a, and is defined by

$$a^y = x \quad \text{(exponential form)}$$

| TABLE 5.3 |

Logarithmic Form	Exponential Form
$\log_{10} 100 = 2$	$10^2 = 100$
$\log_{10} 0.1 = -1$	$10^{-1} = 0.1$
$\log_2 x = y$	$2^y = x$
$\log_a 1 = 0 \; (a > 0)$	$a^0 = 1$
$\log_a a = 1 \; (a > 0)$	$a^1 = a$

From the definition, we know that $\log_3 81 = 4$ because $3^4 = 81$. In this case the logarithm, 4, is the exponent to which we have to raise the base 3 to obtain 81. In general, if $y = \log_a x$, then y is the exponent to which the base a must be raised to obtain x.

The a is called the **base** in both $\log_a x = y$ and $a^y = x$, and y is the *logarithm* in $\log_a x = y$ and the *exponent* in $a^y = x$. Thus **a logarithm is an exponent.**

Table 5.3 shows some logarithmic equations and their equivalent exponential forms.

EXAMPLE 1   Logarithms and Exponential Forms

(a) Write $64 = 4^3$ in logarithmic form.
(b) Write $\log_4 \left(\frac{1}{64} \right) = -3$ in exponential form.
(c) If $4 = \log_2 x$, find x.
(d) Evaluate: $\log_2 8$
(e) Evaluate: $\log_5 \left(\frac{1}{25} \right)$

Solution

(a) In $64 = 4^3$, the base is 4 and the exponent (or logarithm) is 3. Thus $64 = 4^3$ is equivalent to $3 = \log_4 64$.
(b) In $\log_4 \left(\frac{1}{64} \right) = -3$, the base is 4 and the logarithm (or exponent) is -3. Thus $\log_4 \left(\frac{1}{64} \right) = -3$ is equivalent to $4^{-3} = \frac{1}{64}$.
(c) If $4 = \log_2 x$, then $2^4 = x$ and $x = 16$.
(d) If $y = \log_2 8$, then $8 = 2^y$. Because $2^3 = 8$, $\log_2 8 = 3$.
(e) If $y = \log_5 \left(\frac{1}{25} \right)$, then $\frac{1}{25} = 5^y$. Because $5^{-2} = \frac{1}{25}$, $\log_5 \left(\frac{1}{25} \right) = -2$.

EXAMPLE 2   Graphing a Logarithmic Function

Graph $y = \log_2 x$.

Solution

We may graph $y = \log_2 x$ by graphing $x = 2^y$. The table of values (found by substituting values of y and calculating x) and the graph are shown in Figure 5.15.

$x = 2^y$	y
$\frac{1}{8}$	-3
$\frac{1}{4}$	-2
$\frac{1}{2}$	-1
1	0
2	1
4	2
8	3

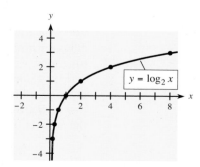

Figure 5.15

From the definition of logarithms, we see that every logarithm has a base. Most applications of logarithms involve logarithms to the base 10 (called **common logarithms**) or logarithms to the base e (called **natural logarithms**). In fact, logarithms to the base 10 and to the base e are the only ones that have function keys on calculators. Thus it is important to be familiar with their names and designations.

| **Common and Natural Logarithms** | **Common logarithms:** | $\log x$ | means | $\log_{10} x$. |
| | **Natural logarithms:** | $\ln x$ | means | $\log_e x$. |

Values of common and natural logarithmic functions are usually found with a calculator. For example, a calculator gives $\log 2 \approx 0.301$ and $\ln 2 \approx 0.693$.

EXAMPLE 3 Doubling Time for an Investment | APPLICATION PREVIEW |

If P is invested for t years at interest rate r, compounded continuously, then the future value of the investment is given by $S = Pe^{rt}$. The doubling time for this investment can be found by solving for t in $S = Pe^{rt}$ when $S = 2P$. That is, we must solve $2P = Pe^{rt}$, or (equivalently) $2 = e^{rt}$. Express this equation in logarithmic form and then solve for t to find the doubling-time formula.

Solution
In logarithmic form, $2 = e^{rt}$ is equivalent to $\log_e 2 = rt$. Solving for t gives the doubling-time formula

$$t = \frac{\log_e 2}{r} = \frac{\ln 2}{r}$$

Note that if the interest rate is $r = 10\%$, compounded continuously, the time required for the investment to double is

$$t = \frac{\ln 2}{0.10} \approx \frac{0.693}{0.10} = 6.93$$

In general we can approximate the doubling time for an investment at $r\%$, compounded continuously, with $\frac{70}{r}$. (In economics, this is called the **Rule of 70.**)

EXAMPLE 4 Market Share

Suppose that after a company introduces a new product, the number of months m before its market share is s percent can be modeled by

$$m = 20 \ln \left(\frac{40}{40 - s} \right)$$

When will the company's product have a 35% share of the market?

Solution
A 35% market share means $s = 35$. Hence

$$m = 20 \ln \left(\frac{40}{40 - s} \right) = 20 \ln \left(\frac{40}{40 - 35} \right) = 20 \ln \left(\frac{40}{5} \right) = 20 \ln 8 \approx 41.6$$

Thus, the market share will be 35% after about 41.6 months.

EXAMPLE 5 Graphing the Natural Logarithm

Graph $y = \ln x$.

Solution
We can graph $y = \ln x$ by evaluating $y = \ln x$ for $x > 0$ (including some values $0 < x < 1$) with a calculator. The graph is shown in Figure 5.16.

x	$y = \ln x$
0.05	−2.996
0.10	−2.303
0.50	−0.693
1	0.000
2	0.693
3	1.099
5	1.609
10	2.303

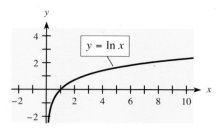

Figure 5.16

Note that because $\ln x$ is a standard function on a graphing utility, such a utility could be used to obtain its graph. Note also that the graphs of $y = \log_2 x$ (Figure 5.15) and $y = \ln x$ (Figure 5.16) are very similar. The shapes of graphs of equations of the form $y = \log_a x$ with $a > 1$ are similar to these two graphs.

Graphs of Logarithmic Functions

Equation: $y = \log_a x$ $(a > 1)$
x-intercept: $(1, 0)$
Domain: All positive reals
Range: All reals
Asymptote: y-axis (negative half)

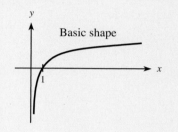

Basic shape

---

1. What asymptote does the graph of $y = \log_a x$ approach when $a > 1$?
2. For $a > 1$, does the equation $y = \log_a x$ represent the same function as the equation $x = a^y$?
3. For what values of x is $y = \log_a x$, $a > 0$, $a \neq 1$, defined?
4. (a) Write $4 = \log_3 x$ in exponential form, and find x.
   (b) Write $e^x = 31$ in logarithmic form, and approximate x.

Modeling with Logarithmic Functions

The basic shape of a logarithmic function is important for two reasons. First, when we graph a logarithmic function, we know that the graph should have this shape. Second, when data points have this basic shape, they suggest a logarithmic model.

EXAMPLE 6   Life Expectancy

The expected life span of people in the United States depends on their year of birth (see the table and scatter plot, with $x = 0$ in 1900, in Figure 5.17). In Section 2.5, "Modeling; Fitting Curves to Data with Graphing Utilities," we modeled life span with a linear function and with a quadratic function. However, the scatter plot suggests that a better model may be logarithmic.

(a) Use technology to find a logarithmic equation that models the data.
(b) The National Center for Health Statistics projects the expected life span for people born in 2000 to be 77.0 and that for those born in 2010 to be 78.1. Use your model to project the life spans for those years.
(c) Do the expected life spans for 2015 and 2020, as given in the table, agree with the calculations found with the model found in part (a)?

Life Span		Life Span	
Year	**(years)**	**Year**	**(years)**
1920	54.1	1994	75.7
1930	59.7	1996	76.1
1940	62.9	1998	76.7
1950	68.2	1999	76.7
1960	69.7	2000	77.0
1970	70.8	2001	77.2
1975	72.6	2002	77.3
1980	73.7	2003	77.5
1987	75.0	2004	77.8
1988	74.9	2005	77.9
1989	75.2	2010	78.1
1990	75.4	2015	78.9
1992	75.8	2020	79.5

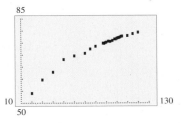

Figure 5.17

Source: National Center for Health Statistics

Solution

(a)   A graphing calculator gives the logarithmic model

$$L(x) = 11.027 + 14.304 \ln x$$

where x is the number of years since 1900. Figure 5.18 shows the scatter plot and graph of the model.

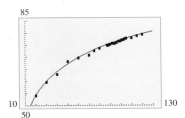

Figure 5.18

(b)   For the year 2000, the value of x is 100, so the projected life span is $L(100) = 76.9$. For 2010, the model gives 78.3 as the expected life span. These calculations closely approximate the projections from the National Center for Health Statistics.

(c)   Yes, the values from the model match perfectly.

Properties of Logarithms

The definition of the logarithmic function and the previous examples suggest a special relationship between the logarithmic function $y = \log_a x$ and the exponential function $y = a^x$ ($a > 0$, $a \neq 1$). Because we can write $y = \log_a x$ in exponential form as $x = a^y$, we see that the connection between

$$y = \log_a x \quad \text{and} \quad y = a^x$$

is that x and y have been interchanged from one function to the other. This is true for the functional description and hence for the ordered pairs or coordinates that satisfy these functions. This is illustrated in Table 5.4 for the functions $y = \log x$ ($y = \log_{10} x$) and $y = 10^x$.

■ | TABLE 5.4 | ▊▊▊▊▊▊▊▊▊▊▊▊▊▊▊▊▊▊▊▊▊▊▊▊▊▊▊▊▊▊

$y = \log_{10} x = \log x$		$y = 10^x$	
Coordinates	**Justification**	**Coordinates**	**Justification**
$(1000, 3)$	$3 = \log 1000$	$(3, 1000)$	$1000 = 10^3$
$(100, 2)$	$2 = \log 100$	$(2, 100)$	$100 = 10^2$
$\left(\frac{1}{10}, -1\right)$	$-1 = \log \frac{1}{10}$	$\left(-1, \frac{1}{10}\right)$	$\frac{1}{10} = 10^{-1}$

In general we say that $y = f(x)$ and $y = g(x)$ are **inverse functions** if, whenever the pair (a, b) satisfies $y = f(x)$, the pair (b, a) satisfies $y = g(x)$. Furthermore, because the values of the x- and y-coordinates are interchanged for inverse functions, their graphs are reflections of each other about the line $y = x$.

Thus for $a > 0$ and $a \neq 1$, the logarithmic function $y = \log_a x$ (also written $x = a^y$) and the exponential function $y = a^x$ are inverse functions.

The logarithmic function $y = \log x$ is the inverse of the exponential function $y = 10^x$. Thus the graphs of $y = \log x$ and $y = 10^x$ are reflections of each other about the line $y = x$. Some values of x and y for these functions are given in Table 5.4, and their graphs are shown in Figure 5.19.

This inverse relationship is a consequence of the definition of the logarithmic function. We can use this definition to discover several other properties of logarithms.

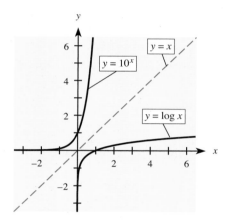

Figure 5.19

Because logarithms are exponents, the properties of logarithms can be derived from the properties of exponents. (The properties of exponents are discussed in Chapter 0, "Algebraic Concepts.") The following properties of logarithms are useful in simplifying expressions that contain logarithms.

Logarithmic Property I   If $a > 0$, $a \neq 1$, then $\log_a a^x = x$, for any real number x.

To prove this result, note that the exponential form of $y = \log_a a^x$ is $a^y = a^x$, so $y = x$. That is, $\log_a a^x = x$.

EXAMPLE   7   Logarithmic Property I

Use Property I to simplify each of the following.
(a) $\log_4 4^3$ (b) $\ln e^x$

Solution
(a) $\log_4 4^3 = 3$
Check: The exponential form is $4^3 = 4^3$. ✔

(b) $\ln e^x = \log_e e^x = x$
Check: The exponential form is $e^x = e^x$. ✔

We note that two special cases of Property I are used frequently; these are when $x = 1$ and $x = 0$.

Special Cases of Logarithmic Property I   Because $a^1 = a$, we have $\log_a a = 1$.
Because $a^0 = 1$, we have $\log_a 1 = 0$.

The logarithmic form of $y = a^{\log_a x}$ is $\log_a y = \log_a x$, so $y = x$. This means that $a^{\log_a x} = x$ and proves Property II.

Logarithmic Property II

If $a > 0$, $a \neq 1$, then $a^{\log_a x} = x$, for any positive real number x.

EXAMPLE 8   **Logarithmic Property II**

Use Property II to simplify each of the following.
(a) $2^{\log_2 4}$ (b) $e^{\ln x}$

Solution
(a) $2^{\log_2 4} = 4$
Check: The logarithmic form is $\log_2 4 = \log_2 4$. ✔

(b) $e^{\ln x} = x$
Check: The logarithmic form is $\log_e x = \ln x$. ✔

If $u = \log_a M$ and $v = \log_a N$, then their exponential forms are $a^u = M$ and $a^v = N$, respectively. Thus

$$\log_a (MN) = \log_a (a^u \cdot a^v) = \log_a (a^{u+v}) = u + v = \log_a M + \log_a N$$

and Property III is established.

Logarithmic Property III

If $a > 0$, $a \neq 1$, and M and N are positive real numbers, then
$$\log_a (MN) = \log_a M + \log_a N$$

EXAMPLE 9   **Logarithmic Property III**

(a) Find $\log_2 (4 \cdot 16)$, if $\log_2 4 = 2$ and $\log_2 16 = 4$.
(b) Find $\ln 77$, if $\ln 7 = 1.9459$ and $\ln 11 = 2.3979$ (to 4 decimal places).

Solution
(a) $\log_2 (4 \cdot 16) = \log_2 4 + \log_2 16 = 2 + 4 = 6$
Check: $\log_2 (4 \cdot 16) = \log_2 (64) = 6$, because $2^6 = 64$. ✔

(b) $\ln 77 = \ln (7 \cdot 11) = \ln 7 + \ln 11 = 1.9459 + 2.3979 = 4.3438$
Check: Using a calculator, we can see that $e^{4.3438} \approx 77$. ✔

Logarithmic Property IV

If $a > 0$, $a \neq 1$, and M and N are positive real numbers, then
$$\log_a (M/N) = \log_a M - \log_a N$$

The proof of this property is left to the student.

EXAMPLE 10   **Logarithmic Property IV**

(a) Evaluate $\log_3 \left(\frac{9}{27}\right)$.
(b) Find $\log_{10} \left(\frac{16}{5}\right)$, if $\log_{10} 16 = 1.2041$ and $\log_{10} 5 = 0.6990$ (to 4 decimal places).

Solution
(a) $\log_3 \left(\frac{9}{27}\right) = \log_3 9 - \log_3 27 = 2 - 3 = -1$
Check: $\log_3 \left(\frac{1}{3}\right) = -1$ because $3^{-1} = \frac{1}{3}$. ✔

(b) $\log_{10}\left(\frac{16}{5}\right) = \log_{10}16 - \log_{10}5 = 1.2041 - 0.6990 = 0.5051$

Check: Using a calculator, we can see that $10^{0.5051} \approx 3.2 = \frac{16}{5}$. ✔

Logarithmic Property V

If $a > 0$, $a \neq 1$, M is a positive real number, and N is any real number, then

$$\log_a(M^N) = N\log_a M$$

The proof of this property is left to the student.

EXAMPLE 11   Logarithmic Property V

(a) Simplify $\log_3(9^2)$.
(b) Simplify $\ln 8^{-4}$, if $\ln 8 = 2.0794$ (to 4 decimal places).

Solution
(a) $\log_3(9^2) = 2\log_3 9 = 2 \cdot 2 = 4$
(b) $\ln 8^{-4} = -4\ln 8 \approx -8.3178$

✓ CHECKPOINT   5. Simplify:

(a) $6^{\log_6 x}$ (b) $\log_7 7^3$ (c) $\ln\left(\frac{1}{e^2}\right)$ (d) $\log 1$

6. If $\log_7 20 = 1.5395$ and $\log_7 11 = 1.2323$, find the following.

(a) $\log_7 220 = \log_7(20 \cdot 11)$ (b) $\log_7\left(\frac{11}{20}\right)$ (c) $\log_7 20^4$

Change of Base   With a calculator, we can directly evaluate only those logarithms with base 10 or base e. Also, logarithms with base 10 or base e are the only ones that are standard functions on a graphing calculator. Thus, if we had a way to express a logarithmic function with any base in terms of a logarithm with base 10 or base e, we would be able to evaluate the original logarithmic function and graph it with a graphing calculator.

In general, if we use the properties of logarithms, we can write

$$y = \log_b x \quad \text{in the form} \quad b^y = x$$

If we take the base a logarithm of both sides, we have

$$\log_a b^y = \log_a x$$
$$y\log_a b = \log_a x$$
$$y = \frac{\log_a x}{\log_a b}$$

This gives us the **change-of-base formula** from base b to base a.

Change-of-Base Formulas

If $a \neq 1$, $b \neq 1$, $a > 0$, $b > 0$, then

$$\log_b x = \frac{\log_a x}{\log_a b}$$

For calculation purposes, we can convert logarithms to base e or base 10.

Base e: $\log_b x = \dfrac{\ln x}{\ln b}$ Base 10: $\log_b x = \dfrac{\log x}{\log b}$

EXAMPLE 12   ### Change-of-Base Formula

Evaluate $\log_7 15$ by using a change-of-base formula.

Solution

$$\log_7 15 = \frac{\ln 15}{\ln 7} = \frac{2.70805}{1.94591} = 1.39166 \text{ (approximately)}$$

As a check, a calculator shows that $7^{1.39166} \approx 15.$ ✔

Calculator Note   The change-of-base formula expands the capability of graphing calculators so they can be used to evaluate logarithms and to graph logarithmic functions to any base. See Appendix A, Section 5.2, for details.

Figure 5.20(a) shows the graph of $y = \log_2 x = \dfrac{\ln x}{\ln 2}$. Note that it is exactly the same as the graph in Figure 5.15 in Example 2.

Figure 5.20(b) shows the graph of $y = \log_7 x = \dfrac{\ln x}{\ln 7}$.

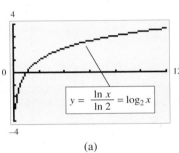

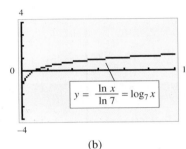

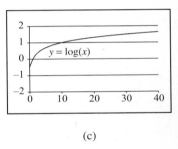

(a)   (b)   (c)

Figure 5.20

Spreadsheet Note   The graph of $y = \log x$ can be created with Excel by entering the formula "$= \log 10(x)$" (see Figure 5.20(c)). The graph of $y = \ln x$ can be created with Excel by entering the formula "$= \ln (x)$", and for any other base a the graph of $y = \log_a x$ can be created by entering the formula "$= \log (x, a)$". See Appendix B, Section 5.2, for details.

Natural logarithms, $y = \ln x$ (and the inverse exponentials with base e), have many practical applications, some of which are considered in the next section. Common logarithms, $y = \log x$, were widely used for computation before computers and calculators became popular. They also have several applications to scaling variables, where the purpose is to reduce the scale of variation when a natural physical variable covers a wide range.

EXAMPLE 13   ### Richter Scale

The Richter scale is used to measure the intensity of an earthquake. The magnitude on the Richter scale of an earthquake of intensity I is given by

$$R = \log (I/I_0)$$

where I_0 is a certain minimum intensity used for comparison.

(a) Find R if I is 15,800,000 times as great as I_0.
(b) As of 2014, the 1964 Alaskan earthquake was the most violent U.S. earthquake and the second strongest ever; it measured 9.2 on the Richter scale. Find the intensity of the 1964 Alaskan earthquake.

Solution

(a) If $I = 15,800,000 I_0$, then $I/I_0 = 15,800,000$. Hence

$$R = \log (15,800,000)$$
$$= 7.2 \text{ (approximated to 1 decimal place)}$$

(b) For $R = 9.2$, it follows that

$$9.2 = \log (I/I_0)$$

Rewriting this in exponential form gives

$$10^{9.2} = I/I_0$$

and from a calculator we obtain

$$I/I_0 = 1{,}580{,}000{,}000 \text{ (approximately)}$$

Thus the intensity is 1,580,000,000 times I_0.

Note that a Richter scale measurement that is 2 units larger means that the intensity is $10^2 = 100$ *times* greater.

✓ CHECKPOINT
ANSWERS

1. The (negative) y-axis
2. Yes
3. $x > 0$ is the domain of $\log_a x$.
4. (a) $3^4 = x = 81$ (b) $\log_e 31 = \ln 31 = x \approx 3.434$
5. (a) x (b) 3   (c) -2 (d) 0
6. (a) 2.7718   (b) -0.3072 (c) 6.1580

| EXERCISES | 5.2

In Problems 1–4, use the definition of a logarithmic function to rewrite each equation in exponential form.

1. $4 = \log_2 16$
2. $4 = \log_3 81$
3. $\dfrac{1}{2} = \log_4 2$
4. $-2 = \log_3 \left(\dfrac{1}{9}\right)$

In Problems 5–14, solve for x by writing the equation in exponential form.

5. $\log_3 x = 4$
6. $\log_4 x = -2$
7. $\log_{16} x = -\dfrac{1}{2}$
8. $\log_{25} x = \dfrac{1}{2}$
9. $\log_7 (3x + 1) = 2$
10. $\log_3 (7 - x) = 3$
11. $\log(4x - 7) = 2$
12. $\log(1.34 - x) = -1$
13. $\ln (2x + 5) = 2.2$ (to 3 decimal places)
14. $\ln (2 - x) = -1.4$ (to 3 decimal places)

In Problems 15–18, write the equation in logarithmic form.

15. $2^5 = 32$
16. $5^3 = 125$
17. $4^{-1} = \dfrac{1}{4}$
18. $9^{1/2} = 3$

In Problems 19 and 20, write the equation in logarithmic form and solve for x.

19. $e^{3x+5} = 0.55$ (to 3 decimal places)
20. $10^{2x+1} = 0.25$ (to 3 decimal places)

In Problems 21–26, graph each function.

21. $y = \log_3 x$
22. $y = \log_4 x$
23. $y = \ln x$
24. $y = \log_9 x$
25. $y = \log_2 (-x)$
26. $y = \ln (-x)$

In Problems 27 and 28, use properties of logarithms or a definition to simplify each expression. Check each result with a change-of-base formula.

27. (a) $\log_3 27$ (b) $\log_5 \left(\dfrac{1}{5}\right)$
28. (a) $\log_4 16$ (b) $\log_9 3$
29. If $f(x) = \ln (x)$, find $f(e^x)$.
30. If $f(x) = \log (x)$, find $f(10^x)$.
31. If $f(x) = \log (x)$, find $f(10^{-7})$.
32. If $f(x) = \ln (x)$, find $f(\sqrt{e})$.
33. If $f(x) = e^x$, find $f(\ln 3)$.
34. If $f(x) = 10^x$, find $f(\log 2)$.

In Problems 35 and 36, evaluate each logarithm by using properties of logarithms and the following facts.

$$\log_a x = 3.1 \quad \log_a y = 1.8 \quad \log_a z = 2.7$$

35. (a) $\log_a (xy)$ (b) $\log_a \left(\dfrac{x}{z}\right)$
    (c) $\log_a (x^4)$ (d) $\log_a \sqrt{y}$
36. (a) $\log_a (yz)$ (b) $\log_a \left(\dfrac{z}{y}\right)$
    (c) $\log_a (y^6)$ (d) $\log_a \sqrt[3]{z}$

Write each expression in Problems 37–40 as the sum or difference of two logarithmic functions containing no exponents.

37. $\log \left(\dfrac{x}{x+1}\right)$
38. $\ln [(x + 1)(4x + 5)]$
39. $\log_7 (x\sqrt[3]{x + 4})$
40. $\log_5 \left(\dfrac{x^2}{\sqrt{x + 4}}\right)$

Use the properties of logarithms to write each expression in Problems 41–44 as a single logarithm.

41. $\ln x - \ln y$

42. $\log_3 (x + 1) + \log_3 (x - 1)$

43. $\log_5 (x + 1) + \dfrac{1}{2} \log_5 x$

44. $\log (2x + 1) - \dfrac{1}{3} \log (x + 1)$

In Problems 45–48, use a calculator to determine whether expression (a) is equivalent to expression (b). If they are equivalent, state what properties are being illustrated. If they are not equivalent, rewrite expression (a) so that they are equivalent.

45. (a) $\ln \sqrt{4 \cdot 6}$

    (b) $\dfrac{1}{2} (\ln 4 + \ln 6)$

46. (a) $\log \dfrac{\sqrt{56}}{23}$

    (b) $\dfrac{1}{2} \log 56 - \log 23$

47. (a) $\log \sqrt[3]{\dfrac{8}{5}}$

    (b) $\dfrac{1}{3} \log 8 - \log 5$

48. (a) $\dfrac{\log_2 34}{17}$

    (b) $\log_2 34 - \log_2 17$

49. (a) Use a graphing utility to graph $f(x) = \ln x$ and $f(x - c) = \ln (x - c)$ for $c = -4, -2, 1$, and 5 on the same axes.

    (b) For each c-value, identify the vertical asymptote and the domain of $y = \ln (x - c)$.

    (c) For each c-value, find the x-intercept of $y = \ln (x - c)$.

    (d) Write a sentence that explains precisely how the graphs of $y = f(x)$ and $y = f(x - c)$ are related.

50. Use a graphing utility to graph $f(x) = \ln x$ and $f(ax) = \ln (ax)$ for $a = -2, -1, -0.5, 0.2$, and 3. Explain the differences between the graphs

    (a) when $a > 0$ and when $a < 0$.

    (b) when $|a| > 1$ and when $0 < |a| < 1$.

In Problems 51 and 52, use a change-of-base formula to evaluate each logarithm.

51. (a) $\log_2 17$ (b) $\log_5 (0.78)$

52. (a) $\log_3 12$ (b) $\log_8 (0.15)$

In Problems 53–56, use a change-of-base formula to rewrite each logarithm. Then use a graphing utility to graph the function.

53. $y = \log_5 x$ 54. $y = \log_6 x$

55. $y = \log_{13} x$ 56. $y = \log_{16} x$

57. Prove logarithmic Property IV.

58. Prove logarithmic Property V.

APPLICATIONS

Richter scale Use the formula $R = \log (I/I_0)$ in Problems 59–62. (*Source:* Earthquake data from the U.S. Geological Survey.)

59. The most devastating earthquake since 2000 was the Haiti quake in 2010 that measured 7.0 on the Richter scale and resulted in more than 222,500 deaths, 300,000 injuries, and 1.3 million displaced persons. The largest quake of that year was the 8.8 quake that struck offshore Maule, Chile. How many times more intense was the quake in Chile?

60. In May of 2008, an earthquake measuring 6.8 on the Richter scale struck near the east coast of Honshu, Japan. In March of 2011, a quake measuring 9.0 struck that same region. How many times more intense was the 2011 quake than the one in 2008?

61. The most destructive earthquake in the United States was the 1906 San Francisco quake that measured 7.8 on the Richter scale. The quake and subsequent fires that burned for several days destroyed 80% of the city. This 1906 quake was the seventeenth most violent in the United States. Among the 40 most severe U.S. quakes, the only one that occurred east of the Mississippi River shook Charleston, South Carolina, in 1886 and measured 7.3. How many times more intense was the San Francisco quake?

62. The world's strongest earthquake struck Chile in 1960 and measured 9.5 on the Richter scale. The 2010 Chilean quake at 8.8 was the world's sixth largest. Find the ratio of their intensities.

Decibel readings **In Problems 63–66, use the fact that the loudness of sound (in decibels) perceived by the human ear depends on intensity levels according to**

$$L = 10 \log(I/I_0)$$

where I_0 is the threshold of hearing for the average human ear.

63. Find the loudness when I is 10,000 times I_0. This is the intensity level of the average voice.

64. A sound that causes pain has intensity about 10^{14} times I_0. Find the decibel reading for this threshold.

65. Graph the equation for loudness of sound in decibels. Use I/I_0 as the independent variable.

66. The background noise level of a relatively quiet room is about $L_1 = 32$ decibels and of a heated argument can exceed $L_2 = 66$ decibels. Find the ratio I_2/I_1 of these associated intensities.

pH levels **In Problems 67–70, use the following information. Chemists use the pH (hydrogen potential) of a solution to measure its acidity or basicity. The pH is given by the formula**

$$\text{pH} = -\log[\text{H}^+]$$

where $[\text{H}^+]$ is the concentration of hydrogen ions in moles per liter.

67. Most common solutions have pH ranges between 1 and 14. What values of $[\text{H}^+]$ are associated with these extremes?

68. Find the approximate pH of each of the following.

    (a) blood: $[\text{H}^+] = 3.98 \times 10^{-8}$

              $= 0.0000000398$

(b) beer: $[H^+] = 6.31 \times 10^{-5} = 0.0000631$
(c) vinegar: $[H^+] = 6.3 \times 10^{-3} = 0.0063$
69. Sometimes pH is defined as the logarithm of the reciprocal of the concentration of hydrogen ions. Write an equation that represents this sentence, and explain how it and the equation given in the information preceding Problem 67 can both represent pH.
70. Find the approximate hydrogen ion concentration $[H^+]$ for each of the following.
(a) apples: pH $= 3.0$ (b) eggs: pH $= 7.79$
(c) water (neutral): pH $= 7.0$

Doubling time **In Problems 71 and 72, use the formula**

$$2 = \left(1 + \frac{r}{100n}\right)^{nt}$$

to find the doubling time t, in years, for an investment at $r\%$ compounded n times per year. Write each exponential statement in logarithmic form. Then use a change-of-base formula to find the doubling time.
71. 8% compounded quarterly
72. 7.2% compounded monthly
73. *Women in the workforce* For selected years from 1970 and projected to 2050, the number, in millions, of women in the workforce is given by

$$w(x) = 37.6 \ln x - 81.2$$

where x is the number of years past 1950 (*Source:* U.S. Bureau of Labor Statistics).
(a) Graph this function for x representing 1960–2030.
(b) What does this model predict to be the number of women in the workforce in 2030?
(c) Use the graph drawn in part (a) to estimate the year in which the number will reach 80 million.
74. *Life span update* In Example 6 we used data from 1920 to 2020 and found that the life span in the United States depended on the year of birth according to the equation

$$L(x) = 11.027 + 14.304 \ln x$$

where x is the number of years after 1900. Using data from 1920 to 1989, the model

$$\ell(x) = 11.616 + 14.144 \ln x$$

where x is the number of years after 1900, predicts life span as a function of birth year. Use both models to predict the life spans for people born in 1999 and in 2015. Did adding data from 1990 to 2020 give predictions that were quite different from or very similar to predictions based on the model found earlier?
75. *Modeling Diabetes* As the following table shows, projections indicate that the percent of U.S. adults with diabetes could dramatically increase.
(a) Find a logarithmic model that fits the data in the table, with $x = 0$ in 2000.

(b) Graph the function and the data on the same axes and comment on the fit.
(c) Use the model to predict the percent of U.S. adults with diabetes in 2027.

Year	Percent	Year	Percent	Year	Percent
2010	15.7	2025	24.2	2040	31.4
2015	18.9	2030	27.2	2045	32.1
2020	21.1	2035	29.0	2050	34.3

Source: Centers for Disease Control and Prevention

76. *Modeling Female workers* The percent of all workers 16 years and older that are female, for selected years from 1970 and projected to 2040, is given in the following table.
(a) Find the logarithmic function that models the percent as a function of the years, with x equal to the number of years past 1960.
(b) Visually determine whether this model is a good fit for the data.
(c) Use the model to predict the percent of workers who are females in 2045.

Year	Percent	Year	Percent
1970	38.1	2015	48.3
1980	42.5	2020	48.1
1990	45.2	2030	48.0
2000	46.6	2040	47.9
2010	47.9		

Source: Bureau of Labor Statistics

77. *Modeling Internet usage* The percent of the U.S. population that uses the Internet, during selected years from 2000, is given in the following table.
(a) Find the logarithmic function that models the percent as a function of the years, with x equal to the number of years after 1990.
(b) Visually determine whether this model is a good fit for the data.
(c) Use the model to predict the percent of Internet users in the United States in 2020.

Year	Percent	Year	Percent
2000	67	2008	80
2002	71	2010	82
2005	79	2011	82
2007	79		

Source: Digital Future Report, USC Annenberg

78. *Modeling Demographics* The table below gives the millions of White non-Hispanic individuals in the U.S. civilian non-institutional population 16 years and older for selected years from 1980 and projected to 2050.

(a) Find a logarithmic function that models the data, with x equal to the number of years past 1970 and y equal to the White non-Hispanic population, in millions.

(b) Graph the function and the data on the same set of axes.

(c) What does the model predict this demographic group's population to be in 2043?

Year	Millions	Year	Millions
1980	136.8	2020	166.3
1990	146.5	2030	168.8
2000	153.1	2040	169.7
2010	162.1	2050	169.4
2015	164.6		

Source: U.S. Census Bureau

OBJECTIVES

5.3

- To solve exponential and logarithmic equations
- To solve exponential growth or decay equations when sufficient data are known
- To solve exponential equations representing demand, supply, or total cost when sufficient data are known
- To model and solve problems involving Gompertz curves and logistic functions

Equations and Applications with Exponential and Logarithmic Functions

▮| APPLICATION PREVIEW |▮

A company's sales decline following an advertising campaign so that the number of sales is $S = 2000(2^{-0.1x})$, where x is the number of days after the campaign ends. When should the company begin a new campaign? In other words, how many days will elapse before sales drop below 350 (see Example 4)?

In this section, we discuss applications of exponential and logarithmic functions to the solutions of problems involving exponential growth and decay, and supply and demand. With exponential decay, we consider various applications, including decay of radioactive materials and decay of sales following an advertising campaign. With exponential growth, we focus on population growth and growth that can be modeled by Gompertz curves and logistic functions. Finally, we consider applications of demand functions that can be modeled by exponential functions.

Solving Exponential Equations

Questions such as the one in the Application Preview can be answered by solving an equation in which the variable appears in the exponent, called an **exponential equation.** Logarithmic properties are useful in converting an equation of this type to one that can be solved easily. In this section we limit our discussion and applications to equations involving a single exponential.

Solving Exponential Equations

Procedure	Example
To solve an exponential equation by using properties of logarithms:	Solve: $4(25^{2x}) = 312{,}500$
1. Isolate the exponential by rewriting the equation with a base raised to a power on one side.	1. $\dfrac{4(25^{2x})}{4} = \dfrac{312{,}500}{4}$ $25^{2x} = 78{,}125$
2. Take the logarithm (either base e or base 10) of both sides.	2. We choose base e, although base 10 would work similarly. $\ln (25^{2x}) = \ln (78{,}125)$
3. Use a property of logarithms to remove the variable from the exponent.	3. Using logarithmic Property V gives $2x \ln 25 = \ln (78{,}125)$
4. Solve for the variable.	4. Dividing both sides by $2 \ln 25$ gives $x = \dfrac{\ln (78{,}125)}{2 \ln 25} = 1.75$

In Step 2 we noted that using a logarithm base 10 would work similarly, and it gives the same result (try it). Unless the exponential in the equation has base e or base 10, the choice of a logarithm in Step 2 makes no difference. However, if the exponential in the equation has base e, then choosing a base e logarithm is slightly easier (see Examples 3 and 5), and similarly for choosing a base 10 logarithm when the equation has a base 10 exponential.

EXAMPLE 1   **Solving an Exponential Equation**

Solve the equation $6(4^{3x-2}) = 120$.

Solution

We first divide both sides by 6 to isolate the exponential.

$$4^{3x-2} = 20$$

Taking the logarithm, base 10, of both sides leads to the solution.

$$\log 4^{3x-2} = \log 20$$
$$(3x - 2)\log 4 = \log 20$$
$$3x - 2 = \frac{\log 20}{\log 4}$$
$$x = \frac{1}{3}\left(\frac{\log 20}{\log 4} + 2\right) \approx 1.387$$

An alternate method of solving the equation is to write $4^{3x-2} = 20$ in logarithmic form.

$$\log_4 20 = 3x - 2$$
$$x = \frac{\log_4 20 + 2}{3} \approx 1.387$$

The change-of-base formula can be used to verify that these solutions are the same. ∎

Solving Logarithmic Equations   A logarithmic equation is one in which the variable appears in a logarithm, such as $2 = \log_5(x + 1)$. The definition of logarithms allows us to express a logarithmic statement such as $2 = \log_5(x + 1)$ in an equivalent exponential form as follows:

$$5^2 = x + 1 \quad \text{or} \quad 25 = x + 1$$

In this form we can easily find $x = 24$.

To solve any logarithmic equation, we use logarithm properties to express the equation as a single logarithmic statement of the form $A = \log_b(X)$, where X is an expression in the variable x. We can translate the single logarithmic statement to exponential form, then solve. Because $\log_b(X)$ is defined only when $X > 0$, a quick check that our solutions do *not* result in the logarithm of a negative quantity is a good idea.

EXAMPLE 2   **Solve the following for x.**

(a) $3\log_8(5x - 9) = 4$ (b) $\log(60x) - \log(x - 50) = 2$

Solution

(a)   First we divide both sides by 3; then translate to exponential form.

$$\log_8(5x - 9) = \frac{4}{3} \quad \Rightarrow \quad 5x - 9 = 8^{4/3}$$

This is equivalent to

$$5x - 9 = 16, \quad \text{so} \quad 5x = 25.$$

Thus, the solution is $x = 5$.   (Note that $5x - 9$ is positive when $x = 5$.)

(b) First we use Logarithm Property IV to write the left side as a single logarithm.

$$\log\left(\frac{60x}{x-50}\right) = 2$$

Next we translate to exponential form (note that this is a base 10 logarithm).

$$10^2 = \frac{60x}{x-50}$$

We multiply both sides by $(x-50)$ and then complete the solution.

$$100(x-50) = 60x \quad \Rightarrow \quad 100x - 5000 = 60x$$
$$40x = 5000 \quad \Rightarrow \quad x = 125$$

The solution is $x = 125$.
(Note that $60x$ and $x - 50$ are positive when $x = 125$.)

Growth and Decay   Recall that **exponential decay models** are those that can be described by a function of the following form.

Decay Models $f(x) = C(a^{-x})$ with $a > 1$ and $C > 0$ or $f(x) = C(b^x)$ with $0 < b < 1$ and $C > 0$

Some applications that use exponential decay models are radioactive decay, demand curves, sales decay, and blood pressure in the aorta, illustrated in the following example.

EXAMPLE   3   **Pressure in the Aorta**

Medical research has shown that over short periods of time when the valves to the aorta of a normal adult close, the pressure in the aorta is a function of time and can be modeled by the equation

$$P = 95e^{-0.491t}$$

where t is in seconds. How long will it be before the pressure reaches 80?

Solution
Setting $P = 80$ and solving for t will give us the length of time before the pressure reaches 80.

$$80 = 95e^{-0.491t}$$

To solve this equation for t, we first isolate the exponential containing t by dividing both sides by 95.

$$\frac{80}{95} = e^{-0.491t}$$

Because e is the base of the exponential, we take the logarithm, base e, of both sides, then use logarithmic Property I to simplify the right-hand side of the expression.

$$\ln\left(\frac{80}{95}\right) = \ln e^{-0.491t} = -0.491t$$

Evaluating the left-hand side with a calculator gives $-0.172 = -0.491t$. Thus,

$$\frac{-0.172}{-0.491} = t \quad \text{so} \quad t = 0.35 \text{ second}   \text{(approximately)}$$

EXAMPLE 4   Sales Decay | APPLICATION PREVIEW |

A company finds that its daily sales begin to fall after the end of an advertising campaign, and the decline is such that the number of sales is $S = 2000(2^{-0.1x})$, where x is the number of days after the campaign ends.

(a) How many sales will be made 10 days after the end of the campaign?
(b) If the company does not want sales to drop below 350 per day, when should it start a new campaign?

Solution

(a) If $x = 10$, sales are given by $S = 2000(2^{-1}) = 1000$.
(b) Setting $S = 350$ and solving for x will give us the number of days after the end of the campaign when sales will reach 350.

$$350 = 2000(2^{-0.1x})$$

$$\frac{350}{2000} = 2^{-0.1x} \quad \text{so} \quad 0.175 = 2^{-0.1x}$$

With the base 2 exponential isolated, we take logarithms of both sides. This time we choose base 10 logarithms and complete the solution as follows.

$$\log 0.175 = \log (2^{-0.1x})$$

$$\log 0.175 = (-0.1x)(\log 2) \qquad \text{Property V}$$

$$\frac{\log 0.175}{\log 2} = -0.1x$$

$$-2.515 \approx -0.1x \quad \text{so} \quad x \approx 25.15$$

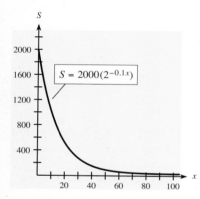

Thus sales will be 350 at day 25.15, and fall below 350 during the 26th day after the end of the campaign. If a new campaign isn't begun on or before the 26th day, sales will drop below 350. (See Figure 5.21.)

Figure 5.21

In business, economics, biology, and the social sciences, **exponential growth models** describe the growth of money, bacteria, or population.

Growth Models $f(x) = C(a^x)$ with $a > 1$ and $C > 0$

The function $y = P_0 e^{ht}$ can be used to model population growth for humans, insects, or bacteria.

EXAMPLE 5   Population

The population of a certain city was 30,000 in 1990 and 40,500 in 2000. If the formula $P = P_0 e^{ht}$ applies to the growth of the city's population, what population is predicted for the year 2020?

Solution

Letting $t = 0$ in 1990 gives $P_0 = 30,000$, and when $t = 10$, $P = 40,500$. Using these values we find h in the formula.

$$40,500 = 30,000e^{h(10)}$$

$$1.35 = e^{10h} \qquad \text{Isolate the exponential.}$$

Taking the natural logarithms of both sides and using logarithmic Property I give

$$\ln 1.35 = \ln e^{10h} = 10h$$

$$0.3001 = 10h \quad \text{so} \quad h \approx 0.0300$$

Thus the formula for this population is $P = P_0 e^{0.03t}$. To predict the population for the year 2020, we reset the most recent data point (for 2000) as $t = 0$, $P_0 = 40{,}500$, and find P for $t = 20$. This gives

$$P = 40{,}500e^{0.03(20)} = 40{,}500e^{0.6} \approx 73{,}796$$

✓ **CHECKPOINT**

1. Suppose the sales of a product, in dollars, are given by $S = 1000e^{-0.07x}$, where x is the number of days after the end of an advertising campaign.
   (a) What are sales 2 days after the end of the campaign?
   (b) How long will it be before sales are $300?

Sometimes cost, revenue, demand, and supply may also be modeled by exponential or logarithmic equations. For example, suppose the demand for a product is given by $p = 30(3^{-q/2})$, where q is the number of thousands of units demanded at a price of p dollars per unit. Then the graph of the demand curve is as given in Figure 5.22.

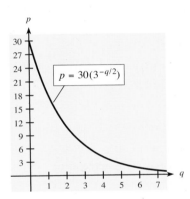

Figure 5.22

EXAMPLE 6   **Demand**

Suppose the demand function for q thousand units of a certain commodity is given by

$$p = 30(3^{-q/2})$$

(a) At what price per unit will the demand equal 4000 units?
(b) How many units, to the nearest thousand units, will be demanded if the price is $17.32?

Solution

(a) If 4000 units are demanded, then $q = 4$ and

$$p = 30(3^{-4/2}) = 30(0.1111) \approx 3.33 \,\text{dollars}$$

(b) If $p = 17.32$, then $17.32 = 30(3^{-q/2})$

$$0.5773 = 3^{-q/2} \qquad \text{Isolate the exponential.}$$

$$\ln 0.5773 = \ln 3^{-q/2} = -\frac{q}{2}\ln 3$$

$$\frac{-2 \ln 0.5773}{\ln 3} = q \quad \text{so} \quad 1.000 \approx q$$

The number of units demanded would be approximately 1000 units.

✓ **CHECKPOINT**

2. Suppose the monthly demand for a product is given by $p = 400e^{-0.003x}$, where p is the price in dollars and x is the number of units. How many units will be demanded when the price is $100?

Gompertz Curves and Logistic Functions

Gompertz Curves

One family of curves that has been used to describe human growth and development, the growth of organisms in a limited environment, and the growth of many types of organizations is the family of **Gompertz curves**. These curves are graphs of equations of the form

$$N = Ca^{R^t}$$

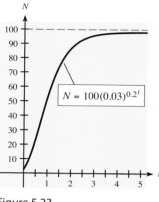

where t represents the time, R $(0 < R < 1)$ is a constant that depends on the population, a represents the proportion of initial growth, C is the maximum possible number of individuals, and N is the number of individuals at a given time t.

For example, the equation $N = 100(0.03)^{0.2^t}$ could be used to predict the size of a deer herd introduced on a small island. Here the maximum number of deer C would be 100, the proportion of the initial growth a is 0.03, and R is 0.2. For this example, t represents time, measured in decades. The graph of this equation is given in Figure 5.23.

Figure 5.23

EXAMPLE 7   Organizational Growth

A hospital administrator predicts that the growth in the number of hospital employees will follow the Gompertz equation

$$N = 2000(0.6)^{0.5^t}$$

where t represents the number of years after the opening of a new facility.

(a) What is the number of employees when the facility opens?
(b) How many employees are predicted after 1 year of operation?
(c) Graph the curve.
(d) What is the maximum value of N that the curve will approach?

Solution

(a) The facility opens when $t = 0$, so $N = 2000(0.6)^{0.5^0} = 2000(0.6)^1 = 1200$.
(b) In 1 year, $t = 1$, so $N = 2000(0.6)^{0.5} = 2000\sqrt{0.6} \approx 1549$.
(c) The graph is shown in Figure 5.24.
(d) From the graph we can see that as larger values of t are substituted in the function, the values of N approach, but never reach, 2000. We say that the line $N = 2000$ (dashed) is an **asymptote** for this curve and that 2000 is the maximum possible value.

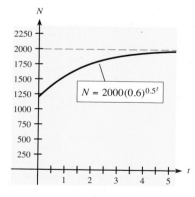

Figure 5.24

EXAMPLE 8   Wildlife Populations

The Gompertz equation

$$N = 100(0.03)^{0.2^t}$$

predicts the size of a deer herd on a small island t decades from now. During what year will the deer population reach or exceed 70?

Solution

We solve the equation with $N = 70$.

$$70 = 100(0.03)^{0.2^t}$$

$$0.7 = 0.03^{0.2^t} \qquad \text{Isolate the exponential.}$$

$$\ln 0.7 = \ln 0.03^{0.2^t} = 0.2^t \ln 0.03$$

$$\frac{\ln 0.7}{\ln 0.03} = 0.2^t \qquad \text{Again, isolate the exponential.}$$

$$\ln\left(\frac{\ln 0.7}{\ln 0.03}\right) = t \ln 0.2 \qquad \text{Take the logarithm of both sides.}$$

$$\ln(0.10172) \approx t(-1.6094)$$

$$\frac{-2.2855}{-1.6094} \approx t \quad \text{so} \quad t \approx 1.42 \text{ decades}$$

The population will exceed 70 in just over 14 years, or during the 15th year. ◼

Calculator Note   Some graphing calculators have a SOLVER feature or program that can be used to solve an equation. Solution with such a feature or program may not be successful unless a reasonable guess at the solution (which can be seen from a graph) is chosen to start the process used to solve the equation. Figure 5.25 shows the equation from Example 8 and its solution with the SOLVER feature of a graphing calculator. ◼

```
EQUATION SOLVER
eqn:0=100(.03)^(
.2^X)-70▮
```

```
100(.03)^(.2^...=0
 X=1.4201015868...
 bound=(-1E99,1...
```

Figure 5.25

✓ CHECKPOINT

3. Suppose the number of employees at a new regional hospital is predicted by the Gompertz curve

$$N = 3500(0.1)^{0.5^t}$$

where t is the number of years after the hospital opens.
(a) How many employees did the hospital have when it opened?
(b) What is the expected upper limit on the number of employees?

Logistic Functions

Gompertz curves describe situations in which growth is limited. There are other equations that model this phenomenon under different assumptions. Two examples are

(a) $y = c(1 - e^{-ax}), \quad a > 0$ 	See Figure 5.26(a).

(b) $y = \dfrac{A}{1 + ce^{-ax}}, \quad a > 0$ 	See Figure 5.26(b).

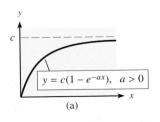

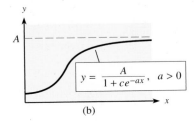

Figure 5.26   (a)   (b)

These equations have many applications. In general, both (a) and (b) can be used to model learning, sales of new products, and population growth, and (b) can be used to describe the spread of epidemics. The equation

$$y = \frac{A}{1 + ce^{-ax}} \qquad a > 0$$

is called a **logistic function,** and the graph in Figure 5.26(b) is called a **logistic curve.**

EXAMPLE 9   Computer Tablets

In recent years, computer tablets have been one of the most frequently purchased personal electronic devices. One company's revenues from the sales of computer tablets from 2010 to 2015 can be modeled by the logistic function

$$y = \frac{9.46}{1 + 53.08e^{-1.28x}}$$

where x is the number of years past 2009 and y is in millions of dollars.

(a) Graph this function.
(b) Use the function to estimate the sales revenue for 2015.

Solution

(a) The graph of this function is shown in Figure 5.27. Note that the graph is an S-shaped curve with a relatively slow initial rise, then a steep climb, followed by a leveling off. It is reasonable that sales would eventually level off. Very seldom will exponential growth continue indefinitely, so logistic functions often better represent many types of sales and organizational growth.
(b) For the 2015 estimate, use $x = 6$ in the function.

$$y = \frac{9.46}{1 + 53.08e^{-1.28(6)}} = \frac{9.46}{1 + 53.08e^{-7.68}} \approx 9.234$$

Thus the model estimates that the 2015 sales revenue from computer tablets for this company is about $9.234 million.

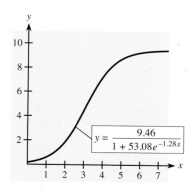

Figure 5.27

1. (a) $S \approx \$869.36$
    (b) $x \approx 17$
2. $x \approx 462$
3. (a) 350
    (b) 3500

| EXERCISES | 5.3

In Problems 1–22, solve each equation. Give answers correct to 3 decimal places in Problems 1–12.

1. $8^{3x} = 32{,}768$
2. $7^{2x} = 823{,}543$
3. $0.13P = P(2^{-x})$
4. $0.05A = A(1.06)^{-x}$
5. $25{,}000 = 10{,}000(1.05)^{2x}$
6. $75{,}000 = 15{,}000(1.02)^{4x}$
7. $10{,}000 = 1500e^{0.10x}$
8. $2500 = 600e^{0.05x}$
9. $78 = 100 - 100e^{-0.01x}$
10. $500 = 600 - 600e^{-0.4x}$
11. $55 = \dfrac{60}{1 + 5e^{-0.6x}}$
12. $150 = \dfrac{200}{1 + 30e^{-0.3x}}$
13. $\log x = 5$
14. $\ln x = 8$
15. $\log_4(9x + 1) = 3$
16. $\log_5(x + 2) = 2$
17. $\ln x - \ln 5 = 10$
18. $\ln x + \ln 8 = 5$
19. $7 + \log(8x) = 25 - 2\log x$
20. $3\log x + 10 = \log(3x) + 14$
21. $\ln(x + 2) + \ln x = \ln(x + 12)$
22. $\log_4 x - \log_4(x + 3) = \log_4(x - 2)$

For Problems 23 and 24, let $f(x) = \dfrac{A}{1 + ce^{-x}}$. Use a graphing utility to make the requested graphs.

23. (a) Fix $A = 100$ and graph $y = f(x) = \dfrac{100}{1 + ce^{-x}}$
    for $c = 0.25$, 1, 9, and 49.
    (b) What effect does c have on the graphs?

24. (a) Fix $c = 1$ and graph $y = f(x) = \dfrac{A}{1 + e^{-x}}$ for
    $A = 50$, 100, and 150.
    (b) What effect does A have on the graphs?

APPLICATIONS

25. *Sales decay* The sales decay for a product is given by $S = 50{,}000e^{-0.8x}$, where S is the monthly sales and x is the number of months that have passed since the end of a promotional campaign.
    (a) What will be the sales 4 months after the end of the campaign?
    (b) How many months after the end of the campaign will sales drop below 1000, if no new campaign is initiated?

26. *Sales decay* The sales of a product decline after the end of an advertising campaign, with the sales decay given by $S = 100{,}000e^{-0.5x}$, where S represents the weekly sales and x represents the number of weeks since the end of the campaign.
    (a) What will be the sales for the tenth week after the end of the campaign?
    (b) During what week after the end of the campaign will sales drop below 400?

27. *Inflation* The purchasing power P (in dollars) of an annual amount of A dollars after t years of 5% inflation decays according to

$$P = Ae^{-0.05t}$$

(*Source: Viewpoints*, VALIC)

(a) How long will it be before a pension of $60,000 per year has a purchasing power of $30,000?
(b) How much pension A would be needed so that the purchasing power P is $50,000 after 15 years?

28. *Product reliability* A statistical study shows that the fraction of television sets of a certain brand that are still in service after x years is given by $f(x) = e^{-0.15x}$.
    (a) What fraction of the sets are still in service after 5 years?
    (b) After how many years will the fraction still in service be 1/10?

29. *Radioactive half-life* An initial amount of 100 g of the radioactive isotope thorium-234 decays according to

$$Q(t) = 100e^{-0.02828t}$$

where t is in years. How long before half of the initial amount has disintegrated? This time is called the half-life of this isotope.

30. *Radioactive half-life* A breeder reactor converts stable uranium-238 into the isotope plutonium-239. The decay of this isotope is given by

$$A(t) = A_0 e^{-0.00002876t}$$

where $A(t)$ is the amount of the isotope at time t, in years, and A_0 is the original amount.
    (a) If $A_0 = 500$ lb, how much will be left after a human lifetime (use $t = 80$ years)?
    (b) Find the half-life of this isotope.

31. *Population growth* If the population of a certain county was 100,000 in 1998 and 110,517 in 2008, and if the formula $y = P_0 e^{ht}$ applies to the growth of the county's population, estimate the population of the county in 2023.

32. *Population growth* The population of a certain city grows according to the formula $y = P_0 e^{0.03t}$. If the population was 250,000 in 2000, estimate the year in which the population reaches 350,000.

33. *Health care* For the years from 2006 and projected to 2021, the national health care expenditures H, in billions of dollars, can be modeled by

$$H = 2009e^{0.05194t}$$

where t is the number of years past 2005 (*Source*: U.S. Department of Health and Human Services). When are national health care expenditures expected to reach $4.0 trillion (that is, $4000 billion)?

34. *U.S. debt* For selected years from 1900 to 2013, the national debt d, in billions of dollars, can be modeled by

$$d = 1.60e^{0.0834t}$$

where t is the number of years past 1900 (*Source*: Bureau of Public Debt, U.S. Treasury). How long will it be before the debt is predicted to reach $30 trillion (that is, $30,000 billion)?

35. *Demand* The demand function for a certain commodity is given by $p = 100e^{-q/2}$.
    (a) At what price per unit will the quantity demanded equal 6 units?
    (b) If the price is $1.83 per unit, how many units will be demanded, to the nearest unit?

36. *Demand* The demand function for a product is given by $p = 3000e^{-q/3}$.
    (a) At what price per unit will the quantity demanded equal 6 units?
    (b) If the price is $149.40 per unit, how many units will be demanded, to the nearest unit?

37. *Supply* If the supply function for a product is given by $p = 100e^q/(q + 1)$, where q represents the number of hundreds of units, what will be the price when the producers are willing to supply 300 units?

38. *Supply* If the supply function for a product is given by $p = 200(2^q)$, where q represents the number of hundreds of units, what will be the price when the producers are willing to supply 500 units?

39. *Total cost* The total cost function for x units of a product is given by

$$C(x) = 2500 \ln (2x + 1) + 1500$$

    (a) Find the total cost of producing 80 items.
    (b) How many units can be produced before total costs reach $16,000?

40. *Total cost* The total cost function for a product is

$$C(x) = 800 \ln (x + 10) + 1700$$

    where x is the number of units produced.
    (a) Find the total cost of producing 100 units.
    (b) Producing how many units will give total costs of $7500?

41. *Demographics* The millions of White non-Hispanic individuals in the U.S. civilian non-institutional population 16 years and older for selected years from 1980 and projected to 2050 can be modeled by the function

$$y = 96.12 + 17.43 \ln x$$

    where x is equal to the number of years past 1970 (*Source:* U.S. Census Bureau). Find the year in which the number of White non-Hispanics is expected to reach 166.5 million.

42. *Diabetes* Centers for Disease Control and Prevention data from 2010 and projected to 2050 indicate that adult diabetes in the United States could dramatically increase. With $x = 0$ in 2000, the percent of U.S. adults with diabetes can be modeled by

$$y = -13.0 + 11.9 \ln x$$

    Use the model to find the year in which the percent of U.S. adults with diabetes is predicted to reach 30%.

43. *Compound interest* If $8500 is invested at 11.5% compounded continuously, the future value S at any time t (in years) is given by

$$S = 8500e^{0.115t}$$

    (a) What is the amount after 18 months?
    (b) How long before the investment doubles?

44. *Compound interest* If $1000 is invested at 10% compounded continuously, the future value S at any time t (in years) is given by $S = 1000e^{0.1t}$.
    (a) What is the amount after 1 year?
    (b) How long before the investment doubles?

45. *Compound interest* If $5000 is invested at 9% per year compounded monthly, the future value S at any time t (in months) is given by $S = 5000(1.0075)^t$.
    (a) What is the amount after 1 year?
    (b) How long before the investment doubles?

46. *Compound interest* If $10,000 is invested at 1% per month, the future value S at any time t (in months) is given by $S = 10,000(1.01)^t$.
    (a) What is the amount after 1 year?
    (b) How long before the investment doubles?

Profits **An investment services company experienced dramatic growth in the last two decades. The following models for the company's revenue R and expenses or costs C (both in millions of dollars) are functions of the years past 1990.**

$$R(t) = 21.4e^{0.131t} \quad \text{and} \quad C(t) = 18.6e^{0.131t}$$

Use these models in Problems 47 and 48.

47. (a) Use the models to predict the company's profit in 2020.
    (b) How long before the profit found in part (a) is predicted to double?

48. Use the models to find how long before the company's profit reaches $500 million.

49. *Purchasing power* Using Social Security Administration data for selected years from 2012 and projected to 2050, with a purchasing power of $1.00 in 2012, the function

$$P(x) = 1.078(1.028^{-x})$$

    gives the purchasing power of a 2012 dollar as a function of x, the number of years past 2010.
    (a) Find and interpret $P(18)$.
    (b) Solve algebraically to find the year when the purchasing power of a 2012 dollar is expected to reach $0.48.

50. *China's shale-natural gas* The function that models the growth in the number of billions of cubic feet of shale-natural gas in China, with x as the number of years after 2010, is

$$y = 0.0117(1.75^x)$$

    Find the year when the number of cubic feet is projected to be 2.5 billion by solving algebraically (*Source:* Sanford C. Bernstein).

51. *Supply* Suppose the supply of x units of a product at price p dollars per unit is given by

$$p = 10 + 5 \ln (3x + 1)$$

How many units would be supplied when the price is $50 each?

52. *Demand* Say the demand function for a product is given by $p = 100/\ln(q + 1)$.
    (a) What will be the price if 19 units are demanded?
    (b) How many units, to the nearest unit, will be demanded if the price is $29.40?

GOMPERTZ CURVES AND LOGISTIC FUNCTIONS APPLICATIONS

53. *Sales growth* The president of a company predicts that sales will increase after she assumes office and that the number of monthly sales will follow the curve given by $N = 3000(0.2)^{0.6^t}$, where t represents the months since she assumed office.
    (a) What will be the sales when she assumes office?
    (b) What will be the sales after 3 months?
    (c) What is the expected upper limit on sales?
    (d) Graph the curve.

54. *Organizational growth* Because of a new market opening, the number of employees of a firm is expected to increase according to the equation $N = 1400(0.5)^{0.3^t}$, where t represents the number of years after the new market opens.
    (a) What is the level of employment when the new market opens?
    (b) How many employees should be working at the end of 2 years?
    (c) What is the expected upper limit on the number of employees?
    (d) Graph the curve.

55. *Organizational growth* Suppose that the equation $N = 500(0.02)^{0.7^t}$ represents the number of employees working t years after a company begins operations.
    (a) How many employees are there when the company opens (at $t = 0$)?
    (b) After how many years will at least 100 employees be working?

56. *Sales growth* A firm predicts that sales will increase during a promotional campaign and that the number of daily sales will be given by $N = 200(0.01)^{0.8^t}$, where t represents the number of days after the campaign begins. How many days after the beginning of the campaign would the firm expect to sell at least 60 units per day?

57. *Drugs in the bloodstream* The concentration y of a certain drug in the bloodstream t hours after an oral dosage (with $0 \le t \le 15$) is given by the equation
$$y = 100(1 - e^{-0.462t})$$
    (a) What is y after 1 hour ($t = 1$)?
    (b) How long does it take for y to reach 50?

58. *Population growth* Suppose that the number y of otters t years after otters were reintroduced into a wild and scenic river is given by
$$y = 2500 - 2490e^{-0.1t}$$

(a) Find the population when the otters were reintroduced (at $t = 0$).
(b) How long will it be before the otter population numbers 1500?

59. *Spread of disease* On a college campus of 10,000 students, a single student returned to campus infected by a disease. The spread of the disease through the student body is given by
$$y = \frac{10{,}000}{1 + 9999e^{-0.99t}}$$
where y is the total number infected at time t (in days).
    (a) How many are infected after 4 days?
    (b) The school will shut down if 50% of the students are ill. During what day will it close?

60. *Spread of a rumor* The number of people $N(t)$ in a community who are reached by a particular rumor at time t is given by the equation
$$N(t) = \frac{50{,}500}{1 + 100e^{-0.7t}}$$
    (a) Find $N(0)$.
    (b) What is the upper limit on the number of people affected?
    (c) How long before 75% of the upper limit is reached?

61. *Market share* Suppose that the market share y (as a percent) that a company expects t months after a new product is introduced is given by $y = 40 - 40e^{-0.05t}$.
    (a) What is the market share after the first month (to the nearest percent)?
    (b) How long (to the nearest month) before the market share is 25%?

62. *Advertising* An advertising agency has found that when it promotes a new product in a certain market of 350,000, the number of people x who are aware of the product t days after the ad campaign is initiated is given by
$$x = 350{,}000(1 - e^{-0.077t})$$
    (a) How many people (to the nearest thousand) are aware after 1 week?
    (b) How long (to the nearest day) before 300,000 are aware of the new product?

63. *Pollution* Pollution levels in a lake have been modeled by the equation
$$x = 0.05 + 0.18e^{-0.38t}$$
where x is the volume of pollutants (in cubic kilometers) and t is the time (in years).
    (a) Find the initial pollution levels; that is, find x when $t = 0$.
    (b) How long before x is 30% of that initial level?

64. *Fish length* Suppose that the length x (in centimeters) of an individual of a certain species of fish is given by
$$x = 50 - 40e^{-0.05t}$$

where t is its age in months.
(a) Find the length after 1 year.
(b) How long (to the nearest month) will it be until the length is 45 cm?

65. **U.S. civilian labor force** With U.S. Bureau of Labor Statistics data since 1950 and projected to 2040, the total civilian labor force age 16 years and older (in millions) can be modeled by

$$L = \frac{197}{1 + 3.65e^{-0.037t}}$$

where t is the number of years after 1940.
(a) Use the model to estimate the size of the civilian labor force in 2015.
(b) Use the model to estimate the year when the civilian labor force is predicted to reach 170 million.

66. **Chemical reaction** When two chemicals, A and B, react to form another chemical C (such as in the digestive process), this is a special case of the **law of mass action,** which is fundamental to studying chemical reaction rates. Suppose that chemical C is formed from A and B according to

$$x = \frac{120[1 - (0.6)^{3t}]}{4 - (0.6)^{3t}}$$

where x is the number of pounds of C formed in t minutes.
(a) How much of C is present when the reaction begins?
(b) How much of C is formed in 4 minutes?
(c) How long does it take to form 10 lb of C?

67. **Modeling Diabetes** The following table gives the total number of U.S adults with diabetes for selected years from 2010 and projected to 2050.
(a) Find the logistic function that models these data. Use x equal to the number of years past 2000.
(b) Use the model to predict the number of U.S. adults expected to have diabetes in 2028.

(c) According to the model, what is the expected upper limit on the number of U.S. adults with diabetes?
(d) In what year does the model predict that the number of U.S. adults with diabetes will reach 80.0 million?

Year	Number (millions)	Year	Number (millions)
2010	32.3	2035	76.2
2015	37.3	2040	84.1
2020	50.0	2045	91.7
2025	59.5	2050	100.0
2030	68.3		

Source: Centers for Disease Control and Prevention

68. **Modeling Endangered species** The following table gives the numbers of species in the United States that were endangered in various years from 1990 to 2012.
(a) Find the logistic function that models these data. Use x as the number of years past 1980.
(b) Use the model to predict the number of endangered species in 2020.
(c) When does the model predict that 1088 species will be endangered?

Year	Endangered Species
1990	442
2003	987
2006	1009
2007	1037
2008	1049
2010	1061
2011	1058
2012	1086

Source: U.S. Fish and Wildlife Service

Chapter 5 Summary & Review

KEY TERMS AND FORMULAS

Section 5.1

Exponential functions (p. 317)
Growth functions (p. 319)
$\quad f(x) = a^x \quad (a > 1)$
$\quad f(x) = C(a^x) \quad (C > 0, \ a > 1)$

$e \approx 2.71828$ (p. 320)
Decay functions (p. 321)
$\quad f(x) = C(a^{-x}) \quad (C > 0, \ a > 1)$
$\quad f(x) = C(b^x) \quad (C > 0, \ 0 < b < 1)$

Section 5.2

Logarithmic function (p. 329)
$\quad y = \log_a x$, defined by $x = a^y$
Common logarithm (p. 331)
$\quad \log x = \log_{10} x$
Natural logarithm (p. 331)
$\quad \ln x = \log_e x$

Graphs of logarithmic functions (p. 332)
Inverse functions (p. 334)
Logarithmic Properties I–V (pp. 334–336)
$\quad$ I. $\log_a a^x = x$
$\quad$ II. $a^{\log_a x} = x$
$\quad$ III. $\log_a (MN) = \log_a M + \log_a N$

IV. $\log_a (M/N) = \log_a M - \log_a N$
V. $\log_a (M^N) = N(\log_a M)$
Change-of-base formula (p. 336)

$$\log_b x = \frac{\log_a x}{\log_a b}$$

Calculation formulas

Base e: $\log_b x = \dfrac{\ln x}{\ln b}$

Base 10: $\log_b x = \dfrac{\log x}{\log b}$

Section 5.3

Solving exponential equations (p. 341)
  Isolate the exponential; take logarithm of both sides.
Solving logarithmic equations (p. 342)
  Obtain form $A = \log_b X$; solve equivalent exponential
  equation
Exponential growth and decay (p. 343)
  Growth models
  $f(x) = Ca^x$ $(a>1, C>0)$

Decay models
  $f(x) = Ca^{-x}$ $(a>1, C>0)$
Gompertz curves (p. 346)
  $N = Ca^{R^t}$
Logistic functions (p. 348)

$$y = \frac{A}{1 + ce^{-ax}} \quad (a>0)$$

REVIEW EXERCISES

Sections 5.1 and 5.2

1. Write each statement in logarithmic form.
  (a) $2^x = y$ (b) $3^y = 2x$
2. Write each statement in exponential form.
  (a) $\log_7 \left(\dfrac{1}{49}\right) = -2$ (b) $\log_4 x = -1$

Graph the following functions.
3. $y = e^x$
4. $y = e^{-x}$
5. $y = \log_2 x$
6. $y = 2^x$
7. $y = \frac{1}{2}(4^x)$
8. $y = \ln x$
9. $y = \log_4 x$
10. $y = 3^{-2x}$
11. $y = \log x$
12. $y = 10(2^{-x})$

In Problems 13–20 evaluate each logarithm without using a calculator. In Problems 13–17, check with the change-of-base formula.
13. $\log_5 1$
14. $\log_2 8$
15. $\log_{25} 5$
16. $\log_3 \left(\dfrac{1}{3}\right)$
17. $\log_3 3^8$
18. $\ln e$
19. $e^{\ln 5}$
20. $10^{\log 3.15}$

In Problems 21–24, if $\log_a x = 1.2$ and $\log_a y = 3.9$, find each of the following by using the properties of logarithms.
21. $\log_a \left(\dfrac{x}{y}\right)$
22. $\log_a \sqrt{x}$
23. $\log_a (xy)$
24. $\log_a (y^4)$

In Problems 25 and 26, use the properties of logarithms to write each expression as the sum or difference of two logarithmic functions containing no exponents.

25. $\log (yz)$
26. $\ln \sqrt{\dfrac{x+1}{x}}$

27. Is it true that $\ln x + \ln y = \ln (x + y)$ for all positive values of x and y?
28. If $f(x) = \ln x$, find $f(e^{-2})$.
29. If $f(x) = 2^x + \log (7x - 4)$, find $f(2)$.
30. If $f(x) = e^x + \ln (x + 1)$, find $f(0)$.
31. If $f(x) = \ln (3e^x - 5)$, find $f(\ln 2)$.

In Problems 32 and 33, use a change-of-base formula to evaluate each logarithm.
32. $\log_9 2158$
33. $\log_{12} (0.0195)$

In Problems 34 and 35, rewrite each logarithm by using a change-of-base formula, then graph the function with a graphing utility.
34. $y = \log_{\sqrt{3}} x$
35. $f(x) = \log_{11} (2x - 5)$

Section 5.3

In Problems 36–42, solve each equation.
36. $6^{4x} = 46{,}656$
37. $8000 = 250(1.07)^x$
38. $11{,}000 = 45{,}000e^{-0.05x}$
39. $312 = 300 + 300e^{-0.08x}$
40. $\log_3(4x - 5) = 3$
41. $\ln (2x - 1) - \ln 3 = \ln 9$
42. $3 + 2 \log_2 x = \log_2(x + 3) + 5$

APPLICATIONS

Section 5.1

43. *Medicare spending* The graph in the figure on the following page shows the projected federal spending for Medicare as a percent of the gross domestic product. If these expenditures were modeled as a function of time, which of a growth exponential, a decay exponential, or a logarithm would be the best model? Justify your answer.

A Consuming Problem

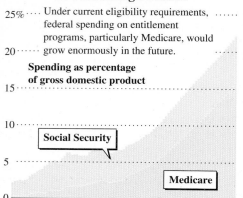

25% ···· Under current eligibility requirements, ······
       federal spending on entitlement
       programs, particularly Medicare, would
20 ····· grow enormously in the future. ······

**Spending as percentage
of gross domestic product**

15 ···········

10 ··········

5 ··········

Social Security

Medicare

0
'60 '70 '80 '90 '00 '10 '20 '30 '40 '50
Source: Congressional Budget Office

44. *Consumer price index* By using Social Security Administration data for selected years from 2012 and projected to 2050, the U.S. consumer price index (CPI) can be modeled by the function

$$C(t) = 92.7e^{0.0271t}$$

where t is the number of years past 2010. With the reference year as 2012, a 2016 CPI = 108.58 means goods and services that cost $100.00 in 2012 are expected to cost $108.58 in 2016.
(a) Find $C(15)$ and explain its meaning.
(b) Graph the model.

45. *Inflation* The purchasing power P of a $60,000 pension after t years of 3% annual inflation is modeled by

$$P(t) = 60,000(0.97)^t$$

(a) What is the purchasing power after 20 years?
(b) Graph this function for $t = 0$ to $t = 25$ with a graphing utility.

46. **Modeling** *Average annual wage* The following table shows the U.S. average annual wage in thousands of dollars for selected years from 2012 and projected to 2050.
(a) Find an exponential function that models these data. Use x equal to the number of years past 2010.
(b) Graph the model and the data on the same axes.
(c) What does the model predict that the average annual wage will be in 2054?

Year	Average annual wage (thousands of dollars)	Year	Average annual wage (thousands of dollars)
2012	44.6	2030	93.2
2014	48.6	2035	113.2
2016	53.3	2040	137.6
2018	58.7	2045	167.1
2020	63.7	2050	202.5
2025	76.8		

Source: Social Security Administration

Section 5.2

47. *Poverty threshold* The average poverty threshold for 1990–2011 for a single individual can be modeled by

$$y = -4199.9 + 4436.3\ln x$$

where x is the number of years past 1980 and y is the annual income in dollars (*Source:* U.S. Bureau of the Census).
(a) What does the model predict as the poverty threshold in 2018?
(b) Graph this function for $x = 0$ to $x = 40$ and $y \geq 0$.

48. **Modeling** *U.S. population* The following table gives the total U.S. population, in millions, for selected years from 1990 and projected to 2050.
(a) Find a logarithmic function model for the data. Use x as the number of years past 1950 and report the model with four significant digit coefficients.
(b) Use the model to find the expected U.S. population in 2018.
(c) Use the reported model to find the x-value when the total U.S. population is predicted to reach 400 million.

Year	U.S. population (in millions)	Year	U.S. population (in millions)
1990	259.6	2020	342.9
2000	287.9	2030	369.5
2010	315.2	2040	390.8
2015	328.4	2050	409.1

Source: Social Security Administration

49. *Stellar magnitude* The stellar magnitude M of a star is related to its brightness B as seen from earth according to

$$M = -\frac{5}{2}\log(B/B_0)$$

where B_0 is a standard level of brightness (the brightness of the star Vega).
(a) Find the magnitude of Venus if its brightness is 36.3 times B_0.
(b) Find the brightness (as a multiple of B_0) of the North Star if its magnitude is 2.1.
(c) If the faintest stars have magnitude 6, find their brightness (as a multiple of B_0).
(d) Is a star with magnitude -1.0 brighter than a star with magnitude $+1.0$?

Section 5.3

50. *Sales decay* The sales decay for a product is given by $S = 50,000e^{-0.1x}$, where S is the weekly sales (in dollars) and x is the number of weeks that have passed since the end of an advertising campaign.
(a) What will sales be 6 weeks after the end of the campaign?
(b) How many weeks will pass before sales drop below $15,000?

51. **Sales decay** The sales decay for a product is given by $S = 50{,}000e^{-0.6x}$, where S is the monthly sales (in dollars) and x is the number of months that have passed since the end of an advertising campaign. What will sales be 6 months after the end of the campaign?

52. **Compound interest** If $1000 is invested at 12%, compounded monthly, the future value S at any time t (in years) is given by

$$S = 1000(1.01)^{12t}$$

How long will it take for the amount to double?

53. **Compound interest** If $5000 is invested at 13.5%, compounded continuously, then the future value S at any time t (in years) is given by $S = 5000e^{0.135t}$.
   (a) What is the amount after 9 months?
   (b) How long will it be before the investment doubles?

54. **World population** With data from the International Data Base of the U.S. Bureau of the Census, the accompanying figure shows a scatter plot of actual or projected world population (in billions) in 5-year increments from 1950 to 2050 ($x = 0$ in 1945). Which of the following functions would be the best model: exponential growth, exponential decay, logarithmic, or logistic? Explain.

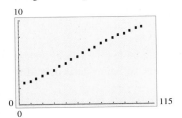

55. **Advertising and sales** Because of a new advertising campaign, a company predicts that sales will increase and that the yearly sales will be given by the equation

$$N = 10{,}000(0.3)^{0.5t}$$

where t represents the number of years after the start of the campaign.
   (a) What are the sales when the campaign begins?
   (b) What are the predicted sales for the third year?
   (c) What are the maximum predicted sales?

56. **Spread of a disease** The spread of a highly contagious virus in a high school can be described by the logistic function

$$y = \frac{5000}{1 + 1000e^{-0.8x}}$$

where x is the number of days after the virus is identified in the school and y is the total number of people who are infected by the virus in the first x days.
   (a) Graph the function for $0 \le x \le 15$.
   (b) How many students had the virus when it was first discovered?
   (c) What is the total number infected by the virus during the first 15 days?
   (d) In how many days will the total number infected reach 3744?

Chapter 5 TEST

In Problems 1–4, graph the functions.
1. $y = 5^x$
2. $y = 3^{-x}$
3. $y = \log_5 x$
4. $y = \ln x$

In Problems 5–8, use technology to graph the functions.
5. $y = 3^{0.5x}$
6. $y = \ln(0.5x)$
7. $y = e^{2x}$
8. $y = \log_7 x$

In Problems 9–12, use a calculator to give a decimal approximation of the numbers to three decimal places.
9. e^4
10. $3^{-2.1}$
11. $\ln 4$
12. $\log 21$

13. Use the definition of a logarithmic function to write $\log_7 x = 3.1$ in exponential form. Then find x to three decimal places.

14. Write $3^{2x} = 27$ in logarithmic form.

In Problems 15 and 16, solve each equation for x to 3 decimal places.
15. $3 + 6e^{-2x} = 7$
16. $8 - \log_3(5x - 13) = 5$

In Problems 17–20, simplify the expressions, using properties or definitions of logarithms.
17. $\log_2 8$
18. $e^{\ln x^4}$
19. $\log_7 7^3$
20. $\ln e^{x^2}$

21. Write $\ln(M \cdot N)$ as a sum involving M and N.

22. Write $\ln\left(\dfrac{x^3 - 1}{x + 2}\right)$ as a difference involving two binomials.

23. Write $\log_4(x^3 + 1)$ as a base e logarithm using a change-of-base formula.

24. Solve for x: $47{,}500 = 1500(1.015)^{6x}$

25. The graph in the following figure shows the number of active workers who will be (or have been)

supporting each Social Security beneficiary. What type of function might be an appropriate model for this situation?

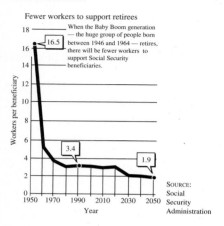

Fewer workers to support retirees

When the Baby Boom generation — the huge group of people born between 1946 and 1964 — retires, there will be fewer workers to support Social Security beneficiaries.

SOURCE: Social Security Administration

26. With data from the U.S. Energy Information Administration, the following figure shows a scatter plot of tons of carbon dioxide (CO_2) emissions per person for selected years from 2010 and projected to 2040, with x as the number of years past 2010.
    (a) Which of the following functions would be an appropriate model: growth exponential, decay exponential, logarithmic, or logistic?
    (b) The point (20, 14.8) is one of the data points plotted; interpret this point in terms of the application.

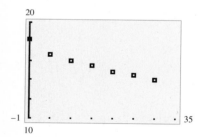

27. The total national health expenditures per capita (in dollars) for 2006 and projected to 2021 can be modeled with the equation

$$H(t) = 6791e^{0.04343t}$$

where t is the number of years past 2005 (*Source:* U.S. Centers for Medicare & Medicaid Services).
    (a) Find the predicted per capita health expenditures for 2018.

(b) According to the model, how long will it take for the 2018 expenditures to double?

28. A company plans to phase out one model of its product and replace it with a new model. An advertising campaign for the product being replaced just ended, and typically after such a campaign, monthly sales volume S (in dollars) decays according to

$$S = 22{,}000e^{-0.35t}$$

where t is in months. When the monthly sales volume for this product reaches \$2500, the company plans to discontinue production and launch the new model. How long will it be until this happens?

29. The total U.S. personal income I (in billions of dollars) from 1988 and projected to 2018 can be modeled by

$$I = \frac{70{,}290}{1 + 18.26e^{-0.058t}}$$

where t is the number of years past 1985 (*Source:* U.S. Department of Labor).
    (a) What does the model predict for the total U.S. personal income in 2015?
    (b) When will the total U.S. personal income reach \$25,000 billion?

30. **Modeling** The following table gives the projected population, in thousands, of Americans over 100 years of age.
    (a) Create an exponential function that models this population as a function of the number of years past 2010.
    (b) According to this model, what is the projected population of centenarians in 2052?
    (c) When will this population reach 1,030,000 according to this model?

Year	Population (1000s)	Year	Population (1000s)
2015	78	2040	230
2020	106	2045	310
2025	143	2050	442
2030	168	2055	564
2035	188	2060	690

Source: U.S. Census Bureau

Chapter **Warm-Up**

Prerequisite Problem Type	For Section	Answer	Section for Review
What is $\dfrac{(-1)^n}{2n}$, if (a) $n = 1$? (b) $n = 2$? (c) $n = 3$?	**6.1**	(a) $-\frac{1}{2}$ (b) $\frac{1}{4}$ (c) $-\frac{1}{6}$	0.2 Signed numbers
(a) What is $(-2)^6$? (b) What is $\dfrac{\frac{1}{4}\left[1 - \left(\frac{1}{2}\right)^6\right]}{1 - \frac{1}{2}}$?	**6.2**	(a) 64 (b) $\frac{63}{128}$	0.2 Signed numbers
If $f(x) = \dfrac{1}{2x}$, what is (a) $f(2)$? (b) $f(4)$?	**6.1**	(a) $\frac{1}{4}$ (b) $\frac{1}{8}$	1.2 Function notation
Evaluate: $e^{(0.08)(20)}$	**6.2**	4.95303	5.1 Exponential functions
Evaluate: (a) $\dfrac{1 - (1.05)^{-16}}{0.05}$ (b) $5000 + 5000\left[\dfrac{1-(1.059)^{-9}}{0.059}\right]$	**6.3** **6.4**	(a) 10.83777 (b) 39,156.96575	0.3 Integral exponents
Solve: (a) $1100 = 1000 + 1000(0.058)t$ (b) $12,000 = P(1.03)^6$ (c) $850 = A_n\left[\dfrac{0.0065}{1 - (1.0065)^{-360}}\right]$	**6.1–6.5**	(a) $t \approx 1.72$ (b) $P \approx 10,049.81$ (c) $A_n \approx 118,076.79$	1.1 Linear equations
Solve: (a) $2 = (1.08)^n$ (b) $20,000 = 10,000e^{0.08t}$	**6.2**	(a) $n \approx 9.01$ (b) $t \approx 8.66$	5.3 Solutions of exponential equations

6.1

- To find the future value of and the amount of interest from a simple interest investment
- To find the interest due on a simple interest loan
- To find the time required for a simple interest investment to reach a goal
- To write a specified number of terms of a sequence
- To find specified terms and sums of specified numbers of terms of arithmetic sequences

Simple Interest; Sequences

▮ | APPLICATION PREVIEW |

Mary Spaulding purchased some Wind-Gen Electric stock for $6125.00. After 6 months, the stock had risen in value by $138.00 and had paid dividends totaling $144.14. One way to evaluate this investment and compare it with a bank savings plan is to find the simple interest rate that these gains represent. (See Example 3.)

In this section we begin our study of the mathematics of finance by considering simple interest. Simple interest forms the basis for all calculations involving interest that is paid on an investment or that is due on a loan. Also, we can evaluate short-term investments (such as in stocks or real estate) by calculating their simple interest rates.

Simple Interest   If a sum of money P (called the **principal**) is invested for a time period t (frequently in years) at an interest rate r per period, the **simple interest** is given by the following formula.

Simple Interest

The **simple interest** I is given by

$$I = Prt$$

where $I =$ interest (in dollars)
$P =$ principal (in dollars)
$r =$ annual interest rate (written as a decimal)
$t =$ time (in years)*

Note that the time measurements for r and t must agree.

Simple interest is paid on investments involving time certificates issued by banks and on certain types of bonds, such as some U.S. government bonds and municipal bonds. The interest for a given period is paid to the investor, and the principal remains the same.

If you borrow money from a friend or a relative, interest on your loan might be calculated with the simple interest formula. We'll consider some simple interest loans in this section, but interest on loans from banks and other lending institutions is calculated using methods discussed later.

EXAMPLE   1   Simple Interest

(a) If $8000 is invested for 2 years at an annual interest rate of 9%, how much interest will be received at the end of the 2-year period?
(b) If $4000 is borrowed for 39 weeks at an annual interest rate of 15%, how much interest is due at the end of the 39 weeks?

Solution

(a) The interest is $I = Prt =$ $8000(0.09)(2) =$ $1440.
(b) Use $I = Prt$ with $t = 39/52 = 0.75$ year. Thus

$$I = \$4000(0.15)(0.75) = \$450$$

*Periods of time other than years can be used, as can other monetary systems.

Future Value

The **future amount of an investment,** or its **future value,** at the end of an interest period is the sum of the principal and the interest. Thus, in Example 1(a), the future value is

$$S = \$8000 + \$1440 = \$9440$$

Future Value	If we use the letter S to denote the **future value** of an investment, then we have Future value of investment: $S = P + I$ where P is the principal (in dollars) and I is the interest (in dollars).

The principal P of an investment is also called the **present value** of the investment. The present value of a loan is the original loan amount, which is also called the **face value** of the loan.

EXAMPLE 2 Loans and Investments

(a) If $2000 is borrowed for one-half year at a simple interest rate of 12% per year, what amount must be repaid at the end of the half-year?

(b) An investor wants to have $20,000 in 9 months. If the best available simple interest rate is 6.05% per year, how much must be invested now to yield the desired amount?

Solution

(a) The interest for the half-year period is $I = \$2000(0.12)(0.5) = \$120$. Thus the amount that must be repaid for the period is

$$S = P + I = \$2000 + \$120 = \$2120$$

(b) We know that $S = P + I = P + Prt$. In this case, we must solve for P, the present value. Also, the time 9 months is $(9/12)$ of a year.

$$\$20,000 = P + P(0.0605)(9/12) = P + 0.045375P$$
$$\$20,000 = 1.045375P$$
$$\frac{\$20,000}{1.045375} = P \quad \text{so} \quad P \approx \$19{,}131.89$$

EXAMPLE 3 Return on an Investment | APPLICATION PREVIEW |

Mary Spaulding bought Wind-Gen Electric stock for $6125.00. After 6 months, the value of her shares had risen by $138.00 and dividends totaling $144.14 had been paid. Find the simple interest rate she earned on this investment if she sold the stock at the end of the 6 months.

Solution

To find the simple interest rate that Mary earned on this investment, we find the rate that would yield an amount of simple interest equal to all of Mary's gains (that is, equal to the rise in the stock's price plus the dividends she received). Thus the principal is $6125.00, the time is 1/2 year, and the interest earned is the total of all gains (that is, interest $I = \$138.00 + \$144.14 = \$282.14$). Using these values in $I = Prt$ gives

$$\$282.14 = (\$6125)r(0.5) = \$3062.5r$$
$$r = \frac{\$282.14}{\$3062.5} \approx 0.092 = 9.2\%$$

Thus Mary's return was equivalent to an annual simple interest rate of about 9.2%.

EXAMPLE 4 Duration of an Investment

If $1000 is invested at 5.8% simple interest, how long will it take to grow to $1100?

Solution

We use $P = \$1000$, $S = \$1100$, and $r = 0.058$ in $S = P + Prt$ and solve for t.

$$\$1100 = \$1000 + \$1000(0.058)t$$

$$\$100 = \$58t \quad \text{so} \quad \frac{\$100}{\$58} = t \quad \text{and} \quad t \approx 1.72 \text{ years}$$

✓ **CHECKPOINT**

1. What is the simple interest formula?
2. If $8000 is invested at 6% simple interest for 9 months, find the future value of the investment.
3. If a $2500 investment grows to $2875 in 15 months, what simple interest rate was earned?

Sequences

Let's look at the monthly future values of a $2000 investment that earns 1% simple interest for each of 5 months.

Month	Interest ($I = Prt$)	Future Value of the Investment
1	($2000)(0.01)(1) = $20	$2000 + $20 = $2020
2	($2000)(0.01)(1) = $20	$2020 + $20 = $2040
3	($2000)(0.01)(1) = $20	$2040 + $20 = $2060
4	($2000)(0.01)(1) = $20	$2060 + $20 = $2080
5	($2000)(0.01)(1) = $20	$2080 + $20 = $2100

These future values are outputs that result when the inputs are positive integers that correspond to the number of months of the investment. Outputs (such as these future values) that arise uniquely from positive integer inputs define a special type of function.

Sequence

A function whose domain is the set of positive integers is called a **sequence function**. The set of function outputs of a sequence function

$$f(1) = a_1, f(2) = a_2, \ldots, f(n) = a_n, \ldots$$

forms an ordered list called a **sequence**. The outputs $a_1, a_2, a_3, \ldots$ are called **terms** of the sequence, with a_1 the first term, a_2 the second term, and so on.

Because calculations involving interest often result from using positive integer inputs, sequences are the basis for most of the financial formulas derived in this chapter.

EXAMPLE 5 Terms of a Sequence

Write the first four terms of the sequence whose nth term is $a_n = (-1)^n/(2n)$.

Solution

The first four terms of the sequence are as follows:

$$a_1 = \frac{(-1)^1}{2(1)} = -\frac{1}{2} \qquad a_2 = \frac{(-1)^2}{2(2)} = \frac{1}{4}$$

$$a_3 = \frac{(-1)^3}{2(3)} = -\frac{1}{6} \qquad a_4 = \frac{(-1)^4}{2(4)} = \frac{1}{8}$$

We usually write these terms in the form $-\frac{1}{2}, \frac{1}{4}, -\frac{1}{6}, \frac{1}{8}$.

Arithmetic Sequences   The sequence 2020, 2040, 2060, 2080, 2100, . . . can also be described in the following way:

$$a_1 = 2020, \quad a_n = a_{n-1} + 20 \quad \text{for } n > 1$$

This sequence is an example of a special kind of sequence called an **arithmetic sequence.** In such a sequence, each term after the first can be found by adding a constant to the preceding term. Thus we have the following definition.

Arithmetic Sequences | A sequence is called an **arithmetic sequence** (progression) if there exists a number d, called the **common difference,** such that
$$a_n = a_{n-1} + d \quad \text{for } n > 1$$

EXAMPLE 6   Arithmetic Sequences

Write the next three terms of each of the following arithmetic sequences.
(a) 1, 3, 5, ...
(b) 9, 6, 3, ...
(c) $\frac{1}{2}, \frac{5}{6}, \frac{7}{6}, \ldots$

Solution
(a) The common difference is 2, so the next three terms are 7, 9, 11.
(b) The common difference is -3, so the next three terms are 0, -3, -6.
(c) The common difference is $\frac{1}{3}$, so the next three terms are $\frac{3}{2}, \frac{11}{6}, \frac{13}{6}$.

Because each term after the first term in an arithmetic sequence is obtained by adding d to the preceding term, the second term is $a_1 + d$, the third is $(a_1 + d) + d = a_1 + 2d, \ldots$, and the nth term is $a_1 + (n-1)d$. Thus we have the following formula.

nth Term of an Arithmetic Sequence | The **nth term of an arithmetic sequence** (progression) is given by
$$a_n = a_1 + (n-1)d$$
where a_1 is the first term and d is the common difference between successive terms.

EXAMPLE 7 nth Terms of Arithmetic Sequences

(a) Find the 11th term of the arithmetic sequence with first term 3 and common difference -2.
(b) If the first term of an arithmetic sequence is 4 and the 9th term is 20, find the 75th term.

Solution
(a) The 11th term is $a_{11} = 3 + (11 - 1)(-2) = -17$.
(b) Substituting the values $a_1 = 4$, $a_n = 20$, and $n = 9$ in $a_n = a_1 + (n-1)d$ gives $20 = 4 + (9-1)d$. Solving this equation gives $d = 2$. Therefore, the 75th term is $a_{75} = 4 + (75 - 1)(2) = 152$.

Sum of an Arithmetic Sequence

Consider the arithmetic sequence with first term a_1, common difference d, and nth term a_n. The first n terms of an arithmetic sequence can be written in two ways, as follows.

From a_1 to a_n: $a_1, a_1 + d, a_1 + 2d, a_1 + 3d, \ldots, a_1 + (n-1)d$
From a_n to a_1: $a_n, a_n - d, a_n - 2d, a_n - 3d, \ldots, a_n - (n-1)d$

If we let s_n represent the sum of the first n terms of the sequence just described, then we have the following equivalent forms for the sum.

$$s_n = a_1 + (a_1 + d) + (a_1 + 2d) + \cdots + [a_1 + (n-1)d] \qquad (1)$$
$$s_n = a_n + (a_n - d) + (a_n - 2d) + \cdots + [a_n - (n-1)d] \qquad (2)$$

If we add equations (1) and (2) term by term, we obtain

$$2s_n = (a_1 + a_n) + (a_1 + a_n) + (a_1 + a_n) + \cdots + (a_1 + a_n)$$

in which $(a_1 + a_n)$ appears as a term n times. Thus,

$$2s_n = n(a_1 + a_n) \qquad \text{so} \qquad s_n = \frac{n}{2}(a_1 + a_n)$$

Sum of an Arithmetic Sequence

The **sum of the first n terms of an arithmetic sequence** is given by the formula

$$s_n = \frac{n}{2}(a_1 + a_n)$$

where a_1 is the first term of the sequence and a_n is the nth term.

EXAMPLE   8   **Sums of Arithmetic Sequences**

Find the sum of
(a) the first 10 terms of the arithmetic sequence with first term 2 and common difference 4
(b) the first 91 terms of the arithmetic sequence $\frac{1}{4}, \frac{7}{12}, \frac{11}{12}, \ldots$.

Solution
(a) We are given the values $n = 10$, $a_1 = 2$, and $d = 4$. Thus the 10th term is $a_{10} = 2 + (10 - 1)4 = 38$, and the sum of the first 10 terms is

$$s_{10} = \frac{10}{2}(2 + 38) = 200$$

(b) The first term is $\frac{1}{4}$ and the common difference is $\frac{1}{3}$. Therefore, the 91st term is $a_{91} = \frac{1}{4} + (91 - 1)\left(\frac{1}{3}\right) = 30\frac{1}{4} = \frac{121}{4}$. The sum of the first 91 terms is

$$s_{91} = \frac{91}{2}\left(\frac{1}{4} + \frac{121}{4}\right) = \frac{91}{2}\left(\frac{122}{4}\right) = \frac{91(61)}{4} = \left(\frac{5551}{4}\right) = 1387\frac{3}{4}$$

✓ CHECKPOINT

4. Of the following sequences, identify each arithmetic sequence and state its common difference.
    (a) 1, 4, 9, 16, ...
    (b) 1, 4, 7, 10, ...
    (c) 1, 2, 4, 8, ...
5. Given the arithmetic sequence $-10, -6, -2, \ldots$, find
    (a) the 51st term
    (b) the sum of the first 51 terms.

Technology Note

Finally, we should note that many graphing calculators, some graphics software packages, and spreadsheets have the capability of defining sequence functions and then operating on them by finding additional terms, graphing the terms, or summing a fixed number of terms.

 **CHECKPOINT**
ANSWERS

1. $I = Prt$
2. $S = \$8360$
3. $r = 0.12$, or 12%
4. Only (b) is an arithmetic sequence; the common difference is 3.
5. (a) $a_{51} = 190$
    (b) $s_{51} = 4590$

| EXERCISES | 6.1

SIMPLE INTEREST

In Problems 1–4, find the requested value and tell what the other numbers represent.

1. Find r: $250 = 1000(r)(4)$
2. Find t: $1500 = 5000(0.05)(t)$
3. Find P: $9600 = P + P(0.05)(4)$
4. Find P: $11,800 = P + P(0.03)(6)$
5. \$10,000 is invested for 6 years at an annual simple interest rate of 16%.
    (a) How much interest will be earned?
    (b) What is the future value of the investment at the end of the 6 years?
6. \$800 is invested for 5 years at an annual simple interest rate of 14%.
    (a) How much interest will be earned?
    (b) What is the future value of the investment at the end of the 5 years?
7. \$1000 is invested for 3 months at an annual simple interest rate of 12%.
    (a) How much interest will be earned?
    (b) What is the future value of the investment after 3 months?
8. \$1800 is invested for 9 months at an annual simple interest rate of 15%.
    (a) How much interest will be earned?
    (b) What is the future value of the investment after 9 months?
9. If you borrow \$800 for 6 months at 16% annual simple interest, how much must you repay at the end of the 6 months?
10. If you borrow \$1600 for 2 years at 14% annual simple interest, how much must you repay at the end of the 2 years?
11. If you lend \$3500 to a friend for 15 months at 8% annual simple interest, find the future value of the loan.
12. Mrs. Gonzalez lent \$2500 to her son Luis for 7 months at 9% annual simple interest. What is the future value of this loan?
13. A couple bought some stock for \$30 per share that pays an annual dividend of \$0.90 per share. After 1 year the price of the stock was \$33. Find the simple interest rate on the growth of their investment.
14. Jenny Reed bought SSX stock for \$16 per share. The annual dividend was \$1.50 per share, and after 1 year SSX was selling for \$35 per share. Find the simple interest rate of growth of her money.

15. (a) To buy a Treasury bill (T-bill) that matures to \$10,000 in 6 months, you must pay \$9750. What annual simple interest rate does this earn?
    (b) If the bank charges a fee of \$40 to buy a T-bill, what is the actual interest rate you earn?
16. Janie Christopher lent \$6000 to a friend for 90 days at 12%. After 30 days, she sold the note to a third party for \$6000. What annual simple interest rate did the third party receive? Use 360 days in a year.
17. A firm buys 12 file cabinets at \$140 each, with the bill due in 90 days. How much must the firm deposit now to have enough to pay the bill if money is worth 12% simple interest per year? Use 360 days in a year.
18. A student has a savings account earning 9% simple interest. She must pay \$1500 for first-semester tuition by September 1 and \$1500 for second-semester tuition by January 1. How much must she earn in the summer (by September 1) in order to pay the first-semester bill on time and still have the remainder of her summer earnings grow to \$1500 between September 1 and January 1?
19. If you want to earn 15% annual simple interest on an investment, how much should you pay for a note that will be worth \$13,500 in 10 months?
20. What is the present value of an investment at 6% annual simple interest if it is worth \$832 in 8 months?
21. If \$5000 is invested at 8% annual simple interest, how long does it take to be worth \$9000?
22. How long does it take for \$8500 invested at 11% annual simple interest to be worth \$13,000?
23. A retailer owes a wholesaler \$500,000 due in 45 days. If the payment is 15 days late, there is a 1% penalty charge. The retailer can get a 45-day certificate of deposit (CD) paying 6% or a 60-day certificate paying 7%. Is it better to take the 45-day certificate and pay on time or to take the 60-day certificate and pay late with the penalty?
24. An investor owns several apartment buildings. The taxes on these buildings total \$30,000 per year and are due before April 1. The late fee is 1/2% per month up to 6 months, at which time the buildings are seized by the authorities and sold for back taxes. If the investor has \$30,000 available on March 31, will he save money by paying the taxes at that time or by investing the money at 8% and paying the taxes and the penalty on September 30?

25. Bill Casler bought a $2000, 9-month certificate of deposit (CD) that would earn 8% annual simple interest. Three months before the CD was due to mature, Bill needed his CD money, so a friend agreed to lend him money and receive the value of the CD when it matured.
    (a) What is the value of the CD when it matures?
    (b) If their agreement allowed the friend to earn a 10% annual simple interest return on his loan to Bill, how much did Bill receive from his friend?

26. Suppose you lent $5000 to friend 1 for 18 months at an annual simple interest rate of 9%. After 1 year you need money for an emergency and decide to sell the note to friend 2.
    (a) How much does friend 1 owe when the loan is due?
    (b) If your agreement with friend 2 means she earns simple interest at an annual rate of 12%, how much did friend 2 pay you for the note?

SEQUENCES

27. Write the first ten terms of the sequence defined by $a_n = 3n$.
28. Write the first seven terms of the sequence defined by $a_n = 2/n$.
29. Write the first six terms of the sequence whose nth term is $(-1)^n/(2n + 1)$.
30. Write the first five terms of the sequence whose nth term is $a_n = (-1)^n/(n^2)$.
31. Write the first four terms and the 10th term of the sequence whose nth term is

$$a_n = \frac{n - 4}{n(n + 2)}$$

32. Write the sixth term of the sequence whose nth term is

$$a_n = \frac{n(n - 1)}{n + 3}$$

ARITHMETIC SEQUENCES

In Problems 33–36, (a) identify d and a_1 and (b) write the next three terms.

33. 2, 5, 8, ...
34. 3, 9, 15, ...
35. $3, \frac{9}{2}, 6, \ldots$
36. 2, 2.75, 3.5, ...

37. Find the 83rd term of the arithmetic sequence with first term 6 and common difference $-\frac{1}{2}$.
38. Find the 66th term of the arithmetic sequence with first term $\frac{1}{2}$ and common difference $-\frac{1}{3}$.
39. Find the 100th term of the arithmetic sequence with first term 5 and eighth term 19.
40. Find the 73rd term of the arithmetic sequence with first term 20 and 10th term 47.
41. Find the sum of the first 38 terms of the arithmetic sequence with first term 2 and 38th term 113.
42. Find the sum of the first 56 terms of the arithmetic sequence with first term 6 and 56th term 226.

43. Find the sum of the first 70 terms of the arithmetic sequence with first term 10 and common difference $\frac{1}{2}$.
44. Find the sum of the first 80 terms of the arithmetic sequence with first term 12 and common difference -3.
45. Find the sum of the first 150 terms of the arithmetic sequence $6, \frac{9}{2}, 3, \ldots$.
46. Find the sum of the first 200 terms of the arithmetic sequence 12, 9, 6, ...

APPLICATIONS

47. *Bee reproduction* A female bee hatches from a fertilized egg, whereas a male bee hatches from an unfertilized egg. Thus a female bee has a male parent and a female parent, but a male bee has only a female parent. Therefore, the number of ancestors of a male bee follows the *Fibonacci sequence*

$$1, 2, 3, 5, 8, 13, \ldots$$

Observe the pattern and write three more terms of the sequence.

48. *Salaries* Suppose you are offered a job with a relatively low starting salary but with a $3000 raise for each of the next 7 years. How much more than your starting salary would you be making in the eighth year?
49. *Profit* A new firm loses $4000 in its first month, but its profit increases by $800 in each succeeding month for the next year. What is its profit in the 12th month?
50. *Pay raises* If you make $36,000 and get $2400 raises each year, in how many years will your salary double?
51. *Salaries* Suppose you are offered two identical jobs: one paying a starting salary of $40,000 with yearly raises of $2000 and one paying a starting salary of $36,000 with yearly raises of $2400. Which job will pay you more for your 10th year on the job?
52. *Profit* A new firm loses $4000 in its first month, but its profit increases by $800 in each succeeding month for the next year. What is its profit for the year?
53. *Pay raises* If you are an employee, would you rather be given a raise of $2000 at the end of each year (plan I) or a raise of $600 at the end of each 6-month period (plan II)? Consider the table for an employee whose base salary is $40,000 per year (or $20,000 per 6-month period), and answer parts (a)–(g).

| Period (months) | Salary Received per 6-Month Period | |
	Plan I	Plan II
0–6	$20,000	$20,000
6–12	20,000	20,600
12–18	21,000	21,200
18–24	21,000	21,800
24–30	22,000	22,400
30–36	22,000	23,000

(a) Find the sum of the raises for plan I for the first 3 years.

(b) Find the sum of the raises for plan II for the first 3 years.

(c) Which plan is better, and by how much?

(d) Find the sum of the raises in plan I for 5 years.

(e) Find the sum of the raises in plan II for 5 years.

(f) Which plan is better, and by how much?

(g) Do you want plan I or plan II?

54. *Pay raises* As an employee, would you prefer being given a $2400 raise each year for 5 years or a $400 raise each quarter for 5 years?

OBJECTIVES

6.2

- To find the future value of and interest earned when interest is compounded at regular intervals or continuously
- To find the annual percentage yield (APY), or the effective annual interest rate, of money invested at compound interest
- To find the time it takes for an investment to reach a specified amount
- To find specified terms, and sums of specified numbers of terms, of geometric sequences

Compound Interest; Geometric Sequences

■ | APPLICATION PREVIEW |

A common concern for young parents is how they will pay for their children's college educations. To address this, there are an increasing number of college savings plans, such as the so-called "529 plans," which are tax-deferred.

Suppose Jim and Eden established such a plan for their baby daughter Maura. If this account earns 9.8% compounded quarterly and if their goal is to have $200,000 by Maura's 18th birthday, what would be the impact of having $10,000 in the account by Maura's first birthday? (See Example 3.)

A compound interest investment (such as Jim and Eden's account) is one in which interest is paid into the account at regular intervals. In this section we consider investments of this type and develop formulas that enable us to determine the impact of making a $10,000 investment in Maura's college tuition account by her first birthday.

Compound Interest   In the previous section we discussed simple interest. A second method of paying interest is the **compound interest** method, where the interest for each period is added to the principal before interest is calculated for the next period. With compound interest, both the interest added and the principal earn interest for the next period. With this method, the principal grows as the interest is added to it. Think of it like building a snowman. You start with a snowball the size of your fist (your investment), and as you roll the snowball around the yard, the snowball picks up additional snow (interest). The more you roll it, the snowball itself (principal) keeps growing, and as it does, the amount of snow it picks up along the way (interest) also grows. This method is used in investments such as savings accounts and some U.S. government bonds.

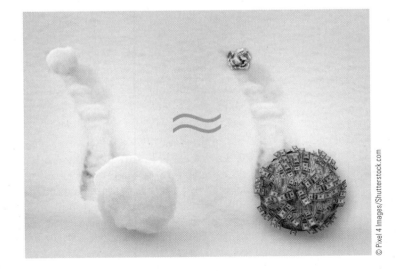

An understanding of compound interest is important not only for people planning careers with financial institutions but also for anyone planning to invest money. To see how compound interest is computed, consider the following table, which tracks the annual growth of $20,000 invested for 3 years at 10% compounded annually. (Notice that the ending principal for each year becomes the beginning principal for the next year.)

Year	Beginning Principal $= P$	10% Annual Interest $= I$	Ending Principal $= P + I$
1	$20,000	0.10($20,000) = $2000	$22,000
2	$22,000	0.10($22,000) = $2200	$24,200
3	$24,200	0.10($24,200) = $2400	$26,620

Note that the future value for each year can be found by multiplying the beginning principal for that year by $1 + 0.10$, or 1.10. That is,

First year: $\$20,000(1.10) = \$22,000$
Second year: $[\$20,000(1.10)](1.10) = \$20,000(1.10)^2 = \$24,200$
Third year: $[\$20,000(1.10)^2](1.10) = \$20,000(1.10)^3 = \$26,620$

This suggests that if we maintained this investment for n years, the future value at the end of this time would be $\$20,000(1.10)^n$. Thus we have the following general formula.

Future Value (Annual Compounding)

If $\$P$ is invested at an interest rate of r per year (expressed as a decimal), compounded annually, the future value S at the end of the nth year is

$$S = P(1 + r)^n$$

EXAMPLE   1   Annual Compounding

If $3000 is invested for 4 years at 9% compounded annually, how much interest is earned?

Solution
The future value is

$$S = \$3000(1 + 0.09)^4$$
$$\approx \$3000(1.4115816)$$
$$= \$4234.7448$$
$$\approx \$4234.74$$

Because $3000 of this amount was the original investment, the interest earned is $\$4234.74 - \$3000 = \$1234.74$.

Some accounts have the interest compounded semiannually, quarterly, monthly, or daily. Unless specifically stated otherwise, a stated interest rate, called the **nominal annual rate,** is the rate per year and is denoted by r. The interest rate *per period*, denoted by i, is the nominal rate divided by the number of interest periods per year. The interest periods are also called *conversion periods*, and the number of periods is denoted by n. Thus, if $100 is invested for 5 years at 6% compounded semiannually (twice a year), it has been invested for $n = 10$ periods (5 years $\times$ 2 periods per year) at $i = 3\%$ per period (6% per year ÷ 2 periods per year). The future value of an investment of this type is found using the following formula.

Future Value (Periodic Compounding)

If $P is invested for t years at a nominal interest rate r, compounded m times per year, then the total number of compounding periods is

$$n = mt$$

the interest rate per compounding period is

$$i = \frac{r}{m} \quad \text{(expressed as a decimal)}$$

and the future value is

$$S = P(1 + i)^n = P\left(1 + \frac{r}{m}\right)^{mt}$$

EXAMPLE 2   Periodic Compounding

For each of the following investments, find the interest rate per period, i, and the number of compounding periods, n.

(a) 12% compounded monthly for 7 years
(b) 7.2% compounded quarterly for 11 quarters

Solution

(a) If the compounding is monthly and $r = 12\% = 0.12$, then $i = 0.12/12 = 0.01$. The number of compounding periods is $n = (7\,\text{yr})(12\,\text{periods}/\text{yr}) = 84$.
(b) $i = 0.072/4 = 0.018, n = 11$ (the number of quarters given)

Once we know i and n, we can calculate the future value from the formula with a calculator.

EXAMPLE 3   Future Value | APPLICATION PREVIEW |

Jim and Eden want to have $200,000 in Maura's college fund on her 18th birthday, and they want to know the impact on this goal of having $10,000 invested at 9.8%, compounded quarterly, on her first birthday. To advise Jim and Eden regarding this, find

(a) the future value of the $10,000 investment
(b) the amount of compound interest that the investment earns
(c) the impact this would have on their goal.

Solution

(a) For this situation, $i = 0.098/4 = 0.0245$ and $n = 4(17) = 68$. Thus the future value of the $10,000 is given by

$$S = P(1 + i)^n = \$10{,}000(1 + 0.0245)^{68} \approx \$51{,}857.73$$

(b) The amount of interest earned is $51,857.73 − $10,000 = $41,857.73.
(c) Thus $10,000 invested by Maura's first birthday grows to an amount that is slightly more than 25% of their goal. This rather large early investment has a substantial impact on their goal.

Technology Note   Graphing calculators and most spreadsheets (including Excel) have built-in finance packages that can be used to solve the compound interest problems of this section and later sections of this chapter.

We can use a graphing calculator to find the future value of a lump sum investment as follows:

1. Under the APPS menu, select Finance, then TVM Solver.
2. (a) Set N = the total number of payments
   (b) Set I% = the annual percentage rate
   (c) Set PV = lump sum invested (with a negative sign because the sum is leaving to go into the investment)
   (d) Set PMT = 0
   (e) Set both P/Y and C/Y equal to the number of compounding periods per year.
4. Highlight END, then put the cursor on FV and press ALPHA ENTER to get the future value.

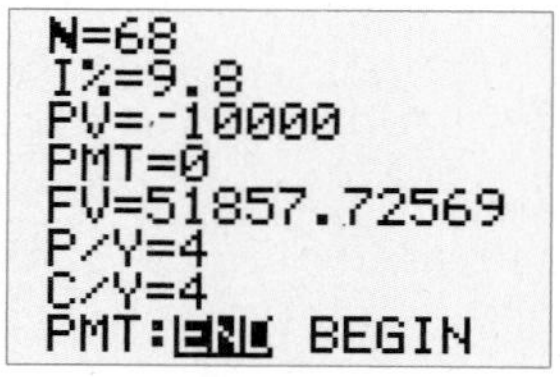

```
N=68
I%=9.8
PV=-10000
PMT=0
FV=51857.72569
P/Y=4
C/Y=4
PMT:END BEGIN
```

Figure 6.1

Figure 6.1 shows that when $10,000 is invested at 9.8% compounded quarterly for 17 years, the future value is about $51,857.73, as we found in Example 3. See Appendix A, Section 6.2, for more details.

We can also use Excel to find the future value of the same lump sum investment by using the formula "= fv(F2, B2, C2, A2, 0)" where

1. Cell F2 has the periodic interest rate as a decimal.
2. Cell B2 has the number of periods.
3. Cell C2 has the value 0.
4. Cell A2 has the lump sum investment amount P.

Cell B4 of Table 6.1 shows the future value for this investment. See Appendix B, Section 6.2, for complete details.

| TABLE 6.1 |

	A	B	C	D	E	F
1	Principal	Number of Periods	Payment	Annual Rate	Periods per Year	Periodic Rate
2	−10000	68	0	0.098	4	0.0245
3						
4	Future Value	$51,857.73				

We saw previously that compound interest calculations are based on those for simple interest, except that interest payments are added to the principal. In this way, interest is earned on both principal and previous interest payments. Let's examine the effect of this compounding by comparing compound interest and simple interest. If the investment in Example 3 had been at simple interest, the interest earned would have been $Prt = \$10,000(0.098)(17) = \$16,660$. This is almost $25,200 less than the amount of compound interest earned. And this difference would have been magnified over a longer period of time. Try reworking Example 3's investment over 30 years and compare the compound interest earned with the simple interest earned. This comparison begins to shed some light on why Albert Einstein characterized compound interest as "the most powerful force in the Universe."

In each of Examples 1 and 3 the beginning principal of the investment, P, also called the **present value** of the investment, and the interest rate, r, were known. Next we consider examples where one of these quantities must be found.

EXAMPLE 4 Present Value

What amount must be invested now in order to have $12,000 after 3 years if money is worth 6% compounded semiannually?

Solution

We need to find the present value P, knowing that the future value is $S = \$12,000$. Use $i = 0.06/2 = 0.03$ and $n = 3(2) = 6$.

$$S = P(1 + i)^n$$
$$\$12,000 = P(1 + 0.03)^6 = P(1.03)^6 \approx P(1.1940523)$$
$$P \approx \frac{\$12,000}{1.1940523} \approx \$10,049.81$$

EXAMPLE   5   **Rate Earned**

As Figure 6.2 shows, three years after Google stock was first sold publicly, its share price had risen 500%. Google's 500% increase means that $10,000 invested in Google stock at its initial public offering (I.P.O.) was worth $60,000 three years later. What interest rate compounded annually does this represent? (For similar information and calculations regarding Microsoft's annual compounding performance, see Problem 33 in the exercises for this section.)

Figure 6.2

Source: Based on data from Google Finance

Solution

We use $P = \$10,000$, $S = \$60,000$, and $n = 3$ in the formula $S = P(1 + i)^n$, and solve for i.

$$\$60,000 = \$10,000(1 + i)^3$$
$$6 = (1 + i)^3$$

At this point we take the cube root (third root) of both sides (or, equivalently, raise both sides to the 1/3 power).

$$6^{(1/3)} = [(1 + i)^3]^{(1/3)}$$
$$1.817 \approx 1 + i \quad \text{so} \quad 0.817 \approx i$$

Thus, this investment earned about 81.7% compounded annually.

✓ CHECKPOINT

1. If $5000 is invested at 6%, compounded quarterly, for 5 years, find
   (a) the number of compounding periods per year, m
   (b) the number of compounding periods for the investment, n
   (c) the interest rate for each compounding period, i
   (d) the future value of the investment.
2. Find the present value of an investment that is worth $12,000 after 5 years at 9% compounded monthly.

If we invest a sum of money, say $100, then the higher the interest rate, the greater the future value. Figure 6.3 shows a graphical comparison of the future values when $100 is invested at 5%, 8%, and 10%, all compounded annually over a period of 30 years. Note that higher interest rates yield consistently higher future values and have dramatically higher future values after 15 to 20 years. Note also that these graphs of the future values are growth exponentials.

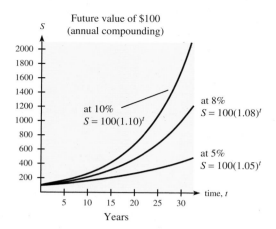

Figure 6.3

Spreadsheet Note
We can also find the future values of investments after n periods with Excel by entering formulas for specific investments. This method is useful when comparing investments with different interest rates. Table 6.2 shows a portion of a spreadsheet that tracks the monthly growth of two investments, both compounded monthly and both with $P = \$1000$, but one at 6% (giving $i = 0.005$) and the other at 6.9% (giving $i = 0.00575$). ■

| TABLE 6.2 |

TWO INVESTMENTS AT DIFFERENT INTEREST RATES

	A	B	C
1	Month #	$ = 1000(1.005)^n	$ = 1000(1.00575)^n
2	22	$1115.97	$1134.44
3	23	$1121.55	$1140.96
4	24	$1127.16	$1147.52

Continuous Compounding

Because more frequent compounding means that interest is paid more often (and hence more interest on interest is earned), it would seem that the more frequently the interest is compounded, the larger the future value will become. To determine the interest that results from *continuous* compounding (compounding every instant), consider an investment of $1 for 1 year at a 100% interest rate. If the interest is compounded m times per year, the future value is given by

$$S = \left(1 + \frac{1}{m}\right)^m$$

Table 6.3 shows the future values that result as the number of compounding periods increases.

| TABLE 6.3 |

Compounded	Number of Periods per Year	Future Value of $1
Annually	1	$\left(1 + \frac{1}{1}\right)^1 = 2$
Monthly	12	$\left(1 + \frac{1}{12}\right)^{12} = 2.6130\ldots$
Daily	360 (business year)	$\left(1 + \frac{1}{360}\right)^{360} = 2.7145\ldots$
Hourly	8640	$\left(1 + \frac{1}{8640}\right)^{8640} = 2.71812\ldots$
Each minute	518,400	$\left(1 + \frac{1}{518,400}\right)^{518,400} = 2.71827\ldots$

Table 6.3 shows that as the number of periods per year increases, the future value increases, although not very rapidly. In fact, no matter how often the interest is compounded, the future value will never exceed $2.72. We say that as the number of periods increases, the future value approaches a limit, which is the number e:

$$e = 2.7182818\ldots.$$

We discussed the number e and the function $y = e^x$ in Chapter 5, "Exponential and Logarithmic Functions." The discussion here shows one way the number we call e may be derived. We will define e more formally later.

Future Value (Continuous Compounding)	In general, if \$$P$ is invested for t years at a nominal rate r (expressed as a decimal), compounded continuously, then the future value is given by the exponential function $$S = Pe^{rt}$$

EXAMPLE 6   Continuous Compounding

(a) Find the future value if $1000 is invested for 20 years at 8%, compounded continuously.
(b) What amount must be invested at 6.5%, compounded continuously, so that it will be worth $25,000 after 8 years?

Solution

(a) The future value is

$$S = \$1000e^{(0.08)(20)} = \$1000e^{1.6}$$
$$\approx \$1000(4.95303) \quad \text{(because } e^{1.6} \approx 4.95303\text{)}$$
$$= \$4953.03$$

(b) Solve for the present value P in $\$25{,}000 = Pe^{(0.065)(8)}$.

$$\$25{,}000 = Pe^{(0.065)(8)} = Pe^{0.52} \approx P(1.68202765)$$
$$\frac{\$25{,}000}{1.68202765} \approx P \quad \text{so} \quad P \approx \$14{,}863.01$$

EXAMPLE 7   Comparing Investments

How much more will you earn if you invest $1000 for 5 years at 8% compounded continuously instead of at 8% compounded quarterly?

Solution

If the interest is compounded continuously, the future value at the end of the 5 years is

$$S = \$1000e^{(0.08)(5)} = \$1000e^{0.4} \approx \$1491.82$$

If the interest is compounded quarterly, the future value at the end of the 5 years is

$$S = \$1000(1.02)^{20} \approx \$1485.95$$

Thus the extra interest earned by compounding continuously is

$$\$1491.82 - \$1485.95 = \$5.87$$

Annual Percentage Yield

As Example 7 shows, when we invest money at a given compound interest rate, the method of compounding affects the amount of interest we earn. As a result, a rate of 8% can earn more than 8% interest if compounding is more frequent than annually.

For example, suppose $1 is invested for 1 year at 8%, compounded semiannually. Then $i = 0.08/2 = 0.04$, $n = 2$, the future value is $S = \$1(1.04)^2 = \$1.0816$, and the interest earned for the year is $\$1.0816 - \$1 = \$0.0816$. Note that this amount of interest represents an annual percentage yield of 8.16%, so we say that 8% compounded semi-annually has an **annual percentage yield (APY),** or **effective annual rate,** of 8.16%. Similarly, if $1 is invested at 8% compounded continuously, then the interest earned is $1(e^{0.08}) − $1 = $0.0833, for an APY of 8.33%.

Banks acknowledge this difference between stated nominal interest rates and annual percentage yields by posting both rates for their investments. Note that the annual percentage yield is equivalent to the stated rate when compounding is annual. In general, the annual percentage yield equals I/P, or just I if $P = $1. Hence we can calculate the APY with the following formulas.

Annual Percentage Yield (APY)	Let r represent the annual (nominal) interest rate for an investment. Then the **annual percentage yield (APY)*** is found as follows. **Periodic Compounding.** If m is the number of compounding periods per year, then $i = r/m$ is the interest rate per period, and $$APY = \left(1 + \frac{r}{m}\right)^m - 1 = (1 + i)^m - 1$$ **Continuous Compounding** $$APY = e^r - 1$$

Thus, although we cannot directly compare two nominal rates with different compounding periods, we can compare their corresponding APYs.

EXAMPLE 8 Comparing Yields

Suppose a young couple such as Jim and Eden from our Application Preview found three different investment companies that offered college savings plans: (a) one at 10% compounded annually, (b) another at 9.8% compounded quarterly, and (c) a third at 9.65% compounded continuously. Find the annual percentage yield (APY) for each of these three plans to discover which plan is best.

Solution
(a) For annual compounding, the stated rate is the APY. Thus, $APY = 10\%$.
(b) Because the number of periods per year is $m = 4$ and the nominal rate is $r = 0.098$, the rate per period is $i = r/m = 0.098/4 = 0.0245$. Thus,

$$APY = (1 + 0.0245)^4 - 1 \approx 1.10166 - 1 = 0.10166 = 10.166\%$$

(c) For continuous compounding and a nominal rate of 9.65%, we have

$$APY = e^{0.0965} - 1 \approx 1.10131 - 1 = 0.10131 = 10.131\%$$

Hence we see that of these three choices, 9.8% compounded quarterly is best. Furthermore, even 9.65% compounded continuously has a higher APY than 10% compounded annually.

✓ **CHECKPOINT**

3. For each future value formula below, decide which is used for interest that is compounded periodically and which is used for interest that is compounded continuously.
   (a) $S = P(1 + i)^n$ (b) $S = Pe^{rt}$
4. If $5000 is invested at 6% compounded continuously for 5 years, find the future value of the investment.
5. Find the annual percentage yield of an investment that earns 7% compounded semiannually.

* Note that the annual percentage yield is also called the **effective annual rate.**

EXAMPLE 9   **Doubling Time**

How long does it take an investment of $10,000 to double if it is invested at
(a) 8%, compounded annually
(b) 8%, compounded continuously?

Solution

(a) We solve for n in $20,000 = \$10,000(1 + 0.08)^n$.

$$2 = 1.08^n$$

Taking the logarithm, base e, of both sides of the equation gives

$$\ln 2 = \ln 1.08^n$$
$$\ln 2 = n \ln 1.08 \quad \text{Logarithm Property V}$$
$$n = \frac{\ln 2}{\ln 1.08} \approx 9.0 \text{ (years)}$$

(b) Solve for t in $20,000 = \$10,000e^{0.08t}$.

$$2 = e^{0.08t} \quad \text{Isolate the exponential.}$$
$$\ln 2 = \ln e^{0.08t} \quad \text{Take "ln" of both sides.}$$
$$\ln 2 = 0.08t \quad \text{Logarithm Property I}$$
$$t = \frac{\ln 2}{0.08} \approx 8.7 \text{ (years)}$$

Spreadsheet Note   To understand better the effect of compounding periods on an investment, we can use a spreadsheet to compare different compounding schemes. Table 6.4 shows a spreadsheet that tracks the growth at 5-year intervals of a $100 investment for quarterly compounding and continuous compounding (both at 10%).

| TABLE 6.4 |

COMPARISON OF TWO INVESTMENTS WITH DIFFERENT COMPOUNDING SCHEMES

	A	B	C
1	Year	S = 100(1.025)^(4n)	S = 100*exp(.10n)
2	5	163.86	164.87
3	10	268.51	271.83
4	15	439.98	448.17
5	20	720.96	738.91
6	25	1181.37	1218.25
7	30	1935.81	2008.55

✓ CHECKPOINT   6. How long does it take $5000 to double if it is invested at 9% compounded monthly?

Geometric Sequences   If P is invested at an interest rate of i per period, compounded at the end of each period, the future value at the end of each succeeding period is

$$P(1 + i), P(1 + i)^2, P(1 + i)^3, \ldots, P(1 + i)^n, \ldots$$

The future values for each of the succeeding periods form a sequence in which each term (after the first) is found by multiplying the previous term by the same number. Such a sequence is called a **geometric sequence.**

Geometric Sequence	A sequence is called a **geometric sequence** (progression) if there exists a number r, called the **common ratio,** such that $$a_n = ra_{n-1} \quad \text{for } n > 1$$

Geometric sequences form the foundation for other applications involving compound interest.

EXAMPLE 10   Geometric Sequences

Write the next three terms of the following geometric sequences.
(a) $1, 3, 9, \ldots$ (b) $4, 2, 1, \ldots$ (c) $3, -6, 12, \ldots$

Solution
(a) The common ratio is 3, so the next three terms are 27, 81, 243.
(b) The common ratio is $\frac{1}{2}$, so the next three terms are $\frac{1}{2}, \frac{1}{4}, \frac{1}{8}$.
(c) The common ratio is -2, so the next three terms are $-24, 48, -96$.

Because each term after the first in a geometric sequence is obtained by multiplying the previous term by r, the second term is $a_1 r$, the third is $a_1 r^2$, etc., and the nth term is $a_1 r^{n-1}$. Thus we have the following formula.

nth Term of a Geometric Sequence	The **nth term of a geometric sequence** (progression) is given by $$a_n = a_1 r^{n-1}$$ where a_1 is the first term of the sequence and r is the common ratio.

EXAMPLE 11 nth Term of a Geometric Sequence

Find the seventh term of the geometric sequence with first term 5 and common ratio -2.

Solution
The seventh term is $a_7 = 5(-2)^{7-1} = 5(64) = 320$.

EXAMPLE 12   Ball Rebounding

A ball is dropped from a height of 125 feet. If it rebounds $\frac{3}{5}$ of the height from which it falls every time it hits the ground, how high will it bounce after it strikes the ground for the fifth time?

Solution
The first rebound is $\frac{3}{5}(125) = 75$ feet; the second rebound is $\frac{3}{5}(75) = 45$ feet. The heights of the rebounds form a geometric sequence with first term 75 and common ratio $\frac{3}{5}$. Thus the fifth term is

$$a_5 = 75\left(\frac{3}{5}\right)^4 = 75\left(\frac{81}{625}\right) = \frac{243}{25} = 9\frac{18}{25} \text{ feet}$$

Sum of a Geometric Sequence

Next we develop a formula for the sum of a geometric sequence, a formula that is important in our study of annuities. The sum of the first n terms of a geometric sequence is

$$s_n = a_1 + a_1 r + a_1 r^2 + \cdots + a_1 r^{n-1} \qquad (1)$$

If we multiply Equation (1) by r, we have

$$rs_n = a_1 r + a_1 r^2 + a_1 r^3 + \cdots + a_1 r^n \qquad (2)$$

Subtracting Equation (2) from Equation (1), we obtain

$$s_n - rs_n = a_1 + (a_1 r - a_1 r) + (a_1 r^2 - a_1 r^2) + \cdots + (a_1 r^{n-1} - a_1 r^{n-1}) - a_1 r^n$$

Thus

$$s_n(1 - r) = a_1 - a_1 r^n \quad \text{so} \quad s_n = \frac{a_1 - a_1 r^n}{1 - r} \quad \text{if } r \neq 1$$

This gives the following.

Sum of a Geometric Sequence	The **sum of the first n terms of the geometric sequence** with first term a_1 and common ratio r is $$s_n = \frac{a_1(1 - r^n)}{1 - r} \quad \text{provided that } r \neq 1$$

EXAMPLE 13 Sums of Geometric Sequences

(a) Find the sum of the first five terms of the geometric progression with first term 4 and common ratio -3.

(b) Find the sum of the first six terms of the geometric sequence $\frac{1}{4}, \frac{1}{8}, \frac{1}{16}, \ldots$.

Solution

(a) We are given that $n = 5$, $a_1 = 4$, and $r = -3$. Thus

$$s_5 = \frac{4[1 - (-3)^5]}{1 - (-3)} = \frac{4[1 - (-243)]}{4} = 244$$

(b) We know that $n = 6$, $a_1 = \frac{1}{4}$, and $r = \frac{1}{2}$. Thus

$$s_6 = \frac{\frac{1}{4}\left[1 - \left(\frac{1}{2}\right)^6\right]}{1 - \frac{1}{2}} = \frac{\frac{1}{4}\left(1 - \frac{1}{64}\right)}{\frac{1}{2}} = \frac{1 - \frac{1}{64}}{2} = \frac{64 - 1}{128} = \frac{63}{128}$$

✓ CHECKPOINT

7. Identify any geometric sequences among the following and give each one's common ratio.
   (a) 1, 4, 9, 16, …
   (b) 1, 4, 7, 10, …
   (c) 1, 4, 16, 64, …
8. (a) Find the 40th term of the geometric sequence $8, 6, \frac{9}{2}, \ldots$.
   (b) Find the sum of the first 20 terms of the geometric sequence 2, 6, 18, ….

✓ CHECKPOINT ANSWERS

1. (a) $m = 4$ (b) $n = 20$ (c) $i = 0.015$ (d) $S \approx \$6734.28$
2. $P \approx \$7664.40$
3. (a) Periodic compounding
   (b) Continuous compounding
4. $S \approx \$6749.29$
5. APY ≈ 0.0712, or 7.12%
6. $n \approx 92.8$ months
7. Only (c) is geometric with common ratio $r = 4$
8. (a) $a_{40} = 8(3/4)^{39} \approx 0.0001$
   (b) $s_{20} = 3{,}486{,}784{,}400$

| EXERCISES | 6.2

COMPOUND INTEREST

In Problems 1–4, find the requested value and identify each of the other values as the periodic rate, the number of periods, the principal, or the future value.

1. Find S: $S = 2000(1 + 0.02)^{24}$
2. Find S: $S = 15{,}000(1 + 0.005)^{360}$
3. Find P: $25{,}000 = P(1 + 0.03)^{48}$
4. Find P: $100{,}000 = P(1 + 0.06)^{25}$

For each investment situation in Problems 5–8, identify (a) the annual interest rate, (b) the length of the investment in years, (c) the periodic interest rate, and (d) the number of periods of the investment.

5. 8% compounded quarterly for 7 years
6. 12% compounded monthly for 3 years
7. 9% compounded monthly for 5 years
8. 10% compounded semiannually for 8 years
9. Find the future value if $8000 is invested for 10 years at 12% compounded annually.
10. What is the future value if $8600 is invested for 8 years at 10% compounded semiannually?
11. What are the future value and the interest earned if $3200 is invested for 5 years at 8% compounded quarterly?
12. What interest will be earned if $6300 is invested for 3 years at 12% compounded monthly?
13. What lump sum do parents need to deposit in an account earning 10%, compounded monthly, so that it will grow to $80,000 for their son's college fund in 18 years?
14. What lump sum should be deposited in an account that will earn 9%, compounded quarterly, to grow to $1.2 million for retirement in 25 years?
15. What present value amounts to $10,000 if it is invested for 10 years at 6% compounded annually?
16. What present value amounts to $300,000 if it is invested at 7%, compounded semiannually, for 15 years?
17. Find the future value if $5100 is invested for 4 years at 9% compounded continuously.
18. Find the interest that will result if $8000 is invested at 7%, compounded continuously, for 8 years.
19. What is the compound interest if $410 is invested for 10 years at 8% compounded continuously?
20. If $8000 is invested at 8.5% compounded continuously, find the future value after $4\frac{1}{2}$ years.
21. Grandparents want to make a gift of $100,000 for their grandchild's 20th birthday. How much would have to be invested on the day of their grandchild's birth if their investment could earn
    (a) 10.5% compounded continuously
    (b) 11% compounded continuously?
    (c) Describe the effect that this slight change in the interest rate makes over the 20 years of this investment.
22. Suppose an individual wants to have $200,000 available for her child's education. Find the amount that would

have to be invested at 12%, compounded continuously, if the number of years until college is
(a) 7 years   (b) 14 years.
(c) Does leaving the money invested twice as long mean that only half as much is needed initially? Explain why or why not.

23. Which investment will earn more money, a $1000 investment for 5 years at 8% compounded annually or a $1000 investment for 5 years compounded continuously at 7%?
24. How much more interest will be earned if $5000 is invested for 6 years at 7% compounded continuously, instead of at 7% compounded quarterly?
25. Find the annual percentage yield for an investment at
    (a) 7.3% compounded monthly
    (b) 6% compounded continuously.
26. What is the annual percentage yield (or effective annual rate) for a nominal rate of (a) 8.4% compounded quarterly and (b) 10% compounded continuously?

In Problems 27 and 28, rank each interest rate and compounding scheme in order from highest yield to lowest yield.

27. 8% compounded quarterly, 8% compounded monthly, 8% compounded annually
28. 6% compounded continuously, 6% compounded semiannually, 6% compounded monthly
29. Two different investment companies offer college savings plans, one at 8.2% compounded continuously and the other at 8.4% compounded quarterly. Which is the better investment?
30. For life insurance policies, some of the premium pays for the cost of the insurance, and the remainder goes toward the cash value of the policy and earns interest like a savings account. Suppose that, on the cash value of their policies, one insurance company pays 4.8% compounded monthly and another pays 4.82% compounded semiannually. Which company offers a higher yield?
31. The figure shows a graph of the future value of $100 at 8% compounded annually, along with the graph of $100 at 8% compounded continuously. Which is which? Explain.

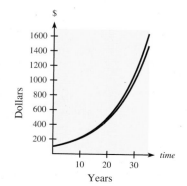

32. The figure shows a graph of the future value of $350 at 6% compounded monthly, along with the graph of $350 at 6% compounded annually. Which is which? Explain.

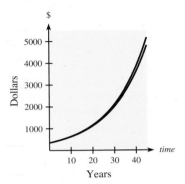

33. Microsoft's stock price peaked at 6118% of its I.P.O. price more than 13 years after the I.P.O. (*Source: Bloomberg Financial Markets*). Suppose that $10,000 invested in Microsoft at its I.P.O. price had been worth $600,000 (6000% of the I.P.O. price) after exactly 13 years. What interest rate, compounded annually, does this represent?

34. If $10,000 had been invested in the Sagamore Capital Opportunity Fund on September 30, 2004, it would have been worth $46,649.55 on September 30, 2014. What interest rate, compounded annually, did this investment earn?

35. How long (in years) would $700 have to be invested at 11.9%, compounded continuously, to earn $300 interest?

36. How long (in years) would $600 have to be invested at 8%, compounded continuously, to amount to $970?

37. At what nominal rate, compounded quarterly, would $20,000 have to be invested to amount to $26,425.82 in 7 years?

38. At what nominal rate, compounded annually, would $10,000 have to be invested to amount to $14,071 in 7 years?

39. For her 1st birthday, Ruth's grandparents invested $1000 in an 18-year certificate for her that pays 8% compounded annually. How much will the certificate be worth on Ruth's 19th birthday?

40. To help their son buy a car on his 16th birthday, a boy's parents invest $7500 on his 10th birthday. If the investment pays 9% compounded continuously, how much is available on his 16th birthday?

41. (a) A 40-year-old man has $432,860 in an IRA account. He decides to make no additional contributions to the account but expects it to grow at 7.5% compounded annually. How much does he expect to have in the account when he retires at age 62?
    (b) How much more money would the man have if his investments earned 8.5% compounded annually?

42. (a) The purchase of Alaska cost the United States $7 million in 1869. If this money had been placed in a savings account paying 6% compounded annually, how much money would be available from this investment in 2015?
    (b) If the $7 million earned 7% compounded annually since 1869, how much would be available in 2015?
    (c) Do you think either amount would purchase Alaska in 2015? Explain in light of the value of Alaska's resources or perhaps the price per acre of land.

43. A couple needs $45,000 as a down payment for a home. If they invest the $30,000 they have at 8% compounded quarterly, how long will it take for the money to grow into $45,000?

44. How long does it take for an account containing $8000 to be worth $15,000 if the money is invested at 9% compounded monthly?

45. Mary Stahley invested $2500 in a 36-month certificate of deposit (CD) that earned 8.5% annual simple interest. When the CD matured, she invested the full amount in a mutual fund that had an annual growth equivalent to 18% compounded annually. How much was the mutual fund worth after 9 years?

46. Suppose Patrick Goldsmith deposited $1000 in an account that earned simple interest at an annual rate of 7% and left it there for 4 years. At the end of the 4 years, Patrick deposited the entire amount from that account into a new account that earned 7% compounded quarterly. He left the money in this account for 6 years. How much did he have after the 10 years?

 In Problems 47 and 48, use a spreadsheet or financial program on a calculator or computer.

47. Track the future values of two investments of $5000, one at 6.3% compounded quarterly and another at 6.3% compounded monthly for each interest payment period for 10 years.
    (a) How long does it take each investment to be worth more than $7500?
    (b) What are the values of each investment after 3 years, 7 years, and 10 years?

48. Track the future values of two investments of $1000, one at 6.0% compounded semiannually and one at 6.6% compounded semiannually for each interest payment period for 25 years.
    (a) How long before the difference between these investments is $50?
    (b) How much sooner does the 6.6% investment reach $1500?

GEOMETRIC SEQUENCES

For each geometric sequence given in Problems 49 and 50, write the next three terms.

49. (a) 3, 6, 12, . . .
    (b) 81, 54, 36, . . .

50. (a) 4, 12, 36, . . .
    (b) 32, 40, 50, . . .

In Problems 51–60, write an expression that gives the requested term or sum.

51. The 13th term of the geometric sequence with first term 10 and common ratio 2

52. The 11th term of the geometric sequence with first term 6 and common ratio 3

53. The 16th term of the geometric sequence with first term 4 and common ratio $\frac{3}{2}$

54. The 20th term of the geometric sequence with first term 3 and common ratio -2

55. The sum of the first 17 terms of the geometric sequence with first term 6 and common ratio 3

56. The sum of the first 14 terms of the geometric sequence with first term 3 and common ratio 4

57. The sum of the first 35 terms of the geometric sequence 1, 3, 9, . . .

58. The sum of the first 14 terms of the geometric sequence 16, 64, 256, . . .

59. The sum of the first 18 terms of the geometric sequence 6, 4, $\frac{8}{3}$, . . .

60. The sum of the first 31 terms of the geometric sequence 9, -6, 4, . . .

APPLICATIONS

61. *Inflation* A house that 20 years ago was worth $160,000 has increased in value by 4% each year because of inflation. What is its worth today?

62. *Inflation* If inflation causes the cost of automobiles to increase by 3% each year, what should a car cost today if it cost $25,000 6 years ago?

63. *Population growth* Suppose a country has a population of 20 million and projects a growth rate of 2% per year for the next 20 years. What will the population of this country be in 10 years?

64. *Spread of AIDS* Suppose a country is so devastated by the AIDS epidemic that its population decreases by 0.5% each year for a 4-year period. If the population was originally 10 million, what is the population at the end of the 4-year period?

65. *Population growth* If the rate of growth of a population continues at 2%, in how many years will the population double?

66. *Population* If a population of 8 million begins to increase at a rate of 0.1% each month, in how many months will it be 10 million?

67. *Ball rebounding* A ball is dropped from a height of 128 feet. If it rebounds $\frac{3}{4}$ of the height from which it falls every time it hits the ground, how high will it bounce after it strikes the ground for the fourth time?

68. *Water pumping* A pump removes $\frac{1}{3}$ of the water in a container with every stroke. What amount of water is still in a container after 5 strokes if it originally contained 81 cm^3?

69. *Depreciation* A machine is valued at $10,000. If the depreciation at the end of each year is 20% of its value at the beginning of the year, find its value at the end of 4 years.

70. *Profit* Suppose a new business makes a $1000 profit in its first month and has its profit increase by 10% each month for the next 2 years. How much profit will the business earn in its 12th month?

71. *Bacterial growth* The size of a certain bacteria culture doubles each hour. If the number of bacteria present initially is 5000, how many would be present at the end of 6 hours?

72. *Bacterial growth* If a bacteria culture increases by 20% every hour and 2000 are present initially, how many will be present at the end of 10 hours?

73. *Profit* If changing market conditions cause a company earning $8,000,000 in 2015 to project a loss of 2% of its profit in each of the next 5 years, what profit does it project in 2020?

74. *Profit* Suppose a new business makes a $1000 profit in its first month and has its profit increase by 10% each month for the next 2 years. How much profit will it earn in its first year?

75. *Chain letters* Suppose you receive a chain letter with six names on it, and to keep the chain unbroken, you are to mail a dime to the person whose name is at the top, cross out the top name, add your name to the bottom, and mail it to five friends. If your friends mail out five letters each, and no one breaks the chain, you will eventually receive dimes. How many sets of mailings before your name is at the top of the list to receive dimes? How many dimes would you receive? (This is a geometric sequence with first term 5.)

76. *Chain letters* Mailing chain letters that involve sending money has been declared illegal because most people would receive nothing while a comparative few would profit. Suppose the chain letter in Problem 75 were to go through 12 unbroken progressions.
    (a) How many people would receive money?
    (b) How much money would these people receive as a group?

77. *Chain letters* How many letters would be mailed if the chain letter in Problem 75 went through 12 unbroken progressions?

- To compute the future values of ordinary annuities and annuities due
- To compute the payments required in order for ordinary annuities and annuities due to have specified future values
- To compute the payment required to establish a sinking fund
- To find how long it will take to reach a savings goal

Future Values of Annuities

| APPLICATION PREVIEW |

Twins graduate from college together and start their careers. Twin 1 invests $2000 at the end of each of 8 years in an account that earns 10%, compounded annually. After the initial 8 years, no additional contributions are made, but the investment continues to earn 10%, compounded annually. Twin 2 invests no money for 8 years but then contributes $2000 at the end of each year for a period of 36 years (to age 65) to an account that pays 10%, compounded annually. How much money does each twin have at age 65? (See Examples 1 and 2.)

In this section we consider ordinary annuities and annuities due, and we develop a formula for each type of annuity that allows us to find its future value—that is, a formula for the value of the account after regular deposits have been made over a period of time.

Each twin's contributions form an annuity. An **annuity** is a financial plan characterized by regular payments. We can view an annuity as a savings plan in which the regular payments are contributions to the account, and then we can ask what the total value of the account will become (as in the Application Preview). Also, we can view an annuity as a payment plan (such as for retirement) in which regular payments are made from an account, often to an individual.

Ordinary Annuities   Most people save (or invest) money by depositing relatively small amounts at different times. If a depositor makes equal deposits at regular intervals, he or she is contributing to an annuity. The payments (deposits) may be made weekly, monthly, quarterly, yearly, or at any other interval of time. The sum of all payments plus all interest earned is called the **future amount of the annuity** or its **future value.**

In this text we will deal with annuities in which the payments begin and end on fixed dates, and we will deal first with annuities in which the payments are made at the end of each of the equal payment intervals. This type of annuity is called an **ordinary annuity** (and also an **annuity immediate**). The ordinary annuities we will consider have payment intervals that coincide with the compounding period of the interest.

Suppose you invested $100 at the end of each year for 5 years in an account that paid interest at 10%, compounded annually. How much money would you have in the account at the end of the 5 years?

Because you are making payments at the end of each period (year), this annuity is an ordinary annuity.

To find the future value of your annuity at the end of the 5 years, we compute the future value of each payment separately and add the amounts (see Figure 6.4). The $100 invested *at the end* of the first year will draw interest for 4 years, so it will amount to $100(1.10)^4$. Figure 6.4 shows similar calculations for years 2–4. The $100 invested at the end of the fifth year will draw no interest, so it will amount to $100.

Thus the future value of the annuity is given by

$$S = 100 + 100(1.10) + 100(1.10)^2 + 100(1.10)^3 + 100(1.10)^4$$

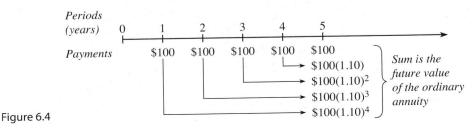

Figure 6.4

The terms of this sum are the first five values of the geometric sequence having $a_1 = 100$ and $r = 1.10$. Thus

$$S = \frac{100[1 - (1.10)^5]}{1 - 1.10} \approx \frac{100(-0.61051)}{-0.10} = 610.51$$

Thus the investment ($100 at the end of each year for 5 years, at 10%, compounded annually) would return $610.51.

Because every such annuity will take the same form, we can state that if a periodic payment R is made for n periods at an interest rate i *per period*, the **future amount of the annuity**, or its **future value**, will be given by

$$S = R \cdot \frac{1 - (1 + i)^n}{1 - (1 + i)} \quad \text{or} \quad S = R\left[\frac{(1 + i)^n - 1}{i}\right]$$

Future Value of an Ordinary Annuity

If $R is deposited at the end of each period for n periods in an annuity that earns interest at a rate of i per period, the **future value of the annuity** will be

$$S = R \cdot s_{\overline{n}|i} = R \cdot \left[\frac{(1 + i)^n - 1}{i}\right]$$

where $s_{\overline{n}|i}$ is read "s, n angle i" and represents the future value of an ordinary annuity of $1 per period for n periods with an interest rate of i per period.

In the Application Preview, we described savings plans for twins. In the next two examples, we answer the questions posed in the Application Preview.

EXAMPLE 1 **Future Value for Twin 2** | APPLICATION PREVIEW |

Twin 2 in the Application Preview invests $2000 at the end of each year for 36 years (until age 65) in an account that pays 10%, compounded annually. How much does twin 2 have at age 65?

Solution

This savings plan is an ordinary annuity with $i = 0.10$, $n = 36$, and $R = 2000. The future value (to the nearest dollar) is

$$S = R\left[\frac{(1 + i)^n - 1}{i}\right] = $2000\left[\frac{(1.10)^{36} - 1}{0.10}\right] \approx $598,254$$

EXAMPLE 2 **Future Value for Twin 1** | APPLICATION PREVIEW |

Twin 1 invests $2000 at the end of each of 8 years in an account that earns 10%, compounded annually. After the initial 8 years, no additional contributions are made, but the investment continues to earn 10%, compounded annually, for 36 more years (until twin 1 is age 65). How much does twin 1 have at age 65?

Solution

We seek the future values of two different investments. The first is an ordinary annuity with $R = 2000, $n = 8$ periods, and $i = 0.10$. The second is a compound interest investment with $n = 36$ periods and $i = 0.10$ and whose principal (that is, its present value) is the future value of this twin's ordinary annuity.

We first find the future value of the ordinary annuity.

$$S = R\left[\frac{(1 + i)^n - 1}{i}\right] = $2000\left[\frac{(1 + 0.10)^8 - 1}{0.10}\right] \approx $22,871.78$$

This amount is the principal of the compound interest investment. If no deposits or withdrawals were made for the next 36 years, the future value of this investment would be

$$S = P(1 + i)^n = \$22,871.78(1 + 0.10)^{36} = \$707,028.03, \text{ to the nearest cent}$$

Thus, at age 65, twin 1's investment is worth about $707,028.

Looking back at Examples 1 and 2, we can extract the following summary and see which twin was the wiser.

	Contributions	Account Value at Age 65
Twin 1	$2000/year for 8 years = $16,000	$707,028
Twin 2	$2000/year for 36 years = $72,000	$598,254

Note that twin 1 contributed $56,000 less than twin 2 but had $108,774 more at age 65. This illustrates the powerful effect that time and compounding have on investments.

Technology Note

We can use a graphing calculator to find the future value of an ordinary annuity as follows:

1. Under the APPS menu, select Finance, then TVM Solver.
2. Set N = the total number of payments, I% = the annual percentage rate, and PV = 0.
3. Set PMT = periodic payment (with a "-" because the money is leaving) and both P/Y and C/Y equal to the number of compounding periods per year.
4. Highlight END, then put the cursor on FV and press ALPHA ENTER to get the future value.

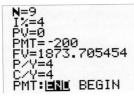

Figure 6.5

Figure 6.5 shows that when $200 is invested at the end of each quarter for $2\frac{1}{4}$ years at 4%, compounded quarterly, the future value is about $1873.71. See Appendix A, Section 6.3, for further details.

We can also use Excel to find the future value of an ordinary annuity by using the formula "= fv(F2, B2, C2, A2, 0)" with the periodic interest rate as a decimal in cell F2, the number of periods in cell B2, the value 0 in cell A2, and the periodic payment in cell C2. Table 6.5 shows the Excel display for the future value of the annuity above; cell B4 shows the future value is $1873.71. See Appendix B, Section 6.3, for details.

TABLE 6.5

	A	B	C	D	E	F
1	Principal	Number of Periods	Payment	Annual Rate	Periods per Year	Periodic Rate
2	0	9	−200	0.04	4	0.01
3	Ordinary Annuity					
4	Future Value	$1873.71				

Figure 6.6 on the next page shows a comparison (each graphed as a smooth curve) of the future values of two annuities that are invested at 6% compounded monthly. One annuity has monthly payments of $100, and one has payments of $125. Note the impact of a slightly larger contribution on the future value of the annuity after 5 years, 10 years, 15 years, and 20 years. Of course, a slightly higher interest rate also can have a substantial impact over time; try a graphical comparison yourself.

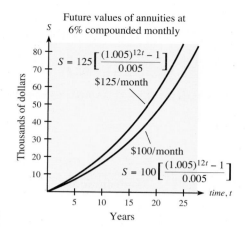

Figure 6.6

Spreadsheet Note   Excel also can be used to compare investments such as those compared graphically in Figure 6.6. Table 6.6 shows the future values at the end of every two years for the first 10 years of two ordinary annuities: one of $100 per month and a second of $125 per month and both at 6%, compounded monthly.

| TABLE 6.6 |

	A	B	C
1		Future Value for $R = \$100$	Future Value for $R = \$125$
2	End of Year #	at 6% compounded monthly	at 6% compounded monthly
3	2	2543.20	3178.99
4	4	5409.78	6762.23
5	6	8640.89	10,801.11
6	8	12,282.85	15,353.57
7	10	16,387.93	20,484.92

Sometimes we want to know how long it will take for an annuity to reach a desired future value.

EXAMPLE 3   Time to Reach a Goal

A small business invests $1000 at the end of each month in an account that earns 6% compounded monthly. How long will it take until the business has $100,000 toward the purchase of its own office building?

Solution

This is an ordinary annuity with $S = \$100{,}000$, $R = \$1000$, $i = 0.06/12 = 0.005$, and $n = $ the number of months. To answer the question of how long, solve for n.

$$\text{Use } S = R\left[\frac{(1 + i)^n - 1}{i}\right] \text{ and solve for } n \text{ in } 100{,}000 = 1000\left[\frac{(1 + 0.005)^n - 1}{0.005}\right].$$

This is an exponential equation. Hence, we isolate $(1.005)^n$, take the natural logarithm of both sides, and then solve for n as follows.

$$100{,}000 = \frac{1000}{0.005}[(1.005)^n - 1]$$

$$0.5 = (1.005)^n - 1$$

$$1.5 = (1.005)^n$$
$$\ln(1.5) = \ln[(1.005)^n] = n[\ln(1.005)]$$
$$n = \frac{\ln(1.5)}{\ln(1.005)} \approx 81.3$$

Because this investment is monthly, after 82 months the company will be able to purchase its own office building.

Sinking Funds

Consumers who are saving for an anticipated purchase by using a regular savings plan to obtain some specified future amount need to know what periodic deposit will allow them to reach their goal. Similarly, some borrowers, such as municipalities, may have a debt that must be paid in a single large sum on a specified future date. If these borrowers make periodic deposits that will produce that sum on a specified date, we say that they have established a **sinking fund.** If the deposits (into the sinking fund or toward the consumer's goal) are all the same size and are made regularly, they form an ordinary annuity whose future value (on a specified date) is the desired amount. To find the size of these periodic deposits, we solve for R in the equation for the future value of an annuity.

EXAMPLE 4   Sinking Fund

A company establishes a sinking fund to discharge a debt of $300,000 due in 5 years by making equal semiannual deposits, the first due in 6 months. If the deposits are placed in an account that pays 6%, compounded semiannually, what is the size of the deposits?

Solution
For this sinking fund, we want to find the payment size, R, given that the future value is $S = \$300,000$, $n = 2(5) = 10$, and $i = 0.06/2 = 0.03$. Thus we have

$$S = R\left[\frac{(1+i)^n - 1}{i}\right]$$

$$\$300,000 = R\left[\frac{(1+0.03)^{10} - 1}{0.03}\right] \approx R(11.463879)$$

$$\frac{\$300,000}{11.463879} \approx R \quad \text{so} \quad R \approx \$26,169.15$$

Thus the semiannual deposit is $26,169.15.

Calculator Note

Example 6 can also be solved with a graphing calculator and TVM as follows: Enter N = 10, I% = 6, PV = 0, FV = 300000, P/Y and C/Y = 2, and select END. Then put the cursor on PMT and press ALPHA ENTER to get the semiannual deposit of $26,169.15. See Figure 6.7.

```
N=10
I%=6
PV=0
PMT=-26169.151…
FV=300000
P/Y=2
C/Y=2
PMT:END BEGIN
```

Figure 6.7

✓ CHECKPOINT

1. Suppose that $500 is deposited at the end of every quarter for 6 years in an account that pays 8%, compounded quarterly.
   (a) What is the total number of payments (periods)?
   (b) What is the interest rate per period?
   (c) What formula is used to find the future value of the annuity?
   (d) Find the future value of the annuity.
2. A sinking fund of $100,000 is to be established with equal payments at the end of each half-year for 15 years. Find the amount of each payment if money is worth 10%, compounded semiannually.

Annuities Due   Deposits in savings accounts, rent payments, and insurance premiums are examples of **annuities due.** Unlike an ordinary annuity, an annuity due has the periodic payments made at the *beginning* of the period. The *term* of an annuity due is from the first payment to the end of one period after the last payment. Thus an annuity due draws interest for one period more than the ordinary annuity.

We can find the future value of an annuity due by treating each payment as though it were made at the *end* of the preceding period in an ordinary annuity. Then that amount, $Rs_{\overline{n}|i}$, remains in the account for one additional period (see Figure 6.8) and its future value is $Rs_{\overline{n}|i}(1 + i)$.

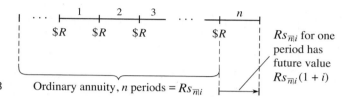

Figure 6.8   Ordinary annuity, n periods $= Rs_{\overline{n}|i}$

Thus the formula for the future value of an annuity due is as follows.

Future Value of an Annuity Due

$$S_{\text{due}} = Rs_{\overline{n}|i}(1 + i) = R\left[\frac{(1 + i)^n - 1}{i}\right](1 + i)$$

EXAMPLE 5   Future Value

Find the future value of an investment if $150 is deposited at the beginning of each month for 9 years and the interest rate is 7.2%, compounded monthly.

Solution
Because deposits are made at the *beginning* of each month, this is an annuity due with $R = \$150$, $n = 9(12) = 108$, and $i = 0.072/12 = 0.006$.

$$S_{\text{due}} = R\left[\frac{(1 + i)^n - 1}{i}\right](1 + i) = \$150\left[\frac{(1 + 0.006)^{108} - 1}{0.006}\right](1 + 0.006)$$

$$\approx \$150(151.3359308)(1.006) \approx \$22{,}836.59$$

✓ CHECKPOINT

3. Suppose $100 is deposited at the beginning of each month for 3 years in an account that pays 6%, compounded monthly.
    (a) What is the total number of payments (or periods)?
    (b) What is the interest rate per period?
    (c) What formula is used to find the future value of the annuity?
    (d) Find the future value.

We can also use the formula for the future value of an annuity due to determine the payment size required to reach an investment goal.

EXAMPLE 6   Required Payment

Suppose a company wants to have $450,000 after $2\frac{1}{2}$ years to modernize its production equipment. How much of each previous quarter's profits should be deposited at the beginning of the current quarter to reach this goal, if the company's investment earns 6.8%, compounded quarterly?

Solution

We seek the payment size, R, for an annuity due with $S_{due} = \$450{,}000$, $n = (2.5)(4) = 10$, and $i = 0.068/4 = 0.017$.

$$S_{due} = R\left[\frac{(1+i)^n - 1}{i}\right](1+i)$$

$$\$450{,}000 = R\left[\frac{(1+0.017)^{10} - 1}{0.017}\right](1+0.017)$$

$$\$450{,}000 \approx R(10.80073308)(1.017) \approx (10.98434554)R$$

$$R = \frac{\$450{,}000}{10.98434554} \approx \$40{,}967.39$$

Thus, the company needs to deposit about $\$40{,}967$ at the beginning of each quarter for the next $2\frac{1}{2}$ years to reach its goal.

Technology Note   Solving investment problems involving annuities due with a graphing calculator uses the same operations as those for ordinary annuities *except* that the PMT is changed from END to BEGIN. See Appendix A, Section 6.3, for details.

Solving investment problems involving annuities due with Excel uses the same formulas as those for ordinary annuities *except* that the last component in fv(F2, B2, C2, A2, 1) is 1 instead of 0. See Appendix B, Section 6.3, for details.

✓ **CHECKPOINT ANSWERS**

1. (a) $n = 24$ periods   (b) $i = 0.02$ per period

   (c) $S = R\left[\dfrac{(1+i)^n - 1}{i}\right]$ (d) $S \approx \$15{,}210.93$

2. $R \approx \$1505.14$

3. (a) $n = 36$ periods   (b) $i = 0.005$ per period

   (c) $S_{due} = R\left[\dfrac{(1+i)^n - 1}{i}\right](1+i)$ (d) $S_{due} \approx \$3953.28$

| EXERCISES | 6.3

ORDINARY ANNUITIES

In Problems 1–4, find the requested value (to the nearest dollar), and tell what each of the other values represents.

1. Find S: $S = 2500\left[\dfrac{(1+0.02)^{60} - 1}{0.02}\right]$

2. Find S: $S = 1000\left[\dfrac{(1+0.03)^{25} - 1}{0.03}\right]$

3. Find R: $80{,}000 = R\left[\dfrac{(1+0.04)^{30} - 1}{0.04}\right]$

4. Find R: $25{,}000 = R\left[\dfrac{(1+0.06)^{15} - 1}{0.06}\right]$

5. The figure shows a graph that compares the future values, at 8% compounded annually, of an annuity of $1000 per year and one of $1120 per year.
   (a) Decide which graph corresponds to which annuity.

   (b) Verify your conclusion to (a) by finding the value of each annuity and the difference between them at $t = 25$ years.

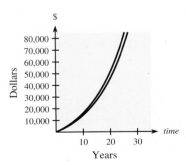

6. The figure shows a graph that compares the future values, at 9% compounded monthly, of an annuity of $50 per month and one of $60 per month.

(a) Decide which graph corresponds to which annuity.
(b) Use the graph to estimate (to the nearest 10 months) how long it will be before the larger annuity is $10,000 more than the smaller one.

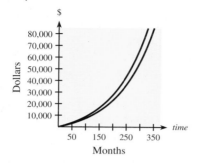

7. Find the future value of an annuity of $1300 paid at the end of each year for 5 years, if interest is earned at a rate of 6%, compounded annually.
8. Find the future value of an annuity of $5000 paid at the end of each year for 10 years, if it earns 9%, compounded annually.
9. Find the future value of an ordinary annuity of $80 paid quarterly for 3 years, if the interest rate is 8%, compounded quarterly.
10. Find the future value of an ordinary annuity of $300 paid quarterly for 5 years, if the interest rate is 12%, compounded quarterly.
11. The Weidmans want to save $40,000 in 2 years for a down payment on a house. If they make monthly deposits in an account paying 12%, compounded monthly, what is the size of the payments that are required to meet their goal?
12. A sinking fund is established to discharge a debt of $80,000 in 10 years. If deposits are made at the end of each 6-month period and interest is paid at the rate of 8%, compounded semiannually, what is the amount of each deposit?
13. If $2500 is deposited at the end of each quarter in an account that earns 5% compounded quarterly, after how many quarters will the account contain $80,000?
14. If $4000 is deposited at the end of each half year in an account that earns 6.2% compounded semiannually, how long will it be before the account contains $120,000?
15. In this section's Application Preview, we considered the investment strategies of twins and found that starting early and stopping was a significantly better strategy than waiting, in terms of total contributions made as well as total value in the account at retirement. Suppose now that twin 1 invests $2000 at the end of each year for 10 years only (until age 33) in an account that earns 8%, compounded annually. Suppose that twin 2 waits until turning 40 to begin investing. How much must twin 2 put aside at the end of each year for the next 25 years in an account that earns 8% compounded annually in order to have the same amount as twin 1 at the end of these 25 years (when they turn 65)?

16. (a) Patty Stacey deposits $2000 at the end of each of 5 years in an IRA. If she leaves the money that has accumulated in the IRA account for 25 additional years, how much is in her account at the end of the 30-year period? Assume an interest rate of 9%, compounded annually.
    (b) Suppose that Patty's husband delays starting an IRA for the first 10 years he works but then makes $2000 deposits at the end of each of the next 15 years. If the interest rate is 9%, compounded annually, and if he leaves the money in his account for 5 additional years, how much will be in his account at the end of the 30-year period?
    (c) Does Patty or her husband have more IRA money?

ANNUITIES DUE

17. Find the future value of an annuity due of $100 each quarter for $2\frac{1}{2}$ years at 12%, compounded quarterly.
18. Find the future value of an annuity due of $1500 each month for 3 years if the interest rate is 12%, compounded monthly.
19. Find the future value of an annuity due of $200 paid at the beginning of each 6-month period for 8 years if the interest rate is 6%, compounded semiannually.
20. A house is rented for $3600 per quarter, with each quarter's rent payable in advance. If money is worth 8%, compounded quarterly, and the rent is deposited in an account, what is the future value of the rent for one year?
21. How much must be deposited at the beginning of each year in an account that pays 8%, compounded annually, so that the account will contain $24,000 at the end of 5 years?
22. What is the size of the payments that must be deposited at the beginning of each 6-month period in an account that pays 7.8%, compounded semiannually, so that the account will have a future value of $120,000 at the end of 15 years?
23. A company wants to have $800,000 for office renovations. If it can deposit $40,000 at the beginning of each quarter into an account that earns 5.2% compounded quarterly, how long before the company reaches its goal?
24. Seana wants to save $20,000 toward a new car purchase. She can contribute $400 at the beginning of each month into an account that earns 4.8% compounded monthly. How long until the account reaches her goal?

MISCELLANEOUS PROBLEMS

In Problems 25–42, (a) state whether the problem relates to an ordinary annuity or an annuity due, and then (b) solve the problem.

25. Parents agree to invest $500 (at 10%, compounded semiannually) for their son on the December 31 or June 30 following each semester that he makes the dean's list during his 4 years in college. If he makes the

dean's list in each of the 8 semesters, how much money will his parents have to give him when he graduates?

26. Jake Werkheiser decides to invest $2000 in an IRA at the end of each year for the next 10 years. If he makes these investments, and if the certificates pay 12%, compounded annually, how much will he have at the end of the 10 years?

27. How much will have to be invested at the beginning of each year at 10%, compounded annually, to pay off a debt of $50,000 in 8 years?

28. If $1000 is deposited at the beginning of each quarter into an account that earns 8%, compounded quarterly, how long until the account contains $31,000?

29. A family wants to have a $200,000 college fund for their children at the end of 20 years. What contribution must be made at the end of each quarter if their investment pays 7.6%, compounded quarterly?

30. If $2000 is deposited at the end of each quarter into an account that earns 6% compounded quarterly, how long until the account reaches $50,000?

31. A couple has determined that they need $1.5 million to establish an annuity when they retire in 25 years. How much money should they deposit at the end of each month in an investment plan that pays 10%, compounded monthly, so they will have the $1.5 million in 25 years?

32. Sam deposits $500 at the end of every 6 months in an account that pays 8%, compounded semiannually. How much will he have at the end of 8 years?

33. A company deposits $12,000 at the beginning of each quarter into an account that earns 7.2% compounded quarterly. How much will be in this account after 5 years?

34. Sofia can deposit $350 at the beginning of each month into an account that earns 4.2% compounded monthly. How long before the account contains $17,000?

35. Mr. Gordon plans to invest $300 at the end of each month in an account that pays 9%, compounded monthly. After how many months will the account be worth $50,000?

36. For 3 years, $400 is placed in a savings account at the beginning of each 6-month period. If the account pays interest at 10%, compounded semiannually, how much will be in the account at the end of the 3 years?

37. Grandparents plan to open an account on their grandchild's birthday and contribute each month until she goes to college. How much must they contribute at the beginning of each month in an investment that pays 12%, compounded monthly, if they want the balance to be $180,000 at the end of 18 years?

38. How much money should a couple deposit at the end of each month in an investment plan that pays 7.5%, compounded monthly, so they will have $800,000 in 30 years?

39. Jane Adele deposits $500 in an account at the beginning of each 3-month period for 9 years. If the account pays interest at the rate of 8%, compounded quarterly, how much will she have in her account after 9 years?

40. A company establishes a sinking fund to discharge a debt of $750,000 due in 8 years by making equal semiannual deposits, the first due in 6 months. If the investment pays 12%, compounded semiannually, what is the size of the deposits?

41. A sinking fund is established by a working couple so that they will have $60,000 to pay for part of their daughter's education when she enters college. If they make deposits at the end of each 3-month period for 10 years, and if interest is paid at 12%, compounded quarterly, what size deposits must they make?

42. A property owner has several rental units and wants to build more. How much of each month's rental income should be deposited at the beginning of each month in an account that earns 6.6%, compounded monthly, if the goal is to have $100,000 at the end of 4 years?

COMBINED APPLICATIONS

Problems 43–46 are complex financial problems that require several skills, perhaps some from previous sections.

43. Suppose a recent college graduate's first job allows her to deposit $100 at the end of each month in a savings plan that earns 9%, compounded monthly. This savings plan continues for 8 years before new obligations make it impossible to continue. If the accrued amount remains in the plan for the next 15 years without deposits or withdrawals, how much money will be in the account 23 years after the plan began?

44. Suppose a young couple deposits $1000 at the end of each quarter in an account that earns 7.6%, compounded quarterly, for a period of 8 years. After the 8 years, they start a family and find they can contribute only $200 per quarter. If they leave the money from the first 8 years in the account and continue to contribute $200 at the end of each quarter for the next $18\frac{1}{2}$ years, how much will they have in the account (to help with their child's college expenses)?

45. A small business owner contributes $3000 at the end of each quarter to a retirement account that earns 8% compounded quarterly.
    (a) How long will it be until the account is worth $150,000?
    (b) Suppose when the account reaches $150,000, the business owner increases the contributions to $5000 at the end of each quarter. What will the total value of the account be after 15 more years?

46. A young executive deposits $300 at the end of each month for 8 years and then increases the deposits. If the account earns 7.2%, compounded monthly, how much (to the nearest dollar) should each new deposit be in order to have a total of $400,000 after 25 years?

OBJECTIVES

6.4

- To compute the present values of ordinary annuities, annuities due, and deferred annuities
- To compute the payments from various annuities
- To find how long an annuity will last
- To apply present values to bond pricing

Present Values of Annuities

|| APPLICATION PREVIEW ||

If you wanted to receive, at retirement, $1000 at the end of each month for 16 years, what lump sum would you need to invest in an annuity that paid 9%, compounded monthly? (See Example 1.) We call this lump sum the present value of the annuity. Note that the annuity in this case is an account from which a person receives equal periodic payments (withdrawals).

In this section, we will find present values of annuities, compute payments from annuities, and find how long annuities will last.

We have discussed how contributing to an annuity program will result in a sum of money, and we have called that sum the future value of the annuity. Just as the term *annuity* is used to describe an account in which a person makes equal periodic payments (deposits), this term is also used to describe an account from which a person receives equal periodic payments (withdrawals). That is, if you invest a lump sum of money in an account today, so that at regular intervals you will receive a fixed sum of money, you have established an annuity. The single sum of money required to purchase an annuity that will provide these payments at regular intervals is the **present value** of the annuity.

Ordinary Annuities

Suppose we wish to invest a lump sum of money (denoted by A_n) in an annuity that earns interest at rate i per period in order to receive (withdraw) payments of size $R from this account at the end of each of n periods (after which time the account balance will be $0). Recall that receiving payments at the end of each period means that this is an ordinary annuity.

To find a formula for A_n, we can find the present value of each future payment and then add these present values (see Figure 6.9).

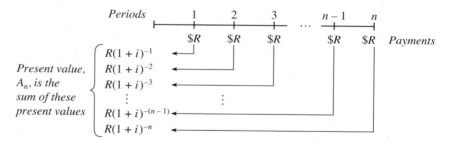

Figure 6.9

Figure 6.9 shows that we can express A_n as follows.

$$A_n = R(1 + i)^{-1} + R(1 + i)^{-2} + R(1+i)^{-3} + \cdots + R(1 + i)^{-(n-1)} + R(1 + i)^{-n} \quad (1)$$

Multiplying both sides of equation (1) by $(1 + i)$ gives

$$(1 + i)A_n = R + R(1 + i)^{-1} + R(1 + i)^{-2} + \cdots + R(1 + i)^{-(n-2)} + R(1 + i)^{-(n-1)} \quad (2)$$

If we subtract Equation (1) from Equation (2), we obtain $iA_n = R - R(1 + i)^{-n}$. Then solving for A_n gives the following.

Present Value of an Ordinary Annuity

If a payment of $R is to be made at the end of each period for n periods from an account that earns interest at a rate of i per period, then the account is an **ordinary annuity,** and the **present value** is

$$A_n = R \cdot a_{\overline{n}|i} = R \cdot \left[\frac{1 - (1 + i)^{-n}}{i} \right]$$

where $a_{\overline{n}|i}$ represents the present value of an ordinary annuity of $1 per period for n periods, with an interest rate of i per period.

For example, if money is worth 8%, compounded semiannually, then an annuity that pays $1500 at the end of each 6-month period for 2 years has $R = \$1500$, $i = 0.08/2 = 0.04$, and $n = (2)(2) = 4$. Thus, the present value of this annuity is

$$A_n = \$1500 \left[\frac{1 - (1 + 0.04)^{-4}}{0.04} \right] \approx \$5444.84$$

EXAMPLE   1   Present Value | APPLICATION PREVIEW |

Find the lump sum that one must invest in an annuity in order to receive $1000 at the end of each month for the next 16 years, if the annuity pays 9%, compounded monthly.

Solution

The sum we seek is the present value of an ordinary annuity, A_n, with $R = \$1000$, $i = 0.09/12 = 0.0075$, and $n = (16)(12) = 192$.

$$A_n = R \left[\frac{1 - (1 + i)^{-n}}{i} \right]$$

$$= \$1000 \left[\frac{1 - (1.0075)^{-192}}{0.0075} \right] \approx \$101{,}572.77$$

Thus the required lump sum, to the nearest dollar, is $101,573.

Technology Note

We can use a graphing calculator to find the present value of an ordinary annuity as follows:

1. Under the APPS menu, select Finance, then TVM Solver.
2. Set N = the total number of payments, I% = the annual percentage rate, and FV = 0.
3. Set PMT = the periodic payment and both P/Y and C/Y equal to the number of compounding periods.
4. Highlight END, then put the cursor on PV and press ALPHA ENTER to get the present value.

Figure 6.10

Figure 6.10 shows the present value of the ordinary annuity in Example 1. Note that PV is negative because this money leaves the investor to start the annuity. See Appendix A, Section 6.4, for complete details for ordinary annuities (and annuities due, introduced later).

We can also use Excel to find the present value of an ordinary annuity by using the *new* formula "= pv(F2, B2, C2, A2, 0)" with the periodic interest rate as a decimal in cell F2, the number of periods in cell B2, the value 0 in cell A2, and the periodic payment in cell C2. Table 6.7 on the next page gives the present value for the annuity of Example 1. The ($101,572.77) means the present value is negative (this money leaves the investor to start the annuity). See Appendix B, Section 6.4, for complete details for ordinary annuities and annuities due.

| TABLE 6.7 |

	A	B	C	D	E	F
1	Future Value	Number of Periods	Payment	Annual Rate	Periods per Year	Periodic Rate
2	0	192	1000	0.09	12	0.0075
3						
4	Present Value	($101,572.77)				

It is important to note that all annuities involve both periodic payments and a lump sum of money. It is whether this lump sum is in the present or in the future that distinguishes problems that use formulas for present values of annuities from those that use formulas for future values of annuities. In Example 1, the lump sum was needed now (in the present) to generate the $1000 payments, so we used the present value formula.

Figure 6.11 shows a graph that compares the present value of an annuity of $1000 per year at an interest rate of 6%, compounded annually, with the same annuity at an interest rate of 10%, compounded annually. Note the impact that the higher interest rate has on the present value needed to establish such an annuity for a longer period of time.

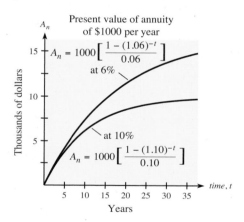

Figure 6.11

Spreadsheet Note

The analysis shown graphically in Figure 6.11 can also be done with a spreadsheet, as Table 6.8 shows for years 5, 10, 15, 20, and 25. Note that at 6% interest, a present value of more than $12,500 is needed to generate 25 years of $1000 payments, but at an interest rate of 10%, the necessary present value is less than $10,000.

| TABLE 6.8 |

PRESENT VALUE GIVING $R = \$1000$ FOR N YEARS

	A	B	C
	Year number	at 6% compounded annually	at 10% compounded annually
2	5	4212.36	3790.79
3	10	7360.09	6144.57
4	15	9712.25	7606.08
5	20	11469.92	8513.56
6	25	12783.36	9077.04

Our graphical and spreadsheet comparisons in Figure 6.11 and Table 6.8 and those from other sections emphasize the truth of the saying "Time is money." We have seen that, given enough time, relatively small differences in contributions or in interest rates can result in substantial differences in amounts (both present and future values).

EXAMPLE 2   Payments from an Annuity

Suppose that a couple plans to set up an ordinary annuity with a $100,000 inheritance they received. What is the size of the quarterly payments they will receive for the next 6 years (while their children are in college) if the account pays 7%, compounded quarterly?

Solution

The $100,000 is the amount the couple has now, so it is the present value of an ordinary annuity whose payment size, R, we seek. Using present value $A_n = \$100,000$, $n = 6(4) = 24$, and $i = 0.07/4 = 0.0175$, we solve for R.

$$A_n = R\left[\frac{1 - (1 + i)^{-n}}{i}\right]$$

$$\$100,000 = R\left[\frac{1 - (1 + 0.0175)^{-24}}{0.0175}\right]$$

$$\$100,000 \approx R(19.46068565)$$

$$R \approx \frac{\$100,000}{19.46068565} \approx \$5138.57$$

✓ CHECKPOINT

1. Suppose an annuity pays $2000 at the end of each 3-month period for $3\frac{1}{2}$ years and money is worth 4%, compounded quarterly.
    (a) What is the total number of periods?
    (b) What is the interest rate per period?
    (c) What formula is used to find the present value of the annuity?
    (d) Find the present value.
2. An inheritance of $400,000 will provide how much at the end of each year for the next 20 years, if money is worth 7%, compounded annually?

EXAMPLE 3   Number of Payments from an Annuity

An inheritance of $250,000 is invested at 9%, compounded monthly. If $2500 is withdrawn at the end of each month, how long will it be until the account balance is $0?

Solution

The regular withdrawals form an ordinary annuity with present value $A_n = \$250,000$, payment $R = \$2500$, $i = 0.09/12 = 0.0075$, and $n =$ the number of months.

Use $A_n = R\left[\dfrac{1 - (1 + i)^{-n}}{i}\right]$ and solve for n in $250,000 = 2500\left[\dfrac{1 - (1.0075)^{-n}}{0.0075}\right]$.

This is an exponential equation, and to solve it we isolate $(1.0075)^{-n}$ and then take the natural logarithm of both sides.

$$\frac{250,000(0.0075)}{2500} = 1 - (1.0075)^{-n}$$

$$0.75 = 1 - (1.0075)^{-n}$$

$$(1.0075)^{-n} = 0.25$$

$$\ln\left[(1.0075)^{-n}\right] = \ln(0.25) \implies -n\left[\ln(1.0075)\right] = \ln(0.25)$$

$$-n = \frac{\ln(0.25)}{\ln(1.0075)} \approx -185.5, \text{ so } n \approx 185.5$$

Thus, the account balance will be $0 in 186 months (with the last payment less than $2500). ■

Bond Pricing

Bonds are investments with a fixed rate of return, similar to a bank certificate of deposit (CD), but unlike CDs (and like stocks), bonds can be traded. And, as is also true of stocks, the trading or market price of a bond may fluctuate.

Most commonly, bonds are issued by the government, corporations, or municipalities for periods of 10 years or longer. Bonds actually constitute a loan in which the issuer of the bond is the borrower, the bond holders (or purchasers) are the lenders, and the interest payments to the bond holders are called **coupons.** In the simplest case, a bond's issue price, or **par value,** is the same as its **maturity value,** and the coupons are paid semiannually.

For example, if a corporation plans to issue $5000 bonds at 6% semiannually, then the maturity value is $5000, the **coupon rate** is 6%, and each semiannual coupon payment will be

$$(\$5000)(0.06/2) = (\$5000)(0.03) = \$150$$

The coupons are paid at the end of every 6 months and constitute an ordinary annuity. At maturity, the bond holder receives the final coupon payment of $150 plus the $5000 maturity value of the bond.

Because the amount of the coupon is fixed by the coupon rate for the entire term of the bond, the market price of the bond is strongly influenced by current interest rates. If a $5000 bond pays a 6% coupon rate, but market interest rates are higher than that, an investor will typically invest in the bond only if the bond's price makes its rate of return comparable to the market rate. The rate of return that the investor requires in order to buy the bond is called the **yield rate.**

At any moment in time the market price of a bond is the sum of the present value of the bond's maturity value, P, and the present value of the annuity of future coupon payments, A_n. See Figure 6.12.

Market Price of a Bond = P + A_n

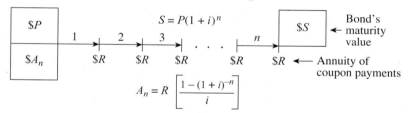

Figure 6.12

EXAMPLE 4   Bond Pricing

Suppose a 15-year corporate bond has a maturity value of $10,000 and coupons at 5% paid semiannually. If an investor wants to earn a yield of 7.2% compounded semiannually, what should he or she pay for this bond?

Solution

Each semiannual coupon payment is

$$(\$10,000)(0.05/2) = (\$10,000)(0.025) = \$250$$

Since the desired rate of return is 7.2% semiannually and the bond is for 15 years, we set $i = 0.072/2 = 0.036$ and $n = (15)(2) = 30$.

With these values of i and n, the market price of this bond is the sum of the following present values, (1) and (2).

(1) the principal (or present value) of a compound interest investment at $i = 0.036$ for $n = 30$ periods with future value $S = \$10,000$, the bond's maturity value

$$S = P(1 + i)^n$$
$$\$10,000 = P(1 + 0.036)^{30} = P(1.036)^{30}$$
$$P = \frac{\$10,000}{(1.036)^{30}} \approx \$3461.05$$

(2)   the present value of the ordinary annuity formed by the coupon payments of $R = \$250$ at $i = 0.036$ for $n = 30$ periods

$$A_n = R\left[\frac{1 - (1 + i)^{-n}}{i}\right]$$

$$A_n = \$250\left[\frac{1 - (1.036)^{-30}}{0.036}\right] \approx \$4540.94$$

Thus, to earn the desired 7.2% yield, the market price an investor should pay for this bond is

$$\text{Price} = \$3461.05 + \$4540.94 = \$8001.99$$

Note that in Example 4 the bond's market price is less than its maturity value. In this case the bond is said to be **selling at a discount.** This has to be the case in order for the yield rate to exceed the coupon rate. Similarly, if the yield rate is lower than the coupon rate, then the market price of the bond will exceed its maturity value. When this happens, the bond is said to be **selling at a premium.** In general, the market price of a bond moves in the opposite direction from current yield rates.

Annuities Due   Recall that an annuity due is one in which payments are made at the beginning of each period. This means that the present value of an annuity due of n payments (denoted $A_{(n,\text{due})}$) of $\$R$ at interest rate i per period can be viewed as an initial payment of $\$R$ plus the payment program for an ordinary annuity of $n - 1$ payments of $\$R$ at interest rate i per period (see Figure 6.13).

Present Value of an Annuity Due

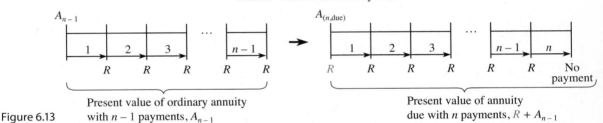

Figure 6.13   Present value of ordinary annuity with $n - 1$ payments, A_{n-1} Present value of annuity due with n payments, $R + A_{n-1}$

From Figure 6.13, we have

$$A_{(n,\text{due})} = R + A_{n-1} = R + R\left[\frac{1 - (1 + i)^{-(n-1)}}{i}\right]$$

$$= R\left[1 + \frac{1 - (1 + i)^{-(n-1)}}{i}\right] = R\left[\frac{i}{i} + \frac{1 - (1 + i)^{-(n-1)}}{i}\right]$$

$$= R\left[\frac{(1 + i) - (1 + i)^{-(n-1)}}{i}\right] = R(1 + i)\left[\frac{1 - (1 + i)^{-n}}{i}\right]$$

Thus we have the following formula for the present value of an annuity due.

Present Value of an Annuity Due

If a payment of $\$R$ is to be made at the beginning of each period for n periods from an account that earns interest rate i per period, then the account is an **annuity due,** and its **present value** is given by

$$A_{(n,\text{due})} = R\left[\frac{1 - (1 + i)^{-n}}{i}\right](1 + i) = Ra_{\overline{n}|i}(1 + i)$$

where $a_{\overline{n}|i}$ denotes the present value of an ordinary annuity of $\$1$ per period for n periods at interest rate i per period.

EXAMPLE 5   Lottery Prize

A lottery prize worth $1,200,000 is awarded in payments of $10,000 at the beginning of each month for 10 years. Suppose money is worth 7.8%, compounded monthly. What is the *real* value of the prize?

Solution

The *real* value of this prize is its present value when it is awarded. That is, it is the present value of an annuity due with $R = \$10,000$, $i = 0.078/12 = 0.0065$, and $n = 12(10) = 120$. Thus

$$A_{(120,\text{due})} = \$10,000 \left[\frac{1 - (1 + 0.0065)^{-120}}{0.0065} \right] (1 + 0.0065)$$

$$\approx \$10,000(83.1439199)(1.0065) \approx \$836,843.55.$$

This means the lottery operator needs this amount to generate the 120 monthly payments of $10,000 each. ∎

EXAMPLE 6   Court Settlement Payments

Suppose that a court settlement results in a $750,000 award. If this is invested at 9%, compounded semiannually, how much will it provide at the beginning of each half-year for a period of 7 years?

Solution

Because payments are made at the beginning of each half-year, this is an annuity due. We seek the payment size, R, and use the present value $A_{(n,\text{due})} = \$750,000$, $n = 2(7) = 14$, and $i = 0.09/2 = 0.045$.

$$A_{(n,\text{due})} = R \left[\frac{1 - (1 + i)^{-n}}{i} \right] (1 + i)$$

$$\$750,000 = R \left[\frac{1 - (1 + 0.045)^{-14}}{0.045} \right] (1 + 0.045)$$

$$\$750,000 \approx R(10.682852)$$

$$R \approx \frac{\$750,000}{10.682852} \approx \$70,205.97$$ ∎

✓ CHECKPOINT   3. What lump sum will be needed to generate payments of $5000 at the beginning of each quarter for a period of 5 years if money is worth 7%, compounded quarterly?

Deferred Annuities   A **deferred annuity** is one in which the first payment is made not at the beginning or end of the first period, but at some later date. An annuity that is deferred for k periods and then has payments of $R per period at the end of each of the next n periods is an ordinary deferred annuity and can be illustrated by Figure 6.14.

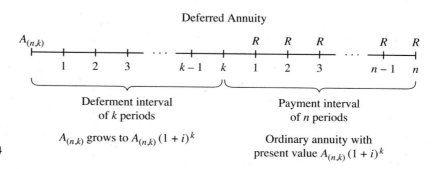

Deferred Annuity

Figure 6.14

We now consider how to find the present value of such a deferred annuity when the interest rate is i per period. If payment is deferred for k periods, then the present value deposited now, denoted by $A_{(n,k)}$, is a compound interest investment for these k periods, and its future value is $A_{(n,k)}(1 + i)^k$. This amount then becomes the present value of the ordinary annuity for the next n periods. From Figure 6.14, we see that we have two equivalent expressions for the amount at the beginning of the first payment period.

$$A_{(n,k)}(1 + i)^k = R\left[\frac{1 - (1 + i)^{-n}}{i}\right]$$

Multiplying both sides by $(1 + i)^{-k}$ gives the following.

Present Value of a Deferred Annuity

The **present value of a deferred annuity** of $R per period for n periods, deferred for k periods with interest rate i per period, is given by

$$A_{(n,k)} = R\left[\frac{1 - (1 + i)^{-n}}{i}\right](1 + i)^{-k} = Ra_{\overline{n}|i}\,(1 + i)^{-k}$$

EXAMPLE 7   Present Value of a Deferred Annuity

A deferred annuity is purchased that will pay $10,000 per quarter for 15 years after being deferred for 5 years. If money is worth 6% compounded quarterly, what is the present value of this annuity?

Solution

We use $R = \$10{,}000$, $n = 4(15) = 60$, $k = 4(5) = 20$, and $i = 0.06/4 = 0.015$ in the formula for the present value of a deferred annuity.

$$A_{(60,20)} = R\left[\frac{1 - (1 + i)^{-60}}{i}\right](1 + i)^{-20}$$

$$= \$10{,}000\left[\frac{1 - (1.015)^{-60}}{0.015}\right](1.015)^{-20} \approx \$292{,}386.85$$

✓ CHECKPOINT

4. Suppose an annuity at 6% compounded semiannually will pay $5000 at the end of each 6-month period for 5 years with the first payment deferred for 10 years.
   (a) What is the number of payment periods and the number of deferral periods?
   (b) What is the interest rate per period?
   (c) What formula is used to find the present value of this annuity?
   (d) Find the present value of this annuity.

EXAMPLE 8   Lottery Prize Payments

Suppose a lottery prize of $50,000 is invested by a couple for future use as their child's college fund. The family plans to use the money as 8 semiannual payments at the end of each 6-month period after payments are deferred for 10 years. How much would each payment be if the money can be invested at 8.6% compounded semiannually?

Solution

We seek the payment R for a deferred annuity with $n = 8$ payment periods, deferred for $k = 2(10) = 20$ periods, $i = 0.086/2 = 0.043$, and $A_{(n,k)} = \$50,000$.

$$A_{(n,k)} = R\left[\frac{1 - (1 + i)^{-n}}{i}\right](1 + i)^{-k}$$

$$\$50,000 = R\left[\frac{1 - (1.043)^{-8}}{0.043}\right](1.043)^{-20}$$

$$\$50,000 \approx R(2.865122499)$$

$$R \approx \frac{\$50,000}{2.865122499} \approx \$17,451.26$$

In Example 8, note the effect of the deferral time. The family receives $8(\$17,451.26) = \$139,610.08$ from the original $\$50,000$ investment.

✓ **CHECKPOINT ANSWERS**

1. (a) $n = 14$
   (b) $i = 0.01$
   (c) $A_n = R\left[\dfrac{1 - (1 + i)^{-n}}{i}\right]$
   (d) $A_n = \$2000\left[\dfrac{1 - (1.01)^{-14}}{0.01}\right] \approx \$26,007.41$
2. $R \approx \$37,757.17$
3. $A_{(20,\text{due})} \approx \$85,230.28$
4. (a) $n = 10$ payment periods; $k = 20$ deferral periods
   (b) $i = 0.03$
   (c) $A_{(n,k)} = R\left[\dfrac{1 - (1 + i)^{-n}}{i}\right](1 + i)^{-k}$
   (d) $A_{(n,k)} \approx \$23,614.83$

| EXERCISES | 6.4

ORDINARY ANNUITIES

In Problems 1–4, find the requested value (to the nearest dollar), and tell what each of the other values represents.

1. Find A_n: $A_n = 1300\left[\dfrac{1 - (1 + 0.04)^{-30}}{0.04}\right]$

2. Find A_n: $A_n = 2550\left[\dfrac{1 - (1 + 0.01)^{-120}}{0.01}\right]$

3. Find R: $135{,}000 = R\left[\dfrac{1 - (1 + 0.005)^{-360}}{0.005}\right]$

4. Find R: $25{,}000 = R\left[\dfrac{1 - (1 + 0.02)^{-20}}{0.02}\right]$

5. Find the present value of an annuity of $6000 paid at the end of each 6-month period for 8 years if the interest rate is 8%, compounded semiannually.

6. Find the present value of an annuity that pays $3000 at the end of each 6-month period for 6 years if the interest rate is 6%, compounded semiannually.

7. Suppose a state lottery prize of $5 million is to be paid in 20 payments of $250,000 each at the end of each of the next 20 years. If money is worth 10%, compounded annually, what is the present value of the prize?

8. How much is needed in an account that earns 8.4% compounded monthly in order to withdraw $1000 at the end of each month for 20 years?

9. With a present value of $135,000, what is the size of the withdrawals that can be made at the end of each quarter for the next 10 years if money is worth 6.4%, compounded quarterly?

10. If $88,000 is invested in an annuity that earns 5.8%, compounded quarterly, what payments will it provide at the end of each quarter for the next $5\frac{1}{2}$ years?

11. A personal account earmarked as a retirement supplement contains $242,400. Suppose $200,000 is used to establish an annuity that earns 6%, compounded quarterly, and pays $4500 at the end of each quarter. How long will it be until the account balance is $0?

12. A professional athlete invested $2.5 million of a bonus in an account that earns 6.8%, compounded semiannually. If $120,000 is to be withdrawn at the end of each six months, how long will it be until the account balance is $0?

13. Suppose that a 25-year government bond has a maturity value of $1000 and a coupon rate of 6%,

with coupons paid semiannually. Find the market price of the bond if the yield rate is 5% compounded semiannually. Is this bond selling at a discount or at a premium?

14. Suppose that a 10-year corporate bond has a maturity value of $25,000 and a coupon rate of 7%, with coupons paid semiannually. Find the market price of the bond if the yield rate is 8% compounded semiannually. Is this bond selling at a discount or at a premium?

15. The figure shows a graph that compares the present values of two ordinary annuities of $1000 annually, one at 8% compounded annually and one at 10% compounded annually.
    (a) Determine which graph corresponds to the 8% rate and which to the 10% rate.
    (b) Use the graph to estimate the difference between the present values of these annuities for 25 years.
    (c) Write a sentence that explains this difference.

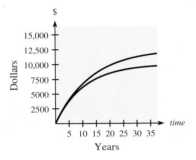

16. The figure shows a graph that compares the present values of two ordinary annuities of $800 quarterly, one at 6% compounded quarterly and one at 9% compounded quarterly.
    (a) Determine which graph corresponds to the 6% rate and which to the 9% rate.
    (b) Use the graph to estimate the difference between the present values of these annuities for 25 years (100 quarters).
    (c) Write a sentence that explains this difference.

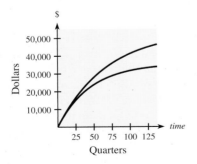

ANNUITIES DUE

17. Explain the difference between an ordinary annuity and an annuity due.

18. Is there any difference between the present values in parts (a) and (b)? Explain.

(a) An annuity due that pays $1000 at the beginning of each year for 10 years
(b) Taking $1000 now and establishing an ordinary annuity that pays $1000 at the end of each year for 9 years

19. Find the present value of an annuity due that pays $3000 at the beginning of each quarter for the next 7 years. Assume that money is worth 5.8%, compounded quarterly.

20. Find the present value of an annuity due that pays $25,000 every 6 months for the next $2\frac{1}{2}$ years if money is worth 6.2%, compounded semiannually.

21. What amount must be set aside now to generate payments of $50,000 at the beginning of each year for the next 12 years if money is worth 5.92%, compounded annually?

22. Suppose an annuity will pay $15,000 at the beginning of each year for the next 7 years. How much money is needed to start this annuity if it earns 7.3%, compounded annually?

23. A year-end bonus of $25,000 will generate how much money at the beginning of each month for the next year, if it can be invested at 6.48%, compounded monthly?

24. A couple inherits $89,000. How much can this generate at the beginning of each month over the next 5 years, if money is worth 6.3%, compounded monthly?

MISCELLANEOUS PROBLEMS FOR ORDINARY ANNUITIES AND ANNUITIES DUE

In Problems 25–40, (a) decide whether the problem relates to an ordinary annuity or an annuity due, and then (b) solve the problem.

25. An insurance settlement of $1.5 million must replace Trixie Eden's income for the next 40 years. What income will this settlement provide at the end of each month if it is invested in an annuity that earns 8.4%, compounded monthly?

26. A local library receives a bequest of $100,000 from a prominent local family. How much will this provide at the beginning of each 3-month period for the next $2\frac{1}{2}$ years if money is worth 7.4% compounded quarterly?

27. A company wants to have $40,000 at the beginning of each 6-month period for the next $4\frac{1}{2}$ years. If an annuity is set up for this purpose, how much must be invested now if the annuity earns 6.68%, compounded semiannually?

28. Is it more economical to buy an automobile for $29,000 cash or to pay $8000 down and $3000 at the end of each quarter for 2 years, if money is worth 8% compounded quarterly?

29. Dr. Jane Kodiak plans to sell her practice to an HMO. The HMO will pay her $1.5 million now or will make a $500,000 partial payment now and make additional payments of $140,000 at the end of each year for the next 10 years. If money is worth 6.5%, compounded

annually, is it better to take $1.5 million now or $500,000 now and $140,000 at the end of each year for the next 10 years? Justify your choice.

30. As a result of a court settlement, an accident victim is awarded $1.2 million. The attorney takes one-third of this amount, another third is used for immediate expenses, and the remaining third is used to set up an annuity. What amount will this annuity pay at the beginning of each quarter for the next 5 years if the annuity earns 7.6%, compounded quarterly?

31. Recent sales of some real estate and record profits make it possible for a manufacturer to set aside $800,000 in a fund to be used for modernization and remodeling. How much can be withdrawn from this fund at the beginning of each half-year for the next 3 years if the fund earns 7.7%, compounded semiannually?

32. A $2.4 million state lottery pays $10,000 at the beginning of each month for 20 years. How much money must the state actually have in hand to set up the payments for this prize if money is worth 6.3%, compounded monthly?

33. How long will an account worth $2.2 million provide $10,000 at the end of each month, if money is worth 5.4% compounded monthly?

34. A college class's 25th reunion gift is $8.6 million. How many semiannual payments of $250,000 will this provide at the beginning of each 6-month period if money is worth 4.4% compounded semiannually?

35. A used piece of rental equipment has $2\frac{1}{2}$ years of useful life remaining. When rented, the equipment brings in $800 per month (paid at the beginning of the month). If the equipment is sold now and money is worth 4.8%, compounded monthly, what must the selling price be to recoup the income that the rental company loses by selling the equipment "early"?

36. As a result of a court settlement, a financial firm agreed to pay $13.4 million to Ford Motor Company, with $10 million of it going to a Ford charitable trust (*Source: The New York Times*). If the trust invested this money at 6.3%, compounded annually, how much could be awarded to worthwhile organizations at the end of each year for the next 20 years?

37. As the contestant with the longest winning streak in the history of *Jeopardy,* Ken Jennings won more than $2.5 million. Suppose he invested $1.5 million in an ordinary annuity that earned 7.2%, compounded monthly. How much would he receive at the end of each month for the next 20 years?

38. Suppose Becky has her choice of $10,000 at the end of each month for life or a single prize of $1.5 million. She is 35 years old and her life expectancy is 40 more years.
    (i)   Find the present value of the annuity if money is worth 7.2%, compounded monthly.
    (ii) If she takes the $1.5 million, spends $700,000 of it, and invests the remainder at 7.2% compounded monthly, what amount will she receive at the end of each month for the next 40 years?

39. Juanita Domingo's parents want to establish a college trust for her. They want to make 16 quarterly withdrawals of $2000, with the first withdrawal 3 months from now. If money is worth 7.2%, compounded quarterly, how much must be deposited now to provide for this trust?

40. A retiree inherits $93,000 and invests it at 6.6%, compounded monthly, in an annuity that provides an amount at the end of each month for the next 12 years. Find the monthly amount.

41. A 10-year Emmaco Corporate bond has a par value of $10,000 with coupons at 7.8% paid semiannually.
    (a) If this bond is bought to yield 10% compounded semiannually, find its price.
    (b) Suppose that after this bond has been held for 2 years, the desired yield is 8% compounded semiannually. Find the selling price.

42. Kodicom, Inc. has 15-year bonds with a $5000 maturity value and a quoted coupon rate of 12% paid semiannually. The current yield is 10% compounded semiannually.
    (a) Compute the price of these bonds.
    (b) Suppose that with 12 years remaining until maturity, the yield rate drops to 8% compounded semiannually. Find the new price of these bonds.

COMBINED APPLICATIONS

Problems 43–46 are complex financial problems that require several skills, perhaps some from previous sections.

For each of Problems 43 and 44, answer the following questions.
(a) How much is in the account after the last deposit is made?
(b) How much was deposited?
(c) What is the amount of each withdrawal?
(d) What is the total amount withdrawn?

43. Suppose an individual makes an initial investment of $2500 in an account that earns 7.8%, compounded monthly, and makes additional contributions of $100 at the end of each month for a period of 12 years. After these 12 years, this individual wants to make withdrawals at the end of each month for the next 5 years (so that the account balance will be reduced to $0).

44. Suppose that Nam Banh deposits his $12,500 bonus in an account that earns 8%, compounded quarterly, and makes additional deposits of $500 at the end of each quarter for the next $22\frac{1}{2}$ years, until he retires. To supplement his retirement, Nam wants to make withdrawals at the end of each quarter for the next 12 years (at which time the account balance will be $0).

45. A young couple wants to have a college fund that will pay $30,000 at the end of each half-year for 8 years.
    (a) If they can invest at 8%, compounded semiannually, how much do they need to invest at the end of each 6-month period for the next 18 years in order to begin making their college withdrawals 6 months after their last investment?

(b) Suppose 8 years after beginning the annuity payments, they receive an inheritance of $38,000 that they contribute to the account, and they continue to make their regular payments as found in part (a). How many college withdrawals will they be able to make before the account balance is $0?

46. A recent college graduate begins a savings plan at age 27 by investing $400 at the end of each month in an account that earns 7.5%, compounded monthly.
    (a) If this plan is followed for 10 years, how much should the monthly contributions be for the next 28 years in order to be able to withdraw $10,000 at the end of each month from the account for the next 25 years?
    (b) What is the total amount contributed?
    (c) What is the total amount withdrawn?

DEFERRED ANNUITIES

47. Find the present value of an annuity of $2000, at the end of each quarter for 5 years after being deferred for 3 years, if money is worth 8% compounded quarterly.
48. Find the present value of an annuity of $2000 per year at the end of each of 8 years after being deferred for 6 years, if money is worth 7% compounded annually.
49. The terms of a single parent's will indicate that a child will receive an ordinary annuity of $16,000 per year from age 18 to age 24 (so the child can attend college) and that the balance of the estate goes to a niece. If the parent dies on the child's 14th birthday, how much money must be removed from the estate to purchase the annuity? (Assume an interest rate of 6%, compounded annually.)
50. On his 48th birthday, a man wants to set aside enough money to provide an income of $1500 at the end of each month from his 60th birthday to his 65th birthday. If he earns 6%, compounded monthly, how much will this supplemental retirement plan cost him on his 48th birthday?
51. The semiannual tuition payment at a major university is expected to be $30,000 for the 4 years beginning 18 years from now. What lump sum payment should the university accept now, in lieu of tuition payments beginning 18 years, 6 months from now? Assume that money is worth 7%, compounded semiannually, and that tuition is paid at the end of each half-year for 4 years.
52. A community is soliciting pledges for a fitness center building project to begin in 3 years. If money is worth 6%, compounded quarterly, how much must

a family deposit now in order to contribute $2500 at the end of each quarter for $2\frac{1}{2}$ years after the project begins?

53. Danny Metzger's parents invested $1600 when he was born. This money is to be used for Danny's college education and is to be withdrawn in four equal annual payments beginning when Danny is age 19. Find the amount that will be available each year, if money is worth 6%, compounded annually.
54. Carol Goldsmith received a trust fund inheritance of $10,000 on her 30th birthday. She plans to use the money to supplement her income with 20 quarterly payments beginning on her 60th birthday. If money is worth 7.6% compounded quarterly, how much will each quarterly payment be?
55. The May 18, 2013, Powerball, worth $590.5 million and won by an 84-year-old resident of Zephyrillis, Florida, was the largest individual jackpot ever. (Note that in March 2012 three ticket holders split the largest-ever Powerball prize of $656 million.) Rather than take the prize in 30 annual installments totaling the $590.5 million, the winner elected a single prize payment of $370.9 million (after taxes, about $278 million). Suppose the winner set aside $150 million of the after-tax amount in a fund that earns 4.5% compounded monthly. After a deferral period of 16 years, how much would be available to the winner's heirs at the end of each month for the next 50 years?
56. A couple received a $134,000 inheritance the year they turned 48 and invested it in a fund that earns 7.7% compounded semiannually. If this amount is deferred for 14 years (until they retire), how much will it provide at the end of each half-year for the next 20 years after they retire?

In Problems 57 and 58, use a spreadsheet or financial program on a calculator or computer.
57. Suppose a couple have $100,000 at retirement that they can invest in an ordinary annuity that earns 7.8%, compounded monthly. Track the balance in this annuity account until it reaches $0, if the couple receive the following monthly payments.
    (a) $1000   (b) $2500
58. Suppose you invested $250,000 in an annuity that earned interest compounded monthly. This annuity paid $3000 at the end of each month. Experiment with the following different interest rates (compounded monthly) to see how long it will be, with each rate, until this annuity has an account balance of $0.
    (a) 6.5%   (b) 9%

Loans and Amortization

| APPLICATION PREVIEW |

Chuckie and Angelica have been married for 4 years and are ready to buy their first home. They have saved $30,000 for a down payment, and their budget can accommodate a monthly mortgage payment of $1200.00. They want to know in what price range they can purchase a home if the rate for a 30-year loan is 7.8% compounded monthly. (See Example 2.)

When businesses, individuals, or families (such as Chuckie and Angelica) borrow money to make a major purchase, four questions commonly arise:

1. What will the payments be?
2. How much can be borrowed and still fit a budget?
3. What is the payoff amount of the loan before the final payment is due?
4. What is the total of all payments needed to pay off the loan?

In this section we discuss the most common way that consumers and businesses discharge debts—regular payments of fixed size made on a loan (called amortization)—and determine ways to answer Chuckie and Angelica's question (Question 2) and the other three questions posed above.

Amortization

Just as we invest money to earn interest, banks and lending institutions lend money and collect interest for its use. Federal law now requires that the full cost of any loan and the **true annual percentage rate (APR)** be disclosed with the loan. Because of this law, loans now are usually paid off by a series of partial payments with interest charged on the unpaid balance at the end of each payment period.

This type of loan is usually repaid by making all payments (including principal and interest) of equal size. This process of repaying the loan is called **amortization.**

When a bank makes a loan of this type, it is purchasing from the borrower an ordinary annuity that pays a fixed return each payment period. The lump sum the bank gives to the borrower (the principal of the loan) is the present value of the ordinary annuity, and each payment the bank receives from the borrower is a payment from the annuity. Hence, to find the size of these periodic payments, we solve for R in the formula for the present value of an ordinary annuity,

$$A_n = R\left[\frac{1-(1+i)^{-n}}{i}\right]$$

which yields the following algebraically equivalent formula.

Amortization Formula

If the debt of $\$A_n$, with interest at a rate of i per period, is amortized by n equal periodic payments (each payment being made at the end of a period), the size of each payment is

$$R = A_n \cdot \left[\frac{i}{1-(1+i)^{-n}}\right]$$

For example, suppose a debt of $1000 with interest at 16%, compounded quarterly, is to be amortized by 20 equal quarterly payments over the next 5 years. To find the size of each payment, we use $A_n = \$1000$, $n = 20$, and $i = 0.16/4 = 0.04$. Thus we have

$$R = A_n\left[\frac{i}{1-(1+i)^{-n}}\right] = \$1000\left[\frac{0.04}{1-(1.04)^{-20}}\right] \approx \$73.58$$

EXAMPLE 1   **Buying a Home**

A man buys a house for $200,000. He makes a $50,000 down payment and agrees to amortize the rest of the debt with quarterly payments over the next 10 years. If the interest on the debt is 12%, compounded quarterly, find (a) the size of the quarterly payments, (b) the total amount of the payments, and (c) the total amount of interest paid.

Solution

(a) We know that $A_n = \$200,000 - \$50,000 = \$150,000$, $n = 4(10) = 40$, and $i = 0.12/4 = 0.03$. Thus, for the quarterly payment, we have

$$R = \$150,000 \left[\frac{0.03}{1 - (1.03)^{-40}} \right]$$

$$\approx (\$150,000)(0.043262378) \approx \$6489.36$$

(b) The man made 40 payments of $6489.36, so his payments totaled

$$(40)(\$6489.36) = \$259,574.40$$

plus the $50,000 down payment, or $309,574.40.

(c) Of the $309,574.40 paid, $200,000 was for payment of the house. The remaining $109,574.40 was the total amount of interest paid.

 Technology Note   We can use a graphing calculator to find the payment size to amortize a debt as follows:

1. Under the APPS menu, select Finance, then TVM Solver.
2. Set N = the total number of payments, I% = the annual percentage rate, and PV = the amount borrowed.
3. Set FV = 0 and both P/Y and C/Y equal to the number of compounding periods.
4. Highlight END, then put the cursor on PMT and press ALPHA ENTER to get the payment size. (The payment is negative because it is leaving.)

```
N=40
I%=12
PV=150000
PMT=-6489.3566…
FV=0
P/Y=4
C/Y=4
PMT:END BEGIN
```

Figure 6.15

Figure 6.15 shows the quarterly payment for the loan in Example 1. See Appendix A, Section 6.5, for more details.

We can also use Excel to find the payment size to amortize a debt by using the *new* formula "= Pmt(F2, B2, A2, C2, 0)" with the periodic interest rate as a decimal in cell F2, the number of periods in cell B2, the loan amount in cell A2, and C2 = 0. Cell B4 of Table 6.9 gives the payment size for the loan in Example 1. See Appendix B, Section 6.5, for more details.

| **TABLE 6.9** |

	A	B	C	D	E	F
1	Loan Amount	Number of Periods	Future Value	Annual Rate	Periods per Year	Periodic Rate
2	150,000	40	0	0.12	4	0.03
3						
4	Payment	($6,489.36)				

EXAMPLE 2   **Affordable Home**   **| APPLICATION PREVIEW |**

Chuckie and Angelica have $30,000 for a down payment, and their budget can accommodate a monthly mortgage payment of $1200.00. What is the most expensive home they can buy if they can borrow money for 30 years at 7.8%, compounded monthly?

Solution

We seek the amount that Chuckie and Angelica can borrow, or A_n, knowing that $R = \$1200$, $n = 30(12) = 360$, and $i = 0.078/12 = 0.0065$. We can use these values in the amortization formula and solve for A_n (or use the formula for the present value of an ordinary annuity).

$$R = A_n \left[\frac{i}{1 - (1 + i)^{-n}} \right]$$

$$\$1200 = A_n \left[\frac{0.0065}{1 - (1.0065)^{-360}} \right]$$

$$A_n = \$1200 \left[\frac{1 - (1.0065)^{-360}}{0.0065} \right]$$

$$A_n \approx \$166,696.65$$

Thus, if they borrow $166,697 (to the nearest dollar) and put down $30,000, the most expensive home they can buy would cost $166,697 + $30,000 = $196,697.   ■

✓ CHECKPOINT

1. A debt of $25,000 is to be amortized with equal quarterly payments over 6 years, and money is worth 7%, compounded quarterly.
   (a) Find the total number of payments.
   (b) Find the interest rate per period.
   (c) Write the formula used to find the size of each payment.
   (d) Find the amount of each payment.
2. A new college graduate determines that she can afford a car payment of $400 per month. If the auto manufacturer is offering a special 2.1% financing rate, compounded monthly for 5 years, how much can she borrow and still have a $400 monthly payment?

Amortization Schedule

We can construct an **amortization schedule** that summarizes all the information regarding the amortization of a loan.

For example, a loan of $10,000 with interest at 10% could be repaid in 5 equal annual payments of size

$$R = \$10,000 \left[\frac{0.10}{1 - (1 + 0.10)^{-5}} \right] \approx \$10,000(0.263797) = \$2637.97$$

Each time this $2637.97 payment is made, some is used to pay the interest on the unpaid balance, and some is used to reduce the principal. For the first payment, the unpaid balance is $10,000, so the interest payment is 10% of $10,000, or $1000. The remaining $1637.97 is applied to the principal. Hence, after this first payment, the unpaid balance is $10,000 − $1637.97 = $8362.03.

For the second payment of $2637.97, the amount used for interest is 10% of $8362.03, or $836.20; the remainder, $1801.77, is used to reduce the principal.

This information for these two payments and for the remaining payments is summarized in the following amortization schedule.

Period	Payment	Interest	Balance Reduction	Unpaid Balance
				10000.00
1	2637.97	1000.00	1637.97	8362.03
2	2637.97	836.20	1801.77	6560.26
3	2637.97	656.03	1981.94	4578.32
4	2637.97	457.83	2180.14	2398.18
5	2638.00	239.82	2398.18	0.00
Total	13189.88	3189.88	10000.00	

Note that the last payment was increased by 3¢ so that the balance was reduced to $0 at the end of the 5 years. Such an adjustment is normal in amortizing a loan.

Spreadsheet Note

The preceding amortization schedule involves only a few payments. For loans involving more payments, a spreadsheet program is an excellent tool to develop an amortization schedule. The spreadsheet requires the user to understand the interrelationships among the columns. The accompanying spreadsheet output in Table 6.10 shows the amortization schedule for the first, sixth, twelfth, eighteenth, and twenty-fourth monthly payments on a $100,000 loan amortized for 30 years at 6%, compounded monthly. It is interesting to observe how little the unpaid balance changes during these first 2 years—and, consequently, how much of each payment is devoted to paying interest due rather than to reducing the debt. In fact, the column labeled "Total Interest" shows a running total of how much has been paid toward interest. We see that after 12 payments of $599.55, a total of $7194.60 has been paid, and $5966.59 of this has been interest payments. ■

| TABLE 6.10 |

	A	B	C	D	E	F
1	Payment Number	Payment Amount	Interest	Balance Reduction	Unpaid Balance	Total Interest
2	0	0	0	0	$100,000.00	$0.00
3	1	$599.55	$500.00	$99.55	$99,900.45	$500.00
4	6	$599.55	$497.49	$102.06	$99,395.18	$2,992.48
5	12	$599.55	$494.39	$105.16	$98,771.99	$5,966.59
6	18	$599.55	$491.19	$108.36	$98,129.87	$8,921.77
7	24	$599.55	$487.90	$111.65	$97,468.25	$11,857.45

Unpaid Balance of a Loan

Many people who borrow money, such as for a car or a home, do not pay on the loan for its entire term. Rather, they pay off the loan early by making a final lump sum payment. The unpaid balance found in the amortization schedule is the "payoff amount" of the loan and represents the lump sum payment that must be made to complete payment on the loan. When the number of payments is large, we may wish to find the unpaid balance of a loan without constructing an amortization schedule.

Recall that calculations for amortization of a debt are based on the present value formula for an ordinary annuity. Because of this, the **unpaid balance of a loan** (also called the **payoff amount** and the **outstanding principal of the loan**) is the present value needed to generate all the remaining payments.

Unpaid Balance or Payoff Amount of a Loan

For a loan of n payments of $R per period at interest rate i per period, the **unpaid balance,** or **payoff amount,** after k payments have been made is the present value of an ordinary annuity with $n - k$ payments. That is, with $n - k$ payments remaining,

$$\text{Unpaid balance} = A_{n-k} = R\left[\frac{1 - (1 + i)^{-(n-k)}}{i}\right]$$

EXAMPLE   3   Unpaid Balance

In Example 1, we found that the quarterly payment for a loan of $150,000 at 12%, compounded quarterly, for 10 years is $6489.36 (to the nearest cent). Find the unpaid balance immediately after the 15th payment.

Solution

The unpaid balance after the 15th payment is the present value of the annuity with $40 - 15 = 25$ payments remaining. Thus we use $R = \$6489.36$, $i = 0.03$, and $n - k = 25$ in the formula for the unpaid balance of a loan.

$$A_{n-k} = R\left[\frac{1 - (1+i)^{-(n-k)}}{i}\right] = \$6489.36\left[\frac{1 - (1.03)^{-25}}{0.03}\right]$$

$$\approx \$113{,}000.18$$

✓ **CHECKPOINT**   3. A 42-month auto loan has monthly payments of $411.35. If the interest rate is 8.1%, compounded monthly, find the unpaid balance immediately after the 24th payment.

With monthly payments of $599.55

Months

Figure 6.16

The curve in Figure 6.16 shows the unpaid balance of a $100,000 loan at 6%, compounded monthly, for 30 years (with monthly payments of $599.55, as in Table 6.10). In the figure, the straight line represents how the unpaid balance would decrease if each payment diminished the debt by the same amount. Note how the curve decreases slowly at first and more rapidly as the unpaid balance nears zero. The reason for this behavior is that when the unpaid balance is large, much of each payment is devoted to interest. Similarly, when the debt decreases, more of each payment goes toward the principal.

A common application of determining the unpaid balance of a loan arises when a loan is refinanced. If interest rates drop during the term of a loan, refinancing often is considered because it may result in a lower periodic payment or fewer payments.

EXAMPLE 4   Loan Refinancing

Four years ago Benencorp decided to expand its production capacity and borrowed $1.3 million for 20 years at 5.2% compounded quarterly. After making 16 quarterly payments of $26,235.37, Benencorp is considering refinancing this loan for 15 years at 4.8% compounded quarterly, with refinancing charges of $5000 added to the amount of the new (refinanced) loan.

(a) Find the payoff amount of Benencorp's original loan.
(b) Find the amount of the new loan and the new quarterly payment.
(c) Should Benencorp refinance?

Solution

(a) The payoff amount of the loan is the unpaid balance after 16 payments. Thus, $n - k = 80 - 16 = 64$ payments remaining, $R = \$26{,}235.37$, $i = 0.052/4 = 0.013$, and

$$A_{n-k} = R\left[\frac{1 - (1+i)^{-(n-k)}}{i}\right] = 26{,}235.37\left[\frac{1 - (1.013)^{-64}}{0.013}\right] \approx 1{,}135{,}148.82$$

(b) The new loan needs to cover this unpaid balance and the refinancing charges of $5000, so that the amount of the new (refinanced) loan is

$$A_n = \$1{,}135{,}148.82 + \$5000 = \$1{,}140{,}148.82$$

This amount will be financed for 15 years at 4.8% compounded quarterly, so we use $n = (15)(4) = 60$ and $i = 0.048/4 = 0.012$. Thus, the new quarterly payment is

$$R = A_n\left[\frac{i}{1 - (1+i)^{-n}}\right] = \$1{,}140{,}148.82\left[\frac{0.012}{1 - (1.012)^{-60}}\right] \approx \$26{,}766.30$$

(c)   At first it seems Benencorp should not refinance because this new payment is higher than the original. But, let's compare the total amounts paid from here on:

$$\text{Original} = (\$26{,}235.37)(64) = \$1{,}679{,}063.68$$
$$\text{Refinance} = (\$26{,}766.30)(60) = \$1{,}605{,}978.00$$

Thus, Benencorp should refinance because it completes making payments 1 year sooner and saves $73,085.68.

✓ CHECKPOINT ANSWERS

1. (a) $n = 24$ payments
   (b) $i = 0.0175$ per period
   (c) $R = A_n \left[\dfrac{i}{1 - (1 + i)^{-n}} \right]$
   (d) $R \approx \$1284.64$
2. $A_n \approx \$22{,}764.08$
3. $A_{n-k} \approx \$6950.13$

| EXERCISES | 6.5

1. Two loans are for the same amount at the same interest rate; one is paid off in 10 years and the other in 25 years.
   (a) Which loan results in more of each payment being directed toward principal? Explain.
   (b) Which loan results in a lower periodic payment? Explain.
2. When a debt is amortized, which interest rate is better for the borrower, 10% or 6%? Explain.
3. A debt of $8000 is to be amortized with 8 equal semiannual payments. If the interest rate is 12%, compounded semiannually, what is the size of each payment?
4. A loan of $10,000 is to be amortized with 10 equal quarterly payments. If the interest rate is 6%, compounded quarterly, what is the periodic payment?
5. A recent graduate's student loans total $18,000. If these loans are at 4.2%, compounded quarterly, for 10 years, what are the quarterly payments?
6. For equipment upgrades a business borrowed $400,000 at 8%, compounded semiannually, for 5 years. What are the semiannual payments?
7. A homeowner planning a kitchen remodeling can afford a $600 monthly payment. How much can the homeowner borrow for 5 years at 6%, compounded monthly, and still stay within the budget?
8. AdriAnne and Anna's Auto Repair wants to add a new service bay. How much can they borrow at 5%, compounded quarterly for $4\frac{1}{2}$ years, if the desired quarterly payment is $10,000?

In Problems 9–12, develop an amortization schedule for the loan described.
9. $100,000 for 3 years at 9% compounded annually
10. $30,000 for 5 years at 7% compounded annually
11. $20,000 for 1 year at 12% compounded quarterly
12. $50,000 for $2\frac{1}{2}$ years at 10% compounded semiannually

13. A $10,000 loan is to be amortized for 10 years with quarterly payments of $334.27. If the interest rate is 6%, compounded quarterly, what is the unpaid balance immediately after the sixth payment?
14. A debt of $8000 is to be amortized with 8 equal semiannual payments of $1288.29. If the interest rate is 12%, compounded semiannually, find the unpaid balance immediately after the fifth payment.
15. When Maria Acosta bought a car $2\frac{1}{2}$ years ago, she borrowed $28,000 for 48 months at 8.1% compounded monthly. Her monthly payments are $684.88, but she'd like to pay off the loan early. How much will she owe just after her payment at the $2\frac{1}{2}$-year mark?
16. Six-and-a-half years ago, a small business borrowed $50,000 for 10 years at 9%, compounded semiannually, in order to update some equipment. Now the company would like to pay off this loan. Find the payoff amount just after the company makes the 14th semiannual payment of $3843.81.

Problems 17–20 describe a debt to be amortized. In each problem, find:
(a) **the size of each payment.**
(b) **the total amount paid for each purchase.**
(c) **the total interest paid over the life of the loan.**
17. A man buys a house for $350,000. He makes a $150,000 down payment and amortizes the rest of the purchase price with semiannual payments over the next 10 years. The interest rate on the debt is 12%, compounded semiannually.
18. Sean Lee purchases $20,000 worth of supplies for his restaurant by making a $3000 down payment and amortizing the remaining cost with quarterly payments over the next 5 years. The interest rate on the debt is 16%, compounded quarterly.

19. A woman buys an apartment house for $1,250,000 by making a down payment of $250,000 and amortizing the rest of the purchase price with monthly payments over the next 10 years. The interest rate on the debt is 7.2%, compounded monthly.

20. John Fare purchased $10,000 worth of equipment by making a $2000 down payment and promising to pay the remainder of the cost in semiannual payments over the next 4 years. The interest rate on the debt is 10%, compounded semiannually.

21. A man buys a car for $36,000. If the interest rate on the loan is 12%, compounded monthly, and if he wants to make monthly payments of $900 for 36 months, how much must he put down?

22. A woman buys a car for $40,000. If the interest rate on the loan is 12%, compounded monthly, and if she wants to make monthly payments of $700 for 3 years, how much must she have for a down payment?

23. A couple purchasing a home budget $1800 per month for their loan payment. If they have $20,000 available for a down payment and are considering a 25-year loan, how much can they spend on the home at each of the following rates?
    (a) 6.9% compounded monthly
    (b) 7.5% compounded monthly

24. A developer wants to buy a certain parcel of land. The developer feels she can afford payments of $44,000 each half-year for the next 7 years. How much can she borrow and hold to this budget at each of the following interest rates?
    (a) 8.9% compounded semiannually
    (b) 7.3% compounded semiannually

25. A couple who borrow $90,000 for 30 years at 7.2%, compounded monthly, must make monthly payments of $610.91.
    (a) Find their unpaid balance after 1 year.
    (b) During that first year, how much interest do they pay?

26. A company that purchases a piece of equipment by borrowing $250,000 for 10 years at 6%, compounded monthly, has monthly payments of $2775.51.
    (a) Find the unpaid balance on this loan after 1 year.
    (b) During that first year, how much interest does the company pay?

27. When Otto and Millie bought their home, they borrowed $200,000 for 30 years at 6% compounded monthly. After making 120 payments of $1199.10, they plan to refinance at 4.5% compounded monthly for 15 years, with refinancing costs of $750 added to the amount of the new loan.
    (a) Find the amount of the new loan (amount refinanced).
    (b) Find their new monthly payment.
    (c) Find the amount saved by refinancing.

28. In order to upgrade its equipment, Simon Reilly Chemicals (SRC) borrowed $2.8 million at 6.4%

compounded quarterly for 20 years. After making 18 quarterly payments of $62,297.39, SRC plans to refinance this loan at 5.2% compounded quarterly for 10 years, with refinancing charges of $12,000 added to the amount refinanced.
    (a) Find the amount refinanced.
    (b) Find SRC's new quarterly payment.
    (c) Find the amount saved by refinancing.

29. A recent college graduate buys a new car by borrowing $18,000 at 8.4%, compounded monthly, for 5 years. She decides to pay an extra $15 per payment.
    (a) What is the monthly payment required by the loan, and how much does she decide to pay each month?
    (b) How many payments (that include the extra $15) will she make?
    (c) How much will she save by paying the extra $15?

30. A young couple buying their first home borrow $85,000 for 30 years at 7.2%, compounded monthly, and make payments of $576.97. After 3 years, they are able to make a one-time payment of $2000 along with their 36th payment.
    (a) Find the unpaid balance immediately after they pay the extra $2000 and their 36th payment.
    (b) How many regular payments of $576.97 will amortize the unpaid balance from part (a)?
    (c) How much will the couple save over the life of the loan by paying the extra $2000?

31. Jadele, Inc., borrowed $12.8 million at 7.2% compounded quarterly for 30 years for construction of a new manufacturing facility. After making 42 quarterly payments of $261,094.80, it plans to refinance the existing loan for an amount that includes an additional $1.1 million for expansion. Jadele can refinance at 6.6% compounded quarterly for 25 years, with refinancing costs of $10,000 added to the refinanced amount.
    (a) Find the total amount refinanced.
    (b) Find the new quarterly payment.
    (c) If Jadele decides to continue to pay $261,094.80 per quarter on the refinanced amount, how long will it take to pay off the new loan?

32. When Gustavo and Serrana bought their home, they had a 5.7% loan with monthly payments of $870.60 for 30 years. After making 78 monthly payments, they plan to refinance for an amount that includes an additional $35,000 to remodel their kitchen. They can refinance at 4.8% compounded monthly for 25 years with refinancing costs of $625 included with the amount refinanced.
    (a) Find the amount refinanced.
    (b) Find their new monthly payment.
    (c) How long will it take to pay off this new loan if they pay $1200 each month?

A debt of $100,000 is amortized at 6%, compounded monthly, over 25 years with 300 monthly payments of $644.30 each. The following figure includes two graphs: One shows the total amount paid (in monthly payments) as a function of time (in months), and the other shows the amount paid toward the principal of the debt as a function of time. Use this figure to complete Problems 33 and 34.

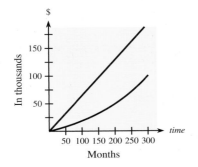

33. (a) Correctly label each graph.
    (b) Draw a vertical segment whose length represents the total amount of interest paid on the debt after 250 months.
34. Draw a vertical segment whose length represents the outstanding principal of the debt (or the payoff amount of the loan) after 150 months.
35. What difference does 0.5% make on a loan? To answer this question, find (to the nearest dollar) the monthly payment and total interest paid over the life of the loan for each of the following.
    (a) An auto loan of $15,000 at 8.0% versus 8.5%, compounded monthly, for 4 years.
    (b) A mortgage loan of $80,000 at 6.75% versus 7.25%, compounded monthly, for 30 years.
    (c) In each of these 0.5% differences, what seems to have the greatest effect on the borrower: amount borrowed, interest rate, or duration of the loan? Explain.
36. Some banks now have biweekly mortgages (that is, with payments every other week). Compare a 20-year, $100,000 loan at 8.1% by finding the payment size and the total interest paid over the life of the loan under each of the following conditions.
    (a) Payments are monthly, and the rate is 8.1%, compounded monthly.
    (b) Payments are biweekly, and the rate is 8.1%, compounded biweekly.
37. Many banks charge points on mortgage loans. Each point is the equivalent of a 1% charge on the amount borrowed and is paid before the loan is made as part of the closing costs of buying a home (closing costs include points, title fees, attorney's fees, assessor's fees, and so on).
    (a) If $100,000 is borrowed for 25 years, for each of the following, find the payment size and the total paid over the life of the loan (including points).
        (i) $7\frac{1}{2}$%, compounded monthly, with 0 points

        (ii) $7\frac{1}{4}$%, compounded monthly, with 1 point
        (iii) 7%, compounded monthly, with 2 points
    (b) Which loan in part (a) has the lowest total cost over the life of the loan?
38. Time-share sales provide an opportunity for vacationers to own a resort condo for 1 week (or more) each year forever. The owners may use their week at their own condo or trade the week and vacation elsewhere. Time-share vacation sales usually require payment in full or financing through the time-share company, and interest rates are usually in the 13% to 18% range. Suppose the cost to buy a 1-week time share in a 3-bedroom condo is $21,833. Also suppose a 10% down payment is required, with the balance financed for 15 years at 16.5%, compounded monthly.
    (a) Find the monthly payment.
    (b) Determine the total cost over the life of the loan.
    (c) Suppose maintenance fees for this condo are $400 per year. Find the annual cost of the condo over the life of the loan. Assume that the annual maintenance fees remain constant.
    (d) Use part (c) and the 10% down payment to determine the average annual cost for having this vacation condo for 1 week over the life of the loan.

COMBINED APPLICATIONS

Problems 39 and 40 are complex financial problems that require several skills, perhaps some from previous sections.

39. During four years of college, Nolan MacGregor's student loans are $4000, $3500, $4400, and $5000 for freshman year through senior year, respectively. Each loan amount gathers interest of 1%, compounded quarterly, while Nolan is in school and 3%, compounded quarterly, during a 6-month grace period after graduation.
    (a) What is the loan balance after the grace period? Assume the freshman year loan earns 1% interest for 3/4 year during the first year, then for 3 full years until graduation. Make similar assumptions for the loans for the other years.
    (b) After the grace period, the loan is amortized over the next 10 years at 3%, compounded quarterly. Find the quarterly payment.
    (c) If Nolan decides to pay an additional $90 per payment, how many payments will amortize the debt?
    (d) How much will Nolan save by paying the extra $90 with each payment?
40. Clark and Lana take a 30-year home mortgage of $121,000 at 7.8%, compounded monthly. They make their regular monthly payments for 5 years, then decide to pay $1000 per month.
    (a) Find their regular monthly payment.

(b) Find the unpaid balance when they begin paying the $1000.

(c) How many payments of $1000 will it take to pay off the loan?

(d) How much interest will they save by paying the loan in this way?

Use a spreadsheet or financial program on a calculator or computer to complete Problems 41 and 42.

41. Develop an amortization schedule for a 4-year car loan if $16,700 is borrowed at 8.2%, compounded monthly.

42. Develop an amortization schedule for a 10-year mortgage loan of $80,000 at 7.2%, compounded monthly.

Chapter 6 Summary & Review

KEY TERMS AND FORMULAS

Section 6.1

Simple interest (p. 362)
$$I = Prt$$
Future value of a simple interest investment (p. 363)
$$S = P + I$$
Sequence function (p. 364)
Arithmetic sequence (p. 365)
$$a_n = a_{n-1} + d \quad (n > 1)$$

Common difference, d
nth term of an arithmetic sequence (p. 365)
$$a_n = a_1 + (n-1)d$$
Sum of first n terms (p. 366)
$$s_n = \frac{n}{2}(a_1 + a_n)$$

Section 6.2

Future value of compound interest investment (p. 370)
Periodic compounding
$$S = P(1 + i)^n = P\left(1 + \frac{r}{m}\right)^{mt}$$
Continuous compounding
$$S = Pe^{rt}$$
Annual percentage yield (p. 376)
Periodic compounding
$$APY = \left(1 + \frac{r}{m}\right)^m - 1$$
$$= (1 + i)^m - 1$$

Continuous compounding
$$APY = e^r - 1$$
Geometric sequence (p. 378)
$$a_n = ra_{n-1} \quad (n > 1)$$
Common ratio, r
nth term of a geometric sequence (p. 378)
$$a_n = a_1 r^{n-1}$$
Sum of first n terms (p. 379)
$$s_n = \frac{a_1(1 - r^n)}{1 - r} \quad (\text{if } r \neq 1)$$

Section 6.3

Future values of annuities (p. 383)
Ordinary annuity (p. 384)
$$S = R\left[\frac{(1 + i)^n - 1}{i}\right]$$

Sinking fund (p. 387)
Annuity due (p. 388)
$$S_{due} = R\left[\frac{(1 + i)^n - 1}{i}\right](1 + i)$$

Section 6.4

Present values of annuities (p. 392)
Ordinary annuity (p. 393)
$$A_n = R\left[\frac{1 - (1 + i)^{-n}}{i}\right]$$
Bond pricing (p. 396)

Annuity due (p. 397)
$$A_{(n,due)} = R\left[\frac{1 - (1 + i)^{-n}}{i}\right](1 + i)$$
Deferred annuity (p. 399)
$$A_{(n,k)} = R\left[\frac{1 - (1 + i)^{-n}}{i}\right](1 + i)^{-k}$$

Section 6.5

True annual percentage rate (APR) (p. 404)
Amortization (p. 404)
$$R = A_n\left[\frac{i}{1 - (1 + i)^{-n}}\right]$$
Amortization schedule (p. 406)

Unpaid balance ($n - k$ payments left) (p. 407)
$$A_{n-k} = R\left[\frac{1 - (1 + i)^{-(n-k)}}{i}\right]$$
Loan refinancing (p. 408)

REVIEW EXERCISES

Section 6.1

1. Find the first 4 terms of the sequence with nth term

$$a_n = \frac{1}{n^2}$$

2. Identify any arithmetic sequences and find the common differences.
   (a) $12, 7, 2, -3, \ldots$ (b) $1, 3, 6, 10, \ldots$
   (c) $\frac{1}{6}, \frac{1}{3}, \frac{1}{2}, \frac{2}{3}, \ldots$
3. Find the 80th term of the arithmetic sequence with first term -2 and common difference 3.
4. Find the 36th term of the arithmetic sequence with third term 10 and eighth term 25.
5. Find the sum of the first 60 terms of the arithmetic sequence $\frac{1}{3}, \frac{1}{2}, \frac{2}{3}, \ldots$

Section 6.2

6. Identify any geometric sequences and their common ratios.
   (a) $\frac{1}{4}, 2, 16, 128, \ldots$ (b) $16, -12, 9, -\frac{27}{4}, \ldots$
   (c) $4, 16, 36, 64, \ldots$
7. Find the fourth term of the geometric sequence with first term 64 and eighth term $\frac{1}{2}$.
8. Find the sum of the first 16 terms of the geometric sequence $\frac{1}{9}, \frac{1}{3}, 1, \ldots$

APPLICATIONS

Section 6.1

9. *Loans* If $8000 is borrowed at 12% simple interest for 3 years, what is the future value of the loan at the end of the 3 years?
10. *Loan rate* Mary Toy borrowed $2000 from her parents and repaid them $2100 after 9 months. What simple interest rate did she pay?
11. *Tuition* How much summer earnings must a college student deposit on August 31 in order to have $3000 for tuition and fees on December 31 of the same year, if the investment earns 6% simple interest?
12. *Contest payments* Suppose the winner of a contest receives $10 on the first day of the month, $20 on the second day, $30 on the third day, and so on for a 30-day month. What is the total won?
13. *Salaries* Suppose you are offered two identical jobs: one paying a starting salary of $40,000 with yearly raises of $2000 and one paying a starting salary of $36,000 with yearly raises of $2500. Which job will pay more money over a 10-year period?

Section 6.2

14. *Investments* An investment is made at 8%, compounded quarterly, for 10 years.
    (a) Find the number of periods.
    (b) Find the interest rate per period.

15. *Future value* Write the formula for the future value of a compound interest investment, if interest is compounded
    (a) periodically   (b) continuously.
16. *Comparing rates* Which compounding method, at 6%, earns more money?
    (a) semiannually   (b) monthly
17. *Interest* If $1000 is invested for 4 years at 8%, compounded quarterly, how much interest will be earned?
18. *Savings goal* How much must one invest now in order to have $18,000 in 4 years if the investment earns 5.4%, compounded monthly?
19. *Future value* What is the future value if $1000 is invested for 6 years at 8%, compounded continuously?
20. *College fund* A couple received an inheritance and plan to invest some of it for their grandchild's college education. How much must they invest if they would like the fund to have $100,000 after 15 years, and their investment earns 10.31%, compounded continuously?
21. *Investments* If $15,000 is invested at 6%, compounded quarterly, how long will it be before it grows to $25,000?
22. *Investment rates* (a) If an initial investment of $35,000 grows to $257,000 in 15 years, what annual interest rate, continuously compounded, was earned? (b) What is the annual percentage yield on this investment?
23. *Comparing yields* Find the annual percentage yield equivalent to a nominal rate of 7.2% (a) compounded quarterly and (b) compounded continuously.
24. *Chess legend* Legend has it that when the king of Persia wanted to reward the inventor of chess with whatever he desired, the inventor asked for one grain of wheat on the first square of the chessboard, with the number of grains doubled on each square thereafter for the remaining 63 squares. Find the number of grains on the 64th square. (The sum of all the grains of wheat on all the squares would cover Alaska more than 3 inches deep with wheat!)
25. *Chess legend* If, in Problem 24, the king granted the inventor's wish for *half* a chessboard, how many grains would the inventor receive?

Section 6.3

26. *Annuity* Find the future value of an ordinary annuity of $800 paid at the end of every 6-month period for 10 years, if it earns interest at 12%, compounded semiannually.
27. *Sinking fund* How much would have to be invested at the end of each year at 6%, compounded annually, to pay off a debt of $80,000 in 10 years?
28. *Annuity* Find the future value of an annuity due of $800 paid at the beginning of every 6-month period for 10 years, if it earns interest at 12%, compounded semiannually.

29. *Construction fund* A company wants to have $250,000 available in $4\frac{1}{2}$ years for new construction. How much must be deposited at the beginning of each quarter to reach this goal if the investment earns 10.2%, compounded quarterly?

30. *Time to reach a goal* If $1200 is deposited at the end of each quarter in an account that earns 7.2%, compounded quarterly, how long will it be until the account is worth $60,000?

Section 6.4

31. *Annuity* What lump sum would have to be invested at 9%, compounded semiannually, to provide an annuity of $10,000 at the end of each half-year for 10 years?

32. *Cruise fund* A couple wish to set up an annuity that will provide 6 monthly payments of $3000 while they take an extended cruise. How much of a $15,000 inheritance must be set aside if they plan to leave in 5 years and want the first payment before they leave? Assume that money is worth 7.8%, compounded monthly.

33. *Powerball lottery* Winners of lotteries receive the jackpot distributed over a period of years, usually 20 or 25 years. The winners of a Powerball lottery elected to take a one-time cash payout rather than receive the $295.7 million jackpot in 25 annual payments beginning on the date the lottery was won.
    (a) How much money would the winners have received at the beginning of each of the 25 years?
    (b) If the value of money was 5.91%, compounded annually, what one-time payout did they receive in lieu of the annual payments?

34. *Payment from an annuity* A recent college graduate's gift from her grandparents is $20,000. How much will this provide at the end of each month for the next 12 months while the graduate travels? Assume that money is worth 6.6%, compounded monthly.

35. *Payment from an annuity* An IRA of $250,000 is rolled into an annuity that pays a retired couple at the beginning of each quarter for the next 20 years. If the annuity earns 6.2%, compounded quarterly, how much will the couple receive each quarter?

36. *Bond pricing* Suppose that a 30-year municipal bond has a maturity value of $5000 and a coupon rate of 8%, with coupons paid semiannually. Find the market price of the bond if the current yield rate is 10% compounded semiannually. Is this bond selling at a discount or at a premium?

37. *Duration of an annuity* A retirement account that earns 6.8%, compounded semiannually, contains $488,000. How long can $40,000 be withdrawn at the end of each half-year until the account balance is $0?

Section 6.5

38. *Amortization* A debt of $1000 with interest at 12%, compounded monthly, is amortized by 12 monthly payments (of equal size). What is the size of each payment?

39. *Loan payoff* A debt of $8000 is amortized with eight semiannual payments of $1288.29 each. If money is worth 12%, compounded semiannually, find the unpaid balance after five payments have been made.

40. *Cash value* A woman paid $90,000 down for a house and agreed to pay 18 quarterly payments of $4500 each. If money is worth 4%, compounded quarterly, how much would the house have cost if she had paid cash?

41. *Amortization schedule* Complete the amortization schedule for the next two payments of a loan for 30 years at 7.5%, compounded monthly, with monthly payments of $699.22.

Payment Number	Payment Amount	Interest	Balance Reduction	Unpaid Balance
56	$699.22	$594.67	$104.55	$95,042.20

42. *Loan refinancing* A corporation borrowed $750,000 for 15 years at 5.4% compounded semiannually. After making 17 payments of $36,795.60, it refinances at 4.8% compounded semiannually for 5 years, with refinancing costs of $2200 added to the new loan.
    (a) Find the amount of the new loan.
    (b) Find the new semiannual payment.
    (c) Find the amount saved by refinancing.

Sections 6.1–6.5

MISCELLANEOUS FINANCIAL PROBLEMS

Identify which of the following formulas applies to each situation in Problems 43–48.

$$I = Prt \qquad S = P(1 + i)^n \qquad S = Pe^{rt}$$

$$S = R\left[\frac{(1 + i)^n - 1}{i}\right] \qquad A_n = R\left[\frac{1 - (1 + i)^{-n}}{i}\right]$$

43. The future value of a series of payments, with interest compounded when the payments are made
44. The simple interest earned on an investment
45. The present value of a series of payments, with interest compounded when the payments are made
46. The future value of an investment that earns interest compounded periodically
47. The regular payment size needed to amortize a debt, when interest is compounded when the payments are made
48. The future value of an investment that earns interest compounded continuously
49. If an initial investment of $2500 grows to $38,000 in 18 years, what annual interest rate, compounded annually, did this investment earn?
50. How much must be deposited at the end of each month in an account that earns 8.4%, compounded monthly, if the goal is to have $40,000 after 10 years?
51. What is the future value if $1000 is invested for 6 years at 8% (a) simple interest and (b) compounded semiannually?

52. Quarterly payments of $500 are deposited in an account that pays 8%, compounded quarterly. How much will have accrued in the account at the end of 4 years if each payment is made at the end of each quarter?

53. If $8000 is invested at 7%, compounded continuously, how long will it be before it grows to $22,000?

54. An investment broker bought some stock at $87.89 per share and sold it after 3 months for $105.34 per share. What was the annual simple interest rate earned on this transaction?

55. A couple feels they can afford a monthly house payment of $2000 and would like a 30-year fixed-rate loan. Currently the rate for such a loan is 4.8% compounded monthly. To the nearest dollar, how much can the couple afford to borrow?

56. A $5000 Mauranol, Inc., corporate bond matures in 10 years and has a coupon rate of 7.2% paid semiannually.
    (a) If the yield rate is 8% compounded semiannually, find the bond's market price.
    (b) Three years later the yield rate is 5.8%. If the bond holder wishes to sell at this time, what is the bond's current market price?
    (c) If you bought a $5000 Mauranol, Inc., bond at the price in part (a), collected 3 years of coupons, and sold at the price in part (b), what amount would you have earned on your original investment?
    (d) Suppose you made a single investment with principal equal to the amount paid in part (a), and after 3 years you received a single lump sum return equal to the amount from part (c). What interest rate compounded semiannually would you have earned?

57. Kevin Patrick paid off the loan he took out to buy his car, but once the loan was paid, he continued to deposit $400 on the first of each month in an account that paid 5.4%, compounded monthly. After four years of making these deposits, Kevin was ready to buy a new car. How much did he have in the account?

58. A young couple receive an inheritance of $72,000 that they want to set aside for a college fund for their two children. How much will this provide at the end of each half-year for a period of 9 years if it is deferred for 11 years and can be invested at 7.3%, compounded semiannually?

59. A bank is trying to decide whether to advertise some new 18-month certificates of deposit (CDs) at 6.52%, compounded quarterly, or at 6.48%, compounded continuously. Which rate is a better investment for the consumer who buys such a CD? Which rate is better for the bank?

60. To purchase a home, a couple borrowed $280,000 at 5.1% compounded monthly for 25 years. After making 70 payments of $1653.21, they plan to refinance at 4.2% compounded monthly for 15 years, with refinancing costs of $1100 added to the new loan.
    (a) Find the amount refinanced.
    (b) Find the new monthly payment.

(c) If this couple decides to make payments of $2000 per month on this refinanced loan, how long will it take to pay off the loan?
(d) How much is saved in total by refinancing and making monthly payments of $2000 on the refinanced amount?

61. A divorce settlement of $40,000 is paid in $1000 payments at the end of each of 40 months. What is the present value of this settlement if money is worth 12%, compounded monthly?

62. If $8000 is invested at 12%, compounded continuously, for 3 years, what is the total interest earned at the end of the 3 years?

63. A couple borrowed $184,000 to buy a condominium. Their loan was for 25 years and money is worth 6%, compounded monthly.
    (a) Find their monthly payment size.
    (b) Find the total amount they would pay over 25 years.
    (c) Find the total interest they would pay over 25 years.
    (d) Find the unpaid balance after 7 years.

COMBINED APPLICATIONS

Problems 64–67 are complex financial problems that require skills from several sections.

64. Suppose a salesman invests his $12,500 bonus in a fund that earns 10.8%, compounded monthly. Suppose also that he makes contributions of $150 at the end of each month to this fund.
    (a) Find the future value after $12\frac{1}{2}$ years.
    (b) If after the $12\frac{1}{2}$ years, the fund is used to set up an annuity, how much will it pay at the end of each month for the next 10 years?

65. Three years from now, a couple plan to spend 4 months traveling in China, Japan, and Southeast Asia. When they take their trip, they would like to withdraw $10,000 at the beginning of each month to cover their expenses for that month. Starting now, how much must they deposit at the beginning of each month for the next 3 years so that the account will provide the money they want while they are traveling? Assume that such an account pays 6.6%, compounded monthly.

66. At age 22, Aruam Sdlonyer receives a $4000 IRA from her parents. At age 30, she decides that at age 67 she'd like to have a retirement fund that would pay $20,000 at the end of each month for 20 years. Suppose all investments earn 8.4%, compounded monthly. How much does Aruam need to deposit at the end of each month from ages 30 to 67 to realize her goal?

67. A company borrows $2.6 million for 15 years at 5.6%, compounded quarterly. After 2 years of regular payments, the company's profits are such that management feels it can increase the quarterly payments to $70,000 each. How long will it take to pay off the loan, and how much interest will be saved?

Chapter 6 TEST

1. If $8000 is invested at 7%, compounded continuously, how long will it be before it grows to $47,000?

2. Suppose you invest $100 at the end of each month in an account that earns 6.9%, compounded monthly. What is the future value of the account after $5\frac{1}{2}$ years?

3. To buy a municipal bond that matures to $10,000 in 9 months, you must pay $9510. What simple interest rate is earned?

4. A debt of $280,000 is amortized with 40 equal semiannual payments of $14,357.78. If interest is 8.2%, compounded semiannually, find the unpaid balance of the debt after 25 payments have been made.

5. If an investment of $1000 grew to $13,500 in 9 years, what interest rate, compounded annually, did this investment earn?

6. A couple borrowed $97,000 at 7.2%, compounded monthly, for 25 years to purchase a condominium.
   (a) Find their monthly payment.
   (b) Over the 25 years, how much interest will they pay?

7. If you borrow $2500 for 15 months at 4% simple interest, how much money must you repay after the 15 months?

8. How much must you put aside at the beginning of each half-year if, in 6 years, you want to have $12,000, and the current interest rate is 6.2%, compounded semiannually?

9. Find the annual percentage yield (the effective annual rate) for an investment that earns 8.4%, compounded monthly.

10. An accountant wants to withdraw $3000 from an investment at the beginning of each quarter for the next 15 years. How much must be deposited originally if the investment earns 6%, compounded quarterly? Assume that after the 15 years, the balance is zero.

11. If $10,000 is invested at 7%, compounded continuously, what is the value of the investment after 20 years?

12. A $780,000 IRA is used to supplement a retired couple's income with payments at the end of each quarter for the next 15 years. If money is worth 8% compounded quarterly, what is the size of each payment?

13. What amount must you invest in an account that earns 6.8%, compounded quarterly, if you want to have $9500 after 5 years?

14. If $1500 is deposited at the end of each half-year in a retirement account that earns 8.2%, compounded semiannually, how long will it be before the account contains $500,000?

15. Maxine deposited $400 at the beginning of each month for 15 years in an account that earned 6%, compounded monthly. Find the value of the account after the 15 years.

16. Grandparents plan to establish a college trust for their youngest grandchild. How much is needed now so the trust, which earns 6.4%, compounded quarterly, will provide $4000 at the end of each quarter for 4 years after being deferred for 10 years?

17. A couple borrows $180,000 at 5.4% compounded monthly for 30 years. After making 80 payments of $1010.76, they refinance at 4.8% compounded monthly for 25 years, with refinancing costs of $550 added to the new loan.
   (a) Find the amount refinanced.
   (b) Find the new monthly payment.
   (c) How much is saved by refinancing?

18. Suppose that a 10-year corporate bond has a maturity value of $10,000 and a coupon rate of 10%, with coupons paid semiannually. Find the market price of the bond if the current yield rate is 6% compounded semiannually. Is this bond selling at a discount or at a premium?

19. The following sequence is arithmetic: 298.8, 293.3, 287.8, 282.3, ...
   (a) If you were not told that this sequence was arithmetic, how could you tell that it was?
   (b) Find the 51st term of this sequence.
   (c) Find the sum of the first 51 terms.

20. A 400-milligram dose of heart medicine is taken daily. During each 24-hour period, the body eliminates 40% of this drug (so that 60% remains in the body). Thus the amount of drug in the bloodstream just after the 31st dose is given by

$$400 + 400(0.6) + 400(0.6)^2 + 400(0.6)^3 + \ldots + 400(0.6)^{29} + 400(0.6)^{30}$$

Find the level of the drug in the bloodstream at this time.

OBJECTIVES

9.1

- To use graphs and numerical tables to find limits of functions, when they exist
- To find limits of polynomial functions
- To find limits of rational functions
- To find limits of piecewise defined functions

Limits

| APPLICATION PREVIEW |

Although everyone recognizes the value of eliminating any and all particulate pollution from smokestack emissions of factories, company owners are concerned about the cost of removing this pollution. Suppose that USA Steel has shown that the cost C of removing p percent of the particulate pollution from the emissions at one of its plants is

$$C = C(p) = \frac{7300p}{100 - p}$$

To investigate the cost of removing as much of the pollution as possible, we can evaluate the limit as p (the percent) approaches 100 from values less than 100. (See Example 6.) Using a limit is important in this case, because this function is undefined at $p = 100$ (it is impossible to remove 100% of the pollution).

In various applications we have seen the importance of the slope of a line as a rate of change. In particular, the slope of a linear total cost, total revenue, or profit function for a product tells us the marginals or rates of change of these functions. When these functions are not linear, how do we define marginals (and slope)?

We can get an idea about how to extend the concept of slope (and rate of change) to functions that are not linear. Observe that for many curves, if we take a very close (or "zoom-in") view near a point, the curve appears straight. See Figure 9.1. We can think of the slope of the "straight" line as the slope of the curve. The mathematical process used to obtain this "zoom-in" view is the process of taking limits. The concept of limit is essential to the study of calculus.

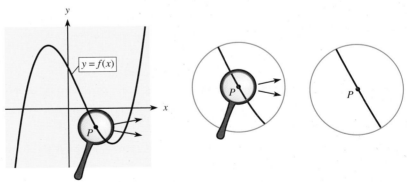

Figure 9.1   When we zoom in near point P, the curve appears straight.

Concept of a Limit   We have used the notation $f(c)$ to indicate the value of a function $f(x)$ at $x = c$. If we need to discuss a value that $f(x)$ approaches as x approaches c, we use the idea of a *limit*. For example, if

$$f(x) = \frac{x^2 - x - 6}{x + 2}$$

then we know that $x = -2$ is not in the domain of $f(x)$, so $f(-2)$ does not exist even though $f(x)$ exists for every value of $x \neq -2$. Figure 9.2 on the next page shows the graph of $y = f(x)$ with an open circle where $x = -2$. The open circle indicates that $f(-2)$ does not exist but shows that points near $x = -2$ have functional values that lie on the line on either side of the open circle. Even though $f(-2)$ is not defined, the figure shows that as x approaches -2 from either side of -2, the graph approaches the open circle at $(-2, -5)$ and the values of $f(x)$ approach -5. Thus -5 is the limit of $f(x)$ as x approaches -2, and we write

$$\lim_{x \to -2} f(x) = -5, \quad \text{or} \quad f(x) \to -5 \quad \text{as} \quad x \to -2$$

| TABLE 9.1 |

Left of −2	
x	$f(x) = \dfrac{x^2 - x - 6}{x + 2}$
−3.000	−6.000
−2.500	−5.500
−2.100	−5.100
−2.010	−5.010
−2.001	−5.001

Right of −2	
x	$f(x) = \dfrac{x^2 - x - 6}{x + 2}$
−1.000	−4.000
−1.500	−4.500
−1.900	−4.900
−1.990	−4.990
−1.999	−4.999

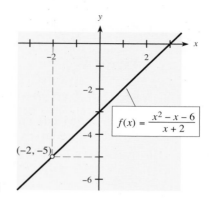

$$f(x) = \frac{x^2 - x - 6}{x + 2}$$

Figure 9.2

This conclusion is fairly obvious from the graph, but it is not so obvious from the equation for $f(x)$.

We can use the values near $x = -2$ in Table 9.1 to help verify that $f(x) \to -5$ as $x \to -2$. Note that to the left of −2, the values of $f(x)$ get very close to −5 as x gets very close to −2, and to the right of −2, the values of $f(x)$ get very close to −5 as x gets very close to −2. Hence, Table 9.1 and Figure 9.2 indicate that the value of $f(x)$ approaches −5 as x approaches −2 from both sides of $x = -2$.

From our discussion of the graph in Figure 9.2 and Table 9.1, we see that as x approaches −2 from either side of −2, the limit of the function is the value L that the function approaches. This limit L is not necessarily the value of the function at $x = -2$. This leads to our intuitive definition of **limit.**

Limit

Let $f(x)$ be a function defined on an open interval containing c, except perhaps at c. Then

$$\lim_{x \to c} f(x) = L$$

is read "the **limit** of $f(x)$ as x approaches c equals L." The number L exists if we can make values of $f(x)$ as close to L as we desire by choosing values of x sufficiently close to c. When the values of $f(x)$ do not approach a single finite value L as x approaches c, we say the limit does not exist.

As the definition states, a limit as $x \to c$ can exist only if the function approaches a single finite value as x approaches c from both the left and right of c.

EXAMPLE   1   Limits

Figure 9.3 shows three functions for which the limit exists as x approaches 2. Use this figure to find the following.

(a) $\lim\limits_{x \to 2} f(x)$ and $f(2)$ (if it exists)

(b) $\lim\limits_{x \to 2} g(x)$ and $g(2)$ (if it exists)

(c) $\lim\limits_{x \to 2} h(x)$ and $h(2)$ (if it exists)

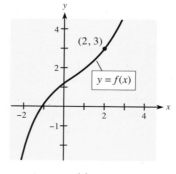

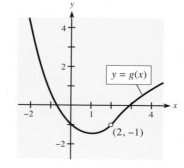

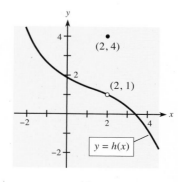

Figure 9.3   (a)   (b)   (c)

Solution

(a) From the graph in Figure 9.3(a), we see that as x approaches 2 from both the left and the right, the graph approaches the point $(2, 3)$. Thus $f(x)$ approaches the single value 3. That is,

$$\lim_{x \to 2} f(x) = 3$$

The value of $f(2)$ is the y-coordinate of the point on the graph at $x = 2$. Thus $f(2) = 3$.

(b) Figure 9.3(b) shows that as x approaches 2 from both the left and the right, the graph approaches the open circle at $(2, -1)$. Thus

$$\lim_{x \to 2} g(x) = -1$$

The figure also shows that at $x = 2$ there is no point on the graph. Thus $g(2)$ is undefined.

(c) Figure 9.3(c) shows that

$$\lim_{x \to 2} h(x) = 1$$

The figure also shows that at $x = 2$ there is a point on the graph at $(2, 4)$. Thus $h(2) = 4$, and we see that $\lim_{x \to 2} h(x) \neq h(2)$. ∎

As Example 1 shows, the limit of the function as x approaches c may or may not be the same as the value of the function at $x = c$.

In Example 1 we saw that the limit as x approaches 2 meant the limit as x approaches 2 from both the left and the right. We can also consider limits only from the left or only from the right; these are called **one-sided limits.**

One-Sided Limits

Limit from the Right: $\lim_{x \to c^+} f(x) = L$

means the values of $f(x)$ approach the value L as $x \to c$ but $x > c$.

Limit from the Left: $\lim_{x \to c^-} f(x) = M$

means the values of $f(x)$ approach the value M as $x \to c$ but $x < c$.

Note that when one or both one-sided limits fail to exist, then the limit does not exist. Also, when the one-sided limits differ, such as if $L \neq M$ above, then the values of $f(x)$ do not approach a *single* value as x approaches c, and $\lim_{x \to c} f(x)$ does not exist.

EXAMPLE 2   One-Sided Limits

Using the functions graphed in Figure 9.4, determine why the limit as $x \to 2$ does not exist for

(a) $f(x)$.
(b) $g(x)$.
(c) $h(x)$.

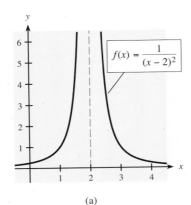

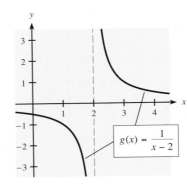

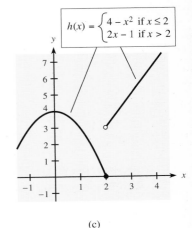

Figure 9.4   (a)   (b)   (c)

Solution

(a) As $x \to 2$ from the left side and the right side of $x = 2$, $f(x)$ increases without bound, which we denote by saying that $f(x)$ approaches ∞ as $x \to 2$. In this case, $\lim\limits_{x \to 2} f(x)$ does not exist [denoted by $\lim\limits_{x \to 2} f(x)$ DNE] because $f(x)$ does not approach a finite value as $x \to 2$. In this case, we write

$$f(x) \to \infty \text{ as } x \to 2$$

The graph has a vertical asymptote at $x = 2$.

(b) As $x \to 2$ from the left, $g(x)$ approaches $-\infty$, and as $x \to 2$ from the right, $g(x)$ approaches ∞, so $g(x)$ does not approach a finite value as $x \to 2$. Therefore, the limit does not exist. The graph of $y = g(x)$ has a vertical asymptote at $x = 2$.
In this case we summarize by writing

$$\lim\limits_{x \to 2^-} g(x) \text{ DNE} \qquad \text{or} \qquad g(x) \to -\infty \text{ as } x \to 2^-$$

$$\lim\limits_{x \to 2^+} g(x) \text{ DNE} \qquad \text{or} \qquad g(x) \to \infty \text{ as } x \to 2^+$$

and

$$\lim\limits_{x \to 2} g(x) \text{ DNE}$$

(c) As $x \to 2$ from the left, the graph approaches the point at $(2, 0)$, so $\lim\limits_{x \to 2^-} h(x) = 0$. As $x \to 2$ from the right, the graph approaches the open circle at $(2, 3)$, so $\lim\limits_{x \to 2^+} h(x) = 3$. Because these one-sided limits differ, $\lim\limits_{x \to 2} h(x)$ does not exist. ■

Examples 1 and 2 illustrate the following two important facts regarding limits.

The Limit

1. The limit $\lim\limits_{x \to c} f(x) = L$ only if the following two conditions are satisfied:

   (a) The limit L is a finite value (real number).
   (b) The limit as x approaches c from the left equals the limit as x approaches c from the right. That is, we must have

$$\lim\limits_{x \to c^-} f(x) = \lim\limits_{x \to c^+} f(x)$$

   Figure 9.4 and Example 2 illustrate cases where $\lim\limits_{x \to c} f(x)$ does not exist.

2. The limit $\lim\limits_{x \to c} f(x)$ and the function value $f(c)$ are independent. When $\lim\limits_{x \to c} f(x)$ exists, $f(c)$ may be (i) the same as the limit, (ii) undefined, or (iii) defined but different from the limit (see Figure 9.3 and Example 1).

✓ **CHECKPOINT**

1. Can $\lim\limits_{x \to c} f(x)$ exist if $f(c)$ is undefined?
2. Does $\lim\limits_{x \to c} f(x)$ exist if $f(c) = 0$?
3. Does $f(c) = 1$ if $\lim\limits_{x \to c} f(x) = 1$?
4. If $\lim\limits_{x \to c^-} f(x) = 0$, does $\lim\limits_{x \to c} f(x)$ exist?
5. Let $\lim\limits_{x \to c} f(x) = 4$.
   (a) Does $\lim\limits_{x \to c^+} f(x) = 4$?   (b) Find $\lim\limits_{x \to c^-} f(x)$.

Properties of Limits; Algebraic Evaluation

We have seen that the value of the limit of a function as $x \to c$ will not always be the same as the value of the function at $x = c$. However, there are many functions for which the limit and the functional value agree [see Figure 9.3(a)], and for these functions we can easily evaluate limits, as the following properties indicate.

Properties of Limits

If k is a constant, $\lim\limits_{x \to c} f(x) = L$, and $\lim\limits_{x \to c} g(x) = M$, then the following are true.

I. $\lim\limits_{x \to c} k = k$

II. $\lim\limits_{x \to c} x = c$

III. $\lim\limits_{x \to c} [f(x) \pm g(x)] = L \pm M$

IV. $\lim\limits_{x \to c} [f(x) \cdot g(x)] = LM$

V. $\lim\limits_{x \to c} \dfrac{f(x)}{g(x)} = \dfrac{L}{M}$ if $M \neq 0$

VI. $\lim\limits_{x \to c} \sqrt[n]{f(x)} = \sqrt[n]{\lim\limits_{x \to c} f(x)} = \sqrt[n]{L}$,
     provided that $L > 0$ when n is even.

If f is a polynomial function, then Properties I–IV imply that $\lim\limits_{x \to c} f(x)$ can be found by evaluating $f(c)$. Moreover, if h is a rational function whose denominator is not zero at $x = c$, then Property V implies that $\lim\limits_{x \to c} h(x)$ can be found by evaluating $h(c)$. The following summarizes these observations and recalls the definitions of polynomial and rational functions.

Function	Definition	Limit
Polynomial function	The function $f(x) = a_n x^n + a_{n-1} x^{n-1} + \cdots + a_1 x + a_0,$ where $a_n \neq 0$ and n is a positive integer, is called a **polynomial function** of degree n.	$\lim\limits_{x \to c} f(x) = f(c)$ for all values c (by Properties I–IV)
Rational function	The function $h(x) = \dfrac{f(x)}{g(x)}$ where both $f(x)$ and $g(x)$ are polynomial functions, is called a **rational function.**	$\lim\limits_{x \to c} h(x) = \lim\limits_{x \to c} \dfrac{f(x)}{g(x)} = \dfrac{f(c)}{g(c)}$ when $g(c) \neq 0$ (by Property V)

EXAMPLE   3   Limits

Find the following limits, if they exist.

(a) $\lim\limits_{x \to -1} (x^3 - 2x)$ (b) $\lim\limits_{x \to 4} \dfrac{x^2 - 4x}{x - 2}$

Solution

(a)   Note that $f(x) = x^3 - 2x$ is a polynomial, so

$$\lim_{x \to -1} f(x) = f(-1) = (-1)^3 - 2(-1) = 1$$

Figure 9.5(a) on the next page shows the graph of $f(x) = x^3 - 2x$.

(b)   Note that this limit has the form

$$\lim_{x \to c} \frac{f(x)}{g(x)}$$

where $f(x)$ and $g(x)$ are polynomials and $g(c) \neq 0$. Therefore, we have

$$\lim_{x \to 4} \frac{x^2 - 4x}{x - 2} = \frac{4^2 - 4(4)}{4 - 2} = \frac{0}{2} = 0$$

Figure 9.5(b) shows the graph of $g(x) = \dfrac{x^2 - 4x}{x - 2}$.

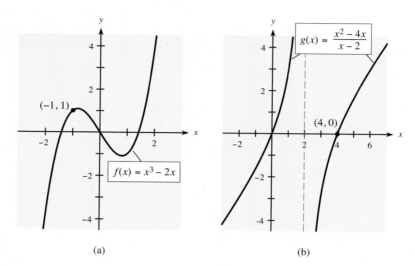

Figure 9.5   (a)   (b)

We have seen that we can use Property V to find the limit of a rational function $f(x)/g(x)$ as long as the denominator is *not* zero. If the limit of the denominator of $f(x)/g(x)$ *is* zero, then there are two possible cases.

Rational Functions: Evaluating Limits of the Form $\lim\limits_{x \to c} \dfrac{f(x)}{g(x)}$ where $\lim\limits_{x \to c} g(x) = 0$

Type I. If $\lim\limits_{x \to c} f(x) = 0$ and $\lim\limits_{x \to c} g(x) = 0$, then $\lim\limits_{x \to c} \dfrac{f(x)}{g(x)}$ has the **0/0 indeterminate form** at $x = c$. We can factor $x - c$ from $f(x)$ and $g(x)$, reduce the fraction, and then find the limit of the resulting expression, if it exists.

Type II. If $\lim\limits_{x \to c} f(x) \neq 0$ and $\lim\limits_{x \to c} g(x) = 0$, then $\lim\limits_{x \to c} \dfrac{f(x)}{g(x)}$ does not exist. In this case, the values of $f(x)/g(x)$ become unbounded as x approaches c; the line $x = c$ is a vertical asymptote.

EXAMPLE 4   0/0 Indeterminate Form

Evaluate the following limits, if they exist.

(a) $\lim\limits_{x \to 2} \dfrac{x^2 - 4}{x - 2}$ (b) $\lim\limits_{x \to 1} \dfrac{x^2 - 3x + 2}{x^2 - 1}$

Solution

(a) This limit has the 0/0 indeterminate form at $x = 2$ because both the numerator and denominator equal zero when $x = 2$. Thus we can factor $x - 2$ from both the numerator and the denominator and reduce the fraction. (We can divide by $x - 2$ because $x - 2 \neq 0$ while $x \to 2$.)

$$\lim_{x \to 2} \frac{x^2 - 4}{x - 2} = \lim_{x \to 2} \frac{(x - 2)(x + 2)}{x - 2} = \lim_{x \to 2} (x + 2) = 4$$

Figure 9.6(a) shows the graph of $f(x) = (x^2 - 4)/(x - 2)$. Note the open circle at $(2, 4)$.

(b) By substituting 1 for x in $(x^2 - 3x + 2)/(x^2 - 1)$, we see that the expression has the 0/0 indeterminate form at $x = 1$, so $x - 1$ is a factor of both the numerator and the denominator. (We can then reduce the fraction because $x - 1 \neq 0$ while $x \to 1$.)

$$\lim_{x \to 1} \frac{x^2 - 3x + 2}{x^2 - 1} = \lim_{x \to 1} \frac{(x - 1)(x - 2)}{(x - 1)(x + 1)} = \lim_{x \to 1} \frac{x - 2}{x + 1}$$
$$= \frac{1 - 2}{1 + 1} = \frac{-1}{2} \qquad \text{(by Property V)}$$

Figure 9.6(b) shows the graph of $g(x) = (x^2 - 3x + 2)/(x^2 - 1)$. Note the open circle at $(1, -\frac{1}{2})$.

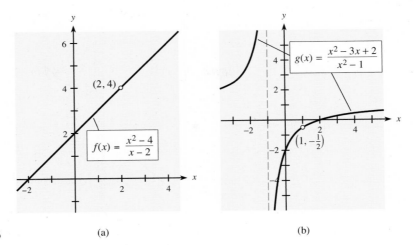

Figure 9.6
(a)
(b)

Note that although both problems in Example 4 had the 0/0 indeterminate form, they had different answers.

EXAMPLE 5 Limit with $a/0$ Form

Find $\lim\limits_{x \to 1} \dfrac{x^2 + 3x + 2}{x - 1}$, if it exists.

Solution

Substituting 1 for x in the function results in 6/0, so this limit has the form $a/0$, with $a \neq 0$, and is like the Type II form discussed previously. Hence the limit does not exist. Because the numerator is not zero when $x = 1$, we know that $x - 1$ is *not* a factor of the numerator, and we cannot divide numerator and denominator as we did in Example 4. Table 9.2 confirms that this limit does not exist, because the values of the expression become unbounded as x approaches 1.

| TABLE 9.2 |

Left of $x = 1$		Right of $x = 1$	
x	$\dfrac{x^2 + 3x + 2}{x - 1}$	x	$\dfrac{x^2 + 3x + 2}{x - 1}$
0.5	−7.5	1.5	17.5
0.7	−15.3	1.2	35.2
0.9	−55.1	1.1	65.1
0.99	−595.01	1.01	605.01
0.999	−5995.001	1.001	6005.001
0.9999	−59,995.0001	1.0001	60,005.0001
$\lim\limits_{x \to 1^-} \dfrac{x^2 + 3x + 2}{x - 1}$ DNE		$\lim\limits_{x \to 1^+} \dfrac{x^2 + 3x + 2}{x - 1}$ DNE	
$(f(x) \to -\infty$ as $x \to 1^-)$		$(f(x) \to \infty$ as $x \to 1^+)$	

The left-hand and right-hand limits do not exist. Thus $\lim\limits_{x \to 1} \dfrac{x^2 + 3x + 2}{x - 1}$ does not exist.

In Example 5, even though the left-hand and right-hand limits do not exist (see Table 9.2), knowledge that the functional values are unbounded (that is, that they become infinite) is helpful in graphing. The graph is shown in Figure 9.7 on the next page. We see that $x = 1$ is a vertical asymptote.

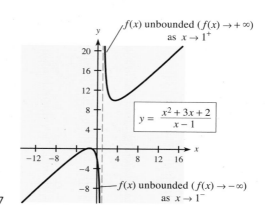

Figure 9.7

EXAMPLE 6 Cost-Benefit | APPLICATION PREVIEW |

USA Steel has shown that the cost C of removing p percent of the particulate pollution from the smokestack emissions at one of its plants is

$$C = C(p) = \frac{7300p}{100 - p}$$

Investigate the cost of removing as much of the pollution as possible.

Solution

First note that the costs of removing 90% and 99% of the pollution are found as follows:

Removing 90%: $C(90) = \dfrac{7300(90)}{100 - 90} = \dfrac{657,000}{10} = 65,700$ (dollars)

Removing 99%: $C(99) = \dfrac{7300(99)}{100 - 99} = \dfrac{722,700}{1} = 722,700$ (dollars)

The cost of removing 100% of the pollution is undefined because the denominator of the function is 0 when $p = 100$. To see what the cost approaches as p approaches 100 from values smaller than 100, we evaluate $\displaystyle\lim_{x \to 100^-} \frac{7300p}{100 - p}$. This limit has the Type II form for rational functions. Thus $\dfrac{7300\,p}{100 - p} \to \infty$ as $x \to 100^-$, which means that as the amount of pollution that is removed approaches 100%, the cost increases without bound. (That is, it is cost prohibitive to remove 100% of the pollution.)

© iStockphoto.com/steba2

✓ CHECKPOINT

6. Evaluate the following limits (if they exist).

(a) $\displaystyle\lim_{x \to -3} \frac{2x^2 + 5x - 3}{x^2 - 9}$ (b) $\displaystyle\lim_{x \to 5} \frac{x^2 - 3x - 3}{x^2 - 8x + 1}$ (c) $\displaystyle\lim_{x \to -3/4} \frac{4x}{4x + 3}$

In Problems 7–10, assume that f, g, and h are polynomials.

7. Does $\displaystyle\lim_{x \to c} f(x) = f(c)$?

8. Does $\displaystyle\lim_{x \to c} \frac{g(x)}{h(x)} = \frac{g(c)}{h(c)}$?

9. If $g(c) = 0$ and $h(c) = 0$, can we be certain that

(a) $\displaystyle\lim_{x \to c} \frac{g(x)}{h(x)} = 0$?   (b) $\displaystyle\lim_{x \to c} \frac{g(x)}{h(x)}$ exists?

10. If $g(c) \neq 0$ and $h(c) = 0$, what can be said about $\displaystyle\lim_{x \to c} \frac{g(x)}{h(x)}$ and $\displaystyle\lim_{x \to c} \frac{h(x)}{g(x)}$?

Limits of Piecewise Defined Functions

As we noted in Section 2.4, "Special Functions and Their Graphs," many applications are modeled by piecewise defined functions. To see how we evaluate a limit involving a piecewise defined function, consider the following example.

EXAMPLE 7   **Limits of a Piecewise Defined Function**

Find $\lim\limits_{x \to 1^-} f(x)$, $\lim\limits_{x \to 1^+} f(x)$, and $\lim\limits_{x \to 1} f(x)$, if they exist, for

$$f(x) = \begin{cases} x^2 + 1 & \text{if } x \le 1 \\ x + 2 & \text{if } x > 1 \end{cases}$$

Solution

Because $f(x)$ is defined by $x^2 + 1$ when $x < 1$,

$$\lim_{x \to 1^-} f(x) = \lim_{x \to 1^-} (x^2 + 1) = 2$$

Because $f(x)$ is defined by $x + 2$ when $x > 1$,

$$\lim_{x \to 1^+} f(x) = \lim_{x \to 1^+} (x + 2) = 3$$

And because

$$2 = \lim_{x \to 1^-} f(x) \ne \lim_{x \to 1^+} f(x) = 3$$

$\lim\limits_{x \to 1} f(x)$ does not exist.

Table 9.3 and Figure 9.8 show these results numerically and graphically.

| TABLE 9.3 |

Left of 1	
x	**$f(x) = x^2 + 1$**
0.9	1.81
0.99	1.98
0.999	1.998
0.9999	1.9998

Right of 1	
x	**$f(x) = x + 2$**
1.01	3.01
1.001	3.001
1.0001	3.0001
1.00001	3.00001

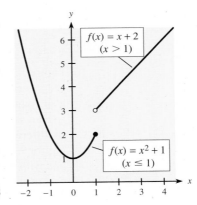

Figure 9.8

Calculator Note   We have used graphical, numerical, and algebraic methods to understand and evaluate limits. Graphing calculators can be especially effective when exploring limits graphically or numerically. See the following example and Appendix A, Section 9.1, for details.

EXAMPLE 8   **Limits: Graphically, Numerically, and Algebraically**

Consider the following limits.

(a) $\lim\limits_{x \to 5} \dfrac{x^2 + 2x - 35}{x^2 - 6x + 5}$ (b) $\lim\limits_{x \to -1} \dfrac{2x}{x + 1}$

Investigate each limit by using the following methods.

(i)   Graphically: Graph the function with a graphing calculator and trace near the limiting x-value.

(ii) Numerically: Use the table feature of a graphing calculator to evaluate the function very close to the limiting x-value.

(iii) Algebraically: Use properties of limits and algebraic techniques.

Solution

(a) $\displaystyle\lim_{x\to5}\frac{x^2+2x-35}{x^2-6x+5}$

(i) Figures 9.9(a) and 9.9(b) show the graph of $y=(x^2+2x-35)/(x^2-6x+5)$. Tracing near $x=5$ will show y-values getting close to 3.

(ii) Figure 9.9(c) shows a table for $y_1=(x^2+2x-35)/(x^2-6x+5)$ with x-values approaching 5 from both sides (note that the function is undefined at $x=5$). Again, the y-values approach 3 as x approaches 5 from both sides.

Both (i) and (ii) strongly suggest $\displaystyle\lim_{x\to5}\frac{x^2+2x-35}{x^2-6x+5}=3$.

(iii) Algebraic evaluation of this limit confirms what the graph and the table suggest.

$$\lim_{x\to5}\frac{x^2+2x-35}{x^2-6x+5}=\lim_{x\to5}\frac{(x+7)(x-5)}{(x-1)(x-5)}=\lim_{x\to5}\frac{x+7}{x-1}=\frac{12}{4}=3$$

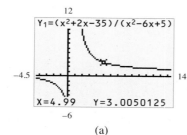

(a)

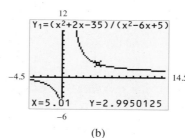

(b)

X	Y₁	
4.9	3.0513	
4.99	3.005	
4.999	3.0005	
5	ERROR	
5.001	2.9995	
5.01	2.995	
5.1	2.9512	
X=4.9		

(c)

Figure 9.9

(b) $\displaystyle\lim_{x\to-1}\frac{2x}{x+1}$

(i) Figure 9.10(a) shows the graph of $y=2x/(x+1)$; it indicates a break in the graph near $x=-1$. Evaluation confirms that the break occurs at $x=-1$ and also suggests that the function becomes unbounded near $x=-1$. In addition, we can see that as x approaches -1 from opposite sides, the function is headed in different directions. All this suggests that the limit does not exist.

(ii) Figure 9.10(b) shows a graphing calculator table of values for $y_1=2x/(x+1)$ and with x-values approaching $x=-1$ from both sides. The table reinforces our preliminary conclusion from the graph that the limit does not exist, because the function values are not approaching a single value and are becoming unbounded near $x=-1$.

(iii) Algebraically we see that this limit has the form $-2/0$. Thus $\displaystyle\lim_{x\to-1}\frac{2x}{x+1}$ DNE.

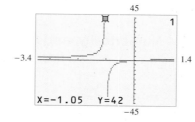

(a)

X	Y₁	
-1.1	22	
-1.01	202	
-1.001	2002	
-1	ERROR	
-.999	-1998	
-.99	-198	
-.9	-18	
X=-.9		

(b)

Figure 9.10

✓ **CHECKPOINT**
ANSWERS

1. Yes. See Figure 9.2 and Table 9.1.
2. Not necessarily. See Figure 9.4(c).
3. Not necessarily. See Figure 9.3(c).
4. Not necessarily. See Figure 9.4(c).
5. (a) Yes   (b) 4

6. (a) $\lim\limits_{x\to -3} \dfrac{2x^2 + 5x - 3}{x^2 - 9} = \dfrac{7}{6}$

    (b) $\lim\limits_{x\to 5} \dfrac{x^2 - 3x - 3}{x^2 - 8x + 1} = -\dfrac{1}{2}$

    (c) $\lim\limits_{x\to -3/4} \dfrac{4x}{4x + 3}$ does not exist.

7. Yes, Properties I–IV yield this result.
8. Not necessarily. If $h(c) \neq 0$, then this is true. Otherwise, it is not true.
9. For both (a) and (b), $g(x)/h(x)$ has the 0/0 indeterminate form at $x = c$. In this case we can make no general conclusion about the limit.

10. $\lim\limits_{x\to c} \dfrac{g(x)}{h(x)}$ does not exist and $\lim\limits_{x\to c} \dfrac{h(x)}{g(x)} = 0$

| EXERCISES | 9.1

In Problems 1–6, a graph of $y = f(x)$ is shown and a c-value is given. For each problem, use the graph to find the following, whenever they exist.
(a) $\lim\limits_{x\to c} f(x)$ and   (b) $f(c)$

In Problems 7–10, use the graph of $y = f(x)$ and the given c-value to find the following, whenever they exist.
(a) $\lim\limits_{x\to c^-} f(x)$ (b) $\lim\limits_{x\to c^+} f(x)$
(c) $\lim\limits_{x\to c} f(x)$ (d) $f(c)$

1. $c = 4$

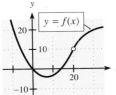

2. $c = 6$

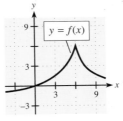

7. $c = -10$

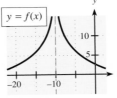

8. $c = 2$

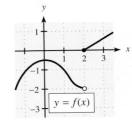

3. $c = 20$

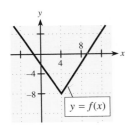

4. $c = -10$

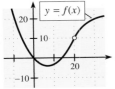

9. $c = -4\frac{1}{2}$

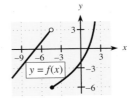

10. $c = 2$

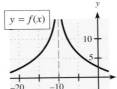

5. $c = -8$

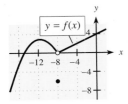

6. $c = -2$

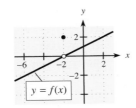

In Problems 11–14, complete each table and predict the limit, if it exists.

11. $f(x) = \dfrac{2 - x - x^2}{x - 1}$

$\lim\limits_{x \to 1} f(x) = ?$

x	$f(x)$
0.9	
0.99	
0.999	
1.001	
1.01	
1.1	

12. $f(x) = \dfrac{2x + 1}{\frac{1}{4} - x^2}$

$\lim\limits_{x \to -0.5} f(x) = ?$

x	$f(x)$
−0.51	
−0.501	
−0.5001	
−0.4999	
−0.499	
−0.49	

13. $f(x) = \begin{cases} 5x - 1 & \text{for } x < 1 \\ 8 - 2x - x^2 & \text{for } x \geq 1 \end{cases}$

$\lim\limits_{x \to 1} f(x) = ?$

x	$f(x)$
0.9	
0.99	
0.999	
1.001	
1.01	
1.1	

14. $f(x) = \begin{cases} 4 - x^2 & \text{for } x \leq -2 \\ x^2 + 2x & \text{for } x > -2 \end{cases}$

$\lim\limits_{x \to -2} f(x) = ?$

x	$f(x)$
−2.1	
−2.01	
−2.001	
−1.999	
−1.99	

In Problems 15–38, use properties of limits and algebraic methods to find the limits, if they exist.

15. $\lim\limits_{x \to -35} (34 + x)$

16. $\lim\limits_{x \to 80} (82 - x)$

17. $\lim\limits_{x \to -1} (4x^3 - 2x^2 + 2)$

18. $\lim\limits_{x \to 3} (2x^3 - 12x^2 + 5x + 3)$

19. $\lim\limits_{x \to -1/2} \dfrac{4x - 2}{4x^2 + 1}$

20. $\lim\limits_{x \to -1/3} \dfrac{1 - 3x}{9x^2 + 1}$

21. $\lim\limits_{x \to 3} \dfrac{x^2 - 9}{x - 3}$

22. $\lim\limits_{x \to -4} \dfrac{x^2 - 16}{x + 4}$

23. $\lim\limits_{x \to 7} \dfrac{x^2 - 8x + 7}{x^2 - 6x - 7}$

24. $\lim\limits_{x \to -5} \dfrac{x^2 + 8x + 15}{x^2 + 5x}$

25. $\lim\limits_{x \to 10} \dfrac{3x^2 - 30x}{x^2 - 100}$

26. $\lim\limits_{x \to -6} \dfrac{2x^2 - 72}{3x^2 + 18x}$

27. $\lim\limits_{x \to -2} \dfrac{x^2 + 4x + 4}{x^2 + 3x + 2}$

28. $\lim\limits_{x \to 10} \dfrac{x^2 - 8x - 20}{x^2 - 11x + 10}$

29. $\lim\limits_{x \to 3} f(x)$, where $f(x) = \begin{cases} 10 - 2x & \text{if } x < 3 \\ x^2 - x & \text{if } x \geq 3 \end{cases}$

30. $\lim\limits_{x \to 5} f(x)$, where $f(x) = \begin{cases} 7x - 10 & \text{if } x < 5 \\ 25 & \text{if } x \geq 5 \end{cases}$

31. $\lim\limits_{x \to -1} f(x)$, where $f(x) = \begin{cases} x^2 + \dfrac{4}{x} & \text{if } x \leq -1 \\ 3x^3 - x - 1 & \text{if } x > -1 \end{cases}$

32. $\lim\limits_{x \to 2} f(x)$, where $f(x) = \begin{cases} \dfrac{x^3 - 4}{x - 3} & \text{if } x \leq 2 \\ \dfrac{3 - x^2}{x} & \text{if } x > 2 \end{cases}$

33. $\lim\limits_{x \to 2} \dfrac{x^2 + 6x + 9}{x - 2}$

34. $\lim\limits_{x \to 5} \dfrac{x^2 - 6x + 8}{x - 5}$

35. $\lim\limits_{x \to -1} \dfrac{x^2 + 5x + 6}{x + 1}$

36. $\lim\limits_{x \to 3} \dfrac{x^2 + 2x - 3}{x - 3}$

37. $\lim\limits_{h \to 0} \dfrac{(x + h)^3 - x^3}{h}$

38. $\lim\limits_{h \to 0} \dfrac{2(x + h)^2 - 2x^2}{h}$

In Problems 39–42, graph each function with a graphing calculator and use it to predict the limit. Check your work either by using the table feature of the calculator or by finding the limit algebraically.

39. $\lim\limits_{x \to 10} \dfrac{x^2 - 19x + 90}{3x^2 - 30x}$

40. $\lim\limits_{x \to -3} \dfrac{x^4 + 3x^3}{2x^4 - 18x^2}$

41. $\lim\limits_{x \to -1} \dfrac{x^3 - x}{x^2 + 2x + 1}$

42. $\lim\limits_{x \to 5} \dfrac{x^2 - 7x + 10}{x^2 - 10x + 25}$

In Problems 43–46, use the table feature of a graphing calculator to predict each limit. Check your work by using either a graphical or an algebraic approach.

43. $\lim\limits_{x \to -2} \dfrac{x^4 - 4x^2}{x^2 + 8x + 12}$

44. $\lim\limits_{x \to -4} \dfrac{x^3 + 4x^2}{2x^2 + 7x - 4}$

45. $\lim\limits_{x \to 4} f(x)$, where $f(x) = \begin{cases} 12 - \dfrac{3}{4}x & \text{if } x \leq 4 \\ x^2 - 7 & \text{if } x > 4 \end{cases}$

46. $\lim\limits_{x \to 7} f(x)$, where $f(x) = \begin{cases} 2 + x - x^2 & \text{if } x \leq 7 \\ 13 - 9x & \text{if } x > 7 \end{cases}$

47. Use values 0.1, 0.01, 0.001, 0.0001, and 0.00001 to approximate

$$\lim\limits_{a \to 0} (1 + a)^{1/a}$$

to three decimal places. This limit equals the special number e that is discussed in Section 5.1, "Exponential Functions," and Section 6.2, "Compound Interest; Geometric Sequences."

48. (a) If $\lim\limits_{x \to 2^+} f(x) = 5$, $\lim\limits_{x \to 2^-} f(x) = 5$, and $f(2) = 0$, find $\lim\limits_{x \to 2} f(x)$, if it exists. Explain your conclusions.

(b) If $\lim\limits_{x \to 0^+} f(x) = 3$, $\lim\limits_{x \to 0^-} f(x) = 0$, and $f(0) = 0$, find $\lim\limits_{x \to 0} f(x)$, if it exists. Explain your conclusions.

49. If $\lim\limits_{x \to 3} f(x) = 4$ and $\lim\limits_{x \to 3} g(x) = -2$, find

(a) $\lim\limits_{x \to 3} [f(x) + g(x)]$

(b) $\lim\limits_{x \to 3} [f(x) - g(x)]$

(c) $\lim\limits_{x \to 3} [f(x) \cdot g(x)]$

(d) $\lim\limits_{x \to 3} \dfrac{g(x)}{f(x)}$

50. If $\lim_{x \to -2} f(x) = 6$ and $\lim_{x \to -2} g(x) = 3$, find

   (a) $\lim_{x \to -2} [5f(x) - 4g(x)]$ (b) $\lim_{x \to -2} [g(x)]^2$

   (c) $\lim_{x \to -2} [4 - xf(x)]$ (d) $\lim_{x \to -2} \left[\dfrac{f(x)}{g(x)} \right]$

51. If $\lim_{x \to 2} [f(x) + g(x)] = 5$ and $\lim_{x \to 2} g(x) = 11$, find

   (a) $\lim_{x \to 2} f(x)$

   (b) $\lim_{x \to 2} \{[f(x)]^2 - [g(x)]^2\}$

   (c) $\lim_{x \to 2} \dfrac{3g(x)}{f(x) - g(x)}$

52. If $\lim_{x \to 5} [f(x) - g(x)] = 8$ and $\lim_{x \to 5} g(x) = 2$, find

   (a) $\lim_{x \to 5} f(x)$ (b) $\lim_{x \to 5} \{[g(x)]^2 - f(x)\}$

   (c) $\lim_{x \to 5} \left[\dfrac{2xg(x)}{4 - f(x)} \right]$

APPLICATIONS

53. *Revenue* The total revenue for a product is given by

   $$R(x) = 1600x - x^2$$

   where x is the number of units sold. What is $\lim_{x \to 100} R(x)$?

54. *Profit* If the profit function for a product is given by

   $$P(x) = 92x - x^2 - 1760$$

   find $\lim_{x \to 40} P(x)$.

55. *Sales and training* The average monthly sales volume (in thousands of dollars) for a firm depends on the number of hours x of training of its sales staff, according to

   $$S(x) = \frac{4}{x} + 30 + \frac{x}{4}, \quad 4 \le x \le 100$$

   (a) Find $\lim_{x \to 4^+} S(x)$.   (b) Find $\lim_{x \to 100^-} S(x)$.

56. *Sales and training* During the first 4 months of employment, the monthly sales S (in thousands of dollars) for a new salesperson depend on the number of hours x of training, as follows:

   $$S = S(x) = \frac{9}{x} + 10 + \frac{x}{4}, \quad x \ge 4$$

   (a) Find $\lim_{x \to 4^+} S(x)$.   (b) Find $\lim_{x \to 10} S(x)$.

57. *Advertising and sales* Suppose that the daily sales S (in dollars) t days after the end of an advertising campaign are

   $$S = S(t) = 400 + \frac{2400}{t + 1}$$

   (a) Find $S(0)$.   (b) Find $\lim_{t \to 7} S(t)$.

   (c) Find $\lim_{t \to 14} S(t)$.

58. *Advertising and sales* Sales y (in thousands of dollars) are related to advertising expenses x (in thousands of dollars) according to

   $$y = y(x) = \frac{200x}{x + 10}, \quad x \ge 0$$

   (a) Find $\lim_{x \to 10} y(x)$.   (b) Find $\lim_{x \to 0} y(x)$.

59. *Productivity* During an 8-hour shift, the rate of change of productivity (in units per hour) of infant activity centers assembled after t hours on the job is

   $$r(t) = \frac{128(t^2 + 6t)}{(t^2 + 6t + 18)^2}, \quad 0 \le t \le 8$$

   (a) Find $\lim_{t \to 4} r(t)$.   (b) Find $\lim_{t \to 8} r(t)$.

   (c) Is the rate of productivity higher near the lunch break (at $t = 4$) or near quitting time (at $t = 8$)?

60. *Revenue* If the revenue for a product is $R(x) = 100x - 0.1x^2$, and the average revenue per unit is

   $$\overline{R}(x) = \frac{R(x)}{x}, \quad x > 0$$

   find (a) $\lim_{x \to 100} \dfrac{R(x)}{x}$ and   (b) $\lim_{x \to 0^+} \dfrac{R(x)}{x}$

61. *Cost-benefit* Suppose that the cost C of obtaining water that contains p percent impurities is given by

   $$C(p) = \frac{120{,}000}{p} - 1200$$

   (a) Find $\lim_{p \to 100^-} C(p)$, if it exists. Interpret this result.

   (b) Find $\lim_{p \to 0^+} C(p)$, if it exists.

   (c) Is complete purity possible? Explain.

62. *Cost-benefit* Suppose that the cost C of removing p percent of the particulate pollution from the smokestacks of an industrial plant is given by

   $$C(p) = \frac{730{,}000}{100 - p} - 7300$$

   (a) Find $\lim_{p \to 80} C(p)$

   (b) Find $\lim_{p \to 100^-} C(p)$ if it exists.

   (c) Can 100% of the particulate pollution be removed? Explain.

63. *Federal income tax* The following table shows part of the April 15, 2015, tax rate schedule for single filers. Use this schedule and create a table of values that could be used to find the following limits, if they exist. Let x represent the amount of taxable income, and let $T(x)$ represent the tax due.

   (a) $\lim_{x \to 36{,}900^-} T(x)$ (b) $\lim_{x \to 36{,}900^+} T(x)$

   (c) $\lim_{x \to 36{,}900} T(x)$

Single Filers

If taxable income is over—	But not over—	The tax is:
$0	$9075	10% of the amount over $0
$9075	$36,900	$907.50 plus 15% of the amount over 9075
$36,900	$89,350	$5081.25 plus 25% of the amount over 36,900
$89,350	$186,350	$18,193.75 plus 28% of the amount over 89,350

Source: Internal Revenue Service

64. *Parking costs* The Ace Parking Garage charges $5.00 for parking for 2 hours or less and $1.50 for each extra hour or part of an hour after the 2-hour minimum. The parking charges for the first 5 hours could be written as a function of the time as follows:

$$f(t) = \begin{cases} \$5.00 & \text{if } 0 < t \le 2 \\ \$6.50 & \text{if } 2 < t \le 3 \\ \$8.00 & \text{if } 3 < t \le 4 \\ \$9.50 & \text{if } 4 < t \le 5 \end{cases}$$

(a) Find $\lim_{t \to 1} f(t)$, if it exists.

(b) Find $\lim_{t \to 2} f(t)$, if it exists.

65. *Municipal water rates* The Corner Water Corp. of Shippenville, Pennsylvania, has the following rates per 1000 gallons of water used.

Usage (x)	Cost per 1000 Gallons ($C(x)$)
First 10,000 gallons	$15.96
Next 110,000 gallons	13.56
Over 120,000 gallons	Additional 11.04

If Corner Water has a monthly service fee of $12.76, write a function $C = C(x)$ that models the charges (where x is thousands of gallons) and find $\lim_{x \to 10} C(x)$ (that is, as usage approaches 10,000 gallons).

66. *Airport parking* Long-term parking at Savannah Airport is free for the first half-hour and costs $1.00 for each hour or part of an hour thereafter. If $C = C(t)$ is the charge for t hours in Savannah's long-term parking, create a table of values for parking costs close to $t = 1/2$ and $t = 2$ and use them to find the following limits, if they exist.

(a) $\lim_{t \to 0.5^-} C(t)$ (b) $\lim_{t \to 0.5^+} C(t)$

(c) $\lim_{t \to 0.5} C(t)$ (d) $\lim_{t \to 2} C(t)$

Dow Jones Industrial Average **The graph in the figure shows the Dow Jones Industrial Average (DJIA) on a particularly tumultuous day in August 2011. Use the graph**

for Problems 67 and 68, with t as the time of day and $D(t)$ as the DJIA at time t.

67. Estimate $\lim_{t \to 9.30\text{AM}^+} D(t)$, if it exists. Explain what this limit corresponds to.

68. Estimate $\lim_{t \to 4.00\text{PM}^-} D(t)$, if it exists. Explain what this limit corresponds to.

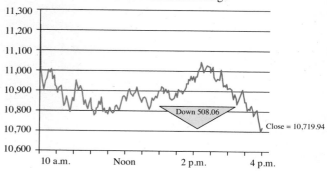

Dow Jones Industrial Average

Source: Google Finance, August 10, 2011

Obesity **Obesity (BMI $\ge$ 30) is a serious problem in the United States and expected to get worse. Being overweight increases the risk of diabetes, heart disease, and many other ailments, but the severely obese (BMI $\ge$ 40) are most at risk and the most expensive to treat. The following table shows the percent of obese Americans who are severely obese for selected years from 1990 and projected to 2030.**

Percent Obese Who Are Severely Obese

Year	1990	2000	2010	2015	2020	2025	2030
Percent	6.30	9.95	15.9	18.6	21.1	23.8	26.3

Source: American Journal of Preventive Medicine 42 (June 2012): 563–570. ajpmonline.org

The percent of obese American adults who are severely obese can be modeled by the function

$$S(x) = \frac{0.264x^2 + 10.7x - 66.9}{-0.00850x^2 + 1.25x + 0.854}$$

where x is the number of years after 1980. Use this function in Problems 69 and 70.

69. (a) Find $\lim_{x \to 60} S(x)$, if it exists.

(b) What does this limit predict?

(c) Does this prediction seem plausible? Explain.

70. (a) Find $\lim_{x \to 40} S(x)$, if it exists.

(b) What does this limit estimate?

(c) Is the function accurate as $x \to 40$? Explain.

OBJECTIVES
  9.2

- To determine whether a function is continuous or discontinuous at a point
- To determine where a function is discontinuous
- To find limits at infinity and horizontal asymptotes

Continuous Functions; Limits at Infinity

■| APPLICATION PREVIEW |■

Suppose that a friend of yours and her husband have a taxable income of $148,850 and she tells you that she doesn't want to make any more money because that would put them in a higher tax bracket. She makes this statement because the tax rate schedule for married taxpayers filing a joint return (part of which is shown in the table) appears to have a jump in taxes for taxable income at $148,850.

Married Filing Jointly or Qualifying Widow(er)

If taxable income is over	But not over	The tax is:
$0	$18,150	10% of the amount over $0
$18,150	$73,800	$1,815.00 plus 15% of the amount over $18,150
$73,800	$148,850	$10,162.50 plus 25% of the amount over $73,800
$148,850	$226,850	$28,925.00 plus 28% of the amount over $148,850
$226,850	$405,100	$50,765.00 plus 33% of the amount over $226,850

Source: Internal Revenue Service

To see whether the couple's taxes would jump to some higher level, we will write the function that gives income tax for married taxpayers with taxable incomes up to $405,100 as a function of taxable income and show that the function is continuous (see Example 3). That is, we will see that the tax paid does not jump at $148,850 even though the tax on income above $148,850 is collected at a higher rate. In this section, we will show how to determine whether a function is continuous, and we will investigate some different types of discontinuous functions.

Continuous Functions
We have found that $f(c)$ is the same as the limit as $x \to c$ for any polynomial function $f(x)$ and any real number c. Any function for which this special property holds is called a **continuous function.** The graphs of such functions can be drawn without lifting the pencil from the paper, and graphs of others may have holes, vertical asymptotes, or jumps that make it impossible to draw them without lifting the pencil. In general, we define continuity of a function at the value $x = c$ as follows.

Continuity at a Point

The function f is **continuous at $x = c$** if *all* of the following conditions are satisfied.

1. $f(c)$ exists   2. $\lim\limits_{x \to c} f(x)$ exists   3. $\lim\limits_{x \to c} f(x) = f(c)$

The figure at the left illustrates these three conditions.
If one or more of the conditions above do not hold, we say the function is **discontinuous at $x = c$.**

If a function is discontinuous at one or more points, it is called a **discontinuous function.** Figure 9.11 on the next page shows graphs of some functions that are discontinuous at $x = 2$.

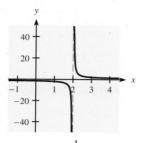

(a) $f(x) = \dfrac{1}{x-2}$

$\lim\limits_{x\to 2} f(x)$ and $f(2)$ do not exist.

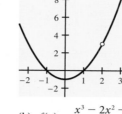

(b) $f(x) = \dfrac{x^3 - 2x^2 - x + 2}{x-2}$

$f(2)$ does not exist.

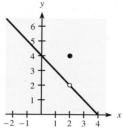

(c) $f(x) = \begin{cases} 4-x & \text{if } x \neq 2 \\ 4 & \text{if } x = 2 \end{cases}$

$\lim\limits_{x\to 2} f(x) = 2 \neq 4 = f(2)$

Figure 9.11

We have seen that $\lim\limits_{x\to c} f(x) = f(c)$ for every real number c, if $f(x)$ is a polynomial, and $\lim\limits_{x\to c} h(x) = h(c)$ if $h(x) = \dfrac{f(x)}{g(x)}$ is a rational function and $g(c) \neq 0$. So, we have the following.

Polynomial and Rational Functions

Every polynomial function is continuous for all real numbers.
Every rational function is continuous at all values of x except those that make the denominator 0.

EXAMPLE 1   Discontinuous Functions

For what values of x, if any, are the following functions continuous?

(a) $h(x) = \dfrac{3x+2}{4x-6}$ (b) $f(x) = \dfrac{x^2 - x - 2}{x^2 - 4}$

Solution

(a) This is a rational function, so it is continuous for all values of x except for those that make the denominator, $4x - 6$, equal to 0. Because $4x - 6 = 0$ at $x = 3/2$, $h(x)$ is continuous for all real numbers except $x = 3/2$. Figure 9.12(a) shows a vertical asymptote at $x = 3/2$.

(b) This is a rational function, so it is continuous everywhere except where the denominator is 0. To find the zeros of the denominator, we factor $x^2 - 4$.

$$f(x) = \frac{x^2 - x - 2}{x^2 - 4} = \frac{x^2 - x - 2}{(x-2)(x+2)}$$

Because the denominator is 0 for $x = 2$ and for $x = -2$, $f(2)$ and $f(-2)$ do not exist (recall that division by 0 is undefined). Thus the function is continuous except at $x = 2$ and $x = -2$. The graph of this function (see Figure 9.12(b)) shows a hole at $x = 2$ and a vertical asymptote at $x = -2$. ∎

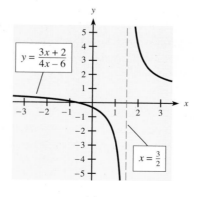

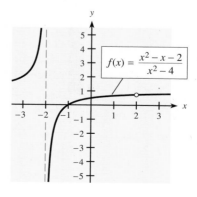

Figure 9.12   (a)   (b)

✓ **CHECKPOINT**

1. Find any x-values where the following functions are discontinuous.

   (a) $f(x) = x^3 - 3x + 1$ (b) $g(x) = \dfrac{x^3 - 1}{(x - 1)(x + 2)}$

If the pieces of a piecewise defined function are polynomials, the only values of x where the function might be discontinuous are those at which the definition of the function changes.

EXAMPLE 2   Piecewise Defined Functions

Determine the values of x, if any, for which the following functions are discontinuous.

$g(x) = \begin{cases} (x+2)^3 + 1 & \text{if } x \le -1 \\ 3 & \text{if } x > -1 \end{cases}$

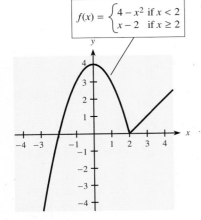

Figure 9.13

$f(x) = \begin{cases} 4 - x^2 & \text{if } x < 2 \\ x - 2 & \text{if } x \ge 2 \end{cases}$

Figure 9.14

(a) $g(x) = \begin{cases} (x+2)^3 + 1 & \text{if } x \le -1 \\ 3 & \text{if } x > -1 \end{cases}$ (b) $f(x) = \begin{cases} 4 - x^2 & \text{if } x < 2 \\ x - 2 & \text{if } x \ge 2 \end{cases}$

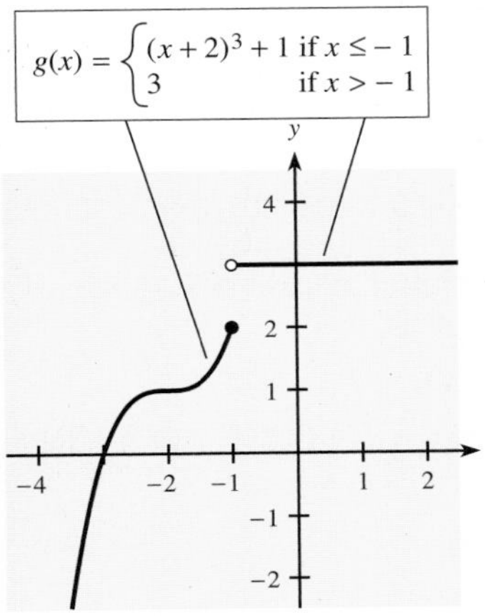

Solution

(a) $g(x)$ is a piecewise defined function in which each part is a polynomial. Thus, to see whether a discontinuity exists, we need only check the value of x for which the definition of the function changes—that is, at $x = -1$. Note that $x = -1$ satisfies $x \le -1$, so $g(-1) = (-1+2)^3 + 1 = 2$. Because $g(x)$ is defined differently for $x < -1$ and $x > -1$, we use left- and right-hand limits.

For $x \to -1^-$, we know that $x < -1$, so $g(x) = (x+2)^3 + 1$:

$$\lim_{x \to -1^-} g(x) = \lim_{x \to -1^-} [(x+2)^3 + 1] = (-1+2)^3 + 1 = 2$$

Similarly, for $x \to -1^+$, we know that $x > -1$, so $g(x) = 3$:

$$\lim_{x \to -1^+} g(x) = \lim_{x \to -1^+} 3 = 3$$

Because the left- and right-hand limits differ, $\lim_{x \to -1} g(x)$ does not exist, so $g(x)$ is discontinuous at $x = -1$. This result is confirmed by examining the graph of g, shown in Figure 9.13.

(b) As with $g(x)$, $f(x)$ is continuous everywhere except perhaps at $x = 2$, where the definition of $f(x)$ changes. Because $x = 2$ satisfies $x \ge 2$, $f(2) = 2 - 2 = 0$. The left- and right-hand limits are

Left: $\lim_{x \to 2^-} f(x) = \lim_{x \to 2^-} (4 - x^2) = 4 - 2^2 = 0$

Right: $\lim_{x \to 2^+} f(x) = \lim_{x \to 2^+} (x - 2) = 2 - 2 = 0$

Because the right- and left-hand limits are equal, we conclude that $\lim_{x \to 2} f(x) = 0$. The limit is equal to the functional value, or:

$$\lim_{x \to 2} f(x) = f(2)$$

so we conclude that f is continuous at $x = 2$ and thus f is continuous for all values of x. This result is confirmed by the graph of f, shown in Figure 9.14.

EXAMPLE 3   Taxes | APPLICATION PREVIEW |

A partial tax rate schedule for married taxpayers filing a joint return (shown in the table) appears to have a jump in taxes for taxable income at $148,850.

Married Filing Jointly or Qualifying Widow(er)		
If taxable income is over—	**But not over—**	**The tax is:**
$0	$18,150	10% of the amount over $0
$18,150	$73,800	$1,815.00 plus 15% of the amount over $18,150
$73,800	$148,850	$10,162.50 plus 25% of the amount over $73,800
$148,850	$226,850	$28,925.00 plus 28% of the amount over $148,850
$226,850	$405,100	$50,765.00 plus 33% of the amount over $226,850

Source: Internal Revenue Service

(a) Use the table and write the function that gives income tax for married taxpayers in this income range as a function of taxable income, x.

(b) Is the function in part (a) continuous at $x = 148{,}850$?

(c) A married friend of yours and her husband have a taxable income of \$148,850, and she tells you that she doesn't want to make any more money because doing so would put her in a higher tax bracket. What would you tell her to do if she is offered a raise?

Solution

(a) The function that gives the tax due for married taxpayers with $0 \le x \le 405{,}100$ is

$$T(x) = \begin{cases} 0.10x & \text{if } 0 \le x \le 18{,}150 \\ 1815.00 + 0.15(x - 18{,}150) & \text{if } 18{,}150 < x \le 73{,}800 \\ 10{,}162.50 + 0.25(x - 73{,}800) & \text{if } 73{,}800 < x \le 148{,}850 \\ 28{,}925.00 + 0.28(x - 148{,}850) & \text{if } 148{,}850 < x \le 226{,}850 \\ 50{,}765.00 + 0.33(x - 226{,}850) & \text{if } 226{,}850 < x \le 405{,}100 \end{cases}$$

(b) If this function is continuous at $x = 148{,}850$, there is no jump in taxes at \$148,850. We examine the three conditions for continuity at $x = 148{,}850$:

(i) $T(148{,}850) = 28{,}925$ so $T(148{,}850)$ exists.

(ii) Because the function is piecewise defined near $x = 148{,}850$, we evaluate $\lim_{x \to 148{,}850} T(x)$ by evaluating one-sided limits:

From the left, we evaluate $\lim_{x \to 148{,}850^-} T(x)$:

$$\lim_{x \to 148{,}850^-} [10{,}162.50 + 0.25(x - 73{,}800)] = 28{,}925$$

From the right, we evaluate $\lim_{x \to 148{,}850^+} T(x)$:

$$\lim_{x \to 148{,}850^+} [28{,}925.00 + 0.28(x - 148{,}850)] = 28{,}925$$

Because these one-sided limits agree, the limit exists and is

$$\lim_{x \to 148{,}850} T(x) = 28{,}925.$$

(iii) Because $\lim_{x \to 148{,}850} T(x) = T(148{,}850) = 28{,}925$, the function is continuous at $x = 148{,}850$.

(c) If your friend earned more than \$148,850, she and her husband would pay taxes at a higher rate *only* on the amount of money *above* \$148,850. Thus she should take any raise that is offered. ∎

✓ CHECKPOINT

2. If $f(x)$ and $g(x)$ are polynomials, $h(x) = \begin{cases} f(x) & \text{if } x \le a \\ g(x) & \text{if } x > a \end{cases}$ is continuous everywhere except perhaps at _____.

Limits at Infinity   We have seen that the graph of $y = 1/x$ has a vertical asymptote at $x = 0$ (shown in Figure 9.15(a)). By graphing $y = 1/x$ and evaluating the function for very large x-values, we can see that $y = 1/x$ never becomes negative for positive x-values regardless of how large the x-value is. Although no value of x makes $1/x$ equal to 0, it is easy to see that $1/x$ approaches 0 as x gets very large. This is denoted by

$$\lim_{x \to \infty} \frac{1}{x} = 0$$

and means that the line $y = 0$ (the x-axis) is a horizontal asymptote for $y = 1/x$. We also see that $y = 1/x$ approaches 0 as x decreases without bound, and we denote this by

$$\lim_{x \to -\infty} \frac{1}{x} = 0$$

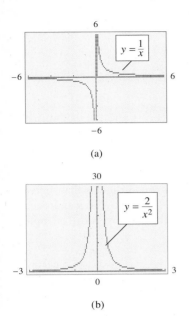

(a)

(b)

Figure 9.15

These limits for $f(x) = 1/x$ can also be established with numerical tables.

x	$f(x) = 1/x$	x	$f(x) = 1/x$
100	0.01	-100	-0.01
100,000	0.00001	$-100,000$	-0.00001
100,000,000	0.00000001	$-100,000,000$	-0.00000001
$\downarrow$	$\downarrow$	$\downarrow$	$\downarrow$
∞	0	$-\infty$	0
$\lim\limits_{x\to\infty} \dfrac{1}{x} = 0$		$\lim\limits_{x\to-\infty} \dfrac{1}{x} = 0$	

We can use the graph of $y = 2/x^2$ in Figure 9.15(b) to see that the x-axis ($y = 0$) is a horizontal asymptote and that

$$\lim_{x\to\infty} \frac{2}{x^2} = 0 \quad \text{and} \quad \lim_{x\to-\infty} \frac{2}{x^2} = 0$$

By using graphs and/or tables of values, we can generalize the results for the functions shown in Figure 9.15 and conclude the following.

Limits at Infinity

If c is any constant, then

1. $\lim\limits_{x\to\infty} c = c$ and $\lim\limits_{x\to-\infty} c = c$.

2. $\lim\limits_{x\to\infty} \dfrac{c}{x^p} = 0$, where $p > 0$.

3. $\lim\limits_{x\to-\infty} \dfrac{c}{x^n} = 0$, where $n > 0$ is any integer.

In order to use these properties for finding the limits of rational functions as x approaches ∞ or $-\infty$, we first divide each term of the numerator and denominator by the highest power of x present and then determine the limit of the resulting expression.

EXAMPLE 4 **Limits at Infinity**

Find each of the following limits, if they exist.

(a) $\lim\limits_{x\to\infty} \dfrac{2x - 1}{x + 2}$ (b) $\lim\limits_{x\to-\infty} \dfrac{x^2 + 3}{1 - x}$

Solution

(a) The highest power of x present is x^1, so we divide each term in the numerator and denominator by x and then use the properties for limits at infinity.

$$\lim_{x\to\infty} \frac{2x - 1}{x + 2} = \lim_{x\to\infty} \frac{\dfrac{2x}{x} - \dfrac{1}{x}}{\dfrac{x}{x} + \dfrac{2}{x}} = \lim_{x\to\infty} \frac{2 - \dfrac{1}{x}}{1 + \dfrac{2}{x}}$$

$$= \frac{2 - 0}{1 + 0} = 2 \quad \text{(by Properties 1 and 2)}$$

Figure 9.16(a) on the next page shows the graph of this function with the y-coordinates of the graph approaching 2 as x approaches ∞ and as x approaches $-\infty$. That is, $y = 2$ is a horizontal asymptote. Note also that there is a discontinuity (vertical asymptote) where $x = -2$.

(b) We divide each term in the numerator and denominator by x^2 and then use the properties.

$$\lim_{x \to -\infty} \frac{x^2 + 3}{1 - x} = \lim_{x \to -\infty} \frac{\dfrac{x^2}{x^2} + \dfrac{3}{x^2}}{\dfrac{1}{x^2} - \dfrac{x}{x^2}} = \lim_{x \to -\infty} \frac{1 + \dfrac{3}{x^2}}{\dfrac{1}{x^2} - \dfrac{1}{x}}$$

This limit does not exist because the numerator approaches 1 and the denominator approaches 0 through positive values. Thus

$$\frac{x^2 + 3}{1 - x} \to \infty \text{ as } x \to -\infty$$

The graph of this function, shown in Figure 9.16(b), has y-coordinates that increase without bound as x approaches $-\infty$ and that decrease without bound as x approaches ∞. (There is no horizontal asymptote.) Note also that there is a vertical asymptote at $x = 1$.

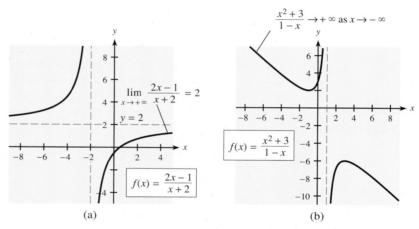

Figure 9.16   (a)   (b)

In our work with limits at infinity, we have mentioned horizontal asymptotes several times. The connection between these concepts follows.

Limits at Infinity and Horizontal Asymptotes	If $\lim\limits_{x \to \infty} f(x) = b$ or $\lim\limits_{x \to -\infty} f(x) = b$, where b is a constant, then the line $y = b$ is a horizontal asymptote for the graph of $y = f(x)$. Otherwise, $y = f(x)$ has no horizontal asymptotes.

✓ CHECKPOINT

3. (a) Evaluate $\lim\limits_{x \to \infty} \dfrac{x^2 - 4}{2x^2 - 7}$.

    (b) What does part (a) say about horizontal asymptotes for $f(x) = (x^2 - 4)/(2x^2 - 7)$?

Calculator Note   We can use the graphing and table features of a graphing calculator to help locate and investigate discontinuities and limits at infinity (horizontal asymptotes). A graphing calculator can be used to focus our attention on a possible discontinuity and to support or suggest appropriate algebraic calculations. See the following example.

EXAMPLE 5   Limits with Technology

Use a graphing utility to investigate the continuity of the following functions.

(a) $f(x) = \dfrac{x^2 + 1}{x + 1}$ (b) $g(x) = \dfrac{x^2 - 2x - 3}{x^2 - 1}$

(c) $h(x) = \dfrac{|x + 1|}{x + 1}$ (d) $k(x) = \begin{cases} \dfrac{-x^2}{2} - 2x & \text{if } x \le -1 \\ \dfrac{x}{2} + 2 & \text{if } x > -1 \end{cases}$

Solution

(a) Figure 9.17(a) shows that $f(x)$ has a discontinuity (vertical asymptote) near $x = -1$. Because $f(-1)$ DNE, we know that $f(x)$ is not continuous at $x = -1$.

(b) Figure 9.17(b) shows that $g(x)$ is discontinuous (vertical asymptote) near $x = 1$, and this looks like the only discontinuity. However, the denominator of $g(x)$ is zero at $x = 1$ and $x = -1$, so $g(x)$ must have discontinuities at both of these x-values. Evaluating or using the table feature confirms that $x = -1$ is a discontinuity (a hole, or missing point). The figure also shows a horizontal asymptote; evaluation of $\lim_{x \to \infty} g(x)$ confirms this is the line $y = 1$.

(c) Figure 9.17(c) shows a discontinuity (jump) at $x = -1$. We also see that $h(-1)$ DNE, which confirms the observations from the graph.

(d) The graph in Figure 9.17(d) appears to be continuous. The only "suspicious" x-value is $x = -1$, where the formula for $k(x)$ changes. Evaluating $k(-1)$ and examining a table near $x = -1$ indicates that $k(x)$ is continuous there. Algebraic evaluations of the two one-sided limits confirm this. ■

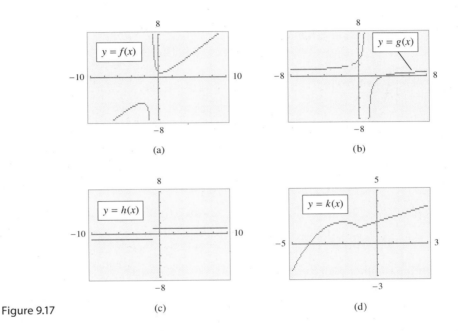

(a)   (b)

(c)   (d)

Figure 9.17

Continous Functions and Limits at Infinity

• The following information is useful in discussing continuity of functions.

A. A polynomial function is continuous everywhere.

B. A rational function is a function of the form $\dfrac{f(x)}{g(x)}$, where $f(x)$ and $g(x)$ are polynomials.

    1. If $g(x) \neq 0$ at any value of x, the function is continuous everywhere.

    2. If $g(c) = 0$, the function is discontinuous at $x = c$.

       (a) If $g(c) = 0$ and $f(c) \neq 0$, then there is a vertical asymptote at $x = c$.

       (b) If $g(c) = 0$ and $\lim_{x \to c} \dfrac{f(x)}{g(x)} = L$, then the graph has a missing point at (c, L).

C. A piecewise defined function may have a discontinuity at any x-value where the function changes its formula. One-sided limits must be used to see whether the limit exists.

• The following steps are useful when we are evaluating limits at infinity for a rational function $f(x) = p(x)/q(x)$.

    1. Divide both $p(x)$ and $q(x)$ by the highest power of x found in either polynomial.

    2. Use the properties of limits at infinity to complete the evaluation.

1. (a) This is a polynomial function, so it is continuous at all values of x (discontinuous at none).

   (b) This is a rational function. It is discontinuous at $x = 1$ and $x = -2$ because these values make its denominator 0.

2. $x = a$

3. (a) $\displaystyle\lim_{x \to \infty} \frac{x^2 - 4}{2x^2 - 7} = \frac{1}{2}$

   (b) The line $y = 1/2$ is a horizontal asymptote.

| EXERCISES | 9.2

In Problems 1 and 2, refer to the figure. For each given x-value, use the figure to determine whether the function is continuous or discontinuous at that x-value. If the function is discontinuous, state which of the three conditions that define continuity is not satisfied.

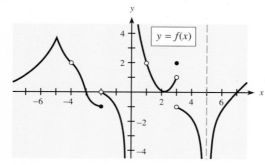

1. (a) $x = -5$ (b) $x = 1$ (c) $x = 3$ (d) $x = 0$
2. (a) $x = 2$ (b) $x = -4$ (c) $x = -2$ (d) $x = 5$

In Problems 3–8, determine whether each function is continuous or discontinuous at the given x-value. Examine the three conditions in the definition of continuity.

3. $f(x) = \dfrac{x^2 - 4}{x - 2}$, $x = -2$

4. $y = \dfrac{x^2 - 9}{x + 3}$, $x = 3$

5. $y = \dfrac{x^2 - x - 12}{x^2 + 3x}$, $x = -3$

6. $f(x) = \dfrac{x^2 - 6x + 8}{x^2 + x - 20}$, $x = 4$

7. $f(x) = \begin{cases} x - 3 & \text{if } x \le 2 \\ 4x - 7 & \text{if } x > 2 \end{cases}$, $x = 2$

8. $f(x) = \begin{cases} x^2 + 1 & \text{if } x \le 1 \\ 2x^2 - 1 & \text{if } x > 1 \end{cases}$, $x = 1$

In Problems 9–16, determine whether the given function is continuous. If it is not, identify where it is discontinuous and which condition fails to hold. You can verify your conclusions by graphing each function with a graphing utility.

9. $f(x) = 4x^2 - 1$

10. $y = 5x^2 - 2x$

11. $g(x) = \dfrac{4x^2 + 3x + 2}{x + 2}$

12. $y = \dfrac{4x^2 + 4x + 1}{x + 1/2}$

13. $y = \dfrac{x}{x^2 + 1}$

14. $y = \dfrac{2x - 1}{x^2 + 3}$

15. $f(x) = \begin{cases} 3 & \text{if } x \le 1 \\ x^2 + 2 & \text{if } x > 1 \end{cases}$

16. $f(x) = \begin{cases} x^3 + 10 & \text{if } x \le -2 \\ 2 & \text{if } x > -2 \end{cases}$

In Problems 17–20, use the trace and table features of a graphing calculator to investigate whether each of the following functions has any discontinuities.

17. $y = \dfrac{x^2 - 5x - 6}{x + 1}$

18. $y = \dfrac{x^2 - 5x + 4}{x - 4}$

19. $f(x) = \begin{cases} x - 4 & \text{if } x \le 3 \\ x^2 - 8 & \text{if } x > 3 \end{cases}$

20. $f(x) = \begin{cases} x^2 + 4 & \text{if } x \ne 4 \\ 8 & \text{if } x = 4 \end{cases}$

Each of Problems 21–24 contains a function and its graph. For each problem, answer parts (a) and (b).

(a) Use the graph to determine, as well as you can,
 (i) vertical asymptotes. (ii) $\displaystyle\lim_{x \to \infty} f(x)$.
 (iii) $\displaystyle\lim_{x \to -\infty} f(x)$.   (iv) horizontal asymptotes.

(b) Check your conclusions in (a) by using the functions to determine items (i)–(iv) analytically.

21. $f(x) = \dfrac{8}{x + 2}$

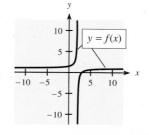

22. $f(x) = \dfrac{x - 3}{x - 2}$

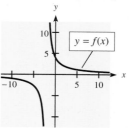

23. $f(x) = \dfrac{2(x+1)^3(x+5)}{(x-3)^2(x+2)^2}$

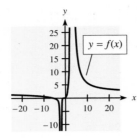

24. $f(x) = \dfrac{4x^2}{x^2 - 4x + 4}$

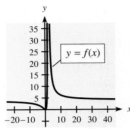

In Problems 25–32, complete (a) and (b).
(a) Use analytic methods to evaluate each limit.
(b) What does the result from part (a) tell you about horizontal asymptotes?
You can verify your conclusions by graphing the functions with a graphing calculator.

25. $\lim\limits_{x \to \infty} \dfrac{3}{x+1}$

26. $\lim\limits_{x \to -\infty} \dfrac{4}{x^2 - 2x}$

27. $\lim\limits_{x \to \infty} \dfrac{x^3 - 1}{x^3 + 4}$

28. $\lim\limits_{x \to -\infty} \dfrac{3x^2 + 2}{x^2 - 4}$

29. $\lim\limits_{x \to -\infty} \dfrac{5x^3 - 4x}{3x^3 - 2}$

30. $\lim\limits_{x \to \infty} \dfrac{4x^2 + 5x}{x^2 - 4x}$

31. $\lim\limits_{x \to \infty} \dfrac{3x^2 + 5x}{6x + 1}$

32. $\lim\limits_{x \to -\infty} \dfrac{5x^3 - 8}{4x^2 + 5x}$

In Problems 33 and 34, use a graphing calculator to complete (a) and (b).
(a) Graph each function using a window with $0 \le x \le 300$ and $-2 \le y \le 2$. What does the graph indicate about $\lim\limits_{x \to \infty} f(x)$?
(b) Use the table feature with x-values larger than 10,000 to investigate $\lim\limits_{x \to \infty} f(x)$. Does the table support your conclusions in part (a)?

33. $f(x) = \dfrac{x^2 - 4}{3 + 2x^2}$

34. $f(x) = \dfrac{5x^3 - 7x}{1 - 3x^3}$

In Problems 35 and 36, complete (a)–(c). Use analytic methods to find (a) any points of discontinuity and (b) limits as $x \to \infty$ and $x \to -\infty$. (c) Then explain why, for these functions, a graphing calculator is better as a support tool for the analytic methods than as the primary tool for investigation.

35. $f(x) = \dfrac{1000x - 1000}{x + 1000}$

36. $f(x) = \dfrac{3000x}{4350 - 2x}$

For Problems 37 and 38, let
$$f(x) = \dfrac{a_n x^n + a_{n-1}x^{n-1} + \cdots + a_1 x + a_0}{b_m x^m + b_{m-1}x^{m-1} + \cdots + b_1 x + b_0}$$
be a rational function.

37. If $m = n$, show that $\lim\limits_{x \to \infty} f(x) = \dfrac{a_n}{b_n}$, and hence that $y = \dfrac{a_n}{b_n}$ is a horizontal asymptote.

38. (a) If $m > n$, show that $\lim\limits_{x \to \infty} f(x) = 0$ and hence that $y = 0$ is a horizontal asymptote.
(b) If $m < n$, find $\lim\limits_{x \to \infty} f(x)$. What does this say about horizontal asymptotes?

APPLICATIONS

39. *Sales volume* Suppose that the weekly sales volume (in thousands of units) for a product is given by
$$y = \dfrac{32}{(p+8)^{2/5}}$$
where p is the price in dollars per unit. Is this function continuous
(a) for all values of p?   (b) at $p = 24$?
(c) for all $p \ge 0$?
(d) What is the domain for this application?

40. *Worker productivity* Suppose that the average number of minutes M that it takes a new employee to assemble one unit of a product is given by
$$M = \dfrac{40 + 30t}{2t + 1}$$
where t is the number of days on the job. Is this function continuous
(a) for all values of t?   (b) at $t = 14$?
(c) for all $t \ge 0$?
(d) What is the domain for this application?

41. *Demand* Suppose that the demand for a product is defined by the equation
$$p = \dfrac{200,000}{(q+1)^2}$$
where p is the price and q is the quantity demanded.
(a) Is this function discontinuous at any value of q? What value?
(b) Because q represents quantity, we know that $q \ge 0$. Is this function continuous for $q \ge 0$?

42. *Advertising and sales* The sales volume y (in thousands of dollars) is related to advertising expenditures x (in thousands of dollars) according to
$$y = \dfrac{200x}{x + 10}$$
(a) Is this function discontinuous at any points?
(b) Advertising expenditures x must be nonnegative. Is this function continuous for these values of x?

43. *Annuities* If an annuity makes an infinite series of equal payments at the end of the interest periods, it is called a **perpetuity**. If a lump sum investment of A_n is needed to result in n periodic payments of R when the interest rate per period is i, then
$$A_n = R\left[\dfrac{1 - (1+i)^{-n}}{i}\right]$$

(a) Evaluate $\lim_{n \to \infty} A_n$ to find a formula for the lump sum payment for a perpetuity.

(b) Find the lump sum investment needed to make payments of $100 per month in perpetuity if interest is 12%, compounded monthly.

44. **Response to adrenalin** Experimental evidence suggests that the response y of the body to the concentration x of injected adrenalin is given by

$$y = \frac{x}{a + bx}$$

where a and b are experimental constants.

(a) Is this function continuous for all x?

(b) On the basis of your conclusion in part (a) and the fact that in the context of the application $x \geq 0$ and $y \geq 0$, must a and b be both positive, be both negative, or have opposite signs?

45. **Cost-benefit** Suppose that the cost C of removing p percent of the impurities from the waste water in a manufacturing process is given by

$$C(p) = \frac{9800p}{101 - p}$$

Is this function continuous for all those p-values for which the problem makes sense?

46. **Pollution** Suppose that the cost C of removing p percent of the particulate pollution from the exhaust gases at an industrial site is given by

$$C(p) = \frac{8100p}{100 - p}$$

Describe any discontinuities for $C(p)$. Explain what each discontinuity means.

47. **Pollution** The percent p of particulate pollution that can be removed from the smokestacks of an industrial plant by spending C dollars is given by

$$p = \frac{100C}{7300 + C}$$

Find the percent of the pollution that could be removed if spending C were allowed to increase without bound. Can 100% of the pollution be removed? Explain.

48. **Cost-benefit** The percent p of impurities that can be removed from the waste water of a manufacturing process at a cost of C dollars is given by

$$p = \frac{100C}{8100 + C}$$

Find the percent of the impurities that could be removed if cost were no object (that is, if cost were allowed to increase without bound). Can 100% of the impurities be removed? Explain.

49. **Federal income tax** The tax owed by a married couple filing jointly and their tax rates can be found in the following tax rate schedule.

Married Filing Jointly or Qualifying Widow(er)

If taxable income is over—	But not over—	The tax rate is:
$0	$18,150	10%
$18,150	$73,800	15%
$73,800	$148,850	25%
$148,850	$226,850	28%
$226,850	$405,100	33%
$405,100	$457,600	35%
$457,600	no limit	39.6%

Source: Internal Revenue Service

From this schedule, the tax rate $R(x)$ is a function of taxable income x, as follows.

$$R(x) = \begin{cases} 0.10 & \text{if} & 0 \leq x \leq 18{,}150 \\ 0.15 & \text{if} & 18{,}150 < x \leq 73{,}800 \\ 0.25 & \text{if} & 73{,}800 < x \leq 148{,}850 \\ 0.28 & \text{if} & 148{,}850 < x \leq 226{,}850 \\ 0.33 & \text{if} & 226{,}850 < x \leq 405{,}100 \\ 0.35 & \text{if} & 405{,}100 < x \leq 457{,}600 \\ 0.396 & \text{if} & x > 457{,}600 \end{cases}$$

Identify any discontinuities in $R(x)$.

50. **Calories and temperature** Suppose that the number of calories of heat required to raise 1 gram of water (or ice) from $-40°C$ to $x°C$ is given by

$$f(x) = \begin{cases} \frac{1}{2}x + 20 & \text{if } -40 \leq x < 0 \\ x + 100 & \text{if } 0 \leq x \end{cases}$$

(a) What can be said about the continuity of the function $f(x)$?

(b) What happens to water at $0°C$ that accounts for the behavior of the function at $0°C$?

51. **Electrical usage costs** The monthly charge in dollars for x kilowatt-hours (kWh) of electricity used by a residential consumer of Excelsior Electric Membership Corporation from November through June is given by the function

$$C(x) = \begin{cases} 20 + 0.188x & \text{if} & 0 \leq x \leq 100 \\ 38.80 + 0.15(x - 100) & \text{if} & 100 < x \leq 500 \\ 98.80 + 0.10(x - 500) & \text{if} & x > 500 \end{cases}$$

(a) What is the monthly charge if 1100 kWh of electricity is consumed in a month?

(b) Find $\lim_{x \to 100} C(x)$ and $\lim_{x \to 500} C(x)$, if the limits exist.

(c) Is C continuous at $x = 100$ and at $x = 500$?

52. **Postage costs** First-class postage for a standard letter is 49 cents for the first ounce or part of an ounce that a letter weighs plus an additional 21 cents for each additional ounce or part of an ounce. Use the table or graph of the postage function, $f(x)$, to determine the following.

(a) $\lim_{x \to 2.5} f(x)$

(b) $f(2.5)$

(c) Is $f(x)$ continuous at 2.5?
(d) $\lim\limits_{x \to 4} f(x)$
(e) $f(4)$
(f) Is $f(x)$ continuous at 4?

Weight x	Postage $f(x)$
$0 < x \leq 1$	$0.49
$1 < x \leq 2$	0.70
$2 < x \leq 3$	0.91
$3 < x \leq 4$	1.12
$4 < x \leq 5$	1.33

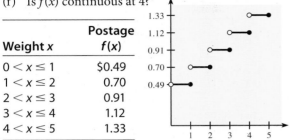

Postage Function

53. **Modeling** *U.S. workforce* Since 1950 the U.S. workforce has seen the arrival of the Baby Boomers and the
changing role of women, among other influences. The
data in the table show the millions of men and women
in the U.S. workforce for selected years from 1950 and
projected to 2050. Complete the following to explore
the dynamics of the changing roles of men and women
in the workforce.
(a) With x representing the number of years past 1950,
use the data in the table to find a linear model for the
number of men in the workforce, $m(x)$, and a model
for the number of women in the workforce, $w(x)$.
Report each model with three significant digits.
(b) Use the results from part (a) to find the function
$r(x)$ that gives the ratio of men to women in the
U.S. workforce.
(c) Find $\lim\limits_{x \to 0} r(x)$ and $\lim\limits_{x \to 100} r(x)$, and interpret their
meanings.
(d) Find $\lim\limits_{x \to \infty} r(x)$ and interpret its meaning.

	Workforce (in millions)	
Year	**Men**	**Women**
1950	43.8	18.4
1960	46.4	23.2
1970	51.2	31.5
1980	61.5	45.5
1990	69.0	56.8
2000	75.2	65.7
2010	82.2	75.5
2015	84.2	78.6
2020	85.4	79.3
2030	88.5	81.6
2040	94.0	86.5
2050	100.3	91.5

Source: U.S. Bureau of Labor Statistics

54. *U.S. smart phones* Using data from 2010 and projected
to 2016, the fraction of U.S. cell phone users who are
smart phone users can be modeled by the function

$$f(t) = \frac{21.35t + 69.59}{4.590t + 233.1}$$

where t is equal to the number of years after 2010
(*Source:* emarketer.com).
(a) Is the function continuous for years from 2010
onward?
(b) Evaluate $\lim\limits_{t \to \infty} f(t)$ if it exists to find a horizontal
asymptote.
(c) When can we be sure this model is no longer valid
for this application?
(d) Does the $\lim\limits_{t \to \infty} f(t)$ give the long-term projection of
the fraction of smart phone users?

OBJECTIVES

9.3

- To define and find average rates of change
- To define the derivative as a rate of change
- To use the definition of derivative to find derivatives of functions
- To use derivatives to find slopes of tangents to curves

Rates of Change and Derivatives

▮ APPLICATION PREVIEW ▮

In Chapter 1, "Linear Equations and Functions," we studied linear revenue
functions and defined the marginal revenue for a product as the rate of change
of the revenue function. For linear revenue functions, this rate is also the slope of
the line that is the graph of the revenue function. In this section, we will define
marginal revenue as the rate of change of the revenue function, even when the
revenue function is not linear.

Thus, if an oil company's revenue (in thousands of dollars) is given by

$$R = 100x - x^2, \quad x \geq 0$$

where x is the number of thousands of barrels of oil sold per day, we can find and
interpret the marginal revenue when 20,000 barrels are sold (see Example 4).

We will discuss the relationship between the *instantaneous rate of change* of
a function at a given point and the slope of the line tangent to the graph of the
function at that point. We will see how the derivative of a revenue function can
be used to find both the slope of its tangent line and its marginal revenue.

Average Rates of Change

For linear functions, we have seen that the slope of the line measures the average rate of change of the function and can be found from any two points on the line. However, for a function that is not linear, the slope between different pairs of points no longer always gives the same number, but it can be interpreted as an **average rate of change.**

Average Rate of Change

The **average rate of change** of a function $y = f(x)$ from $x = a$ to $x = b$ is defined by

$$\text{Average rate of change} = \frac{f(b) - f(a)}{b - a}$$

The figure shows that this average rate is the same as the slope of the segment (or secant line) joining the points $(a, f(a))$ and $(b, f(b))$.

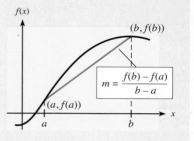

EXAMPLE 1   **Total Cost**

Suppose a company's total cost in dollars to produce x units of its product is given by

$$C(x) = 0.01x^2 + 25x + 1500$$

Find the average rate of change of total cost for the second 100 units produced (from $x = 100$ to $x = 200$).

Solution

The average rate of change of total cost from $x = 100$ to $x = 200$ units is

$$\frac{C(200) - C(100)}{200 - 100} = \frac{[0.01(200)^2 + 25(200) + 1500] - [0.01(100)^2 + 25(100) + 1500]}{100}$$

$$= \frac{6900 - 4100}{100} = \frac{2800}{100} = 28 \text{ dollars per unit}$$

EXAMPLE 2   **Elderly in the Workforce**

Figure 9.18 shows the percents of elderly men and of elderly women in the workforce in selected years from 1970 and projected to 2040. Find and interpret the average rate of change of the percent of (a) elderly men in the workforce and (b) elderly women in the workforce from 1970 to 2040.

Elderly in the Workforce, 1970–2040

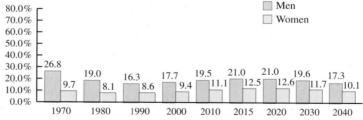

Figure 9.18   *Source:* Bureau of the Census, U.S. Department of Commerce

Solution

(a) From 1970 to 2040, the annual average rate of change in the percent of elderly men in the workforce is

$$\frac{\text{Change in men's percent}}{\text{Change in years}} = \frac{17.3 - 26.8}{2040 - 1970} = \frac{-9.5}{70} \approx -0.136 \text{ percentage points per year}$$

This means that from 1970 to 2040, *on average*, the percent of elderly men in the workforce dropped by 0.136 percentage points per year.

(b) Similarly, the average rate of change for women is

$$\frac{\text{Change in women's percent}}{\text{Change in years}} = \frac{10.1 - 9.7}{2040 - 1970} = \frac{0.4}{70} \approx 0.0057 \text{ percentage points per year}$$

In like manner, this means that from 1970 to 2040, *on average*, the percent of elderly women in the workforce increased by 0.0057 percentage points each year. ▪

Instantaneous Rates of Change: Velocity

Another common rate of change is velocity. For instance, if we travel 200 miles in our car over a 4-hour period, we know that we averaged 50 mph. However, during that trip there may have been times when we were traveling on an Interstate at faster than 50 mph and times when we were stopped at a traffic light. Thus, for the trip we have not only an average velocity but also instantaneous velocities (or instantaneous speeds as displayed on the speedometer). Let's see how average velocity can lead us to instantaneous velocity.

Suppose a ball is thrown straight upward at 64 feet per second from a spot 96 feet above ground level. The equation that describes the height y of the ball after x seconds is

$$y = f(x) = 96 + 64x - 16x^2$$

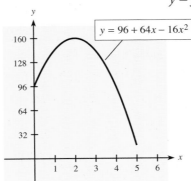

Figure 9.19 shows the graph of this function for $0 \le x \le 5$. The average velocity of the ball over a given time interval is the change in the height divided by the length of time that has passed. Table 9.4 shows some average velocities over time intervals beginning at $x = 1$.

Figure 9.19

TABLE 9.4

AVERAGE VELOCITIES

Time (seconds)			Height (feet)			Average Velocity (ft/sec)
Beginning	Ending	Change (Δx)	Beginning	Ending	Change (Δy)	($\Delta y / \Delta x$)
1	2	1	144	160	16	$16/1 = 16$
1	1.5	0.5	144	156	12	$12/0.5 = 24$
1	1.1	0.1	144	147.04	3.04	$3.04/0.1 = 30.4$
1	1.01	0.01	144	144.3184	0.3184	$0.3184/0.01 = 31.84$

In Table 9.4, the smaller the time interval, the more closely the average velocity approximates the instantaneous velocity at $x = 1$. Thus the instantaneous velocity at $x = 1$ is closer to 31.84 feet per second than to 30.4 feet per second.

If we represent the change in time by h, then the average velocity from $x = 1$ to $x = 1 + h$ approaches the instantaneous velocity at $x = 1$ as h approaches 0. (Note that h can be positive or negative.) This is illustrated in the following example.

EXAMPLE 3   **Velocity**

Suppose a ball is thrown straight upward so that its height $f(x)$ (in feet) is given by the equation

$$f(x) = 96 + 64x - 16x^2$$

where x is time (in seconds).
(a) Find the average velocity from $x = 1$ to $x = 1 + h$.
(b) Find the instantaneous velocity at $x = 1$.

Solution

(a) Let h represent the change in x (time) from 1 to $1 + h$. Then the corresponding change in $f(x)$ (height) is

$$f(1 + h) - f(1) = [96 + 64(1 + h) - 16(1 + h)^2] - [96 + 64 - 16]$$
$$= 96 + 64 + 64h - 16(1 + 2h + h^2) - 144$$
$$= 16 + 64h - 16 - 32h - 16h^2 = 32h - 16h^2$$

The average velocity V_{av} is the change in height divided by the change in time.

$$V_{av} = \frac{f(1 + h) - f(1)}{1 + h - 1} = \frac{32h - 16h^2}{h} = 32 - 16h$$

(b) The instantaneous velocity V is the limit of the average velocity as h approaches 0.

$$V = \lim_{h \to 0} V_{av} = \lim_{h \to 0} (32 - 16h) = 32 \text{ feet per second}$$

Note that average velocity is found over a time interval. Instantaneous velocity is usually called **velocity,** and it can be found at any time x, as follows.

Velocity

Suppose that an object moving in a straight line has its position y at time x given by $y = f(x)$. Then the **velocity** function for the object at time x is

$$V = \lim_{h \to 0} \frac{f(x + h) - f(x)}{h}$$

provided that this limit exists.

The instantaneous rate of change of any function (commonly called *rate of change*) can be found in the same way we find velocity. The function that gives this instantaneous rate of change of a function f is called the **derivative** of f.

Derivative

If f is a function given by $y = f(x)$, then the **derivative** of $f(x)$ at any value x, denoted $f'(x)$, is a new function defined by

$$f'(x) = \lim_{h \to 0} \frac{f(x + h) - f(x)}{h}$$

if this limit exists. If $f'(c)$ exists, we say that f is **differentiable** at c.

The following procedure illustrates how to find the derivative of a function $y = f(x)$ at any value x.

Derivative Using the Definition

Procedure	Example
To find the derivative of $y = f(x)$ at any value x:	Find the derivative of $f(x) = 4x^2$.
1. Let h represent the change in x from x to $x + h$.	1. The change in x from x to $x + h$ is h.
2. The corresponding change in $y = f(x)$ is $$f(x + h) - f(x)$$	2. The change in $f(x)$ is $$\begin{aligned} f(x + h) - f(x) &= 4(x + h)^2 - 4x^2 \\ &= 4(x^2 + 2xh + h^2) - 4x^2 \\ &= 4x^2 + 8xh + 4h^2 - 4x^2 \\ &= 8xh + 4h^2 \end{aligned}$$

(Continued)

3. Form the **difference quotient** $\dfrac{f(x + h) - f(x)}{h}$ and simplify.

3. $\dfrac{f(x + h) - f(x)}{h} = \dfrac{8xh + 4h^2}{h}$

$\qquad = 8x + 4h$

4. Find $\lim\limits_{h \to 0} \dfrac{f(x + h) - f(x)}{h}$ to determine $f'(x)$, the derivative of $f(x)$.

4. $f'(x) = \lim\limits_{h \to 0} \dfrac{f(x + h) - f(x)}{h}$

$f'(x) = \lim\limits_{h \to 0} (8x + 4h) = 8x$

Note that in the example above, we could have found the derivative of the function $f(x) = 4x^2$ at a particular value of x, say $x = 3$, by evaluating the derivative formula at that value:

$$f'(x) = 8x \quad \text{so} \quad f'(3) = 8(3) = 24$$

In addition to $f'(x)$, the derivative of $y = f(x)$ may be denoted by

$$\frac{dy}{dx}, \quad y', \quad \frac{d}{dx} f(x), \quad D_x y, \quad \text{or} \quad D_x f(x)$$

We can, of course, use variables other than x and y to represent functions and their derivatives. For example, we can represent the derivative of the function $p = 2q^2 - 1$ by dp/dq.

✓ CHECKPOINT

1. Find the average rate of change of $f(x) = 30 - x - x^2$ over $[1, 4]$.
2. For the function $y = f(x) = x^2 - x + 1$, find

(a) $f(x + h) - f(x)$.

(b) $\dfrac{f(x + h) - f(x)}{h}$.

(c) $f'(x) = \lim\limits_{h \to 0} \dfrac{f(x + h) - f(x)}{h}$.

(d) $f'(2)$.

For linear functions, we defined the **marginal revenue** for a product as the rate of change of the total revenue function for the product. If the total revenue function for a product is not linear, we define the marginal revenue for the product as the instantaneous rate of change, or the derivative, of the revenue function.

Marginal Revenue

Suppose that the total revenue function for a product is given by $R = R(x)$, where x is the number of units sold. Then the **marginal revenue** at x units is

$$\overline{MR} = R'(x) = \lim\limits_{h \to 0} \frac{R(x + h) - R(x)}{h}$$

provided that the limit exists.

Note that the marginal revenue (derivative of the revenue function) can be found by using the steps in the Procedure/Example box beginning on the preceding page. These steps can also be combined, as they are in Example 4.

EXAMPLE 4   Revenue | APPLICATION PREVIEW |

Suppose that an oil company's revenue (in thousands of dollars) is given by the equation

$$R = R(x) = 100x - x^2, \quad x \geq 0$$

where x is the number of thousands of barrels of oil sold each day.

(a) Find the function that gives the marginal revenue at any value of x.
(b) Find the marginal revenue when 20,000 barrels are sold (that is, at $x = 20$).

Solution

(a) The marginal revenue function is the derivative of $R(x)$.

$$R'(x) = \lim_{h \to 0} \frac{R(x+h) - R(x)}{h} = \lim_{h \to 0} \frac{[100(x+h) - (x+h)^2] - (100x - x^2)}{h}$$

$$= \lim_{h \to 0} \frac{100x + 100h - (x^2 + 2xh + h^2) - 100x + x^2}{h}$$

$$= \lim_{h \to 0} \frac{100h - 2xh - h^2}{h} = \lim_{h \to 0} (100 - 2x - h) = 100 - 2x$$

Thus, the marginal revenue function is $\overline{MR} = R'(x) = 100 - 2x$.

(b) The function found in part (a) gives the marginal revenue at *any* value of x. To find the marginal revenue when 20 units are sold, we evaluate $R'(20)$.

$$R'(20) = 100 - 2(20) = 60$$

Hence the marginal revenue at $x = 20$ is 60 thousand dollars per thousand barrels of oil. Because the marginal revenue is used to approximate the revenue from the sale of one additional unit, we interpret $R'(20) = 60$ to mean that the expected revenue from the sale of the next thousand barrels (after 20,000) will be approximately $60,000. [*Note:* The actual revenue from this sale is $R(21) - R(20) = 1659 - 1600 = 59$ thousand dollars.]

Tangent to a Curve

Just as average rates of change are connected with slopes, so are instantaneous rates (derivatives). In fact, the slope of the graph of a function at any point is the same as the derivative at that point. To show this, we define the slope of a curve at a point on the curve as the slope of the line tangent to the curve at the point.

In geometry, a **tangent** to a circle is defined as a line that has one point in common with the circle. [See Figure 9.20(a).] This definition does not apply to all curves, as Figure 9.20(b) shows. Many lines can be drawn through the point A that touch the curve only at A. One of the lines, line l, looks like it is tangent to the curve, in the same sense as a line is tangent to a circle.

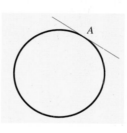

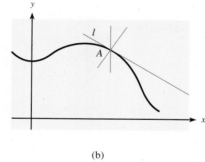

Figure 9.20   (a)   (b)

In Figure 9.21, the line l represents the tangent line to the curve at point A and shows that secant lines (s_1, s_2, etc.) through A approach line l as the second points (Q_1, Q_2, etc.) approach A. (For points and secant lines to the left of A, there would be a similar figure and conclusion.) This means that as we choose points on the curve closer and closer to A (from both sides of A), the limiting position of the secant lines through A is the **tangent line** to the curve at A.

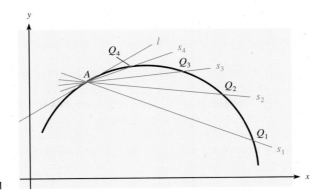

Figure 9.21

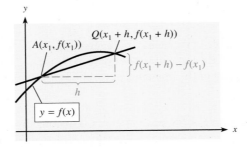

Figure 9.22

From Figure 9.22, we see that the slope of an arbitrary secant line through $A(x_1, f(x_1))$ and $Q(x_1 + h, f(x_1 + h))$ is given by

$$m_{AQ} = \frac{f(x_1 + h) - f(x_1)}{h}$$

Thus, as Q approaches A, the slope of the secant line AQ approaches the **slope of the tangent** line at A, and we have the following.

Slope of the Tangent

The **slope of the tangent** to the graph of $y = f(x)$ at point $A(x_1, f(x_1))$ is

$$m = \lim_{h \to 0} \frac{f(x_1 + h) - f(x_1)}{h}$$

if this limit exists. That is, $m = f'(x_1)$, the derivative at $x = x_1$.

EXAMPLE 5   Slope of the Tangent

Find the slope of $y = f(x) = x^2$ at the point $A(2, 4)$.

Solution
The formula for the slope of the tangent to $y = f(x)$ at $(2, 4)$ is

$$m = f'(2) = \lim_{h \to 0} \frac{f(2 + h) - f(2)}{h}$$

Thus for $f(x) = x^2$, we have

$$m = f'(2) = \lim_{h \to 0} \frac{(2 + h)^2 - 2^2}{h}$$

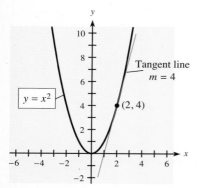

Figure 9.23

Taking the limit immediately would result in both the numerator and the denominator approaching 0. To avoid this, we simplify the fraction before taking the limit.

$$m = \lim_{h \to 0} \frac{4 + 4h + h^2 - 4}{h} = \lim_{h \to 0} \frac{4h + h^2}{h} = \lim_{h \to 0} (4 + h) = 4$$

Thus the slope of the tangent to $y = x^2$ at $(2, 4)$ is 4 (see Figure 9.23).

The statement "the slope of the tangent to the curve at $(2, 4)$ is 4" is frequently simplified to the statement "the slope of the curve at $(2, 4)$ is 4." Knowledge that the slope is a positive number on an interval tells us that the function is increasing on that interval, which means that a point moving along the graph of the function rises as it moves to the right on that interval. If the derivative (and thus the slope) is negative on an interval, the curve is decreasing on the interval; that is, a point moving along the graph falls as it moves to the right on that interval.

EXAMPLE 6   Tangent Line

Given $y = f(x) = 3x^2 + 2x + 11$, find

(a) the derivative of $f(x)$ at any point $(x, f(x))$.
(b) the slope of the tangent to the curve at $(1, 16)$.
(c) the equation of the line tangent to $y = 3x^2 + 2x + 11$ at $(1, 16)$.

Solution
(a) The derivative of $f(x)$ at any value x is denoted by $f'(x)$ and is

$$y' = f'(x) = \lim_{h \to 0} \frac{f(x + h) - f(x)}{h}$$

$$= \lim_{h \to 0} \frac{[3(x + h)^2 + 2(x + h) + 11] - (3x^2 + 2x + 11)}{h}$$

$$= \lim_{h \to 0} \frac{3(x^2 + 2xh + h^2) + 2x + 2h + 11 - 3x^2 - 2x - 11}{h}$$

$$= \lim_{h \to 0} \frac{6xh + 3h^2 + 2h}{h} = \lim_{h \to 0} (6x + 3h + 2) = 6x + 2$$

(b) The derivative is $f'(x) = 6x + 2$, so the slope of the tangent to the curve at $(1, 16)$ is $f'(1) = 6(1) + 2 = 8$.
(c) The equation of the tangent line uses the given point $(1, 16)$ and the slope $m = 8$. Using $y - y_1 = m(x - x_1)$ gives $y - 16 = 8(x - 1)$, or $y = 8x + 8$.

The discussion in this section indicates that the derivative of a function has several interpretations.

Interpretations of the Derivative

For a given function, each of the following means "find the **derivative**."

1. Find the **velocity** of an object moving in a straight line.
2. Find the **instantaneous rate of change** of a function.
3. Find the **marginal revenue** for a given revenue function.
4. Find the **slope of the tangent** to the graph of a function.

That is, all the terms printed in boldface are mathematically the same, and the answers to questions about any one of them give information about the others.

Note in Figure 9.23 that near the point of tangency at $(2, 4)$, the tangent line and the function look coincident. In fact, if we graphed both with a graphing calculator and repeatedly zoomed in near the point $(2, 4)$, the two graphs would eventually appear as one. Try this for yourself. Thus the derivative of $f(x)$ at the point where $x = a$ can be approximated by finding the slope between $(a, f(a))$ and a second point that is nearby.

In addition, we know that the slope of the tangent to $f(x)$ at $x = a$ is defined by

$$f'(a) = \lim_{h \to 0} \frac{f(a + h) - f(a)}{h}$$

Hence we could also estimate $f'(a)$—that is, the slope of the tangent at $x = a$—by evaluating

$$\frac{f(a + h) - f(a)}{h} \quad \text{when } h \approx 0 \text{ and } h \neq 0$$

EXAMPLE   7   **Approximating the Slope of the Tangent Line**

(a) Let $f(x) = 2x^3 - 6x^2 + 2x - 5$. Use $\dfrac{f(a + h) - f(a)}{h}$ and two values of h to make estimates of the slope of the tangent to $f(x)$ at $x = 1$ on opposite sides of $x = 1$.

(b) Use the following table of values of x and $g(x)$ to estimate $g'(3)$.

x	1	1.9	2.7	2.9	2.999	3	3.002	3.1	4	5
$g(x)$	1.6	4.3	11.4	10.8	10.513	10.5	10.474	10.18	6	-5

Solution

A graphing calculator can facilitate the following calculations.

(a) We can use $h = 0.0001$ and $h = -0.0001$ as follows:

With $h = 0.0001$: $f'(1) \approx \dfrac{f(1 + 0.0001) - f(1)}{0.0001} = \dfrac{f(1.0001) - f(1)}{0.0001} \approx -4$

With $h = -0.0001$: $f'(1) \approx \dfrac{f(1 + (-0.0001)) - f(1)}{-0.0001} = \dfrac{f(0.9999) - f(1)}{-0.0001} \approx -4$

(b) We use the given table and measure the slope between $(3, 10.5)$ and another point that is nearby (the closer, the better). Using $(2.999, 10.513)$, we obtain

$$g'(3) \approx \frac{y_2 - y_1}{x_2 - x_1} = \frac{10.5 - 10.513}{3 - 2.999} = \frac{-0.013}{0.001} = -13$$

Calculator Note   Most graphing calculators have a feature called the **numerical derivative** that can approximate the derivative of a function at a point. To find the numerical derivative of $f(x)$ at $x = c$ with a graphing calculator, choose the MATH menu and select 8:nDeriv. Next enter the function, x, and the value, c, so that the display shows nDeriv($f(x)$, x, c), and press ENTER. The numerical derivative will appear. The numerical derivative of $f(x) = 2x^3 - 6x^2 + 2x - 5$ with respect to x at $x = 1$ found in part (a) of Example 7 can also be found as follows on many graphing calculators:

$$\text{nDeriv}(2x^3 - 6x^2 + 2x - 5, x, 1) \approx -3.999998 \approx -4$$

Notice both methods give the same approximation.

Differentiability and Continuity   So far we have talked about how the derivative is defined, what it represents, and how to find it. However, there are functions for which derivatives do not exist at every value of x. Figure 9.24 on the next page shows some common cases where $f'(c)$ does not exist but where $f'(x)$ exists for all other values of x. These cases occur where there is a discontinuity, a corner, or a vertical tangent line.

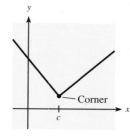

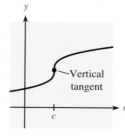

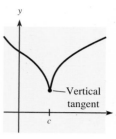

| (a) Not differentiable at $x = c$ | (b) Not differentiable at $x = c$ | (c) Not differentiable at $x = c$ | (d) Not differentiable at $x = c$ |

Figure 9.24

From Figure 9.24 we see that a function may be continuous at $x = c$ even though $f'(c)$ does not exist. Thus continuity does not imply differentiability at a point. However, differentiability does imply continuity.

Differentiability Implies Continuity

If a function f is differentiable at $x = c$, then f is continuous at $x = c$.

✓ **CHECKPOINT**

3. Which of the following are given by $f'(c)$?
   (a) The slope of the tangent when $x = c$
   (b) The y-coordinate of the point where $x = c$
   (c) The instantaneous rate of change of $f(x)$ at $x = c$
   (d) The marginal revenue at $x = c$, if $f(x)$ is the revenue function
4. Must a graph that has no discontinuity, corner, or cusp at $x = c$ be differentiable at $x = c$?

Calculator Note

We can use a graphing calculator to explore the relationship between secant lines and tangent lines. For example, if the point (a, b) lies on the graph of $y = x^2$, then the equation of the secant line to $y = x^2$ from $(1, 1)$ to (a, b) has the equation

$$y - 1 = \frac{b - 1}{a - 1}(x - 1), \quad \text{or} \quad y = \frac{b - 1}{a - 1}(x - 1) + 1$$

Figure 9.25 illustrates the secant lines for three different choices for the point (a, b).

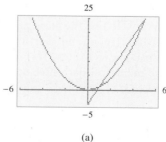

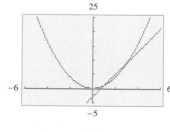

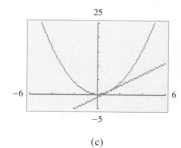

Figure 9.25   (a)   (b)   (c)

We see that as the point (a, b) moves closer to $(1, 1)$, the secant line looks more like the tangent line to $y = x^2$ at $(1, 1)$. Furthermore, (a, b) approaches $(1, 1)$ as $a \to 1$, and the slope of the secant approaches the following limit.

$$\lim_{a \to 1} \frac{b - 1}{a - 1} = \lim_{a \to 1} \frac{a^2 - 1}{a - 1} = \lim_{a \to 1} (a + 1) = 2$$

This limit, 2, is the slope of the tangent line at $(1, 1)$. That is, the derivative of $y = x^2$ at $(1, 1)$ is 2. [Note that a graphing calculator's calculation of the numerical derivative of $f(x) = x^2$ with respect to x at $x = 1$ gives $f'(1) = 2$.]

✓ CHECKPOINT
ANSWERS

1. -6
2. (a) $f(x + h) - f(x) = 2xh + h^2 - h$
   (b) $\dfrac{f(x + h) - f(x)}{h} = 2x + h - 1$
   (c) $f'(x) = 2x - 1$
   (d) $f'(2) = 3$
3. Parts (a), (c), and (d) are given by $f'(c)$. The y-coordinate where $x = c$ is given by $f(c)$.
4. No. See Figure 9.24(c).

| EXERCISES | 9.3

In Problems 1–4, for each given function find the average rate of change over each specified interval.

1. $f(x) = x^2 + x - 12$ over (a) $[0, 5]$ and (b) $[-3, 10]$
2. $f(x) = 6 - x - x^2$ over (a) $[-1, 2]$ and (b) $[1, 10]$
3. For $f(x)$ given by the table, over (a) $[2, 5]$ and (b) $[3.8, 4]$

x	0	2	2.5	3	3.8	4	5
$f(x)$	14	20	22	19	17	16	30

4. For $f(x)$ given in the table, over (a) $[3, 3.5]$ and (b) $[2, 6]$

x	1	2	3	3.5	3.7	6
$f(x)$	40	25	18	15	18	38

5. Given $f(x) = 2x - x^2$, find the average rate of change of $f(x)$ over each of the following pairs of intervals.
   (a) $[2.9, 3]$ and $[2.99, 3]$ (b) $[3, 3.1]$ and $[3, 3.01]$
   (c) What do the calculations in parts (a) and (b) suggest the instantaneous rate of change of $f(x)$ at $x = 3$ might be?
6. Given $f(x) = x^2 + 3x + 7$, find the average rate of change of $f(x)$ over each of the following pairs of intervals.
   (a) $[1.9, 2]$ and $[1.99, 2]$
   (b) $[2, 2.1]$ and $[2, 2.01]$
   (c) What do the calculations in parts (a) and (b) suggest the instantaneous rate of change of $f(x)$ at $x = 2$ might be?
7. In the Procedure/Example box in this section, we were given $f(x) = 4x^2$ and found $f'(x) = 8x$. Find
   (a) the instantaneous rate of change of $f(x)$ at $x = 4$.
   (b) the slope of the tangent to the graph of $y = f(x)$ at $x = 4$.
   (c) the point on the graph of $y = f(x)$ at $x = 4$.

8. In Example 6 in this section, we were given $f(x) = 3x^2 + 2x + 11$ and found $f'(x) = 6x + 2$. Find
   (a) the instantaneous rate of change of $f(x)$ at $x = 6$.
   (b) the slope of the tangent to the graph of $y = f(x)$ at $x = 6$.
   (c) the point on the graph of $y = f(x)$ at $x = 6$.
9. Let $f(x) = 3x^2 - 2x$.
   (a) Use the definition of derivative and the Procedure/Example box in this section to verify that $f'(x) = 6x - 2$.
   (b) Find the instantaneous rate of change of $f(x)$ at $x = -1$.
   (c) Find the slope of the tangent to the graph of $y = f(x)$ at $x = -1$.
   (d) Find the point on the graph of $y = f(x)$ at $x = -1$.
10. Let $f(x) = 9 - \dfrac{1}{2}x^2$.
    (a) Use the definition of derivative and the Procedure/Example box in this section to verify that $f'(x) = -x$.
    (b) Find the instantaneous rate of change of $f(x)$ at $x = 2$.
    (c) Find the slope of the tangent to the graph of $y = f(x)$ at $x = 2$.
    (d) Find the point on the graph of $y = f(x)$ at $x = 2$.

In Problems 11–14, the tangent line to the graph of $f(x)$ at $x = 1$ is shown. On the tangent line, P is the point of tangency and A is another point on the line.
(a) **Find the coordinates of the points P and A.**
(b) **Use the coordinates of P and A to find the slope of the tangent line.**
(c) **Find $f'(1)$.**
(d) **Find the instantaneous rate of change of $f(x)$ at P.**

11.

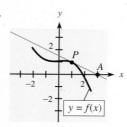

12.

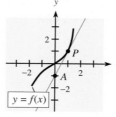

13.

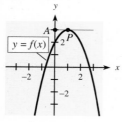

14.

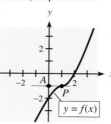

For each function in Problems 15–18, find
(a) the derivative, by using the definition.
(b) the instantaneous rate of change of the function at any value and at the given value.
(c) the slope of the tangent at the given value.

15. $f(x) = 5x^2 + 6x - 11;\quad x = -2$
16. $f(x) = 16x^2 - 4x + 2;\quad x = 1$
17. $p(q) = 2q^2 + q + 5;\quad q = 10$
18. $p(q) = 2q^2 - 4q + 5;\quad q = 2$

For each function in Problems 19–22, approximate $f'(a)$ in the following ways.
(a) Use the numerical derivative feature of a graphing calculator.
(b) Use $\dfrac{f(a + h) - f(a)}{h}$ with $h = 0.0001$.
(c) Graph the function on a graphing calculator. Then zoom in near the point until the graph appears straight, pick two points, and find the slope of the line you see.

19. $f'(2)$ for $f(x) = 3x^4 - 7x - 5$
20. $f'(-1)$ for $f(x) = 2x^3 - 11x + 9$
21. $f'(4)$ for $f(x) = (2x - 1)^3$
22. $f'(3)$ for $f(x) = \dfrac{3x + 1}{2x - 5}$

In Problems 23 and 24, use the given tables to approximate $f'(a)$ as accurately as you can.

23.

x	12.0	12.99	13	13.1	$a = 13$
$f(x)$	1.41	17.42	17.11	22.84	

24.

x	-7.4	-7.50	-7.51	-7	$a = -7.5$
$f(x)$	22.12	22.351	22.38	24.12	

In the figures given in Problems 25 and 26, at each point A and B draw an approximate tangent line and then use it to complete parts (a) and (b).
(a) Is $f'(x)$ greater at point A or at point B? Explain.
(b) Estimate $f'(x)$ at point B.

25.

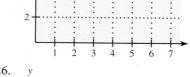

26.

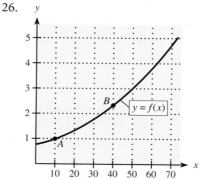

In Problems 27 and 28, a point (a, b) on the graph of $y = f(x)$ is given, and the equation of the line tangent to the graph of $f(x)$ at (a, b) is given. In each case, find $f'(a)$ and $f(a)$.
27. $(4, -11);\quad 7x - 3y = 61$
28. $(-1, 6);\quad x + 10y = 59$
29. If the instantaneous rate of change of $f(x)$ at $(2, -4)$ is 5, write the equation of the line tangent to the graph of $f(x)$ at $x = 2$.
30. If the instantaneous rate of change of $g(x)$ at $(-1, -2)$ is $1/2$, write the equation of the line tangent to the graph of $g(x)$ at $x = -1$.

Because the derivative of a function represents both the slope of the tangent to the curve and the instantaneous rate of change of the function, it is possible to use information about one to gain information about the other. In Problems 31 and 32, use the graph of the function $y = f(x)$ given in Figure 9.26.

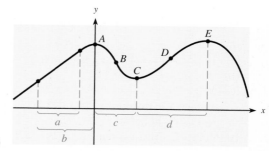

Figure 9.26

31. (a) Over what interval(s) (a) through (d) is the rate of change of $f(x)$ positive?
     (b) Over what interval(s) (a) through (d) is the rate of change of $f(x)$ negative?

EXAMPLE 3   Tangent Line

Write the equation of the tangent line to the graph of $y = x^3$ at $x = 1$.

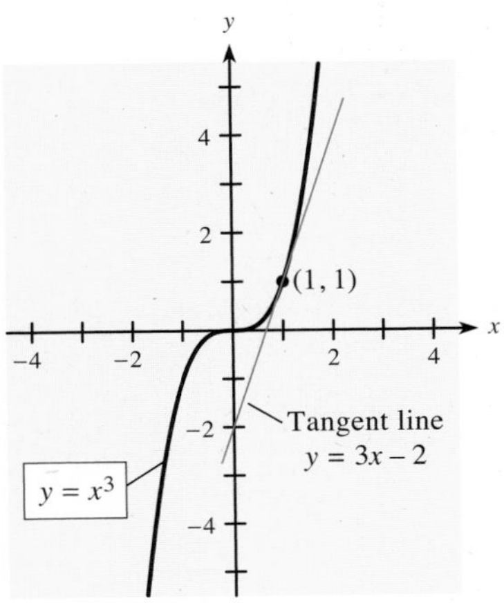

Solution

Writing the equation of the tangent line to $y = x^3$ at $x = 1$ involves three steps.

Figure 9.28

1. Evaluate the function to find the point of tangency.
    At $x = 1$: $y = (1)^3 = 1$, so the point is $(1, 1)$

2. Evaluate the derivative to find the slope of the tangent.
    At any point: $m_{\text{tan}} = y' = 3x^2$
    At $x = 1$: $m_{\text{tan}} = y'\big|_{x=1} = 3(1^2) = 3$

3. Use $y - y_1 = m(x - x_1)$ with the point $(1, 1)$ and slope $m = 3$.

$$y - 1 = 3(x - 1) \Rightarrow y = 3x - 3 + 1 \Rightarrow y = 3x - 2$$

Figure 9.28 shows the graph of $y = x^3$ and the tangent line at $x = 1$.

Derivative of a Constant   A function of the form $y = f(x) = c$, where c is a constant, is called a **constant function.** We can show that the derivative of a constant function is 0, as follows.

$$f'(x) = \lim_{h \to 0} \frac{f(x + h) - f(x)}{h} = \lim_{h \to 0} \frac{c - c}{h} = \lim_{h \to 0} 0 = 0$$

We can state this rule formally.

Constant Function Rule   If $f(x) = c$, where c is a constant, then $f'(x) = 0$.

EXAMPLE 4   Derivative of a Constant

Find the derivative of the function defined by $y = 4$.

Solution

Because 4 is a constant, $\dfrac{dy}{dx} = 0$.

Recall that the function defined by $y = 4$ has a horizontal line as its graph. Thus the slope of the line (and the derivative of the function) is 0.

Derivative of $y = c \cdot u(x)$ We now can take derivatives of constant functions and powers of x. But we do not yet have a rule for taking derivatives of functions of the form $f(x) = 4x^5$ or $g(t) = \frac{1}{2} t^2$. The following rule provides a method for handling functions of this type.

Coefficient Rule   If $f(x) = c \cdot u(x)$, where c is a constant and $u(x)$ is a differentiable function of x, then $f'(x) = c \cdot u'(x)$.

The Coefficient Rule says that the derivative of a constant times a function is the constant times the derivative of the function.

Using Properties of Limits II and IV (from Section 9.1, "Limits"), we can show

$$\lim_{h \to 0} c \cdot g(h) = c \cdot \lim_{h \to 0} g(h)$$

We can use this result to verify the Coefficient Rule. If $f(x) = c \cdot u(x)$, then

$$f'(x) = \lim_{h \to 0} \frac{f(x+h) - f(x)}{h} = \lim_{h \to 0} \frac{c \cdot u(x+h) - c \cdot u(x)}{h}$$

$$= \lim_{h \to 0} c \cdot \left[\frac{u(x+h) - u(x)}{h} \right] = c \cdot \lim_{h \to 0} \frac{u(x+h) - u(x)}{h}$$

so $f'(x) = c \cdot u'(x)$.

EXAMPLE 5   **Coefficient Rule for Derivatives**

Find the derivatives of the following functions.

(a) $f(x) = 4x^5$ (b) $g(t) = \dfrac{1}{2}t^2$ (c) $p = \dfrac{5}{\sqrt{q}}$

Solution

(a) $f'(x) = 4(5x^4) = 20x^4$

(b) $g'(t) = \frac{1}{2}(2t) = t$

(c) $p = \dfrac{5}{\sqrt{q}} = 5q^{-1/2}$,   so $\dfrac{dp}{dq} = 5\left(-\dfrac{1}{2} q^{-3/2} \right) = -\dfrac{5}{2\sqrt{q^3}}$

EXAMPLE 6   **World Tourism**

World tourism has grown into one of the world's major industries. Since 1990 the receipts from world tourism y, in billions of dollars, can be modeled by the function

$$y = 15.9x^{1.18}$$

where x is the number of years past 1980 (*Source:* World Tourism Organization).

(a) Name the function that models the rate of change of the receipts from world tourism.
(b) Find the function from part (a).
(c) Find the rate of change in world tourism in 2020.

Solution

(a) The rate of change of world tourism receipts is modeled by the derivative.

(b) $\dfrac{dy}{dx} = 15.9(1.18x^{1.18-1}) = 18.762x^{0.18}$

(c) $\dfrac{dy}{dx}\bigg|_{x=40} = 18.762(40^{0.18}) \approx 36.45$

Thus, the model estimates that world tourism receipts will change by about $36.45 billion per year in 2020.

Derivatives of Sums and Differences   In Example 6 of Section 9.3, "Rates of Change and Derivatives," we found the derivative of $f(x) = 3x^2 + 2x + 11$ to be $f'(x) = 6x + 2$. This result, along with the results of several of the derivatives calculated in the exercises for that section, suggest that we can find the derivative of a function by finding the derivatives of its terms and combining them. The following rules state this formally.

Sum Rule   If $f(x) = u(x) + v(x)$, where u and v are differentiable functions of x, then $f'(x) = u'(x) + v'(x)$.

We can prove this rule as follows. If $f(x) = u(x) + v(x)$, then

$$f'(x) = \lim_{h\to 0}\frac{f(x+h)-f(x)}{h} = \lim_{h\to 0}\frac{[u(x+h)+v(x+h)]-[u(x)+v(x)]}{h}$$

$$= \lim_{h\to 0}\left[\frac{u(x+h)-u(x)}{h}+\frac{v(x+h)-v(x)}{h}\right]$$

$$= \lim_{h\to 0}\frac{u(x+h)-u(x)}{h}+\lim_{h\to 0}\frac{v(x+h)-v(x)}{h}$$

$$= u'(x)+v'(x)$$

A similar rule applies to the difference of functions.

Difference Rule

If $f(x) = u(x) - v(x)$, where u and v are differentiable functions of x, then $f'(x) = u'(x) - v'(x)$.

EXAMPLE 7   Sum and Difference Rules

Find the derivatives of the following functions.

(a) $y = 3x + 5$
(b) $f(x) = 4x^3 - 2x^2 + 5x - 3$
(c) $p = \frac{1}{3}q^3 + 2q^2 - 3$
(d) $u(x) = 5x^4 + x^{1/3}$
(e) $y = 4x^3 + \sqrt{x}$
(f) $s = 5t^6 - \dfrac{1}{t^2}$

Solution

(a) $y' = 3\cdot 1 + 0 = 3$

(b) The rules regarding the derivatives of sums and differences of two functions also apply if more than two functions are involved. We may think of the functions that are added and subtracted as terms of the function f. Then it would be correct to say that we may take the derivative of a function term by term. Thus,

$$f'(x) = 4(3x^2) - 2(2x) + 5(1) - 0 = 12x^2 - 4x + 5$$

(c) $\dfrac{dp}{dq} = \frac{1}{3}(3q^2) + 2(2q) - 0 = q^2 + 4q$

(d) $u'(x) = 5(4x^3) + \frac{1}{3}x^{-2/3} = 20x^3 + \dfrac{1}{3x^{2/3}}$

(e) We may write the function as $y = 4x^3 + x^{1/2}$, so

$$y' = 4(3x^2) + \frac{1}{2}x^{-1/2} = 12x^2 + \frac{1}{2x^{1/2}} = 12x^2 + \frac{1}{2\sqrt{x}}$$

(f) We may write $s = 5t^6 - 1/t^2$ as $s = 5t^6 - t^{-2}$, so

$$\frac{ds}{dt} = 5(6t^5) - (-2t^{-3}) = 30t^5 + 2t^{-3} = 30t^5 + \frac{2}{t^3}$$

Each derivative in Example 7 has been *simplified*. This means that the final form of the derivative contains no negative exponents and the use of radicals or fractional exponents matches the original problem.

Also, in part (a) of Example 7, we saw that the derivative of $y = 3x + 5$ is 3. Because the slope of a line is the same at all points on the line, it is reasonable that the derivative of a linear equation is a constant. In particular, the slope of the graph of the equation $y = mx + b$ is m at all points on its graph because the derivative of $y = mx + b$ is $y' = f'(x) = m$.

EXAMPLE 8 Personal Income | APPLICATION PREVIEW |

Suppose that t is the number of years past 1960 and that

$$I = I(t) = 6.29t^2 - 51.7t + 601$$

models the U.S. total personal income in billions of current dollars. For 2018, find the model's prediction for

(a) the U.S. total personal income.
(b) the rate of change of U.S. total personal income.

Solution

(a) For 2018, $t = 58$ and

$$I(58) = 6.29(58^2) - 51.7(58) + 601 \approx 18{,}762 \text{ billion (current dollars)}$$

(b) The rate of change of U.S. total personal income is given by

$$I'(t) = 12.58t - 51.7$$

The predicted rate for 2018 is

$$I'(58) = \$677.94 \text{ billion (current dollars) per year}$$

This predicts that U.S. total personal income will change by about $677.94 billion from 2018 to 2019.

✓ **CHECKPOINT**

1. True or false: The derivative of a constant times a function is equal to the constant times the derivative of the function.
2. True or false: The derivative of the sum of two functions is equal to the sum of the derivatives of the two functions.
3. True or false: The derivative of the difference of two functions is equal to the difference of the derivatives of the two functions.
4. Does the Coefficient Rule apply to $f(x) = x^n/c$, where c is a constant? Explain.
5. Find the derivative of each of the following functions.

   (a) $f(x) = x^{10} - 10x + 5$ (b) $s = \dfrac{1}{t^5} - 10^7 + 1$

6. Find the slope of the line tangent to $f(x) = x^3 - 4x^2 + 1$ at $x = -1$.

EXAMPLE 9 Horizontal Tangents

Find all points on the graph of $f(x) = x^3 + 3x^2 - 45x + 4$ where the tangent line is horizontal.

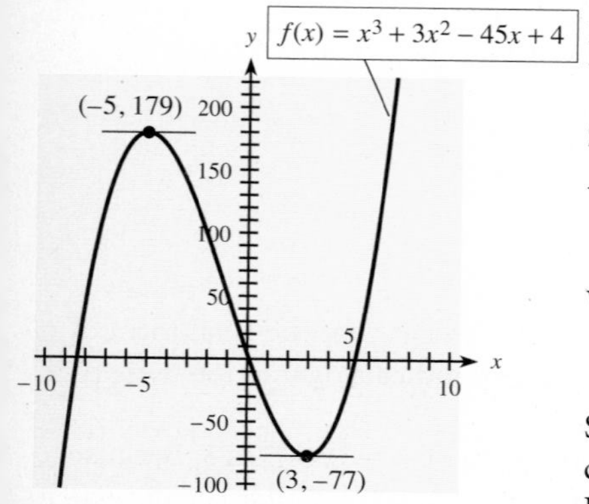

$f(x) = x^3 + 3x^2 - 45x + 4$

$(-5, 179)$

$(3, -77)$

Figure 9.29

Solution

A horizontal line has slope equal to 0. Thus, to find the desired points, we solve $f'(x) = 0$.

$$f'(x) = 3x^2 + 6x - 45$$

We solve $3x^2 + 6x - 45 = 0$ as follows:

$$3x^2 + 6x - 45 = 0 \Longrightarrow 3(x^2 + 2x - 15) = 0 \Longrightarrow 3(x + 5)(x - 3) = 0$$

Solving $3(x + 5)(x - 3) = 0$ gives $x = -5$ and $x = 3$. The y-coordinates for these x-values come from $f(x)$. The desired points are $(-5, f(-5)) = (-5, 179)$ and $(3, f(3)) = (3, -77)$. Figure 9.29 shows the graph of $y = f(x)$ with these points and the tangent lines at them indicated.

Marginal Revenue The marginal revenue $R'(x)$ is used to estimate the change in revenue caused by the sale of one additional unit.

EXAMPLE 10   **Revenue**

Suppose that a manufacturer of a product knows that because of the demand for this product, his revenue is given by

$$R(x) = 1500x - 0.02x^2, \qquad 0 \le x \le 1000$$

where x is the number of units sold and $R(x)$ is in dollars.

(a) Find the marginal revenue at $x = 500$.
(b) Find the change in revenue caused by the increase in sales from 500 to 501 units.

Solution
(a) The marginal revenue for any value of x is

$$R'(x) = 1500 - 0.04x$$

The marginal revenue at $x = 500$ is

$$R'(500) = 1500 - 20 = 1480 \,(\text{dollars per unit})$$

We can interpret this to mean that the approximate revenue from the sale of the 501st unit will be $1480.

(b) The revenue at $x = 500$ is $R(500) = 745{,}000$, and the revenue at $x = 501$ is $R(501) = 746{,}479.98$, so the change in revenue is

$$R(501) - R(500) = 746{,}479.98 - 745{,}000 = 1479.98 \,(\text{dollars})$$

Notice that the marginal revenue at $x = 500$ is a good estimate of the revenue from the 501st unit. ∎

Calculator Note

We have mentioned that graphing calculators have a numerical derivative feature that can be used to estimate the derivative of a function at a specific value of x. This feature can also be used to check the derivative of a function that has been computed with a formula. See Appendix A, Section 9.4, for details. We graph both the derivative calculated with a formula and the numerical derivative. If the two graphs lie on top of one another, the computed derivative agrees with the numerical derivative. Figure 9.30 illustrates this idea for the derivative of $f(x) = \frac{1}{3}x^3 - 2x^2 + 4$. Figure 9.30(a) shows $f'(x) = x^2 - 4x$ as y_1 and the calculator's numerical derivative of $f(x)$ as y_2. Figure 9.30(b) shows the graphs of both y_1 and y_2 (the graphs are coincident). ∎

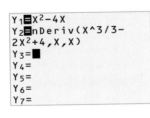

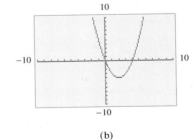

Figure 9.30   (a)   (b)

EXAMPLE 11   **Comparing $f(x)$ and $f'(x)$**

(a) Graph $f(x) = x^3 - 3x + 3$ and its derivative $f'(x)$ on the same set of axes so that all values of x that make $f'(x) = 0$ are in the x-range.
(b) Investigate the graph of $y = f(x)$ near values of x where $f'(x) = 0$. Does the graph of $y = f(x)$ appear to turn at values where $f'(x) = 0$?
(c) Compare the interval of x values where $f'(x) < 0$ with the interval where the graph of $y = f(x)$ is decreasing from left to right.
(d) What is the relationship between the intervals where $f'(x) > 0$ and where the graph of $y = f(x)$ is increasing from left to right?

Solution

(a) The graphs of $f(x) = x^3 - 3x + 3$ and $f'(x) = 3x^2 - 3$ are shown in Figure 9.31.

(b) The values where $f'(x) = 0$ are the x-intercepts, $x = -1$ and $x = 1$. The graph of $y = x^3 - 3x + 3$ appears to turn at both these values.

(c) $f'(x) < 0$ where the graph of $y = f'(x)$ is below the x-axis, for $-1 < x < 1$. The graph of $y = f(x)$ appears to be decreasing on this interval.

(d) They appear to be the same intervals.

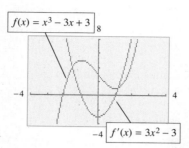

Figure 9.31

1. True, by the Coefficient Rule.
2. True, by the Sum Rule.
3. True, by the Difference Rule.
4. Yes, $f(x) = x^n/c = (1/c)x^n$, so the coefficient is $(1/c)$.
5. (a) $f'(x) = 10x^9 - 10$

    (b) $\dfrac{ds}{dt} = \dfrac{-5}{t^6}$

6. The slope of the tangent at $x = -1$ is $f'(-1) = 11$.

| EXERCISES | 9.4

Find the derivatives of the functions in Problems 1–14.

1. $y = 4$
2. $f(s) = 6$
3. $f(t) = t$
4. $s = t^2$
5. $y = 6 - 8x + 2x^2$
6. $y = 12 + 2x - 7x^3$
7. $f(x) = 3x^4 - x^6$
8. $f(x) = 3x^4 - x^9$
9. $y = 10x^5 - 3x^3 + 5x - 11$
10. $y = 3x^5 - 5x^3 - 8x + 8$
11. $w = z^7 - 3z^6 + 13$
12. $u = 2t^{10} - 5t^5 - 9$
13. $g(x) = 2x^{12} - 5x^6 + 9x^4 + x - 5$
14. $h(x) = 12x^{20} + 8x^{10} - 2x^7 + 17x - 9$

In Problems 15–18, at the indicated points, find
(a) the slope of the tangent to the curve, and
(b) the instantaneous rate of change of the function.

15. $y = 7x^2 + 2x + 1, \quad x = 2$
16. $C(x) = 3x^2 - 5, \quad (3, 22)$
17. $P(x) = x^3 - 6x, \quad (2, -4)$
18. $R(x) = 16x + x^2, \quad x = 1$

In Problems 19–26, find the derivative of each function.

19. $y = x^{-5} + x^{-8} - 3$
20. $y = x^{-1} - x^{-2} + 13$
21. $z = 3t^{11/3} - 2t^{7/4} - t^{1/2} + 8$
22. $w = 5u^{8/5} - 3u^{5/6} + u^{1/3} + 5$

23. $f(x) = 5x^{-4/5} + 2x^{-4/3}$
24. $f(x) = 6x^{-8/3} - x^{-2/3}$
25. $g(x) = \dfrac{3}{x^5} + \dfrac{2}{x^4} + 6\sqrt[3]{x}$
26. $h(x) = \dfrac{7}{x^7} - \dfrac{3}{x^3} + 8\sqrt{x}$

In Problems 27–30, write the equation of the tangent line to each curve at the indicated point. As a check, graph both the function and the tangent line.

27. $y = x^3 - 5x^2 + 7 \quad$ at $x = 1$
28. $y = x^4 - 4x^3 - 2 \quad$ at $x = 2$
29. $f(x) = 4x^2 - \dfrac{1}{x} \quad$ at $x = -\dfrac{1}{2}$
30. $f(x) = \dfrac{x^3}{3} - \dfrac{3}{x^3} \quad$ at $x = -1$

In Problems 31–34, find the coordinates of points where the graph of $f(x)$ has horizontal tangents. As a check, graph $f(x)$ and see whether the points you found look as though they have horizontal tangents.

31. $f(x) = -x^3 + 9x^2 - 15x + 6$
32. $f(x) = \dfrac{1}{3}x^3 - 3x^2 - 16x + 8$

33. $f(x) = x^4 - 4x^3 + 9$
34. $f(x) = 3x^5 - 5x^3 + 2$

In Problems 35 and 36, find each derivative at the given x-value (a) with the appropriate rule and (b) with the numerical derivative feature of a graphing calculator.

35. $y = 5 - 2\sqrt{x}$ at $x = 4$
36. $y = 1 + 3x^{2/3}$ at $x = -8$

In Problems 37–40, complete the following.
(a) Calculate the derivative of each function with the appropriate formula.
(b) Check your result from part (a) by graphing your calculated derivative and the numerical derivative of the given function with respect to x evaluated at x.

37. $f(x) = 2x^3 + 5x - \pi^4 + 8$
38. $f(x) = 3x^2 - 8x + 2^5 - 20$
39. $h(x) = \dfrac{10}{x^3} - \dfrac{10}{\sqrt[5]{x^2}} + x^2 + 1$
40. $g(x) = \dfrac{5}{x^{10}} + \dfrac{4}{\sqrt[4]{x^3}} + x^5 - 4$

The tangent line to a curve at a point closely approximates the curve near the point. In fact, for x-values close enough to the point of tangency, the function and its tangent line are virtually indistinguishable. Problems 41 and 42 explore this relationship. Use each given function and the indicated point to complete the following.
(a) Write the equation of the tangent line to the curve at the indicated point.
(b) Use a graphing calculator to graph both the function and its tangent line. Be sure your graph shows the point of tangency.
(c) Repeatedly zoom in on the point of tangency. Do the function and the tangent line eventually become indistinguishable?

41. $f(x) = 3x^2 + 2x$ at $x = 1$
42. $f(x) = 4x - x^2$ at $x = 5$

For each function in Problems 43–46, do the following.
(a) Find $f'(x)$
(b) Graph both $f(x)$ and $f'(x)$ with a graphing utility.
(c) Use the graph of $f'(x)$ to identify x-values where $f'(x) = 0$, $f'(x) > 0$, and $f'(x) < 0$.
(d) Use the graph of $f(x)$ to identify x-values where $f(x)$ has a maximum or minimum point, where the graph of $f(x)$ is rising, and where the graph of $f(x)$ is falling.

43. $f(x) = 8 - 2x - x^2$
44. $f(x) = x^2 + 4x - 12$
45. $f(x) = x^3 - 12x - 5$
46. $f(x) = 7 - 3x^2 - \dfrac{x^3}{3}$

APPLICATIONS

47. *Revenue* Suppose that a wholesaler expects that his monthly revenue, in dollars, for an electronic game will be
$$R(x) = 100x - 0.1x^2, \quad 0 \le x \le 800$$
where x is the number of units sold. Find his marginal revenue and interpret it when the quantity sold is
(a) $x = 300$.　　　(b) $x = 600$.

48. *Revenue* The total revenue, in dollars, for a commodity is described by the function
$$R = 300x - 0.02x^2$$
(a) What is the marginal revenue when 40 units are sold?
(b) Interpret your answer to part (a).

49. *Metabolic rate* According to Kleiber's law the metabolic rate q of the vast majority of animals is related to the animal's mass M according to
$$q = kM^{3/4}$$
where k is a constant. This means that a cat, with mass about 100 times that of a mouse, has a metabolism about $100^{3/4} \approx 32$ times greater than that of a mouse. Find the function that describes the rate of change of the metabolic rate with respect to mass.

50. *Capital investment and output* The monthly output of a certain product is
$$Q(x) = 800x^{5/2}$$
where x is the capital investment in millions of dollars. Find dQ/dx, which can be used to estimate the effect on the output if an additional capital investment of $1 million is made.

51. *Demand* The demand for q units of a product depends on the price p (in dollars) according to
$$q = \frac{1000}{\sqrt{p}} - 1, \quad \text{for } p > 0$$
Find and explain the meaning of the instantaneous rate of change of demand with respect to price when the price is
(a) \$25.　　　(b) \$100.

52. *Demand* Suppose that the demand for a product depends on the price p according to
$$D(p) = \frac{50,000}{p^2} - \frac{1}{2}, \quad p > 0$$
where p is in dollars. Find and explain the meaning of the instantaneous rate of change of demand with respect to price when
(a) $p = 50$.　　　(b) $p = 100$.

53. *Cost and average cost* Suppose that the total cost function, in dollars, for the production of x units of a product is given by
$$C(x) = 4000 + 55x + 0.1x^2$$

Then the average cost of producing x items is

$$\overline{C(x)} = \frac{\text{total cost}}{x} = \frac{4000}{x} + 55 + 0.1x$$

(a) Find the instantaneous rate of change of average cost with respect to the number of units produced, at any level of production.
(b) Find the level of production at which this rate of change equals zero.
(c) At the value found in part (b), find the instantaneous rate of change of cost and find the average cost. What do you notice?

54. **Cost and average cost** Suppose that the total cost function, in dollars, for a certain commodity is given by

$$C(x) = 40,500 + 190x + 0.2x^2$$

where x is the number of units produced.
(a) Find the instantaneous rate of change of the average cost

$$\overline{C} = \frac{40,500}{x} + 190 + 0.2x$$

for any level of production.
(b) Find the level of production where this rate of change equals zero.
(c) At the value found in part (b), find the instantaneous rate of change of cost and find the average cost. What do you notice?

55. **Cost-benefit** Suppose that for a certain city the cost C, in dollars, of obtaining drinking water that contains p percent impurities (by volume) is given by

$$C = \frac{120,000}{p} - 1200$$

(a) Find the rate of change of cost with respect to p when impurities account for 10% (by volume).
(b) Write a sentence that explains the meaning of your answer in part (a).

56. **Cost-benefit** Suppose that the cost C, in dollars, of processing the exhaust gases at an industrial site to ensure that only p percent of the particulate pollution escapes is given by

$$C(p) = \frac{8100(100 - p)}{p}$$

(a) Find the rate of change of cost C with respect to the percent of particulate pollution that escapes when $p = 2$ (percent).
(b) Write a sentence interpreting your answer to part (a).

57. **Wind chill** One form of the formula that meteorologists use to calculate wind chill temperature (WC) is

$$WC = 35.74 + 0.6215t - 35.75s^{0.16} + 0.4275t\, s^{0.16}$$

where s is the wind speed in mph and t is the actual air temperature in degrees Fahrenheit. Suppose temperature is constant at 15°.
(a) Express wind chill WC as a function of wind speed s.
(b) Find the rate of change of wind chill with respect to wind speed when the wind speed is 25 mph.
(c) Interpret your answer to part (b).

58. **Allometric relationships—crabs** For fiddler crabs, data gathered by Thompson[*] show that the allometric relationship between the weight C of the claw and the weight W of the body is given by

$$C = 0.11W^{1.54}$$

Find the function that gives the rate of change of claw weight with respect to body weight.

Recall that for all modeling problems, use the unrounded model for any calculations unless instructed otherwise.

59. **Modeling Consumer price index** The table below gives the U.S. consumer price index (CPI) for selected years from 2012 and projected to 2050. With the reference year as 2012, a 2020 CPI = 120.56 means goods and services that cost $100.00 in 2012 are expected to cost $120.56 in 2020.
(a) Find the quadratic function that is the best fit for the data, with x as the number of years past 2010 and y as the CPI in dollars. Report the model as $y = f(x)$ with three significant digit coefficients.
(b) Use the data to find the average rate of change of the CPI from 2012 to 2020.
(c) Find the derivative of the reported model found in part (a).
(d) Find the instantaneous rate of change of the CPI for the year 2020.
(e) Use the rate of change from part (d) to predict the CPI for 2022.

Year	CPI	Year	CPI
2012	100.00	2030	158.90
2014	104.00	2035	182.43
2016	108.58	2040	209.44
2018	114.09	2045	240.45
2020	120.56	2050	276.05
2025	138.41		

Source: Social Security Administration

60. **Modeling E-commerce** The following table gives the online sales, in billions of dollars, from 2000 and projected to 2017.
(a) Model these data with a power function $E(t)$, where t is the number of years past 1990. Report the model with three significant digit coefficients.

*d'Arcy Thompson, *On Growth and Form* (Cambridge, England: Cambridge University Press, 1961).

(b) Use the reported model from part (a) to find the function that models the rate of change of online sales.

(c) Use the result from part (b) to find and interpret the rate of change of online sales in 2020.

Year	Sales ($billion)	Year	Sales ($billion)
2000	28	2009	134
2001	34	2010	171
2002	44	2011	202
2003	56	2012	226
2004	70	2013	259
2005	87	2014	297
2006	106	2015	339
2007	126	2016	386
2008	132	2017	434

Source: U.S. Census Bureau, Forrester Research, Inc.

61. **Modeling *U.S. population*** The table gives the U.S. population to the nearest million for selected years from 1950 and projected to 2050.

Year	Total	Year	Total
1950	160	2010	315
1960	190	2015	328
1970	215	2020	343
1980	235	2030	370
1990	260	2040	391
2000	288	2050	409

Source: Social Security Administration

(a) Find a cubic function $P(t)$ that models these data, where P is the U.S. population in millions and t is the number of years past 1950. Report the model with three significant digit coefficients.

(b) Use the part (a) result to find the function that models the instantaneous rate of change of the U.S. population.

(c) Find and interpret the instantaneous rates of change in 2000 and 2025.

62. **Modeling *Gross domestic product*** The table shows U.S. gross domestic product (GDP) in billions of dollars for selected years from 2000 to 2070 (actual and projected).

Year	GDP	Year	GDP
2000	9143	2040	79,680
2005	12,145	2045	103,444
2010	16,174	2050	133,925
2015	21,270	2055	173,175
2020	27,683	2060	224,044
2025	35,919	2065	290,042
2030	46,765	2070	375,219
2035	61,100		

Source: Social Security Administration Trustees Report

(a) Model these data with a cubic function $g = g(t)$, where g is in billions of dollars and t represents the number of years past 2000. Report the model with three significant digit coefficients.

(b) Use the reported model to find the predicted instantaneous rate of change of the GDP in 2025.

(c) Interpret your answer to part (b).

- To use the Product Rule to find the derivatives of certain functions
- To use the Quotient Rule to find the derivatives of certain functions

The Product Rule and the Quotient Rule

| APPLICATION PREVIEW |

When medicine is administered, reaction (measured in change of blood pressure or temperature) can be modeled by

$$R = m^2\left(\frac{c}{2} - \frac{m}{3}\right)$$

where c is a positive constant and m is the amount of medicine absorbed into the blood.* The rate of change of R with respect to m is the sensitivity of the body to medicine. To find an expression for sensitivity as a function of m, we calculate dR/dm. We can find this derivative with the Product Rule for derivatives. See Example 5.

*Source: R. M. Thrall et al., *Some Mathematical Models in Biology*, U.S. Department of Commerce, 1967.

Product Rule   We have simple formulas for finding the derivatives of the sums and differences of functions. But we are not so lucky with products. The derivative of a product is *not* the product of the derivatives. To see this, we consider the function $f(x) = x \cdot x$. Because this function is $f(x) = x^2$, its derivative is $f'(x) = 2x$. But the product of the derivatives of x and x would give $1 \cdot 1 = 1 \neq 2x$. Thus we need a different formula to find the derivative of a product. This formula is given by the **Product Rule.**

Product Rule   If $f(x) = u(x) \cdot v(x)$, where u and v are differentiable functions of x, then

$$f'(x) = u(x) \cdot v'(x) + v(x) \cdot u'(x)$$

Thus the derivative of a product of two functions is the first function times the derivative of the second plus the second function times the derivative of the first.

We can prove the Product Rule as follows. If $f(x) = u(x) \cdot v(x)$, then

$$\lim_{h \to 0} \frac{f(x+h) - f(x)}{h} = \lim_{h \to 0} \frac{u(x+h) \cdot v(x+h) - u(x) \cdot v(x)}{h}$$

Subtracting and adding $u(x+h) \cdot v(x)$ in the numerator gives

$$f'(x) = \lim_{h \to 0} \frac{u(x+h) \cdot v(x+h) - u(x+h) \cdot v(x) + u(x+h) \cdot v(x) - u(x) \cdot v(x)}{h}$$

$$= \lim_{h \to 0} \left\{ u(x+h) \left[\frac{v(x+h) - v(x)}{h} \right] + v(x) \left[\frac{u(x+h) - u(x)}{h} \right] \right\}$$

Properties III and IV of limits (from Section 9.1, "Limits") give

$$f'(x) = \lim_{h \to 0} u(x+h) \cdot \lim_{h \to 0} \frac{v(x+h) - v(x)}{h} + \lim_{h \to 0} v(x) \cdot \lim_{h \to 0} \frac{u(x+h) - u(x)}{h}$$

Because u is differentiable and hence continuous, it follows that $\lim\limits_{h \to 0} u(x+h) = u(x)$, so we have the formula we seek:

$$f'(x) = u(x) \cdot v'(x) + v(x) \cdot u'(x)$$

EXAMPLE   1   Product Rule

(a) Find dy/dx if $y = (2x^3 + 3x + 1)(x^2 + 4)$.
(b) At the point where $x = 1$, find the slope of the tangent to the graph of

$$y = f(x) = (4x^3 + 5x^2 - 6x + 5)(x^3 - 4x^2 + 1)$$

Solution

(a) Using the Product Rule with $u(x) = 2x^3 + 3x + 1$ and $v(x) = x^2 + 4$, we have

$$\frac{dy}{dx} = (2x^3 + 3x + 1)(2x) + (x^2 + 4)(6x^2 + 3)$$

$$= 4x^4 + 6x^2 + 2x + 6x^4 + 3x^2 + 24x^2 + 12$$

$$= 10x^4 + 33x^2 + 2x + 12$$

(b) $f'(x) = (4x^3 + 5x^2 - 6x + 5)(3x^2 - 8x) + (x^3 - 4x^2 + 1)(12x^2 + 10x - 6)$
    If we substitute $x = 1$ into $f'(x)$, we find that the slope of the curve at $x = 1$ is
    $f'(1) = 8(-5) + (-2)(16) = -72$.

Quotient Rule   For a quotient of two functions, we might be tempted to take the derivative of the numerator divided by the derivative of the denominator; but this is incorrect. With the example $f(x) = x^3/x$ (which equals x^2 if $x \neq 0$), this approach would give $3x^2/1 = 3x^2$ as the derivative, rather than $2x$. Thus, finding the derivative of a function that is the quotient of two functions requires the **Quotient Rule.**

Quotient Rule	If $f(x) = \dfrac{u(x)}{v(x)}$, where u and v are differentiable functions of x, with $v(x) \neq 0$, then $$f'(x) = \frac{v(x) \cdot u'(x) - u(x) \cdot v'(x)}{[v(x)]^2}$$

The preceding formula says that the derivative of a quotient is the denominator times the derivative of the numerator minus the numerator times the derivative of the denominator, all divided by the square of the denominator.

To see that this rule is reasonable, again consider the function $f(x) = x^3/x$, $x \neq 0$. Using the Quotient Rule, with $u(x) = x^3$ and $v(x) = x$, we get

$$f'(x) = \frac{x(3x^2) - x^3(1)}{x^2} = \frac{3x^3 - x^3}{x^2} = \frac{2x^3}{x^2} = 2x$$

We see that $f'(x) = 2x$ is the correct derivative. The proof of the Quotient Rule is left for the student in the exercises in this section.

EXAMPLE 2   Quotient Rule

(a)   If $f(x) = \dfrac{x^2 - 4x}{x + 5}$, find $f'(x)$.

(b)   If $f(x) = \dfrac{x^3 - 3x^2 + 2}{x^2 - 4}$, find the instantaneous rate of change of $f(x)$ at $x = 3$.

Solution
(a)   Using the Quotient Rule with $u(x) = x^2 - 4x$ and $v(x) = x + 5$, we get

$$f'(x) = \frac{(x + 5)(2x - 4) - (x^2 - 4x)(1)}{(x + 5)^2}$$

$$= \frac{2x^2 + 6x - 20 - x^2 + 4x}{(x + 5)^2} = \frac{x^2 + 10x - 20}{(x + 5)^2}$$

(b)   We evaluate $f'(x)$ at $x = 3$ to find the desired rate of change. Using the Quotient Rule with $u(x) = x^3 - 3x^2 + 2$ and $v(x) = x^2 - 4$, we get

$$f'(x) = \frac{(x^2 - 4)(3x^2 - 6x) - (x^3 - 3x^2 + 2)(2x)}{(x^2 - 4)^2}$$

$$= \frac{(3x^4 - 6x^3 - 12x^2 + 24x) - (2x^4 - 6x^3 + 4x)}{(x^2 - 4)^2} = \frac{x^4 - 12x^2 + 20x}{(x^2 - 4)^2}$$

Thus, the instantaneous rate of change at $x = 3$ is $f'(3) = 33/25 = 1.32$

EXAMPLE 3   Quotient Rule

Use the Quotient Rule to find the derivative of $y = 1/x^3$.

Solution
Letting $u(x) = 1$ and $v(x) = x^3$, we get

$$y' = \frac{x^3(0) - 1(3x^2)}{(x^3)^2} = -\frac{3x^2}{x^6} = -\frac{3}{x^4}$$

Note that we could have found the derivative more easily by rewriting y.

$$y = 1/x^3 = x^{-3} \quad \text{gives} \quad y' = -3x^{-4} = -\frac{3}{x^4}$$

Recall that we proved the Powers of x Rule for positive integer powers and assumed that it was true for all real number powers. In Problem 38 of the exercises in this section, you will be asked to use the Quotient Rule to show that the Powers of x Rule applies to negative integers.

It is not necessary to use the Quotient Rule when the denominator of the function in question contains only a constant. For example, the function $y = (x^3 - 3x)/3$ can be written $y = \frac{1}{3}(x^3 - 3x)$, so the derivative is $y' = \frac{1}{3}(3x^2 - 3) = x^2 - 1$.

✓ CHECKPOINT

1. True or false: The derivative of the product of two functions is equal to the product of the derivatives of the two functions.
2. True or false: The derivative of the quotient of two functions is equal to the quotient of the derivatives of the two functions.
3. Find $f'(x)$ for each of the following.
   (a) $f(x) = (x^{12} + 8x^5 - 7)(10x^7 - 4x + 19)$ Do not simplify.
   (b) $f(x) = \dfrac{2x^4 + 3}{3x^4 + 2}$ Simplify.
4. If $y = \frac{4}{3}(x^2 + 3x - 4)$, does finding y' require the Product Rule? Explain.
5. If $y = f(x)/c$, where c is a constant, does finding y' require the Quotient Rule? Explain.

EXAMPLE   4   Marginal Revenue

Suppose that the revenue function for a flash drive is given by

$$R(x) = 10x + \frac{100x}{3x + 5}$$

where x is the number of flash drives sold and R is in dollars.

(a) Find the marginal revenue function.
(b) Find the marginal revenue when $x = 15$.

Solution
(a) We must use the Quotient Rule to find the marginal revenue (the derivative).

$$\overline{MR} = R'(x) = 10 + \frac{(3x + 5)(100) - 100x(3)}{(3x + 5)^2}$$

$$= 10 + \frac{300x + 500 - 300x}{(3x + 5)^2} = 10 + \frac{500}{(3x + 5)^2}$$

(b) The marginal revenue when $x = 15$ is $R'(15)$.

$$R'(15) = 10 + \frac{500}{[(3)(15) + 5]^2} = 10 + \frac{500}{(50)^2} = 10.20 \text{ (dollars per unit)}$$

Recall that $R'(15)$ estimates the revenue from the sale of the 16th flash drive.

16th $10.20

$R'(15) = \$10.20$

EXAMPLE 5 Sensitivity to a Drug | APPLICATION PREVIEW |

When medicine is administered, reaction (measured in change of blood pressure or temperature) can be modeled by

$$R = m^2\left(\frac{c}{2} - \frac{m}{3}\right)$$

where c is a positive constant and m is the amount of medicine absorbed into the blood. The rate of change of R with respect to m is the sensitivity of the body to medicine. Find an expression for sensitivity s as a function of m.

Solution
The sensitivity is the rate of change of R with respect to m, or the derivative. Thus

$$s = \frac{dR}{dm} = m^2\left(0 - \frac{1}{3}\right) + \left(\frac{c}{2} - \frac{1}{3}m\right)(2m)$$

$$= -\frac{1}{3}m^2 + mc - \frac{2}{3}m^2 = mc - m^2$$

✓ CHECKPOINT ANSWERS

1. False. The derivative of a product is $\dfrac{d}{dx}(fg) = f \cdot \dfrac{dg}{dx} + g \cdot \dfrac{df}{dx}$

2. False. The derivative of a quotient is $\dfrac{d}{dx}\left(\dfrac{f}{g}\right) = \dfrac{g \cdot f' - f \cdot g'}{g^2}$

3. (a) $f'(x) = (x^{12} + 8x^5 - 7)(70x^6 - 4) + (10x^7 - 4x + 19)(12x^{11} + 40x^4)$
   (b) $f'(x) = \dfrac{-20x^3}{(3x^4 + 2)^2}$

4. No; y' can be found with the Coefficient Rule: $y' = \dfrac{4}{3}(2x + 3)$

5. No; y' can be found with the Coefficient Rule: $y' = \left(\dfrac{1}{c}\right)f'(x)$

| EXERCISES | 9.5

In Problems 1–4, find the derivative and simplify.
1. $y = (5x + 3)(x^2 - 2x)$
2. $s = (t^4 + 1)(t^3 - 1)$
3. $f(x) = (x^{12} + 3x^4 + 4)(2x^3 - 1)$
4. $y = (3x^7 + 4)(8x^6 - 6x^4 - 9)$

In Problems 5–8, find the derivative, but do not simplify your answer.
5. $y = (7x^6 - 5x^4 + 2x^2 - 1)(4x^9 + 3x^7 - 5x^2 + 3x)$
6. $y = (9x^9 - 7x^7 - 6x)(3x^5 - 4x^4 + 3x^3 - 8)$
7. $y = (x^2 + x + 1)(\sqrt[3]{x} - 2\sqrt{x} + 5)$
8. $y = (\sqrt[5]{x} - 2\sqrt[4]{x} + 1)(x^3 - 5x - 7)$

In Problems 9 and 10, at each indicated point find
(a) the slope of the tangent line, and
(b) the instantaneous rate of change of the function.
9. $y = (x^2 + 1)(x^3 - 4x)$ at $(-2, 0)$
10. $y = (x^3 - 3)(x^2 - 4x + 1)$ at $(2, -15)$

In Problems 11–20, find the indicated derivatives and simplify.
11. $\dfrac{dp}{dq}$ for $p = \dfrac{q^2 + 3}{2q - 1}$
12. $C'(x)$ for $C(x) = \dfrac{2x^3}{3x^4 + 2}$
13. $\dfrac{dy}{dx}$ for $y = \dfrac{1 - 2x^2}{x^4 - 2x^2 + 5}$
14. $\dfrac{ds}{dt}$ for $s = \dfrac{t^3 - 4}{t^3 - 2t^2 - t - 5}$
15. $\dfrac{dz}{dx}$ for $z = x^2 + \dfrac{x^2}{1 - x - 2x^2}$
16. $\dfrac{dy}{dx}$ for $y = 200x - \dfrac{100x}{3x + 1}$
17. $\dfrac{dp}{dq}$ for $p = \dfrac{3\sqrt[3]{q}}{1 - q}$

18. $\dfrac{dy}{dx}$ for $y = \dfrac{2\sqrt{x} - 1}{1 - 4\sqrt{x^3}}$

19. y' for $y = \dfrac{x(x^2 + 4)}{x - 2}$

20. $f'(x)$ for $f(x) = \dfrac{(x + 1)(x - 2)}{x^2 + 1}$

In Problems 21 and 22, at the indicated point for each function, find
(a) **the slope of the tangent line, and**
(b) **the instantaneous rate of change of the function.**

21. $y = \dfrac{x^2 + 1}{x + 3}$ at $(2, 1)$

22. $y = \dfrac{x^2 - 4x}{x^2 + 2x}$ at $\left(2, -\dfrac{1}{2}\right)$

In Problems 23–26, write the equation of the tangent line to the graph of the function at the indicated point. Check the reasonableness of your answer by graphing both the function and the tangent line.

23. $y = (9x^2 - 6x + 1)(1 + 2x)$ at $x = 1$

24. $y = (4x^2 + 4x + 1)(7 - 2x)$ at $x = 0$

25. $y = \dfrac{3x^4 - 2x - 1}{4 - x^2}$ at $x = 1$

26. $y = \dfrac{x^2 - 4x}{2x - x^3}$ at $x = 2$

In Problems 27–30, use the numerical derivative feature of a graphing calculator to find the derivative of each function at the given x-value.

27. $y = \left(4\sqrt{x} + \dfrac{3}{x}\right)\left(3\sqrt[3]{x} - \dfrac{5}{x^2} - 25\right)$ at $x = 1$

28. $y = (3\sqrt[4]{x^5} + \sqrt[5]{x^4} - 1)\left(\dfrac{2}{x^3} - \dfrac{1}{\sqrt{x}}\right)$ at $x = 1$

29. $f(x) = \dfrac{4x - 4}{3x^{2/3}}$ at $x = 1$

30. $f(x) = \dfrac{3\sqrt[3]{x} + 1}{x + 2}$ at $x = -1$

In Problems 31–34, complete the following.
(a) **Find the derivative of each function, and check your work by graphing both your calculated derivative and the numerical derivative of the function.**
(b) **Use your graph of the derivative to find points where the original function has horizontal tangent lines.**
(c) **Use a graphing calculator to graph the function and indicate the points found in part (b) on the graph.**

31. $f(x) = (x^2 + 4x + 4)(x - 7)$

32. $f(x) = (x^2 - 14x + 49)(2x + 1)$

33. $y = \dfrac{x^2}{x - 2}$

34. $y = \dfrac{x^2 - 7}{4 - x}$

In Problems 35 and 36,
(a) **find $f'(x)$.**
(b) **graph both $f(x)$ and $f'(x)$ with a graphing utility.**
(c) **identify the x-values where $f'(x) = 0, f'(x) > 0$, and $f'(x) < 0$.**
(d) **identify x-values where $f(x)$ has a maximum point or a minimum point, where $f(x)$ is increasing, and where $f(x)$ is decreasing.**

35. $f(x) = \dfrac{10x^2}{x^2 + 1}$

36. $f(x) = \dfrac{8 - x^2}{x^2 + 4}$

37. Prove the Quotient Rule for differentiation. (*Hint:* Add $[-u(x) \cdot v(x) + u(x) \cdot v(x)]$ to the expanded numerator and use steps similar to those used to prove the Product Rule.)

38. Use the Quotient Rule to show that the Powers of x Rule applies to negative integer powers. That is, show that $(d/dx)x^n = nx^{n-1}$ when $n = -k, k > 0$, by finding the derivative of $f(x) = 1/(x^k)$.

APPLICATIONS

39. *Cost-benefit* If the cost C (in dollars) of removing p percent of the particulate pollution from the exhaust gases at an industrial site is given by

$$C(p) = \dfrac{8100p}{100 - p}$$

find the rate of change of C with respect to p.

40. *Cost-benefit* If the cost C (in dollars) of removing p percent of the impurities from the waste water in a manufacturing process is given by

$$C(p) = \dfrac{9800p}{101 - p}$$

find the rate of change of C with respect to p.

41. *Revenue* Suppose the revenue (in dollars) from the sale of x units of a product is given by

$$R(x) = \dfrac{60x^2 + 74x}{2x + 2}$$

Find the marginal revenue when 49 units are sold. Interpret your result.

42. *Revenue* The revenue (in dollars) from the sale of x units of a product is given by

$$R(x) = \dfrac{3000}{2x + 2} + 80x - 1500$$

Find the marginal revenue when 149 units are sold. Interpret your result.

43. *Revenue* A travel agency will plan a group tour for groups of size 25 or larger. If the group contains exactly 25 people, the cost is $300 per person. If each person's cost is reduced by $10 for each additional person above the 25, then the revenue is given by

$$R(x) = (25 + x)(300 - 10x)$$

where x is the number of additional people above 25. Find the marginal revenue if the group contains 30 people. Interpret your result.

44. **Revenue** McRobert's Electronics sells 200 TVs per month at a price of $400 per unit. Market research indicates that the store can sell one additional TV for each $1 it reduces the price. In this case the total revenue is

$$R(x) = (200 + x)(400 - x)$$

where x is the number of additional TVs beyond the 200. If the store sells a total of 250 TVs, find the marginal revenue. Interpret your result.

45. **Response to a drug** The reaction R to an injection of a drug is related to the dosage x (in milligrams) according to

$$R(x) = x^2\left(500 - \frac{x}{3}\right)$$

where 1000 mg is the maximum dosage. If the rate of reaction with respect to the dosage defines the sensitivity to the drug, find the sensitivity.

46. **Nerve response** The number of action potentials produced by a nerve, t seconds after a stimulus, is given by

$$N(t) = 25t + \frac{4}{t^2 + 2} - 2$$

Find the rate at which the action potentials are produced by the nerve.

47. **Test reliability** If a test having reliability r is lengthened by a factor n, the reliability of the new test is given by

$$R = \frac{nr}{1 + (n - 1)r}, \quad 0 < r \le 1$$

Find the rate at which R changes with respect to n.

48. **Advertising and sales** The sales of a product s (in thousands of dollars) are related to advertising expenses (in thousands of dollars) by

$$s = \frac{200x}{x + 10}$$

Find and interpret the meaning of the rate of change of sales with respect to advertising expenses when
(a) $x = 10$.   (b) $x = 20$.

49. **Candidate recognition** Suppose that the proportion P of voters who recognize a candidate's name t months after the start of the campaign is given by

$$P(t) = \frac{13t}{t^2 + 100} + 0.18$$

(a) Find the rate of change of P when $t = 6$, and explain its meaning.
(b) Find the rate of change of P when $t = 12$, and explain its meaning.
(c) One month prior to the election, is it better for $P'(t)$ to be positive or negative? Explain.

50. **Endangered species population** It is determined that a wildlife refuge can support a group of up to 120 of a certain endangered species. If 75 are introduced onto the refuge and their population after t years is given by

$$p(t) = 75\left(1 + \frac{4t}{t^2 + 16}\right)$$

find the rate of population growth after t years. Find the rate after each of the first 7 years.

51. **Wind chill** In January 2014 the so-called "Polar Vortex" of dense, frigid air plunged deep into the United States and resulted in record cold temperatures and dangerous wind chills. If s is the wind speed in miles per hour and $s \ge 5$, then the wind chill (in degrees Fahrenheit) for an air temperature of 0°F can be approximated by the function

$$f(s) = \frac{289.173 - 58.5731s}{s + 1}$$

(a) At what rate is the wind chill changing when the wind speed is 20 mph?
(b) Explain the meaning of your answer to part (a).

52. **Response to injected adrenalin** Experimental evidence has shown that the response y of a muscle is related to the concentration of injected adrenaline x according to the equation

$$y = \frac{x}{a + bx}$$

where a and b are constants. Find the rate of change of response with respect to the concentration.

53. **Social Security beneficiaries** The table gives the number of millions of Social Security beneficiaries (actual and projected) for selected years from 1950 through 2030.

Year	Number of Beneficiaries (millions)	Year	Number of Beneficiaries (millions)
1950	2.9	2000	44.8
1960	14.3	2010	53.3
1970	25.2	2020	68.8
1980	35.1	2030	82.7
1990	39.5		

Source: Social Security Trustees Report

With $B(t)$ representing the number of beneficiaries (in millions) t years past 1950, these data can be modeled by the function

$$B(t) = (0.01t + 3)(0.0238t^2 - 9.79t + 3100) - 9290$$

(a) Find the function that gives the instantaneous rate of change of the number of beneficiaries.
(b) Find and interpret the instantaneous rate of change in 2020.
(c) Use the data to determine which of the average rates of change (from 2010 to 2020, from 2020 to 2030, or from 2010 to 2030) best approximates the instantaneous rate from part (b).

54. *Emissions* The table shows data for sulfur dioxide emissions from electricity generation (in millions of short tons) for selected years from 2000 and projected to 2035. These data can be modeled by the function

$$E(x) = (0.001x - 0.062)(-0.18x^2 + 8.2x - 200)$$

where x is the number of years past 2000.
(a) Find the function that models the rate of change of these emissions.
(b) Find and interpret $E'(20)$.

Year	Short Tons (in millions)
2000	11.4
2005	10.2
2008	7.6
2015	4.7
2020	4.2
2025	3.8
2030	3.7
2035	3.8

Source: U.S. Department of Energy

55. *Females in the workforce* For selected years from 1950 and with projections to 2050, the table shows the percent of total U.S. workers who were female.

Year	% Female	Year	% Female
1950	29.6	2010	47.9
1960	33.4	2015	48.3
1970	38.1	2020	48.1
1980	42.5	2030	48.0
1990	45.2	2040	47.9
2000	46.6	2050	47.7

Source: U.S. Bureau of the Census

Assume these data can be modeled with the function

$$p(t) = \frac{78.6t + 2090}{1.38t + 64.1}$$

where $p(t)$ is the percent of the U.S. workforce that is female and t is the number of years past 1950.
(a) Find the function that models the instantaneous rate of change of the percent of U.S. workers who were female.
(b) Use the function from part (a) to find the instantaneous rates of change in 2005 and in 2020.
(c) Interpret each of the rates of change in part (b).

56. *Alzheimer's* As the Baby Boom generation ages and the proportion of the U.S population over 65 increases, the number of Americans with Alzheimer's disease and other dementia is projected to grow each year. With data from the Social Security Administration and the Alzheimer's Association for selected years from 2000 and projected to 2050, the percent of the U.S. population with Alzheimer's can be modeled with the function

$$A(t) = \frac{0.34t^2 + 1.3t + 450}{-0.012t^2 + 3.3t + 260}$$

where t is the number of years past 1990.
(a) Find the function that gives the instantaneous rate of change of $A(t)$.
(b) Use your answer in part (a) to find and interpret the instantaneous rate of change of the percent of the U.S. population with Alzheimer's in 2025.

OBJECTIVES

9.6

- To use the Chain Rule to differentiate functions
- To use the Power Rule to differentiate functions

The Chain Rule and the Power Rule

▌| APPLICATION PREVIEW |▌

The demand x for a product is given by

$$x = \frac{98}{\sqrt{2p + 1}} - 1$$

where p is the price per unit. To find how fast demand is changing when price is $24, we take the derivative of x with respect to p. If we write this function with a power rather than a radical, it has the form

$$x = 98(2p + 1)^{-1/2} - 1$$

The formulas learned so far cannot be used to find this derivative. We use a new formula, the Power Rule, to find this derivative. (See Example 6.) In this section we will discuss the Chain Rule and the Power Rule, which is one of the results of the Chain Rule, and we will use these formulas to solve applied problems.

Composite Functions   Recall from Section 1.2, "Functions," that if f and g are functions, then the composite functions g of f (denoted $g \circ f$) and f of g (denoted $f \circ g$) are defined as follows:

$$(g \circ f)(x) = g(f(x)) \quad \text{and} \quad (f \circ g)(x) = f(g(x))$$

EXAMPLE 1   **Composite Function**

If $f(x) = 3x^2$ and $g(x) = 2x - 1$, find $F(x) = f(g(x))$.

Solution
Substituting $g(x) = 2x - 1$ for x in $f(x)$ gives

$$f(g(x)) = f(2x - 1) = 3(2x - 1)^2 \quad \text{or} \quad F(x) = 3(2x - 1)^2$$ ∎

Chain Rule   We could find the derivative of the function $F(x) = 3(2x - 1)^2$ by expanding the expression $3(2x - 1)^2$. Then

$$F(x) = 3(4x^2 - 4x + 1) = 12x^2 - 12x + 3$$

so $F'(x) = 24x - 12$. But we can also use a very powerful rule, called the **Chain Rule,** to find derivatives of composite functions. If we write the composite function $y = f(g(x))$ in the form $y = f(u)$, where $u = g(x)$, we state the Chain Rule as follows.

Chain Rule

If f and g are differentiable functions with $y = f(u)$, and $u = g(x)$, then y is a differentiable function of x, and

$$\frac{dy}{dx} = f'(u) \cdot g'(x)$$

or, equivalently,

$$\frac{dy}{dx} = \frac{dy}{du} \cdot \frac{du}{dx}$$

Note that dy/du represents the derivative of $y = f(u)$ *with respect to u* and du/dx represents the derivative of $u = g(x)$ *with respect to x.* For example, if $y = 3(2x - 1)^2$, then the outside function, f, is the squaring function, and the inside function, g, is $2x - 1$, so we may write $y = f(u) = 3u^2$, where $u = g(x) = 2x - 1$. Then the derivative is

$$\frac{dy}{dx} = \frac{dy}{du} \cdot \frac{du}{dx} = 6u \cdot 2 = 12u$$

To write this derivative in terms of x, we substitute $2x - 1$ for u. Thus

$$\frac{dy}{dx} = 12(2x - 1) = 24x - 12$$

Note that we get the same result by using the Chain Rule as we did by expanding $f(x) = 3(2x - 1)^2$. The Chain Rule is important because it is not always possible to rewrite the function as a polynomial. Consider the following example.

EXAMPLE 2   **Chain Rule**

If $y = \sqrt{x^2 - 1}$, find $\dfrac{dy}{dx}$.

Solution
If we write this function as $y = f(u) = \sqrt{u} = u^{1/2}$, with $u = x^2 - 1$, we can find the derivative.

$$\frac{dy}{dx} = \frac{dy}{du} \cdot \frac{du}{dx} = \frac{1}{2} \cdot u^{-1/2} \cdot 2x = u^{-1/2} \cdot x = \frac{1}{\sqrt{u}} \cdot x = \frac{x}{\sqrt{u}}$$

To write this derivative in terms of x alone, we substitute $x^2 - 1$ for u. Then

$$\frac{dy}{dx} = \frac{x}{\sqrt{x^2 - 1}}$$

Note that we could not find the derivative of a function like that of Example 2 by the methods learned previously.

EXAMPLE 3   Allometric Relationships

The relationship between the length L (in meters) and weight W (in kilograms) of a species of fish in the Pacific Ocean is given by $W = 10.375L^3$. The rate of growth in length is given by $\frac{dL}{dt} = 0.36 - 0.18L$, where t is measured in years.

(a) Determine a formula for the rate of growth in weight $\frac{dW}{dt}$ in terms of L.

(b) If a fish weighs 30 kilograms, approximate its rate of growth in weight using the formula found in part (a).

Solution

(a) The rate of change uses the Chain Rule, as follows:

$$\frac{dW}{dt} = \frac{dW}{dL}\cdot\frac{dL}{dt} = 31.125L^2\,(0.36 - 0.18L) = 11.205L^2 - 5.6025L^3$$

(b) From $W = 10.375L^3$ and $W = 30$ kg, we can find L by solving

$$30 = 10.375L^3$$

$$\frac{30}{10.375} = L^3 \quad \text{so} \quad L = \sqrt[3]{\frac{30}{10.375}} \approx 1.4247 \text{ m}$$

Hence, the rate of growth in weight is

$$\frac{dW}{dt} = 11.205(1.4247)^2 - 5.6025(1.4247)^3 \approx 6.542 \text{ kilograms/year}$$

Power Rule   The Chain Rule is very useful and will be extremely important with functions that we will study later. A special case of the Chain Rule, called the **Power Rule,** is useful for the algebraic functions we have studied so far, composite functions where the outside function is a power.

Power Rule   If $y = u^n$, where u is a differentiable function of x, then

$$\frac{dy}{dx} = nu^{n-1}\cdot\frac{du}{dx}$$

EXAMPLE 4   Power Rule

(a) If $y = (x^2 - 4x)^6$, find $\frac{dy}{dx}$.   (b) If $p = \frac{4}{3q^2 + 1}$, find $\frac{dp}{dq}$.

Solution

(a) This has the form $y = u^n = u^6$, with $u = x^2 - 4x$. Thus, by the Power Rule,

$$\frac{dy}{dx} = nu^{n-1}\cdot\frac{du}{dx} = 6u^5\,(2x - 4)$$

Substituting $x^2 - 4x$ for u gives

$$\frac{dy}{dx} = 6(x^2 - 4x)^5 (2x - 4) = (12x - 24)(x^2 - 4x)^5$$

(b) We can use the Power Rule to find dp/dq if we write the equation in the form

$$p = 4(3q^2 + 1)^{-1}$$

Then

$$\frac{dp}{dq} = 4[-1(3q^2 + 1)^{-2}(6q)] = \frac{-24q}{(3q^2 + 1)^2}$$

The derivative of the function in Example 4(b) can also be found by using the Quotient Rule, but the Power Rule provides a more efficient method.

EXAMPLE 5   Power Rule with Radicals

Find the derivatives of (a) $y = 3\sqrt[3]{x^2 - 3x + 1}$ and (b) $g(x) = \dfrac{1}{\sqrt{(x^2 + 1)^3}}$.

Solution
(a) Because $y = 3(x^2 - 3x + 1)^{1/3}$, we can make use of the Power Rule with $u = x^2 - 3x + 1$.

$$y' = 3\left(nu^{n-1}\frac{du}{dx}\right) = 3\left[\frac{1}{3}u^{-2/3}(2x - 3)\right]$$

$$= (x^2 - 3x + 1)^{-2/3}(2x - 3) = \frac{2x - 3}{(x^2 - 3x + 1)^{2/3}}$$

(b) Writing $g(x)$ as a power gives $g(x) = (x^2 + 1)^{-3/2}$. Then

$$g'(x) = -\frac{3}{2}(x^2 + 1)^{-5/2}(2x) = -3x \cdot \frac{1}{(x^2 + 1)^{5/2}} = \frac{-3x}{\sqrt{(x^2 + 1)^5}}$$

✓ **CHECKPOINT**

1. (a) If $f(x) = (3x^4 + 1)^{10}$, does $f'(x) = 10(3x^4 + 1)^9$?
   (b) If $f(x) = (2x + 1)^5$, does $f'(x) = 10(2x + 1)^4$?
   (c) If $f(x) = \dfrac{[u(x)]^n}{c}$, where c is a constant, does $f'(x) = \dfrac{n[u(x)]^{n-1} \cdot u'(x)}{c}$?

2. (a) If $f(x) = \dfrac{12}{2x^2 - 1}$, find $f'(x)$ by using the Power Rule (not the Quotient Rule).
   (b) If $f(x) = \dfrac{\sqrt{x^3 - 1}}{3}$, find $f'(x)$ by using the Power Rule (not the Quotient Rule).

EXAMPLE 6   Demand | APPLICATION PREVIEW |

The demand for x hundred units of a product is given by

$$x = 98(2p + 1)^{-1/2} - 1$$

where p is the price per unit in dollars. Find the rate of change of the demand with respect to price when $p = 24$.

Solution
The rate of change of demand with respect to price is

$$\frac{dx}{dp} = 98\left[-\frac{1}{2}(2p + 1)^{-3/2}(2)\right] = -98(2p + 1)^{-3/2}$$

When $p = 24$, the rate of change is

$$\frac{dx}{dp}\bigg|_{p=24} = -98(48 + 1)^{-3/2} = -98 \cdot \frac{1}{49^{3/2}} = -\frac{2}{7}$$

This means that when the price is $24, demand is changing at the rate of $-2/7$ hundred units per dollar, or if the price changes by $1, demand will change by about $-200/7$ units.

✓ **CHECKPOINT ANSWERS**

1. (a) No, $f'(x) = 10(3x^4 + 1)^9 (12x^3)$.   (b) Yes   (c) Yes

2. (a) $f'(x) = \dfrac{-48x}{(2x^2 - 1)^2}$ (b) $f'(x) = \dfrac{x^2}{2\sqrt{x^3 - 1}}$

| EXERCISES | 9.6

In Problems 1–4, find $\dfrac{dy}{du}, \dfrac{du}{dx}$, and $\dfrac{dy}{dx}$.

1. $y = u^3$ and $u = x^2 + 1$
2. $y = u^4$ and $u = x^2 + 4x$
3. $y = u^4$ and $u = 4x^2 - x + 8$
4. $y = u^{10}$ and $u = x^2 + 5x$

Differentiate the functions in Problems 5–22.

5. $f(x) = (3x^5 - 2)^{20}$
6. $g(x) = (3 - 2x)^{10}$
7. $h(x) = \frac{3}{4}(x^5 - 2x^3 + 5)^8$
8. $k(x) = \frac{5}{7}(2x^3 - x + 6)^{14}$
9. $s(t) = 5t - 3(2t^4 + 7)^3$
10. $p(q) = 4(3q^2 - 1)^4 - 13q$
11. $g(x) = (x^4 - 5x)^{-2}$ 12. $p = (q^3 + 1)^{-5}$
13. $f(s) = \dfrac{3}{(2s^5 + 1)^4}$ 14. $g(t) = \dfrac{1}{4t^3 + 1}$
15. $g(x) = \dfrac{1}{(2x^3 + 3x + 5)^{3/4}}$
16. $y = \dfrac{1}{(3x^3 + 4x + 1)^{3/2}}$
17. $y = \sqrt{3x^2 + 4x + 9}$ 18. $y = \sqrt{x^2 + 3x}$
19. $y = \dfrac{11(x^3 - 7)^6}{9}$ 20. $y = \dfrac{5\sqrt{1 - x^3}}{6}$
21. $z = \dfrac{(3w + 1)^5 - 3w}{7}$
22. $y = \dfrac{\sqrt{2x - 1} - \sqrt{x}}{2}$

At the indicated point, for each function in Problems 23–26, find
(a) the slope of the tangent line, and
(b) the instantaneous rate of change of the function.
You may use the numerical derivative feature on a graphing calculator to check your work.

23. $y = (x^3 + 2x)^4$ at $x = 2$
24. $y = \sqrt{5x^2 + 2x}$ at $x = 1$
25. $y = \sqrt{x^3 + 1}$ at $(2, 3)$
26. $y = (4x^3 - 5x + 1)^3$ at $(1, 0)$

In Problems 27–30, write the equation of the line tangent to the graph of each function at the indicated point. As a check, graph both the function and the tangent line you found to see whether it looks correct.

27. $y = (x^2 - 3x + 3)^3$ at $(2, 1)$
28. $y = (x^2 + 1)^3$ at $(2, 125)$
29. $y = \sqrt{3x^2 - 2}$ at $x = 3$
30. $y = \dfrac{1}{(x^3 - x)^3}$ at $x = 2$

 In Problems 31 and 32, complete the following for each function.
(a) Find $f'(x)$.
(b) Check your result in part (a) by graphing both it and the numerical derivative of the function.
(c) Find x-values for which the slope of the tangent is 0.
(d) Find points (x, y) where the slope of the tangent is 0.
(e) Use a graphing utility to graph the function and locate the points found in part (d).

31. $f(x) = (x^2 - 4)^3 + 12$
32. $f(x) = 10 - (x^2 - 2x - 8)^2$

 In Problems 33 and 34, do the following for each function $f(x)$.
(a) Find $f'(x)$.
(b) Graph both $f(x)$ and $f'(x)$ with a graphing utility.
(c) Determine x-values where $f'(x) = 0, f'(x) > 0$, $f'(x) < 0$.
(d) Determine x-values for which $f(x)$ has a maximum or minimum point, where the graph is increasing, and where it is decreasing.

33. $f(x) = 12 - 3(1 - x^2)^{4/3}$
34. $f(x) = 3 + \dfrac{1}{16}(x^2 - 4x)^4$

In Problems 35 and 36, find the derivative of each function.

35. (a) $y = \dfrac{2x^3}{3}$ (b) $y = \dfrac{2}{3x^3}$

   (c) $y = \dfrac{(2x)^3}{3}$ (d) $y = \dfrac{2}{(3x)^3}$

36. (a) $y = \dfrac{3}{(5x)^5}$ (b) $y = \dfrac{3x^5}{5}$

   (c) $y = \dfrac{3}{5x^5}$ (d) $y = \dfrac{(3x)^5}{5}$

APPLICATIONS

37. *Ballistics* Ballistics experts are able to identify the weapon that fired a certain bullet by studying the markings on the bullet. Tests are conducted by firing into a bale of paper. If the distance s, in inches, that the bullet travels into the paper is given by

$$s = 27 - (3 - 10t)^3$$

for $0 \le t \le 0.3$ second, find the velocity of the bullet one-tenth of a second after it hits the paper.

38. *Population of microorganisms* Suppose that the population of a certain microorganism at time t (in minutes) is given by

$$P = 1000 - 1000(t + 10)^{-1}$$

Find the rate of change of population.

39. *Revenue* The revenue from the sale of a product is

$$R = 1500x + 3000(2x + 3)^{-1} - 1000 \text{ dollars}$$

where x is the number of units sold. Find the marginal revenue when 100 units are sold. Interpret your result.

40. *Revenue* The revenue from the sale of x units of a product is

$$R = 15(3x + 1)^{-1} + 50x - 15 \text{ dollars}$$

Find the marginal revenue when 40 units are sold. Interpret your result.

41. *Pricing and sales* Suppose that the weekly sales volume y (in thousands of units sold) depends on the price per unit (in dollars) of the product according to

$$y = 32(3p + 1)^{-2/5}, \quad p > 0$$

   (a) What is the rate of change in sales volume when the price is $21?
   (b) Interpret your answer to part (a).

42. *Pricing and sales* A chain of auto service stations has found that its monthly sales volume S (in thousands of dollars) is related to the price p (in dollars) of an oil change according to

$$S = \dfrac{98}{\sqrt{p + 5}}, \quad p > 10$$

   (a) What is the rate of change of sales volume when the price is $44?
   (b) Interpret your answer to part (a).

43. *Demand* Suppose that the demand for q units of a product priced at p per unit is described by

$$p = \dfrac{200{,}000}{(q + 1)^2}$$

   (a) What is the rate of change of price with respect to the quantity demanded when $q = 49$?
   (b) Interpret your answer to part (a).

Stimulus-response **The relation between the magnitude of a sensation y and the magnitude of the stimulus x is given by**

$$y = k(x - x_0)^n$$

where k is a constant, x_0 is the threshold of effective stimulus, and n depends on the type of stimulus. Find the rate of change of sensation with respect to the amount of stimulus for each of Problems 44–46.

44. For the stimulus of visual brightness $y = k(x - x_0)^{1/3}$
45. For the stimulus of warmth $y = k(x - x_0)^{8/5}$
46. For the stimulus of electrical stimulation $y = k(x - x_0)^{7/2}$
47. *Demand* If the demand for q units of a product priced at p per unit is described by the equation

$$p = \dfrac{100}{\sqrt{2q + 1}}$$

find the rate of change of p with respect to q.

48. *Advertising and sales* The daily sales S (in thousands of dollars) attributed to an advertising campaign are given by

$$S = 1 + \dfrac{3}{t + 3} - \dfrac{18}{(t + 3)^2}$$

where t is the number of weeks the campaign runs. What is the rate of change of sales at
   (a) $t = 8$?   (b) $t = 10$?
   (c) Should the campaign be continued after the 10th week? Explain.

49. *Body-heat loss* The description of body-heat loss due to convection involves a coefficient of convection, K_c, which depends on wind velocity according to the following equation.

$$K_c = 4\sqrt{4v + 1}$$

Find the rate of change of the coefficient with respect to the wind velocity.

50. *Data entry speed* The data entry speed (in entries per minute) of a data clerk trainee is

$$S = 10\sqrt{0.8x + 4}, \quad 0 \le x \le 100$$

where x is the number of hours of training he has had. What is the rate at which his speed is changing and what does this rate mean when he has had
   (a) 15 hours of training?
   (b) 40 hours of training?

51. *Investments* If an IRA is a variable-rate investment for 20 years at rate r percent per year, compounded monthly, then the future value S that accumulates from an initial investment of $1000 is

$$S = 1000\left[1 + \dfrac{0.01r}{12}\right]^{240}$$

What is the rate of change of S with respect to r and what does it tell us if the interest rate is (a) 6%? (b) 12%?

52. *Concentration of body substances* The concentration C of a substance in the body depends on the quantity of the substance Q and the volume V through which it is distributed. For a static substance, this is given by

$$C = \frac{Q}{V}$$

For a situation like that in the kidneys, where the fluids are moving, the concentration is the ratio of the rate of change of quantity with respect to time and the rate of change of volume with respect to time.
(a) Formulate the equation for concentration of a moving substance.
(b) Show that this is equal to the rate of change of quantity with respect to volume.

53. *National health expenditures* The table shows the total national expenditures for health (both actual and projected, in billions of dollars) for the years from 2001 to 2018. (These data include expenditures for medical research and medical facilities construction.)

Year	Amount	Year	Amount
2001	$1469	2010	$2624
2002	1602	2011	2770
2003	1735	2012	2931
2004	1855	2013	3111
2005	1981	2014	3313
2006	2113	2015	3541
2007	2241	2016	3790
2008	2379	2017	4062
2009	2509	2018	4353

Source: U.S. Centers for Medicare and Medicaid Services

Assume these data can be modeled with the function

$$A(t) = 445(0.1t + 1)^3 - 2120(0.1t + 1)^2$$
$$+ 4570(0.1t + 1) - 1600$$

where $A(t)$ is in billions of dollars and t is the number of years past 2000.
(a) Use this model to determine and interpret the instantaneous rates of change of the total national health expenditures in 2008 and 2015.
(b) Use the data to find an average rate of change that approximates the 2015 instantaneous rate.

54. *Energy use* Energy use per dollar of GDP indexed to 1980 means that energy use for any year is viewed as a percent of the use per dollar of GDP in 1980. The following data show the energy use per dollar of GDP, as a percent, for selected years from 1985 and projected to 2035.

Energy Use per Dollar of GDP

Year	Percent	Year	Percent
1985	83	2015	51
1990	79	2020	45
1995	75	2025	41
2000	67	2030	37
2005	60	2035	34
2010	56		

Source: U.S. Department of Energy

These data can be modeled with the function

$$E(t) = 0.0039(0.4t + 2)^3 - 0.13(0.4t + 2)^2$$
$$- 1.4(0.4t + 2) + 91$$

where $E(t)$ is the energy use per dollar of GDP (indexed to 1980) and t is the number of years past 1980.
(a) Use this model to find and interpret the instantaneous rates of change of energy use per dollar of GDP in 2000 and 2025.
(b) Use the data in the table to find an average rate of change that approximates the 2025 instantaneous rate.

55. *Gross domestic product* The table shows U.S. gross domestic product (GDP) in billions of dollars for selected years from 2000 to 2070 (actual and projected).

Year	GDP	Year	GDP
2000	9143	2040	79,680
2005	12,145	2045	103,444
2010	16,174	2050	133,925
2015	21,270	2055	173,175
2020	27,683	2060	224,044
2025	35,919	2065	290,042
2030	46,765	2070	375,219
2035	61,100		

Source: Social Security Administration Trustees Report

Assume the GDP can be modeled with the function

$$G(t) = 212.9(0.2t + 5)^3 - 5016(0.2t + 5)^2$$
$$+ 8810.4t + 104,072$$

where $G(t)$ is in billions of dollars and t is the number of years past 2000.
(a) Use the model to find and interpret the instantaneous rates of change of the GDP in 2005 and 2015.
(b) Use the data in the table to find the average rate of change of the GDP from 2005 to 2015.
(c) How well does your answer from part (b) approximate the instantaneous rate of change of GDP in 2010?

56. *Diabetes* The figure shows the percent of the U.S. population with diabetes (diagnosed and undiagnosed) for selected years from 2010 and projections to 2050. Assume this percent can be modeled by

$$y = 6.97(0.5x + 5)^{0.495}$$

where y is the percent and x is the number of years past 2010.

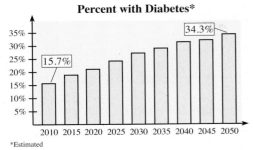

Percent with Diabetes*

34.3%

15.7%

2010 2015 2020 2025 2030 2035 2040 2045 2050

*Estimated

Source: Centers for Disease Control and Prevention

(a)   Use the figure to find the average rate of change from 2010 to 2050.

(b)   Use the model to find the instantaneous rate of change of the U.S. population with diabetes in 2020. Is the average rate found in part (a) a good approximation of the 2020 instantaneous rate?

(c)   Use the model to find and interpret the instantaneous rate of change of the percent of the U.S. population with diabetes in 2050.

OBJECTIVE

9.7

- To use derivative formulas separately and in combination with each other

Using Derivative Formulas

■ | APPLICATION PREVIEW | ■■■■■■■■■■

Suppose the weekly revenue function for a product is given by

$$R(x) = \frac{36,000,000x}{(2x + 500)^2}$$

where $R(x)$ is the dollars of revenue from the sale of x units. We can find marginal revenue by finding the derivative of the revenue function. This revenue function contains both a quotient and a power, so its derivative is found by using both the Quotient Rule and the Power Rule, but in which order are these rules applied? (See Example 4.) In this section we consider functions whose derivatives require more than one derivative formula and discuss how we decide the order in which to apply the formulas.

We have used the Power Rule to find the derivatives of functions like

$$y = (x^3 - 3x^2 + x + 1)^5$$

but we have not found the derivatives of functions like

$$y = [(x^2 + 1)(x^3 + x + 1)]^5$$

This function is different because the function u (which is raised to the fifth power) is the product of two functions, $(x^2 + 1)$ and $(x^3 + x + 1)$. The equation is of the form $y = u^5$, where $u = (x^2 + 1)(x^3 + x + 1)$. This means that the Product Rule should be used to find du/dx. Then

$$\frac{dy}{dx} = 5u^4 \cdot \frac{du}{dx}$$
$$= 5[(x^2 + 1)(x^3 + x + 1)]^4 [(x^2 + 1)(3x^2 + 1) + (x^3 + x + 1)(2x)]$$
$$= 5[(x^2 + 1)(x^3 + x + 1)]^4 (5x^4 + 6x^2 + 2x + 1)$$
$$= (25x^4 + 30x^2 + 10x + 5)[(x^2 + 1)(x^3 + x + 1)]^4$$

A different type of problem involving the Power Rule and the Product Rule is finding the derivative of $y = (x^2 + 1)^5 (x^3 + x + 1)$. We may think of y as the *product* of two functions, one of which is a power. Thus the fundamental formula we should use is the Product

Rule. The two function8s are $u(x) = (x^2 + 1)^5$ and $v(x) = x^3 + x + 1$. The Product Rule gives

$$\frac{dy}{dx} = u(x) \cdot v'(x) + v(x) \cdot u'(x)$$

$$= (x^2 + 1)^5 \, (3x^2 + 1) + (x^3 + x + 1)[5(x^2 + 1)^4(2x)]$$

Note that the Power Rule was used to find $u'(x)$, since $u(x) = (x^2 + 1)^5$.
We can simplify dy/dx by factoring $(x^2 + 1)^4$ from both terms:

$$\frac{dy}{dx} = (x^2 + 1)^4[(x^2 + 1)(3x^2 + 1) + (x^3 + x + 1) \cdot 5 \cdot 2x]$$

$$= (x^2 + 1)^4(13x^4 + 14x^2 + 10x + 1)$$

EXAMPLE   1   Power of a Quotient

If $y = \left(\dfrac{x^2}{x - 1}\right)^5$, find y'.

Solution
We again have an equation of the form $y = u^n$, but this time u is a quotient. Thus we will need the Quotient Rule to find du/dx.

$$y' = nu^{n-1} \cdot \frac{du}{dx} = 5u^4 \frac{(x - 1) \cdot 2x - x^2 \cdot 1}{(x - 1)^2}$$

Substituting for u and simplifying give

$$y' = 5\left(\frac{x^2}{x - 1}\right)^4 \cdot \frac{2x^2 - 2x - x^2}{(x - 1)^2} = \frac{5x^8(x^2 - 2x)}{(x - 1)^6} = \frac{5x^{10} - 10x^9}{(x - 1)^6}$$

EXAMPLE   2   Quotient of Two Powers

Find $f'(x)$ if $f(x) = \dfrac{(x - 1)^2}{(x^4 + 3)^3}$.

Solution
This function is the quotient of two functions, $(x - 1)^2$ and $(x^4 + 3)^3$, so we must use the Quotient Rule to find the derivative of $f(x)$, but taking the derivatives of $(x - 1)^2$ and $(x^4 + 3)^3$ will require the Power Rule.

$$f'(x) = \frac{[v(x) \cdot u'(x) - u(x) \cdot v'(x)]}{[v(x)]^2}$$

$$= \frac{(x^4 + 3)^3[2(x - 1)(1)] - (x - 1)^2[3(x^4 + 3)^2 \, 4x^3]}{[(x^4 + 3)^3]^2}$$

$$= \frac{2(x^4 + 3)^3(x - 1) - 12x^3(x - 1)^2(x^4 + 3)^2}{(x^4 + 3)^6}$$

We see that 2, $(x^4 + 3)^2$, and $(x - 1)$ are all factors in both terms of the numerator, so we can factor them from both terms and reduce the fraction.

$$f'(x) = \frac{2(x^4 + 3)^2(x - 1)[(x^4 + 3) - 6x^3(x - 1)]}{(x^4 + 3)^6}$$

$$= \frac{2(x - 1)(-5x^4 + 6x^3 + 3)}{(x^4 + 3)^4}$$

EXAMPLE 3   **Product with a Power**

Find $f'(x)$ if $f(x) = (x^2 - 1)\sqrt{3 - x^2}$.

Solution

The function is the product of two functions, $x^2 - 1$ and $\sqrt{3 - x^2}$. Therefore, we will use the Product Rule to find the derivative of $f(x)$, but the derivative of $\sqrt{3 - x^2} = (3 - x^2)^{1/2}$ will require the Power Rule.

$$f'(x) = u(x) \cdot v'(x) + v(x) \cdot u'(x)$$

$$= (x^2 - 1)\left[\frac{1}{2}(3 - x^2)^{-1/2}(-2x)\right] + (3 - x^2)^{1/2}(2x)$$

$$= (x^2 - 1)[-x(3 - x^2)^{-1/2}] + (3 - x^2)^{1/2}(2x)$$

$$= \frac{-x^3 + x}{(3 - x^2)^{1/2}} + 2x(3 - x^2)^{1/2}$$

We can combine these terms over the common denominator $(3 - x^2)^{1/2}$ as follows:

$$f'(x) = \frac{-x^3 + x}{(3 - x^2)^{1/2}} + \frac{2x(3 - x^2)^1}{(3 - x^2)^{1/2}} = \frac{-x^3 + x + 6x - 2x^3}{(3 - x^2)^{1/2}} = \frac{-3x^3 + 7x}{(3 - x^2)^{1/2}}$$

We should note that in Example 3 we could have written $f'(x)$ in the form

$$f'(x) = (-x^3 + x)(3 - x^2)^{-1/2} + 2x(3 - x^2)^{1/2}$$

Now the factor $(3 - x^2)$, to different powers, is contained in both terms of the expression. Thus we can factor $(3 - x^2)^{-1/2}$ from both terms. (We choose the $-1/2$ power because it is the smaller of the two powers.) Dividing $(3 - x^2)^{-1/2}$ into the first term gives $(-x^3 + x)$, and dividing it into the second term gives $2x(3 - x^2)^1$. (Why?) Thus we have

$$f'(x) = (3 - x^2)^{-1/2}[(-x^3 + x) + 2x(3 - x^2)] = \frac{-3x^3 + 7x}{(3 - x^2)^{1/2}}$$

which agrees with our previous answer.

✓ CHECKPOINT

1. If a function has the form $y = [u(x)]^n \cdot v(x)$, where n is a constant, we begin to find the derivative by using the _____ Rule and then use the _____ Rule to find the derivative of $[u(x)]^n$.
2. If a function has the form $y = [u(x)/v(x)]^n$, where n is a constant, we begin to find the derivative by using the _____ Rule and then use the _____ Rule.
3. Find the derivative of each of the following and simplify.
   (a) $f(x) = 3x^4(2x^4 + 7)^5$ (b) $g(x) = \dfrac{(4x + 3)^7}{2x - 9}$

EXAMPLE 4   **Revenue** | APPLICATION PREVIEW |

Suppose that the weekly revenue function for a product is given by

$$R(x) = \frac{36{,}000{,}000x}{(2x + 500)^2}$$

where $R(x)$ is the dollars of revenue from the sale of x units.

(a) Find the marginal revenue function.
(b) Find the marginal revenue when 50 units are sold.

Solution

(a) $\overline{MR} = R'(x)$

$$= \frac{(2x + 500)^2(36{,}000{,}000) - 36{,}000{,}000x[2(2x + 500)^1(2)]}{(2x + 500)^4}$$

$$= \frac{36{,}000{,}000(2x + 500)(2x + 500 - 4x)}{(2x + 500)^4} = \frac{36{,}000{,}000(500 - 2x)}{(2x + 500)^3}$$

(b) $\overline{MR}(50) = R'(50) = \dfrac{36{,}000{,}000(500 - 100)}{(100 + 500)^3} = \dfrac{36{,}000{,}000(400)}{(600)^3} = \dfrac{200}{3} \approx 66.67$

The marginal revenue is \$66.67 when 50 units are sold. That is, the predicted revenue from the sale of the 51st unit is approximately \$66.67.   ■

It may be helpful to review the formulas needed to find the derivatives of various types of functions. Table 9.5 presents examples of different types of functions and the formulas needed to find their derivatives.

■| TABLE 9.5 |

SUMMARY OF DERIVATIVE FORMULAS

Examples	Formulas
$f(x) = 14$	If $f(x) = c$, then $f'(x) = 0$.
$y = x^4$	If $f(x) = x^n$, then $f'(x) = nx^{n-1}$.
$g(x) = 5x^3$	If $g(x) = cf(x)$, then $g'(x) = cf'(x)$.
$y = 3x^2 + 4x$	If $f(x) = u(x) + v(x)$, then $f'(x) = u'(x) + v'(x)$.
$y = (x^2 - 2)(x + 4)$	If $f(x) = u(x) \cdot v(x)$, then $f'(x) = u(x) \cdot v'(x) + v(x) \cdot u'(x)$.
$f(x) = \dfrac{x^3}{x^2 + 1}$	If $f(x) = \dfrac{u(x)}{v(x)}$ then $f'(x) = \dfrac{v(x) \cdot u'(x) - u(x) \cdot v'(x)}{[v(x)]^2}$.
$y = (x^3 - 4x)^{10}$	If $y = u^n$ and $u = g(x)$, then $\dfrac{dy}{dx} = nu^{n-1} \cdot \dfrac{du}{dx}$.
$y = \left(\dfrac{x - 1}{x^2 + 3}\right)^3$	Power Rule, then Quotient Rule to find $\dfrac{du}{dx}$, where $u = \dfrac{x - 1}{x^2 + 3}$.
$y = (x + 1)\sqrt{x^3 + 1}$	Product Rule, then Power Rule to find $v'(x)$, where $v(x) = \sqrt{x^3 + 1}$.
$y = \dfrac{(x^2 - 3)^4}{x + 1}$	Quotient Rule, then Power Rule to find the derivative of the numerator.

✓ CHECKPOINT ANSWERS

1. Product, Power
2. Power, Quotient
3. (a) $f'(x) = 12x^3(12x^4 + 7)(2x^4 + 7)^4$

   (b) $g'(x) = \dfrac{2(24x - 129)(4x + 3)^6}{(2x - 9)^2}$

| EXERCISES | 9.7

Find the derivatives of the functions in Problems 1–32. Simplify and express the answer using positive exponents only.

1. $f(x) = \pi^4$

2. $f(x) = \dfrac{1}{4}$

3. $g(x) = \dfrac{4}{x^4}$

4. $y = \dfrac{x^4}{4}$

5. $g(x) = 5x^3 + \dfrac{4}{x}$

6. $y = 3x^2 + 4\sqrt{x}$

7. $y = (x^2 - 2)(x + 4)$

8. $y = (x^3 - 5x^2 + 1)(x^3 - 3)$

9. $f(u) = \dfrac{u^3 + 1}{u^2}$

10. $C(w) = \dfrac{1 + w^2 - w^4}{1 + w^4}$

11. $y = \dfrac{(x^3 - 4x)^{10}}{10}$

12. $y = \dfrac{5}{2}(3x^4 - 6x^2 + 2)^5$

13. $y = \dfrac{5}{3}x^3(4x^5 - 5)^3$

14. $y = 3x^4(2x^5 + 1)^7$

15. $y = (x - 1)^2(x^2 + 1)$

16. $f(x) = (5x^3 + 1)(x^4 + 5x)^2$

17. $y = \dfrac{(x^2 - 4)^3}{x^2 + 1}$

18. $y = \dfrac{(x^2 - 3)^4}{x}$

19. $p = [(q + 1)(q^3 - 3)]^3$

20. $s = [(4 - t^2)(t^2 + 5t)]^4$

21. $R(x) = [x^2(x^2 + 3x)]^4$

22. $c(x) = [x^3(x^2 + 1)]^{-3}$

23. $y = \left(\dfrac{2x - 1}{x^2 + x}\right)^4$

24. $y = \left(\dfrac{5 - x^2}{x^4}\right)^3$

25. $g(x) = (8x^4 + 3)^2(x^3 - 4x)^3$

26. $y = (3x^3 - 4x)^3(4x^2 - 8)^2$

27. $f(x) = \dfrac{\sqrt[3]{x^2 + 5}}{4 - x^2}$

28. $g(x) = \dfrac{\sqrt[3]{2x - 1}}{2x + 1}$

29. $y = x^2\sqrt[4]{4x - 3}$

30. $y = 3x\sqrt[3]{4x^4 + 3}$

31. $c(x) = 2x\sqrt{x^3 + 1}$

32. $R(x) = x\sqrt[3]{3x^3 + 2}$

In Problems 33 and 34, find the derivative of each function.

33. (a) $F_1(x) = \dfrac{3(x^4 + 1)^5}{5}$

(b) $F_2(x) = \dfrac{3}{5(x^4 + 1)^5}$

(c) $F_3(x) = \dfrac{(3x^4 + 1)^5}{5}$

(d) $F_4(x) = \dfrac{3}{(5x^4 + 1)^5}$

34. (a) $G_1(x) = \dfrac{2(x^3 - 5)^3}{3}$

(b) $G_2(x) = \dfrac{(2x^3 - 5)^3}{3}$

(c) $G_3(x) = \dfrac{2}{3(x^3 - 5)^3}$

(d) $G_4(x) = \dfrac{2}{(3x^3 - 5)^3}$

APPLICATIONS

35. *Physical output* The total physical output P of workers is a function of the number of workers, x. The function $P = f(x)$ is called the physical productivity function. Suppose that the physical productivity of x construction workers is given by

$$P = 10(3x + 1)^3 - 10$$

Find the marginal physical productivity, dP/dx.

36. *Revenue* Suppose that the revenue function for a certain product is given by

$$R(x) = 15(2x + 1)^{-1} + 30x - 15$$

where x is in thousands of units and R is in thousands of dollars.
(a) Find the marginal revenue when 2000 units are sold.
(b) How is revenue changing when 2000 units are sold?

37. *Revenue* Suppose that the revenue in dollars from the sale of x campers is given by

$$R(x) = 60{,}000x + 40{,}000(10 + x)^{-1} - 4000$$

(a) Find the marginal revenue when 10 units are sold.
(b) How is revenue changing when 10 units are sold?

38. *Production* Suppose that the production of x items of a new line of products is given by

$$x = 200[(t + 10) - 400(t + 40)^{-1}]$$

where t is the number of weeks the line has been in production. Find the rate of production, dx/dt.

39. *National consumption* If the national consumption function is given by

$$C(y) = 2(y + 1)^{1/2} + 0.4y + 4$$

find the marginal propensity to consume, dC/dy.

40. *Demand* Suppose that the demand function for q units of an appliance priced at $\$p$ per unit is given by

$$p = \dfrac{400(q + 1)}{(q + 2)^2}$$

Find the rate of change of price with respect to the number of appliances.

41. *Volume* When squares of side x inches are cut from the corners of a 12-inch-square piece of cardboard, an open-top box can be formed by folding up the sides. The volume of this box is given by

$$V = x(12 - 2x)^2$$

Find the rate of change of volume with respect to the size of the squares.

42. *Advertising and sales* Suppose that sales (in thousands of dollars) are directly related to an advertising campaign according to

$$S = 1 + \dfrac{3t - 9}{(t + 3)^2}$$

where t is the number of weeks of the campaign.
(a) Find the rate of change of sales after 3 weeks.
(b) Interpret the result in part (a).

43. *Advertising and sales* An inferior product with an extensive advertising campaign does well when it is released, but sales decline as people discontinue use of the product. If the sales S (in thousands of dollars) after t weeks are given by

$$S(t) = \dfrac{200t}{(t + 1)^2}, \qquad t \geq 0$$

what is the rate of change of sales when $t = 9$? Interpret your result.

44. *Advertising and sales* An excellent film with a very small advertising budget must depend largely on word-of-mouth advertising. If attendance at the film after t weeks is given by

$$A = \frac{100t}{(t + 10)^2}$$

what is the rate of change in attendance and what does it mean when (a) $t = 10$? (b) $t = 20$?

45. *Per capita expenditures for U.S. health care* The dollars spent per person per year for health care (projected to 2018) are shown in the table. These data can be modeled by

$$y = \frac{4.38(x - 10)^2 + 78(x - 10) + 1430}{0.0029x + 0.25}$$

where x is the number of years past 1990 and y is the per capita expenditures for health care.

(a) Find the instantaneous rate of change of per capita health care expenditures in 2005 and 2015.

(b) Interpret the rate of change for 2015 found in part (a).

(c) Use the data to find the average rate of change of per capita health care expenditures from 2004 to 2006. How well does this approximate the instantaneous rate of change in 2005?

Year	$ per Person	Year	$ per Person
2000	4789	2010	8465
2002	5563	2012	9275
2004	6331	2014	10,289
2006	7091	2016	11,520
2008	7826	2018	12,994

Source: U.S. Medicare and Medicaid Services

OBJECTIVE

9.8

- To find second derivatives and higher-order derivatives of certain functions

Higher-Order Derivatives

| APPLICATION PREVIEW |

Since cell phones were introduced, their popularity has increased enormously. Figure 9.32(a) shows a graph of the billions of worldwide cellular subscribers (actual and projected) as a function of the number of years past 1990 (*Source:* International Telecommunications Union and Key Global Telecom Indicators). Note that the number of subscribers is always increasing and that the rate of change of that number (as seen from tangent lines to the graph) is always positive. However, the tangent lines shown in Figure 9.32(b) indicate that the rate of change of the number of subscribers is greater at B than at either A or C.

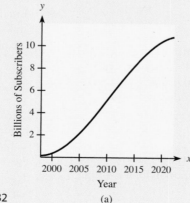

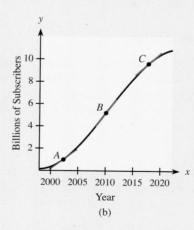

Figure 9.32   (a)   (b)

Furthermore, the rate of change of the number of subscribers (the slopes of tangents) increases from A to B and then decreases from B to C. To learn how the rate of change of the number of subscribers is changing, we are interested in finding the derivative of the rate of change of the number of subscribers—that is, the derivative of the derivative of the number of subscribers. (See Example 4.) This is called the second derivative. In this section we will discuss second and higher-order derivatives.

Second Derivatives   Because the derivative of a function is itself a function, we can take a derivative of the derivative. The derivative of a first derivative is called a **second derivative.** We can find the second derivative of a function f by differentiating it twice. If f' represents the first derivative of a function, then f'' represents the second derivative of that function.

EXAMPLE 1   **Second Derivative**

(a) Find the second derivative of $y = x^4 - 3x^2 + x^{-2}$.
(b) If $f(x) = 3x^3 - 4x^2 + 5$, find $f''(x)$.

Solution
(a) The first derivative is $y' = 4x^3 - 6x - 2x^{-3}$.
     The second derivative, which we may denote by y'', is

$$y'' = 12x^2 - 6 + 6x^{-4}$$

(b) The first derivative is $f'(x) = 9x^2 - 8x$.
     The second derivative is $f''(x) = 18x - 8$.   ■

It is also common to use $\dfrac{d^2y}{dx^2}$ and $\dfrac{d^2f(x)}{dx^2}$ to denote the second derivative of a function.

EXAMPLE 2   **Second Derivative**

If $y = \sqrt{2x - 1}$, find d^2y/dx^2.

Solution
The first derivative is

$$\frac{dy}{dx} = \frac{1}{2}(2x - 1)^{-1/2}(2) = (2x - 1)^{-1/2}$$

The second derivative is

$$\frac{d^2y}{dx^2} = -\frac{1}{2}(2x - 1)^{-3/2}(2) = -(2x - 1)^{-3/2}$$

$$= \frac{-1}{(2x - 1)^{3/2}} = \frac{-1}{\sqrt{(2x - 1)^3}}$$ ■

Higher-Order Derivatives   We can also find third, fourth, fifth, and higher derivatives, continuing indefinitely. The third, fourth, and fifth derivatives of a function f are denoted by $f''', f^{(4)}$, and $f^{(5)}$, respectively. Other notations for the third and fourth derivatives include

$$y''' = \frac{d^3y}{dx^3} = \frac{d^3f(x)}{dx^3}, \qquad y^{(4)} = \frac{d^4y}{dx^4} = \frac{d^4f(x)}{dx^4}$$

EXAMPLE 3   **Higher-Order Derivatives**

Find the first four derivatives of $f(x) = 4x^3 + 5x^2 + 3$.

Solution

$$f'(x) = 12x^2 + 10x, \qquad f''(x) = 24x + 10, \qquad f'''(x) = 24, \qquad f^{(4)}(x) = 0$$ ■

Just as the first derivative, $f'(x)$, can be used to determine the rate of change of a function $f(x)$, the second derivative, $f''(x)$, can be used to determine the rate of change of $f'(x)$.

EXAMPLE 4   **Worldwide Cellular Subscriberships** | APPLICATION PREVIEW |

By using International Telecommunications Union and Key Global Telecom Indicators data from 1990 and projected to 2020, the billions of world cell phone subscriberships can be modeled by the function

$$C(t) = -0.000728t^3 + 0.0414t^2 - 0.296t + 0.340$$

where t is the number of years past 1990.

(a) Find the instantaneous rate of change of world cell phone subscriberships.
(b) Find the instantaneous rate of change of the function found in part (a).
(c) For what t-value does the second derivative of $C(t)$ equal zero?
(d) Find the instantaneous rate of change of the world cell phone subscriberships in 2005 and in 2015.
(e) Use the second derivative to approximate how fast the instantaneous rate of change of world cell phone subscriberships is changing in 2005 and in 2015.
(f) Explain the meaning of $C'(25)$ and $C''(25)$.

Solution

(a) The instantaneous rate of change of $C(t)$ is

$$C'(t) = -0.002184t^2 + 0.0828t - 0.296$$

(b) The instantaneous rate of change of $C'(t)$ is

$$C''(t) = -0.004368t + 0.0828$$

(c) To find the t-value when $C''(t) = -0.004368t + 0.0828 = 0$, we solve as follows.

$$0.0828 = 0.004368t \Rightarrow t = \frac{0.0828}{0.004368} \approx 18.96$$

Thus $C''(t) = 0$ in 2009.

(d) We find these rates of change by evaluating the derivative
In 2005: $C'(15) = -0.002184(15)^2 + 0.0828(15) - 0.296 \approx 0.455$ billion per year
In 2015: $C'(25) = -0.002184(25)^2 + 0.0828(25) - 0.296 \approx 0.409$ billion per year

(e) In 2005: $C''(15) = -0.004368(15) + 0.0828 \approx 0.0173$ billion per year per year
In 2015: $C''(25) = -0.004368(25) + 0.0828 \approx -0.0264$ billion per year per year

(f) In 2015 the number of world cell phone subscriberships increased at a rate of 0.409 billion per year, but the rate of change decreased at a rate of 0.0264 billion per year per year. Thus, in 2015 the number of world cell phone subscriberships was increasing but at a decreasing (slower) rate. See Figure 9.32.

EXAMPLE 5   **Rate of Change of a Derivative**

Let $f(x) = 3x^4 + 6x^3 - 3x^2 + 4$.

(a) How fast is $f(x)$ changing at (1, 10)?
(b) How fast is $f'(x)$ changing at (1, 10)?
(c) Is $f'(x)$ increasing or decreasing at (1, 10)?

Solution

(a) Because $f'(x) = 12x^3 + 18x^2 - 6x$, we have

$$f'(1) = 12 + 18 - 6 = 24$$

Thus the rate of change of $f(x)$ at (1, 10) is 24 (y units per x unit).

(b) Because $f''(x) = 36x^2 + 36x - 6$, we have

$$f''(1) = 66$$

Thus the rate of change of $f'(x)$ at (1, 10) is 66 (y units per x unit per x unit).

(c) Because $f''(1) = 66 > 0$, $f'(x)$ is increasing at (1, 10).

EXAMPLE 6   Acceleration

Suppose that a particle travels according to the equation

$$s = 100t - 16t^2 + 200$$

where s is the distance in feet and t is the time in seconds. Then ds/dt is the velocity, and $d^2s/dt^2 = dv/dt$ is the acceleration of the particle. Find the acceleration.

Solution

The velocity is $v = ds/dt = 100 - 32t$ feet per second, and the acceleration is

$$\frac{dv}{dt} = \frac{d^2s}{dt^2} = -32 \text{ (feet/second)/second} = -32 \text{ feet/second}^2$$

✓ CHECKPOINT

Suppose that the distance a particle travels is given by

$$s = 4x^3 - 12x^2 + 6$$

where s is in feet and x is in seconds.
1. Find the function that describes the velocity of this particle.
2. Find the function that describes the acceleration of this particle.
3. Is the acceleration always positive?
4. When does the *velocity* of this particle increase?

Calculator Note

We can use the numerical derivative feature of a graphing calculator to find the second derivative of a function at a point. Figure 9.33 shows how the numerical derivative feature of a graphing calculator can be used to find $f''(2)$ if $f(x) = \sqrt{x^3 - 1}$. See Appendix A, Section 9.8, for details.

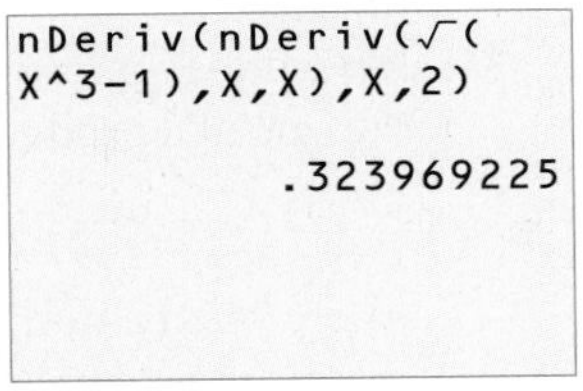

```
nDeriv(nDeriv(√(
X^3-1),X,X),X,2)


        .323969225
```

Figure 9.33

The figure shows that $f''(2) = 0.323969225 \approx 0.32397$. We can check this result by calculating $f''(x)$ with formulas.

$$f'(x) = \frac{1}{2}(x^3 - 1)^{-\frac{1}{2}}(3x^2)$$

$$f''(x) = \frac{1}{2}(x^3 - 1)^{-\frac{1}{2}}(6x) + (3x^2)\left[-\frac{1}{4}(x^3 - 1)^{-\frac{3}{2}}(3x^2)\right]$$

$$f''(2) = 0.3239695483 \approx 0.32397$$

Thus we see that the numerical derivative approximation is quite accurate.

**✓ CHECKPOINT
ANSWERS**

1. The velocity is described by $s'(x) = 12x^2 - 24x$.
2. The acceleration is described by $s''(x) = 24x - 24$.
3. No; acceleration is negative when $x < 1$ second, zero when $x = 1$ second, and positive when $x > 1$ second.
4. The velocity increases when the acceleration is positive, after 1 second.

| EXERCISES | 9.8

In Problems 1–6, find the second derivative.

1. $f(x) = 2x^{10} - 18x^5 - 12x^3 + 4$

2. $y = 6x^5 - 3x^4 + 12x^2$

3. $g(x) = x^3 - \dfrac{1}{x}$

4. $h(x) = x^2 - \dfrac{1}{x^2}$

5. $y = x^3 - \sqrt{x}$

6. $y = 3x^2 - \sqrt[3]{x^2}$

In Problems 7–12, find the third derivative.

7. $y = x^5 - 16x^3 + 12$

8. $y = 6x^3 - 12x^2 + 6x$

9. $f(x) = 2x^9 - 6x^6$

10. $f(x) = 3x^5 - x^6$

11. $y = 1/x$

12. $y = 1/x^2$

In Problems 13–24, find the indicated derivative.

13. If $y = x^5 - x^{1/2}$, find $\dfrac{d^2y}{dx^2}$.

14. If $y = x^4 + x^{1/3}$, find $\dfrac{d^2y}{dx^2}$.

15. If $f(x) = \sqrt{x + 1}$, find $f'''(x)$.

16. If $f(x) = \sqrt{x - 5}$, find $f'''(x)$.

17. Find $\dfrac{d^4y}{dx^4}$ if $y = 4x^3 - 16x$.

18. Find $y^{(4)}$ if $y = x^6 - 15x^3$.

19. Find $f^{(4)}(x)$ if $f(x) = \sqrt{x}$.

20. Find $f^{(4)}(x)$ if $f(x) = 1/x$.

21. Find $y^{(4)}$ if $y' = \sqrt{4x - 1}$.

22. Find $y^{(5)}$ if $\dfrac{d^2y}{dx^2} = \sqrt[3]{3x + 2}$.

23. Find $f^{(6)}(x)$ if $f^{(4)}(x) = x(x + 1)^{-1}$.

24. Find $f^{(3)}(x)$ if $f'(x) = \dfrac{x^2}{x^2 + 1}$.

25. If $f(x) = 16x^2 - x^3$, what is the rate of change of $f'(x)$ at $(1, 15)$?

26. If $y = 36x^2 - 6x^3 + x$, what is the rate of change of y' at $(1, 31)$?

In Problems 27–30, use the numerical derivative feature of a graphing calculator to approximate the given second derivatives.

27. $f''(3)$ for $f(x) = x^3 - \dfrac{27}{x}$

28. $f''(-1)$ for $f(x) = \dfrac{x^2}{4} - \dfrac{4}{x^2}$

29. $f''(21)$ for $f(x) = \sqrt{x^2 + 4}$

30. $f''(3)$ for $f(x) = \dfrac{1}{\sqrt{x^2 + 7}}$

In Problems 31 and 32, do the following for each function $f(x)$.

(a) Find $f'(x)$ and $f''(x)$.

(b) Graph $f(x)$, $f'(x)$, and $f''(x)$ with a graphing utility.

(c) Identify x-values where $f''(x) = 0$, $f''(x) > 0$, and $f''(x) < 0$.

(d) Identify x-values where $f'(x)$ has a maximum point or a minimum point, where $f'(x)$ is increasing, and where $f'(x)$ is decreasing.

(e) When $f(x)$ has a maximum point, is $f''(x) > 0$ or $f''(x) < 0$?

(f) When $f(x)$ has a minimum point, is $f''(x) > 0$ or $f''(x) < 0$?

31. $f(x) = x^3 - 3x^2 + 5$

32. $f(x) = 2 + 3x - x^3$

APPLICATIONS

33. *Acceleration* A particle travels as a function of time according to the formula

$$s = 100 + 10t + 0.01t^3$$

where s is in meters and t is in seconds. Find the acceleration of the particle when $t = 2$.

34. *Acceleration* If the formula describing the distance s (in feet) an object travels as a function of time (in seconds) is

$$s = 100 + 160t - 16t^2$$

what is the acceleration of the object when $t = 4$?

35. *Revenue* The revenue (in dollars) from the sale of x units of a certain product can be described by

$$R(x) = 100x - 0.01x^2$$

Find the instantaneous rate of change of the marginal revenue.

36. *Revenue* Suppose that the revenue (in dollars) from the sale of a product is given by

$$R = 70x + 0.5x^2 - 0.001x^3$$

where x is the number of units sold. How fast is the marginal revenue $\overline{MR}$ changing when $x = 100$?

37. *Sensitivity* When medicine is administered, reaction (measured in change of blood pressure or temperature) can be modeled by

$$R = m^2 \left(\dfrac{c}{2} - \dfrac{m}{3} \right)$$

where c is a positive constant and m is the amount of medicine absorbed into the blood (*Source:* R. M. Thrall et al., *Some Mathematical Models in Biology,* U.S. Department of Commerce, 1967). The sensitivity to the medication is defined to be the rate of change of reaction R with respect to the amount of medicine m absorbed in the blood.

(a) Find the sensitivity.

(b) Find the instantaneous rate of change of sensitivity with respect to the amount of medicine absorbed in the blood.

(c) Which order derivative of reaction gives the rate of change of sensitivity?

38. *Photosynthesis* The amount of photosynthesis that takes place in a certain plant depends on the intensity of light x according to the equation

$$f(x) = 145x^2 - 30x^3$$

(a) Find the rate of change of photosynthesis with respect to the intensity.
(b) What is the rate of change when $x = 1$? When $x = 3$?
(c) How fast is the rate found in part (a) changing when $x = 1$? When $x = 3$?

39. *Revenue* The revenue (in thousands of dollars) from the sale of a product is

$$R = 15x + 30(4x + 1)^{-1} - 30$$

where x is the number of units sold.
(a) At what rate is the marginal revenue $\overline{MR}$ changing when the number of units being sold is 25?
(b) Interpret your result in part (a).

40. *Advertising and sales* The sales of a product S (in thousands of dollars) are given by

$$S = \frac{600x}{x + 40}$$

where x is the advertising expenditure (in thousands of dollars).
(a) Find the rate of change of sales with respect to advertising expenditure.
(b) Use the second derivative to find how this rate is changing at $x = 20$.
(c) Interpret your result in part (b).

41. *Advertising and sales* The daily sales S (in thousands of dollars) that are attributed to an advertising campaign are given by

$$S = 1 + \frac{3}{t + 3} - \frac{18}{(t + 3)^2}$$

where t is the number of weeks the campaign runs.
(a) Find the rate of change of sales at any time t.
(b) Use the second derivative to find how this rate is changing at $t = 15$.
(c) Interpret your result in part (b).

42. *Advertising and sales* A product with a large advertising budget has its sales S (in millions of dollars) given by

$$S = \frac{500}{t + 2} - \frac{1000}{(t + 2)^2}$$

where t is the number of months the product has been on the market.
(a) Find the rate of change of sales at any time t.
(b) What is the rate of change of sales at $t = 2$?
(c) Use the second derivative to find how this rate is changing at $t = 2$.
(d) Interpret your results from parts (b) and (c).

43. *Average annual wage* By using Social Security Administration data for selected years from 2012 and projected to 2050, the U.S. average annual wage, in thousands of dollars, can be modeled by

$$W(t) = 0.0212t^{2.11}$$

where t is the number of years past 1975.
(a) Use the model to find a function that models the instantaneous rate of change of W.
(b) Find a function that models the rate at which the instantaneous rate from part (a) is changing.
(c) Find and interpret $W(50)$, $W'(50)$, and $W''(50)$.

44. *Demographics* The makeup of various groups within the U.S. population may reshape the electorate in ways that could change political representation and policies. By using U.S. Department of Labor data from 1980 and projected to 2050 for the civilian non-institutional population ages 16 and older, in millions, the population of those who are non-White or Hispanic can be modeled by the function

$$P(t) = 0.707t^{1.17} + 20.0$$

where t is the number of years past 1970.
(a) Find the function that models the instantaneous rate of change of the population of non-Whites or Hispanics.
(b) Find the function that models how fast the rate found in part (a) changes.
(c) Find and interpret $P(55)$, $P'(55)$, and $P''(55)$.

45. Modeling *Economic dependency ratio* The economic dependency ratio is defined as the number of persons in the total population who are not in the workforce per 100 in the workforce. Since 1960, Baby Boomers in the workforce coupled with a decrease in the birth rate have caused a significant decrease in the economic dependency ratio.

The table shows the economic dependency ratio for selected years from 1960 and projected to 2050.

Year	Ratio	Year	Ratio
1960	150.4	2015	91.9
1970	140.4	2020	97.4
1980	108.9	2030	106.4
1990	98.3	2040	109.0
2000	93.9	2050	111.4
2010	90.3		

Source: U.S. Bureau of Labor Statistics

(a) Model these data with a cubic function, $R(x)$, where $R(x)$ is the economic dependency ratio and x is the number of years past 1950. Report the model with three significant digit coefficients.
(b) Use the reported model from part (a) to find the function that models the rate of change of $R(x)$.

(c) Find the function that gives the rate of change of
     $R'(x)$.
(d) Find and interpret $R'(90)$ and $R''(90)$.

46. **Modeling U.S. population** The table gives the U.S.
    population to the nearest million for selected years
    from 1950 and projected to 2050.

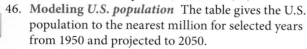

Year	Total	Year	Total
1950	160	2010	315
1960	190	2015	328
1970	215	2020	343
1980	235	2030	370
1990	260	2040	391
2000	288	2050	409

Source: Social Security Administration

(a) Find a cubic function $P(t)$ that models these data,
     where P is the U.S. population in millions and t is
     the number of years past 1950. Report the model
     with three significant digit coefficients.
(b) Use the reported model to find the function that
     models the instantaneous rate of change of the
     U.S. population.

(c) Use the second derivative to determine how fast
     this rate was changing in 2000 and 2020.
(d) Write sentences that explain the meanings of
     $P'(70)$ and $P''(70)$.

47. **Income by age** The median income $f(x)$, in thousands
    of dollars, is a function of the age of workers ages
    20–62, x, and can be modeled by

$$f(x) = 0.000864x^3 - 0.128x^2 + 6.61x - 62.6$$

(a) Find the instantaneous rate of change of the
     median income function.
(b) Find the instantaneous rate of change of the median
     income for 25-year-old and 55-year-old workers.
(c) Find the second derivative of the median income
     function.
(d) Use the second derivative to determine how fast
     the instantaneous rate of change in the median
     income of workers is changing for 25-year-old and
     55-year-old workers.
(e) Explain the meaning $f'(55)$ and $f''(55)$.

OBJECTIVES

9.9

- To find the marginal cost
  and marginal revenue
  at different levels of
  production
- To find the marginal profit
  function, given information
  about cost and revenue

Applications: Marginals and Derivatives

| APPLICATION PREVIEW |

If the total cost in dollars to produce x kitchen blenders is given by

$$C(x) = 0.001x^3 - 0.3x^2 + 32x + 2500$$

what is the marginal cost function, and what does it tell us about how costs are
changing when $x = 80$ and $x = 200$ blenders are produced? See Example 3.
    In Section 1.6, "Applications of Functions in Business and Economics," we
defined the marginals for linear total cost, total revenue, and profit functions as
the rate of change or slope of the respective function. In Section 9.3, we extended
the notion of marginal revenue to nonlinear total revenue functions by defining
marginal revenue as the derivative of total revenue. In this section, we extend the
notion of marginal to nonlinear functions for any total cost or profit function.

Marginal Revenue   As we saw earlier, the instantaneous rate of change (the derivative) of the revenue function
gives the **marginal revenue function.**

Marginal Revenue   If $R = R(x)$ is the total revenue function for a commodity, then the **marginal
revenue function** is $\overline{MR} = R'(x)$.

Recall that if the demand function for a product in a monopoly market is $p = f(x)$,
then the total revenue from the sale of x units is

$$R(x) = px = f(x) \cdot x$$

EXAMPLE **1**   **Revenue and Marginal Revenue**

If the demand for a product in a monopoly market is given by

$$p = 16 - 0.02x$$

where x is the number of units and p is the price per unit, (a) find the total revenue function, and (b) find the marginal revenue for this product at $x = 40$.

Solution

(a)   The total revenue function is

$$R(x) = px = (16 - 0.02x)x = 16x - 0.02x^2$$

(b)   The marginal revenue function is

$$\overline{MR} = R'(x) = 16 - 0.04x$$

At $x = 40$, $R'(40) = 16 - 1.6 = 14.40$ dollars per unit. Thus the 41st item sold will increase the total revenue by approximately $14.40.

The marginal revenue is an approximation or estimate of the revenue gained from the sale of 1 additional unit. We have used marginal revenue in Example 1 to find that the revenue from the sale of the 41st item will be approximately $14.40. The actual increase in revenue from the sale of the 41st item is

$$R(41) - R(40) = 622.38 - 608 = \$14.38$$

Marginal revenue (and other marginals) can be used to predict for more than one additional unit. For instance, in Example 1, $\overline{MR}\,(40) = \$14.40$ per unit means that the expected or approximate revenue for the 41st through the 45th items sold would be 5($14.40) = $72.00. The actual revenue for these 5 items is $R(45) - R(40) = \$679.50 - \$608 = \$71.50$.

EXAMPLE **2**   **Maximum Revenue**

Use the graphs in Figure 9.34 to determine the x-value where the revenue function has its maximum. What is happening to the marginal revenue at and near this x-value?

Solution

Figure 9.34(a) shows that the total revenue function has a maximum value at $x = 400$. After that, the total revenue function decreases. This means that the total revenue will be reduced each time a unit is sold if more than 400 are produced and sold. The graph of the marginal revenue function in Figure 9.34(b) shows that the marginal revenue is positive to the left of 400. This indicates that the rate at which the total revenue is changing is positive

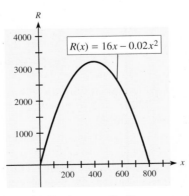

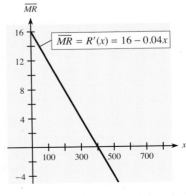

Figure 9.34   (a) Total revenue function   (b) Marginal revenue function

until 400 units are sold; thus the total revenue is increasing. Then, at 400 units, the rate of change is 0. After 400 units are sold, the marginal revenue is negative, which indicates that the total revenue is now decreasing. It is clear from looking at either graph that 400 units should be produced and sold to maximize the total revenue function $R(x)$. That is, the *total revenue* function has its maximum at $x = 400$. ∎

Marginal Cost   As with marginal revenue, the derivative of a total cost function gives the **marginal cost function.**

Marginal Cost   If $C = C(x)$ is a total cost function for a commodity, then its derivative, $\overline{MC} = C'(x)$, is the **marginal cost function.**

Notice that the linear total cost function with equation

$$C(x) = 300 + 6x \qquad \text{(in dollars)}$$

has marginal cost $6 per unit because its slope is 6. Taking the derivative of $C(x)$ also gives

$$\overline{MC} = C'(x) = 6$$

which verifies that the marginal cost is $6 per unit at all levels of production.

EXAMPLE 3   Marginal Cost | APPLICATION PREVIEW |

Suppose the daily total cost in dollars for a certain factory to produce x kitchen blenders is

$$C(x) = 0.001x^3 - 0.3x^2 + 32x + 2500$$

(a) Find the marginal cost function for these blenders.
(b) Find and interpret the marginal cost when $x = 80$ and $x = 200$.

Solution
(a) The marginal cost function is the derivative of $C(x)$.

$$\overline{MC} = C'(x) = 0.003x^2 - 0.6x + 32$$

(b) $C'(80) = 0.003(80)^2 - 0.6(80) + 32 = 3.2$ dollars per unit
$C'(200) = 0.003(200)^2 - 0.6(200) + 32 = 32$ dollars per unit

These values for the marginal cost can be used to *estimate* the amount that total cost would change if production were increased by one blender. Thus,

$$C'(80) = 3.2$$

means total cost would increase by *about* $3.20 if an 81st blender were produced. Note that

$$C(81) - C(80) = 3.141 \approx \$3.14$$

is the actual increase in total cost for an 81st blender.
      Also, $C'(200) = 32$ means that total cost would increase by *about* $32 if a 201st blender were produced.
      Whenever $C'(x)$ is positive it means that an additional unit produced adds to or increases the total cost. In addition, the value of the derivative (or marginal cost) measures how fast $C(x)$ is increasing. Thus, our calculations above indicate that $C(x)$ is increasing faster at $x = 200$ than at $x = 80$. The graphs of the total cost function and the marginal cost function in Figure 9.35(a) and (b) also illustrate these facts. ∎

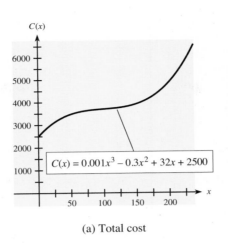

(a) Total cost

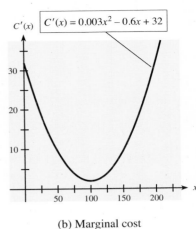

(b) Marginal cost

Figure 9.35

The graphs of many marginal cost functions tend to be U-shaped; they eventually will rise, even though there may be an initial interval where they decrease. Looking at the marginal cost graph in Figure 9.35(b), we see that marginal cost reaches its minimum near $x = 100$. We can also see this in Figure 9.35(a) by noting that tangent lines drawn to the total cost graph would have slopes that decrease until about $x = 100$ and then would increase.

Because producing more units can never reduce the total cost of production, the following properties are valid for total cost functions.

1. The total cost can never be negative. If there are fixed costs, the cost of producing 0 units is positive; otherwise, the cost of producing 0 units is 0.
2. The total cost function is always increasing; the more units produced, the higher the total cost. Thus the marginal cost is always positive.
3. There may be limitations on the units produced, such as those imposed by plant space.

EXAMPLE 4   Total and Marginal Cost

Suppose the graph in Figure 9.36 shows the monthly total cost for producing a product.

(a) Estimate the total cost of producing 400 items.
(b) Estimate the cost of producing the 401st item.
(c) Will producing the 151st item cost more or less than producing the 401st item?

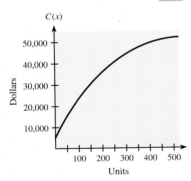

Figure 9.36

Solution

(a) The total cost of producing 400 items is the height of the total cost graph when $x = 400$, or about $50,000.

(b) The approximate cost of the 401st item is the marginal cost when $x = 400$, or the slope of the tangent line drawn to the graph at $x = 400$. Figure 9.37 shows the total cost graph with a tangent line at $x = 400$.

Note that the tangent line passes through the point $(0, 40{,}000)$, so we can find the slope by using the points $(0, 40{,}000)$ and $(400, 50{,}000)$.

$$m = \frac{y_2 - y_1}{x_2 - x_1} = \frac{50{,}000 - 40{,}000}{400 - 0} = \frac{10{,}000}{400} = 25$$

Thus the marginal cost at $x = 400$ is 25 dollars per item, so the approximate cost of the 401st item is $25.

(c) From Figure 9.37 we can see that if a tangent line to the graph were drawn where $x = 150$, it would be steeper than the one at $x = 400$. Because the slope of the tangent is the marginal cost and the marginal cost predicts the cost of the next item, this means that it would cost more to produce the 151st item than to produce the 401st.

Figure 9.37

Suppose the total cost function for a commodity is $C(x) = 0.01x^3 - 0.9x^2 + 33x + 3000$.
1. Find the marginal cost function.
2. What is the marginal cost if $x = 50$ units are produced?
3. Use marginal cost to estimate the cost of producing the 51st unit.
4. Calculate $C(51) - C(50)$ to find the actual cost of producing the 51st unit.
5. True or false: For products that have linear cost functions, the actual cost of producing the $(x + 1)$st unit is equal to the marginal cost at x.

Marginal Profit   As with marginal cost and marginal revenue, the derivative of a profit function for a commodity will give us the **marginal profit function** for the commodity.

Marginal profit   If $P = P(x)$ is the profit function for a commodity, then the **marginal profit function** is $\overline{MP} = P'(x)$.

EXAMPLE 5   Marginal Profit

If the total profit, in thousands of dollars, for a product is given by $P(x) = 20\sqrt{x + 1} - 2x - 22$, what is the marginal profit at a production level of 15 units?

Solution
The marginal profit function is

$$\overline{MP} = P'(x) = 20 \cdot \frac{1}{2}(x + 1)^{-1/2} - 2 = \frac{10}{\sqrt{x + 1}} - 2$$

If 15 units are produced, the marginal profit is

$$P'(15) = \frac{10}{\sqrt{15 + 1}} - 2 = \frac{1}{2}$$

This means that the profit from the sale of the 16th unit is approximately $\frac{1}{2}$ (thousand dollars), or $500.

In a **competitive market,** each firm is so small that its actions in the market cannot affect the price of the product. The price of the product is determined in the market by the intersection of the market demand curve (from all consumers) and the market supply curve (from all firms that supply this product). The firm can sell as little or as much as it desires at the given market price, which it cannot change.
    Therefore, a firm in a competitive market has a total revenue function given by $R(x) = px$, where p is the market equilibrium price for the product and x is the quantity sold.

EXAMPLE 6   Profit in a Competitive Market

A firm in a competitive market must sell its product for $200 per unit. The cost per unit (per month) is $80 + x$, where x represents the number of units sold per month. Find the marginal profit function.

Solution
If the cost per unit is $80 + x$, then the total cost of x units is given by the equation $C(x) = (80 + x)x = 80x + x^2$. The revenue per unit is $200, so the total revenue is given by $R(x) = 200x$. Thus the profit function is

$$P(x) = R(x) - C(x) = 200x - (80x + x^2), \quad \text{or} \quad P(x) = 120x - x^2$$

The marginal profit is $P'(x) = 120 - 2x$.

The marginal profit in Example 6 is not always positive, so producing and selling a certain number of items will maximize profit. Note that the marginal profit will be negative (that is, profit will decrease) if more than 60 items per month are produced. We will discuss methods of maximizing total revenue and profit, and of minimizing average cost, in the next chapter.

✓ CHECKPOINT

If the total profit function for a product is $P(x) = 20\sqrt{x + 1} - 2x - 22$, then the marginal profit and its derivative are

$$P'(x) = \frac{10}{\sqrt{x + 1}} - 2 \quad \text{and} \quad P''(x) = \frac{-5}{\sqrt{(x + 1)^3}}$$

6. Is $P''(x) < 0$ for all values of $x \geq 0$?
7. Is the marginal profit decreasing for all $x \geq 0$?

EXAMPLE   7   **Marginal Profit**

Figure 9.38 shows graphs of a company's total revenue and total cost functions.

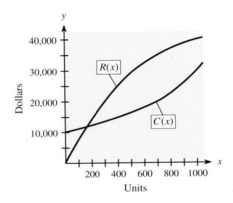

Figure 9.38

(a) If 100 units are being produced and sold, will producing the 101st item increase or decrease the profit?
(b) If 300 units are being produced and sold, will producing the 301st item increase or decrease the profit?
(c) If 1000 units are being produced and sold, will producing the 1001st item increase or decrease the profit?

Solution
At a given x-value, the slope of the tangent line to each function gives the marginal at that x-value.
(a) At $x = 100$, we can see that the graph of $R(x)$ is steeper than the graph of $C(x)$. Thus, the tangent line to $R(x)$ will be steeper than the tangent line to $C(x)$. Hence $\overline{MR}(100) > \overline{MC}(100)$, which means that the revenue from the 101st item will exceed the cost. Therefore, profit will increase when the 101st item is produced. Note that at $x = 100$, total costs are greater than total revenue, so the company is losing money but should still sell the 101st item because it will reduce the amount of loss.
(b) At $x = 300$, we can see that the tangent line to $R(x)$ again will be steeper than the tangent line to $C(x)$. Hence $\overline{MR}(300) > \overline{MC}(300)$, which means that the revenue from the 301st item will exceed the cost. Therefore, profit will increase when the 301st item is produced.
(c) At $x = 1000$, we can see that the tangent line to $C(x)$ will be steeper than the tangent line to $R(x)$. Hence $\overline{MC}(1000) > \overline{MR}(1000)$, which means that the cost of the 1001st item will exceed the revenue. Therefore, profit will decrease when the 1001st item is produced.

EXAMPLE 8 Profit and Marginal Profit

In Example 5, we found that the profit (in thousands of dollars) for a company's products is given by $P(x) = 20\sqrt{x + 1} - 2x - 22$ and its marginal profit is given by $P'(x) = \dfrac{10}{\sqrt{x + 1}} - 2$.

(a) Use the graphs of $P(x)$ and $P'(x)$ to determine the relationship between the two functions.

(b) When is the marginal profit 0? What is happening to profit at this level of production?

Solution

(a) By comparing the graphs of the two functions (shown in Figure 9.39), we see that for $x > 0$, profit $P(x)$ is increasing over the interval where the marginal profit $P'(x)$ is positive, and profit is decreasing over the interval where the marginal profit $P'(x)$ is negative.

(b) By using ZERO or SOLVER, or by using algebra, we see that $P'(x) = 0$ when $x = 24$. This level of production ($x = 24$) is where profit is maximized, at 30 (thousand dollars).

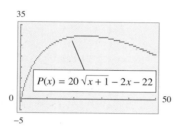

Figure 9.39

1. $\overline{MC} = C'(x) = 0.03x^2 - 1.8x + 33$
2. $C'(50) = 18$
3. The 51st unit will cost approximately $18 to produce.
4. $C(51) - C(50) = 18.61$
5. True   6. Yes   7. Yes, because $P''(x) < 0$ for $x \geq 0$.

| EXERCISES | 9.9

MARGINAL REVENUE, COST, AND PROFIT

In Problems 1–8, total revenue is in dollars and x is the number of units.

1. (a) If the total revenue function for a product is $R(x) = 4x$, what is the marginal revenue function for that product?
   (b) What does this marginal revenue function tell us?

2. If the total revenue function for a product is $R(x) = 32x$, what is the marginal revenue for the product? What does this mean?

3. Suppose that the total revenue function for a commodity is $R = 36x - 0.01x^2$.
   (a) Find $R(100)$ and tell what it represents.
   (b) Find the marginal revenue function.
   (c) Find the marginal revenue at $x = 100$, and tell what it predicts about the sale of the next unit and the next 3 units.

(d) Find $R(101) - R(100)$ and explain what this value represents.

4. Suppose that the total revenue function for a commodity is $R(x) = 25x - 0.05x^2$.
   (a) Find $R(50)$ and tell what it represents.
   (b) Find the marginal revenue function.
   (c) Find the marginal revenue at $x = 50$, and tell what it predicts about the sale of the next unit and the next 2 units.
   (d) Find $R(51) - R(50)$ and explain what this value represents.

5. Suppose that demand for local cable TV service is given by

$$p = 80 - 0.4x$$

where p is the monthly price in dollars and x is the number of subscribers (in hundreds).

(a) Find the total revenue as a function of the number of subscribers.

(b) Find the number of subscribers when the company charges $50 per month for cable service. Then find the total revenue for $p = \$50$.

(c) How could the company attract more subscribers?

(d) Find and interpret the marginal revenue when the price is $50 per month. What does this suggest about the monthly charge to subscribers?

6. Suppose that in a monopoly market, the demand function for a product is given by

$$p = 160 - 0.1x$$

where x is the number of units and p is the price in dollars.

(a) Find the total revenue from the sale of 500 units.

(b) Find and interpret the marginal revenue at 500 units.

(c) Is more revenue expected from the 501st unit sold or from the 701st? Explain.

7. (a) Graph the marginal revenue function from Problem 3.

(b) At what value of x will total revenue be maximized for Problem 3.

(c) What is the maximum revenue?

8. (a) Graph the marginal revenue function from Problem 4.

(b) Determine the number of units that must be sold to maximize total revenue.

(c) What is the maximum revenue?

In Problems 9–16, cost is in dollars and x is the number of units. Find the marginal cost functions for the given cost functions.

9. $C(x) = 40 + 8x$

10. $C(x) = 200 + 16x$

11. $C(x) = 500 + 13x + x^2$

12. $C(x) = 300 + 10x + \frac{1}{100}x^2$

13. $C = x^3 - 6x^2 + 24x + 10$

14. $C = 0.1x^3 - 1.5x^2 + 9x + 15$

15. $C = 400 + 27x + x^3$

16. $C(x) = 50 + 48x + x^3$

17. Suppose that the cost function for a commodity is

$$C(x) = 40 + x^2 \quad \text{dollars}$$

(a) Find the marginal cost at $x = 5$ units and tell what this predicts about the cost of producing 1 additional unit.

(b) Calculate $C(6) - C(5)$ to find the actual cost of producing 1 additional unit.

18. Suppose that the cost function for a commodity is

$$C(x) = 300 + 6x + \frac{1}{20}x^2 \text{ dollars}$$

(a) Find the marginal cost at $x = 8$ units and tell what this predicts about the cost of producing 1 additional unit.

(b) Calculate $C(9) - C(8)$ to find the actual cost of producing 1 additional unit.

19. If the cost function for a commodity is

$$C(x) = x^3 - 4x^2 + 30x + 20 \quad \text{dollars}$$

find the marginal cost at $x = 4$ units and tell what this predicts about the cost of producing 1 additional unit and 3 additional units.

20. If the cost function for a commodity is

$$C(x) = \tfrac{1}{90}x^3 + 4x^2 + 4x + 10 \quad \text{dollars}$$

find the marginal cost at $x = 3$ units and tell what this predicts about the cost of producing 1 additional unit and 2 additional units.

21. If the cost function for a commodity is

$$C(x) = 300 + 4x + x^2$$

graph the marginal cost function.

22. If the cost function for a commodity is

$$C(x) = x^3 - 12x^2 + 63x + 15$$

graph the marginal cost function.

In each of Problems 23 and 24, the graph of a company's total cost function is shown. For each problem, use the graph to answer the following questions.

(a) Will the 101st item or the 501st item cost more to produce? Explain.

(b) Does this total cost function represent a manufacturing process that is getting more efficient or less efficient? Explain.

23.

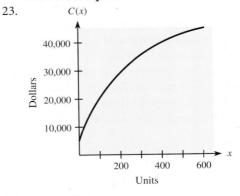

24.

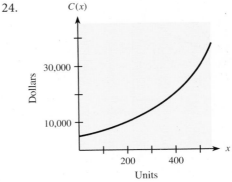

In Problems 25–28, cost, revenue, and profit are in dollars and x is the number of units.

25. If the total profit function is $P(x) = 5x - 25$, find the marginal profit. What does this mean?
26. If the total profit function is $P(x) = 16x - 32$, find the marginal profit. What does this mean?
27. Suppose that the total revenue function for a product is $R(x) = 50x$ and that the total cost function is $C(x) = 1900 + 30x + 0.01x^2$.
    (a) Find the profit from the production and sale of 500 units.
    (b) Find the marginal profit function.
    (c) Find $\overline{MP}$ at $x = 500$ and explain what it predicts.
    (d) Find $P(501) - P(500)$ and explain what this value represents.
28. Suppose that the total revenue function is given by

    $$R(x) = 46x$$

    and that the total cost function is given by

    $$C(x) = 100 + 30x + \tfrac{1}{10}x^2$$

    (a) Find $P(100)$.
    (b) Find the marginal profit function.
    (c) Find $\overline{MP}$ at $x = 100$ and explain what it predicts.
    (d) Find $P(101) - P(100)$ and explain what this value represents.

In each of Problems 29 and 30, the graphs of a company's total revenue function and total cost function are shown. For each problem, use the graph to answer the following questions.

(a) From the sale of 100 items, 400 items, and 700 items, rank from smallest to largest the amount of profit received. Explain your choices and note whether any of these scenarios results in a loss.
(b) From the sale of the 101st item, the 401st item, and the 701st item, rank from smallest to largest the amount of profit received. Explain your choices, and note whether any of these scenarios results in a loss.

29.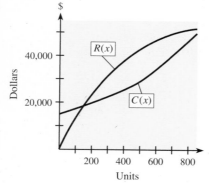

30.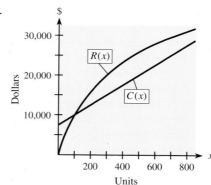

In each of Problems 31 and 32, the graph of a company's profit function is shown. For each problem, use the graph to answer the following questions about points A, B, and C.

(a) Rank from smallest to largest the amounts of profit received at these points. Explain your choices, and note whether any point results in a loss.
(b) Rank from smallest to largest the marginal profit at these points. Explain your choices, and note whether any marginal is negative and what this means.

31.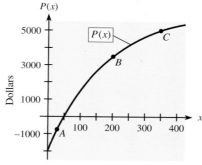

32.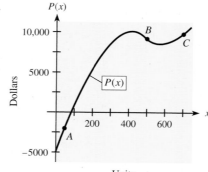

33. (a) Graph the marginal profit function for the profit function $P(x) = 30x - x^2 - 200$, where $P(x)$ is in thousands of dollars and x is hundreds of units.

(b) What level of production and sales will give a 0 marginal profit?

(c) At what level of production and sales will profit be at a maximum?

(d) What is the maximum profit?

34. (a) Graph the marginal profit function for the profit function $P(x) = 16x - 0.1x^2 - 100$, where $P(x)$ is in hundreds of dollars and x is hundreds of units.

(b) What level of production and sales will give a 0 marginal profit?

(c) At what level of production and sales will profit be at a maximum?

(d) What is the maximum profit?

35. The price of a product in a competitive market is $300. If the cost per unit of producing the product is $160 + 0.1x$ dollars, where x is the number of units produced per month, how many units should the firm produce and sell to maximize its profit?

36. The cost per unit of producing a product is $60 + 0.2x$ dollars, where x represents the number of units produced per week. If the equilibrium price determined by a competitive market is $220, how many units should the firm produce and sell each week to maximize its profit?

37. If the daily cost per unit of producing a product by the Ace Company is $10 + 0.1x$ dollars, and if the price on the competitive market is $70, what is the maximum daily profit the Ace Company can expect on this product?

38. The Mary Ellen Candy Company produces chocolate Easter bunnies at a cost per unit of $0.40 + 0.005x$ dollars, where x is the number produced. If the price on the competitive market for a bunny this size is $10.00, how many should the company produce to maximize its profit?

Chapter 9 **Summary & Review**

KEY TERMS AND FORMULAS

Section 9.1

Limit (p. 536)
One-sided limits (p. 537)
Properties of limits (p. 539)
Polynomial functions (p. 539)

Limits of rational functions (p. 540)
   0/0 indeterminate form
Limits of piecewise defined functions (p. 543)

Section 9.2

Continuous function (p. 549)
Limit at infinity (p. 553)

Vertical asymptote (p. 553)
Horizontal asymptote (p. 554)

Section 9.3

Average rate of change of f over $[a, b]$ (p. 560)
$$\frac{f(b) - f(a)}{b - a}$$
Average velocity (p. 561)
Instantaneous rate of change (p. 561)
Velocity (p. 562)
Derivative of $f(x)$ (p. 562)
$$f'(x) = \lim_{h \to 0} \frac{f(x + h) - f(x)}{h}$$

Derivative notation (p. 563)
$$y', \ f'(x), \ \frac{dy}{dx}, \ \frac{df(x)}{dx}$$
Marginal revenue (p. 563)
$$MR = R'(x)$$
Slope of a tangent (p. 565)
Tangent line (p. 566)
Interpretations of the derivative (p. 566)
Differentiability and continuity (p. 567)

Section 9.4

Powers of x Rule (p. 573)
$$\frac{d(x^n)}{dx} = nx^{n-1}$$
Constant Function Rule (p. 575)
$$\frac{d(c)}{dx} = 0 \quad \text{for constant } c$$
Coefficient Rule (p. 575)
$$\frac{d}{dx}[c \cdot f(x)] = c \cdot f'(x)$$

Sum Rule (p. 576)
$$\frac{d}{dx}(u + v) = \frac{du}{dx} + \frac{dv}{dx}$$
Difference Rule (p. 577)
$$\frac{d}{dx}(u - v) = \frac{du}{dx} - \frac{dv}{dx}$$

Section 9.5

Product Rule (p. 584)

$$\frac{d}{dx}(uv) = uv' + vu'$$

Quotient Rule (p. 585)

$$\frac{d}{dx}\left(\frac{u}{v}\right) = \frac{vu' - uv'}{v^2}$$

Section 9.6

Chain Rule (p. 591)

$$\frac{dy}{dx} = \frac{dy}{du} \cdot \frac{du}{dx}$$

Power Rule (p. 592)

$$\frac{d}{dx}(u^n) = nu^{n-1}\frac{du}{dx}$$

Section 9.7

Derivative formulas summary (p. 600)

Section 9.8

Second derivative of $f(x)$ (p. 603)

$$f''(x) = \frac{d}{dx}(f'(x))$$

Higher-order derivatives (p. 603)

Acceleration (p. 605)

Section 9.9

Marginal revenue function (p. 608)

$$\overline{MR} = R'(x)$$

Marginal cost function (p. 610)

$$\overline{MC} = C'(x)$$

Marginal profit function (p. 612)

$$\overline{MP} = P'(x)$$

REVIEW EXERCISES

Section 9.1

In Problems 1–6, use the graph of $y = f(x)$ in Figure 9.40 to find the functional values and limits, if they exist.

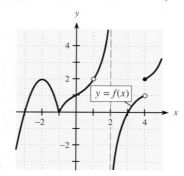

Figure 9.40

1. (a) $f(-2)$ (b) $\lim\limits_{x \to -2} f(x)$
2. (a) $f(-1)$ (b) $\lim\limits_{x \to -1} f(x)$
3. (a) $f(4)$ (b) $\lim\limits_{x \to 4^-} f(x)$
4. (a) $\lim\limits_{x \to 4^+} f(x)$ (b) $\lim\limits_{x \to 4} f(x)$
5. (a) $f(1)$ (b) $\lim\limits_{x \to 1} f(x)$
6. (a) $f(2)$ (b) $\lim\limits_{x \to 2} f(x)$

In Problems 7–20, find each limit, if it exists.

7. $\lim\limits_{x \to 4}(3x^2 + x + 3)$

8. $\lim\limits_{x \to 4}\dfrac{x^2 - 16}{x + 4}$

9. $\lim\limits_{x \to -1}\dfrac{x^2 - 1}{x + 1}$

10. $\lim\limits_{x \to 5}\dfrac{x^2 - 6x + 5}{x^2 - 5x}$

11. $\lim\limits_{x \to 2}\dfrac{4x^3 - 8x^2}{4x^3 - 16x}$

12. $\lim\limits_{x \to -\frac{1}{2}}\dfrac{x^2 - \frac{1}{4}}{6x^2 + x - 1}$

13. $\lim\limits_{x \to 3}\dfrac{x^2 - 16}{x - 3}$

14. $\lim\limits_{x \to -3}\dfrac{x^2 - x - 12}{2x - 6}$

15. $\lim\limits_{x \to 1}\dfrac{x^2 - 9}{x - 3}$

16. $\lim\limits_{x \to 2}\dfrac{x^2 - 8}{x - 2}$

17. $\lim\limits_{x \to 1}f(x)$ where $f(x) = \begin{cases} 4 - x^2 & \text{if } x < 1 \\ 4 & \text{if } x = 1 \\ 2x + 1 & \text{if } x > 1 \end{cases}$

18. $\lim\limits_{x \to -2}f(x)$ where $f(x) = \begin{cases} x^3 - x & \text{if } x < -2 \\ 2 - x^2 & \text{if } x \geq -2 \end{cases}$

19. $\lim\limits_{h \to 0}\dfrac{3(x + h)^2 - 3x^2}{h}$

20. $\lim\limits_{h \to 0}\dfrac{[(x + h) - 2(x + h)^2] - (x - 2x^2)}{h}$

 In Problems 21 and 22, use tables to investigate each limit. Check your result analytically or graphically.

21. $\lim\limits_{x \to 2}\dfrac{x^2 + 10x - 24}{x^2 - 5x + 6}$

22. $\lim\limits_{x \to -\frac{1}{2}}\dfrac{x^2 + \frac{1}{6}x - \frac{1}{6}}{x^2 + \frac{5}{6}x + \frac{1}{6}}$

Section 9.2

Use the graph of $y = f(x)$ in Figure 9.40 to answer the questions in Problems 23 and 24.

23. Is $f(x)$ continuous at
    (a) $x = -1$?   (b) $x = 1$?

24. Is $f(x)$ continuous at
    (a) $x = -2$?   (b) $x = 2$?

In Problems 25–30, suppose that

$$f(x) = \begin{cases} x^2 + 1 & \text{if } x \le 0 \\ x & \text{if } 0 < x < 1 \\ 2x^2 - 1 & \text{if } x \ge 1 \end{cases}$$

25. What is $\lim\limits_{x \to -1} f(x)$?
26. What is $\lim\limits_{x \to 0} f(x)$, if it exists?
27. What is $\lim\limits_{x \to 1} f(x)$, if it exists?
28. Is $f(x)$ continuous at $x = 0$?
29. Is $f(x)$ continuous at $x = 1$?
30. Is $f(x)$ continuous at $x = -1$?

For the functions in Problems 31–34, determine which are continuous. Identify discontinuities for those that are not continuous.

31. $y = \dfrac{x^2 + 25}{x - 5}$

32. $y = \dfrac{x^2 - 3x + 2}{x - 2}$

33. $f(x) = \begin{cases} x + 2 & \text{if } x \le 2 \\ 5x - 6 & \text{if } x > 2 \end{cases}$

34. $y = \begin{cases} x^4 - 3 & \text{if } x \le 1 \\ 2x - 3 & \text{if } x > 1 \end{cases}$

In Problems 35 and 36, use the graphs to find (a) the points of discontinuity, (b) $\lim\limits_{x \to \infty} f(x)$, and (c) $\lim\limits_{x \to -\infty} f(x)$.

35.

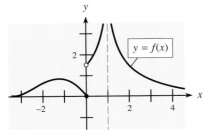

36.

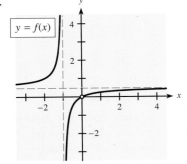

In Problems 37 and 38, evaluate the limits, if they exist. Then state what each limit tells about any horizontal asymptotes.

37. $\lim\limits_{x \to -\infty} \dfrac{2x^2}{1 - x^2}$

38. $\lim\limits_{x \to \infty} \dfrac{3x^{2/3}}{x + 1}$

Section 9.3

39. Find the average rate of change of

$$f(x) = 2x^4 - 3x + 7 \text{ over } [-1, 2]$$

In Problems 40 and 41, decide whether the statements are true or false.

40. $\lim\limits_{h \to 0} \dfrac{f(x + h) - f(x)}{h}$ gives the formula for the slope of the tangent and the instantaneous rate of change of $f(x)$ at any value of x.

41. $\lim\limits_{h \to 0} \dfrac{f(c + h) - f(c)}{h}$ gives the equation of the tangent line to $f(x)$ at $x = c$.

42. Use the definition of derivative to find $f'(x)$ for $f(x) = 3x^2 + 2x - 1$.

43. Use the definition of derivative to find $f'(x)$ if $f(x) = x - x^2$.

Use the graph of $y = f(x)$ in Figure 9.40 to answer the questions in Problems 44–46.

44. Explain which is greater: the average rate of change of f over $[-3, 0]$ or over $[-1, 0]$.

45. Is $f(x)$ differentiable at
    (a) $x = -1$?   (b) $x = 1$?

46. Is $f(x)$ differentiable at
    (a) $x = -2$?   (b) $x = 2$?

47. Let $f(x) = \dfrac{\sqrt[3]{4x}}{(3x^2 - 10)^2}$. Approximate $f'(2)$

    (a) by using the numerical derivative feature of a graphing calculator, and

    (b) by evaluating $\dfrac{f(2 + h) - f(2)}{h}$ with $h = 0.0001$.

48. Use the given table of values for $g(x)$ to
    (a) find the average rate of change of $g(x)$ over $[2, 5]$.
    (b) approximate $g'(4)$ as accurately as possible.

x	2	2.3	3.1	4	4.3	5
$g(x)$	13.2	12.1	9.7	12.2	14.3	18.1

Use the following graph of $f(x)$ to complete Problems 49 and 50.

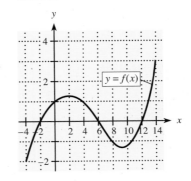

49. Estimate $f'(4)$.
50. Rank the following from smallest to largest and explain.
    A: $f'(2)$ B: $f'(6)$
    C: the average rate of change of $f(x)$ over $[2, 10]$

Section 9.4

51. If $c = 4x^5 - 6x^3$, find c'.
52. If $f(x) = 10x^9 - 5x^6 + 4x - 2^7 + 19$, find $f'(x)$.
53. If $p = q + \sqrt{7}$, find dp/dq.
54. If $y = \sqrt{x}$, find y'.
55. If $f(z) = \sqrt[3]{2^4}$, find $f'(z)$.
56. If $v(x) = 4/\sqrt[3]{x}$, find $v'(x)$.
57. If $y = \dfrac{1}{x} - \dfrac{1}{\sqrt{x}}$, find y'.
58. If $f(x) = \dfrac{3}{2x^2} - \sqrt[3]{x} + 4^5$, find $f'(x)$.
59. Write the equation of the line tangent to the graph of $y = 3x^5 - 6$ at $x = 1$.
60. Write the equation of the line tangent to the curve $y = 3x^3 - 2x$ at the point where $x = 2$.

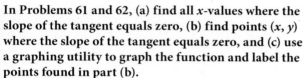

In Problems 61 and 62, (a) find all x-values where the slope of the tangent equals zero, (b) find points (x, y) where the slope of the tangent equals zero, and (c) use a graphing utility to graph the function and label the points found in part (b).
61. $f(x) = x^3 - 3x^2 + 1$ 62. $f(x) = x^6 - 6x^4 + 8$

Section 9.5

63. If $f(x) = (3x - 1)(x^2 - 4x)$, find $f'(x)$.
64. Find y' if $y = (x^4 + 3)(3x^3 + 1)$.
65. If $p = \dfrac{5q^3}{2q^3 + 1}$, find $\dfrac{dp}{dq}$.
66. Find $\dfrac{ds}{dt}$ if $s = \dfrac{\sqrt{t}}{(3t + 1)}$.
67. Find $\dfrac{dy}{dx}$ for $y = \sqrt{x}\,(3x + 2)$.
68. Find $\dfrac{dC}{dx}$ for $C = \dfrac{5x^4 - 2x^2 + 1}{x^3 + 1}$.

Section 9.6

69. If $y = (x^3 - 4x^2)^3$, find y'.
70. If $y = (5x^6 + 6x^4 + 5)^6$, find y'.
71. If $y = (2x^4 - 9)^9$, find $\dfrac{dy}{dx}$.
72. Find $g'(x)$ if $g(x) = \dfrac{1}{\sqrt{x^3 - 4x}}$.

Section 9.7

73. Find $f'(x)$ if $f(x) = x^2(2x^4 + 5)^8$.
74. Find S' if $S = \dfrac{(3x + 1)^2}{x^2 - 4}$.
75. Find $\dfrac{dy}{dx}$ if $y = [(3x + 1)(2x^3 - 1)]^{12}$.
76. Find y' if $y = \left(\dfrac{x + 1}{1 - x^2}\right)^3$.

77. Find y' if $y = x\sqrt{x^2 - 4}$.
78. Find $\dfrac{dy}{dx}$ if $y = \dfrac{x}{\sqrt[3]{3x - 1}}$.

Section 9.8

In Problems 79 and 80, find the second derivatives.
79. $y = \sqrt{x} - x^2$ 80. $y = x^4 - \dfrac{1}{x}$

In Problems 81 and 82, find the fifth derivatives.
81. $y = (2x + 1)^4$ 82. $y = \dfrac{(1 - x)^6}{24}$

83. If $\dfrac{dy}{dx} = \sqrt{x^2 - 4}$, find $\dfrac{d^3y}{dx^3}$.
84. If $\dfrac{d^2y}{dx^2} = \dfrac{x}{x^2 + 1}$, find $\dfrac{d^4y}{dx^4}$.

APPLICATIONS

Sections 9.1 and 9.2

Cost, revenue, and profit In Problems 85–88, assume that a company's monthly total revenue and total cost (both in dollars) are given by

$$R(x) = 140x - 0.01x^2 \quad \text{and} \quad C(x) = 60x + 70{,}000$$

where x is the number of units. (Let $P(x)$ denote the profit function.)

85. Find (a) $\lim\limits_{x \to 4000} R(x)$, (b) $\lim\limits_{x \to 4000} C(x)$, and (c) $\lim\limits_{x \to 4000} P(x)$.
86. Find and interpret (a) $\lim\limits_{x \to 0^+} C(x)$ and (b) $\lim\limits_{x \to 1000} P(x)$.
87. If $\overline{R}(x) = \dfrac{R(x)}{x}$ and $\overline{C}(x) = \dfrac{C(x)}{x}$ are, respectively, the company's average revenue per unit and average cost per unit, find
    (a) $\lim\limits_{x \to 0^+} \overline{R}(x)$.   (b) $\lim\limits_{x \to 0^+} \overline{C}(x)$.
88. Evaluate and explain the meanings of
    (a) $\lim\limits_{x \to \infty} C(x)$.   (b) $\lim\limits_{x \to \infty} \overline{C}(x) = \lim\limits_{x \to \infty} \dfrac{C(x)}{x}$.

Section 9.3

Elderly in the workforce The graph shows the percent of elderly men and women in the workforce for selected years from 1970 and projected to 2040. Use this graph in Problems 89 and 90.

89. For the period from 1990 to 2030, find and interpret the annual average rate of change of
    (a) elderly men in the workforce and
    (b) elderly women in the workforce.
90. (a) Find the annual average rate of change of the percent of elderly men in the workforce from 1970 to 1980 and from 2030 to 2040.
    (b) Find the annual average rate of change of the percent of elderly women in the workforce from 1970 to 1980 and from 2030 to 2040.

Elderly in the Workforce, 1970–2040

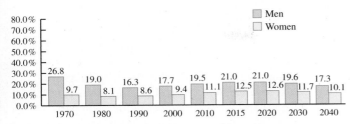

Source: Bureau of the Census, U.S. Department of Commerce

Section 9.4

91. *Demand* Suppose that the demand for x units of a product is given by $x = (100/p) - 1$, where p is the price per unit of the product. Find and interpret the rate of change of demand with respect to price if the price is
    (a) $10.   (b) $20.

92. *Severe weather ice makers* Thunderstorms severe enough to produce hail develop when an upper-level low (a pool of cold air high in the atmosphere) moves through a region where there is warm, moist air at the surface. These storms create an updraft that draws the moist air into subfreezing air above 10,000 feet. Data from the National Weather Service indicates that the strength of the updraft, as measured by its speed s in mph, affects the size of the hail according to

    $$h = 0.000595s^{1.922}$$

    where h is the diameter of the hail (in inches). Find and interpret $h(100)$ and $h'(100)$.

93. *Revenue* The graph shows the revenue function for a commodity. Will the $(A + 1)$st item sold or the $(B + 1)$st item sold produce more revenue? Explain.

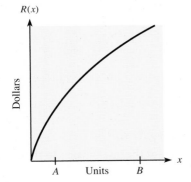

Section 9.5

94. *Revenue* In a 100-unit apartment building, when the price charged per apartment rental is $(830 + 30x)$ dollars, then the number of apartments rented is $100 - x$ and the total revenue for the building is

    $$R(x) = (830 + 30x)(100 - x)$$

where x is the number of $30 rent increases (and also the resulting number of unrented apartments). Find the marginal revenue when $x = 10$. Does this tell you that the rent should be raised (causing more vacancies) or lowered? Explain.

95. *Productivity* Suppose the productivity of a worker (in units per hour) after x hours of training and time on the job is given by

    $$P(x) = 3 + \frac{70x^2}{x^2 + 1000}$$

    (a) Find and interpret $P(20)$.
    (b) Find and interpret $P'(20)$.

Section 9.6

96. *Demand* The demand q for a product at price p is given by

    $$q = 10{,}000 - 50\sqrt{0.02p^2 + 500}$$

    Find the rate of change of demand with respect to price.

97. *Supply* The number of units x of a product that is supplied at price p is given by

    $$x = \sqrt{p - 1}, \quad p \geq 1$$

    If the price p is $10, what is the rate of change of the supply with respect to the price, and what does it tell us?

Section 9.8

98. *Acceleration* Suppose an object moves so that its distance to a sensor, in feet, is given by

    $$s(t) = 16 + 140t + 8\sqrt{t}$$

    where t is the time in seconds. Find the acceleration at time $t = 4$ seconds.

99. *Profit* Suppose a company's profit (in dollars) is given by

    $$P(x) = 70x - 0.1x^2 - 5500$$

    where x is the number of units. Find and interpret $P'(300)$ and $P''(300)$.

Section 9.9

In Problems 100–107, cost, revenue, and profit are in dollars and x is the number of units.

100. *Cost* If the cost function for a particular good is $C(x) = 3x^2 + 6x + 600$, what is the
    (a) marginal cost function?
    (b) marginal cost if 30 units are produced?
    (c) interpretation of your answer in part (b)?

101. *Cost* If the total cost function for a commodity is $C(x) = 400 + 5x + x^3$, what is the marginal cost when 4 units are produced, and what does it mean?

102. **Revenue** The total revenue function for a commodity is $R = 40x - 0.02x^2$, with x representing the number of units.
    (a) Find the marginal revenue function.
    (b) At what level of production will marginal revenue be 0?

103. **Profit** If the total revenue function for a product is given by $R(x) = 60x$ and the total cost function is given by $C = 200 + 10x + 0.1x^2$, what is the marginal profit at $x = 10$? What does the marginal profit at $x = 10$ predict?

104. **Revenue** The total revenue function for a commodity is given by $R = 80x - 0.04x^2$.
    (a) Find the marginal revenue function.
    (b) What is the marginal revenue at $x = 100$?
    (c) Interpret your answer in part (b).

105. **Revenue** If the revenue function for a product is
    $$R(x) = \frac{60x^2}{2x + 1}$$
    find the marginal revenue.

106. **Profit** A firm has monthly costs given by
    $$C = 45{,}000 + 100x + x^3$$
    where x is the number of units produced per month. The firm can sell its product in a competitive market for \$4600 per unit. Find the marginal profit.

107. **Profit** A small business has weekly costs of
    $$C = 100 + 30x + \frac{x^2}{10}$$
    where x is the number of units produced each week. The competitive market price for this business's product is \$46 per unit. Find the marginal profit.

108. **Cost, revenue, and profit** The graph shows the total revenue and total cost functions for a company. Use the graph to decide (and justify) at which of points A, B, and C
    (a) the revenue from the next item will be least.
    (b) the profit will be greatest.
    (c) the profit from the sale of the next item will be greatest.
    (d) the next item sold will reduce the profit.

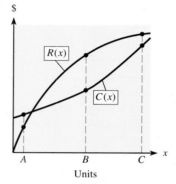

Chapter 9 TEST

1. Evaluate the following limits, if they exist. Use algebraic methods.
    (a) $\displaystyle\lim_{x \to -2} \frac{4x - x^2}{4x - 8}$
    (b) $\displaystyle\lim_{x \to \infty} \frac{8x^2 - 4x + 1}{2 + x - 5x^2}$
    (c) $\displaystyle\lim_{x \to 7} \frac{x^2 - 5x - 14}{x^2 - 6x - 7}$
    (d) $\displaystyle\lim_{x \to -5} \frac{5x - 25}{x + 5}$

2. (a) Write the limit definition for $f'(x)$.
    (b) Use the definition from (a) to find $f'(x)$ for $f(x) = 3x^2 - x + 9$.

3. Let $f(x) = \dfrac{4x}{x^2 - 8x}$. Identify all x-values where $f(x)$ is *not* continuous.

4. Use derivative formulas to find the derivative of each of the following. Simplify, except for part (d).
    (a) $B = 0.523W - 5176$
    (b) $p = 9t^{10} - 6t^7 - 17t + 23$
    (c) $y = \dfrac{3x^3}{2x^7 + 11}$
    (d) $f(x) = (3x^5 - 2x + 3)(4x^{10} + 10x^4 - 17)$
    (e) $g(x) = \frac{3}{4}(2x^5 + 7x^3 - 5)^{12}$
    (f) $y = (x^2 + 3)(2x + 5)^6$
    (g) $f(x) = 12\sqrt{x} - \dfrac{10}{x^2} + 17$

5. Find $\dfrac{d^3y}{dx^3}$ for $y = x^3 - x^{-3}$.

6. Let $f(x) = x^3 - 3x^2 - 24x - 10$.
    (a) Write the equation of the line tangent to the graph of $y = f(x)$ at $x = -1$.
    (b) Find all points (both x- and y-coordinates) where $f'(x) = 0$.

7. Find the average rate of change of $f(x) = 4 - x - 2x^2$ over $[1, 6]$.

8. Use the given tables to evaluate the following limits, if they exist.
    (a) $\displaystyle\lim_{x \to 5} f(x)$ (b) $\displaystyle\lim_{x \to 5} g(x)$ (c) $\displaystyle\lim_{x \to 5^-} g(x)$

x	4.99	4.999	→5←	5.001	5.01
$f(x)$	2.01	2.001	→?←	1.999	1.99

x	4.99	4.999	→5←	5.001	5.01
$g(x)$	−3.99	−3.999	→?←	6.999	6.99

9. Use the definition of continuity to investigate whether $g(x)$ is continuous at $x = -2$. Show your work.

$$g(x) = \begin{cases} 6 - x & \text{if } x \leq -2 \\ x^3 & \text{if } x > -2 \end{cases}$$

In Problems 10 and 11, suppose a company has its total cost for a product given by $C(x) = 200x + 10{,}000$ dollars and its total revenue given by $R(x) = 250x - 0.01x^2$ dollars, where x is the number of units produced and sold.

10. (a) Find the marginal revenue function.
    (b) Find $R(72)$ and $R'(72)$ and tell what each represents or predicts.

11. (a) Form the profit function for this product.
    (b) Find the marginal profit function.
    (c) Find the marginal profit when $x = 1000$, and then write a sentence that interprets this result.

12. Suppose that $f(x)$ is a differentiable function. Use the table of values to approximate $f'(3)$ as accurately as possible.

x	2	2.5	2.999	3	3.01	3.1
$f(x)$	0	18.4	44.896	45	46.05	56.18

13. Use the graph to perform the evaluations (a)–(f) and to answer (g)–(i). If no value exists, so indicate.
    (a) $f(1)$
    (b) $\lim\limits_{x \to 6} f(x)$
    (c) $\lim\limits_{x \to 3} f(x)$
    (d) $\lim\limits_{x \to -4} f(x)$
    (e) $\lim\limits_{x \to -\infty} f(x)$
    (f) Estimate $f'(4)$.
    (g) Find all x-values where $f'(x)$ does not exist.

(h) Find all x-values where $f(x)$ is not continuous.
(i) Rank from smallest to largest: $f'(-2), f'(2)$, and the average rate of change of $f(x)$ over $[-2, 2]$.

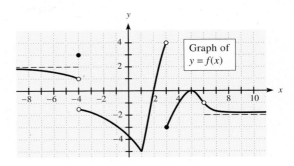

14. Given that the line $y = \frac{2}{3}x - 8$ is tangent to the graph of $y = f(x)$ at $x = 6$, find
    (a) $f'(6)$.
    (b) $f(6)$.
    (c) the instantaneous rate of change of $f(x)$ with respect to x at $x = 6$.

15. The graph shows the total revenue and total cost functions for a company. Use the graph to decide (and justify) at which of points A, B, and C
    (a) profit is the greatest.
    (b) there is a loss.
    (c) producing and selling another item will increase profit.
    (d) the next item sold will decrease profit.

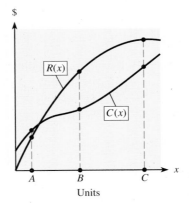

Extended Applications & Group Projects

I. Marginal Return to Sales

A tire manufacturer studying the effectiveness of television advertising and other promotions on sales of its GRIPPER-brand tires attempted to fit data it had gathered to the
equation

$$S = a_0 + a_1 x + a_2 x^2 + b_1 y$$

where S is sales revenue in millions of dollars, x is millions of dollars spent on television
advertising, y is millions of dollars spent on other promotions, and a_0, a_1, a_2, and b_1 are
constants. The data, gathered in two different regions of the country where expenditures
for other promotions were kept constant (at B_1 and B_2), resulted in the following quadratic
equations relating TV advertising and sales.

$$\text{Region 1:} \quad S_1 = 30 + 20x - 0.4x^2 + B_1$$
$$\text{Region 2:} \quad S_2 = 20 + 36x - 1.3x^2 + B_2$$

The company wants to know how to make the best use of its advertising dollars in the
regions and whether the current allocation could be improved. Advise management about
current advertising effectiveness, allocation of additional expenditures, and reallocation
of current advertising expenditures by answering the following questions.

1. In the analysis of sales and advertising, **marginal return to sales** is usually used, and
   it is given by dS_1/dx for Region 1 and dS_2/dx for Region 2.

   (a) Find $\dfrac{dS_1}{dx}$ and $\dfrac{dS_2}{dx}$.

   (b) If \$10 million is being spent on TV advertising in each region, what is the
       marginal return to sales in each region?

2. Which region would benefit more from additional advertising expenditure, if
   \$10 million is currently being spent in each region?

3. If any additional money is made available for advertising, in which region should it
   be spent?

4. How could money already being spent be reallocated to produce more sales revenue?

the tangent to the curve, we see that if $f'(x) > 0$ on an interval, then $f(x)$ is increasing on that interval. A similar conclusion can be reached when the derivative is negative on the interval.

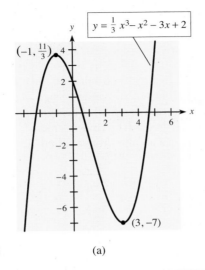

$y = \frac{1}{3}x^3 - x^2 - 3x + 2$

$(-1, \frac{11}{3})$

$(3, -7)$

(a)

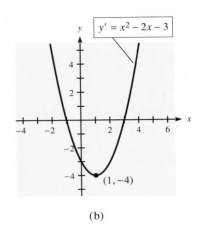

$y' = x^2 - 2x - 3$

$(1, -4)$

(b)

Figure 10.1

Increasing and Decreasing Functions

If f is a function that is differentiable on an interval (a, b), then

  if $f'(x) > 0$ for all x in (a, b), f is increasing on (a, b).

  if $f'(x) < 0$ for all x in (a, b), f is decreasing on (a, b).

Figure 10.1(a) shows the graph of a function, and Figure 10.1(b) shows the graph of its derivative. The figures show that the graph of $y = f(x)$ is increasing for the same x-values for which the graph of $y' = f'(x)$ is above the x-axis (when $f'(x) > 0$). Similarly, the graph of $y = f(x)$ is decreasing for the same x-values $(-1 < x < 3)$ for which the graph of $y' = f'(x)$ is below the x-axis (when $f'(x) < 0$).

The derivative $f'(x)$ can change signs only at values of x at which $f'(x) = 0$ or $f'(x)$ is undefined. We call these values of x **critical values.** The point corresponding to a critical value for x is a **critical point.*** Because a curve changes from increasing to decreasing at a relative maximum and from decreasing to increasing at a relative minimum (see Figure 10.1(a)), we have the following.

Relative Maximum and Minimum

If f has a relative maximum or a relative minimum at $x = x_0$, then $f'(x_0) = 0$ or $f'(x_0)$ is undefined.

Figure 10.2 shows a function with two relative maxima, one at $x = x_1$ and the second at $x = x_3$, and one relative minimum at $x = x_2$. At $x = x_1$ and $x = x_2$, we see that $f'(x) = 0$, and at $x = x_3$ the derivative does not exist.

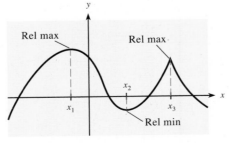

Rel max

Rel max

x_2

x_1

x_3

Rel min

Figure 10.2

*There may be some critical values at which both $f'(x)$ and $f(x)$ are undefined. Critical points do not occur at these values, but studying the derivative on either side of such values may be of interest.

Thus we can find relative maxima and minima for a curve by finding values of x for which the function has critical points. The behavior of the derivative to the left and right of (and near) these points will tell us whether they are relative maxima, relative minima, or neither.

Because the critical values are the only values at which the graph can have turning points, the derivative cannot change sign anywhere except at a critical value. Thus, in an interval between two critical values, the sign of the derivative at any value in the interval will be the sign of the derivative at all values in the interval.

Using the critical values of $f(x)$ and the sign of $f'(x)$ between those critical values, we can create a **sign diagram for $f'(x)$**. The sign diagram for the graph in Figure 10.2 is shown in Figure 10.3. This sign diagram was created from the graph of f, but it is also possible to predict the shape of a graph from a sign diagram.

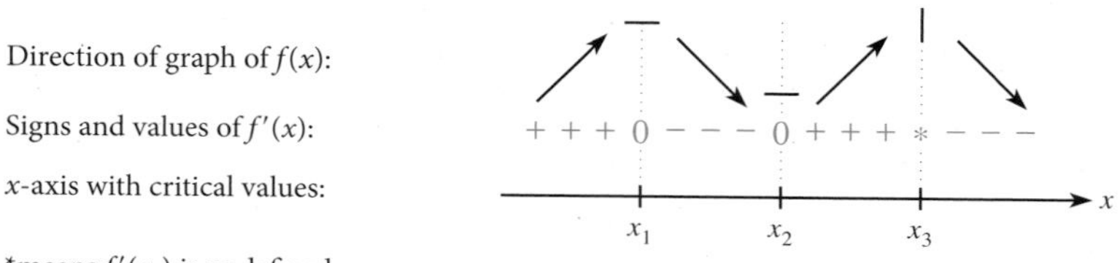

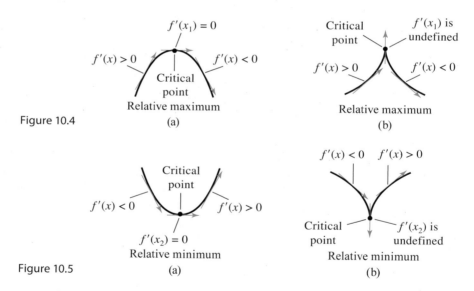

Direction of graph of $f(x)$:

Signs and values of $f'(x)$: $+ + + 0 - - - 0 + + + * - - -$

x-axis with critical values: $x_1 \quad x_2 \quad x_3 \qquad x$

Figure 10.3   *means $f'(x_3)$ is undefined

Figure 10.4 shows two ways that a function can have a relative maximum at a critical point, and Figure 10.5 shows two ways for a relative minimum.

$f'(x_1) = 0$

$f'(x) > 0$ $f'(x) < 0$

Critical point

Relative maximum

Figure 10.4   (a)

Critical point $f'(x_1)$ is undefined

$f'(x) > 0$ $f'(x) < 0$

Relative maximum

(b)

Critical point

$f'(x) < 0$ $f'(x) > 0$

$f'(x_2) = 0$

Relative minimum

Figure 10.5   (a)

$f'(x) < 0$ $f'(x) > 0$

Critical point $f'(x_2)$ is undefined

Relative minimum

(b)

The preceding discussion suggests the following procedure for finding relative maxima and minima of a function.

First-Derivative Test

Procedure

To find relative maxima and minima of a function:

1. Find the first derivative of the function.
2. Set the derivative equal to 0, and solve for values of x that satisfy $f'(x) = 0$. These are called **critical values.** Values that make $f'(x)$ undefined are also critical values.

Example

Find the relative maxima and minima of $f(x) = \frac{1}{3}x^3 - x^2 - 3x + 2$.

1. $f'(x) = x^2 - 2x - 3$
2. $0 = x^2 - 2x - 3 = (x + 1)(x - 3)$ has solutions $x = -1, x = 3$. No values of x make $f'(x) = x^2 - 2x - 3$ undefined. Critical values are -1 and 3.

(Continued)

3. Substitute the critical values into the *original function* to find the **critical points.**
4. Evaluate $f'(x)$ at a value of x to the left and one to the right of each critical point to develop a sign diagram.
    (a) If $f'(x) > 0$ to the left and $f'(x) < 0$ to the right of the critical value, the critical point is a relative maximum point.
    (b) If $f'(x) < 0$ to the left and $f'(x) > 0$ to the right of the critical value, the critical point is a relative minimum point.

3. $f(-1) = \frac{11}{3}$ $f(3) = -7$
   The critical points are $\left(-1, \frac{11}{3}\right)$ and $(3, -7)$.
4. $f'(-2) = 5 > 0$ and $f'(0) = -3 < 0$
   Thus $(-1, 11/3)$ is a relative maximum point.
   $f'(2) = -3 < 0$ and $f'(4) = 5 > 0$
   Thus $(3, -7)$ is a relative minimum point. The sign diagram for $f'(x)$ is

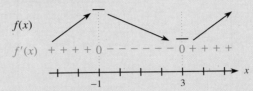

5. Use the information from the sign diagram and selected points to sketch the graph.

5. The information from this sign diagram is shown in Figure 10.6(a). Plotting additional points gives the graph of the function, which is shown in Figure 10.6(b).

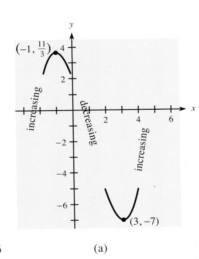

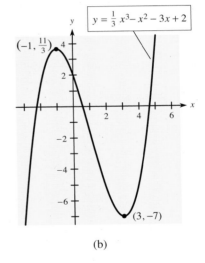

Figure 10.6   (a)   (b)

Because the critical values are the only x-values at which the graph can have turning points, we can test to the left and right of each critical value by testing to the left of the smallest critical value, then testing a value *between* each two successive critical values, and then testing to the right of the largest critical value. The following example illustrates this procedure.

EXAMPLE 1   Maxima and Minima

Find the relative maxima and minima of $f(x) = \frac{1}{4}x^4 - \frac{1}{3}x^3 - 3x^2 + 8$, and sketch its graph.

Solution

1. $f'(x) = x^3 - x^2 - 6x$
2. Setting $f'(x) = 0$ gives $0 = x^3 - x^2 - 6x$. Solving for x gives

$$0 = x(x - 3)(x + 2)$$

$x = 0$	$x - 3 = 0$	$x + 2 = 0$
	$x = 3$	$x = -2$

Thus the critical values are $x = 0$, $x = 3$, and $x = -2$.

3. Substituting the critical values into the original function gives the critical points:

$$f(-2) = \tfrac{8}{3}, \quad \text{so } \left(-2, \tfrac{8}{3}\right) \text{ is a critical point.}$$
$$f(0) = 8, \quad \text{so } (0, 8) \text{ is a critical point.}$$
$$f(3) = -\tfrac{31}{4}, \quad \text{so } \left(3, -\tfrac{31}{4}\right) \text{ is a critical point.}$$

4. Testing $f'(x)$ to the left of the smallest critical value, then between the critical values, and finally to the right of the largest critical value will give the sign diagram. Evaluating $f'(x)$ at the test values $x = -3$, $x = -1$, $x = 1$, and $x = 4$ gives the signs to determine relative maxima and minima.

    The sign diagram for $f'(x)$ is

    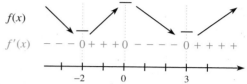

    Thus we have

    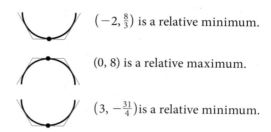

    $\left(-2, \tfrac{8}{3}\right)$ is a relative minimum.

    $(0, 8)$ is a relative maximum.

    $\left(3, -\tfrac{31}{4}\right)$ is a relative minimum.

5. Figure 10.7(a) shows the graph of the function near the critical points, and Figure 10.7(b) shows the graph of the function.

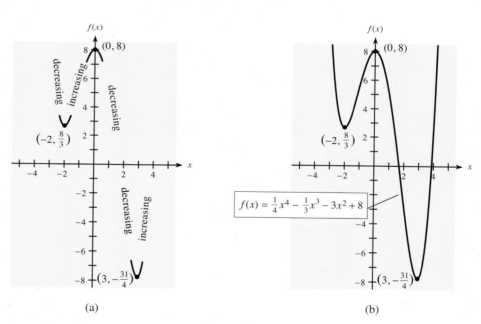

Figure 10.7   (a)   (b)

Note that we substitute the critical values into the *original function* $f(x)$ to find the y-values of the critical points, but we test for relative maxima and minima by substituting values near the critical values into the *derivative of the function,* $f'(x)$.

Only four values were needed to test three critical points in Example 1. This method will work *only if* the critical values are tested in order from smallest to largest.

If the first derivative of f is 0 at x_0 but does not change from positive to negative or from negative to positive as x passes through x_0, then the critical point at x_0 is neither a relative maximum nor a relative minimum. In this case we say that f has a **horizontal point of inflection** (abbreviated HPI) at x_0.

EXAMPLE   2   **Maxima, Minima, and Horizontal Points of Inflection**

Find the relative maxima, relative minima, and horizontal points of inflection of $h(x) = \frac{1}{4}x^4 - \frac{2}{3}x^3 - 2x^2 + 8x + 4$, and sketch its graph.

Solution

1. $h'(x) = x^3 - 2x^2 - 4x + 8$
2. $0 = x^3 - 2x^2 - 4x + 8$ or $0 = x^2(x-2) - 4(x-2)$. Therefore, we have $0 = (x-2)(x^2 - 4)$. Thus $x = -2$ and $x = 2$ are solutions.
3. The critical points are $\left(-2, -\frac{32}{3}\right)$ and $\left(2, \frac{32}{3}\right)$.
4. Using test values, such as $x = -3$, $x = 0$, and $x = 3$, gives the sign diagram for $h'(x)$.

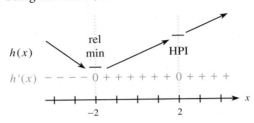

5. Figure 10.8(a) shows the graph of the function near the critical points, and Figure 10.8(b) shows the graph of the function.

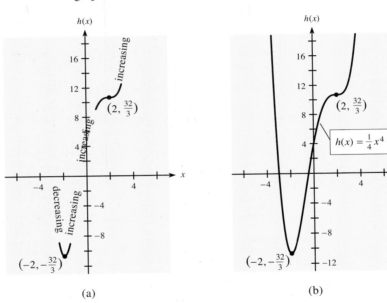

Figure 10.8   (a)   (b)

Technology Note   We can use a graphing calculator as an aid in locating the x-values where $f'(x) = 0$, which are the critical values of $f(x)$, and then making the sign diagram used to classify these critical values, as follows.

1. Enter the derivative of the function in Y1.
2. Graph Y1 and use ZERO to determine the x-values where Y1 $= 0$; this gives the critical values.
3. Use TABLE to evaluate the derivative to the left and right of each critical value. This creates a sign diagram for $f'(x)$ and can be used to determine whether each critical value is a relative maximum, a relative minimum, or neither.
4. Enter the function in Y2 and use TABLE to evaluate the function at each critical value to find the y-coordinates of the critical points.

Figure 10.9 on the next page illustrates steps (2) and (3) above for $f(x) = \frac{1}{3}x^3 - 4x$, which has derivative $f'(x) = x^2 - 4$. See Appendix A, Section 10.1, for details.

Appendix B, Section 10.1, and the online Excel Guide can be used to find the relative maxima and relative minima of functions with Excel.

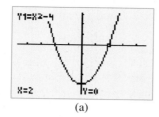
(a)

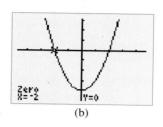
(b)

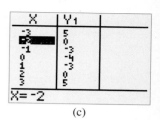
(c)

Figure 10.9

EXAMPLE 3   Undefined Derivatives

Find the relative maxima and minima (if any) of the graph of $y = (x + 2)^{2/3}$.

Solution

1. $y' = f'(x) = \dfrac{2}{3}(x + 2)^{-1/3} = \dfrac{2}{3\sqrt[3]{x + 2}}$

2. $0 = \dfrac{2}{3\sqrt[3]{x + 2}}$ has no solutions; $f'(x)$ is undefined at $x = -2$.

3. $f(-2) = 0$, so the critical point is $(-2, 0)$.

4. The sign diagram for $f'(x)$ is

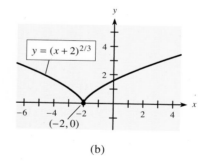

$*$ means $f'(-2)$ is undefined.

Thus a relative minimum occurs at $(-2, 0)$.

5. Figure 10.10(a) shows the graph of the function near the critical points, and Figure 10.10(b) shows the graph of the function.

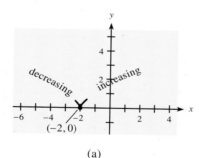
(a)

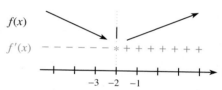
(b)

Figure 10.10

✓ **CHECKPOINT**

1. The x-values of critical points are found where $f'(x)$ is _____ or _____.

2. Decide whether the following are true or false.
    (a) If $f'(1) = 7$, then $f(x)$ is increasing at $x = 1$.
    (b) If $f'(-2) = 0$, then a relative maximum or a relative minimum occurs at $x = -2$.
    (c) If $f'(-3) = 0$ and $f'(x)$ changes from positive on the left to negative on the right of $x = -3$, then a relative minimum occurs at $x = -3$.

3. If $f(x) = 7 + 3x - x^3$, then $f'(x) = 3 - 3x^2$. Use these functions to decide whether the following statements are true or false.
    (a) The only critical value is $x = 1$.
    (b) The critical points are $(1, 0)$ and $(-1, 0)$.

4. If $f'(x)$ has the following partial sign diagram, make a "stick-figure" sketch of $f(x)$ and label where any maxima and minima occur. Assume that $f(x)$ is defined for all real numbers.

$*$ means $f'(0)$ is undefined.

EXAMPLE 4   **Advertising** | APPLICATION PREVIEW |

The weekly sales S of a product during an advertising campaign are given by

$$S = \frac{100t}{t^2 + 100}, \qquad 0 \le t \le 20$$

where t is the number of weeks since the beginning of the campaign and S is in thousands of dollars.
(a) Over what interval are sales increasing? Decreasing?
(b) What are the maximum weekly sales?
(c) Sketch the graph for $0 \le t \le 20$.

Solution
(a) To find where S is increasing, we first find $S'(t)$

$$S'(t) = \frac{(t^2 + 100)100 - (100t)2t}{(t^2 + 100)^2}$$

$$= \frac{10{,}000 - 100t^2}{(t^2 + 100)^2}$$

We see that $S'(t) = 0$ when $10{,}000 - 100t^2 = 0$, or

$$100(100 - t^2) = 0$$
$$100(10 + t)(10 - t) = 0$$
$$t = -10 \quad \text{or} \quad t = 10$$

Because $S'(t)$ is never undefined ($t^2 + 100 \ne 0$ for any real t) and because $0 \le t \le 20$, our only critical value is $t = 10$. Testing $S'(t)$ to the left and right of $t = 10$ gives the sign diagram.

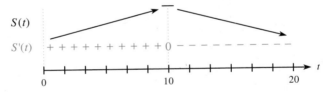

Hence, S is increasing on the interval $[0, 10)$ and decreasing on the interval $(10, 20]$.
(b) Because S is increasing to the left of $t = 10$ and S is decreasing to the right of $t = 10$, the maximum value of S occurs at $t = 10$ and is

$$S = S(10) = \frac{100(10)}{10^2 + 100} = \frac{1000}{200} = 5 \text{(thousand dollars)}$$

(c) Plotting some additional points gives the graph; see Figure 10.11.

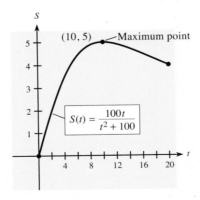

Figure 10.11

Calculator Note   With a graphing calculator, choosing an appropriate viewing window is the key to understanding the graph of a function. To find an appropriate window, set the x-min of the window to the left of the smallest critical value and the x-max to the right of the largest critical value, and set the y-min and y-max to contain the y-coordinates of the critical points. See Example 5 and Appendix A, Section 10.1, for details.   ∎

EXAMPLE 5   Critical Points and Viewing Windows

Find the critical values of $f(x) = 0.0001x^3 + 0.003x^2 - 3.6x + 5$. Use them to determine an appropriate viewing window. Then sketch the graph.

Solution

The critical points are helpful in graphing the function. We begin by finding $f'(x)$.

$$f'(x) = 0.0003x^2 + 0.006x - 3.6$$

Now we solve $f'(x) = 0$ to find the critical values.

$$0 = 0.0003x^2 + 0.006x - 3.6$$
$$0 = 0.0003(x^2 + 20x - 12,000)$$
$$0 = 0.0003(x + 120)(x - 100)$$
$$x = -120 \quad \text{or} \quad x = 100$$

We choose a window that includes $x = -120$ and $x = 100$, and use TABLE to find $f(-120) = 307.4$ and $f(100) = -225$. We then graph $y = f(x)$ in a window that includes $y = -225$ and $y = 307.4$ (see Figure 10.12). On this graph we can see that $(-120, 307.4)$ is a relative maximum and that $(100, -225)$ is a relative minimum.   ∎

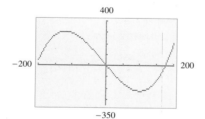

Figure 10.12

EXAMPLE 6   Aging workers

The table shows the millions of Americans who are working full time at selected ages from 27 to 62.
(a) Find a cubic model that gives the number of Americans working full time, y (in millions), as a function of their age, x. Report the model with three significant digits in the coefficients.
(b) Find the relative maximum and minimum of the reported function.

Age	Millions Working Full Time	Age	Millions Working Full Time
27	6.30	47	7.52
32	6.33	52	7.10
37	6.96	57	5.58
42	7.07	62	3.54

Source: Wall Street Journal

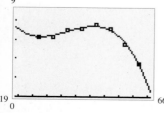

Figure 10.13

Solution
(a) A cubic function that models these data is

$$f(x) = -0.000362x^3 + 0.0401x^2 - 1.39x + 21.7$$

Figure 10.13 shows a graph of the model with the data.

(b) We use $f'(x) = -0.001086x^2 + 0.0802x - 1.39$ and solve $f'(x) = 0$ to find the critical values. We can solve

$$-0.001086x^2 + 0.0802x - 1.39 = 0$$

with the quadratic formula or with a graphing calculator. The two solutions are approximately

$$x = 27.8 \quad \text{and} \quad x = 46.1$$

The sign diagram shows that $x = 27.8$ gives a relative minimum and $x = 46.1$ gives a relative maximum.

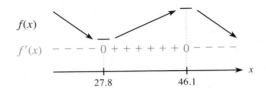

Thus the model indicates a relative minimum of $f(27.8) \approx 6.3$ (million) full-time workers at age 27.8 and a relative maximum of $f(46.1) \approx 7.4$ (million) full-time workers at age 46.1.

Spreadsheet Note   Excel can be used to create sign diagrams that determine the maxima and minima of functions. Details are given in Appendix B, Section 10.1, and the Online Excel Guide.

✓ CHECKPOINT ANSWERS

1. $f'(x) = 0$ or $f'(x)$ is undefined.
2. (a) True. $f(x)$ is increasing when $f'(x) > 0$.
    (b) False. See Figure 10.8.
    (c) False. A relative maximum occurs at $x = -3$.
3. (a) False. Critical values are $x = 1$ and $x = -1$.
    (b) False. Critical points are $(1, 9)$ and $(-1, 5)$.
4.

Horizontal point
of inflection
at $x = 2$

Relative
maximum
at $x = -1$

Relative
minimum
at $x = 0$

| EXERCISES | **10.1**

In Problems 1 and 2, use the indicated points on the graph of $y = f(x)$ to identify points at which $f(x)$ has (a) a relative maximum, (b) a relative minimum, and (c) a horizontal point of inflection.

1.

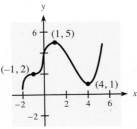

2.

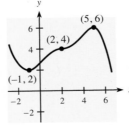

3. Use the graph of $y = f(x)$ in Problem 1 to identify at which of the indicated points the derivative $f'(x)$ (a) changes from positive to negative, (b) changes from negative to positive, and (c) does not change sign.
4. Use the graph of $y = f(x)$ in Problem 2 to identify at which of the indicated points the derivative $f'(x)$ (a) changes from positive to negative, (b) changes from negative to positive, and (c) does not change sign.

In Problems 5 and 6, use the sign diagram for $f'(x)$ to determine (a) the critical values of $f(x)$, (b) intervals on which $f(x)$ increases, (c) intervals on which $f(x)$

decreases, (d) x-values at which relative maxima occur, and (e) x-values at which relative minima occur.

5. $f'(x)$ $\xrightarrow{\;\; ---\; 0 +++++\; 0 ---\;\;}$ x
     3 7

6. $f'(x)$ $\xrightarrow{\;\; +++\,+0+ +++++ +0 ----\;\;}$ x
     -5 8

In Problems 7–10, (a) find the critical values of the function, and (b) make a sign diagram and determine the relative maxima and minima.

7. $y = 2x^3 - 12x^2 + 6$ $\qquad$ 8. $y = x^3 - 3x^2 + 6x + 1$
9. $y = 2x^5 + 5x^4 - 11$ $\qquad$ 10. $y = 15x^3 - x^5 + 7$

For each function and graph in Problems 11–14:
(a) **Estimate the coordinates of the relative maxima, relative minima, or horizontal points of inflection by observing the graph.**
(b) **Use $y' = f'(x)$ to find the critical values.**
(c) **Find the critical points.**
(d) **Do the results in part (c) confirm your estimates in part (a)?**

11. $y = x^3 - 3x + 4$ $\qquad$ 12. $y = x - \frac{1}{3}x^3$

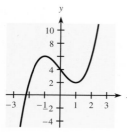 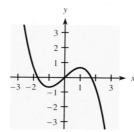

13. $y = x^3 + 3x^2 + 3x - 2$ $\qquad$ 14. $y = x^3 - 6x^2 + 12x + 1$

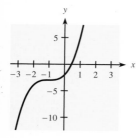 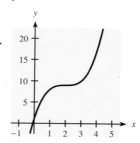

For each function in Problems 15–20:
(a) Find $y' = f'(x)$.
(b) Find the critical values.
(c) Find the critical points.
(d) Find intervals of x-values where the function is increasing and where it is decreasing.
(e) Classify the critical points as relative maxima, relative minima, or horizontal points of inflection. In each case, check your conclusions with a graphing utility.

15. $y = \frac{1}{2}x^2 - x$ $\qquad\qquad$ 16. $y = x^2 + 4x$
17. $y = \dfrac{x^3}{3} + \dfrac{x^2}{2} - 2x + 1$ $\quad$ 18. $y = \dfrac{x^4}{4} - \dfrac{x^3}{3} - 2$
19. $y = x^{2/3}$ $\qquad\qquad$ 20. $y = -(x - 3)^{2/3}$

For each function and graph in Problems 21–24:
(a) Use the graph to identify x-values for which $y' > 0$, $y' < 0$, $y' = 0$, and y' does not exist.
(b) Use the derivative to check your conclusions.

21. $y = 6 - x - x^2$ $\qquad$ 22. $y = \frac{1}{2}x^2 - 4x + 1$

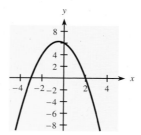 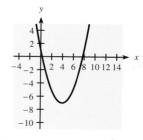

23. $y = 6 + x^3 - \frac{1}{15}x^5$ $\qquad$ 24. $y = x^4 - 2x^2 - 1$

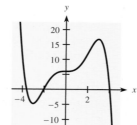 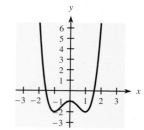

For each function in Problems 25–30, find the relative maxima, relative minima, horizontal points of inflection, and sketch the graph. Check your graph with a graphing utility.

25. $y = \frac{1}{3}x^3 - x^2 + x + 1$
26. $y = \frac{1}{4}x^4 - \frac{2}{3}x^3 + \frac{1}{2}x^2 - 2$
27. $y = \frac{1}{3}x^3 + x^2 - 24x + 20$
28. $C(x) = x^3 - \frac{3}{2}x^2 - 18x + 5$
29. $y = 3x^5 - 5x^3 + 1$
30. $y = \frac{1}{6}x^6 - x^4 + 7$

In Problems 31–36, both a function and its derivative are given. Use them to find critical values, critical points, intervals on which the function is increasing and decreasing, relative maxima, relative minima, and horizontal points of inflection; sketch the graph of each function.

31. $y = (x^2 - 2x)^2$ $\qquad$ $\dfrac{dy}{dx} = 4x(x-1)(x-2)$

32. $f(x) = (x^2 - 4)^2$ $\qquad$ $f'(x) = 4x(x+2)(x-2)$

33. $y = \dfrac{x^3(x-5)^2}{27}$ $\qquad$ $\dfrac{dy}{dx} = \dfrac{5x^2(x-3)(x-5)}{27}$

34. $y = \dfrac{x^2(x-5)^3}{27}$ $\qquad$ $\dfrac{dy}{dx} = \dfrac{5x(x-2)(x-5)^2}{27}$

35. $f(x) = x^{2/3}(x-5)$ $\qquad$ $f'(x) = \dfrac{5(x-2)}{3x^{1/3}}$

36. $f(x) = x - 3x^{2/3}$ $\qquad$ $f'(x) = \dfrac{x^{1/3} - 2}{x^{1/3}}$

In Problems 37–42, use the derivative to locate critical points and determine a viewing window that shows all features of the graph. Use a graphing utility to sketch a complete graph.

37. $f(x) = x^3 - 225x^2 + 15,000x - 12,000$

38. $f(x) = x^3 - 15x^2 - 16,800x + 80,000$

39. $f(x) = x^4 - 160x^3 + 7200x^2 - 40,000$

40. $f(x) = x^4 - 240x^3 + 16,200x^2 - 60,000$

41. $y = 7.5x^4 - x^3 + 2$ 42. $y = 2 - x^3 - 7.5x^4$

In each of Problems 43–46, a graph of $f'(x)$ is given. Use the graph to determine the critical values of $f(x)$, where $f(x)$ is increasing, where it is decreasing, and where it has relative maxima, relative minima, and horizontal points of inflection. In each case sketch a possible graph for $f(x)$ that passes through $(0, 0)$.

43. $f'(x) = x^2 - x - 2$ 44. $f'(x) = 4x - x^2$

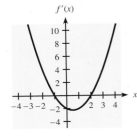

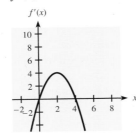

45. $f'(x) = x^3 - 3x^2$ 46. $f'(x) = x(x-2)^2$

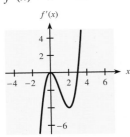

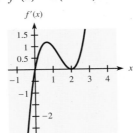

In Problems 47 and 48, two graphs are given. One is the graph of f and the other is the graph of f'. Decide which is which and explain your reasoning.

47.

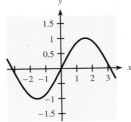

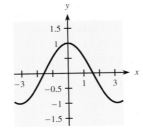

48.

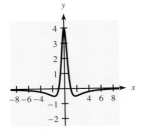

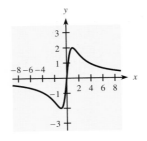

APPLICATIONS

49. *Advertising and sales* Suppose that the daily sales (in dollars) t days after the end of an advertising campaign are given by

$$S = 1000 + \frac{400}{t+1}, \quad t \ge 0$$

Does S increase for all $t \ge 0$, decrease for all $t \ge 0$, or change direction at some point?

50. *Pricing and sales* Suppose that a chain of auto service stations, Quick-Oil, Inc., has found that its monthly sales volume y (in thousands of dollars) is related to the price p (in dollars) of an oil change by

$$y = \frac{90}{\sqrt{p+5}}, \quad p > 10$$

Is y increasing or decreasing for all values of $p > 10$?

51. *Productivity* A time study showed that, on average, the productivity of a worker after t hours on the job can be modeled by

$$P(t) = 27t + 6t^2 - t^3, \quad 0 \le t \le 8$$

where P is the number of units produced per hour.
   (a) Find the critical values of this function.
   (b) Which critical value makes sense in this model?
   (c) For what values of t is P increasing?
   (d) Graph the function for $0 \le t \le 8$.

52. *Production* Analysis of daily output of a factory shows that, on average, the number of units per hour y produced after t hours of production is

$$y = 70t + \frac{1}{2}t^2 - t^3, \quad 0 \le t \le 8$$

   (a) Find the critical values of this function.
   (b) Which critical values make sense in this particular problem?
   (c) For which values of t, for $0 \le t \le 8$, is y increasing?
   (d) Graph this function.

53. *Production costs* Suppose that the average cost, in dollars, of producing a shipment of a certain product is

$$\overline{C} = 5000x + \frac{125,000}{x}, \quad x > 0$$

where x is the number of machines used in the production process.
   (a) Find the critical values of this function.
   (b) Over what interval does the average cost decrease?
   (c) Over what interval does the average cost increase?

54. *Average costs* Suppose the average costs of a mining operation depend on the number of machines used, and average costs, in dollars, are given by

$$\overline{C}(x) = 2900x + \frac{1,278,900}{x}, \quad x > 0$$

where x is the number of machines used.

(a) Find the critical values of $\overline{C}(x)$ that lie in the domain of the problem.

(b) Over what interval in the domain do average costs decrease?

(c) Over what interval in the domain do average costs increase?

(d) How many machines give minimum average costs?

(e) What is the minimum average cost?

55. **Marginal revenue** Suppose the weekly marginal revenue function for selling x units of a product is given by the graph in the figure.

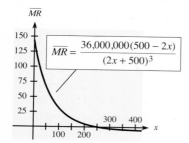

$$\overline{MR} = \frac{36{,}000{,}000(500 - 2x)}{(2x + 500)^3}$$

(a) At each of $x = 150$, $x = 250$, and $x = 350$, what is happening to revenue?

(b) Over what interval is revenue increasing?

(c) How many units must be sold to maximize revenue?

56. **Earnings** Suppose that the rate of change $f'(x)$ of the average annual earnings of new car salespersons is shown in the figure.

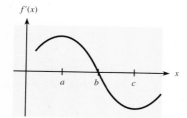

(a) If a, b, and c represent certain years, what is happening to $f(x)$, the average annual earnings of the salespersons, at a, b, and c?

(b) Over what interval (involving a, b, or c) is there an increase in $f(x)$, the average annual earnings of the salespersons?

57. **Revenue** The weekly revenue of a certain recently released film is given by

$$R(t) = \frac{50t}{t^2 + 36}, \quad t \geq 0$$

where R is in millions of dollars and t is in weeks.

(a) Find the critical values.

(b) For how many weeks will weekly revenue increase?

58. **Medication** Suppose that the concentration C of a medication in the bloodstream t hours after an injection is given by

$$C(t) = \frac{0.2t}{t^2 + 1}$$

(a) Determine the number of hours before C attains its maximum.

(b) Find the maximum concentration.

59. **Candidate recognition** Suppose that the proportion P of voters who recognize a candidate's name t months after the start of the campaign is given by

$$P(t) = \frac{13t}{t^2 + 100} + 0.18$$

(a) How many months after the start of the campaign is recognition at its maximum?

(b) To have greatest recognition on November 1, when should a campaign be launched?

60. **Medication** The number of milligrams x of a medication in the bloodstream t hours after a dose is taken can be modeled by

$$x(t) = \frac{2000t}{t^2 + 16}$$

(a) For what t-values is x increasing?

(b) Find the t-value at which x is maximum.

(c) Find the maximum value of x.

61. **Worldwide cell phone subscriberships** In 2013, worldwide cell phone subscriberships surpassed the world's total population of 6.8 billion. Using data from 2009 and projected to 2020, the billions of subscriberships can be modeled by

$$C(t) = 0.000286t^3 - 0.0443t^2 + 1.49t - 5.36$$

where t is equal to the number of years after 2000. When does this model estimate that the number of subscribers reached its maximum, and what maximum does it estimate? *Source: portioresearch.com*

62. **Economic dependency ratio** The economic dependency ratio is defined as the number of persons in the total population who are not in the workforce per 100 in the workforce. Since 1960, Baby Boomers in the workforce and a decrease in the birth rate have caused a significant decrease in the economic dependency ratio. With data for selected years from 1960 and projected to 2050, the economic dependency ratio R can be modeled by the function

$$R(x) = -0.0002x^3 + 0.052x^2 - 4.06x + 192$$

where x is the number of years past 1950 (*Source:* U.S. Department of Labor). Use this model to find the year in which the economic dependency ratio reached its minimum. What was happening in the United States around this time that helps explain why the minimum occurred in this year?

63. **Modeling *China's labor pool*** The following table shows the millions of individuals, ages 15 to 59, in China's labor pool for selected years from 1975 and projected to 2050.
   (a) Find the cubic function $L(t)$ that best models the size of this labor pool, where t is the number of years after 1970. Report the model with three significant digit coefficients.
   (b) Use the reported model to estimate the maximum size of this labor pool before it begins to shrink and the year when the maximum occurs.

Year	Labor Pool (millions)	Year	Labor Pool (millions)
1975	490	2015	920
1980	560	2020	920
1985	650	2025	905
1990	730	2030	875
1995	760	2035	830
2000	800	2040	820
2005	875	2045	800
2010	910	2050	670

Source: United Nations

64. **Modeling *Energy from crude oil*** The table shows the total energy supply from crude oil products, in quadrillion BTUs, for selected years from 2010 and projected to 2040.
   (a) Find the cubic function that is the best model for the data. Use x as the number of years after 2010 and $C(x)$ as the quadrillion BTUs of energy from crude oil products. Report the model with three significant digit coefficients.
   (b) Find the critical values of the reported model.

(c) Find the reported model's critical points and classify them.
(d) Do you think this model will be valid for years past 2040? Explain.

Total Energy Supply from Crude Oil Products (in quadrillion BTUs)

Year	BTUs	Year	BTUs
2010	11.6	2030	13.5
2015	15.6	2035	13.4
2020	16.0	2040	13.1
2025	14.5		

Source: U.S. Energy Information Administration

65. **Modeling *Employment in manufacturing*** The table shows the total employment in U.S. manufacturing, in millions, for selected years from 2010 and projected to 2040.
   (a) Find the cubic function that is the best model for the data. Use t as the number of years after 2010 and $M(t)$ as the millions employed in U.S. manufacturing. Report the model with three significant digit coefficients.
   (b) Find the reported model's critical points and classify them.
   (c) Do you think this model will be accurate for years between the critical points? Explain.

U.S. Employment in Manufacturing (in millions)

Year	Employment	Year	Employment
2010	11.5	2030	12.5
2015	12.4	2035	11.8
2020	12.8	2040	11.0
2025	12.9		

Source: U.S. Department of Energy

10.2

- To determine the concavity of the graph of a function at a point
- To find points of inflection of graphs of functions
- To use the second-derivative test to graph functions

Concavity; Points of Inflection

▌| APPLICATION PREVIEW |▌

Suppose that a retailer wishes to sell his store and uses the graph in Figure 10.14 on the next page to show how profits have increased since he opened the store and the potential for profit in the future. Can we conclude that profits will continue to grow, or should we be concerned about future earnings?

   Note that although profits are still increasing in 2017, they seem to be increasing more slowly than in previous years. Indeed, they appear to have been growing at a decreasing rate since about 2015. We can analyze this situation more carefully by identifying the point at which profit begins to grow more slowly, that is, the *point of diminishing returns*. (See Example 3.)

(Continued)

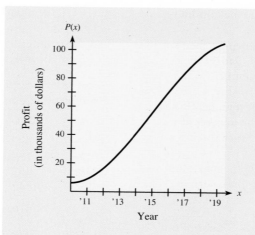

Figure 10.14

Just as we used the first derivative to determine whether a curve was increasing or decreasing on a given interval, we can use the second derivative to determine whether the curve is concave up or concave down on an interval.

Concavity   A curve is said to be **concave up** on an interval (a, b) if at each point on the interval the curve is above its tangent at the point (see Figure 10.15(a)). If the curve is below all its tangents on a given interval, it is **concave down** on the interval (Figure 10.15(b)).

Looking at Figure 10.15(a), we see that the *slopes* of the tangent lines increase over the interval where the graph is concave up. Because $f'(x)$ gives the slopes of those tangents, it follows that $f'(x)$ is increasing over the interval where $f(x)$ is concave up. However, we know that $f'(x)$ is increasing when its derivative, $f''(x)$, is positive. That is, if the second derivative is positive, the curve is concave up.

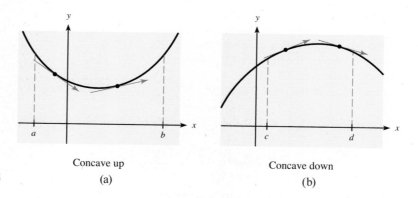

Concave up	Concave down
(a)	(b)

Figure 10.15

Similarly, if the second derivative of a function is negative over an interval, the slopes of the tangents to the graph decrease over that interval. This happens when the tangent lines are above the graph, as in Figure 10.15(b), so the graph must be concave down on this interval.

Thus we see that the second derivative can be used to determine the concavity of a curve.

Concave Up and Concave Down

Assume that the first and second derivatives of function f exist.
The function f is **concave up** on an interval I, if $f''(x) > 0$ on I, and **concave up** at the point $(a, f(a))$, if $f''(a) > 0$.
The function f is **concave down** on an interval I, if $f''(x) < 0$ on I, and **concave down** at the point $(a, f(a))$, if $f''(a) < 0$.

EXAMPLE 1   Concavity at a Point

Is the graph of $f(x) = x^3 - 4x^2 + 3$ concave up or down at the point
(a) $(1, 0)$?   (b) $(2, -5)$?

Solution

(a) We must find $f''(x)$ before we can answer this question.

$$f'(x) = 3x^2 - 8x \qquad f''(x) = 6x - 8$$

Then $f''(1) = 6(1) - 8 = -2$, so the graph is concave down at $(1, 0)$.

(b) Because $f''(2) = 6(2) - 8 = 4$, the graph is concave up at $(2, -5)$. The graph of $f(x) = x^3 - 4x^2 + 3$ is shown in Figure 10.16(a).

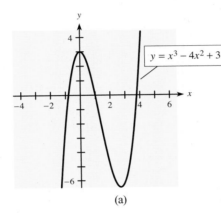

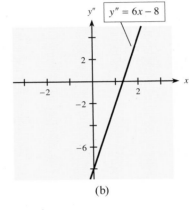

Figure 10.16   (a)   (b)

Points of Inflection   Looking at the graph of $y = x^3 - 4x^2 + 3$ [Figure 10.16(a)], we see that the curve is concave down on the left and concave up on the right. Thus it has changed from concave down to concave up, and from Example 1 we would expect the concavity to change somewhere between $x = 1$ and $x = 2$. Figure 10.16(b) shows the graph of $y'' = f''(x) = 6x - 8$, and we can see that $y'' = 0$ when $x = \frac{4}{3}$ and that $y'' < 0$ for $x < \frac{4}{3}$ and $y'' > 0$ for $x > \frac{4}{3}$. Thus the second derivative changes sign at $x = \frac{4}{3}$, so the concavity of the graph of $y = f(x)$ changes at $x = \frac{4}{3}$, $y = -\frac{47}{27}$. The point where concavity changes is called a **point of inflection.**

Point of Inflection | A point (x_0, y_0) on the graph of a function f is called a **point of inflection** if the curve is concave up on one side of the point and concave down on the other side. The second derivative at this point, $f''(x_0)$, will be 0 or undefined.

In general, we can find points of inflection and information about concavity as follows.

Finding Points of Inflection and Concavity

Procedure	Example
To find the point(s) of inflection of a curve and intervals where it is concave up and where it is concave down:	Find the points of inflection and concavity of the graph of $y = \dfrac{x^4}{2} - x^3 + 5$.
1. Find the second derivative of the function.	1. $y' = f'(x) = 2x^3 - 3x^2$ $y'' = f''(x) = 6x^2 - 6x$
2. Set the second derivative equal to 0, and solve for x. Potential points of inflection occur at these values of x or at values of x where $f(x)$ is defined and $f''(x)$ is undefined.	2. $0 = 6x^2 - 6x = 6x(x - 1)$ has solutions $x = 0$, $x = 1$. $f''(x)$ is defined everywhere.

(Continued)

Finding Points of Inflection and Concavity (*Continued*)

Procedure	Example

3. Find the potential points of inflection.
4. If the second derivative has opposite signs on the two sides of one of these values of x, a point of inflection occurs.
    The curve is concave up where $f''(x) > 0$ and concave down where $f''(x) < 0$.
    The changes in the sign of $f''(x)$ correspond to changes in concavity and occur at points of inflection.

3. $(0, 5)$ and $\left(1, \frac{9}{2}\right)$ are potential points of inflection.
4. A **sign diagram for $f''(x)$** is

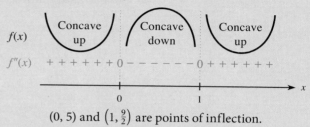

$(0, 5)$ and $\left(1, \frac{9}{2}\right)$ are points of inflection.

See the graph in Figure 10.17.

The graph of $y = \frac{1}{2}x^4 - x^3 + 5$ is shown in Figure 10.17. Note the points of inflection at $(0, 5)$ and $\left(1, \frac{9}{2}\right)$. The point of inflection at $(0, 5)$ is a horizontal point of inflection because $f'(x)$ is also 0 at $x = 0$.

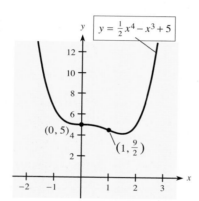

Figure 10.17

EXAMPLE   2   Water Purity

Suppose that a real estate developer wishes to remove pollution from a small lake so that she can sell lakefront homes on a "crystal clear" lake. The graph in Figure 10.18 shows the relation between dollars spent on cleaning the lake and the purity of the water. The point of inflection on the graph is called the **point of diminishing returns** on her investment because it is where the *rate* of return on her investment changes from increasing to decreasing. Show that the rate of change in the purity of the lake, $f'(x)$, is maximized at this point, $x = c$. Assume that $f(c)$, $f'(c)$, and $f''(c)$ are defined.

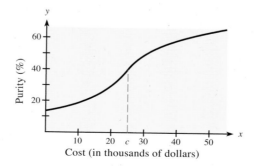

Figure 10.18

Solution

Because $x = c$ is a point of inflection for $f(x)$, we know that the concavity must change at $x = c$. From the figure we see the following.

$$x < c: \quad f(x) \text{ is concave up, so } f''(x) > 0.$$
$$f''(x) > 0 \text{ means that } f'(x) \text{ is increasing.}$$
$$x > c: \quad f(x) \text{ is concave down, so } f''(x) < 0.$$
$$f''(x) < 0 \text{ means that } f'(x) \text{ is decreasing.}$$

Thus $f'(x)$ has $f'(c)$ as its relative maximum.

EXAMPLE 3 | **Diminishing Returns** | **APPLICATION PREVIEW** |

Suppose the annual profit for a store (in thousands of dollars) is given by

$$P(x) = -0.2x^3 + 3x^2 + 6$$

where x is the number of years past 2010. If this model is accurate, find the point of diminishing returns for the profit.

Solution

The point of diminishing returns occurs at the point of inflection. Thus we seek the point where the graph of this function changes from concave up to concave down, if such a point exists.

$$P'(x) = -0.6x^2 + 6x$$
$$P''(x) = -1.2x + 6$$
$$P''(x) = 0 \quad \text{when} \quad 0 = -1.2x + 6 \quad \text{or} \quad \text{when } x = 5$$

Thus $x = 5$ is a possible point of inflection. We test $P''(x)$ to the left and the right of $x = 5$.

$$P''(4) = 1.2 > 0 \Rightarrow \text{concave up to the left of } x = 5$$
$$P''(6) = -1.2 < 0 \Rightarrow \text{concave down to the right of } x = 5$$

Thus $(5, 56)$ is the point of inflection for the graph, and the point of diminishing returns for the profit is when $x = 5$ (in the year 2015) and is $P(5) = 56$ thousand dollars. Figure 10.19 shows the graphs of $P(x)$, $P'(x)$, and $P''(x)$. At $x = 5$, we see that the point of diminishing returns on the graph of $P(x)$ corresponds to the maximum point of the graph of $P'(x)$ and the zero (or x-intercept) of the graph of $P''(x)$.

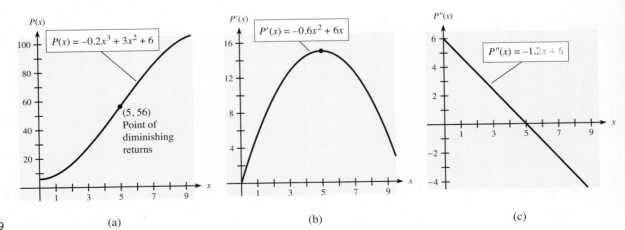

Figure 10.19

(a)   (b)   (c)

✓ **CHECKPOINT**

1. If $f''(x) > 0$, then $f(x)$ is concave _____.
2. At what value of x does the graph $y = \frac{1}{3}x^3 - 2x^2 + 2x$ have a point of inflection?
3. On the graph below, locate any points of inflection (approximately) and label where the curve satisfies $f''(x) > 0$ and $f''(x) < 0$.

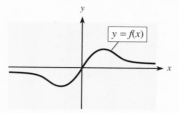

$y = f(x)$

4. Determine whether the following is true or false. If $f''(0) = 0$, then $f(x)$ has a point of inflection at $x = 0$.

Second-Derivative Test

We can use information about points of inflection and concavity to help sketch graphs. For example, if we know that the curve is concave up at a critical point where $f'(x) = 0$, then the point must be a relative minimum because the tangent to the curve is horizontal at the critical point, and only a point at the bottom of a "concave up" curve could have a horizontal tangent [see Figure 10.20(a)].

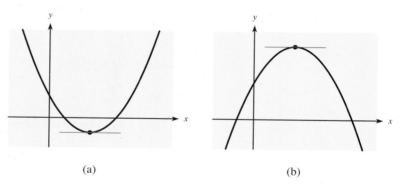

Figure 10.20   (a)   (b)

On the other hand, if the curve is concave down at a critical point where $f'(x) = 0$, then the point is a relative maximum [see Figure 10.20(b)].

Thus we can use the **second-derivative test** to determine whether a critical point where $f'(x) = 0$ is a relative maximum or minimum.

Second-Derivative Test

Procedure

To find relative maxima and minima of a function:

1. Find the critical values of the function.

2. Substitute the critical values into $f(x)$ to find the critical points.

3. Evaluate $f''(x)$ at each critical value for which $f'(x) = 0$.
   (a) If $f''(x_0) < 0$, a relative maximum occurs at x_0.
   (b) If $f''(x_0) > 0$, a relative minimum occurs at x_0.
   (c) If $f''(x_0) = 0$, or $f''(x_0)$ is undefined, the second-derivative test fails; use the first-derivative test.

Example

Find the relative maxima and minima of
$y = f(x) = \frac{1}{3}x^3 - x^2 - 3x + 2$.

1. $f'(x) = x^2 - 2x - 3$
   $0 = (x - 3)(x + 1)$ has solutions $x = -1$ and $x = 3$.
   No values of x make $f'(x)$ undefined.

2. $f(-1) = \frac{11}{3}$ $f(3) = -7$
   The critical points are $\left(-1, \frac{11}{3}\right)$ and $(3, -7)$.

3. $f''(x) = 2x - 2$
   $f''(-1) = 2(-1) - 2 = -4 < 0$, so $\left(-1, \frac{11}{3}\right)$ is a relative maximum point.
   $f''(3) = 2(3) - 2 = 4 > 0$, so $(3, -7)$ is a relative minimum point. (The graph is shown in Figure 10.21.)

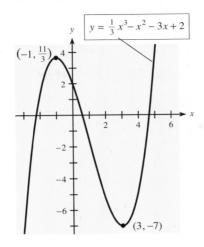

Figure 10.21

Because the second-derivative test (just shown) and the first-derivative test (in Section 10.1) are both methods for classifying critical values, let's compare the advantages and disadvantages of the second derivative test.

Advantage of the Second-Derivative Test	Disadvantages of the Second-Derivative Test
It is quick and easy for many functions.	The second derivative is difficult to find for some functions. The second-derivative test sometimes fails to give results.

EXAMPLE 4   Maxima, Minima, and Points of Inflection

Find the relative maxima and minima and points of inflection of $y = 3x^4 - 4x^3 - 2$.

Solution

$$y' = f'(x) = 12x^3 - 12x^2$$

Solving $0 = 12x^3 - 12x^2 = 12x^2(x - 1)$ gives $x = 1$ and $x = 0$. Thus the critical points are $(1, -3)$ and $(0, -2)$.

$$y'' = f''(x) = 36x^2 - 24x$$
$$f''(1) = 12 > 0 \Rightarrow (1, -3) \text{ is a relative minimum point.}$$
$$f''(0) = 0 \Rightarrow \text{the second-derivative test fails.}$$

Because the second-derivative test fails, we must use the first-derivative test at the critical point $(0, -2)$. A sign diagram for $f'(x)$ shows that $(0, -2)$ is a horizontal point of inflection.

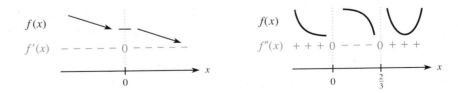

We look for points of inflection by setting $f''(x) = 0$ and solving for x. We find that $0 = 36x^2 - 24x$ has solutions $x = 0$ and $x = \frac{2}{3}$. The sign diagram for $f''(x)$ shows points of inflection at both of these x-values, that is at the points $(0, -2)$ and $\left(\frac{2}{3}, -\frac{70}{27}\right)$. The point $(0, -2)$ is a special point, where the curve changes concavity *and* has a horizontal tangent (see Figure 10.22 on the next page).

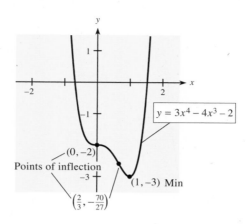

$$y = 3x^4 - 4x^3 - 2$$

$(0, -2)$

Points of inflection

$(1, -3)$ Min

$\left(\frac{2}{3}, -\frac{70}{27}\right)$

Figure 10.22

Calculator Note We can use a graphing calculator to explore the relationships among f, f', and f'', as we did in the previous section for f and f'. See Appendix A, Section 10.2, for details. ▨

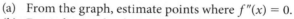

EXAMPLE 5   **Concavity from the Graph of $y = f(x)$**

Figure 10.23 shows the graph of $f(x) = \frac{1}{6}(2x^3 - 3x^2 - 12x + 12)$.

(a) From the graph, estimate points where $f''(x) = 0$.
(b) From the graph, observe intervals where $f''(x) > 0$ and where $f''(x) < 0$.
(c) Check the conclusions from parts (a) and (b) by calculating $f''(x)$ and graphing it.

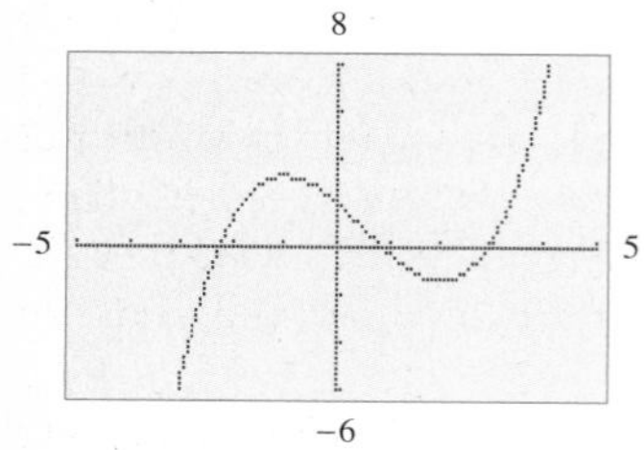

Figure 10.23

Solution

(a) From Figure 10.23, the point of inflection appears to be near $x = \frac{1}{2}$, so we expect $f''(x) = 0$ at (or very near) $x = \frac{1}{2}$.
(b) We see that the graph is concave down (so $f''(x) < 0$) to the left of the point of inflection. That is, $f''(x) < 0$ when $x < \frac{1}{2}$. Similarly, $f''(x) > 0$ when $x > \frac{1}{2}$.
(c) $f(x) = \frac{1}{6}(2x^3 - 3x^2 - 12x + 12)$
$f'(x) = \frac{1}{6}(6x^2 - 6x - 12) = x^2 - x - 2$
$f''(x) = 2x - 1$
Thus $f''(x) = 0$ when $x = \frac{1}{2}$.
Figure 10.24 shows the graph of $f''(x) = 2x - 1$. We see that the graph crosses the x-axis ($f''(x) = 0$) when $x = \frac{1}{2}$, is below the x-axis ($f''(x) < 0$) when $x < \frac{1}{2}$, and is above the x-axis ($f''(x) > 0$) when $x > \frac{1}{2}$. This verifies our conclusions from parts (a) and (b). ▨

Figure 10.24

Spreadsheet Note We can investigate the function in Example 5 by using Excel to find the outputs of $f(x) = \frac{1}{6}(2x^3 - 3x^2 - 12x + 12)$, $f'(x)$, and $f''(x)$ for values of x at and near the critical points and including values where $f''(x) = 0$. The following Excel Spreadsheet illustrates how we extend the Appendix B, Section 10.1, technique for relative maxima and minima by adding a column for $f''(x)$.

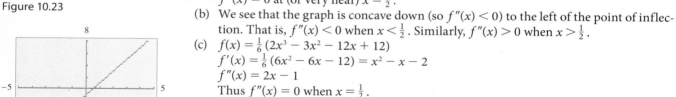

	A	B	C	D
	x	$f(x)$	$f'(x)$	$f''(x)$
1				
2	−2	1.3333	4	−5
3	−1	3.1667	0	−3
4	0	2	−2	−1
5	1/2	0.9167	−2.25	0
6	1	−0.1667	−2	1
7	2	−1.3333	0	3
8	3	0.5	4	5

By looking at column C, we see that $f'(x)$ changes from positive to negative as x passes through the value $x = -1$ and that the derivative changes from negative to positive as x passes through the value $x = 2$. Thus the graph has a relative maximum at $x = -1$ and a relative minimum at $x = 2$. By looking at column D, we can also see that $f''(x)$ changes from negative to positive as x passes through the value $x = 1/2$, so the graph has a point of inflection at $x = 1/2$. ◼

EXAMPLE 6

Concavity from the Graph of $y = f'(x)$

Figure 10.25 shows the graph of $f'(x) = -x^2 - 2x$. Use the graph of $f'(x)$ to do the following.

(a) Find intervals on which $f(x)$ is concave down and concave up.
(b) Find x-values at which $f(x)$ has a point of inflection.
(c) Check the conclusions from parts (a) and (b) by finding $f''(x)$ and graphing it.
(d) For $f(x) = \frac{1}{3}(9 - x^3 - 3x^2)$, calculate $f'(x)$ to verify that this could be $f(x)$.

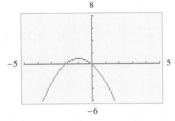

Figure 10.25

Solution

(a) Concavity for $f(x)$ can be found from the sign of $f''(x)$. Because $f''(x)$ is the first derivative of $f'(x)$, wherever the graph of $f'(x)$ is increasing, it follows that $f''(x) > 0$. Thus $f''(x) > 0$ and $f(x)$ is concave up when $x < -1$. Similarly, $f''(x) < 0$, and $f(x)$ is concave down, when $f'(x)$ is decreasing—that is, when $x > -1$.

(b) From (a) we know that $f''(x)$ changes sign at $x = -1$, so $f(x)$ has a point of inflection at $x = -1$. Note that $f'(x)$ has its maximum at the x-value where $f(x)$ has a point of inflection. In fact, points of inflection for $f(x)$ will correspond to relative extrema for $f'(x)$.

(c) For $f'(x) = -x^2 - 2x$, we have $f''(x) = -2x - 2$. Figure 10.26 shows the graph of $y = f''(x)$ and verifies our conclusions from (a) and (b).

(d) If $f(x) = \frac{1}{3}(9 - x^3 - 3x^2)$, then $f'(x) = \frac{1}{3}(-3x^2 - 6x) = -x^2 - 2x$. Figure 10.27 shows the graph of $f(x) = \frac{1}{3}(9 - x^3 - 3x^2)$. Note that the point of inflection and the concavity correspond to what we discovered in parts (a) and (b). ◼

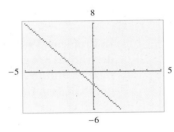

Figure 10.26

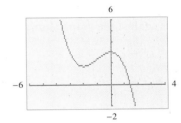

Figure 10.27

The relationships among $f(x)$, $f'(x)$, and $f''(x)$ that we explored in Example 6 can be summarized as follows.

$f(x)$	Concave Up	Concave Down	Point of Inflection	
$f'(x)$	increasing	decreasing	maximum	minimum
$f''(x)$	positive (+)	negative (−)	(+) to (−)	(−) to (+)

---

1. Up
2. At $x = 2$
3. Points of inflection at A, B, and C
   $f''(x) < 0$ to the left of A and between B and C
   $f''(x) > 0$ between A and B and to the right of C

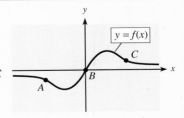

4. (a) False. Consider $f(x) = x^4$.

| EXERCISES | 10.2

In Problems 1 and 2, determine whether each function is concave up or concave down at the indicated points.

1. $f(x) = x^3 - 3x^2 + 1$ at (a) $x = -2$ (b) $x = 3$
2. $f(x) = x^3 + 6x - 4$ at (a) $x = -5$ (b) $x = 7$

In Problems 3–8, use the indicated x-values on the graph of $y = f(x)$ to find the following.

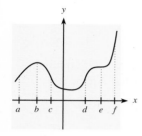

3. Find intervals over which the graph is concave down.
4. Find intervals over which the graph is concave up.
5. Find intervals where $f''(x) > 0$.
6. Find intervals where $f''(x) < 0$.
7. Find the x-coordinates of three points of inflection.
8. Find the x-coordinate of a horizontal point of inflection.

In Problems 9–12, a function and its graph are given. Use the second derivative to determine intervals on which the function is concave up, to determine intervals on which it is concave down, and to locate points of inflection. Check these results against the graph shown.

9. $f(x) = x^3 - 6x^2 + 5x + 6$

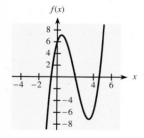

10. $y = x^3 - 9x^2$

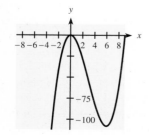

11. $f(x) = \frac{1}{4}x^4 + \frac{1}{2}x^3 - 3x^2 + 3$

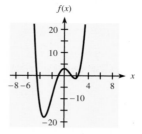

12. $y = 2x^4 - 6x^2 + 4$

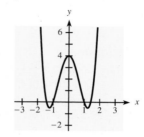

Find the relative maxima, relative minima, and points of inflection, and sketch the graphs of the functions, in Problems 13–18.

13. $y = x^2 - 4x + 2$ 14. $y = x^3 - x^2$
15. $y = \frac{1}{3}x^3 - 2x^2 + 3x + 2$
16. $y = x^3 - 3x^2 + 6$
17. $y = x^4 - 16x^2$
18. $y = x^4 - 8x^3 + 16x^2$

In Problems 19–22, a function and its first and second derivatives are given. Use these to find relative maxima, relative minima, and points of inflection; sketch the graph of each function.

19. $f(x) = 3x^5 - 20x^3$
   $f'(x) = 15x^2(x - 2)(x + 2)$
   $f''(x) = 60x(x^2 - 2)$
20. $f(x) = x^5 - 5x^4$
   $f'(x) = 5x^3(x - 4)$
   $f''(x) = 20x^2(x - 3)$
21. $y = x^{1/3}(x - 4)$ 22. $y = x^{4/3}(x - 7)$
   $y' = \dfrac{4(x - 1)}{3x^{2/3}}$ $y' = \dfrac{7x^{1/3}(x - 4)}{3}$
   $y'' = \dfrac{4(x + 2)}{9x^{5/3}}$ $y'' = \dfrac{28(x - 1)}{9x^{2/3}}$

 In Problems 23 and 24, a function and its graph are given.
(a) From the graph, estimate where $f''(x) > 0$, where $f''(x) < 0$, and where $f''(x) = 0$.
(b) Use (a) to decide where $f'(x)$ has its relative maxima and relative minima.
(c) Verify your results in parts (a) and (b) by finding $f'(x)$ and $f''(x)$ and then graphing each with a graphing utility.

23. $f(x) = -\frac{1}{3}x^3 + x^2 + 8x - 12$

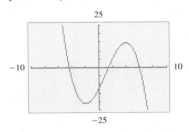

24. $f(x) = \frac{1}{3}x^3 + 2x^2 - 12x - 20$

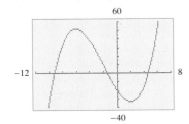

In Problems 25 and 26, $f'(x)$ and its graph are given. Use the graph of $f'(x)$ to determine the following.

(a) **Where is the graph of $f(x)$ concave up and where is it concave down?**

(b) **Where does $f(x)$ have any points of inflection?**

(c) **Find $f''(x)$ and graph it. Then use that graph to check your conclusions from parts (a) and (b).**

(d) **Sketch a possible graph of $f(x)$.**

25. $f'(x) = 4x - x^2$

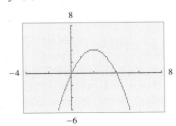

26. $f'(x) = x^2 - x - 2$

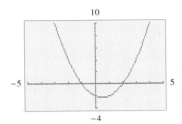

In Problems 27 and 28, use the graph shown in the figure and identify points from A through I that satisfy the given conditions.

27. (a) $f'(x) > 0$ and $f''(x) > 0$

(b) $f'(x) < 0$ and $f''(x) < 0$

(c) $f'(x) = 0$ and $f''(x) > 0$

(d) $f'(x) > 0$ and $f''(x) = 0$

(e) $f'(x) = 0$ and $f''(x) = 0$

28. (a) $f'(x) > 0$ and $f''(x) < 0$

(b) $f'(x) < 0$ and $f''(x) > 0$

(c) $f'(x) = 0$ and $f''(x) < 0$

(d) $f'(x) < 0$ and $f''(x) = 0$

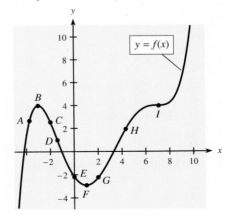

In Problems 29 and 30, a graph is given. Tell where $f(x)$ is concave up, where it is concave down, and where it has points of inflection on the interval $-2 < x < 2$, if the given graph is the graph of

(a) $f(x)$.   (b) $f'(x)$.   (c) $f''(x)$.

29.   30.

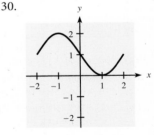

APPLICATIONS

31. *Productivity—diminishing returns* The figure is a typical graph of worker productivity as a function of time on the job.

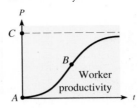

(a) If P represents the productivity and t represents the time, write a mathematical symbol that represents the rate of change of productivity with respect to time.

(b) Which of A, B, and C is the critical point for the rate of change found in part (a)? This point actually corresponds to the point at which the rate of production is maximized, or the point for maximum worker efficiency. In economics, this is called the point of diminishing returns.

(c) Which of A, B, and C corresponds to the upper limit of worker productivity?

32. *Population growth* The figure shows the growth of a population as a function of time.

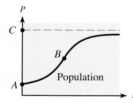

(a) If P represents the population and t represents the time, write a mathematical symbol that represents the rate of change (growth *rate*) of the population with respect to time.

(b) Which of A, B, and C corresponds to the point at which the growth *rate* attains its maximum?

(c) Which of A, B, and C corresponds to the upper limit of population?

33. *Advertising and sales* The figure shows the daily sales volume S as a function of time t since an ad campaign began.

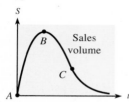

(a) Which of A, B, and C is the point of inflection for the graph?

(b) On which side of C is $d^2S/dt^2 > 0$?

(c) Does the *rate of change* of sales volume attain its minimum at C?

34. *Oxygen purity* The figure shows the oxygen level P (for purity) in a lake t months after an oil spill.

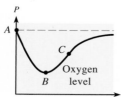

(a) Which of A, B, and C is the point of inflection for the graph?

(b) On which side of C is $d^2P/dt^2 < 0$?

(c) Does the *rate of change* of purity attain its maximum at C?

35. *Production* Suppose that the total number of units produced by a worker in t hours of an 8-hour shift can be modeled by the production function $P(t)$:

$$P(t) = 27t + 12t^2 - t^3$$

(a) Find the number of hours before production is maximized.

(b) Find the number of hours before the rate of production is maximized. That is, find the point of diminishing returns.

36. *Poiseuille's law—velocity of blood* ccording to Poiseuille's law, the speed S of blood through an artery of radius r at a distance x from the artery wall is given by

$$S = k[r^2 - (r - x)^2]$$

where k is a constant. Find the distance x that maximizes the speed.

37. *Advertising and sales—diminishing returns* Suppose that a company's daily sales volume attributed to an advertising campaign is given by

$$S(t) = \frac{3}{t + 3} - \frac{18}{(t + 3)^2} + 1$$

(a) Find how long it will be before sales volume is maximized.

(b) Find how long it will be before the rate of change of sales volume is minimized. That is, find the point of diminishing returns.

38. *Oxygen purity—diminishing returns* Suppose that the oxygen level P (for purity) in a body of water t months after an oil spill is given by

$$P(t) = 500\left[1 - \frac{4}{t + 4} + \frac{16}{(t + 4)^2}\right]$$

(a) Find how long it will be before the oxygen level reaches its minimum.

(b) Find how long it will be before the rate of change of P is maximized. That is, find the point of diminishing returns.

39. *Energy use* Energy use per capita indexed to 1995 means that per capita energy use for any year is viewed as a percent of per capita use in 1995. Using U.S. Department of Energy data for selected years from 1985 and projected to 2035, the per capita energy use, as a percent of the use in 1995, can be modeled by the function

$$E(t) = 0.000772t^3 - 0.0760t^2 + 1.83t + 87.3$$

where t is the number of years past 1980.

(a) Find the critical points for this function.

(b) Use the second-derivative test to classify and interpret these critical points.

40. *Modeling Foreign-born population* The figure gives the percent of the U.S. population that was foreign-born for selected years from 1910 and projected to 2020.

(a) Find the cubic function that is the best fit for the data. Use $x = 0$ to represent 1900, and report the model to three significant digits.

(b) Find the critical point of the reported model when $x > 50$.

(c) Interpret this point in terms of the percent of foreign-born people in the U.S. population.

Percent of Population That Was Foreign-Born, 1910–2020

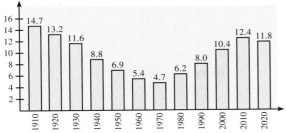

Source: U.S. Bureau of the Census

41. **Modeling** *Civilian labor force* The table gives the size of the U.S. civilian labor force (in millions) for selected years from 1950 and projected to 2050.
    (a) Find a cubic function that models these data, with *x* equal to the number of years after 1950 and *y* equal to the labor force in millions. Report the model with three significant digit coefficients.
    (b) Use the reported model to find the year when the second derivative predicts that the rate of change of the civilian labor force begins to decrease.

Year	Civilian Labor Force (in millions)	Year	Civilian Labor Force (in millions)
1950	62.2	2010	157.7
1960	69.6	2015	162.8
1970	82.8	2020	164.7
1980	106.9	2030	170.1
1990	125.8	2040	180.5
2000	140.9	2050	191.8

Source: U.S. Bureau of Labor Statistics

42. **Modeling** *Elderly men in the workforce* The table gives the percent of men 65 years or older in the workforce for selected years from 1920 and projected to 2030.
    (a) With $x = 0$ representing 1900, find the cubic function that models these data. Report the model with three significant digits.
    (b) Use the reported model to determine when the rate of change of the percent of elderly men in the workforce reached its minimum.
    (c) On the graph of this model, to what does the result in part (b) correspond?

Year	Percent	Year	Percent
1920	55.6	1980	19.0
1930	54.0	1990	16.3
1940	41.8	2000	17.7
1950	45.8	2010	22.6
1960	33.1	2020	27.2
1970	21.8	2030	27.6

Source: U.S. Bureau of the Census

43. **Modeling** *Home health care* The table gives the annual cost per person age 65 and older for home health care from 2006 and projected through 2021. While these annual costs per person may seem modest, the majority of older Americans live healthy, active lives and require no special care.
    (a) With *t* equal to the number of years past 2005, find a cubic function $C(t)$ that models the annual cost per person age 65 and older for home health care. Report the model with three significant digits.
    (b) Find the point of inflection of the reported model. Examine the function on either side of the point of inflection and interpret your results.

Year	Cost (in $)	Year	Cost (in $)
2006	1418	2014	1967
2007	1529	2015	2045
2008	1589	2016	2122
2009	1673	2017	2203
2010	1764	2018	2305
2011	1787	2019	2416
2012	1841	2020	2532
2013	1883	2021	2653

Source: Centers for Medicare and Medicaid Services

OBJECTIVES

10.3

- To find absolute maxima and minima
- To maximize revenue, given the total revenue function
- To minimize the average cost, given the total cost function
- To find the maximum profit from total cost and total revenue functions, or from a profit function

Optimization in Business and Economics

■ | **APPLICATION PREVIEW** |

Suppose a travel agency charges $300 per person for a certain tour when the tour group has 25 people, but will reduce the price by $10 per person for each additional person above the 25. In order to determine the group size that will maximize the revenue, the agency must create a model for the revenue. With such a model, the techniques of calculus can be useful in determining the maximum revenue. (See Example 2.)

Most companies (such as the travel agency) are interested in obtaining the greatest possible revenue or profit. Similarly, manufacturers of products

(Continued)

are concerned about producing their products for the lowest possible average cost per unit. Therefore, rather than just finding the relative maxima or relative minima of a function, we will consider where the absolute maximum or absolute minimum of a function occurs in a given interval.

In this section we will discuss how to find the absolute extrema of a function and then use these techniques to solve applications involving revenue, cost, and profit.

As the name implies, **absolute extrema** are the functional values that are the largest or smallest values over the entire domain of the function (or over the interval of interest).

Absolute Extrema	The value $f(a)$ is the **absolute maximum** of f if $f(a) \geq f(x)$ for all x in the domain of f (or over the interval of interest). The value $f(b)$ is the **absolute minimum** of f if $f(b) \leq f(x)$ for all x in the domain of f (or over the interval of interest).

Let us begin by considering the graph of $y = (x - 1)^2$, shown in Figure 10.28(a). This graph has a relative minimum at $(1, 0)$. Note that the relative minimum is the lowest point on the graph. In this case, the point $(1, 0)$ is an **absolute minimum point**, and 0 is the absolute minimum for the function. Similarly, when there is a point that is the highest point on the graph over the domain of the function, we call the point an **absolute maximum point** of the graph of the function.

In Figure 10.28(a), we see that there is no relative maximum. However, if the domain of the function is restricted to the interval $\left[\frac{1}{2}, 2\right]$, then we get the graph shown in Figure 10.28(b). In this case, there is an absolute maximum of 1 at the point $(2, 1)$ and the absolute minimum of 0 is still at $(1, 0)$.

If the domain of $y = (x - 1)^2$ is restricted to the interval $[2, 3]$, the resulting graph is that shown in Figure 10.28(c). In this case, the absolute minimum is 1 and occurs at the point $(2, 1)$, and the absolute maximum is 4 and occurs at $(3, 4)$.

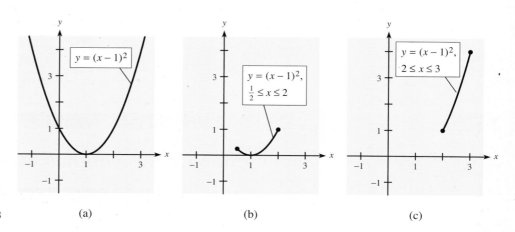

Figure 10.28   (a)   (b)   (c)

As the preceding discussion indicates, if the domain of a continuous function is limited to a closed interval, the absolute maximum or minimum may occur at an endpoint of the domain. In testing functions with limited domains for absolute maxima and minima, we must compare the function values at the endpoints of the domain with the function values at the critical values found by taking derivatives. In the management, life, and social sciences, a limited domain occurs very often, because many quantities are required to be positive, or at least nonnegative.

Maximizing Revenue   Because the marginal revenue is the first derivative of the total revenue, the total revenue function will have a critical point at the point where the marginal revenue equals 0. With the total revenue function $R(x) = 16x - 0.02x^2$, the point where $R'(x) = 0$ is clearly a maximum because $R(x)$ is a parabola that opens downward. But the domain may be limited, the revenue function may not always be a parabola, or the critical point may not always be a maximum, so it is important to verify where the maximum value occurs.

EXAMPLE 1   Revenue

The total revenue in dollars for a firm is given by

$$R(x) = 8000x - 40x^2 - x^3$$

where x is the number of units sold per day. If only 50 units can be sold per day, find the number of units that must be sold to maximize revenue. Find the maximum revenue.

Solution

This revenue function is limited to x in the interval $[0, 50]$. Thus, the maximum revenue will occur at a critical value in this interval or at an endpoint. $R'(x) = 8000 - 80x - 3x^2$, so we must solve $8000 - 80x - 3x^2 = 0$ for x:

$$(40 - x)(200 + 3x) = 0 \quad \text{means} \quad 40 - x = 0 \quad \text{or} \quad 200 + 3x = 0$$

Thus
$$x = 40 \quad \text{or} \quad x = -\frac{200}{3}$$

The negative value of x is not relevant, so for $x = 40$ we use either the second-derivative test or the first-derivative test with a sign diagram.

Second-Derivative Test	First-Derivative Test
$R''(x) = -80 - 6x$, $R''(40) = -320 < 0$, so $x = 40$ gives a relative maximum.	$R(x)$ $R'(x)$ $+ + + + + + + + + 0 - - - - - - -$ $\qquad\qquad\qquad\qquad 40$ $\quad x$

These tests show that a relative maximum occurs at $x = 40$, giving revenue $R(40) = \$192{,}000$. Checking the endpoints $x = 0$ and $x = 50$ gives $R(0) = \$0$ and $R(50) = \$175{,}000$. Thus $R = \$192{,}000$ at $x = 40$ is the (absolute) maximum revenue.   ∎

✓ CHECKPOINT   1. True or false: If $R(x)$ is the revenue function, we find all possible points where $R(x)$ could be maximized by solving $\overline{MR} = 0$ for x.

EXAMPLE 2   Revenue | APPLICATION PREVIEW |

A travel agency will plan tours for groups of 25 or larger. If the group contains exactly 25 people, the price is $300 per person. However, the price per person is reduced by $10 for each additional person above the 25. What size group will produce the largest revenue for the agency?

Solution
The total revenue is

$$R = (\text{number of people})(\text{price per person})$$

The table shows how the revenue is changed by increases in the size of the group.

Number in Group	Price per Person	Revenue
25	300	7500
$25 + 1$	$300 - 10$	7540
$25 + 2$	$300 - 20$	7560
$\vdots$	$\vdots$	$\vdots$
$25 + x$	$300 - 10x$	$(25 + x)(300 - 10x)$

Thus when x is the number of people added to the 25, the total revenue will be

$$R = R(x) = (25 + x)(300 - 10x) \quad \text{or} \quad R(x) = 7500 + 50x - 10x^2$$

This is a quadratic function, so its graph is a parabola that is concave down. Thus, a maximum will occur at its vertex, where $R'(x) = 0$.

$R'(x) = 50 - 20x$, and the solution to $0 = 50 - 20x$ is $x = 2.5$. Thus adding 2.5 people to the group should maximize the total revenue. But we cannot add half a person, so we will test the total revenue function for 27 people and 28 people. This will determine the optimal group size.

For $x = 2$ (giving 27 people) we get $R(2) = 7500 + 50(2) - 10(2)^2 = 7560$. For $x = 3$ (giving 28 people) we get $R(3) = 7500 + 50(3) - 10(3)^2 = 7560$. Note that both 27 and 28 people give the same total revenue and that this revenue is greater than the revenue for 25 people. Thus the revenue is maximized at either 27 or 28 people in the group. (See Figure 10.29.)

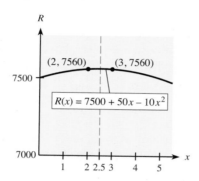

Figure 10.29

Minimizing Average Cost

Because the total cost function is always increasing for $x \geq 0$, the number of units that will make the total cost a minimum is always $x = 0$ units, which gives an absolute minimum. However, it is more useful to find the number of units that will make the **average cost** per unit a minimum.

Average Cost

If the total cost function is $C = C(x)$, then the per unit **average cost function** is

$$\overline{C} = \frac{C(x)}{x}$$

Note that the average cost per unit is undefined if no units are produced.

We can use derivatives to find the minimum of the average cost function, as the next example shows.

EXAMPLE 3   Average Cost

If the total cost function for a commodity is given by $C = \frac{1}{4}x^2 + 4x + 100$ dollars, where x represents the number of units produced, producing how many units will result in a minimum *average cost* per unit? Find the minimum average cost.

Solution
Begin by finding the average cost function and its derivative:

$$\overline{C} = \frac{\dfrac{1}{4}x^2 + 4x + 100}{x} = \frac{1}{4}x + 4 + \frac{100}{x}$$

$$\overline{C}' = \overline{C}'(x) = \frac{1}{4} - \frac{100}{x^2}$$

Setting $\overline{C}' = 0$ gives

$$0 = \frac{1}{4} - \frac{100}{x^2} \quad \text{so} \quad 0 = x^2 - 400 \quad \text{and} \quad x = \pm 20$$

Because the quantity produced must be positive, 20 units should minimize the average cost per unit. We show that it is an absolute minimum by using the second derivative to show $\overline{C}$ is concave up for all positive x.

$$\overline{C}''(x) = \frac{200}{x^3} \quad \text{so} \quad \overline{C}''(x) > 0 \quad \text{when } x > 0$$

Thus the minimum average cost per unit occurs if 20 units are produced. The graph of the average cost per unit is shown in Figure 10.30. The minimum average cost per unit is $\overline{C}(20) = \$14$.

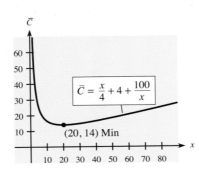

Figure 10.30

✓ CHECKPOINT

2. If $C(x) = 0.01x^2 + 20x + 2500$, form $\overline{C}(x)$, the average cost function, and find the minimum average cost.

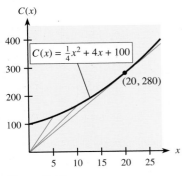

Figure 10.31

The graph of the cost function for the commodity in Example 3 is shown in Figure 10.31, along with several lines that join $(0, 0)$ to a point of the form $(x, C(x))$ on the total cost graph. Note that the slope of each of these lines has the form

$$\frac{C(x) - 0}{x - 0} = \frac{C(x)}{x}$$

so the slope of each line is the *average cost* for the given number of units at the point on $C(x)$. Note that the line from the origin to the point on the curve where $x = 20$ is tangent to the total cost curve. Hence, when $x = 20$, the slope of this line represents both the derivative of the cost function (the *marginal cost*) and the *average cost*. All lines from the origin to points with x-values larger than 20 or smaller than 20 are steeper (and therefore have greater slopes) than the line to the point where $x = 20$. Thus the minimum average cost occurs where the average cost equals the marginal cost. You will be asked to show this analytically in Problems 21 and 22 of the 10.3 Exercises.

Maximizing Profit   We have defined the marginal profit function as the derivative of the profit function. That is,

$$\overline{MP} = P'(x)$$

In this chapter we have seen how to use the derivative to find maxima and minima for various functions. Now we can apply those same techniques in the context of **profit maximization.** We can use marginal profit to maximize profit functions.

If there is a physical limitation on the number of units that can be produced in a given period of time, then the endpoints of the interval caused by these limitations should also be checked.

EXAMPLE 4 **Profit**

Suppose that the production capacity for a certain commodity cannot exceed 30. If the total profit for this commodity is

$$P(x) = 4x^3 - 210x^2 + 3600x - 200 \quad \text{dollars}$$

where x is the number of units sold, find the number of items that will maximize profit.

Solution

The restrictions on capacity mean that $P(x)$ is restricted by $0 \le x \le 30$. The marginal profit function is

$$P'(x) = 12x^2 - 420x + 3600$$

Setting $P'(x)$ equal to 0, we get

$$0 = 12(x - 15)(x - 20)$$

so $P'(x) = 0$ at $x = 15$ *and* $x = 20$. A sign diagram for $P'(x)$ tests these critical values.

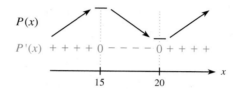

Thus, at (15, 20,050) the total profit function has a *relative* maximum, but we must check the endpoints (0 and 30) before deciding whether it is the absolute maximum.

$$P(0) = -200 \quad \text{and} \quad P(30) = 26,800$$

Thus the absolute maximum profit is $26,800, and it occurs at the endpoint, $x = 30$. Figure 10.32 shows the graph of the profit function.

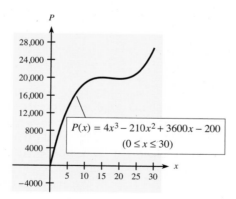

Figure 10.32

In a **monopolistic market,** the seller who has a monopoly controls the supply of a product and can force the price higher by limiting supply.

If the demand function for the product is $p = f(x)$, total revenue for the sale of x units is $R(x) = px = f(x) \cdot x$. Note that the price p is fixed by the market in a competitive market but varies with output for the monopolist.

If $\overline{C} = \overline{C}(x)$ represents the average cost per unit sold, then the total cost for the x units sold is $C = \overline{C} \cdot x = \overline{C}x$. Because we have both total cost and total revenue as a function of the quantity, x, we can maximize the profit function, $P(x) = px - \overline{C}x$, where p represents the demand function $p = f(x)$ and $\overline{C}$ represents the average cost function $\overline{C} = \overline{C}(x)$.

EXAMPLE 5

MONOPOLY

One big player controls supply and dictates pricing.

© Eric Isselee/Shutterstock.com

Profit in a Monopoly Market

The price of a product in dollars is related to the number of units x demanded daily by

$$p = 168 - 0.2x$$

A monopolist finds that the daily average cost for this product is

$$\overline{C} = 120 + x \quad \text{dollars}$$

(a) How many units must be sold daily to maximize profit?
(b) What is the selling price at this "optimal" level of production?
(c) What is the maximum possible daily profit?

Solution

(a) The total revenue function for the product is

$$R(x) = px = (168 - 0.2x)x = 168x - 0.2x^2$$

and the total cost function is

$$C(x) = \overline{C} \cdot x = (120 + x)x = 120x + x^2$$

Thus the profit function is

$$P(x) = R(x) - C(x) = 168x - 0.2x^2 - (120x + x^2) = 48x - 1.2x^2$$

Then $P'(x) = 48 - 2.4x$, so $P'(x) = 0$ when $x = 20$. We see that $P''(20) = -2.4$, so by the second-derivative test, $P(x)$ has a maximum at $x = 20$. That is, selling 20 units will maximize profit.

(b) The selling price is determined by $p = 168 - 0.2x$, so the price that will result from supplying 20 units per day is $p = 168 - 0.2(20) = 164$. That is, the "optimal" selling price is $164 per unit.

(c) The profit at $x = 20$ is $P(20) = 48(20) - 1.2(20)^2 = 960 - 480 = 480$. Thus the maximum possible profit is $480 per day. ∎

COMPETITION

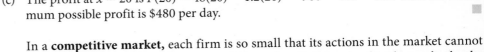

© Stephen Coburn/Shutterstock.com

Several players are so small that individual actions cannot affect product

In a **competitive market,** each firm is so small that its actions in the market cannot affect the price of the product. The price of the product is determined in the market by the intersection of the market demand curve (from all consumers) and market supply curve (from all firms that supply this product). The firm can sell as little or as much as it desires at the market equilibrium price.

Therefore, a firm in a competitive market has a total revenue function given by $R(x) = px$, where p is the market equilibrium price for the product and x is the quantity sold.

EXAMPLE 6

Profit in a Competitive Market

A firm in a competitive market must sell its product for $200 per unit. The average cost per unit (per month) is $\overline{C} = 80 + x$, where x is the number of units sold per month. How many units should be sold to maximize profit?

Solution

If the average cost per unit is $\overline{C} = 80 + x$, then the total cost of x units is given by $C(x) = (80 + x)x = 80x + x^2$. The revenue per unit is $200, so the total revenue is given by $R(x) = 200x$. Thus the profit function is

$$P(x) = R(x) - C(x) = 200x - (80x + x^2), \quad \text{or} \quad P(x) = 120x - x^2$$

Then $P'(x) = 120 - 2x$. Setting $P'(x) = 0$ and solving for x gives $x = 60$. Because $P''(60) = -2$, the profit is maximized when the firm sells 60 units per month. ∎

3. (a) If $p = 5000 - x$ gives the demand function in a monopoly market, find $R(x)$, if it is possible with this information.
   (b) If $p = 5000 - x$ gives the demand function in a competitive market, find $R(x)$, if it is possible with this information.

4. If $R(x) = 400x - 0.25x^2$ and $C(x) = 150x + 0.25x^2 + 8500$ are the total revenue and total cost (both in dollars) for x units of a product, find the number of units that gives maximum profit and find the maximum profit.

Calculator Note

As we have seen, graphing calculators can be used to locate maximum values. In addition, if it is difficult to determine critical values algebraically, we may be able to approximate them graphically. For example, if

$$P(x) = 2500 - \frac{3000}{x + 1} - 12x - x^2 \qquad \text{then} \qquad P'(x) = \frac{3000}{(x + 1)^2} - 12 - 2x$$

Finding the critical values by solving $P'(x) = 0$ is difficult unless we use a graphing approach. Figure 10.33(a) shows the graph of $P(x)$, and Figure 10.33(b) shows the graph of $P'(x)$. These figures indicate that the maximum occurs near $x = 10$.

By adjusting the viewing window for $P'(x)$, we obtain the graph in Figure 10.34. This shows that $P'(x) = 0$ when $x = 9$. The maximum is $P(9) = 2500 - 300 - 108 - 81 = 2011$. See Appendix A, Section 10.3, for additional details. ■

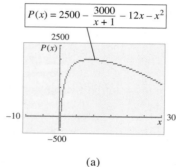

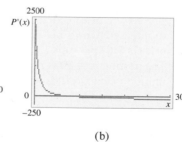

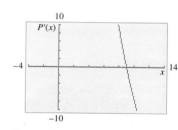

Figure 10.33   (a)   (b)   Figure 10.34

Spreadsheet Note

The solver feature of Excel can also be used to find optimal values of functions. See Appendix B, Section 10.3, and the Online Excel Guide for complete details. ■

1. False. $\overline{MR} = R'(x)$, but there may also be critical points where $R'(x)$ is undefined, or $R(x)$ may be maximized at endpoints of a restricted domain.

2. $\overline{C}(x) = \dfrac{C(x)}{x} = 0.01x + 20 + \dfrac{2500}{x}$

   The minimum average cost per unit is $\overline{C}(500) = 30$ dollars per unit.

3. (a) $R(x) = p \cdot x = 5000x - x^2$
   (b) In a competitive market, we need to know the supply function and find the equilibrium price before we can form $R(x)$.

4. The (absolute) maximum profit occurs when $x = 250$ and is $P(250) = \$22,750$.

| EXERCISES | 10.3

In Problems 1–4, find the absolute maxima and minima for $f(x)$ on the interval $[a, b]$.

1. $f(x) = x^3 - 2x^2 - 4x + 2, [-1, 3]$
2. $f(x) = x^3 - 3x + 3, [-3, 1.5]$
3. $f(x) = x^3 + x^2 - x + 1, [-2, 0]$
4. $f(x) = x^3 - x^2 - x, [-0.5, 2]$

MAXIMIZING REVENUE

5. (a) If the total revenue function for a hammer is $R = 36x - 0.01x^2$, then sale of how many hammers, x, will maximize the total revenue in dollars? Find the maximum revenue.
   (b) Find the maximum revenue if production is limited to at most 1500 hammers.

6. (a) If the total revenue function for a blender is $R(x) = 25x - 0.05x^2$, sale of how many units, x, will provide the maximum total revenue in dollars? Find the maximum revenue.
   (b) Find the maximum revenue if production is limited to at most 200 blenders.

7. If the total revenue function for a computer is $R(x) = 2000x - 20x^2 - x^3$, find the level of sales, x, that maximizes revenue and find the maximum revenue in dollars.

8. A firm has total revenues given by

   $$R(x) = 2800x - 8x^2 - x^3 \text{ dollars}$$

   for x units of a product. Find the maximum revenue from sales of that product.

9. An agency charges $100 per person for a trip to a concert if 70 people travel in a group. But for each person above the 70, the charge will be reduced by $1.00. How many people will maximize the total revenue for the agency if the trip is limited to at most 90 people?

10. A company handles an apartment building with 70 units. Experience has shown that if the rent for each of the units is $1080 per month, all the units will be filled, but 1 unit will become vacant for each $20 increase in the monthly rate. What rent should be charged to maximize the total revenue from the building if the upper limit on the rent is $1300 per month?

11. A cable TV company has 4000 customers paying $110 each month. If each $1 reduction in price attracts 50 new customers, find the price that yields maximum revenue. Find the maximum revenue.

12. If club members charge $5 admission to a classic car show, 1000 people will attend, and for each $1 increase in price, 100 fewer people will attend. What price will give the maximum revenue for the show? Find the maximum revenue.

13. The function $\bar{R}(x) = R(x)/x$ defines the average revenue for selling x units. For

    $$R(x) = 2000x + 20x^2 - x^3$$

    (a) find the maximum average revenue.
    (b) show that $\bar{R}(x)$ attains its maximum at an x-value where $\bar{R}(x) = \overline{MR}$.

14. For the revenue function given by

    $$R(x) = 2800x + 8x^2 - x^3$$

    (a) find the maximum average revenue.
    (b) show that $\bar{R}(x)$ attains its maximum at an x-value where $\bar{R}(x) = \overline{MR}$.

MINIMIZING AVERAGE COST

15. If the total cost function for a lamp is $C(x) = 250 + 33x + 0.1x^2$ dollars, producing how many units, x, will result in a minimum average cost per unit? Find the minimum average cost.

16. If the total cost function for a product is $C(x) = 300 + 10x + 0.03x^2$ dollars, producing how many units, x, will result in a minimum average cost per unit? Find the minimum average cost.

17. If the total cost function for a product is $C(x) = 810 + 0.1x^2$ dollars, producing how many units, x, will result in a minimum average cost per unit? Find the minimum average cost.

18. If the total cost function for a product is $C(x) = 250 + 6x + 0.1x^2$ dollars, producing how many units, x, will minimize the average cost? Find the minimum average cost.

19. If the total cost function for a product is $C(x) = 100(0.02x + 4)^3$ dollars, where x represents the number of hundreds of units produced, producing how many units will minimize average cost? Find the minimum average cost.

20. If the total cost function for a product is $C(x) = (x + 5)^3$ dollars, where x represents the number of hundreds of units produced, producing how many units will minimize average cost? Find the minimum average cost.

21. For the cost function $C(x) = 25 + 13x + x^2$, show that average costs are minimized at the x-value where

    $$\bar{C}(x) = \overline{MC}$$

22. For the cost function $C(x) = 300 + 10x + 0.03x^2$, show that average costs are minimized at the x-value where

    $$\bar{C}(x) = \overline{MC}$$

The graphs in Problems 23 and 24 show total cost functions. For each problem:

(a) **Explain how to use the total cost graph to determine the level of production at which average cost is minimized.**

(b) **Determine that level of production.**

23.

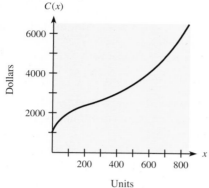

Units

24.

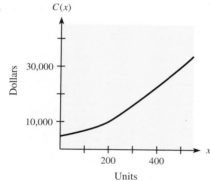

Units

MAXIMIZING PROFIT

25. If the profit function for a product is $P(x) = 5600x + 85x^2 - x^3 - 200,000$ dollars, selling how many items, x, will produce a maximum profit? Find the maximum profit.

26. If the profit function for a commodity is $P = 6400x - 18x^2 - \frac{1}{3}x^3 - 40,000$ dollars, selling how many units, x, will result in a maximum profit? Find the maximum profit.

27. A manufacturer estimates that its product can be produced at a total cost of $C(x) = 45,000 + 100x + x^3$ dollars. If the manufacturer's total revenue from the sale of x units is $R(x) = 4600x$ dollars, determine the level of production x that will maximize the profit. Find the maximum profit.

28. A product can be produced at a total cost $C(x) = 800 + 100x^2 + x^3$ dollars, where x is the number produced. If the total revenue is given by $R(x) = 60,000x - 50x^2$ dollars, determine the level of production, x, that will maximize the profit. Find the maximum profit.

29. A firm can produce only 1000 units per month. The monthly total cost is given by $C(x) = 300 + 200x$ dollars, where x is the number produced. If the total revenue is given by $R(x) = 250x - \frac{1}{100}x^2$ dollars, how

many items, x, should the firm produce for maximum profit? Find the maximum profit.

30. A firm can produce 100 units per week. If its total cost function is $C = 500 + 1500x$ dollars and its total revenue function is $R = 1600x - x^2$ dollars, how many units, x, should it produce to maximize its profit? Find the maximum profit.

31. *Marginal revenue and marginal cost* The figure shows the graph of a quadratic revenue function and a linear cost function.

(a) At which of the four x-values shown is the distance between the revenue and the cost greatest?

(b) At which of the four x-values shown is the profit largest?

(c) At which of the four x-values shown is the slope of the tangent to the revenue curve equal to the slope of the cost line?

(d) What is the relationship between marginal cost and marginal revenue when profit is at its maximum value?

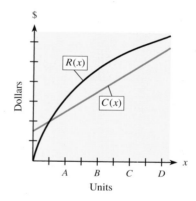

Units

32. *Marginal revenue and marginal cost* The figure shows the graph of revenue function $y = R(x)$ and cost function $y = C(x)$.

(a) At which of the four x-values shown is the profit largest?

(b) At which of the four x-values shown is the slope of the tangent to the revenue curve equal to the slope of the tangent to the cost curve?

(c) What is the relationship between marginal cost and marginal revenue when profit is at its maximum value?

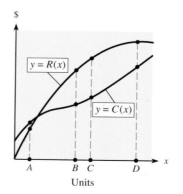

Units

33. A company handles an apartment building with 50 units. Experience has shown that if the rent for each of the units is $720 per month, all of the units will be filled, but 1 unit will become vacant for each $20 increase in this monthly rate. If the monthly cost of maintaining the apartment building is $12 per rented unit, what rent should be charged per month to maximize the profit?

34. A travel agency will plan a tour for groups of size 25 or larger. If the group contains exactly 25 people, the cost is $500 per person. However, each person's cost is reduced by $10 for each additional person above the 25. If the travel agency incurs a cost of $125 per person for the tour, what size group will give the agency the maximum profit?

35. A firm has monthly average costs, in dollars, given by

$$\overline{C} = \frac{45,000}{x} + 100 + x$$

where x is the number of units produced per month. The firm can sell its product in a competitive market for $1600 per unit. If production is limited to 600 units per month, find the number of units that gives maximum profit, and find the maximum profit.

36. A small business has weekly average costs, in dollars, of

$$\overline{C} = \frac{100}{x} + 30 + \frac{x}{10}$$

where x is the number of units produced each week. The competitive market price for this business's product is $46 per unit. If production is limited to 150 units per week, find the level of production that yields maximum profit, and find the maximum profit.

37. The weekly demand function for x units of a product sold by only one firm is $p = 600 - \frac{1}{2}x$ dollars, and the average cost of production and sale is $\overline{C} = 300 + 2x$ dollars.
    (a) Find the quantity that will maximize profit.
    (b) Find the selling price at this optimal quantity.
    (c) What is the maximum profit?

38. The monthly demand function for x units of a product sold by a monopoly is $p = 8000 - x$ dollars, and its average cost is $\overline{C} = 4000 + 5x$ dollars.
    (a) Determine the quantity that will maximize profit.
    (b) Determine the selling price at the optimal quantity.
    (c) Determine the maximum profit.

39. The monthly demand function for a product sold by a monopoly is $p = 1960 - \frac{1}{3}x^2$ dollars, and the average cost is $\overline{C} = 1000 + 2x + x^2$ dollars. Production is limited to 1000 units and x is in hundreds of units.
    (a) Find the quantity that will give maximum profit.
    (b) Find the maximum profit.

40. The monthly demand function for x units of a product sold by a monopoly is $p = 5900 - \frac{1}{2}x^2$ dollars, and its average cost is $\overline{C} = 3020 + 2x$ dollars. If production is limited to 100 units, find the number of units that maximizes profit. Will the maximum profit result in a profit or loss?

41. An industry with a monopoly on a product has its average weekly costs, in dollars, given by

$$\overline{C} = \frac{10,000}{x} + 60 - 0.03x + 0.00001x^2$$

The weekly demand for x units of the product is given by $p = 120 - 0.015x$ dollars. Find the price the industry should set and the number of units it should produce to obtain maximum profit. Find the maximum profit.

42. A large corporation with monopolistic control in the marketplace has its average daily costs, in dollars, given by

$$\overline{C} = \frac{800}{x} + 100x + x^2$$

The daily demand for x units of its product is given by $p = 60,000 - 50x$ dollars. Find the quantity that gives maximum profit, and find the maximum profit. What selling price should the corporation set for its product?

43. Coastal Soda Sales has been granted exclusive market rights to the upcoming Beaufort Seafood Festival. This means that during the festival Coastal will have a monopoly, and it is anxious to take advantage of this position in its pricing strategy. The daily demand function is

$$p = 2 - 0.0004x$$

and the daily total cost function is

$$C(x) = 800 + 0.2x + 0.0001x^2$$

where x is the number of units.
    (a) Determine Coastal's total revenue and profit functions.
    (b) What profit-maximizing price per soda should Coastal charge, how many sodas per day would it expect to sell at this price, and what would be the daily profits?
    (c) If the festival organizers wanted to set an economically efficient price of $1.25 per soda, how would this change the results from part (b)? Would Coastal be willing to provide sodas for the festival at this regulated price? Why or why not?

44. A retiree from a large Atlanta financial services firm decides to keep busy and supplement her retirement income by opening a small upscale folk art company near Charleston, South Carolina. The company, Sand Dollar Art, manufactures and sells in a purely competitive market, and the following monthly market information for x units at p per unit applies:

Demand: $p = 2000 - 4.5x$
Supply: $p = 100 + 0.25x$

(a) Find the market equilibrium quantity and price for this market.

(b) If Sand Dollar Art's monthly cost function is

$$C(x) = 400 + 100x + x^2$$

find the profit-maximizing monthly quantity. What are the total monthly revenues and total monthly costs? What monthly profit does Sand Dollar Art earn?

(c) Assuming that Sand Dollar Art is representative of firms in this competitive market, what is its market share?

MISCELLANEOUS APPLICATIONS

45. **Modeling** *Social Security beneficiaries* The numbers of millions of Social Security beneficiaries for selected years and projected into the future are given in the table.

(a) Find the cubic function that models these data, with x equal to the number of years past 1950. Report the model with three significant digits.

(b) Find the point of inflection of the graph of the reported model for $x > 0$.

(c) Graph this function and discuss what the point of inflection indicates.

Year	Number of Beneficiaries (millions)	Year	Number of Beneficiaries (millions)
1950	2.9	2002	44.8
1960	14.3	2010	53.3
1970	25.2	2020	68.8
1980	35.1	2030	82.7
1990	39.5		

Source: Social Security Trustees Report

46. **Modeling** *Workforce participation: Women* For women age 16 and older, the table gives the percent of this group that participates in the U.S. workforce for selected years from 1950 and projected to 2050.

Year	Percent	Year	Percent
1950	33.9	2010	62.2
1960	37.7	2015	62.1
1970	43.3	2020	60.3
1980	51.5	2030	57.4
1990	57.5	2040	56.7
2000	60.2	2050	56.6

Source: U.S. Bureau of the Census

(a) With x as the number of years past 1940, find a quartic function that models the data. Report the model with three significant digit coefficients.

(b) For the years from 1950 to 2050, determine all critical points of the reported model.

(c) Find the absolute maximum and absolute minimum of the reported model. Interpret the coordinates of each point.

(d) Find the absolute maximum and absolute minimum of the data set.

47. **Dow Jones Industrial Average** The figure shows the Dow Jones Industrial Average for all of 2001, the year of the terrorist attacks on New York City and Washington, D.C.

(a) Approximate when during 2001 the Dow reached its absolute maximum for that year.

(b) When do you think the Dow reached its absolute minimum for this period? What happened to trigger this?

Dow Jones Industrial Average

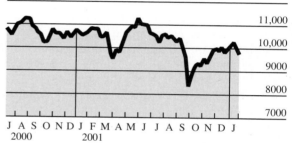

J A S O N D J F M A M J J A S O N D J
2000   2001

Source: From *The Wall Street Journal*, January 17, 2002. Copyright © 2002 by Dow Jones & Co. Reprinted by permission of Dow Jones & Co. via Copyright Clearance Center.

48. **Dow Jones averages** The figure shows the daily Dow Jones Industrial Average (DJIA) and its 30-day moving average from late July to early November. Use the figure to complete the following.

(a) Approximate the absolute maximum point and absolute minimum point for the daily DJIA.

(b) Approximate the absolute maximum point and absolute minimum point for the DJIA 30-day moving average.

$INDU (Dow Jones Industrial Average) INDX

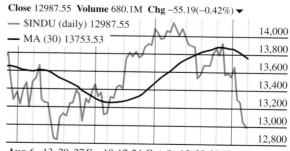

Close 12987.55 Volume 680.1M Chg −55.19(−0.42%) ▼

Aug 6   13 20 27 Sep 10 17 24 Oct 8   15 22 29 Nov 12

Source: StockCharts.com

49. *Social Security support* The graph shows the number of workers, $W = f(t)$, still in the workforce per Social Security beneficiary (historically and projected into the future) as a function of time t, in calendar years with $1950 \le t \le 2050$. Use the graph to answer the following.
    (a) What is the absolute maximum of $f(t)$?
    (b) What is the absolute minimum of $f(t)$?
    (c) Does this graph suggest that Social Security taxes will rise or will fall in the early 21st century? Explain.

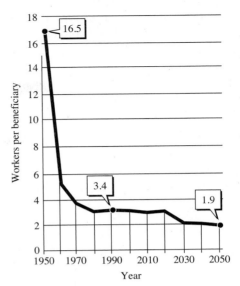

Source: Social Security Administration

10.4

- To apply the procedures for finding maxima and minima to solve problems from the management, life, and social sciences

Applications of Maxima and Minima

■| APPLICATION PREVIEW |■

Suppose that a company needs 1,000,000 items during a year and that preparation costs are $800 for each production run. Suppose further that it costs the company $6 to produce each item and $1 to store each item for up to a year. Find the number of units that should be produced in each production run so that the total costs of production and storage are minimized. This question is answered using an inventory cost model (see Example 4).

This inventory-cost determination is a typical example of the kinds of questions and important business applications that require the use of the derivative for finding maxima and minima. As managers, workers, or consumers, we may be interested in such things as maximum revenue, maximum profit, minimum cost, maximum medical dosage, maximum utilization of resources, and so on.

If we have functions that model cost, revenue, or population growth, we can apply the methods of this chapter to find the maxima and minima of those functions.

EXAMPLE 1   Company Growth

Suppose that a new company begins production in 2015 with eight employees and the growth of the company over the next 10 years is predicted by

$$N = N(t) = 8\left(1 + \frac{160t}{t^2 + 16}\right), \quad 0 \le t \le 10$$

where N is the number of employees t years after 2015.

Determine in what year the number of employees will be maximized and the maximum number of employees.

Solution

This function will have a relative maximum when $N'(t) = 0$.

$$N'(t) = 8\left[\frac{(t^2 + 16)(160) - (160t)(2t)}{(t^2 + 16)^2}\right]$$

$$= 8\left[\frac{160t^2 + 2560 - 320t^2}{(t^2 + 16)^2}\right]$$

$$= 8\left[\frac{2560 - 160t^2}{(t^2 + 16)^2}\right]$$

Because $N'(t) = 0$ when its numerator is 0 (note that this denominator is never 0), we must solve

$$2560 - 160t^2 = 0$$
$$160(4 + t)(4 - t) = 0$$

so
$$t = -4 \text{ or } t = 4$$

We are interested only in positive t-values, so we test $t = 4$.

$$\left.\begin{array}{l} N'(0) = 8\left[\dfrac{2560}{256}\right] > 0 \\[3mm] N'(10) = 8\left[\dfrac{-13,440}{(116)^2}\right] < 0 \end{array}\right\} \Rightarrow \text{relative maximum}$$

The relative maximum is

$$N(4) = 8\left(1 + \frac{640}{32}\right) = 168$$

At $t = 0$, the number of employees is $N(0) = 8$, and it increases to $N(4) = 168$. After $t = 4$ (in 2019), $N(t)$ decreases to $N(10) = 118$ (approximately), so $N(4) = 168$ is the maximum number of employees. Figure 10.35 verifies these conclusions.

Sometimes we must develop the function we need from the statement of the problem. In this case, it is important to understand what is to be maximized or minimized and to express that quantity as a function of *one* variable.

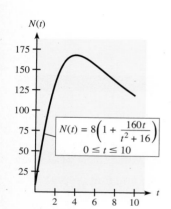

Figure 10.35

EXAMPLE 2 **Minimizing Cost**

A farmer needs to enclose a rectangular pasture containing 1,600,000 square feet. Suppose that along the road adjoining his property he wants to use a more expensive fence and that he needs no fence on one side perpendicular to the road because a river bounds his property on that side. If the fence costs $15 per foot along the road and $10 per foot along the two remaining sides that must be fenced, what dimensions of his rectangular field will minimize his cost?

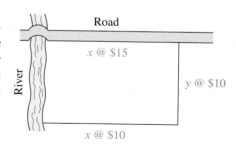

Figure 10.36

Solution

In Figure 10.36, x represents the length of the pasture along the road (and parallel to the road) and y represents the width. The cost function for the fence used is

$$C = 15x + 10y + 10x = 25x + 10y$$

We cannot use a derivative to find where C is minimized unless we write C as a function of x or y only. Because the area of the rectangular field must be 1,600,000 square feet, we have

$$A = xy = 1,600,000$$

Solving for y in terms of x and substituting give C as a function of x.

$$y = \frac{1,600,000}{x}$$

$$C = 25x + 10\left(\frac{1,600,000}{x}\right) = 25x + \frac{16,000,000}{x}$$

To find $C'(x)$, we first rewrite: $C = 25x + 16,000,000x^{-1}$. Then

$$C'(x) = 25 - 16,000,000x^{-2} = 25 - \frac{16,000,000}{x^2}$$

We find the critical values of C by solving $C'(x) = 0$ as follows:

$$0 = 25 - \frac{16,000,000}{x^2}$$

$$0 = 25x^2 - 16,000,000 \qquad \text{(multiply both sides by } x^2\text{)}$$

$$25x^2 = 16,000,000$$

$$x^2 = 640,000 \Rightarrow x = \pm\sqrt{640,000} = \pm 800$$

We use $x = 800$ feet because $x = -800$ is meaningless in this application. Testing to see whether $x = 800$ gives the minimum cost, we find

$$C''(x) = \frac{32,000,000}{x^3}$$

$C''(x) > 0$ for $x > 0$, so $C(x)$ is concave up for all positive x. Thus $x = 800$ gives the absolute minimum, and $C(800) = 40,000$ is the minimum cost. The other dimension of the rectangular field is $y = 1,600,000/800 = 2000$ feet. Figure 10.37 verifies that $C(x)$ reaches its minimum (of 40,000) at $x = 800$.

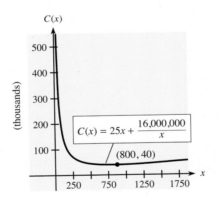

Figure 10.37

$x = 800$ ft @ $15/ft = $12,000 for the road side

EXAMPLE 3   **Postal Restrictions**

Postal restrictions limit the size of packages sent through the mail. If the restrictions are that the length plus the girth may not exceed 108 inches, find the volume of the largest box with square cross section that can be mailed.

Solution

Let l equal the length of the box, and let s equal a side of the square end. See Figure 10.38. The volume we seek to maximize is given by

$$V = s^2 l$$

We can use the restriction that girth plus length equals 108,

$$4s + l = 108$$

to express V as a function of s or l. Because $l = 108 - 4s$, the equation for V becomes

$$V = s^2(108 - 4s) = 108s^2 - 4s^3$$

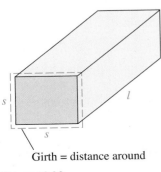

Girth = distance around

Figure 10.38

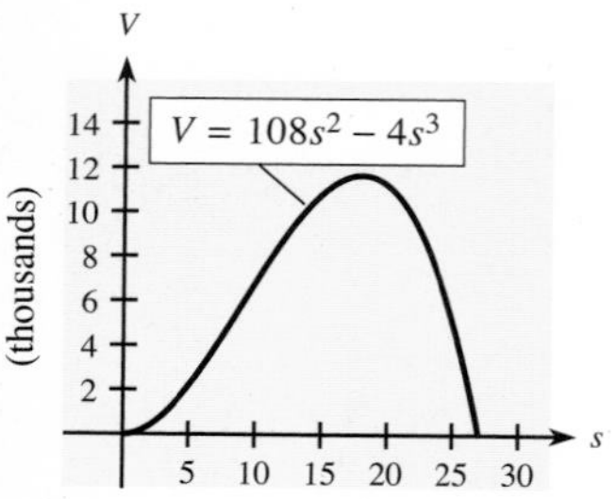

We solve $dV/ds = 0$ to find the critical values.

$$\frac{dV}{ds} = 216s - 12s^2$$

$$0 = s(216 - 12s)$$

The critical values are $s = 0$, $s = \frac{216}{12} = 18$. The critical value $s = 0$ will not maximize the volume, for in this case, $V = 0$. Testing to the left and right of $s = 18$ gives

$$V'(17) > 0 \quad \text{and} \quad V'(19) < 0$$

Thus $s = 18$ inches and $l = 108 - 4(18) = 36$ inches yield a maximum volume of 11,664 cubic inches. Once again we can verify our results graphically. Figure 10.39 shows that $V = 108s^2 - 4s^3$ achieves its maximum when $s = 18$.

Figure 10.39

(graph) $V = 108s^2 - 4s^3$, axis label (thousands), horizontal axis s.

✓ CHECKPOINT

Suppose we want to find the minimum value of $C = 5x + 2y$ and we know that x and y must be positive and that $xy = 1000$.
1. What equation do we differentiate to solve this problem?
2. Find the critical values.
3. Find the minimum value of C.

We next consider **inventory cost models**, in which x items are produced in each production run and items are removed from inventory at a fixed constant rate. Because items are removed at a constant rate, the average number stored at any time is $x/2$. Also, when $x = 0$, new items must be added to inventory from a production run. Thus the number of units in storage changes with time and is illustrated in Figure 10.40. In these models there are costs associated with both production and storage, but lowering one of these costs means increasing the other. To see how inventory cost models work, consider the following example.

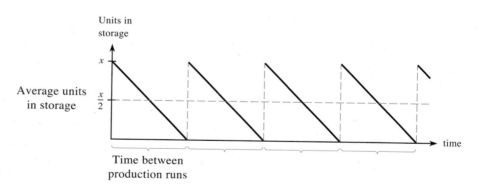

Figure 10.40

Units in storage / Average units in storage / Time between production runs / time

EXAMPLE 4   Inventory Cost Model | APPLICATION PREVIEW |

Suppose that a company needs 1,000,000 items during a year and that preparation costs are $800 for each production run. Suppose further that it costs the company $6 to produce each item and $1 to store an item for up to a year. If each production run consists of x items, find x so that the total costs of production and storage are minimized.

Solution
The total production costs are given by

$$\binom{\text{No. of}}{\text{runs}}\binom{\text{cost}}{\text{per run}} + \binom{\text{no. of}}{\text{items}}\binom{\text{cost}}{\text{per item}} = \left(\frac{1,000,000}{x}\right)(\$800) + (1,000,000)(\$6)$$

The total storage costs are

$$\binom{\text{Average}}{\text{no. stored}}\binom{\text{storage cost}}{\text{per item}} = \left(\frac{x}{2}\right)(\$1)$$

Thus the total costs of production and storage are

$$C = \left(\frac{1{,}000{,}000}{x}\right)(800) + 6{,}000{,}000 + \frac{x}{2} = \frac{800{,}000{,}000}{x} + 6{,}000{,}000 + \frac{x}{2}$$

We wish to find x so that C is minimized.

$$C' = \frac{-800{,}000{,}000}{x^2} + \frac{1}{2}$$

If $x > 0$, critical values occur when $C' = 0$.

$$0 = \frac{-800{,}000{,}000}{x^2} + \frac{1}{2}$$

$$\frac{800{,}000{,}000}{x^2} = \frac{1}{2}$$

$$1{,}600{,}000{,}000 = x^2$$

$$x = \pm 40{,}000$$

Because x must be positive, we test $x = 40{,}000$ with the second derivative.

$$C''(x) = \frac{1{,}600{,}000{,}000}{x^3}, \quad \text{so} \quad C''(40{,}000) > 0$$

Note that $x = 40{,}000$ yields an absolute minimum value of C, because $C'' > 0$ for all $x > 0$. That is, production runs of 40,000 items yield minimum total costs for production and storage. ■

Technology Note   Problems of the types we've studied in this section could also be solved (at least approximately) with a graphing calculator or Excel. With this approach, our first goal is still to express the quantity to be maximized or minimized as a function of one variable. Then that function can be graphed, and the (at least approximate) optimal value can be obtained from the graph. This method is especially useful with problems that have critical values that are difficult to find algebraically, like the one in Example 5. ■

EXAMPLE 5   Property Development

A developer of a campground has to pay for utility line installation to the community center from a transformer on the street at the corner of her property. Because of local restrictions, the lines must be underground on her property. Suppose that the costs are $50 per meter along the street and $100 per meter underground. How far from the transformer should the line enter the property to minimize installation costs? See Figure 10.41.

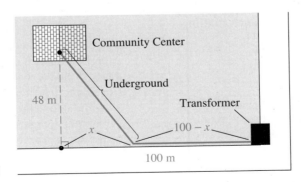

Figure 10.41

Solution
If the developer had the cable placed underground from the community center perpendicular to the street and then to the transformer, then $x = 0$ in Figure 10.41 and the cost would be

$$\$100(48) + \$50(100) = \$9800$$

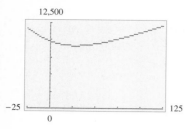

Figure 10.42

It may be possible to save some money by placing the cable on a diagonal to the street, but then only $x \leq 100$ makes sense. By using the Pythagorean Theorem, we find that the length of the underground cable that meets the street x meters closer to the transformer is

$$\sqrt{48^2 + x^2} = \sqrt{2304 + x^2} \quad \text{meters}$$

Thus the cost C of installation is given by

$$C = 100\sqrt{2304 + x^2} + 50(100 - x) \quad \text{dollars}$$

Figure 10.42 shows the graph of this function over an interval for x that contains $0 \leq x \leq 100$. Because any extrema must occur in this interval, we can find the minimum by using MIN on a graphing calculator or Excel. See Appendices A and B, Section 10.4, and the Online Excel Guide for the steps. The minimum cost is $9156.92, when $x = 27.7$ meters (that is, when the cable meets the street 72.3 meters from the transformer). ▪

✓ CHECKPOINT
ANSWERS

1. We must differentiate C, but first C must be expressed as a function of one variable:

$$C(x) = 5x + \frac{2000}{x}$$

2. $C'(x) = 5 - 2000/x^2$, so $C'(x) = 0$ when $x = \pm 20$. The only relevant critical value is $x = 20$.

3. The minimum value occurs when $x = 20$ and $y = 50$ and is $C = 200$.

| EXERCISES | 10.4

APPLICATIONS

1. **Return to sales** The manufacturer of GRIPPER tires modeled its return to sales from television advertising expenditures in two regions, as follows:

   Region 1:　$S_1 = 30 + 20x_1 - 0.4x_1^2$
   Region 2:　$S_2 = 20 + 36x_2 - 1.3x_2^2$

   where S_1 and S_2 are the sales revenue in millions of dollars and x_1 and x_2 are millions of dollars of expenditures for television advertising.
   (a) What advertising expenditures would maximize sales revenue in each district?
   (b) How much money will be needed to maximize sales revenue in both districts?

2. **Projectiles** A ball thrown into the air from a building 100 ft high travels along a path described by

   $$y = \frac{-x^2}{110} + x + 100$$

   where y is its height in feet and x is the horizontal distance from the building in feet. What is the maximum height the ball will reach?

3. **Profit** The profit from a grove of orange trees is given by $x(200 - x)$ dollars, where x is the number of orange trees per acre. How many trees per acre will maximize the profit?

4. **Reaction rates** The velocity v of an autocatalytic reaction can be represented by the equation

   $$v = x(a - x)$$

   where a is the amount of material originally present and x is the amount that has been decomposed at any given time. Find the maximum velocity of the reaction.

5. **Productivity** Analysis of daily output of a factory during an 8-hour shift shows that the hourly number of units y produced after t hours of production is

   $$y = 70t + \tfrac{1}{2}t^2 - t^3, \quad 0 \leq t \leq 8$$

   (a) After how many hours will the hourly number of units be maximized?
   (b) What is the maximum hourly output?

6. **Productivity** A time study showed that, on average, the productivity of a worker after t hours on the job can be modeled by

   $$P = 27t + 6t^2 - t^3, \quad 0 \leq t \leq 8$$

   where P is the number of units produced per hour. After how many hours will productivity be maximized? What is the maximum productivity?

7. **Consumer expenditure** Suppose that the demand x (in units) for a product is $x = 10,000 - 100p$, where p dollars is the market price per unit. Then the consumer expenditure for the product is

   $$E = px = 10,000p - 100p^2$$

   For what market price will expenditure be greatest?

8. **Production costs** Suppose that the monthly cost in dollars of mining a certain ore is related to the number of pieces of equipment used, according to

   $$C = 25,000x + \frac{870,000}{x}, \quad x > 0$$

where x is the number of pieces of equipment used. Using how many pieces of equipment will minimize the cost?

Medication **For Problems 9 and 10, consider that when medicine is administered, reaction (measured in change of blood pressure or temperature) can be modeled by**

$$R = m^2 \left(\frac{c}{2} - \frac{m}{3} \right)$$

where c is a positive constant and m is the amount of medicine absorbed into the blood (*Source: R. M. Thrall et al., Some Mathematical Models in Biology, U.S. Department of Commerce, 1967*).

9. Find the amount of medicine that is being absorbed into the blood when the reaction is maximum.
10. The rate of change of reaction R with respect to the amount of medicine m is defined to be the sensitivity.
    (a) Find the sensitivity, S.
    (b) Find the amount of medicine that is being absorbed into the blood when the sensitivity is maximum.
11. *Advertising and sales* An inferior product with a large advertising budget sells well when it is introduced, but sales fall as people discontinue use of the product. Suppose that the weekly sales S are given by

$$S = \frac{200t}{(t+1)^2}, \quad t \ge 0$$

where S is in millions of dollars and t is in weeks. After how many weeks will sales be maximized?

12. *Revenue* A newly released film has its weekly revenue given by

$$R(t) = \frac{50t}{t^2 + 36}, \quad t \ge 0$$

where R is in millions of dollars and t is in weeks.
    (a) After how many weeks will the weekly revenue be maximized?
    (b) What is the maximum weekly revenue?

13. *News impact* Suppose that the percent p (as a decimal) of people who could correctly identify two of eight defendants in a drug case t days after their trial began is given by

$$p(t) = \frac{6.4t}{t^2 + 64} + 0.05$$

Find the number of days before the percent is maximized, and find the maximum percent.

14. *Candidate recognition* Suppose that in an election year the proportion p of voters who recognize a certain candidate's name t months after the campaign started is given by

$$p(t) = \frac{7.2t}{t^2 + 36} + 0.2$$

After how many months is the proportion maximized?

15. *Minimum fence* Two equal rectangular lots are to be enclosed by fencing the perimeter of a rectangular lot and then putting a fence across its middle. If each lot is to contain 1200 square feet, what is the minimum amount of fence needed to enclose the lots (include the fence across the middle)?

16. *Minimum fence* The running yard for a dog kennel must contain at least 900 square feet. If a 20-foot side of the kennel is used as part of one side of a rectangular yard with 900 square feet, what dimensions will require the least amount of fencing?

17. *Minimum cost* A rectangular field with one side along a river is to be fenced. Suppose that no fence is needed along the river, the fence on the side opposite the river costs $20 per foot, and the fence on the other sides costs $5 per foot. If the field must contain 45,000 square feet, what dimensions will minimize costs?

18. *Minimum cost* From a tract of land a developer plans to fence a rectangular region and then divide it into two identical rectangular lots by putting a fence down the middle. Suppose that the fence for the outside boundary costs $5 per foot and the fence for the middle costs $2 per foot. If each lot contains 13,500 square feet, find the dimensions of each lot that yield the minimum cost for the fence.

19. *Optimization at a fixed cost* A rectangular area is to be enclosed and divided into thirds. The family has $800 to spend for the fencing material. The outside fence costs $10 per running foot installed, and the dividers cost $20 per running foot installed. What are the dimensions that will maximize the area enclosed? (The answer contains a fraction.)

20. *Minimum cost* A kennel of 640 square feet is to be constructed as shown. The cost is $4 per running foot for the sides and $1 per running foot for the ends and dividers. What are the dimensions of the kennel that will minimize the cost?

21. *Minimum cost* The base of a rectangular box is to be twice as long as it is wide. The volume of the box is 256 cubic inches. The material for the top costs $0.10 per square inch and the material for the sides and bottom costs $0.05 per square inch. Find the dimensions that will make the cost a minimum.

22. *Velocity of air during a cough* According to B. F. Visser, the velocity v of air in the trachea during a cough is related to the radius r of the trachea according to

$$v = ar^2(r_0 - r)$$

where a is a constant and r_0 is the radius of the trachea in a relaxed state. Find the radius r that produces the maximum velocity of air in the trachea during a cough.

23. *Inventory cost model* Suppose that a company needs 1,500,000 items during a year and that preparation

for each production run costs $600. Suppose also that it costs $15 to produce each item and $2 per year to store an item. Use the inventory cost model to find the number of items in each production run so that the total costs of production and storage are minimized.

24. *Inventory cost model* Suppose that a company needs 60,000 items during a year and that preparation for each production run costs $400. Suppose further that it costs $4 to produce each item and $0.75 to store an item for one year. Use the inventory cost model to find the number of items in each production run that will minimize the total costs of production and storage.

25. *Inventory cost model* A company needs 150,000 items per year. It costs the company $360 to prepare a production run of these items and $7 to produce each item. If it also costs the company $0.75 per year for each item stored, find the number of items that should be produced in each run so that total costs of production and storage are minimized.

26. *Inventory cost model* A company needs 450,000 items per year. Production costs are $500 to prepare for a production run and $10 for each item produced. Inventory costs are $2 per item per year. Find the number of items that should be produced in each run so that the total costs of production and storage are minimized.

27. *Volume* A rectangular box with a square base is to be formed from a square piece of metal with 12-inch sides. If a square piece with side x is cut from each corner of the metal and the sides are folded up to form an open box, the volume of the box is $V = (12 - 2x)^2x$. What value of x will maximize the volume of the box?

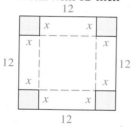

28. *Volume*
    (a) A square piece of cardboard 36 centimeters on a side is to be formed into a rectangular box by cutting squares with length x from each corner and folding up the sides. What is the maximum volume possible for the box?
    (b) Show that if the piece of cardboard is k centimeters on each side, cutting squares of size $k/6$ and folding up the sides gives the maximum volume.

29. *Revenue* The owner of an orange grove must decide when to pick one variety of oranges. She can sell them for $24 a bushel if she sells them now, with each tree yielding an average of 5 bushels. The yield increases by half a bushel per week for the next 5 weeks, but the price per bushel decreases by $1.50 per bushel each week. When should the oranges be picked for maximum return?

30. *Minimum material*
    (a) A box with an open top and a square base is to be constructed to contain 4000 cubic inches. Find

the dimensions that will require the minimum amount of material to construct the box.
    (b) A box with an open top and a square base is to be constructed to contain k cubic inches. Show that the minimum amount of material is used to construct the box when each side of the base is $x = (2k)^{1/3}$ and the height is $y = (k/4)^{1/3}$

31. *Minimum cost* A printer has a contract to print 100,000 posters for a political candidate. He can run the posters by using any number of plates from 1 to 30 on his press. If he uses x metal plates, they will produce x copies of the poster with each impression of the press. The metal plates cost $20.00 to prepare, and it costs $125.00 per hour to run the press. If the press can make 1000 impressions per hour, how many metal plates should the printer make to minimize costs?

32. *Shortest time* A vacationer on an island 8 miles offshore from a point that is 48 miles from town must travel to town occasionally. (See the figure.) The vacationer has a boat capable of traveling 30 mph and can go by auto along the coast at 55 mph. At what point should the car be left to minimize the time it takes to get to town?

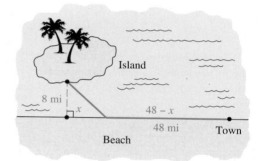

33. *U.S. oil reserves* By using U.S. Department of Energy data for selected years from 2011 and projected to 2040, the U.S. onshore oil reserves in the lower 48 states (in billions of barrels) can be modeled by the function

$$R(t) = -0.00044t^3 + 0.0042t^2 + 0.52t + 19$$

where t is the number of years past 2010.
    (a) In what year does the model predict the onshore oil reserves in the lower 48 states will reach a maximum? Find the predicted maximum. Is this the absolute maximum for the period from 2011 to 2040?
    (b) Find the absolute minimum point for the period from 2011 to 2040.
    (c) Find the t-value of the point of inflection for $R(t)$. At that t-value, is the rate of change of these oil reserves maximum or minimum? Explain.

OBJECTIVES 10.5

- To locate horizontal asymptotes
- To locate vertical asymptotes
- To sketch graphs of functions that have vertical and/or horizontal asymptotes

Rational Functions: More Curve Sketching

| APPLICATION PREVIEW |

Suppose that the total cost of producing a shipment of a product is

$$C(x) = 5000x + \frac{125,000}{x}, \quad x > 0$$

where x is the number of machines used in the production process. To find the number of machines that will minimize the total cost, we find the minimum value of this rational function. (See Example 3.) The graph of this function contains a vertical asymptote at $x = 0$. We will discuss graphs and applications involving asymptotes in this section.

The procedures for using the first-derivative test and the second-derivative test are given in previous sections, but none of the graphs discussed in those sections contains vertical asymptotes or horizontal asymptotes. In this section, we consider how to use information about asymptotes along with the first and second derivatives, and we present a unified approach to curve sketching.

Asymptotes

In Section 2.4, "Special Functions and Their Graphs," we first discussed asymptotes and saw that they are important features of the graphs that have them. Then, in our discussion of limits in Sections 9.1 and 9.2, we discovered the relationship between certain limits and asymptotes. The formal definition of **vertical asymptotes** uses limits.

Vertical Asymptote

The line $x = x_0$ is a **vertical asymptote** of the graph of $y = f(x)$ if the values of $f(x)$ approach ∞ or $-\infty$ as x approaches x_0 (from the left or the right).

From our work with limits, recall that a vertical asymptote will occur on the graph of a function at an x-value at which the denominator (but not the numerator) of the function is equal to zero. These observations allow us to determine where vertical asymptotes occur.

Vertical Asymptote of a Rational Function

The graph of the rational function

$$h(x) = \frac{f(x)}{g(x)}$$

has a vertical asymptote at $x = c$ if $g(c) = 0$ and $f(c) \neq 0$.

Because a **horizontal asymptote** tells us the behavior of the values of the function (y-coordinates) when x increases or decreases without bound, we use limits at infinity to determine the existence of horizontal asymptotes.

Horizontal Asymptote

The graph of a rational function $y = f(x)$ will have a **horizontal asymptote** at $y = b$, for a constant b, if

$$\lim_{x \to \infty} f(x) = b \quad \text{or} \quad \lim_{x \to -\infty} f(x) = b$$

Otherwise, the graph has no horizontal asymptote.

For a rational function f, $\lim_{x \to \infty} f(x) = b$ if and only if $\lim_{x \to -\infty} f(x) = b$, so we only need to find one of these limits to locate a horizontal asymptote. In Problems 37 and 38 in the 9.2 Exercises, the following statements regarding horizontal asymptotes of the graphs of rational functions were proved.

Horizontal Asymptotes of Rational Functions

Consider the rational function $y = \dfrac{f(x)}{g(x)} = \dfrac{a_n x^n + \cdots + a_1 x + a_0}{b_m x^m + \cdots + b_1 x + b_0}$.

1. If $n < m$ (that is, if the degree of the numerator is less than that of the denominator), a horizontal asymptote occurs at $y = 0$ (the x-axis).
2. If $n = m$ (that is, if the degree of the numerator equals that of the denominator), a horizontal asymptote occurs at $y = \dfrac{a_n}{b_m}$ (the ratio of the leading coefficients).
3. If $n > m$ (that is, if the degree of the numerator is greater than that of the denominator), there is no horizontal asymptote.

EXAMPLE 1   Vertical and Horizontal Asymptotes

Find any vertical and horizontal asymptotes for

(a) $f(x) = \dfrac{2x - 1}{x + 2}$ (b) $f(x) = \dfrac{x^2 + 3}{1 - x}$ (c) $g(x) = \dfrac{10x}{x^2 + 9}$

Solution

(a) The denominator of this function is 0 at $x = -2$, and because this value does not make the numerator 0, there is a vertical asymptote at $x = -2$. Because the function is rational, with the degree of the numerator equal to that of the denominator and with the ratio of the leading coefficients equal to 2, the graph of the function has a horizontal asymptote at $y = 2$. The graph is shown in Figure 10.43(a).

(b) At $x = 1$, the denominator of $f(x)$ is 0 and the numerator is not, so a vertical asymptote occurs at $x = 1$. The function is rational with the degree of the numerator greater than that of the denominator, so there is no horizontal asymptote. The graph is shown in Figure 10.43(b).

(c) The denominator of this function is never zero ($x^2 + 9 \geq 9$ for every real number). Therefore, there is no vertical asymptote. This is a rational function with the degree of the numerator less than that of the denominator; thus $y = 0$ (the x-axis) is a horizontal asymptote. The graph is shown in Figure 10.43(c).

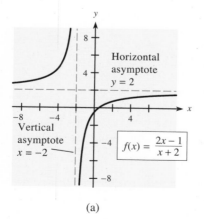

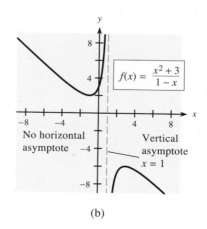

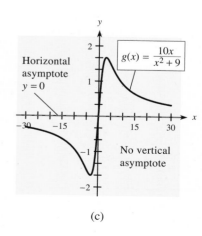

Figure 10.43   (a)   (b)   (c)

More Curve Sketching   We now extend our first- and second-derivative techniques of curve sketching to include functions that have asymptotes.

In general, the following steps are helpful when we sketch the graph of a function.

Graphing Guidelines

1. Determine the domain of the function. The domain may be restricted by the nature of the problem or by the equation.
2. Look for vertical asymptotes, especially if the function is a rational function.
3. Look for horizontal asymptotes, especially if the function is a rational function.
4. Find the relative maxima and minima by using the first-derivative test or the second-derivative test.
5. Use the second derivative to find the points of inflection if this derivative is easily found.
6. Use other information (intercepts, for example) and plot additional points to complete the sketch of the graph.

EXAMPLE 2   ## Graphing with Asymptotes

Sketch the graph of the function $f(x) = \dfrac{x^2}{(x+1)^2}$.

Solution

1. The domain is the set of all real numbers except $x = -1$.
2. Because $x = -1$ makes the denominator 0 and does not make the numerator 0, there is a vertical asymptote at $x = -1$.
3. Because
$$\frac{x^2}{(x+1)^2} = \frac{x^2}{x^2 + 2x + 1}$$
the function is rational with the degree of the numerator equal to that of the denominator and with the ratio of the leading coefficients equal to 1. Hence, the graph of the function has a horizontal asymptote at $y = 1$.
4. To find any maxima and minima, we first find $f'(x)$.
$$f'(x) = \frac{(x+1)^2\,(2x) - x^2\,[2(x+1)]}{(x+1)^4} = \frac{2x(x+1)[(x+1)-x]}{(x+1)^4} = \frac{2x}{(x+1)^3}$$

Thus $f'(x) = 0$ when $x = 0$ (and $y = 0$), and $f'(x)$ is undefined at $x = -1$ (where the vertical asymptote occurs). Using $x = 0$ and $x = -1$ gives the following sign diagram for $f'(x)$. The sign diagram shows that the critical point $(0, 0)$ is a relative minimum and shows how the graph approaches the vertical asymptote at $x = -1$.

*$x = -1$ is a vertical asymptote.

5. The second derivative is
$$f''(x) = \frac{(x+1)^3\,(2) - 2x[3(x+1)^2]}{(x+1)^6}$$

Factoring $(x+1)^2$ from the numerator and simplifying give
$$f''(x) = \frac{2 - 4x}{(x+1)^4}$$

We can see that $f''(0) = 2 > 0$, so the second-derivative test also shows that $(0, 0)$ is a relative minimum. We see that $f''(x) = 0$ when $x = \frac{1}{2}$. Checking $f''(x)$ between $x = -1$ (where it is undefined) and $x = \frac{1}{2}$ shows that the graph is concave up on this interval.

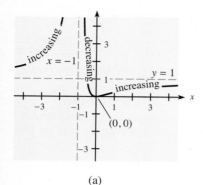

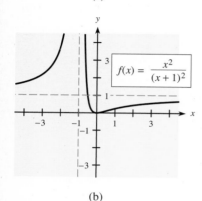

$$f(x) = \frac{x^2}{(x+1)^2}$$

(a)

(b)

Figure 10.44

Note also that $f''(x) < 0$ for $x > \frac{1}{2}$, so the point $\left(\frac{1}{2}, \frac{1}{9}\right)$ is a point of inflection. Also see the sign diagram for $f''(x)$.

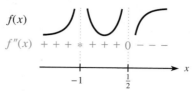

$*x = -1$ is a vertical asymptote.

6. To see how the graph approaches the horizontal asymptote, we check $f(x)$ for large values of $|x|$.

$$f(-100) = \frac{(-100)^2}{(-99)^2} = \frac{10,000}{9,801} > 1, \quad f(100) = \frac{100^2}{101^2} = \frac{10,000}{10,201} < 1$$

Thus the graph has the characteristics shown in Figure 10.44(a). The graph is shown in Figure 10.44(b).

When we wish to learn about a function $f(x)$ or sketch its graph, it is important to understand what information we obtain from $f(x)$, from $f'(x)$, and from $f''(x)$. The following summary may be helpful.

▌ DERIVATIVES AND GRAPHS ▐

Source	Information Provided
$f(x)$	y-coordinates; horizontal asymptotes, vertical asymptotes; domain restrictions
$f'(x)$	Increasing [$f'(x) > 0$]; decreasing [$f'(x) < 0$]; critical points [$f'(x) = 0$ or $f'(x)$ undefined]; sign-diagram tests for maxima and minima
$f''(x)$	Concave up [$f''(x) > 0$]; concave down [$f''(x) < 0$]; possible points of inflection [$f''(x) = 0$ or $f''(x)$ undefined]; sign-diagram tests for points of inflection; second-derivative test for maxima and minima

✓ **CHECKPOINT**

1. Let $f(x) = \dfrac{2x + 10}{x - 1}$ and decide whether the following are true or false.

   (a) $f(x)$ has a vertical asymptote at $x = 1$.
   (b) $f(x)$ has $y = 2$ as its horizontal asymptote.

2. Let $f(x) = \dfrac{x^3 - 16}{x} + 1$; then $f'(x) = \dfrac{2x^3 + 16}{x^2}$ and $f''(x) = \dfrac{2x^3 - 32}{x^3}$.
   Use these to determine whether the following are true or false.
   (a) There are no asymptotes.
   (b) $f'(x) = 0$ when $x = -2$
   (c) A partial sign diagram for $f'(x)$ is

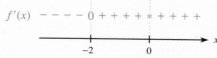

*means $f'(0)$ is undefined.

   (d) There is a relative minimum at $x = -2$.
   (e) A partial sign diagram for $f''(x)$ is

*means $f''(0)$ is undefined.

   (f) There are points of inflection at $x = 0$ and $x = \sqrt[3]{16}$.

EXAMPLE 3   Production Costs | APPLICATION PREVIEW |

Suppose that the total cost of producing a shipment of a certain product is

$$C(x) = 5000x + \frac{125{,}000}{x}, \quad x > 0$$

where x is the number of machines used in the production process.

(a) Determine any asymptotes for $C(x)$.
(b) How many machines should be used to minimize the total cost?
(c) Graph this total cost function.

Solution

(a) Writing this function with all terms over a common denominator gives

$$C(x) = 5000x + \frac{125{,}000}{x} = \frac{5000x^2 + 125{,}000}{x}$$

The domain of $C(x)$ does not include 0, and $C \to \infty$ as $x \to 0^+$, so there is a vertical asymptote at $x = 0$. Thus the cost increases without bound as the number of machines used in the process approaches zero. Because the numerator has a higher degree than the denominator, there is no horizontal asymptote.

(b) Finding the derivative of $C(x)$ gives

$$C'(x) = 5000 - \frac{125{,}000}{x^2} = \frac{5000x^2 - 125{,}000}{x^2}$$

Setting $C'(x) = 0$ and solving for x gives the critical values of x.

$$0 = \frac{5000(x + 5)(x - 5)}{x^2}$$

$$x = 5 \quad \text{or} \quad x = -5$$

Because $C''(x) = 250{,}000x^{-3} = \dfrac{250{,}000}{x^3}$ is positive for all $x > 0$, using 5 machines minimizes the cost at $C(5) = 50{,}000$.

(c) The graph is shown in Figure 10.45.

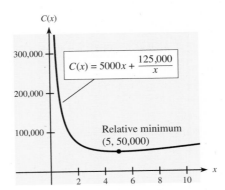

Figure 10.45

EXAMPLE 4   Horizontal and Vertical Asymptotes

Figure 10.46 on the next page shows the graph of $f(x) = \dfrac{71x^2}{28(3 - 2x^2)}$.

(a) Determine whether the function has horizontal or vertical asymptotes, and estimate where they occur.
(b) Check your conclusions to part (a) analytically.

Figure 10.46

Solution

(a) The graph appears to have a horizontal asymptote somewhere between $y = -1$ and $y = -2$, perhaps near $y = -1.5$. Also, there are two vertical asymptotes located approximately at $x = 1.25$ and $x = -1.25$.

(b) The function

$$f(x) = \frac{71x^2}{28(3 - 2x^2)} = \frac{71x^2}{84 - 56x^2}$$

is a rational function with the degree of the numerator equal to that of the denominator and with the ratio of the leading coefficients equal to $-71/56$. Thus the graph of the function has a horizontal asymptote at $y = -71/56 \approx -1.27$.

Vertical asymptotes occur at x-values where $28(3 - 2x^2) = 0$. Solving gives

$$3 - 2x^2 = 0 \quad \text{or} \quad 3 = 2x^2 \quad \text{so} \quad \frac{3}{2} = x^2$$

$$\text{Thus} \qquad \pm\sqrt{\frac{3}{2}} = x \quad \text{or} \quad x \approx \pm 1.225$$

Calculator Note   The procedures previously outlined in this section are necessary to generate a complete and accurate graph. With a graphing calculator, the graph of a function is easily generated as long as the viewing window dimensions are appropriate. We frequently need information provided by derivatives to obtain a window that shows all features of a graph. See Example 5 and Appendix A, Section 10.5, for details.

EXAMPLE 5 Graphing with Technology

The standard viewing window of the graph of $f(x) = \dfrac{x + 10}{x^2 + 300}$ appears blank (check and see). Find any asymptotes, maxima, and minima, and determine an appropriate viewing window. Sketch the graph.

Solution

Because $x^2 + 300 = 0$ has no real solution, there are no vertical asymptotes. The function is rational with the degree of the numerator less than that of the denominator, so the horizontal asymptote is $y = 0$, which is the x-axis.

We then find an appropriate viewing window by locating the critical points.

$$f'(x) = \frac{(x^2 + 300)(1) - (x + 10)(2x)}{(x^2 + 300)^2}$$

$$= \frac{x^2 + 300 - 2x^2 - 20x}{(x^2 + 300)^2} = \frac{300 - 20x - x^2}{(x^2 + 300)^2}$$

$f'(x) = 0$ when the numerator is zero. Thus

$$300 - 20x - x^2 = 0$$
$$0 = x^2 + 20x - 300$$
$$0 = (x + 30)(x - 10)$$
$$x + 30 = 0 \quad x - 10 = 0$$
$$x = -30 \qquad x = 10$$

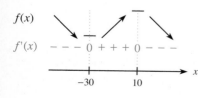

The critical points are $x = -30$, $y = -\frac{1}{60} \approx -0.01666667$ and $x = 10$, $y = \frac{1}{20} = 0.05$. See the sign diagram for $f'(x)$.

Without using the information above, a graphing calculator may not give a useful graph. An x-range that includes -30 and 10 is needed. Because $y = 0$ is a horizontal asymptote, these relative extrema are absolute, and the y-range must be quite small for the shape of the graph to be seen clearly. Figure 10.47 shows the graph.

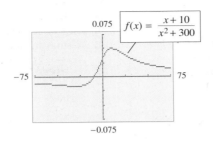

Figure 10.47

1. (a) True. (b) True.
2. (a) False. There are no horizontal asymptotes, but $x = 0$ is a vertical asymptote.
   (b) True
   (c) True
   (d) True
   (e) True
   (f) False, only at $(\sqrt[3]{16}, 1)$. At $x = 0$ there is a vertical asymptote.

| EXERCISES | 10.5

In Problems 1–4, a function and its graph are given. Use the graph to find each of the following, if they exist. Then confirm your results analytically.

(a) vertical asymptotes   (b) $\lim\limits_{x \to \infty} f(x)$

(c) $\lim\limits_{x \to -\infty} f(x)$ (d) horizontal asymptotes

1. $f(x) = \dfrac{x - 4}{x - 2}$ 2. $f(x) = \dfrac{8}{x + 2}$

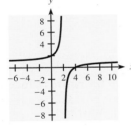

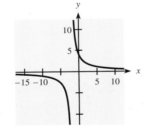

3. $f(x) = \dfrac{3(x^4 + 2x^3 + 6x^2 + 2x + 5)}{(x^2 - 4)^2}$

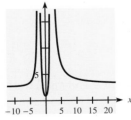

4. $f(x) = \dfrac{x^2}{(x - 2)^2}$

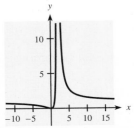

In Problems 5–10, find any horizontal and vertical asymptotes for each function.

5. $y = \dfrac{2x}{x - 3}$ 6. $y = \dfrac{3x - 1}{x + 5}$

7. $y = \dfrac{x + 1}{x^2 - 4}$ 8. $y = \dfrac{4x}{9 - x^2}$

9. $y = \dfrac{3x^3 - 6}{x^2 + 4}$ 10. $y = \dfrac{6x^3}{4x^2 + 9}$

For each function in Problems 11–18, find any horizontal and vertical asymptotes, and use information from the first derivative to sketch the graph.

11. $f(x) = \dfrac{2x + 2}{x - 3}$ 12. $f(x) = \dfrac{5x - 15}{x + 2}$

13. $y = \dfrac{x^2 + 4}{x}$ 14. $y = \dfrac{x^2 + 4}{x^2}$

15. $y = \dfrac{27x^2}{(x + 1)^3}$ 16. $y = \left(\dfrac{x + 2}{x - 3}\right)^2$

17. $f(x) = \dfrac{16x}{x^2 + 1}$ 18. $f(x) = \dfrac{4x^2}{x^4 + 1}$

In Problems 19–24, a function and its first and second derivatives are given. Use these to find any horizontal and vertical asymptotes, critical points, relative maxima, relative minima, and points of inflection. Then sketch the graph of each function.

19. $y = \dfrac{x}{(x - 1)^2}$ 20. $y = \dfrac{(x - 1)^2}{x^2}$

$y' = -\dfrac{x + 1}{(x - 1)^3}$ $y' = \dfrac{2(x - 1)}{x^3}$

$y'' = \dfrac{2x + 4}{(x - 1)^4}$ $y'' = \dfrac{6 - 4x}{x^4}$

21. $y = x + \dfrac{3}{\sqrt[3]{x-3}}$

$y' = 1 - \dfrac{1}{(x-3)^{4/3}}$

$y'' = \dfrac{4}{3(x-3)^{7/3}}$

22. $y = 3\sqrt[3]{x} + \dfrac{1}{x}$

$y' = \dfrac{x^{4/3} - 1}{x^2}$

$y'' = \dfrac{6 - 2x^{4/3}}{3x^3}$

23. $f(x) = \dfrac{9(x-2)^{2/3}}{x^2}$

$f'(x) = \dfrac{12(3-x)}{x^3(x-2)^{1/3}}$

$f''(x) = \dfrac{4(7x^2 - 42x + 54)}{x^4(x-2)^{4/3}}$

24. $f(x) = \dfrac{3x^{2/3}}{x+1}$

$f'(x) = \dfrac{2-x}{x^{1/3}(x+1)^2}$

$f''(x) = \dfrac{2(2x^2 - 8x - 1)}{3x^{4/3}(x+1)^3}$

In Problems 25–28, a function and its graph are given.
(a) Use the graph to estimate the locations of any horizontal or vertical asymptotes.
(b) Use the function to determine precisely the locations of any asymptotes.

25. $f(x) = \dfrac{9x}{17 - 4x}$

26. $f(x) = \dfrac{5 - 13x}{3x + 20}$

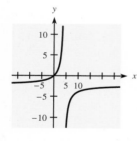

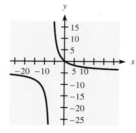

27. $f(x) = \dfrac{20x^2 + 98}{9x^2 - 49}$

28. $f(x) = \dfrac{15x^2 - x}{7x^2 - 35}$

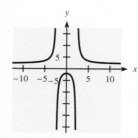

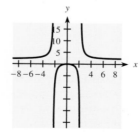

For each function in Problems 29–34, complete the following steps.
(a) Use a graphing calculator to graph the function in the standard viewing window.
(b) Analytically determine the location of any asymptotes and extrema.

(c) Graph the function in a viewing window that shows all features of the graph. State the ranges for *x*-values and *y*-values for your viewing window.

29. $f(x) = \dfrac{x + 25}{x^2 + 1400}$

30. $f(x) = \dfrac{x - 50}{x^2 + 1100}$

31. $f(x) = \dfrac{100(9 - x^2)}{x^2 + 100}$

32. $f(x) = \dfrac{200x^2}{x^2 + 100}$

33. $f(x) = \dfrac{1000x - 4000}{x^2 - 10x - 2000}$

34. $f(x) = \dfrac{900x + 5400}{x^2 - 30x - 1800}$

APPLICATIONS

35. *Cost-benefit* The percent p of particulate pollution that can be removed from the smokestacks of an industrial plant by spending C dollars is given by

$$p = \dfrac{100C}{7300 + C}$$

   (a) Find any C-values at which the rate of change of p with respect to C does not exist. Make sure that these make sense in the problem.
   (b) Find C-values for which p is increasing.
   (c) If there is a horizontal asymptote, find it.
   (d) Can 100% of the pollution be removed?

36. *Cost-benefit* The percent p of impurities that can be removed from the waste water of a manufacturing process at a cost of C dollars is given by

$$p = \dfrac{100C}{8100 + C}$$

   (a) Find any C-values at which the rate of change of p with respect to C does not exist. Make sure that these make sense in the problem.
   (b) Find C-values for which p is increasing.
   (c) Find any horizontal asymptotes.
   (d) Can 100% of the pollution be removed?

37. *Revenue* A recently released film has its weekly revenue given by

$$R(t) = \dfrac{50t}{t^2 + 36}, \quad t \geq 0$$

   where $R(t)$ is in millions of dollars and t is in weeks.
   (a) Graph $R(t)$.
   (b) When will revenue be maximized?
   (c) Suppose that if revenue decreases for 4 consecutive weeks, the film will be removed from theaters and will be released as a video 12 weeks later. When will the video come out?

38. *Minimizing average cost* If the total daily cost, in dollars, of producing plastic rafts for swimming pools is given by

$$C(x) = 500 + 8x + 0.05x^2$$

where x is the number of rafts produced per day, then the average cost per raft produced is given by
$$\overline{C}(x) = C(x)/x, \quad \text{for} \quad x > 0.$$
(a) Graph this function.
(b) Discuss what happens to the average cost as the number of rafts decreases, approaching 0.
(c) Find the level of production that minimizes average cost.

39. **Wind chill** If x is the wind speed in miles per hour and is greater than or equal to 5, then the wind chill (in degrees Fahrenheit) for an air temperature of 0°F can be approximated by the function
$$f(x) = \frac{289.173 - 58.5731x}{x + 1}, \quad x \geq 5$$
(a) Ignoring the restriction $x \geq 5$, does $f(x)$ have a vertical asymptote? If so, what is it?
(b) Does $f(x)$ have a vertical asymptote within its domain?
(c) Does $f(x)$ have a horizontal asymptote? If so, what is it?
(d) In the context of wind chill, does $\lim_{x \to \infty} f(x)$ have a physical interpretation? If so, what is it, and is it meaningful?

40. **Profit** An entrepreneur starts new companies and sells them when their growth is maximized. Suppose that the annual profit for a new company is given by
$$P(x) = 22 - \frac{1}{2}x - \frac{18}{x + 1}$$
where P is in thousands of dollars and x is the number of years after the company is formed. If she wants to sell the company before profits begin to decline, after how many years should she sell it?

41. **Productivity** The figure is a typical graph of worker productivity per hour P as a function of time t on the job.
(a) What is the horizontal asymptote?
(b) What is $\lim_{x \to \infty} P(t)$?
(c) What is the horizontal asymptote for $P'(t)$?
(d) What is $\lim_{x \to \infty} P'(t)$?

42. **Sales volume** The figure shows a typical curve that gives the volume of sales S as a function of time t after an ad campaign.
(a) What is the horizontal asymptote?
(b) What is $\lim_{t \to \infty} S(t)$?
(c) What is the horizontal asymptote for $S'(t)$?
(d) What is $\lim_{t \to \infty} S'(t)$?

43. **Females in the workforce** For selected years from 1950 and projected to 2050, the table shows the percent of total U.S. workers who were female.

Year	% Female	Year	% Female
1950	29.6	2010	47.9
1960	33.4	2015	48.3
1970	38.1	2020	48.1
1980	42.5	2030	48.0
1990	45.2	2040	47.9
2000	46.6	2050	47.7

Source: U.S. Bureau of Labor Statistics

Assume these data can be modeled with the function
$$p(t) = \frac{78.6t + 2090}{1.38t + 64.1}$$
where $p(t)$ is the percent of the U.S. workforce that is female and t is the number of years past 1950.
(a) Find $\lim_{t \to \infty} p(t)$.
(b) Interpret your answer to part (a).
(c) Does $p(t)$ have any vertical asymptotes within its domain $t \geq 0$?
(d) Whenever $p(t) < 0$ or $p(t) > 100$, the model would be inappropriate. Determine whether the model is ever inappropriate for $t \geq 0$.

44. **Modeling Obesity** Obesity (BMI $\geq$ 30) is a serious problem in the United States and expected to get worse. Being overweight increases the risk of diabetes, heart disease, and many other ailments, but the severely obese (BMI $\geq$ 40) are most at risk and are the most expensive to treat. The percent of Americans who are obese and severely obese from 1990 projected to 2030 are shown in the table below. Report the following models with three significant digits.
(a) Find the linear function, $O(x)$, that models the percent of Americans who are obese, with x equal to the number of years past 1980.
(b) Find the linear function, $S(x)$, that models the percent of Americans who are severely obese, with x equal to the number of years past 1980.
(c) Form the rational function $F(x)$ that gives the fraction of obese Americans who are severely obese.
(d) Find $\lim_{x \to \infty} F(x)$ and tell what it means in terms of these data.
(e) What does part (d) tell us about the graph of $y = F(x)$?
(f) Does $F(x)$ have any vertical asymptotes for $x > 0$?

Year	1990	2000	2010	2015	2020	2025	2030
% Obese	12.7	22.1	30.9	34.5	37.4	39.9	42.2
% Severely Obese	0.8	2.2	4.9	6.4	7.9	9.5	11.1

Source: American Journal of Preventive Medicine 42 (June 2012) 563–70, ajpmonline.org

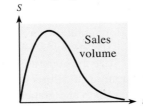

45. *Barometric pressure* The figure shows a barograph readout of the barometric pressure as recorded by Georgia Southern University's meteorological equipment. The figure shows a tremendous drop in barometric pressure on Saturday morning, March 13, 1993.

    (a) If $B(t)$ is barometric pressure expressed as a function of time, as shown in the figure, does $B(t)$ have a vertical asymptote sometime after 8 A.M. on Saturday, March 13, 1993? Explain why or why not.

    (b) Consult your library or some other resource to find out what happened in Georgia (and in the eastern United States) on March 13, 1993, to cause such a dramatic drop in barometric pressure.

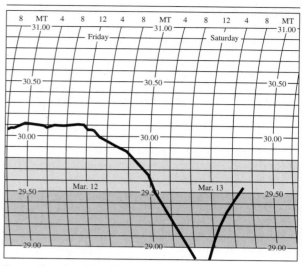

Source: Statesboro Herald, March 14, 1993.

Chapter 10   Summary & Review

KEY TERMS AND FORMULAS

Section 10.1

Relative maxima and minima (p. 630)
Increasing (p. 630)
  $f'(x) > 0$
Decreasing (p. 630)
  $f'(x) < 0$

Critical points (p. 631)
  $f'(x) = 0$ or $f'(x)$ undefined
Sign diagram for $f'(x)$ (p. 632)
First-derivative test (p. 632)
Horizontal point of inflection (p. 634)

Section 10.2

Concave up (p. 644)
  $f''(x) > 0$
Concave down (p. 644)
  $f''(x) < 0$

Point of inflection (p. 645)
  May occur where $f''(x) = 0$ or $f''(x)$ undefined
Sign diagram for $f''(x)$ (p. 646)
Second-derivative test (p. 648)

Section 10.3

Absolute extrema (p. 656)
Maximizing revenue (p. 657)
Average cost (p. 658)
  $\overline{C}(x) = C(x)/x$

Profit maximization (p. 659)
Monopolistic market (p. 660)
  $R(x) = p \cdot x$ where $p = f(x)$ is the demand function
Competitive market (p. 661)
  $R(x) = p \cdot x$ where $p =$ equilibrium price

Section 10.4

Inventory cost models (p. 670)

Section 10.5

Asymptotes for $f(x)/g(x)$ (p. 675)
  Vertical: $x = c$ if $g(c) = 0$ and $f(c) \neq 0$
    y unbounded near $x = c$

Horizontal: $y = b$
  $f(x) \to b$ as $x \to \infty$ or $x \to -\infty$
  Use the highest power terms of $f(x)$ and $g(x)$
Graphing guidelines (p. 677)
Derivatives and graphs (p. 678)

REVIEW EXERCISES

Section 10.1

In Problems 1–4, find all critical points and determine whether they are relative maxima, relative minima, or horizontal points of inflection.

1. $y = -x^2$
2. $p = q^2 - 4q - 5$
3. $f(x) = 1 - 3x + 3x^2 - x^3$
4. $f(x) = \dfrac{3x}{x^2 + 1}$

In Problems 5–10:
(a) Find all critical values, including those at which $f'(x)$ is undefined.
(b) Find the relative maxima and minima, if any exist.
(c) Find the horizontal points of inflection, if any exist.
(d) Sketch the graph.

5. $y = x^3 + x^2 - x - 1$
6. $f(x) = 4x^3 - x^4$
7. $f(x) = x^3 - \dfrac{15}{2}x^2 - 18x + \dfrac{3}{2}$
8. $y = 5x^7 - 7x^5 - 1$
9. $y = x^{2/3} - 1$
10. $y = x^{2/3}(x - 4)^2$

Section 10.2

11. Is the graph of $y = x^4 - 3x^3 + 2x - 1$ concave up or concave down at $x = 2$?
12. Find intervals on which the graph of $y = x^4 - 2x^3 - 12x^2 + 6$ is concave up and intervals on which it is concave down, and find points of inflection.
13. Find the relative maxima, relative minima, and points of inflection of the graph of $y = x^3 - 3x^2 - 9x + 10$.

In Problems 14 and 15, find any relative maxima, relative minima, and points of inflection, and sketch each graph.

14. $y = x^3 - 12x$
15. $y = 2 + 5x^3 - 3x^5$

Section 10.3

16. Given $R = 280x - x^2$, find the absolute maximum and minimum for R when (a) $0 \le x \le 200$ and (b) $0 \le x \le 100$.

17. Given $y = 6400x - 18x^2 - \dfrac{x^3}{3}$, find the absolute maximum and minimum for y when (a) $0 \le x \le 50$ and (b) $0 \le x \le 100$.

Section 10.5

In Problems 18 and 19, use the graphs to find the following items.
(a) vertical asymptotes
(b) horizontal asymptotes
(c) $\displaystyle\lim_{x \to \infty} f(x)$
(d) $\displaystyle\lim_{x \to -\infty} f(x)$

18.

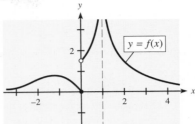

19.

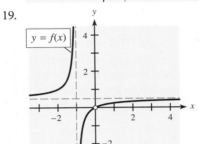

In Problems 20 and 21, find any horizontal asymptotes and any vertical asymptotes.

20. $y = \dfrac{3x + 2}{2x - 4}$
21. $y = \dfrac{x^2}{1 - x^2}$

In Problems 22–24:
(a) Find any horizontal and vertical asymptotes.
(b) Find any relative maxima and minima.
(c) Sketch each graph.

22. $y = \dfrac{3x}{x + 2}$
23. $y = \dfrac{8(x - 2)}{x^2}$
24. $y = \dfrac{x^2}{x - 1}$

Sections 10.1 and 10.2

In Problems 25 and 26, a function and its graph are given.
(a) Use the graph to determine (estimate) x-values where $f'(x) > 0$, where $f'(x) < 0$, and where $f'(x) = 0$.
(b) Use the graph to determine x-values where $f''(x) > 0$, where $f''(x) < 0$, and where $f''(x) = 0$.
(c) Check your conclusions to (a) by finding $f'(x)$ and graphing it with a graphing calculator.
(d) Check your conclusions to (b) by finding $f''(x)$ and graphing it with a graphing calculator.

25. $f(x) = x^3 - 4x^2 + 4x$

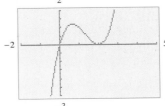

26. $f(x) = 0.0025x^4 + 0.02x^3 - 0.48x^2 + 0.08x + 4$

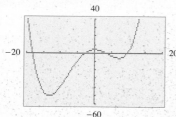

In Problems 27 and 28, $f'(x)$ and its graph are given.
(a) Use the graph of $f'(x)$ to determine (estimate) where the graph of $f(x)$ is increasing, where it is decreasing, and where it has relative extrema.
(b) Use the graph of $f'(x)$ to determine where $f''(x) > 0$, where $f''(x) < 0$, and where $f''(x) = 0$.
(c) Verify that the given $f(x)$ has $f'(x)$ as its derivative, and graph $f(x)$ to check your conclusions in part (a).
(d) Calculate $f''(x)$ and graph it to check your conclusions in part (b).

27. $f'(x) = x^2 + 4x - 5$ $\left(\text{for } f(x) = \dfrac{x^3}{3} + 2x^2 - 5x \right)$

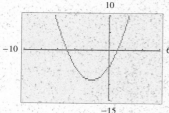

28. $f'(x) = 6x^2 - x^3$ $\left(\text{for } f(x) = 2x^3 - \dfrac{x^4}{4} \right)$

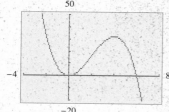

In Problems 29 and 30, $f''(x)$ and its graph are given.
(a) Use the graph to determine (estimate) where the graph of $f(x)$ is concave up, where it is concave down, and where it has points of inflection.
(b) Verify that the given $f(x)$ has $f''(x)$ as its second derivative, and graph $f(x)$ to check your conclusions in part (a).

29. $f''(x) = 4 - x$ $\left(\text{for } f(x) = 2x^2 - \dfrac{x^3}{6} \right)$

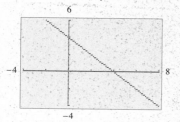

30. $f''(x) = 6 - x - x^2$ $\left(\text{for } f(x) = 3x^2 - \dfrac{x^3}{6} - \dfrac{x^4}{12} \right)$

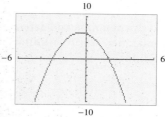

APPLICATIONS

Sections 10.1–10.3

In Problems 31–36, cost, revenue, and profit are in dollars and x is the number of units.

31. *Cost* Suppose the total cost function for a product is
$$C(x) = 3x^2 + 15x + 75$$
How many units will minimize the average cost? Find the minimum average cost.

32. *Revenue* Suppose the total revenue function for a product is given by
$$R(x) = 32x - 0.01x^2$$
(a) How many units will maximize the total revenue? Find the maximum revenue.
(b) If production is limited to 1500 units, how many units will maximize the total revenue? Find the maximum revenue.

33. *Profit* Suppose the profit function for a product is
$$P(x) = 1080x + 9.6x^2 - 0.1x^3 - 50,000$$
Find the maximum profit.

34. *Profit* How many units (x) will maximize profit if $R(x) = 46x - 0.01x^2$ and $C(x) = 0.05x^2 + 10x + 1100$?

35. *Profit* A product can be produced at a total cost of $C(x) = 800 + 4x$, where x is the number produced and is limited to at most 150 units. If the total revenue is given by $R(x) = 80x - \frac{1}{4}x^2$, determine the level of production that will maximize the profit.

36. *Average cost* The total cost function for a product is $C = 2x^2 + 54x + 98$. How many units must be produced to minimize average cost?

37. *Marginal profit* The figure shows the graph of a marginal profit function for a company. At what level of sales will profit be maximized? Explain.

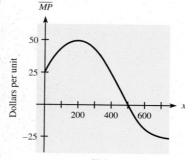

38. *Productivity—diminishing returns* Suppose the productivity P of an individual worker (in number of items produced per hour) is a function of the number of hours of training t according to

$$P(t) = 5 + \frac{95t^2}{t^2 + 2700}$$

Find the number of hours of training at which the rate of change of productivity is maximized. (That is, find the point of diminishing returns.)

39. *Output* The figure shows a typical graph of output y (in thousands of dollars) as a function of capital investment I (also in thousands of dollars).
   (a) Is the point of diminishing returns closest to the point at which $I = 20$, $I = 60$, or $I = 120$? Explain.
   (b) The average output per dollar of capital investment is defined as the total output divided by the amount of capital investment; that is,

$$\text{Average output} = \frac{f(I)}{I}$$

   Calculate the slope of a line from $(0, 0)$ to an arbitrary point $(I, f(I))$ on the output graph. How is this slope related to the average output?
   (c) Is the maximum average output attained when the capital investment is closest to $I = 40$, to $I = 70$, or to $I = 140$? Explain.

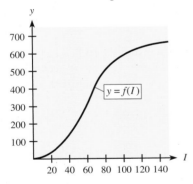

40. *Revenue* MMR II Extreme Bike Shop sells 54 of its most popular mountain bikes per month at a price of $1540 each. Market research indicates that MMR II could sell one more of these bikes if the price were $10 lower. At what selling price will MMR II maximize the revenue from these bikes?

41. *Profit* If in Problem 40 the mountain bikes cost the shop $680 each, at what selling price will MMR II's profit be a maximum?

42. *Profit* Suppose that for a product in a competitive market, the demand function is $p = 1200 - 2x$ and the supply function is $p = 200 + 2x$, where x is the number of units and p is in dollars. A firm's average cost function for this product is

$$\overline{C}(x) = \frac{12,000}{x} + 50 + x$$

Find the maximum profit. (*Hint:* First find the equilibrium price.)

43. *Profit* The monthly demand function for x units of a product sold at $\$p$ per unit by a monopoly is $p = 800 - x$, and its average cost is $\overline{C} = 200 + x$.
   (a) Determine the quantity that will maximize profit.
   (b) Find the selling price at the optimal quantity.

44. *Profit* Suppose that in a monopolistic market, the demand function for a commodity is

$$p = 7000 - 10x - \frac{x^2}{3}$$

where x is the number of units and p is in dollars. If a company's average cost function for this commodity is

$$\overline{C}(x) = \frac{40,000}{x} + 600 + 8x$$

find the maximum profit.

Section 10.4

45. *Reaction to a drug* The reaction R to an injection of a drug is related to the dose x (in milligrams) according to

$$R(x) = x^2\left(500 - \frac{x}{3}\right)$$

Find the dose that yields the maximum reaction.

46. *Productivity* The number of parts produced per hour by a worker is given by

$$N = 4 + 3t^2 - t^3$$

where t is the number of hours on the job without a break. If the worker starts at 8 A.M., when will she be at maximum productivity during the morning?

47. *Population* Population estimates show that the equation $P = 300 + 10t - t^2$ represents the size of the graduating class of a high school, where t represents the number of years after 2015, $0 \le t \le 10$. What will be the largest graduating class in the next 10 years?

48. *Night brightness* Suppose that an observatory is to be built between cities A and B, which are 30 miles apart. For the best viewing, the observatory should be located where the night brightness from these cities is minimum. If the night brightness of city A is 8 times that of city B, then the night brightness b between the two cities and x miles from A is given by

$$b = \frac{8k}{x^2} + \frac{k}{(30 - x)^2}$$

where k is a constant. Find the best location for the observatory; that is, find x that minimizes b.

49. *Product design* A playpen manufacturer wants to make a rectangular enclosure with maximum play area. To remain competitive, he wants the perimeter of the base to be only 16 feet. What dimensions should the playpen have?

50. *Printing design* A page is to contain 56 square inches of print and have a $\frac{3}{4}$-inch margin at the bottom and 1-inch margins at the top and on both sides. Find the

dimensions that minimize the size of the page (and hence the costs for paper).

51. ***Drug sensitivity*** The reaction R to an injection of a drug is related to the dose x, in milligrams, according to

$$R(x) = x^2\left(500 - \frac{x}{3}\right)$$

The sensitivity to the drug is defined by dR/dx. Find the dose that maximizes sensitivity.

52. ***Per capita health care costs*** For the years from 2000 and projected to 2018, the U.S. per capita out-of-pocket cost for health care C (in dollars) can be modeled by the function

$$C(t) = 0.118t^3 - 2.51t^2 + 40.2t + 677$$

where t is the number of years past 2000 (*Source:* U.S. Centers for Medicare and Medicaid Services).
(a) When does the rate of change of health care costs per capita reach its minimum?
(b) On a graph of $C(t)$, what feature occurs at the t-value found in part (a)?

53. ***Inventory cost model*** A company needs to produce 288,000 items per year. Production costs are $1500 to prepare for a production run and $30 for each item produced. Inventory costs are $1.50 per year for each

item stored. Find the number of items that should be produced in each run so that the total costs of production and storage are minimum.

Section 10.5

54. ***Average cost*** Suppose the total cost of producing x units of a product is given by

$$C(x) = 4500 + 120x + 0.05x^2 \quad \text{dollars}$$

(a) Find any asymptotes of the average cost function $\overline{C}(x) = C(x)/x$.
(b) Graph the average cost function.

55. ***Market share*** Suppose a company's percent share of the market (actual and projected) for a new product t quarters after its introduction is given by

$$M(t) = \frac{3.8t^2 + 3}{0.1t^2 + 1}$$

(a) Find the company's market share when the product is introduced.
(b) Find any horizontal asymptote of the graph of $M(t)$, and write a sentence that explains the meaning of this asymptote.

Chapter 10 TEST

Find the local maxima, local minima, points of inflection, and asymptotes, if they exist, for each of the functions in Problems 1–3. Graph each function.

1. $f(x) = x^3 + 6x^2 + 9x + 3$

2. $y = 4x^3 - x^4 - 10$

3. $y = \dfrac{x^2 - 3x + 6}{x - 2}$

In Problems 4–6, use the function $y = 3x^5 - 5x^3 + 2$.

4. Over what intervals is the graph of this function concave up?

5. Find the points of inflection of this function.

6. Find the relative maxima and minima of this function.

7. Find the absolute maximum and minimum for $f(x) = 2x^3 - 15x^2 + 3$ on the interval $[-2, 8]$.

8. Find all horizontal and vertical asymptotes of the function

$$f(x) = \frac{200x - 500}{x + 300}.$$

9. Use the graph of $y = f(x)$ and the indicated points to complete the chart. Enter $+$, $-$, or 0, according to whether f, f', and f'' are positive, negative, or zero at each point.

Point	f	f'	f''
A			
B			
C			

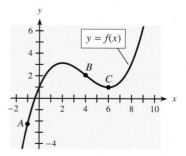

10. Use the figure to complete the following.
(a) $\lim\limits_{x \to -\infty} f(x) = ?$
(b) What is the vertical asymptote?

Solution

(a) We use logarithm Properties III and V to rewrite the function.

$$y = \ln x + \ln (x^5 - 2)^{10} \qquad \text{Property III}$$
$$y = \ln x + 10 \ln (x^5 - 2) \qquad \text{Property V}$$

We now take the derivative.

$$\frac{dy}{dx} = \frac{1}{x} + 10 \cdot \frac{1}{x^5 - 2} \cdot 5x^4$$
$$= \frac{1}{x} + \frac{50x^4}{x^5 - 2}$$

(b) Again we begin by using logarithm properties.

$$f(x) = \ln \left(\frac{\sqrt[3]{3x + 5}}{x^2 + 11} \right)^4 = 4 \ln \left(\frac{\sqrt[3]{3x + 5}}{x^2 + 11} \right) \qquad \text{Property V}$$
$$f(x) = 4 \left[\tfrac{1}{3} \ln (3x + 5) - \ln (x^2 + 11) \right] \qquad \text{Properties IV and V}$$

We now take the derivative.

$$f'(x) = 4 \left(\frac{1}{3} \cdot \frac{1}{3x + 5} \cdot 3 - \frac{1}{x^2 + 11} \cdot 2x \right)$$
$$= 4 \left(\frac{1}{3x + 5} - \frac{2x}{x^2 + 11} \right) = \frac{4}{3x + 5} - \frac{8x}{x^2 + 11}$$

✓ CHECKPOINT

3. If $y = \ln \sqrt[3]{x^2 + 1}$, find y'.

4. Find $f'(x)$ for $f(x) = \ln \left[\dfrac{2x^4}{(5x + 7)^5} \right]$.

EXAMPLE   4   Life Span | APPLICATION PREVIEW |

Assume that the average life span (in years) for people born from 1920 and projected to 2020 can be modeled by

$$l(x) = 11.249 + 14.244 \ln x$$

where x is the number of years past 1900.
(a) Find the function that models the rate of change of life span.
(b) Does $l(x)$ have a maximum value for $x > 0$?
(c) Evaluate $\lim\limits_{x \to \infty} l'(x)$.
(d) What do the results of parts (b) and (c) tell us about the average life span?

Solution

(a) The rate of change of life span is given by the derivative.

$$l'(x) = 0 + 14.244 \left(\frac{1}{x} \right) = \frac{14.244}{x}$$

(b) For $x > 0$, we see that $l'(x) > 0$. Hence $l(x)$ is increasing for all values of $x > 0$, so $l(x)$ never achieves a maximum value. That is, there is no maximum life span.

(c) $\lim\limits_{x \to \infty} l'(x) = \lim\limits_{x \to \infty} \dfrac{14.244}{x} = 0$

(d) If this model is accurate, life span will continue to increase, but at an ever slower rate.

EXAMPLE   5   Cost

Suppose the cost function for x skateboards is given by

$$C(x) = 18{,}250 + 615 \ln (4x + 10)$$

where $C(x)$ is in dollars. Find the marginal cost when 100 units are produced, and explain what it means.

Solution
Marginal cost is given by $C'(x)$.

$$\overline{MC} = C'(x) = 615\left(\frac{1}{4x + 10}\right)(4) = \frac{2460}{4x + 10}$$

$$\overline{MC}(100) = \frac{2460}{4(100) + 10} = \frac{2460}{410} = 6$$

When 100 units are produced, the marginal cost is 6. This means that the approximate cost of producing the 101st skateboard is $6.

Derivative of
$y = \log_a (x)$

So far we have found derivatives of natural logarithmic functions. If we have a logarithmic function with a base other than e, then we can use the **change-of-base formula.**

Change-of-Base Formula

To express a logarithm base a as a natural logarithm, use

$$\log_a x = \frac{\ln x}{\ln a}$$

We can apply this change-of-base formula to find the derivative of a logarithm with any base, as the following example illustrates.

EXAMPLE 6   **Derivative of $y = \log_a (u)$**

If $y = \log_4 (x^3 + 1)$, find dy/dx.

Solution
By using the change-of-base formula, we have

$$y = \log_4 (x^3 + 1) = \frac{\ln (x^3 + 1)}{\ln 4} = \frac{1}{\ln 4} \cdot \ln (x^3 + 1)$$

Thus

$$\frac{dy}{dx} = \frac{1}{\ln 4} \cdot \frac{1}{x^3 + 1} \cdot 3x^2 = \frac{3x^2}{(x^3 + 1) \ln 4}$$

Note that this formula means that logarithms with bases other than e will have the *constant* $1/\ln a$ as a factor in their derivatives (as Example 6 had $1/\ln 4$ as a factor). This means that derivatives involving natural logarithms have a simpler form, and we see why base e logarithms are used more frequently in calculus.

EXAMPLE 7   **Critical Values**

Let $f(x) = x \ln x - x$. Use the graph of the derivative of $f(x)$ for $x > 0$ to answer the following questions.

(a)   At what value a does the graph of $f'(x)$ cross the x-axis (that is, where is $f'(x) = 0$)?
(b)   What value a is a critical value for $y = f(x)$?
(c)   Does $f(x)$ have a relative maximum or a relative minimum at $x = a$?

Solution

$$f'(x) = x \cdot \frac{1}{x} + \ln x - 1 = \ln x. \text{ The graph of } f'(x) = \ln x \text{ is shown in Figure 11.4(a).}$$

(a) The graph crosses the x-axis at $x = 1$, so $f'(a) = 0$ if $a = 1$.
(b) $a = 1$ is a critical value of $f(x)$.
(c) Because $f'(x)$ is negative for $x < 1$, $f(x)$ is decreasing for $x < 1$.
Because $f'(x)$ is positive for $x > 1$, $f(x)$ is increasing for $x > 1$.
Therefore, $f(x)$ has a relative minimum at $x = 1$.
The graph of $f(x) = x \ln x - x$ is shown in Figure 11.4(b). It has a relative minimum at the point $(1, -1)$.

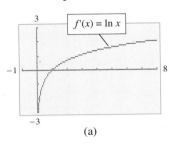

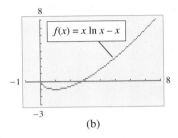

(a)   (b)

Figure 11.4

Calculator Note  As with polynomial functions, critical values involving logarithmic functions can be found by using the SOLVER feature of a graphing calculator. Figure 11.5 shows the steps used to find the two critical values of $y = x^2 - 8 \ln x$ by solving $0 = 2x - \dfrac{8}{x}$ with SOLVER. The critical values are $x = 2$ and $x = -2$. See Appendix A, Section 11.1, for details.

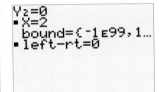

Figure 11.5

Proof That $\dfrac{d}{dx}(\ln\ x) = \dfrac{1}{x}$ For completeness, we now include the formal proof that if $y = \ln\ x$, then $dy/dx = 1/x$.

$$\frac{dy}{dx} = \lim_{h \to 0} \frac{f(x + h) - f(x)}{h}$$

$$= \lim_{h \to 0} \frac{\ln(x + h) - \ln x}{h}$$

$$= \lim_{h \to 0} \frac{\ln\left(\dfrac{x + h}{x}\right)}{h} \qquad \text{Property IV}$$

$$= \lim_{h \to 0} \frac{x}{x} \cdot \frac{1}{h} \ln\left(\frac{x + h}{x}\right) \qquad \text{Introduce } \frac{x}{x}$$

$$= \lim_{h \to 0} \frac{1}{x} \cdot \frac{x}{h} \ln\left(1 + \frac{h}{x}\right)$$

$$= \lim_{h \to 0} \frac{1}{x} \ln\left(1 + \frac{h}{x}\right)^{x/h} \qquad \text{Property V}$$

$$= \frac{1}{x} \lim_{h \to 0} \left[\ln\left(1 + \frac{h}{x}\right)^{x/h}\right]^{*}$$

$$= \frac{1}{x} \ln\left[\lim_{h \to 0} \left(1 + \frac{h}{x}\right)^{x/h}\right]$$

If we let $a = \dfrac{h}{x}$, then $h \to 0$ means $a \to 0$, and we have

$$\frac{dy}{dx} = \frac{1}{x} \ln\left[\lim_{a \to 0}(1 + a)^{1/a}\right]$$

*The next step uses a new limit property for continuous composite functions. In particular, $\lim_{x \to c} \ln(f(x)) = \ln[\lim_{x \to c} f(x)]$ when $\lim_{x \to c} f(x)$ exists and is positive.

In Problem 47 in the 9.1 Exercises, we saw that $\lim_{a\to 0}(1+a)^{1/a}=e$. Hence,

$$\frac{dy}{dx}=\frac{1}{x}\ln\ e=\frac{1}{x}$$

✓ **CHECKPOINT ANSWERS**

1. $y'=\dfrac{6x}{3x^2+2}$

2. $y'=\dfrac{6}{x}$

3. $y'=\dfrac{2x}{3(x^2+1)}$

4. $f'(x)=\dfrac{4}{x}-\dfrac{25}{5x+7}$

| EXERCISES | 11.1

Find the derivatives of the functions in Problems 1–10.

1. $f(x)=4\ln x$
2. $y=3\ln x$
3. $y=\ln 8x$
4. $y=\ln 5x$
5. $y=\ln x^4$
6. $f(x)=\ln x^3$
7. $f(x)=\ln(4x+9)$
8. $y=\ln(6x+1)$
9. $y=\ln(2x^2-x)+3x$
10. $y=\ln(8x^3-2x)-2x$
11. Find dp/dq if $p=\ln(q^2+1)$.
12. Find $\dfrac{ds}{dq}$ if $s=\ln\left(\dfrac{q^2}{4}+1\right)$.

In each of Problems 13–18, find the derivative of the function in part (a). Then find the derivative of the function in part (b) or show that the function in part (b) is the same function as that in part (a).

13. (a) $y=\ln x-\ln(x-1)$
　　(b) $y=\ln\dfrac{x}{x-1}$
14. (a) $y=\ln(x-1)+\ln(2x+1)$
　　(b) $y=\ln[(x-1)(2x+1)]$
15. (a) $y=\frac13\ln(x^2-1)$
　　(b) $y=\ln\sqrt[3]{x^2-1}$
16. (a) $y=3\ln(x^4-1)$
　　(b) $y=\ln(x^4-1)^3$
17. (a) $y=\ln(4x-1)-3\ln x$
　　(b) $y=\ln\left(\dfrac{4x-1}{x^3}\right)$
18. (a) $y=3\ln x-\ln(x+1)$
　　(b) $y=\ln\left(\dfrac{x^3}{x+1}\right)$
19. Find $\dfrac{dp}{dq}$ if $p=\ln\left(\dfrac{q^2-1}{q}\right)$.
20. Find $\dfrac{ds}{dt}$ if $s=\ln[t^3(t^2-1)]$.
21. Find $\dfrac{dy}{dt}$ if $y=\ln\left(\dfrac{t^2+3}{\sqrt{1-t}}\right)$.
22. Find $\dfrac{dy}{dx}$ if $y=\ln\left(\dfrac{3x+2}{x^2-5}\right)^{1/4}$.

23. Find $\dfrac{dy}{dx}$ if $y=\ln(x^3\sqrt{x+1})$.
24. Find $\dfrac{dy}{dx}$ if $y=\ln[x^2(x^4-x+1)]$.

In Problems 25–38, find y'.

25. $y=x-\ln x$
26. $y=x^2\ln(2x+3)$
27. $y=\dfrac{\ln x}{x}$
28. $y=\dfrac{1+\ln x}{x^2}$
29. $y=\ln(x^4+3)^2$
30. $y=\ln(3x+1)^{1/2}$
31. $y=(\ln x)^4$
32. $y=(\ln x)^{-1}$
33. $y=[\ln(x^4+3)]^2$
34. $y=\sqrt{\ln(3x+1)}$
35. $y=\log_4 x$
36. $y=\log_5 x$
37. $y=\log_6(x^4-4x^3+1)$
38. $y=\log_2(1-x-x^2)$

In Problems 39–42, find the relative maxima and relative minima, and sketch the graph with a graphing utility to check your results.

39. $y=x\ln x$
40. $y=x^2\ln x$
41. $y=x^2-8\ln x$
42. $y=\ln x-x$

APPLICATIONS

43. *Marginal cost* Suppose that the total cost (in dollars) for a product is given by

$$C(x)=1500+200\ln(2x+1)$$

where x is the number of units produced.
(a) Find the marginal cost function.
(b) Find the marginal cost when 200 units are produced, and interpret your result.
(c) Total cost functions always increase because producing more items costs more. What then must be true of the marginal cost function? Does it apply in this problem?

44. *Investment* If money is invested at the constant rate r, the time to increase the investment by a factor x is

$$t=\frac{\ln x}{r}$$

(a) At what rate $\dfrac{dt}{dx}$ is the time changing at $x = 2$?

(b) What happens to $\dfrac{dt}{dx}$ as x gets very large? Interpret this result.

45. ***Marginal revenue*** The total revenue, in dollars, from the sale of x units of a product is given by

$$R(x) = \frac{2500x}{\ln(10x + 10)}$$

(a) Find the marginal revenue function.

(b) Find the marginal revenue when 100 units are sold, and interpret your result.

46. ***Supply*** Suppose that the supply of x units of a product at price p dollars per unit is given by

$$p = 10 + 50 \ln(3x + 1)$$

(a) Find the rate of change of supply price with respect to the number of units supplied.

(b) Find the rate of change of supply price when the number of units is 33.

(c) Approximate the price increase associated with the number of units supplied changing from 33 to 34.

47. ***Demand*** The demand function for a product is given by $p = 4000/\ln(x + 10)$, where p is the price per unit in dollars when x units are demanded.

(a) Find the rate of change of price with respect to the number of units sold when 40 units are sold.

(b) Find the rate of change of price with respect to the number of units sold when 90 units are sold.

(c) Find the second derivative to see whether the rate at which the price is changing at 40 units is increasing or decreasing.

48. ***pH level*** The pH of a solution is given by

$$pH = -\log[H^+]$$

where $[H^+]$ is the concentration of hydrogen ions (in gram atoms per liter). What is the rate of change of pH with respect to $[H^+]$?

49. ***Drug concentration*** Concentration (in mg/ml) in the bloodstream of a certain drug is related to the time t (in minutes) after an injection and can be calculated using y in the equation

$$y = A \ln(t) - Bt + C$$

where A, B, and C are positive constants. In terms of A and B, find t at which y (and hence the drug concentration) reaches its maximum.

50. ***Decibels*** The loudness of sound (L, measured in decibels) perceived by the human ear depends on intensity levels (I) according to

$$L = 10 \log(I/I_0)$$

where I_0 is the standard threshold of audibility. If $x = I/I_0$, then using the change-of-base formula, we get

$$L = \frac{10 \ln(x)}{\ln 10}$$

At what rate is the loudness changing with respect to x when the intensity is 100 times the standard threshold of audibility (that is, when $x = 100$)?

51. ***Richter scale*** The Richter scale reading, R, used for measuring the magnitude of an earthquake with intensity I is determined by

$$R = \frac{\ln(I/I_0)}{\ln 10}$$

where I_0 is a standard minimum threshold of intensity. If $I_0 = 1$, what is the rate of change of the Richter scale reading with respect to intensity?

52. ***Women in the workforce*** From 1950 and projected to 2050, the percent of women in the workforce can be modeled by

$$w(x) = 9.42 + 8.70 \ln x$$

where x is the number of years past 1940 (*Source:* U.S. Bureau of Labor Statistics). If this model is accurate, at what rate will the percent be changing in 2020?

53. **Modeling *Obesity*** Obesity (BMI ≥ 30) is a serious problem in the United States and expected to get worse. Being overweight increases the risk of diabetes, heart disease, and many other ailments. The table gives the percent of Americans who are obese for selected years from 1990 and projected to 2030.

Year	1990	2000	2010	2015	2020	2025	2030
% Obese	12.7	22.1	30.9	34.5	37.4	39.9	42.2

Source: American Journal of Preventive Medicine 42 (June 2012).

(a) Find a logarithmic function that models the data, with x equal to the number of years after 1980 and y equal to the percent. Report the model with three significant digits.

(b) Use the reported model to find the instantaneous rate of change of obesity.

(c) At what rate is obesity projected to increase in 2020?

54. **Modeling *Diabetes*** The following table gives the percent of adult Americans with diabetes for selected years from 2010 and projected to 2050.

(a) Find a logarithmic function that models the data, with x equal to the number of years after 2000 and y equal to the percent of the adult American population with diabetes. Report the model with three significant digits.

(b) Use the reported model to find the instantaneous rate of change of the percent of Americans with diabetes.

(c) At what rate is the percent of Americans with diabetes projected to increase in 2030?

Year	Percent	Year	Percent
2010	15.7	2035	29.0
2015	18.9	2040	31.4
2020	21.1	2045	32.1
2025	24.2	2050	34.3
2030	27.2		

OBJECTIVE

11.2

- To find derivatives of exponential functions

Derivatives of Exponential Functions

■ | APPLICATION PREVIEW |

We saw in Chapter 6, "Mathematics of Finance," that the amount that accrues when $100 is invested at 8%, compounded continuously, is

$$S(t) = 100e^{0.08t}$$

where t is the number of years. If we want to find the rate at which the money in this account is growing at the end of 1 year, then we need to find the derivative of this exponential function. (See Example 4.)

Derivative of $y = e^x$ Just as base e logarithms are most convenient, we begin by focusing on base e exponentials. Figure 11.6(a) shows the graph of $f(x) = e^x$, and Figure 11.6(b) shows the same graph with tangent lines drawn to several points.

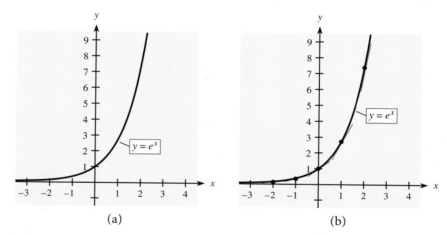

Figure 11.6   (a)   (b)

Note in Figure 11.6(b) that when $x < 0$, tangent lines have slopes near 0, much like the y-coordinates of $f(x) = e^x$. Furthermore, as x increases to $x = 0$ and for $x > 0$, the slopes of the tangents increase just as the values of the function do. This suggests that the function that gives the slope of the tangent to the graph of $f(x) = e^x$ (that is, the derivative) is similar to the function itself. In fact, the derivative of $f(x) = e^x$ is exactly the function itself, which we prove as follows:

From logarithms Property I, we know that

$$\ln e^x = x$$

Taking the derivative, with respect to x, of both sides of this equation, we have

$$\frac{d}{dx}(\ln e^x) = \frac{d}{dx}(x)$$

Using the Chain Rule for logarithms gives

$$\frac{1}{e^x} \cdot \frac{d}{dx}(e^x) = 1$$

and solving for $\dfrac{d}{dx}(e^x)$ yields

$$\frac{d}{dx}(e^x) = e^x$$

Thus we can conclude the following.

Derivative of $y = e^x$	If $y = e^x$, then $\dfrac{dy}{dx} = e^x$.

EXAMPLE 1 **Derivative of an Exponential Function**

If $y = 3e^x + 4x - 11$, find $\dfrac{dy}{dx}$.

Solution

$$\frac{dy}{dx} = 3e^x + 4$$

Derivative of $y = e^u$ As with logarithmic functions, the Chain Rule permits us to expand our derivative formulas.

Derivatives of Exponential Functions	If $y = e^u$, where u is a differentiable function of x, then $$\frac{dy}{dx} = e^u \cdot \frac{du}{dx}$$

EXAMPLE 2 **Derivatives of $y = e^u$**

(a) If $f(x) = e^{4x^3}$ find $f'(x)$.
(b) If $s = 3te^{3t^2 + 5t}$, find ds/dt.
(c) If $u = w/e^{3w}$, find u'.

Solution
(a) $f'(x) = e^{4x^3} \cdot (12x^2) = 12x^2\, e^{4x^3}$
(b) We begin with the Product Rule.

$$\frac{ds}{dt} = 3t \cdot e^{3t^2 + 5t}(6t + 5) + e^{3t^2 + 5t} \cdot 3$$
$$= (18t^2 + 15t)e^{3t^2 + 5t} + 3e^{3t^2 + 5t}$$
$$= 3e^{3t^2 + 5t}(6t^2 + 5t + 1)$$

(c) The function is a quotient. Using the Quotient Rule gives

$$u' = \frac{(e^{3w})(1) - (w)(e^{3w} \cdot 3)}{(e^{3w})^2} = \frac{e^{3w} - 3we^{3w}}{e^{6w}} = \frac{1 - 3w}{e^{3w}}$$

EXAMPLE 3 **Derivatives and Logarithmic Properties**

If $y = e^{\ln x^2}$, find y'.

Solution

$$y' = e^{\ln x^2} \cdot \frac{1}{x^2} \cdot 2x = \frac{2}{x}e^{\ln x^2}$$

By logarithm Property II (see the previous section), $e^{\ln u} = u$, and we can simplify the derivative to

$$y' = \frac{2}{x} \cdot x^2 = 2x$$

Note that if we had used this property *before* taking the derivative, we would have had

$$y = e^{\ln x^2} = x^2$$

Then the derivative is $y' = 2x$.

✓ **CHECKPOINT**   1. If $y = 2e^{4x}$, find y'.   2. If $y = e^{x^2+6x}$, find y'.   3. If $s = te^{t^2}$, find ds/dt.

EXAMPLE 4   **Future Value** | **APPLICATION PREVIEW** |

When \$100 is invested at 8% compounded continuously, the amount that accrues after t years, which is called the future value, is $S(t) = 100e^{0.08t}$. At what rate is the money in this account growing

(a) at the end of 1 year?   (b) at the end of 10 years?

Solution

The rate of growth of the money is given by

$$S'(t) = 100e^{0.08t}(0.08) = 8e^{0.08t}$$

(a) The rate of growth of the money at the end of 1 year is

$$S'(1) = 8e^{0.08} \approx 8.666$$

Thus the future value will change by about \$8.67 during the second year.

(b) The rate of growth of the money at the end of 10 years is

$$S'(10) = 8e^{0.08(10)} \approx 17.804$$

Thus the future value will change by about \$17.80 during the eleventh year.

EXAMPLE 5   **Revenue**

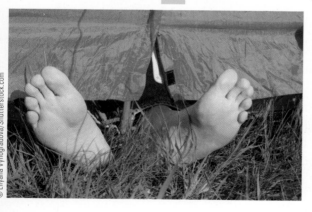

North Forty, Inc. is a manufacturer of wilderness camping equipment. The revenue function for its best-selling tent, the Sierra, can be modeled by the function

$$R(x) = 250xe^{(1-0.01x)}$$

where $R(x)$ is the revenue in thousands of dollars from the sale of x thousand Sierra tents. Find the marginal revenue when 75,000 tents are sold, and explain what it means.

Solution

The marginal revenue function is given by $R'(x)$, and to find this derivative we use the Product Rule.

$$R'(x) = \overline{MR} = 250x[e^{(1-0.01x)} \cdot (-0.01)] + e^{(1-0.01x)}(250)$$
$$\overline{MR} = 250e^{(1-0.01x)}(1 - 0.01x)$$

To find the marginal revenue when 75,000 tents are sold, we use $x = 75$.

$$\overline{MR}(75) = 250e^{(1-0.75)}(1 - 0.75) \approx 80.25$$

This means that the sale of one (thousand) more Sierra tents will yield approximately \$80.25 (thousand) in additional revenue.

✓ **CHECKPOINT**   4. If the sales of a product are given by $S = 1000e^{-0.2x}$, where x is the number of days after the end of an advertising campaign, what is the rate of decline in sales 20 days after the end of the campaign?

Derivative of $y = a^u$ In a manner similar to that used to find the derivative of $y = e^x$, we can develop a formula for the derivative of $y = a^x$ for any base $a > 0$ and $a \neq 1$.

Derivative of $y = a^u$

If $y = a^x$, with $a > 0$, $a \neq 1$, then

$$\frac{dy}{dx} = a^x \ln a$$

If $y = a^u$, with $a > 0$, $a \neq 1$, where u is a differentiable function of x, then

$$\frac{dy}{dx} = a^u \frac{du}{dx} \ln a$$

EXAMPLE 6 **Derivatives of $y = a^u$**

(a) If $y = 4^x$, find dy/dx.   (b) If $y = 5^{x^2+x}$, find y'.

Solution

(a) $\dfrac{dy}{dx} = 4^x \ln 4$

(b) $y' = 5^{x^2+x}(2x + 1) \ln 5$

 Calculator Note   As with other functions, we can make use of a graphing calculator to check derivatives of functions involving exponentials. See Appendix A, Section 11.2, for details.

 EXAMPLE 7 **Technology and Critical Values**

For the function $y = e^x - 3x^2$, complete the following.

(a) Approximate the critical values of the function to four decimal places.
(b) Determine whether relative maxima or relative minima occur at the critical values.

Solution

(a) The derivative is $y' = e^x - 6x$. Using the ZERO feature of a graphing calculator, we find that $y' = 0$ at $x \approx 0.2045$ (see Figure 11.7(a)) and at $x \approx 2.8331$.
(b) From the graph of $y' = e^x - 6x$ in Figure 11.7(a), we can observe where $y' > 0$ and where $y' < 0$. From this we can make a sign diagram to determine relative maxima and relative minima.

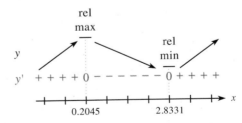

The graph of $y = e^x - 3x^2$ in Figure 11.7(b) shows that the relative maximum point is $(0.2045, 1.1015)$ and that the relative minimum point is $(2.8331, -7.0813)$.

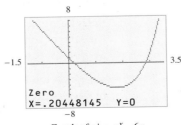

Graph of $y' = e^x - 6x$

(a)

Graph of $y = e^x - 3x^2$

(b)

Figure 11.7

Calculator Note As with other functions, the SOLVER feature of a graphing calculator can also be used to find maxima and minima of functions involving exponentials. See Appendix A, Section 11.2, for details. ∎

✓ CHECKPOINT ANSWERS

1. $y' = 8e^{4x}$
2. $y' = (2x + 6)e^{x^2+6x}$
3. $\dfrac{ds}{dt} = e^{t^2} + 2t^2 e^{t^2}.$
4. The rate of decline is given by $S'(20) = -200e^{-4} \approx -3.663$ sales/day.

| EXERCISES | 11.2

Find the derivatives of the functions in Problems 1–34.

1. $y = 5e^x - x$
2. $y = x^2 - 3e^x$
3. $f(x) = e^x - x^e$
4. $f(x) = 4e^x - \ln x$
5. $g(x) = 500(1 - e^{-0.1x})$
6. $h(x) = 750e^{0.04x}$
7. $y = e^{x^3}$
8. $y = e^{x^2-1}$
9. $y = 6e^{3x^2}$
10. $y = 1 - 2e^{-x^3}$
11. $y = 2e^{(x^2+1)^3}$
12. $y = e^{\sqrt{x^2-9}}$
13. $y = e^{\ln x^3}$
14. $y = e^3 + e^{\ln x}$
15. $y = e^{-1/x}$
16. $y = 2e^{\sqrt{x}}$
17. $y = e^{-1/x^2} + e^{-x^2}$
18. $y = \dfrac{2}{e^{2x}} + \dfrac{e^{2x}}{2}$
19. $s = t^2 e^t$
20. $p = 4qe^{q^3}$
21. $y = e^{x^4} - (e^x)^4$
22. $y = 4(e^x)^3 - 4e^{x^3}$
23. $y = \ln(e^{4x} + 2)$
24. $y = \ln(e^{2x} + 1)$
25. $y = e^{-3x}\ln(2x)$
26. $y = e^{2x^2}\ln(4x)$
27. $y = \dfrac{1 + e^{5x}}{e^{3x}}$
28. $y = \dfrac{x}{1 + e^{2x}}$
29. $y = (e^{3x} + 4)^{10}$
30. $y = \dfrac{e^x - e^{-x}}{e^x + e^{-x}}$
31. $y = 6^x$
32. $y = 3^x$
33. $y = 4^{x^2}$
34. $y = 5^{2x-1}$

35. (a) What is the slope of the line tangent to $y = xe^{-x}$ at $x = 1$?
    (b) Write the equation of the line tangent to the graph of $y = xe^{-x}$ at $x = 1$.
36. (a) What is the slope of the line tangent to $y = e^{-x}/(1 + e^{-x})$ at $x = 0$?
    (b) Write the equation of the line tangent to the graph of $y = e^{-x}/(1 + e^{-x})$ at $x = 0$.
37. The equation for the standard normal probability distribution is
$$y = \frac{1}{\sqrt{2\pi}}e^{-z^2/2}$$
    (a) At what value of z will the curve be at its highest point?
    (b) Graph this function with a graphing utility to verify your answer.

38. (a) Find the mode of the normal distribution* given by
$$y = \frac{1}{\sqrt{2\pi}}e^{-(x-10)^2/2}$$
    (b) What is the mean of this normal distribution?
    (c) Use a graphing utility to verify your answer.

In Problems 39–42, find any relative maxima and minima. Use a graphing utility to check your results.

39. $y = \dfrac{e^x}{x}$
40. $y = \dfrac{x}{e^x}$
41. $y = x - e^x$
42. $y = \dfrac{x^2}{e^x}$

APPLICATIONS

43. **Future value** If $\$P$ is invested for n years at 10% compounded continuously, the future value that results after n years is given by the function
$$S = Pe^{0.1n}$$
    (a) At what rate is the future value growing at any time (for any nonnegative n)?
    (b) At what rate is the future value growing after 1 year ($n = 1$)?
    (c) Is the rate of growth of the future value after 1 year greater than 10%? Why?
44. **Future value** The future value that accrues when $\$700$ is invested at 9%, compounded continuously, is
$$S(t) = 700e^{0.09t}$$
    where t is the number of years.
    (a) At what rate is the money in this account growing when $t = 4$?
    (b) At what rate is it growing when $t = 10$?
45. **Sales decay** After the end of an advertising campaign, the sales of a product are given by
$$S = 100{,}000e^{-0.5t}$$
    where S is weekly sales in dollars and t is the number of weeks since the end of the campaign.

*The mode occurs at the highest point on normal curves and equals the mean.

(a) Find the rate of change of S (that is, the rate of *sales decay*).

(b) Give a reason from looking at the function and another reason from looking at the derivative that explain how you know sales are decreasing.

46. *Sales decay* The sales decay for a product is given by

$$S = 50{,}000e^{-0.8t}$$

where S is the daily sales in dollars and t is the number of days since the end of a promotional campaign. Find the rate of sales decay.

47. *Marginal cost* Suppose that the total cost in dollars of producing x units of a product is given by

$$C(x) = 10{,}000 + 20xe^{x/600}$$

Find the marginal cost when 600 units are produced.

48. *Marginal revenue* Suppose that the revenue in dollars from the sale of x units of a product is given by

$$R(x) = 1000xe^{-x/50}$$

Find the marginal revenue function.

49. *Drugs in a bloodstream* The percent concentration y of a certain drug in the bloodstream at any time t (in hours) is given by

$$y = 100(1 - e^{-0.462t})$$

(a) What function gives the instantaneous rate of change of the concentration of the drug in the bloodstream?

(b) Find the rate of change of the concentration after 1 hour. Give your answer to three decimal places.

50. *Radioactive decay* The amount of the radioactive isotope thorium-234 present at time t in years is given by

$$Q(t) = 100e^{-0.02828t}$$

(a) Find the function that describes how rapidly the isotope is decaying.

(b) Find the rate of radioactive decay of the isotope after 10 years.

51. *Pollution* Pollution levels in Lake Sagamore have been modeled by the equation

$$x = 0.05 + 0.18e^{-0.38t}$$

where x is the volume of pollutants (in cubic kilometers) and t is the time (in years). What is the rate of change of x with respect to time?

52. *Drug concentration* Suppose the concentration $C(t)$, in mg/ml, of a drug in the bloodstream t minutes after an injection is given by

$$C(t) = 20te^{-0.04t}$$

(a) Find the instantaneous rate of change of the concentration after 10 minutes.

(b) Find the maximum concentration and when it occurs.

53. *National health care* With U.S. Department of Health and Human Services data from 2000 and projected to 2018, the total public expenditures for health care H can be modeled by

$$H = 624e^{0.07t}$$

where t is the number of years past 2000 and H is in billions of dollars. If this model is accurate, at what rate will health care expenditures change in 2020?

54. *Personal consumption* By using U.S. Bureau of Labor Statistics data for selected years from 1988 and projected to 2018, the billions of dollars spent for personal consumption in the United States can be modeled by

$$P = 2969e^{0.051t}$$

where t is the number of years past 1985. If this model is accurate, find and interpret the rate of change of personal consumption in 2015.

55. *Richter scale* The intensity of an earthquake is related to the Richter scale reading R by

$$\frac{I}{I_0} = 10^R$$

where I_0 is a standard minimum intensity. If $I_0 = 1$, what is the rate of change of the intensity I with respect to the Richter scale reading?

56. *Decibel readings* The intensity level of sound, I, is given by

$$\frac{I}{I_0} = 10^{L/10}$$

where L is the decibel reading and I_0 is the standard threshold of audibility. If $I/I_0 = y$, at what rate is y changing with respect to L when $L = 20$?

57. *U.S. debt* For selected years from 1900 to 2014, the national debt d, in billions of dollars, can be modeled by

$$d = 1.60e^{0.083t}$$

where t is the number of years past 1900
(*Source:* Bureau of Public Debt, U.S. Treasury).

(a) What function describes how fast the national debt is changing?

(b) Find the instantaneous rate of change of the national debt model $d(t)$ in 1950 and 2025.

58. *Blood pressure* Medical research has shown that between heartbeats, the pressure in the aorta of a normal adult is a function of time in seconds and can be modeled by the equation

$$P = 95e^{-0.491t}$$

(a) Use the derivative to find the rate at which the pressure is changing at any time t.

(b) Use the derivative to find the rate at which the pressure is changing after 0.1 second.

(c) Is the pressure increasing or decreasing?

59. *Spread of disease* Suppose that the spread of a disease through the student body at an isolated college campus can be modeled by

$$y = \frac{10,000}{1 + 9999e^{-0.99t}}$$

where y is the total number affected at time t (in days). Find the rate of change of y.

60. *Spread of a rumor* The number of people $N(t)$ in a community who are reached by a particular rumor at time t (in days) is given by

$$N(t) = \frac{50,500}{1 + 100e^{-0.7t}}$$

Find the rate of change of $N(t)$.

61. *Population* By using Social Security Administration data for selected years from 1950 and projected to 2050, the population of Americans ages 20 to 64 can be modeled by the function

$$P(t) = \frac{250}{1 + 1.91e^{-0.0280t}}$$

where t is the number of years after 1950 and $P(t)$ is in millions.
(a) Find and interpret $P'(45)$.
(b) At what rate is this population projected to increase in 2040?
(c) What does this tell us about this population after 2040?

62. *Carbon dioxide emissions* By using U.S. Department of Energy data for selected years from 2010 and projected to 2032, the millions of metric tons of carbon dioxide (CO_2) emissions from biomass energy combustion in the United States can be modeled with the function

$$E(t) = \frac{1310}{1 + 2.95e^{-0.0619t}}$$

where t is the number of years past 2010.
(a) Find the function that models the rate of change of $E(t)$. Report this function as $E'(t)$ with three significant digits.
(b) Find and interpret $E'(15)$.

63. **Modeling *Severe obesity*** Obesity (BMI $\geq$ 30) increases the risk of diabetes, heart disease, and many other ailments, but the severely obese (BMI $\geq$ 40) are most at risk and are the most expensive to treat. The table gives the percent of the Americans who are severely obese for the years from 1990 and projected to 2030.
(a) Find an exponential function that models the data, with x equal to the number of years after 1980 and y equal to the percent. Report the model with three significant digits.
(b) Use the reported model to find the instantaneous rate of change of severe obesity.
(c) At what rate is severe obesity projected to increase in 2020?

Year	1990	2000	2010	2015	2020	2025	2030
% Severely Obese	0.8	2.2	4.9	6.4	7.9	9.5	11.1

Source: *American Journal of Preventive Medicine* 42 (June 2012)

64. **Modeling *Centenarians*** The following table gives the projected population, in thousands, of Americans over 100 years of age.
(a) Create an exponential function that models the projected population y, in thousands, as a function of the number of years past 2010. Report the model with three significant digits.
(b) Use the reported model to find a function that gives the rate of change in the projected number of centenarians.
(c) What is the projected rate of change in the number of centenarians in 2040?

Year	Centenarians (thousands)	Year	Centenarians (thousands)
2015	78	2040	230
2020	106	2045	310
2025	143	2050	442
2030	168	2055	564
2035	188	2060	690

Source: U.S. Census Bureau

65. *World tourism* Using data from 2000 and projected to 2050, the receipts (in billions of dollars) for world tourism can be modeled by the function

$$y = 165.55(1.055^x)$$

where x is the number of years past 1980.
(a) Write the function that models the rate of change in the tourism receipts. Use four significant digits.
(b) Predict the rate of change of tourism receipts in 2015.

66. *Energy use* When U.S. energy use per dollar of GDP is indexed to 1980, that energy use for any year is viewed as a percent of the use per dollar of GDP in 1980. By using U.S. Department of Energy data for selected years from 1985 and projected to 2035, energy use per dollar of GDP can be modeled by the function

$$E(t) = 96e^{-0.019t}$$

where t is the number of years past 1980.
(a) Find the function that describes how rapidly the energy use per dollar of GDP is changing.
(b) Find and interpret $E(50)$ and $E'(50)$.

67. **Modeling *Annual wages*** The table gives the average annual wage, in thousands of dollars, for selected years from 2012 and projected to 2050.

(a) Find an exponential function that models the data, with x equal to the number of years after 2010 and y equal to the average annual wage in thousands of dollars. Report the model with three significant digits.

(b) Use the reported model to find a function that gives the instantaneous rate of change of the average annual wage. Report this function with three significant digits.

(c) Use the result in part (b) to predict the rate of growth of the average annual wage in 2040.

Year	Annual Wage ($ thousands)	Year	Annual Wage ($ thousands)
2012	44.6	2030	93.2
2014	48.6	2035	113.2
2016	53.3	2040	137.6
2018	58.7	2045	167.1
2020	63.7	2050	202.5
2025	76.8		

Source: Social Security Administration

OBJECTIVES

- To find derivatives by using implicit differentiation
- To find slopes of tangents by using implicit differentiation

11.3

Implicit Differentiation

| APPLICATION PREVIEW |

In the retail electronics industry, suppose the monthly demand for Precision, Inc., headphones is given by

$$p = \frac{10,000}{(x+1)^2}$$

where p is the price in dollars per set of headphones and x is demand in hundreds of sets of headphones. If we want to find the rate of change of the quantity demanded with respect to the price, then we need to find dx/dp. (See Example 8.) Although we can solve this equation for x so that dx/dp can be found, the resulting equation does not define x as a function of p. In this case, and in other cases where we cannot solve equations for the variables we need, we can find derivatives with a technique called implicit differentiation.

Up to this point, functions involving x and y have been written in the form $y = f(x)$, defining y as an *explicit function* of x. However, not all equations involving x and y can be written in the form $y = f(x)$, and we need a new technique for taking their derivatives. For example, solving $y^2 = x$ for y gives $y = \pm\sqrt{x}$ so that y is not a function of x. We can write $y = \sqrt{x}$ and $y = -\sqrt{x}$, but then finding the derivative $\dfrac{dy}{dx}$ at a point on the graph of $y^2 = x$ would require determining which of these functions applies before taking the derivative. Alternatively, we can *imply* that y is a function of x and use a technique called **implicit differentiation**. When y is an implied function of x, we find $\dfrac{dy}{dx}$ by differentiating both sides of the equation with respect to x and then algebraically solving for $\dfrac{dy}{dx}$.

EXAMPLE   1   **Implicit Differentiation**

(a) Use implicit differentiation to find $\dfrac{dy}{dx}$ for $y^2 = x$.

(b) Find the slopes of the tangents to the graph of $y^2 = x$ at the points $(4, 2)$ and $(4, -2)$.

Solution

(a) First take the derivative of both sides of the equation with respect to x.

$$\frac{d}{dx}(y^2) = \frac{d}{dx}(x)$$

Because y is an implied, or implicit, function of x, we can think of $y^2 = x$ as meaning $[u(x)]^2 = x$ for some function u. We use the Chain Rule to take the derivative of y^2 in the same way we would for $[u(x)]^2$. Thus

$$\frac{d}{dx}(y^2) = \frac{d}{dx}(x) \quad \text{gives} \quad 2y\frac{dy}{dx} = 1$$

Solving for $\dfrac{dy}{dx}$ gives $\dfrac{dy}{dx} = \dfrac{1}{2y}$.

(b) To find the slopes of the tangents at the points $(4, 2)$ and $(4, -2)$, we use the coordinates of the points to evaluate $\dfrac{dy}{dx}$ at those points.

$$\left.\frac{dy}{dx}\right|_{(4,\,2)} = \frac{1}{2(2)} = \frac{1}{4} \quad \text{and} \quad \left.\frac{dy}{dx}\right|_{(4,\,-2)} = \frac{1}{2(-2)} = \frac{-1}{4}$$

Figure 11.8 shows the graph of $y^2 = x$ with tangent lines drawn at $(4, 2)$ and $(4, -2)$.

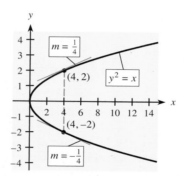

Figure 11.8

As noted previously, solving $y^2 = x$ for y gives the two functions $y = \sqrt{x} = x^{1/2}$ and $y = -\sqrt{x} = -x^{1/2}$; see Figures 11.9(a) and (b).

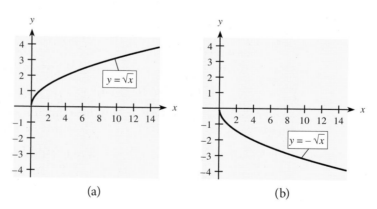

Figure 11.9   (a)   (b)

Let us now compare the results obtained in Example 1 with the results from the derivatives of the two functions $y = \sqrt{x}$ and $y = -\sqrt{x}$. The derivatives of these two functions are as follows:

$$\text{For } y = x^{1/2}, \text{ then } \frac{dy}{dx} = \frac{1}{2}x^{-1/2} = \frac{1}{2\sqrt{x}}$$

$$\text{For } y = -x^{1/2}, \text{ then } \frac{dy}{dx} = -\frac{1}{2}x^{-1/2} = \frac{-1}{2\sqrt{x}}$$

We cannot find the slope of a tangent line at $x = 4$ unless we also know the y-coordinate and hence which function and which derivative to use.

$$\text{At } (4, 2) \text{ use } y = \sqrt{x} \quad \text{so} \quad \frac{dy}{dx}\bigg|_{(4, 2)} = \frac{1}{2\sqrt{4}} = \frac{1}{4}$$

$$\text{At } (4, -2) \text{ use } y = -\sqrt{x} \quad \text{so} \quad \frac{dy}{dx}\bigg|_{(4, -2)} = \frac{-1}{2\sqrt{4}} = \frac{-1}{4}$$

These are the same results that we obtained directly after implicit differentiation. In this example, we could easily solve for y in terms of x and work the problem two different ways. However, sometimes solving explicitly for y is difficult or impossible. For these functions, implicit differentiation is necessary and extends our ability to find derivatives.

EXAMPLE 2 Slope of a Tangent

Find the slope of the tangent to the graph of $x^2 + y^2 - 9 = 0$ at $(\sqrt{5}, 2)$.

Solution
We find the derivative dy/dx from $x^2 + y^2 - 9 = 0$ by taking the derivative term by term on both sides of the equation.

$$\frac{d}{dx}(x^2) + \frac{d}{dx}(y^2) + \frac{d}{dx}(-9) = \frac{d}{dx}(0)$$

$$2x + 2y \cdot \frac{dy}{dx} + 0 = 0$$

Solving for dy/dx gives

$$\frac{dy}{dx} = -\frac{2x}{2y} = -\frac{x}{y}$$

The slope of the tangent to the curve at $(\sqrt{5}, 2)$ is the value of the derivative at this point. Evaluating $dy/dx = -x/y$ at $(\sqrt{5}, 2)$ gives the slope of the tangent as $-\sqrt{5}/2$.

As we have seen in Examples 1 and 2, the Chain Rule yields $\frac{d}{dx}(y^n) = ny^{n-1}\frac{dy}{dx}$. Just as we needed this result to find derivatives of powers of y, the next example discusses how to find the derivative of xy.

EXAMPLE 3 Equation of a Tangent Line

Write the equation of the tangent to the graph of $x^3 + xy + 4 = 0$ at the point $(2, -6)$.

Solution
Note that the second term is the *product* of x and y. Because we are assuming that y is a function of x, and because x is a function of x, we must use the Product Rule to find $\frac{d}{dx}(xy)$.

$$\frac{d}{dx}(xy) = x \cdot 1\frac{dy}{dx} + y \cdot 1 = x\frac{dy}{dx} + y$$

Thus we have

$$\frac{d}{dx}(x^3) + \frac{d}{dx}(xy) + \frac{d}{dx}(4) = \frac{d}{dx}(0)$$

$$3x^2 + \left(x\frac{dy}{dx} + y\right) + 0 = 0$$

Solving for dy/dx gives $\quad \dfrac{dy}{dx} = \dfrac{-3x^2 - y}{x}$

The slope of the tangent to the curve at $x = 2$, $y = -6$ is

$$m = \frac{-3(2)^2 - (-6)}{2} = -3$$

The equation of the tangent line is

$$y - (-6) = -3[x - (2)], \quad \text{or} \quad y = -3x$$

Technology Note   A graphing utility can be used to graph the function of Example 3 and the line that is tangent to the curve at $(2, -6)$. To graph the equation, we solve the equation for y, getting

$$y = \frac{-x^3 - 4}{x}$$

The graph of the equation and the line that is tangent to the curve at $(2, -6)$ are shown in Figure 11.10.

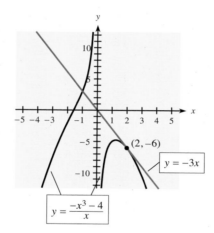

Figure 11.10

EXAMPLE 4   Implicit Differentiation

Find dy/dx if $x^4 + 5xy^4 = 2y^2 + x - 1$.

Solution

By viewing $5xy^4$ as the product $(5x)(y^4)$ and differentiating implicitly, we get

$$\frac{d}{dx}(x^4) + \frac{d}{dx}(5xy^4) = \frac{d}{dx}(2y^2) + \frac{d}{dx}(x) - \frac{d}{dx}(1) \quad (1)$$

$$4x^3 + 5x\left(4y^3\frac{dy}{dx}\right) + y^4(5) = 4y\frac{dy}{dx} + 1$$

To solve for $\dfrac{dy}{dx}$, we first rewrite the equation with terms containing $\dfrac{dy}{dx}$ on one side and the other terms on the other side.

$$20xy^3\frac{dy}{dx} - 4y\frac{dy}{dx} = 1 - 4x^3 - 5y^4$$

Now $\dfrac{dy}{dx}$ is a factor of one side. To complete the solution, we factor out $\dfrac{dy}{dx}$ and divide both sides by its coefficient.

$$(20xy^3 - 4y)\frac{dy}{dx} = 1 - 4x^3 - 5y^4$$

$$\frac{dy}{dx} = \frac{1 - 4x^3 - 5y^4}{20xy^3 - 4y}$$

1. Find the following:

   (a) $\dfrac{d}{dx}(x^3)$ (b) $\dfrac{d}{dx}(y^4)$ (c) $\dfrac{d}{dx}(x^2y^5)$

2. Find $\dfrac{dy}{dx}$ for $x^3 + y^4 = x^2y^5$.

EXAMPLE 5   Production

Suppose that a company's weekly production output is $384,000 and that this output is related to hours of labor x and dollars of capital investment y by

$$384{,}000 = 30x^{1/3}\, y^{2/3}$$

(This relationship is an example of a Cobb-Douglas production function, studied in more detail in Chapter 14.) Find and interpret the rate of change of capital investment with respect to labor hours when labor hours are 512 and capital investment is $64,000.

Solution

The desired rate of change is given by the value of dy/dx when $x = 512$ and $y = 64{,}000$. Taking the derivative implicitly gives

$$\frac{d}{dx}(384{,}000) = \frac{d}{dx}(30x^{1/3}\, y^{2/3})$$

$$0 = 30x^{1/3}\left(\frac{2}{3}y^{-1/3}\frac{dy}{dx}\right) + y^{2/3}(10x^{-2/3})$$

$$0 = \frac{20x^{1/3}}{y^{1/3}}\cdot\frac{dy}{dx} + \frac{10y^{2/3}}{x^{2/3}}$$

$$\frac{-20x^{1/3}}{y^{1/3}}\cdot\frac{dy}{dx} = \frac{10y^{2/3}}{x^{2/3}}$$

Multiplying both sides by $\dfrac{-y^{1/3}}{20x^{1/3}}$ gives

$$\frac{dy}{dx} = \left(\frac{10y^{2/3}}{x^{2/3}}\right)\left(\frac{-y^{1/3}}{20x^{1/3}}\right) = \frac{-y}{2x}$$

When $x = 512$ and $y = 64{,}000$, we obtain

$$\frac{dy}{dx} = \frac{-64{,}000}{2(512)} = -62.5$$

This means that when labor hours are 512 and capital investment is $64,000, if labor hours change by 1 hour, then capital investment could decrease by about $62.50.

EXAMPLE 6   Horizontal and Vertical Tangents

(a) At what point(s) does $x^2 + 4y^2 - 2x + 4y - 2 = 0$ have a horizontal tangent?
(b) At what point(s) does it have a vertical tangent?

Solution

(a) First we find the derivative implicitly, with y' representing $\dfrac{dy}{dx}$.

$$2x + 8y\cdot y' - 2 + 4y' - 0 = 0$$

We isolate the y' terms, factor out y', and solve for y'.

$$8yy' + 4y' = 2 - 2x$$
$$(8y + 4)y' = 2 - 2x$$
$$y' = \frac{2 - 2x}{8y + 4} = \frac{1 - x}{4y + 2}$$

Horizontal tangents will occur where $y' = 0$; that is, where $1 - x = 0$, or $x = 1$. We can now find the corresponding y-value(s) by substituting 1 for x in the original equation and solving.

$$1 + 4y^2 - 2 + 4y - 2 = 0$$
$$4y^2 + 4y - 3 = 0$$
$$(2y - 1)(2y + 3) = 0$$
$$y = \frac{1}{2} \quad \text{or} \quad y = -\frac{3}{2}$$

Thus horizontal tangents occur at $\left(1, \frac{1}{2}\right)$ and $\left(1, -\frac{3}{2}\right)$; see Figure 11.11.

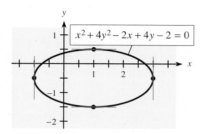

Figure 11.11

(b) Vertical tangents will occur where the derivative is undefined—that is, where $4y + 2 = 0$, or $y = -\frac{1}{2}$. To find the corresponding x-value(s), we substitute $-\frac{1}{2}$ in the equation for y and solve for x.

$$x^2 + 4\left(-\frac{1}{2}\right)^2 - 2x + 4\left(-\frac{1}{2}\right) - 2 = 0$$
$$x^2 - 2x - 3 = 0$$
$$(x - 3)(x + 1) = 0$$
$$x = 3 \quad \text{or} \quad x = -1$$

Thus vertical tangents occur at $\left(3, -\frac{1}{2}\right)$ and $\left(-1, -\frac{1}{2}\right)$; see Figure 11.11.

EXAMPLE 7   Implicit Derivatives with Logarithms and Exponentials

Find dy/dx for each of the following.
(a) $\ln xy = 6$ (b) $4x^2 + e^{xy} = 6y$

Solution
(a) Using the properties of logarithms, we have

$$\ln x + \ln y = 6$$

which leads to the implicit derivative

$$\frac{1}{x} + \frac{1}{y}\frac{dy}{dx} = 0$$

Solving gives $\dfrac{1}{y}\dfrac{dy}{dx} = -\dfrac{1}{x}$ so $\dfrac{dy}{dx} = -\dfrac{y}{x}$

(b) We take the derivative of both sides of $4x^2 + e^{xy} = 6y$ and obtain

$$8x + e^{xy}\left(x\frac{dy}{dx} + y\right) = 6\frac{dy}{dx}$$
$$8x + xe^{xy}\frac{dy}{dx} + ye^{xy} = 6\frac{dy}{dx}$$
$$8x + ye^{xy} = 6\frac{dy}{dx} - xe^{xy}\frac{dy}{dx}$$
$$8x + ye^{xy} = (6 - xe^{xy})\frac{dy}{dx} \quad \text{so} \quad \frac{8x + ye^{xy}}{6 - xe^{xy}} = \frac{dy}{dx}$$

EXAMPLE 8   Demand | APPLICATION PREVIEW |

Suppose the demand for Precision, Inc. headphones is given by

$$p = \frac{10{,}000}{(x + 1)^2}$$

where p is the price per set in dollars and x is in hundreds of headphone sets demanded. Find the rate of change of demand with respect to price when 19 (hundred) sets are demanded.

Solution

The rate of change of demand with respect to price is dx/dp. Using implicit differentiation, we get

$$\frac{d}{dp}(p) = \frac{d}{dp}\left[\frac{10{,}000}{(x + 1)^2}\right] = \frac{d}{dp}[10{,}000(x + 1)^{-2}]$$

$$1 = 10{,}000\left[-2(x + 1)^{-3}\frac{dx}{dp}\right]$$

$$1 = \frac{-20{,}000}{(x + 1)^3} \cdot \frac{dx}{dp}$$

$$\frac{(x + 1)^3}{-20{,}000} = \frac{dx}{dp}$$

When 19 (hundred) headphone sets are demanded we use $x = 19$, and the rate of change of demand with respect to price is

$$\frac{dx}{dp}\bigg|_{x=19} = \frac{(19 + 1)^3}{-20{,}000} = \frac{8000}{-20{,}000} = -0.4$$

This result means that when 19 (hundred) headphone sets are demanded, if the price per set is increased by $1, then the expected change in demand is a decrease of about 0.4 hundred, or 40, headphone sets. ∎

Calculator Note

To graph a function with a graphing calculator, we need to write y as an *explicit* function of x (such as $y = \sqrt{4 - x^2}$). If an equation defines y as an *implicit* function of x, we have to solve for y in terms of x before we can use the graphing calculator. Sometimes we cannot solve for y, and other times, such as for

$$x^{2/3} + y^{2/3} = 8^{2/3}$$

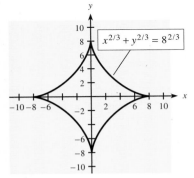

Figure 11.12

y cannot be written as a single function of x. If this equation is solved for y as a single function and a graphing calculator is used to graph that function, the resulting graph usually shows only the portion of the graph that lies in Quadrants I and II. To graph $x^{2/3} + y^{2/3} = 8^{2/3}$, we solve for y.

$$y^{2/3} = 8^{2/3} - x^{2/3} \Rightarrow y^2 = (8^{2/3} - x^{2/3})^3 \Rightarrow y = \pm\sqrt{(8^{2/3} - x^{2/3})^3}$$

Graphing $Y_1 = \sqrt{(8^{2/3} - x^{2/3})^3}$ and $Y_2 = -\sqrt{(8^{2/3} - x^{2/3})^3}$ on a window such as 5:ZSquare gives a complete graph like the one shown in Figure 11.12. In general, for the graph of an implicitly defined function, a graphing calculator must be used carefully (and sometimes cannot be used at all). ∎

✓ CHECKPOINT ANSWERS

1. (a) $\dfrac{d}{dx}(x^3) = 3x^2$ (b) $\dfrac{d}{dx}(y^4) = 4y^3\dfrac{dy}{dx}$

   (c) $\dfrac{d}{dx}(x^2y^5) = x^2\left(5y^4\dfrac{dy}{dx}\right) + y^5(2x)$

2. $\dfrac{dy}{dx} = \dfrac{3x^2 - 2xy^5}{5x^2y^4 - 4y^3}$

| EXERCISES | 11.3

In Problems 1–6, find dy/dx at the given point without first solving for y.

1. $x^2 - 4y - 17 = 0$ at $(1, -4)$
2. $3x^2 - 10y + 400 = 0$ at $(10, 70)$
3. $xy^2 = 8$ at $(2, 2)$
4. $e^y = x$ at $(1, 0)$
5. $x^2 + 3xy - 4 = 0$ at $(1, 1)$
6. $x^2 + 5xy + 4 = 0$ at $(1, -1)$

Find dy/dx for the functions in Problems 7–10.

7. $x^2 + 2y^2 - 4 = 0$
8. $x + y^2 - 4y + 6 = 0$
9. $x^2 + 4x + y^2 - 3y + 1 = 0$
10. $x^2 - 5x + y^3 - 3y - 3 = 0$
11. If $x^2 + y^2 = 4$, find y'.
12. If $p^2 + 4p - q = 4$, find dp/dq.
13. If $xy^2 - y^3 = 1$, find y'.
14. If $p^2 - q = 4$, find dp/dq.
15. If $p^2q = 4p - 2$, find dp/dq.
16. If $x^2 - 3y^4 = 2x^5 + 7y^3 - 5$, find dy/dx.
17. If $3x^5 - 5y^3 = 5x^2 + 3y^5$, find dy/dx.
18. If $x^2 + 3x^2y^4 = y + 8$, find dy/dx.
19. If $x^4 + 2x^3y^2 = x - y^3$, find dy/dx.
20. If $(x + y)^2 = 5x^4y^3$, find dy/dx.
21. Find dy/dx for $x^4 + 3x^3y^2 - 2y^5 = (2x + 3y)^2$.
22. Find y' for $2x + 2y = \sqrt{x^2 + y^2}$.

For Problems 23–26, find the slope of the tangent to the curve.

23. $x^2 + 4x + y^2 + 2y - 4 = 0$ at $(1, -1)$
24. $x^2 - 4x + 2y^2 - 4 = 0$ at $(2, 2)$
25. $x^2 + 2xy + 3 = 0$ at $(-1, 2)$
26. $y + x^2 + xy = 13$ at $(2, 3)$
27. Write the equation of the line tangent to the curve $x^2 - 2y^2 + 4 = 0$ at $(2, 2)$.
28. Write the equation of the line tangent to the curve $x^2 + y^2 + 2x - 3 = 0$ at $(-1, 2)$.
29. Write the equation of the line tangent to the curve $4x^2 + 3y^2 - 4y - 3 = 0$ at $(-1, 1)$.
30. Write the equation of the line tangent to the curve $xy + y^2 = 0$ at $(3, 0)$.
31. If $\ln x = y^2$, find dy/dx.
32. If $\ln (x + y) = y^2$, find dy/dx.
33. If $y^2 \ln x = 4$, find dy/dx.
34. If $\ln (xy - 1) = x + 2$, find dy/dx.
35. Find the slope of the tangent to the curve $y^2 \ln x + x^2y = 3$ at the point $(1, 3)$.
36. Write the equation of the line tangent to the curve $x \ln y + 2xy = 2$ at the point $(1, 1)$.
37. If $xe^y = 6$, find dy/dx.
38. If $x + e^{xy} = 10$, find dy/dx.
39. If $xe^{xy} = 4$, find dy/dx.
40. If $x - xe^y = 3$, find dy/dx.
41. If $ye^x - y = 3$, find dy/dx.

42. If $x^2y = e^{x+y}$, find dy/dx.
43. Find the slope of the line tangent to the graph of $ye^x = y^2 + x - 2$ at $(0, 2)$.
44. Find the slope of the line tangent to the curve $xe^y = 3x^2 + y - 24$ at $(3, 0)$.
45. Write the equation of the line tangent to the curve $xe^y = 2y + 3$ at $(3, 0)$.
46. Write the equation of the line tangent to the curve $ye^x = 2y + 1$ at $(0, -1)$.
47. At what points does the curve defined by $x^2 + 4y^2 - 4x - 4 = 0$ have
    (a) horizontal tangents?
    (b) vertical tangents?
48. At what points does the curve defined by $x^2 + 4y^2 - 4 = 0$ have
    (a) horizontal tangents?
    (b) vertical tangents?
49. In Problem 11, the derivative y' was found to be

    $$y' = \frac{-x}{y}$$

    when $x^2 + y^2 = 4$.
    (a) Take the implicit derivative of the equation for y' to show that

    $$y'' = \frac{-y + xy'}{y^2}$$

    (b) Substitute $-x/y$ for y' in the expression for y'' in part (a) and simplify to show that

    $$y'' = -\frac{(x^2 + y^2)}{y^3}$$

    (c) Does $y'' = -4/y^3$? Why or why not?
50. (a) Find y' implicitly for $x^3 - y^3 = 8$.
    (b) Then, by taking derivatives implicitly, use part (a) to show that

    $$y'' = \frac{2x(y - xy')}{y^3}$$

    (c) Substitute x^2/y^2 for y' in the expression for y'' and simplify to show that

    $$y'' = \frac{2x(y^3 - x^3)}{y^5}$$

    (d) Does $y'' = -16x/y^5$? Why or why not?
51. Find y'' for $\sqrt{x} + \sqrt{y} = 1$ and simplify.
52. Find y'' for $\dfrac{1}{x} - \dfrac{1}{y} = 1$.

 In Problems 53 and 54, find the maximum and minimum values of y. Use a graphing utility to verify your conclusion.

53. $x^2 + y^2 - 9 = 0$ 54. $4x^2 + y^2 - 8x = 0$

APPLICATIONS

55. **Advertising and sales** Suppose that a company's sales volume y (in thousands of units) is related to its advertising expenditures x (in thousands of dollars) according to

$$xy - 20x + 10y = 0$$

Find the rate of change of sales volume with respect to advertising expenditures when $x = 10$ (thousand dollars).

56. **Insect control** Suppose that the number of mosquitoes N (in thousands) in a certain swampy area near a community is related to the number of pounds of insecticide x sprayed on the nesting areas according to

$$Nx - 10x + N = 300$$

Find the rate of change of N with respect to x when 49 pounds of insecticide is used.

57. **Production** Suppose that a company can produce 12,000 units when the number of hours of skilled labor y and unskilled labor x satisfy

$$384 = (x + 1)^{3/4}(y + 2)^{1/3}$$

Find the rate of change of skilled-labor hours with respect to unskilled-labor hours when $x = 255$ and $y = 214$. This can be used to approximate the change in skilled-labor hours required to maintain the same production level when unskilled-labor hours are increased by 1 hour.

58. **Production** Suppose that production of 10,000 units of a certain agricultural crop is related to the number of hours of labor x and the number of acres of the crop y according to

$$300x + 30,000y = 11xy - 0.0002x^2 - 5y$$

Find the rate of change of the number of hours with respect to the number of acres.

59. **Demand** If the demand function for q units of a product at \$$p$ per unit is given by

$$p(q + 1)^2 = 200,000$$

find the rate of change of quantity with respect to price when $p = \$80$. Interpret this result.

60. **Demand** If the demand function for q units of a commodity at \$$p$ per unit is given by

$$p^2(2q + 1) = 100,000$$

find the rate of change of quantity with respect to price when $p = \$50$. Interpret this result.

61. **Radioactive decay** The number of grams of radium, y, that will remain after t years if 100 grams existed originally can be found by using the equation

$$-0.000436t = \ln\left(\frac{y}{100}\right)$$

Use implicit differentiation to find the rate of change of y with respect to t—that is, the rate at which the radium will decay.

62. **Disease control** Suppose the proportion P of people affected by a certain disease is described by

$$\ln\left(\frac{P}{1 - P}\right) = 0.5t$$

where t is the time in months. Find dP/dt, the rate at which P grows.

63. **Temperature-humidity index** The temperature-humidity index (THI) is given by

$$\text{THI} = t - 0.55(1 - h)(t - 58)$$

where t is the air temperature in degrees Fahrenheit and h is the relative humidity. If the THI remains constant, find the rate of change of humidity with respect to temperature if the temperature is 70°F (*Source:* "Temperature-Humidity Indices," *UMAP Journal,* Fall 1989).

OBJECTIVE   11.4

- To use implicit differentiation to solve problems that involve related rates

Related Rates

▮ | APPLICATION PREVIEW | ▮

According to Poiseuille's law, the flow of blood F is related to the radius r of the vessel according to

$$F = kr^4$$

where k is a constant. When the radius of a blood vessel is reduced, such as by cholesterol deposits, the flow of blood is also restricted. Drugs can be administered that increase the radius of the blood vessel and, hence, the flow of blood. The rate of change of the blood flow and the rate of change of the radius of the blood vessel are time rates of change that are related to each other, so they are called related rates. We can use these related rates to find the percent rate of change in the blood flow that corresponds to the percent rate of change in the radius of the blood vessel caused by the drug. (See Example 2.)

Related Rates   We have seen that the derivative represents the instantaneous rate of change of one variable with respect to another. When the derivative is taken with respect to time, it represents the rate at which that variable is changing with respect to time. For example, if distance x is measured in miles and time t in hours, then dx/dt is measured in miles per hour and indicates how fast x is changing. Similarly, if V represents the volume (in cubic feet) of water in a swimming pool and t is time (in minutes), then dV/dt is measured in cubic feet per minute (ft³/min) and might measure the rate at which the pool is being filled with water or being emptied.

Sometimes, two (or more) quantities that depend on time are also related to each other. For example, the height of a tree h (in feet) is related to the radius r (in inches) of its trunk, and this relationship can be modeled by

$$h = kr^{2/3}$$

where k is a constant.* Of course, both h and r are also related to time, so the rates of change dh/dt and dr/dt are related to each other. Thus they are called **related rates.**

The specific relationship between dh/dt and dr/dt can be found by differentiating $h = kr^{2/3}$ implicitly with respect to time t.

EXAMPLE 1   Tree Height and Trunk Radius

Suppose that for a certain type of tree, the height of the tree (in feet) is related to the radius of its trunk (in inches) by

$$h = 15r^{2/3}$$

Suppose that the rate of change of r is $\frac{3}{4}$ inch per year. Find how fast the height is changing when the radius is 8 inches.

Solution

To find how the rates dh/dt and dr/dt are related, we differentiate $h = 15r^{2/3}$ implicitly with respect to time t.

$$\frac{dh}{dt} = 10r^{-1/3}\frac{dr}{dt}$$

Using $r = 8$ inches and $dr/dt = \frac{3}{4}$ inch per year gives

$$\frac{dh}{dt} = 10(8)^{-1/3}(3/4) = \frac{15}{4} = 3\tfrac{3}{4} \text{ feet per year}$$

Percent Rates of Change   The work in Example 1 shows how to obtain related rates, but the different units (feet per year and inches per year) may be somewhat difficult to interpret. For this reason, many applications in the life sciences deal with **percent rates of change.** The percent rate of change of a quantity is the rate of change of the quantity divided by the quantity.

EXAMPLE 2   Blood Flow | APPLICATION PREVIEW |

Poiseuille's law expresses the flow of blood F as a function of the radius r of the vessel according to

$$F = kr^4$$

where k is a constant. When the radius of a blood vessel is restricted, such as by cholesterol deposits, drugs can be administered that will increase the radius of the blood vessel (and hence the blood flow). Find the percent rate of change of the flow of blood that corresponds to the percent rate of change of the radius of a blood vessel caused by the drug.

*T. McMahon, "Size and Shape in Biology," *Science* 179 (1979): 1201.

Solution

We seek the percent rate of change of flow, $(dF/dt)/F$, that results from a given percent rate of change of the radius $(dr/dt)/r$. We first find the related rates of change by differentiating

$$F = kr^4$$

implicitly with respect to time.

$$\frac{dF}{dt} = k\left(4r^3\frac{dr}{dt}\right)$$

Then the percent rate of change of flow can be found by dividing both sides of the equation by F.

$$\frac{\frac{dF}{dt}}{F} = \frac{4kr^3\frac{dr}{dt}}{F}$$

If we replace F on the right side of the equation with kr^4 and reduce, we get

$$\frac{\frac{dF}{dt}}{F} = \frac{4kr^3\frac{dr}{dt}}{kr^4} = 4\left(\frac{\frac{dr}{dt}}{r}\right)$$

Thus we see that the percent rate of change of the flow of blood is 4 times the corresponding percent rate of change of the radius of the blood vessel. This means that a drug that would cause a 12% increase in the radius of a blood vessel at a certain time would produce a corresponding 48% increase in blood flow through that vessel at that time. ■

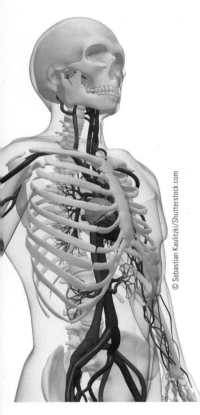

© Sebastian Kaulitzki/Shutterstock.com

Solving Related-Rates Problems

In the examples above, the equation relating the time-dependent variables has been given. For some problems, the original equation relating the variables must first be developed from the statement of the problem. These problems can be solved with the aid of the following procedure.

Solving a Related-Rates Problem

Procedure	Example
To solve a related-rates problem:	Sand falls at a rate of 5 ft³/min on a conical pile, with the diameter always equal to the height of the pile. At what rate is the height increasing when the pile is 10 ft high?
1. Use geometric and/or physical conditions to write an equation that relates the time-dependent variables.	1. The conical pile has its volume given by $$V = \frac{1}{3}\pi r^2 h$$
2. Substitute into the equation values or relationships that are true at *all times*.	2. The radius $r = \frac{1}{2}h$ at all times, so $$V = \frac{1}{3}\pi\left(\frac{1}{4}h^2\right)h = \frac{\pi}{12}h^3$$
3. Differentiate both sides of the equation implicitly with respect to time. This equation is valid for all times.	3. $\dfrac{dV}{dt} = \dfrac{\pi}{12}\left(3h^2\dfrac{dh}{dt}\right) = \dfrac{\pi}{4}h^2\dfrac{dh}{dt}$
4. Substitute the values that are known at the instant specified, and solve the equation.	4. $\dfrac{dV}{dt} = 5$ at all times, so when $h = 10$, $$5 = \frac{\pi}{4}(10^2)\frac{dh}{dt}$$
5. Solve for the specified quantity at the given time.	5. $\dfrac{dh}{dt} = \dfrac{20}{100\pi} = \dfrac{1}{5\pi}$ (feet/minute)

Note that you should *not* substitute numerical values for any quantity that varies with time until after the derivative is taken. If values are substituted before the derivative is taken, that quantity will have the constant value resulting from the substitution and hence will have a derivative equal to zero.

EXAMPLE 3   Hot Air Balloon

A hot air balloon has a velocity of 50 feet per minute and is flying at a constant height of 500 feet. An observer on the ground is watching the balloon approach. How fast is the distance between the balloon and the observer changing when the balloon is 1000 feet from the observer?

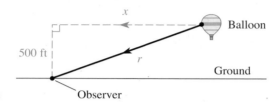

Figure 11.13

Solution

If we let r be the distance between the balloon and the observer and let x be the horizontal distance from the balloon to a point directly above the observer, then we see that these quantities are related by the equation

$$x^2 + 500^2 = r^2 \qquad \text{(See Figure 11.13)}$$

Because the distance x is decreasing, we know that dx/dt must be negative. Thus we are given that $dx/dt = -50$ at all times, and we need to find dr/dt when $r = 1000$. Taking the derivative with respect to t of both sides of the equation $x^2 + 500^2 = r^2$ gives

$$2x \frac{dx}{dt} + 0 = 2r \frac{dr}{dt}$$

Using $dx/dt = -50$ and $r = 1000$, we get

$$2x(-50) = 2000 \frac{dr}{dt}$$

$$\frac{dr}{dt} = \frac{-100x}{2000} = \frac{-x}{20}$$

Using $r = 1000$ in $x^2 + 500^2 = r^2$ gives $x^2 = 750{,}000$. Thus $x = 500\sqrt{3}$, and

$$\frac{dr}{dt} = \frac{-500\sqrt{3}}{20} = -25\sqrt{3} \approx -43.3$$

The distance is decreasing at 43.3 feet per minute.

✓ CHECKPOINT

1. If V represents volume, write a mathematical symbol that represents "the rate of change of volume with respect to time."
2. (a) Differentiate $x^2 + 64 = y^2$ implicitly with respect to time.
   (b) Suppose that we know that y is increasing at 2 units per minute. Use part (a) to find the rate of change of x at the instant when $x = 6$ and $y = 10$.
3. True or false: In solving a related-rates problem, we substitute all numerical values into the equation before we take derivatives.

EXAMPLE 4   Spread of an Oil Slick

Suppose that oil is spreading in a circular pattern from a leak at an offshore rig. If the rate at which the radius of the oil slick is growing is 1 foot per minute at what rate is the area of the oil slick growing when the radius is 600 feet?

Solution

The area of the circular oil slick is given by

$$A = \pi r^2$$

where r is the radius. The rate at which the area is changing is

$$\frac{dA}{dt} = 2\pi r \frac{dr}{dt}$$

Using $r = 600$ feet and $dr/dt = 1$ foot per minute gives

$$\frac{dA}{dt} = 2\pi\,(600\text{ ft})\,(1\text{ ft/min}) = 1200\pi \text{ ft}^2/\text{min}$$

Thus when the radius of the oil slick is 600 feet, the area is growing at the rate of 1200π square feet per minute, or approximately 3770 square feet per minute. ∎

✓ **CHECKPOINT ANSWERS**

1. dV/dt
2. (a) $x\dfrac{dx}{dt} = y\dfrac{dy}{dt}$ (b) $\dfrac{10}{3}$ units per minute
3. False; the numerical value for any variable that is changing with time should not be substituted until after the derivative is taken.

| EXERCISES | 11.4

In Problems 1–4, find dy/dt using the given values.
1. $y = x^3 - 3x$ for $x = 2$, $dx/dt = 4$
2. $y = 3x^3 + 5x^2 - x$ for $x = 4$, $dx/dt = 3$
3. $xy = 4$ for $x = 8$, $dx/dt = -2$
4. $xy = x + 3$ for $x = 3$, $dx/dt = -1$

In Problems 5–8, assume that x and y are differentiable functions of t. In each case, find dx/dt given that $x = 5$, $y = 12$, and $dy/dt = 2$.
5. $x^2 + y^2 = 169$
6. $y^2 - x^2 = 119$
7. $y^2 = 2xy + 24$
8. $x^2(y - 6) = 12y + 6$
9. If $x^2 + y^2 = z^2$, find dy/dt when $x = 3$, $y = 4$, $dx/dt = 10$, and $dz/dt = 2$.
10. If $s = 2\pi r(r + h)$, find dr/dt when $r = 2$, $h = 8$, $dh/dt = 3$, and $ds/dt = 10\pi$.
11. A point is moving along the graph of the equation $y = -4x^2$. At what rate is y changing when $x = 5$ and is changing at a rate of 2 units/sec?
12. A point is moving along the graph of the equation $y = 5x^3 - 2x$. At what rate is y changing when $x = 4$ and is changing at a rate of 3 units/sec?
13. The radius of a circle is increasing at a rate of 2 ft/min. At what rate is its area changing when the radius is 3 ft? (Recall that for a circle, $A = \pi r^2$.)
14. The area of a circle is changing at a rate of 1 in²/sec. At what rate is its radius changing when the radius is 2 in.?

15. The volume of a cube is increasing at a rate of 64 in³/sec. At what rate is the length of each edge of the cube changing when the edges are 6 in. long? (Recall that for a cube, $V = x^3$.)
16. The lengths of the edges of a cube are increasing at a rate of 8 ft/min. At what rate is the surface area changing when the edges are 24 ft long? (Recall that for a cube, $S = 6x^2$.)

APPLICATIONS

17. *Profit* Suppose that the daily profit (in dollars) from the production and sale of x units of a product is given by

$$P = 180x - \frac{x^2}{1000} - 2000$$

At what rate per day is the profit changing when the number of units produced and sold is 100 and is increasing at a rate of 10 units per day?
18. *Profit* Suppose that the monthly revenue and cost (in dollars) for x units of a product are

$$R = 400x - \frac{x^2}{20} \quad \text{and} \quad C = 5000 + 70x$$

At what rate per month is the profit changing if the number of units produced and sold is 200 and is increasing at a rate of 5 units per month?

19. **Demand** Suppose that the price p (in dollars) of a product is given by the demand function

$$p = \frac{1000 - 10x}{400 - x}$$

where x represents the quantity demanded. If the daily demand is *decreasing* at a rate of 20 units per day, at what rate is the price changing when the demand is 20 units?

20. **Supply** The supply function for a product is given by $p = 40 + 100\sqrt{2x + 9}$, where x is the number of units supplied and p is the price in dollars. If the price is increasing at a rate of $1 per month, at what rate is the supply changing when $x = 20$?

21. **Capital investment and production** Suppose that for a particular product, the number of units x produced per month depends on the number of thousands of dollars y invested, with $x = 30y + 20y^2$. At what rate will production increase if $10,000 is invested and if the investment capital is increasing at a rate of $1000 per month?

22. **Boyle's law** Boyle's law for enclosed gases states that at a constant temperature, the pressure is related to the volume by the equation

$$P = \frac{k}{V}$$

where k is a constant. If the volume is increasing at a rate of 5 cubic inches per hour, at what rate is the pressure changing when the volume is 30 cubic inches and $k = 2$ inch-pounds?

Tumor growth **For Problems 23 and 24, suppose that a tumor in a person's body has a spherical shape and that treatment is causing the radius of the tumor to decrease at a rate of 1 millimeter per month.**

23. At what rate is the volume decreasing when the radius is 3 mm? (Recall that $V = \frac{4}{3}\pi r^3$.)

24. At what rate is the surface area of the tumor decreasing when the radius is 3 mm? (Recall that for a sphere, $S = 4\pi r^2$.)

25. **Allometric relationships—fish** For many species of fish, the allometric relationship between the weight W and the length L is approximately $W = kL^3$, where k is a constant. Find the percent rate of change of the weight as a corresponding percent rate of change of the length.

26. **Blood flow** The resistance R of a blood vessel to the flow of blood is a function of the radius r of the blood vessel and is given by

$$R = \frac{k}{r^4}$$

where k is a constant. Find the percent rate of change of the resistance of a blood vessel in terms of the percent rate of change in the radius of the blood vessel.

27. **Allometric relationships—crabs** For fiddler crabs, data gathered by Thompson* show that the allometric relationship between the weight C of the claw and the weight W of the body is given by

$$C = 0.11W^{1.54}$$

Find the percent rate of change of the claw weight in terms of the percent rate of change of the body weight for fiddler crabs.

28. **Body weight and surface area** For human beings, the surface area S of the body is related to the body's weight W according to

$$S = kW^{2/3}$$

where k is a constant. Find the percent rate of change of the body's surface area in terms of the percent rate of change of the body's weight.

29. **Cell growth** A bacterial cell has a spherical shape. If the volume of the cell is increasing at a rate of 4 cubic micrometers per day, at what rate is the radius of the cell increasing when it is 2 micrometers? (Recall that for a sphere, $V = \frac{4}{3}\pi r^3$.)

30. **Water purification** Assume that water is being purified by causing it to flow through a conical filter that has a height of 15 inches and a radius of 5 inches. If the depth of the water is decreasing at a rate of 1 inch per minute when the depth is 6 inches, at what rate is the volume of water flowing out of the filter at this instant?

31. **Volume and radius** Suppose that air is being pumped into a spherical balloon at a rate of 5 in³/min. At what rate is the radius of the balloon increasing when the radius is 5 in.?

32. **Boat docking** Suppose that a boat is being pulled toward a dock by a winch that is 5 ft above the level of the boat deck, as shown in the figure. If the winch is pulling the cable at a rate of 3 ft/min, at what rate is the boat approaching the dock when it is 12 ft from the dock?

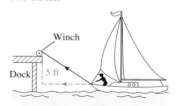

33. **Ladder safety** A 30-ft ladder is leaning against a wall. If the bottom is pulled away from the wall at a rate of 1 ft/sec, at what rate is the top of the ladder sliding down the wall when the bottom is 18 ft from the wall?

34. **Flight** A kite is 30 ft high and is moving horizontally at a rate of 10 ft/min. If the kite string is taut, at what rate is the string being played out when 50 ft of string is out?

*d'Arcy Thompson, *On Growth and Form* (Cambridge, England: Cambridge University Press, 1961).

35. *Flight* A plane is flying at a constant altitude of 1 mile and a speed of 300 mph. If it is flying toward an observer on the ground, how fast is the plane approaching the observer when it is 5 miles from the observer?

36. *Distance* Two boats leave the same port at the same time, with boat A traveling north at 15 knots (nautical miles per hour) and boat B traveling east at 20 knots. How fast is the distance between them changing when boat A is 30 nautical miles from port?

37. *Distance* Two cars are approaching an intersection on roads that are perpendicular to each other. Car A is north of the intersection and traveling south at

40 mph. Car B is east of the intersection and traveling west at 55 mph. How fast is the distance between the cars changing when car A is 15 miles from the intersection and car B is 8 miles from the intersection?

38. *Water depth* Water is flowing into a barrel in the shape of a right circular cylinder at the rate of 200 in^3/min. If the radius of the barrel is 18 in., at what rate is the depth of the water changing when the water is 30 in. deep?

39. *Water depth* Suppose that water is being pumped into a rectangular swimming pool of uniform depth at 10 ft^3/hr. If the pool is 10 ft wide and 25 ft long, at what rate is the water rising when it is 4 ft deep?

OBJECTIVES

11.5

- To find the elasticity of demand
- To find the tax per unit that will maximize tax revenue

Applications in Business and Economics

| APPLICATION PREVIEW |

Suppose that the demand for a product is given by

$$p = \frac{1000}{(q + 1)^2}$$

We can measure how sensitive the demand for this product is to price changes by finding the elasticity of demand. (See Example 2.) This elasticity can be used to measure the effects that price changes have on total revenue. We also consider taxation in a competitive market, which examines how a tax levied on goods shifts market equilibrium. We will find the tax per unit that, despite changes in market equilibrium, maximizes tax revenue.

Elasticity of Demand   We know from the law of demand that consumers will respond to changes in prices; if prices increase, the quantities demanded will decrease. But the degree of responsiveness of the consumers to price changes will vary widely for different products. For example, a price increase in insulin will not greatly decrease the demand for it by diabetics, but a price increase in clothes may cause consumers to buy less and wear their old clothes longer. When the response to price changes is considerable, we say the demand is *elastic*. When price changes cause relatively small changes in demand for a product, the demand is said to be *inelastic* for that product.

Economists measure the **elasticity of demand** as follows.

Elasticity   The **elasticity of demand** at the point (q_A, p_A) is

$$\eta = -\frac{p}{q} \cdot \frac{dq}{dp}\bigg|_{(q_A, p_A)}$$

EXAMPLE 1   **Elasticity**

Find the elasticity of the demand function $p + 5q = 100$ when
(a) the price is $40.   (b) the price is $60.   (c) the price is $50.

Solution
Solving the demand function for q gives $q = 20 - \frac{1}{5}p$. Then $dq/dp = -\frac{1}{5}$ and

$$\eta = -\frac{p}{q}\left(-\frac{1}{5}\right)$$

(a) When $p = 40, q = 12$ and $\eta = -\dfrac{p}{q}\left(\dfrac{1}{5}\right)\Big|_{(12,\,40)} = -\dfrac{40}{12}\left(\dfrac{1}{5}\right) = \dfrac{2}{3}.$

(b) When $p = 60, q = 8$ and $\eta = -\dfrac{p}{q}\left(-\dfrac{1}{5}\right)\Big|_{(8,\,60)} = -\dfrac{60}{8}\left(-\dfrac{1}{5}\right) = \dfrac{3}{2}.$

(c) When $p = 50, q = 10$ and $\eta = -\dfrac{p}{q}\left(-\dfrac{1}{5}\right)\Big|_{(10,\,50)} = -\dfrac{50}{10}\left(\dfrac{1}{5}\right) = 1.$

Note that in Example 1 the demand equation was $p + 5q = 100$, so the demand "curve" is a straight line, with slope $m = -5$. But the elasticity was $\eta = \frac{2}{3}$ at $(12, 40)$, $\eta = \frac{3}{2}$ at $(8, 60)$, and $\eta = 1$ at $(10, 50)$. This illustrates that the elasticity of demand may be different at different points on the demand curve, even though the slope of the demand "curve" is constant. (See Figure 11.14.)

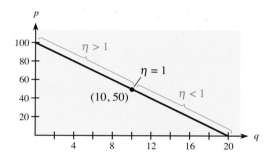

Figure 11.14

This example shows that the elasticity of demand is more than just the slope of the demand curve, which is the rate at which the demand is changing. Recall that the elasticity measures the consumers' degree of responsiveness to a price change.

Economists use η to measure how responsive demand is to price at different points on the demand curve for a product.

Elasticity of Demand

- If $\eta > 1$, the demand is **elastic,** and the percent decrease in demand is greater than the corresponding percent increase in price.
- If $\eta < 1$, the demand is **inelastic,** and the percent decrease in demand is less than the corresponding percent increase in price.
- If $\eta = 1$, the demand is **unitary elastic,** and the percent decrease in demand is approximately equal to the corresponding percent increase in price.

We can also use implicit differentiation to find dq/dp in evaluating the point elasticity of demand.

EXAMPLE 2   Elasticity | APPLICATION PREVIEW |

The demand for a certain product is given by

$$p = \frac{1000}{(q + 1)^2}$$

where p is the price per unit in dollars and q is demand in units of the product. Find the elasticity of demand with respect to price when $q = 19$.

July 10, 2017
Instructor: Karina Roitman

Math 75: Quiz Number 13

Name: Justice Carbajal

3.5/10

Please answer each question in the space below it. Show ALL your work.

1. Given the function $f(x) = e^{-2x^2}$,

(a) Find $f'(x)$

$a = -2x^2 \rightarrow a' = -4x$

$b = e^a \rightarrow b' = e^a$

$\rightarrow (-4x)e^{-2x^2} = f'(x)$

$-4xe^{-2x^2}$

2/2

(b) Find $f''(x)$ and simplify your answer as much as possible by factoring.

fun.	der
$-4x$	-4
e^{-2x^2}	$-4xe^{-2x^2}$

$-4(e^{-2x^2}) + (-4xe^{-2x^2} \cdot -4x)$

$e^{-2x^2}(-4 + (-4x \cdot -4x))$

$e^{-2x^2}(-4 + 16x^2)) \rightarrow e^{-2x^2}(16x^2 + 4)$

$f'' = e^{-2x^2}(16x^2+4)$

-4, not $+4$!

3.5/3.5

(c) Find the values of x where $f'(x) = 0$ and $f''(x) = 0$ and make a sign chart on a number line. Indicated the max/min point, intervals where the functions is increasing or decreasing, and points of inflection. Then use this information to sketch a graph of $f(x)$ on the given grid.

the $f'(x)$ is throwing me off. Maybe I made a mistake. You didn't. Just ignore it. That part can't be zero

kemhue

0/0

July 13, 2017

Instructor: Karina Roitman   Math 75: Quiz Number 15   Name: Justice Carbajal

Please answer each question in the space below it. Show ALL your work.

1. In a certain business, the price p of a product and its demand x are related by the equation $x(p) = 40(p - 15)^2$.

   (a) Find an equation for the elasticity of demand

$x(p) = 40(p - 15)^2$

$= (40p - 600)^2 \rightarrow$ NO! ORDER OF OPERATIONS!

$\eta = \frac{-p}{x} \cdot \frac{dx}{dp}$ $p = 15$ ✗

$\rightarrow$ You need derivative!

$= 1600p^2 - 360,000$

$\boxed{1600p^2 = 360,000}$ NO!!! You can NEVER distribute an exponent over a sum!!!

$\sqrt{p^2} = \sqrt{225}$

$p = 15$!!!

$\rightarrow$ why?! $x \neq 0$ ∴!!

over a sum!!!

(b) Find what the elasticity is when the price is $3 and when the price is $9. What do these values mean? How can you interpret them?

Solution

To find the elasticity, we need to find dq/dp. Using implicit differentiation, we get the following:

$$\frac{d}{dp}(p) = \frac{d}{dp}[1000\,(q+1)^{-2}]$$

$$1 = 1000\left[-2\,(q+1)^{-3}\frac{dq}{dp}\right]$$

$$1 = \frac{-2000}{(q+1)^3}\frac{dq}{dp}$$

$$\frac{(q+1)^3}{-2000} = \frac{dq}{dp}$$

When $q = 19$, we have $p = 1000/(19+1)^2 = 1000/400 = 5/2$ and

$$\frac{dq}{dp}\bigg|_{(q=19)} = \frac{(19+1)^3}{-2000} = \frac{8000}{-2000} = -4$$

The elasticity of demand when $q = 19$ is

$$\eta = \frac{-p}{q}\cdot\frac{dq}{dp} = -\frac{(5/2)}{19}\cdot(-4) = \frac{10}{19} < 1$$

Thus the demand for this product is inelastic.

Elasticity and Revenue

Elasticity is related to revenue in a special way. We can see how by computing the derivative with respect to p of the revenue function

$$R = pq$$

$$\frac{dR}{dp} = p\cdot\frac{dq}{dp} + q\cdot 1$$

$$= \frac{q}{q}\cdot p\cdot\frac{dq}{dp} + q = q\cdot\frac{p}{q}\cdot\frac{dq}{dp} + q$$

$$= q(-\eta) + q$$

$$= q(1-\eta)$$

From this we can summarize the relationship of elasticity and revenue.

Elasticity and Revenue

The rate of change of revenue R with respect to price p is related to elasticity in the following way.

- Elastic ($\eta > 1$) means $\dfrac{dR}{dp} < 0.$ $\begin{cases}\text{Hence if price increases, revenue decreases,}\\\text{and if price decreases, revenue increases.}\end{cases}$

- Inelastic ($\eta < 1$) means $\dfrac{dR}{dp} > 0.$ $\begin{cases}\text{Hence if price increases, revenue increases,}\\\text{and if price decreases, revenue decreases.}\end{cases}$

- Unitary elastic ($\eta = 1$) means $\dfrac{dR}{dp} = 0.$ Hence an increase or decrease in price will not change revenue. Revenue is optimized at this point.

EXAMPLE 3   Elasticity and Revenue

The demand for a product is given by

$$p = 10\sqrt{100 - q}, \qquad 0 \le q \le 100$$

(a) Find the point at which demand is of unitary elasticity, and find intervals in which the demand is inelastic and in which it is elastic.
(b) Find q where revenue is increasing, where it is decreasing, and where it is maximized.
(c) Use a graphing utility to show the graph of the revenue function $R = pq$, with $0 \le q \le 100$, and confirm the results from part (b).

Solution

The elasticity is

$$\eta = \frac{-p}{q} \cdot \frac{dq}{dp} = -\frac{10\sqrt{100 - q}}{q} \cdot \frac{dq}{dp}$$

Finding dq/dp implicitly, we have

$$1 = 10\left[\frac{1}{2}(100 - q)^{-1/2}\left(-\frac{dq}{dp}\right)\right] = \frac{-5}{\sqrt{100 - q}} \cdot \frac{dq}{dp}$$

so

$$\frac{dq}{dp} = \frac{-\sqrt{100 - q}}{5}$$

Thus

$$\eta = \left(-\frac{10\sqrt{100 - q}}{q}\right)\left(\frac{-\sqrt{100 - q}}{5}\right) = \frac{200 - 2q}{q}$$

(a) Unitary elasticity occurs where $\eta = 1$.

$$1 = \frac{200 - 2q}{q}$$
$$q = 200 - 2q$$
$$3q = 200$$
$$q = 66\tfrac{2}{3}$$

so unitary elasticity occurs when $66\tfrac{2}{3}$ units are sold, at a price of $57.74. For values of q between 0 and $66\tfrac{2}{3}$, $\eta > 1$ and demand is elastic. For values of q between $66\tfrac{2}{3}$ and 100, $\eta < 1$ and demand is inelastic.

(b) Because $\eta > 1$ and p decreases when q increases over $0 < q < 66\tfrac{2}{3}$, R increases. Similarly, because $\eta < 1$ and p decreases when q increases over $66\tfrac{2}{3} < q < 100$, R decreases. Thus, revenue is maximized where $\eta = 1$, at $q = 66\tfrac{2}{3}$ and $p = 57.74$.

(c) The graph of this revenue function,

$$R = 10q\sqrt{100 - q}$$

is shown in Figure 11.15. The maximum revenue is $3849 at $q = 66\tfrac{2}{3}$.

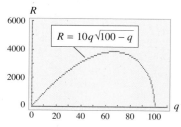

Figure 11.15

✓ CHECKPOINT

1. Write the formula for point elasticity, η.
2. (a) If $\eta > 1$, the demand is called _____.
    (b) If $\eta < 1$, the demand is called _____.
    (c) If $\eta = 1$, the demand is called _____.
3. Find the elasticity of demand for $q = \dfrac{100}{p} - 1$ when $p = 10$ and $q = 9$.

Taxation in a Competitive Market

Many taxes imposed by governments are "hidden." That is, the tax is levied on goods produced, and the producers must pay the tax. Of course, the tax becomes a cost to the producers, and they pass that cost on to the consumer in the form of higher prices for goods.

Suppose the government imposes a tax of t dollars on each unit produced and sold by producers. If we are in pure competition in which the consumers' demand depends only on price, the *demand function* will not change. The tax will change the supply function, of course, because at each level of output q, the firm will want to charge a price $p + t$ per unit, where p is the original price per unit and t is the tax per unit.

The graphs of the market demand function, the original market supply function, and the market supply function after taxes are shown in Figure 11.16. Because the tax added to each item is constant, the graph of the new supply function is t units above the original supply function. If $p = f(q)$ defines the original supply function, then $p = f(q) + t$ defines the supply function after taxation.

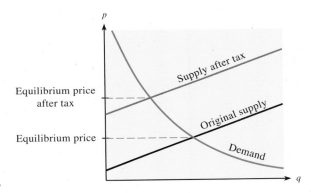

Figure 11.16

Note that after the taxes are imposed, *no* items are supplied at the price that was the equilibrium price before taxation. After the taxes are imposed, the consumers simply have to pay more for the product. Because taxation does not change the demand curve, the quantity purchased at market equilibrium will be less than it was before taxation. Thus governments planning taxes should recognize that they will not collect taxes on the original equilibrium quantity. They will collect on the *new* equilibrium quantity, a quantity reduced by their taxation. Thus a large tax on each item may reduce the quantity demanded at the new market equilibrium so much that very little revenue results from the tax!

If the tax revenue is represented by $T = tq$, where t is the tax per unit and q is the equilibrium quantity of the supply and demand functions after taxation, we can use the following procedure for maximizing the total tax revenue in a competitive market.

Maximizing Total Tax Revenue

Procedure	Example
To find the tax per item (under pure competition) that will maximize total tax revenue:	Suppose the demand and supply functions are given by $p = 600 - q$ and $p = 200 + \frac{1}{3}q$, respectively, where $\$p$ is the price per unit and q is the number of units. Find the tax t that will maximize the total tax revenue T.

1. Write the supply function after taxation.

    1. $p = 200 + \dfrac{1}{3}q + t$

2. Set the demand function and the new supply function equal, and solve for t in terms of q.

    2. $600 - q = 200 + \dfrac{1}{3}q + t$

    $400 - \dfrac{4}{3}q = t$

3. Form the total tax revenue function, $T = tq$, by multiplying the expression for t by q, and then take its derivative with respect to q.

    3. $T = tq = 400q - \dfrac{4}{3}q^2$

    $T'(q) = \dfrac{dT}{dq} = 400 - \dfrac{8}{3}q$

4. Set $T' = 0$, and solve for q. This is the q that should maximize T. Use the second-derivative test to verify it.

    4. $0 = 400 - \dfrac{8}{3}q$

    $q = 150$

    $T''(q) = -\dfrac{8}{3}$. Thus T is maximized at $q = 150$.

5. Substitute the value of q in the equation for t (in Step 2). This is the value of t that will maximize T.

    5. $t = 400 - \dfrac{4}{3}(150) = 200$

    A tax of $200 per item will maximize the total tax revenue. The total tax revenue for the period would be $\$200 \cdot (150) = \$30,000$.

Note that in the example just given, if a tax of $300 were imposed, market equilibrium would occur at $q = 75$, and the total tax revenue the government would receive would be

$$(\$300)(75) = \$22,500$$

Thus, with a tax of $300 per unit rather than $200, the government's tax revenue would be $22,500 rather than $30,000. In addition, with a $300 tax, suppliers would sell only 75 units rather than 150, and consumers would pay $p = 200 + 25 + 300 = \$525$ per item, which is $75 more than the price with a $200 tax. Thus everyone would suffer if the tax rate were raised to $300.

✓ CHECKPOINT

4. For problems involving taxation in a competitive market, if supply is $p = f(q)$ and demand is $p = g(q)$, is the tax t added to $f(q)$ or to $g(q)$?

EXAMPLE 4   Maximizing Tax Revenue

The demand and supply functions for a product are $p = 900 - 20q - \frac{1}{3}q^2$ and $p = 200 + 10q$, respectively, where p is in dollars and q is the number of units. Find the tax per unit that will maximize the tax revenue T.

Solution

After taxation, the supply function is $p = 200 + 10q + t$, where t is the tax per unit. The demand function will meet the new supply function where

$$900 - 20q - \frac{1}{3}q^2 = 200 + 10q + t$$

so

$$t = 700 - 30q - \frac{1}{3}q^2$$

Then the total tax T is $T = tq = 700q - 30q^2 - \frac{1}{3}q^3$, and we maximize T as follows:

$$T'(q) = 700 - 60q - q^2$$
$$0 = -(q + 70)(q - 10)$$
$$q = 10 \quad \text{or} \quad q = -70$$
$$T''(q) = -60 - 2q, \text{ so } T''(q) < 0 \text{ for } q \geq 0$$

Thus the curve is concave down for $q \geq 0$, and $q = 10$ gives an absolute maximum for the tax revenue T. The maximum possible tax revenue is

$$T(10) \approx \$3666.67$$

The tax per unit that maximizes T is

$$t = 700 - 30(10) - \frac{1}{3}(10)^2 \approx \$366.67$$

An infamous example of a tax increase that resulted in decreased tax revenue and economic disaster is the "luxury tax" enacted in 1991. This was a 10% excise tax on the sale of expensive jewelry, furs, airplanes, certain expensive boats, and luxury automobiles. The Congressional Joint Tax Committee had estimated that the luxury tax would raise $6 million from airplanes alone, but it raised only $53,000 while it destroyed the small-airplane market (one company lost $130 million and 480 jobs in a single year). It also capsized the boat market. The luxury tax was repealed at the end of 1993 (except for automobiles).*

✓ CHECKPOINT ANSWERS

1. $\eta = \dfrac{-p}{q} \cdot \dfrac{dq}{dp}$

2. (a) elastic   (b) inelastic   (c) unitary elastic

3. $\eta = \dfrac{10}{9}$ (elastic)

4. Tax t is added to supply: $p = f(q) + t$.

*Fortune, Sept. 6, 1993; Motor Trend, December 1993.

| EXERCISES | 11.5

ELASTICITY OF DEMAND

In Problems 1–8, p is in dollars and q is the number of units.

1. (a) Find the elasticity of the demand function $p + 4q = 80$ at $(10, 40)$.
   (b) How will a price increase affect total revenue?

2. (a) Find the elasticity of the demand function $2p + 3q = 150$ at the price $p = 15$.
   (b) How will a price increase affect total revenue?

3. (a) Find the elasticity of the demand function $p^2 + 2p + q = 49$ at $p = 6$.

   (b) How will a price increase affect total revenue?

4. (a) Find the elasticity of the demand function $pq = 81$ at $p = 3$.
   (b) How will a price increase affect total revenue?

5. Suppose that the demand for a product is given by $pq + p = 5000$.
   (a) Find the elasticity when $p = \$50$ and $q = 99$.
   (b) Tell what type of elasticity this is: unitary, elastic, or inelastic.
   (c) How would revenue be affected by a price increase?

6. Suppose that the demand for a product is given by $2p^2q = 10,000 + 9000p^2$.
   (a) Find the elasticity when $p = \$50$ and $q = 4502$.
   (b) Tell what type of elasticity this is: unitary, elastic, or inelastic.
   (c) How would revenue be affected by a price increase?

7. Suppose that the demand for a product is given by $pq + p + 100q = 50,000$.
   (a) Find the elasticity when $p = \$401$.
   (b) Tell what type of elasticity this is.
   (c) How would a price increase affect revenue?

8. Suppose that the demand for a product is given by

$$(p + 1)\sqrt{q + 1} = 1000$$

   (a) Find the elasticity when $p = \$39$.
   (b) Tell what type of elasticity this is.
   (c) How would a price increase affect revenue?

9. Suppose the demand function for a product is given by

$$p = \frac{1}{2}\ln\left(\frac{5000 - q}{q + 1}\right)$$

   where p is in hundreds of dollars and q is the number of tons.
   (a) What is the elasticity of demand when the quantity demanded is 2 tons and the price is $371?
   (b) Is the demand elastic or inelastic?

10. Suppose the weekly demand function for a product is

$$q = \frac{5000}{1 + e^{2p}} - 1$$

   where p is the price in thousands of dollars and q is the number of units demanded. What is the elasticity of demand when the price is $1000 and the quantity demanded is 595?

In Problems 11 and 12, the demand functions for specialty steel products are given, where p is in dollars and q is the number of units. For both problems:
(a) Find the elasticity of demand as a function of the quantity demanded, q.
(b) Find the point at which the demand is of unitary elasticity and find intervals in which the demand is inelastic and in which it is elastic.
(c) Use information about elasticity in part (b) to decide where the revenue is increasing, where it is decreasing, and where it is maximized.
(d) Graph the revenue function $R = pq$, and use it to find where revenue is maximized. Is it at the same quantity as that determined in part (c)?

11. $p = 120\sqrt[3]{125 - q}$

12. $p = 30\sqrt{49 - q}$

13. South West Electronics Corporation (SWEC) designs high-tech business and residential security systems. The company's marketing analyst has been assigned to analyze market demand for SWEC's top-selling

system, The Terminator. Monthly demand for The Terminator has been estimated as follows:

$$q = 445 - 8p + 25A + 4.5C + 6Y$$

where $q =$ Expected number of system sales per month
   $p =$ Selling price for The Terminator (in dollars)
   $A =$ Advertising (in thousands of dollars)
   $C =$ SWEC's only competitor's average price (in dollars)
   $Y =$ Disposable annual per capita income (in thousands of dollars)

   A recent survey of the potential customer market indicates that monthly advertising is $25,000, per capita disposable income is $80,000 per year, and the average price of the only competitor is $100.
   (a) Based on this information, what is the monthly demand function $p = f(q)$ for The Terminator?
   (b) Find the elasticity of demand for The Terminator.
   (c) If SWEC's current price for The Terminator is $175, is demand elastic, inelastic, or unitary elastic? Is SWEC's revenue for The Terminator maximized at the current price?
   (d) Use the elasticity of demand found in part (b) to determine the price for The Terminator that would maximize SWEC's revenue. Find the maximum revenue.

14. The owner and manager of Pleasantville Deli is considering the expansion of current menu offerings to include a new line of take-out sandwiches. The deli serves primarily the Pleasantville business districts and students from a nearby college, yet it is unclear exactly what level of demand to anticipate for this new product offering and how to price the product in order to maximize sales.
   Over the past few months the information shown in the table was collected from existing customers and from mailings to businesses in the area.

Sandwich Price	$12	10	8	6	4	2
Weekly Demand	0	400	800	1200	1600	2000

   (a) Develop a function $p = f(q)$ that represents this demand schedule.
   (b) Compute the elasticity of demand for the new sandwich.
   (c) Find the elasticity at the possible prices of $4 and $10. Classify these prices as elastic, inelastic, or unitary elastic.
   (d) Determine the price and quantity that would maximize weekly revenues for the new sandwich. Find the maximum weekly revenue.

TAXATION IN A COMPETITIVE MARKET

In Problems 15–24, p is the price per unit in dollars and q is the number of units.

15. If the weekly demand function is $p = 30 - q$ and the supply function before taxation is $p = 6 + 2q$, what tax per item will maximize the total tax revenue?

16. If the demand function for a fixed period of time is given by $p = 38 - 2q$ and the supply function before taxation is $p = 8 + 3q$, what tax per item will maximize the total tax revenue?

17. If the demand and supply functions for a product are $p = 800 - 2q$ and $p = 100 + 0.5q$, respectively, find the tax per unit t that will maximize the tax revenue T.

18. If the demand and supply functions for a product are $p = 2100 - 3q$ and $p = 300 + 1.5q$, respectively, find the tax per unit t that will maximize the tax revenue T.

19. If the weekly demand function is $p = 200 - 2q^2$ and the supply function before taxation is $p = 20 + 3q$, what tax per item will maximize the total tax revenue?

20. If the monthly demand function is $p = 7230 - 5q^2$ and the supply function before taxation is $p = 30 + 30q^2$, what tax per item will maximize the total revenue?

21. Suppose the weekly demand for a product is given by $p + 2q = 840$ and the weekly supply before taxation is given by $p = 0.02q^2 + 0.55q + 7.4$. Find the tax per item that produces maximum tax revenue. Find the tax revenue.

22. If the daily demand for a product is given by the function $p + q = 1000$ and the daily supply before taxation is $p = q^2/30 + 2.5q + 920$, find the tax per item that maximizes tax revenue. Find the tax revenue.

23. If the demand and supply functions for a product are $p = 2100 - 10q - 0.5q^2$ and $p = 300 + 5q + 0.5q^2$, respectively, find the tax per unit t that will maximize the tax revenue T.

24. If the demand and supply functions for a product are $p = 5000 - 20q - 0.7q^2$ and $p = 500 + 10q + 0.3q^2$, respectively, find the tax per unit t that will maximize the tax revenue T.

Chapter 11 Summary & Review

KEY TERMS AND FORMULAS

Section 11.1

Logarithmic function (p. 694)

$y = \log_a x$, defined by $x = a^y$

Natural logarithm (p. 694)

$\ln x = \log_e x; y = \ln (x)$ means $e^y = x$

Derivatives of logarithmic functions (p. 695)

$$\frac{d}{dx}(\ln x) = \frac{1}{x}$$

$$\frac{d}{dx}(\ln u) = \frac{1}{u} \cdot \frac{du}{dx}$$

Logarithmic Properties I–V for natural logarithms (p. 696)

$\ln e^x = x; e^{\ln x} = x$

$\ln (MN) = \ln M + \ln N$

$\ln (M/N) = \ln M - \ln N$

$\ln (M^p) = p (\ln M)$

Change-of-base formula (p. 698)

$$\log_a x = \frac{\ln x}{\ln a}$$

Section 11.2

Derivatives of exponential functions (p. 703)

$$\frac{d}{dx}(e^x) = e^x$$

$$\frac{d}{dx}e^u = e^u \frac{du}{dx}$$

$$\frac{d}{dx}a^u = a^u \frac{du}{dx} \ln a$$

Section 11.3

Implicit differentiation (p. 709)

$$\frac{d}{dx}(y^n) = ny^{n-1} \frac{dy}{dx}$$

Section 11.4

Related rates (p. 718)

Differentiate implicitly with respect to time, t

Percent rates of change (p. 718)

Solving related rates problems (p. 719)

Section 11.5

Elasticity of demand (p. 723)

$$\eta = \frac{-p}{q} \cdot \frac{dq}{dp}$$

Elastic

$\eta > 1$

Inelastic

$\eta < 1$

Unitary elastic

$\eta = 1$

Elasticity and revenue (p. 725)

Taxation in competitive market (p. 727)

Supply function after taxation

$p = f(q) + t$

REVIEW EXERCISES

Sections 11.1 and 11.2

In Problems 1–12, find the derivative of each function.

1. $y = 10e^{3x^2 - x}$

2. $y = 3\ln(4x + 11)$

3. $p = \ln\left(\dfrac{q}{q^2 - 1}\right)$

4. $y = xe^{x^2}$

5. $f(x) = 5e^{2x} - 40e^{-0.1x} + 11$

6. $g(x) = (2e^{3x+1} - 5)^3$

7. $s = \dfrac{3}{4}\ln(x^{12} - 2x^4 + 5)$

8. $w = (t^2 + 1)\ln(t^2 + 1) - t^2$

9. $y = 3^{3x-4}$

10. $y = 1 + \log_8(x^{10})$

11. $y = \dfrac{\ln x}{x}$

12. $y = \dfrac{1 + e^{-x}}{1 - e^{-x}}$

13. Write the equation of the line tangent to $y = 4e^{x^3}$ at $x = 1$.

14. At $x = 1$, write the equation of the line tangent to $y = 8 + 3x^2 \ln x$

Section 11.3

In Problems 15–20, find the indicated derivative.

15. If $y \ln x = 5y^2 + 11$, find dy/dx.

16. Find dy/dx for $e^{xy} = y$.

17. Find dy/dx for $y^2 = 4x - 1$.

18. Find dy/dx for $x^2 + 3y^2 + 2x - 3y + 2 = 0$.

19. Find dy/dx for $3x^2 + 2x^3y^2 - y^5 = 7$.

20. Find the second derivative y'' if $x^2 + y^2 = 1$.

21. Find the slope of the tangent to the curve $x^2 + 4x - 3y^2 + 6 = 0$ at $(3, 3)$.

22. Find the points where tangents to the graph of the equation in Problem 21 are horizontal.

Section 11.4

23. Suppose $3x^2 - 2y^3 = 10y$, where x and y are differentiable functions of t. If $dx/dt = 2$, find dy/dt when $x = 10$ and $y = 5$.

24. A right triangle with legs of lengths x and y has its area given by

$$A = \frac{1}{2}xy$$

If the rate of change of x is 2 units per minute and the rate of change of y is 5 units per minute, find the rate of change of the area when $x = 4$ and $y = 1$.

APPLICATIONS

Section 11.1

25. **Demographics** By using U.S. Census Bureau data for selected years from 1980 and projected to 2040, the number of White non-Hispanic individuals in the U.S.

civilian non-institutional population age 16 years and older, in millions, can be modeled by the function

$$P(t) = 96.1 + 17.4 \ln t$$

where t is the number of years past 1970.
(a) Find $P'(t)$.
(b) Find and interpret $P(58)$ and $P'(58)$.

26. **Life expectancy at age 65** By using Social Security Administration data for selected years from 1950 and projected to 2050, the additional years of life expectancy at age 65 can be modeled by

$$L(y) = -14.6 + 7.10 \ln y$$

where y equals the number of years past 1950.
(a) Find the function that models the rate of change of the years of life expectancy past age 65.
(b) Find and interpret $L(50)$ and $L(80)$.
(c) Find and interpret $L'(50)$ and $L'(80)$.

Section 11.2

27. **Compound interest** If $1000 is invested for n years at 12% compounded continuously, the future value of the investment is given by

$$S = 1000e^{0.12n}$$

(a) Find the function that gives the rate of change of this investment.
(b) Compare the rate at which the future value is growing after 1 year and after 10 years.

28. **Disposable income** Disposable income is the amount available for spending and saving after taxes have been paid and is one gauge for the state of the economy. By using U.S. Energy Administration data for selected years from 2010 and projected to 2040, the total U.S. disposable income, in billions, can be modeled by

$$D(t) = 10{,}020e^{0.02292t}$$

where t is the number of years past 2010.
(a) Find the function that models the rate of change of disposable income.
(b) Find and interpret $D(20)$ and $D'(20)$.

29. **Radioactive decay** A breeder reactor converts stable uranium-238 into the isotope plutonium-239. The decay of this isotope is given by

$$A(t) = A_0 e^{-0.00002876t}$$

where $A(t)$ is the amount of isotope at time t, in years, and A_0 is the original amount. This isotope has a half-life of 24,101 years (that is, half of it will decay away in 24,101 years).
(a) At what rate is $A(t)$ decaying at $t = 24{,}101$ years?
(b) At what rate is $A(t)$ decaying after 1 year?
(c) Is the rate of decay at its half-life greater or less than after 1 year?

30. *Marginal cost* The average cost of producing x units of a product is $\overline{C} = 600e^{x/600}$ dollars per unit. What is the marginal cost when 600 units are produced?

31. *Inflation* The impact of inflation on a $60,000 pension can be measured by the purchasing power P of $60,000 after t years. For an inflation rate of 5% per year, compounded annually, P is given by

$$P = 60{,}000e^{-0.0488t}$$

At what rate is purchasing power changing when $t = 10$? (*Source: Viewpoints, VALIC*)

Section 11.4

32. *Evaporation* A spherical droplet of water evaporates at a rate of 1 mm³/min. Find the rate of change of the radius when the droplet has a radius of 2.5 mm.

33. *Worker safety* A sign is being lowered over the side of a building at the rate of 2 ft/min. A worker handling a guide line is 7 ft away from a spot directly below the sign. How fast is the worker taking in the guide line at the instant the sign is 25 ft from the worker's hands? See the figure.

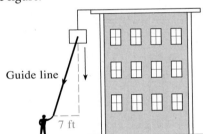

Guide line

7 ft

34. *Environment* Suppose that in a study of water birds, the relationship between the area A of wetlands (in square miles) and the number of different species S of birds found in the area was determined to be

$$S = kA^{1/3}$$

where k is constant. Find the percent rate of change of the number of species in terms of the percent rate of change of the area.

Section 11.5

35. *Taxes* Can increasing the tax per unit sold actually lead to a decrease in tax revenues?

36. *Taxes* Suppose the demand and supply functions for a product are

$$p = 2800 - 8q - \frac{q^2}{3} \quad \text{and} \quad p = 400 + 2q$$

respectively, where p is in dollars and q is the number of units. Find the tax per unit t that will maximize the tax revenue T, and find the maximum tax revenue.

37. *Taxes* Suppose the supply and demand functions for a product are

$$p = 40 + 20q \quad \text{and} \quad p = \frac{5000}{q + 1}$$

respectively, where p is in dollars and q is the number of units. Find the tax t that maximizes the tax revenue T, and find the maximum tax revenue.

38. *Elasticity* A demand function is given by

$$pq = 27$$

where p is in dollars and q is the number of units.
(a) Find the elasticity of demand at $(9, 3)$.
(b) How will a price increase affect total revenue?

39. *Elasticity* Suppose the demand for a product is given by

$$p^2(2q + 1) = 10{,}000$$

where p is in dollars and q is the number of units.
(a) Find the elasticity of demand when $p = \$20$.
(b) How will a price increase affect total revenue?

40. *Elasticity* Suppose the weekly demand function for a product is given by

$$p = 100e^{-0.1q}$$

where p is the price in dollars and q is the number of tons demanded.
(a) What is the elasticity of demand when the price is $36.79 and the quantity demanded is 10?
(b) How will a price increase affect total revenue?

41. *Revenue* A product has the demand function

$$p = 100 - 0.5q$$

where p is in dollars and q is the number of units.
(a) Find the elasticity $\eta(q)$ as a function of q, and graph the function

$$f(q) = \eta(q)$$

(b) Find where $f(q) = 1$, which gives the quantity for which the product has unitary elasticity.
(c) The revenue function for this product is

$$R(q) = pq = (100 - 0.5q)q$$

Graph $R(q)$ and find the q-value for which the maximum revenue occurs.
(d) What is the relationship between elasticity and maximum revenue?

Chapter 11   TEST

In Problems 1–8, find the derivative of each function.

1. $y = 5e^{x^3} + x^2$

2. $y = 4 \ln (x^3 + 1)$

3. $y = \ln (x^4 + 1)^3$

4. $f(x) = 10(3^{2x})$

5. $S = te^{t^4}$

6. $y = \dfrac{e^{x^3+1}}{x}$

7. $y = \dfrac{3 \ln x}{x^4}$

8. $g(x) = 2 \log_5 (4x + 7)$

9. Find y' if $3x^4 + 2y^2 + 10 = 0$.

10. Let $x^2 + y^2 = 100$.

If $\dfrac{dx}{dt} = 2$, find $\dfrac{dy}{dt}$ when $x = 6$ and $y = 8$.

11. Find y' if $xe^y = 10y$.

12. Suppose the weekly revenue and weekly cost (both in dollars) for a product are given by $R(x) = 300x - 0.001x^2$ and $C(x) = 4000 + 30x$, respectively, where x is the number of units produced and sold. Find the rate at which profit is changing with respect to time when the number of units produced and sold is 50 and is increasing at a rate of 5 units per week.

13. Suppose the demand for a product is $p^2 + 3p + q = 1500$, where p is in dollars and q is the number of units. Find the elasticity of demand at $p = 30$. If the price is raised to \$31, does revenue increase or decrease?

14. Suppose the demand function for a product is given by $(p + 1)q^2 = 10,000$, where p is the price and q is the quantity. Find the rate of change of quantity with respect to price when $p = \$99$.

15. The sales of a product are given by $S = 80,000e^{-0.4t}$, where S is the daily sales and t is the number of days after the end of an advertising campaign. Find the rate of sales decay 10 days after the end of the ad campaign.

16. By using U.S. Centers for Medicare and Medicaid Services data from 2000 and projected to 2018, the total U.S. expenditures (in billions of dollars) for health services and supplies can be modeled by

$$y = 1319e^{0.062t}$$

where $t = 0$ in 2000.

(a) Find the function that models the rate of change.
(b) Find the model's value for the rate of change of U.S. expenditures for health services and supplies in 2005 and in 2020.

17. Suppose the demand and supply functions for a product are $p = 1100 - 5q$ and $p = 20 + 0.4q$, respectively, where p is in dollars and q is the number of units. Find the tax per unit t that will maximize the tax revenue $T = tq$.

18. *Modeling* Projections indicate that the percent of U.S. adults with diabetes could dramatically increase, and already in 2007 this disease had cost the country almost \$175 billion. The table gives the percent of U.S. adults with diabetes for selected years from 2010 and projected to 2050.

(a) Find a logarithmic model, $y = f(x)$, for these data. Use $x = 0$ to represent 2000.
(b) Find the function that models the rate of change of the percent of U.S. adults with diabetes.
(c) Find and interpret $f(25)$ and $f'(25)$.

Year	Percent	Year	Percent
2010	15.7	2035	29.0
2015	18.9	2040	31.4
2020	21.1	2045	32.1
2025	24.2	2050	34.3
2030	27.2		

Source: Centers for Disease Control and Prevention

19. Prices for goods and services tend to rise over time, and this results in the erosion of purchasing power. With the 2012 dollar as a reference, a purchasing power of 0.921 for a certain year means that in that year a dollar will purchase 92.1% of the goods and services that could be purchased for \$1.00 in 2012. By using Social Security Administration data for selected years from 2012 and projected to 2050, the purchasing power of a 2012 dollar can be modeled by the function

$$P(t) = 1.078(0.9732^t)$$

where t is the number of years past 2010.

(a) Find the function that models the rate of change of the purchasing power of a 2012 dollar.
(b) Find and interpret $P(18)$ and $P'(18)$.

I. Inflation

Hollingsworth Pharmaceuticals specializes in manufacturing generic medicines. Recently it developed an antibiotic with outstanding profit potential. The new antibiotic's total costs, sales, and sales growth, as well as projected inflation, are described as follows.

Total monthly costs, in dollars, to produce x units (1 unit is 100 capsules):

$$C(x) = \begin{cases} 15,000 + 10x & 0 \le x \le 11,000 \\ 15,000 + 10x + 0.001(x - 11,000)^2 & x \ge 11,000 \end{cases}$$

Sales: 10,000 units per month and growing at 1.25% per month, compounded continuously

Selling price: $34 per unit

Inflation: Approximately 0.25% per month, compounded continuously, affecting both total costs and selling price

Company owners are pleased with the sales growth but are concerned about the projected increase in variable costs when production levels exceed 11,000 units per month. The consensus is that improvements eventually can be made that will reduce costs at higher production levels, thus altering the current cost function model. To plan properly for these changes, Hollingsworth Pharmaceuticals would like you to determine when the company's profits will begin to decrease. To help you determine this, answer the following.

1. If inflation is assumed to be compounded continuously, the selling price and total costs must be multiplied by the factor $e^{0.0025t}$. In addition, if sales growth is assumed to be compounded continuously, then sales must be multiplied by a factor of the form e^{rt}, where r is the monthly sales growth rate (expressed as a decimal) and t is time in months. Use these factors to write each of the following as a function of time t:
   (a) selling price p per unit (including inflation).
   (b) number of units x sold per month (including sales growth).
   (c) total revenue. (Recall that $R = px$.)
2. Determine how many months it will be before monthly sales exceed 11,000 units.
3. If you restrict your attention to total costs when $x \ge 11,000$, then, after expanding and collecting like terms, $C(x)$ can be written as follows:

   $$C(x) = 136,000 - 12x + 0.001x^2 \quad \text{for } x \ge 11,000$$

   Use this form for $C(x)$ with your result from Question 1(b) and with the inflationary factor $e^{0.0025t}$ to express these total costs as a function of time.
4. Form the profit function that would be used when monthly sales exceed 11,000 units by using the total revenue function from Question 1(c) and the total cost function from Question 3. This profit function should be a function of time t.
5. Find how long it will be before the profit is maximized. You may have to solve $P'(t) = 0$ by using a graphing calculator or computer to find the t-intercept of the graph of $P'(t)$. In addition, because $P'(t)$ has large numerical coefficients, you may want to divide both sides of $P'(t) = 0$ by 1000 before solving or graphing.

II. Renewable Electric Power (Modeling)

In the United States, consumers of electric power include all sectors of society—residential, commercial, industrial, and transportation related. Because of this broad dependency, reliable and uninterruptible sources of electric power (and those with the lowest environmental impact) are important. The United States has many sources of electrical power generation—predominately coal, natural gas, nuclear power, and renewable sources. The focus of this application is renewable sources because these will not be depleted, even though some renewables can be significant polluters (such as energy from combustion of wood or municipal waste).

The following table shows data for billions of kilowatt-hours of U.S. electrical power generation for selected years from 2016 and projected to 2040.

Power Generation (Billions of kilowatt-hours)

Year	Renewable	Total	Year	Renewable	Total
2016	629	4233	2030	748	4815
2018	651	4342	2032	764	4880
2020	667	4402	2034	778	4962
2022	683	4483	2036	800	5044
2024	700	4583	2038	825	5132
2026	716	4663	2040	851	5219
2028	730	4745			

Source: U.S. Department of Energy

1. Find an exponential function that models the billions of kilowatt-hours of renewable electric power generation, with x as the number of years after 2010. Store the unrounded model as $r(x)$ in Y_1 on your calculator, and report the rounded model as $R(x)$, with 3 significant digits and with base e.
2. Find a linear model for the billions of kilowatt-hours of total electric power generation, with x as the number of years after 2010. Store the unrounded model as $t(x)$ in Y_2 on your calculator, and report the rounded model as $T(x)$, with 3 significant digits.
3. Use the results of Questions 1 and 2 to create a function that models the percent of total electrical power generation that is renewable. Use the unrounded models in Y_1 and Y_2 to create the unrounded model as $p(x)$ and stored in Y_3, and use the rounded models $R(x)$ and $T(x)$ to report the rounded model as $P(x)$.
4. (a) Use the given data sets to create a data set that corresponds to $p(x)$.
   (b) Graph the data set and the model in Y_3 on the same set of axes.
   (c) How well does the model fit these data points?

In Questions 5–9, use the rounded models $R(x)$ and $P(x)$.

5. Find the function that models the rate of change of
   (a) $R(x)$ (b) $P(x)$
6. Find and interpret
   (a) $R(6)$ and $R'(6)$ (b) $R(25)$ and $R'(25)$
7. Find and interpret
   (a) $P(6)$ and $P'(6)$ (b) $P(25)$ and $P'(25)$
8. Find and interpret $P''(6)$ and $P''(25)$.
9. What does your analysis indicate about how the percent of total U.S. electrical power generation that is renewable is changing?

Indefinite Integrals

When we know the derivative of a function, it is often useful to determine the function itself. For example, accountants can use linear regression to translate information about marginal cost into a linear equation defining (approximately) the marginal cost function and then use the process of antidifferentiation (or integration) as part of finding the (approximate) total cost function. We can also use integration to find total revenue functions from marginal revenue functions, to optimize profit from information about marginal cost and marginal revenue, and to find national consumption from information about marginal propensity to consume.

Integration can also be used in the social and life sciences to predict growth or decay from expressions giving rates of change. For example, we can find equations for population size from the rate of change of growth, we can write equations for the number of radioactive atoms remaining in a substance if we know the rate of the decay of the substance, and we can determine the volume of blood flow from information about rate of flow.

The topics and some representative applications discussed in this chapter include the following.

APPLICATIONS

Revenue, population growth

Revenue, productivity

Real estate inflation, population growth

Cost, revenue, maximum profit, national consumption and savings

Carbon-14 dating, drug in an organ

Prerequisite Problem Type	For Section	Answer	Section for Review
Write as a power: (a) $\sqrt{x}$ (b) $\sqrt{x^2 - 9}$	12.1–12.4	(a) $x^{1/2}$ (b) $(x^2 - 9)^{1/2}$	0.4 Radicals
Expand $(x^2 + 4)^2$.	12.2	$x^4 + 8x^2 + 16$	0.5 Special powers
Divide $x^4 - 2x^3 + 4x^2 - 7x - 1$ by $x^2 - 2x$.	12.3	$x^2 + 4 + \dfrac{x - 1}{x^2 - 2x}$	0.5 Division
Find the derivative of (a) $f(x) = 2x^{1/2}$ (b) $u = x^3 - 3x$	12.1–12.3	(a) $f'(x) = x^{-1/2}$ (b) $u' = 3x^2 - 3$	9.4 Derivatives
If $y = \dfrac{(x^2 + 4)^6}{6}$, what is y'?	12.2	$y' = (x^2 + 4)^5 2x$	9.6 Derivatives
(a) If $y = \ln u$, what is y'? (b) If $y = e^u$, what is y'?	12.3	(a) $y' = \dfrac{1}{u} \cdot u'$ (b) $y' = e^u \cdot u'$	11.1, 11.2 Derivatives
Solve for y: $\ln y = kt + C$	12.5	$y = e^{kt + C}$	5.2 Logarithmic functions
Solve for k: $0.5 = e^{5730k}$	12.5	$k \approx -0.00012097$	5.3 Exponential equations

OBJECTIVE **12.1**

- To find certain indefinite integrals

Indefinite Integrals

■| **APPLICATION PREVIEW** |■

In our study of the theory of the firm, we have worked with total cost, total revenue, and profit functions and have found their marginal functions. In practice, it is often easier for a company to measure marginal cost, revenue, and profit and use these data to form marginal functions from which it can find total cost, revenue, and profit functions. For example, Jarus Technologies manufactures motherboards, and the company's sales records show that the marginal revenue (in dollars per unit) for its motherboards is given by

$$\overline{MR} = 300 - 0.2x$$

where x is the number of units sold. If we want to use this function to find the total revenue function for Jarus Technologies' motherboards, we need to find $R(x)$ from $\overline{MR} = R'(x)$. (See Example 7.) In this situation, we need to be able to reverse the process of differentiation. This reverse process is called antidifferentiation, or integration.

Indefinite Integrals   We have studied procedures for and applications of finding derivatives of a given function. We now turn our attention to reversing this process of differentiation. When we know the derivative of a function, the process of finding the function itself is called **antidifferentiation.** For example, if the derivative of a function is $2x$, we know that the function could be $f(x) = x^2$ because $\dfrac{d}{dx}(x^2) = 2x$. But the function could also be $f(x) = x^2 + 4$ because $\dfrac{d}{dx}(x^2 + 4) = 2x$. It is clear that any function of the form $f(x) = x^2 + C$, where C is an arbitrary constant, will have $f'(x) = 2x$ as its derivative. Thus we say that the **general antiderivative** of $f'(x) = 2x$ is $f(x) = x^2 + C$, where C is an arbitrary constant.

The process of finding an antiderivative is also called **integration.** The function that results when integration takes place is called an **indefinite integral** or, more simply, an **integral.** We can denote the indefinite integral (that is, the general antiderivative) of a function $f(x)$ by $\int f(x)\, dx$. Thus we can write $\int 2x\, dx$ to indicate the general antiderivative of the function $f(x) = 2x$. The expression is read as "the integral of $2x$ with respect to x." In this case, $2x$ is called the **integrand.** The **integral sign,** $\int$, indicates the process of integration, and the dx indicates that the integral is to be taken with respect to x. Because the antiderivative of $2x$ is $x^2 + C$, we can write

$$\int 2x\, dx = x^2 + C$$

EXAMPLE 1   Antidifferentiation

If $f'(x) = 3x^2$, what is $f(x)$?

Solution

The derivative of the function $f(x) = x^3$ is $f'(x) = 3x^2$. But other functions also have this derivative. They will all be of the form $f(x) = x^3 + C$, where C is a constant. Thus we write

$$\int 3x^2\, dx = x^3 + C$$

EXAMPLE 2 Integration

If $f'(x) = x^3$, what is $f(x)$?

Solution

We know that $\dfrac{d}{dx}(x^4) = 4x^3$, so the derivative of $f(x) = \frac{1}{4}x^4$ is $f'(x) = x^3$. Thus

$$f(x) = \int f'(x)\,dx = \int x^3\,dx = \tfrac{1}{4}x^4 + C$$

Powers of x Formula   It is easily seen that

$$\int x^4\,dx = \frac{x^5}{5} + C \text{ because } \frac{d}{dx}\left(\frac{x^5}{5} + C\right) = x^4$$

$$\int x^5\,dx = \frac{x^6}{6} + C \text{ because } \frac{d}{dx}\left(\frac{x^6}{6} + C\right) = x^5$$

In general, we have the following.

Powers of x Formula

$$\int x^n\,dx = \frac{x^{n+1}}{n+1} + C \quad \text{(for } n \neq -1\text{)}$$

In the Powers of x Formula, we see that $n \neq -1$ is essential, because if $n = -1$, then the denominator $n + 1 = 0$. We will discuss the case when $n = -1$ later. (Can you think what function has $1/x$ as its derivative?)

In addition, we can see that this Powers of x Formula applies for any $n \neq -1$ by noting that

$$\frac{d}{dx}\left(\frac{x^{n+1}}{n+1} + C\right) = \frac{d}{dx}\left(\frac{1}{n+1}x^{n+1} + C\right) = \frac{n+1}{n+1}x^n = x^n$$

EXAMPLE 3 Powers of x Formula

Evaluate $\int x^{-1/2}\,dx$.

Solution

Using the formula, we get

$$\int x^{-1/2}\,dx = \frac{x^{-1/2+1}}{-1/2 + 1} + C = \frac{x^{1/2}}{1/2} + C = 2x^{1/2} + C$$

We can check by noting that the derivative of $2x^{1/2} + C$ is $x^{-1/2}$. ✔

Note that the indefinite integral in Example 3 is a function (actually a number of functions, one for each value of C). Graphs of several members of this family of functions are shown in Figure 12.1. Note that at any given x-value, the tangent line to each curve has the same slope, indicating that all family members have the same derivative.

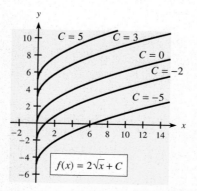

Figure 12.1

EXAMPLE 4   Powers of x Formula

Find (a) $\int \sqrt[3]{x}\, dx$ and (b) $\int \dfrac{1}{x^2}\, dx$.

Solution

(a) $\displaystyle \int \sqrt[3]{x}\, dx = \int x^{1/3}\, dx = \frac{x^{4/3}}{4/3} + C$

$$= \frac{3}{4} x^{4/3} + C = \frac{3}{4} \sqrt[3]{x^4} + C$$

(b) We write the power of x in the numerator so that the integral has the form in the formula above.

$$\int \frac{1}{x^2}\, dx = \int x^{-2}\, dx = \frac{x^{-2+1}}{-2+1} + C = \frac{x^{-1}}{-1} + C = \frac{-1}{x} + C$$

Other Formulas and Properties

Other formulas will be useful in evaluating integrals. The following table shows how some new integration formulas result from differentiation formulas.

Integration Formulas

Derivative	Resulting Integral
$\dfrac{d}{dx}(x) = 1$	$\displaystyle \int 1\, dx = \int dx = x + C$
$\dfrac{d}{dx}[c \cdot u(x)] = c \cdot \dfrac{d}{dx} u(x)$	$\displaystyle \int c\,u(x)\, dx = c \int u(x)\, dx$
$\dfrac{d}{dx}[u(x) \pm v(x)] = \dfrac{d}{dx} u(x) \pm \dfrac{d}{dx} v(x)$	$\displaystyle \int [u(x) \pm v(x)]\, dx = \int u(x)\, dx \pm \int v(x)\, dx$

These formulas indicate that we can integrate functions term by term just as we were able to take derivatives term by term.

EXAMPLE 5   Using Integration Formulas

Evaluate: (a) $\int 4\, dx$ (b) $\int 8x^5 dx$ (c) $\int (x^3 + 4x)\, dx$

Solution

(a) $\int 4\, dx = 4\int dx = 4(x + C_1) = 4x + C$

(Because C_1 is an unknown constant, we can write $4C_1$ as the unknown constant C.)

(b) $\displaystyle \int 8x^5 dx = 8 \int x^5 dx = 8\left(\frac{x^6}{6} + C_1 \right) = \frac{4x^6}{3} + C$

(c) $\displaystyle \int (x^3 + 4x)\, dx = \int x^3\, dx + \int 4x\, dx$

$$= \left(\frac{x^4}{4} + C_1 \right) + \left(4 \cdot \frac{x^2}{2} + C_2 \right)$$

$$= \frac{x^4}{4} + 2x^2 + C_1 + C_2$$

$$= \frac{x^4}{4} + 2x^2 + C$$

Note that we need only one constant because the sum of C_1 and C_2 is just a new constant.

EXAMPLE 6   Integral of a Polynomial

Evaluate $\int (x^2 - 4)^2 \, dx$.

Solution
We expand $(x^2 - 4)^2$ so that the integrand is in a form that fits the basic integration formulas.

$$\int (x^2 - 4)^2 \, dx = \int (x^4 - 8x^2 + 16) \, dx = \frac{x^5}{5} - \frac{8x^3}{3} + 16x + C$$

✓ CHECKPOINT

1. True or false:
   (a) $\int (4x^3 - 2x) \, dx = \int 4x^3 \, dx - \int 2x \, dx$
   $$= (x^4 + C) - (x^2 + C) = x^4 - x^2$$
   (b) $\int \dfrac{1}{3x^2} \, dx = \dfrac{1}{3(x^3/3)} + C = \dfrac{1}{x^3} + C$

2. Evaluate $\int (2x^3 + x^{-1/2} - 4x^{-5}) \, dx$.

EXAMPLE 7   Revenue | APPLICATION PREVIEW |

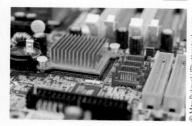
© Max Bukovski/Shutterstock.com

Sales records at Jarus Technologies show that the rate of change of the revenue (that is, the marginal revenue) in dollars per unit for a motherboard is $\overline{MR} = 300 - 0.2x$, where x represents the quantity sold. Find the total revenue function for the product. Then find the total revenue from the sale of 1000 motherboards.

Solution
We know that the marginal revenue can be found by differentiating the total revenue function. That is,

$$R'(x) = 300 - 0.2x$$

Thus integrating the marginal revenue function gives the total revenue function.

$$R(x) = \int (300 - 0.2x) \, dx = 300x - 0.1x^2 + K^*$$

We can use the fact that there is no revenue when no units are sold to evaluate K. Setting $x = 0$ and $R = 0$ gives $0 = 300(0) - 0.1(0)^2 + K$, so $K = 0$. Thus the total revenue function is

$$R(x) = 300x - 0.1x^2$$

The total revenue from the sale of 1000 motherboards is

$$R(1000) = 300(1000) - 0.1(1000^2) = \$200{,}000$$

We can check that the $R(x)$ we found in Example 7 is correct by verifying that $R'(x) = 300 - 0.2x$ and $R(0) = 0$. Also, graphs can help us check the reasonableness of our result. Figure 12.2 shows the graphs of $\overline{MR} = 300 - 0.2x$ and of the $R(x)$ we found. Note that $R(x)$ passes through the origin, indicating $R(0) = 0$. Also, reading both graphs from left to right, we see that $R(x)$ increases when $\overline{MR} > 0$, attains its maximum when $\overline{MR} = 0$, and decreases when $\overline{MR} < 0$.

---

*Here we are using K rather than C to represent the constant of integration to avoid confusion between the constant C and the cost function $C = C(x)$.

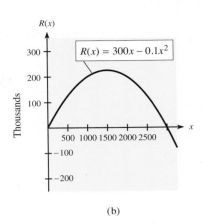

Figure 12.2   (a)   (b)

Calculator Note 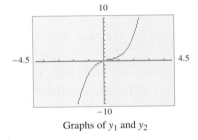 We mentioned in Chapter 9, "Derivatives," that graphing calculators have a numerical derivative feature that can be used to check graphically the derivative of a function that has been calculated with a formula. We can also use the numerical integration feature on graphing calculators to check our integration (if we assume temporarily that the constant of integration is 0). We do this by graphing the integral calculated with a formula and the numerical integral from the graphing calculator on the same set of axes. If the graphs lie on top of one another, the integrals agree. Figure 12.3 illustrates this for the function $f(x) = 3x^2 - 2x + 1$. Its integral, with the constant of integration set equal to 0, is shown as $y_1 = x^3 - x^2 + x$ in Figure 12.3(a), and the graphs of the two integrals are shown in Figure 12.3(b). Of course, it is often easier to use the derivative to check integration. See Appendix A, Section 12.1, for details. ■

```
Y1=X^3-X^2+X
Y2=fnInt(3X^2-2X
+1,X,0,X)
Y3=
Y4=
Y5=
Y6=
Y7=
```

Graphs of y_1 and y_2

Figure 12.3   (a)   (b)

✓ CHECKPOINT ANSWERS

1. (a) False; $\int (4x^3 - 2x)\, dx = x^4 - x^2 + C$

   (b) False; $\int \dfrac{1}{3x^2}\, dx = \dfrac{-1}{3x} + C$

2. $\int (2x^3 + x^{-1/2} - 4x^{-5})\, dx = \dfrac{x^4}{2} + 2x^{1/2} + x^{-4} + C$

| EXERCISES | 12.1

1. If $f'(x) = 4x^3$, what is $f(x)$?
2. If $f'(x) = 5x^4$, what is $f(x)$?
3. If $f'(x) = x^6$, what is $f(x)$?
4. If $g'(x) = x^4$, what is $g(x)$?

Evaluate the integrals in Problems 5–28. Check your answers by differentiating.

5. $\int x^7 dx$
6. $\int x^5\, dx$
7. $\int 8x^3 dx$
8. $\int 16x^9\, dx$

9. $\int (3^3 + x^{13})\, dx$
10. $\int (5^2 + x^{10})\, dx$
11. $\int (3 - x^{3/2})\, dx$
12. $\int (8 + x^{2/3})\, dx$
13. $\int (x^4 - 9x^2 + 3)\, dx$
14. $\int (3x^2 - 4x - 4)\, dx$
15. $\int (13 - 6x + 21x^6)\, dx$
16. $\int (12x^5 + 12x^3 - 7)\, dx$
17. $\int (2 + 2\sqrt{x})\, dx$
18. $\int (17 + \sqrt{x^3})\, dx$
19. $\int 6\sqrt[4]{x}\, dx$
20. $\int 3\sqrt[3]{x^2}\, dx$
21. $\int \dfrac{5}{x^4}\, dx$
22. $\int \dfrac{6}{x^5}\, dx$

23. $\displaystyle\int \frac{dx}{2\sqrt[3]{x^2}}$

24. $\displaystyle\int \frac{2\,dx}{5\sqrt{x^3}}$

25. $\displaystyle\int \left(x^3 - 4 + \frac{5}{x^6}\right) dx$

26. $\displaystyle\int \left(x^3 - 7 - \frac{3}{x^4}\right) dx$

27. $\displaystyle\int \left(x^9 - \frac{1}{x^3} + \frac{2}{\sqrt[3]{x}}\right) dx$

28. $\displaystyle\int \left(3x^8 + \frac{4}{x^8} - \frac{5}{\sqrt[5]{x}}\right) dx$

In Problems 29–32, use algebra to rewrite the integrands; then integrate and simplify.

29. $\int (4x^2 - 1)^2 x^3 \, dx$

30. $\int (x^3 + 1)^2 x \, dx$

31. $\displaystyle\int \frac{x+1}{x^3} \, dx$

32. $\displaystyle\int \frac{x-3}{\sqrt{x}} \, dx$

In Problems 33 and 34, find the antiderivatives and graph the resulting family members that correspond to $C = 0$, $C = 4$, $C = -4$, $C = 8$, and $C = -8$.

33. $\int (2x + 3) \, dx$

34. $\int (4 - x) \, dx$

35. If $\int f(x) \, dx = 2x^9 - 7x^5 + C$, find $f(x)$.

36. If $\int g(x) \, dx = 11x^{10} - 4x^3 + C$, find $g(x)$.

In each of Problems 37–40, a family of functions is given and graphs of some members of the family are shown. Write the indefinite integral that gives the family.

37. $F(x) = 5x - \dfrac{x^2}{4} + C$

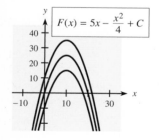

38. $F(x) = \dfrac{x^2}{2} + 3x + C$

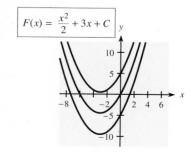

39. $F(x) = x^3 - 3x^2 + C$

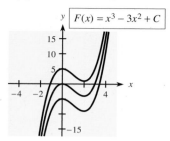

40. $F(x) = 12x - x^3 + C$

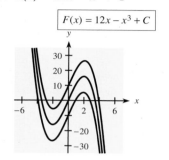

APPLICATIONS

41. **Revenue** If the marginal revenue (in dollars per unit) for a month for a commodity is $\overline{MR} = -0.4x + 30$, find the total revenue function.

42. **Revenue** If the marginal revenue (in dollars per unit) for a month for a commodity is $\overline{MR} = -0.05x + 25$, find the total revenue function.

43. **Revenue** If the marginal revenue (in dollars per unit) for a month is given by $\overline{MR} = -0.3x + 450$, what is the total revenue from the production and sale of 50 units?

44. **Revenue** If the marginal revenue (in dollars per unit) for a month is given by $\overline{MR} = -0.006x + 36$, find the total revenue from the sale of 75 units.

45. **Stimulus-response** Suppose that when a sense organ receives a stimulus at time t, the total number of action potentials is $P(t)$. If the rate at which action potentials are produced is $t^3 + 4t^2 + 6$, and if there are 0 action potentials when $t = 0$, find the formula for $P(t)$.

46. **Projectiles** Suppose that a particle has been shot into the air in such a way that the rate at which its height is changing is $v = 320 - 32t$, in feet per second, and suppose that it is 1600 feet high when $t = 10$ seconds. Write the equation that describes the height of the particle at any time t.

47. **Pollution** A factory is dumping pollutants into a river at a rate given by $dx/dt = t^{3/4}/600$ tons per week, where t is the time in weeks since the dumping began and x is the number of tons of pollutants.
    (a) Find the equation for total tons of pollutants dumped.
    (b) How many tons were dumped during the first year?

48. **Population growth** The rate of growth of the population of a city is predicted to be

$$\frac{dp}{dt} = 1000t^{1.08}$$

where p is the population at time t and t is measured in years from the present. Suppose that the current population is 100,000. What is the predicted
(a) rate of growth 5 years from the present?
(b) population 5 years from the present?

49. *Average cost* The DeWitt Company has found that the rate of change of its average cost for a product is

$$\overline{C}'(x) = \frac{1}{4} - \frac{100}{x^2}$$

where x is the number of units and cost is in dollars. The average cost of producing 20 units is $40.00.
(a) Find the average cost function for the product.
(b) Find the average cost of 100 units of the product.

50. *Oil leakage* An oil tanker hits a reef and begins to leak. The efforts of the workers repairing the leak cause the rate at which the oil is leaking to decrease. The oil was leaking at a rate of 31 barrels per hour at the end of the first hour after the accident, and the rate is decreasing at a rate of one barrel per hour.
(a) What function describes the rate of loss?
(b) How many barrels of oil will leak in the first 6 hours?
(c) When will the oil leak be stopped? How much will have leaked altogether?

51. *Health expenditures per capita* National health expenditures per capita E (in dollars) have risen dramatically since 2000. By using data from the Centers for Medicare and Medicaid Services from 2006 and projected to 2021, the rate of change of health expenditures per capita can be modeled by

$$\frac{dE}{dt} = 41.22t - 116.4$$

dollars per year, where t is the number of years past 2000.
(a) Find the function that models the national health expenditures per capita if these expenditures were $9808 in 2014. Use four significant digits.
(b) Use the model from part (a) to predict the national health expenditures per capita for 2020.

52. *Total taxable payroll* By using Social Security Administration data for selected years from 2012 and projected to 2050, the rate of change of the total U.S. taxable payroll can be modeled by

$$\frac{dP}{dt} = 27.0t + 112$$

billions of dollars per year, where t is the number of years past 2010.
(a) If total U.S. taxable payroll is $7088 billion in 2016, find the function $P(t)$. Use three significant digits.
(b) What does $P(t)$ predict for the total U.S. taxable payroll in 2025?

53. *Wind chill* When the air temperature is 20° F, the rate of change of the wind chill temperature t (°F) is given by

$$\frac{dt}{dw} = -4.352w^{-0.84}$$

where w is wind speed in miles per hour.
(a) Will both the rate of change of wind chill temperature and wind chill temperature decrease as the windspeed increases? Explain.
(b) If the wind chill temperature is 1°F when the wind speed is 31 mph and the air temperature is 20°F, find the function that models the wind chill temperature.

54. *Severe weather ice makers* Hail is produced in severe thunderstorms when an updraft draws moist surface air into subfreezing air above 10,000 feet. The speed of the updraft s, in mph, affects the diameter of hail (in inches). According to National Weather Service data, the rate of change of hail size with respect to updraft speed is

$$\frac{dh}{ds} = 0.001144s^{0.922}$$

inches of diameter per mph of updraft.
(a) When updraft speeds approach 60 mph, hail is golf-ball-sized. Use $h = 1.5$ and $s = 60$ to find a model for $h(s)$.
(b) Use the model to find the hail size for an updraft speed of 100 mph.

55. *U.S. population* With U.S. Census Bureau data (actual and projected) for selected years from 1960 to 2050, the rate of change of U.S. population P can be modeled by

$$\frac{dP}{dt} = -0.0002187t^2 + 0.0276t + 1.98$$

million people per year, where $t = 0$ represents 1960.
(a) In what year does this rate of change reach its maximum?
(b) In 1960, the U.S. population was 181 million. Use this to find a model for $P(t)$.
(c) For 2025, the Census Bureau's predicted U.S. population is 348 million. What does the model predict?

56. *Consumer prices* The consumer price index (CPI) measures how prices have changed for consumers. With 1995 as a reference of 100, a year with CPI = 150 indicates that consumer costs in that year were 1.5 times the 1995 costs. With U.S. Department of Labor data for selected years from 1995 and projected to 2050, the rate of change of the CPI can be modeled by

$$\frac{dC}{dt} = 0.009t^2 - 0.096t + 4.85$$

dollars per year, where $t = 0$ represents 1990.
(a) Find the function that models $C(t)$, if the CPI was 175 in 2010.
(b) What does the model from part (a) predict for the consumer costs in 2030? How does this compare to 2010?

OBJECTIVE   12.2

- To evaluate integrals of the form $\int u^n \cdot u'\,dx = \int u^n du$ if $n \neq -1$

The Power Rule

| APPLICATION PREVIEW |

In the previous section, we saw that total revenue could be found by integrating marginal revenue. That is,

$$R(x) = \int \overline{MR}\,dx$$

For example, if the marginal revenue for a product is given by

$$\overline{MR} = \frac{600}{\sqrt{3x+1}} + 2$$

then

$$R(x) = \int \left[\frac{600}{\sqrt{3x+1}} + 2 \right] dx$$

To evaluate this integral, however, we need a more general formula than the Powers of x Formula. (See Example 8.)

In this section, we will extend the Powers of x Formula to a rule for powers of a function of x.

Differentials   Our goal in this section is to extend the Powers of x Formula,

$$\int x^n dx = \frac{x^{n+1}}{n+1} + C, \quad n \neq -1$$

to powers of a function of x. In order to do this, we must understand the symbol dx.

Recall from Section 9.3, "Rates of Change and Derivatives," that the derivative of $y = f(x)$ with respect to x can be denoted by dy/dx. As we will see, there are advantages to using dy and dx as separate quantities whose ratio dy/dx equals $f'(x)$.

Differentials

If $y = f(x)$ is a differentiable function with derivative $dy/dx = f'(x)$, then the **differential of x** is dx, and the **differential of y** is dy, where

$$dy = f'(x)\,dx$$

Although differentials are useful in certain approximation problems, we are interested in the differential notation at this time.

EXAMPLE 1   Differentials

Find (a) dy if $y = x^3 - 4x^2 + 5$ and (b) du if $u = 5x^4 + 11$.

Solution
(a) $dy = f'(x)\,dx = (3x^2 - 8x)\,dx$
(b) If the dependent variable in a function is u, then $du = u'(x)\,dx$.

$$du = u'(x)\,dx = 20x^3\,dx$$

The Power Rule   In terms of our goal of extending the Powers of x Formula, we would suspect that if x is replaced by a function of x, then dx should be replaced by the differential of that function. Let's see whether this is true.

Recall that if $y = [u(x)]^n$, the derivative of y is

$$\frac{dy}{dx} = n[u(x)]^{n-1} \cdot u'(x)$$

Using this formula for derivatives, we can see that

$$\int n[u(x)]^{n-1} \cdot u'(x)\, dx = [u(x)]^n + C$$

It is easy to see that this formula is equivalent to the following formula, which is called the **Power Rule for Integration.**

Power Rule for Integration

$$\int [u(x)]^n \cdot u'(x)\, dx = \frac{[u(x)]^{n+1}}{n+1} + C, \quad n \neq -1$$

Using the fact that

$$du = u'(x)\, dx \ \text{ or } \ du = u'dx$$

we can write the Power Rule in the following alternative form.

Power Rule (Alternative Form)

If $u = u(x)$, then

$$\int u^n\, du = \frac{u^{n+1}}{n+1} + C, \quad n \neq -1$$

Note that this formula has the same form as the formula

$$\int x^n\, dx = \frac{x^{n+1}}{n+1} + C, \quad n \neq -1$$

with the *function u substituted for x and du substituted for dx.*

EXAMPLE 2 | Power Rule

Evaluate $\int (3x^2 + 4)^5 \cdot 6x\, dx$.

Solution
To use the Power Rule, we must be sure that we have the function $u(x)$, its derivative $u'(x)$, and n.

$$u = 3x^2 + 4, \quad n = 5$$
$$u' = 6x$$

All required parts are present, so the integral is of the form

$$\int (3x^2 + 4)^5 6x\, dx = \int u^5 \cdot u'dx = \int u^5\, du$$
$$= \frac{u^6}{6} + C = \frac{(3x^2 + 4)^6}{6} + C$$

We can check the integration by noting that the derivative of

$$\frac{(3x^2 + 4)^6}{6} + C \ \text{ is } \ (3x^2 + 4)^5 \cdot 6x$$

EXAMPLE 3   Power Rule

Evaluate $\int \sqrt{2x+3} \cdot 2 \, dx$.

Solution

If we let $u = 2x + 3$, then $u' = 2$, and so we have

$$\int \sqrt{2x+3} \cdot 2 \, dx = \int \sqrt{u} \, u' dx = \int \sqrt{u} \, du$$

$$= \int u^{1/2} \, du = \frac{u^{3/2}}{3/2} + C$$

Because $u = 2x + 3$, we have

$$\int \sqrt{2x+3} \cdot 2 \, dx = \frac{2}{3}(2x+3)^{3/2} + C$$

Check: The derivative of $\frac{2}{3}(2x+3)^{3/2} + C$ is $(2x+3)^{1/2} \cdot 2$. ✔

Some members of the family of functions given by

$$\int \sqrt{2x+3} \cdot 2 \, dx = \frac{2}{3}(2x+3)^{3/2} + C$$

are shown in Figure 12.4. Note from the graphs that the domain of each function is $x \geq -3/2$. This is because $2x + 3$ must be nonnegative so that $(2x+3)^{3/2} = (\sqrt{2x+3})^3$ is a real number.

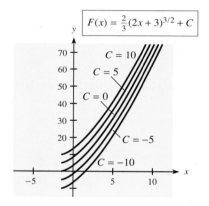

Figure 12.4

EXAMPLE 4   Power Rule

Evaluate $\int x^3(5x^4 + 11)^9 \, dx$.

Solution

If we let $u = 5x^4 + 11$, then $u' = 20x^3$. Thus we do not have an integral of the form $\int u^n \cdot u' dx$, as we had in Example 2 and Example 3; the factor 20 is not in the integrand. To get the integrand in the correct form, we can multiply by 20 and divide it out as follows:

$$\int x^3(5x^4+11)^9 \, dx = \int (5x^4+11)^9 \cdot x^3 \, dx = \int (5x^4+11)^9 \left(\frac{1}{20}\right)(20x^3) \, dx$$

Because $\frac{1}{20}$ is a constant factor, we can factor it outside the integral sign, getting

$$\int (5x^4+11)^9 \cdot x^3 \, dx = \frac{1}{20} \int (5x^4+11)^9 (20x^3) \, dx$$

$$= \frac{1}{20} \int u^9 \cdot u' dx = \frac{1}{20} \cdot \frac{u^{10}}{10} + C$$

$$= \frac{1}{200}(5x^4+11)^{10} + C$$

EXAMPLE 5   **Power Rule**

Evaluate $\int 5x^2\sqrt{x^3 - 4}\, dx$.

Solution

If we let $u = x^3 - 4$, then $u' = 3x^2$. Thus we need the factor 3, rather than 5, in the integrand. If we first reorder the factors and then multiply by the constant factor 3 (and divide it out), we have

$$\int \sqrt{x^3 - 4} \cdot 5x^2\, dx = \int \sqrt{x^3 - 4} \cdot \frac{5}{3}(3x^2)\, dx$$

$$= \frac{5}{3}\int (x^3 - 4)^{1/2} \cdot 3x^2\, dx$$

This integral is of the form $\frac{5}{3}\int u^{1/2} \cdot u'\, dx$, resulting in

$$\frac{5}{3} \cdot \frac{u^{3/2}}{3/2} + C = \frac{5}{3} \cdot \frac{(x^3 - 4)^{3/2}}{3/2} + C = \frac{10}{9}(x^3 - 4)^{3/2} + C \qquad \blacksquare$$

Note that we can factor a constant outside the integral sign to obtain the integrand in the form we seek. But if a variable must be factored outside the integral to obtain the form $u^n \cdot u'\, dx$, we *cannot* use this form and must try something else.

EXAMPLE 6   **Power Rule Fails**

Evaluate $\int (x^2 + 4)^2\, dx$.

Solution

If we let $u = x^2 + 4$, then $u' = 2x$. Because we would have to introduce a variable to get u' in the integral, we cannot solve this problem by using the Power Rule. We must find another method. We can evaluate this integral by squaring and then integrating term by term.

$$\int (x^2 + 4)^2\, dx = \int (x^4 + 8x^2 + 16)\, dx$$

$$= \frac{x^5}{5} + \frac{8x^3}{3} + 16x + C \qquad \blacksquare$$

Note that if we tried to introduce the factor $2x$ into the integral in Example 6, we would get

$$\int (x^2 + 4)^2\, dx = \int (x^2 + 4)^2 \cdot \frac{1}{2x}(2x)\, dx$$

Although it is tempting to factor $1/2x$ outside the integral and use the Power Rule, this leads to an "answer" that does not check. That is, the derivative of the "answer" is not the integrand. (Try it and see.) To emphasize again, we can introduce only *a constant factor* to get an integral in the proper form.

EXAMPLE 7   **Power Rule**

Evaluate:

(a) $\int (2x^2 - 4x)^2(x - 1)\, dx$ (b) $\int \frac{x^2 - 1}{(x^3 - 3x)^3}\, dx$

Solution

(a) If we want to treat this as an integral of the form $\int u^n u'\, dx$, we will have to let $u = 2x^2 - 4x$. Then $u' = 4x - 4$. Multiplying and dividing by 4 will give us this form.

$$\int (2x^2 - 4x)^2 (x - 1)\, dx = \int (2x^2 - 4x)^2 \cdot \frac{1}{4} \cdot 4(x - 1)\, dx$$

$$= \frac{1}{4} \int (2x^2 - 4x)^2 (4x - 4)\, dx$$

$$= \frac{1}{4} \int u^2 u'\, dx = \frac{1}{4} \cdot \frac{u^3}{3} + C$$

$$= \frac{1}{4} \frac{(2x^2 - 4x)^3}{3} + C$$

$$= \frac{1}{12} (2x^2 - 4x)^3 + C$$

(b) This integral can be treated as $\int u^{-3} u'\, dx$ if we let $u = x^3 - 3x$.

$$\int \frac{x^2 - 1}{(x^3 - 3x)^3}\, dx = \int (x^3 - 3x)^{-3} (x^2 - 1)\, dx$$

Then $u' = 3x^2 - 3$ and we can multiply and divide by 3 to get the form we need.

$$= \int (x^3 - 3x)^{-3} \cdot \frac{1}{3} \cdot 3(x^2 - 1)\, dx$$

$$= \frac{1}{3} \int (x^3 - 3x)^{-3} (3x^2 - 3)\, dx$$

$$= \frac{1}{3} \left[\frac{(x^3 - 3x)^{-2}}{-2} \right] + C$$

$$= \frac{-1}{6(x^3 - 3x)^2} + C$$

✓ CHECKPOINT

1. Which of the following can be evaluated with the Power Rule?
    (a) $\int (4x^2 + 1)^{10} (8x\, dx)$
    (b) $\int (4x^2 + 1)^{10} (x\, dx)$
    (c) $\int (4x^2 + 1)^{10} (8\, dx)$
    (d) $\int (4x^2 + 1)^{10}\, dx$

2. Which of the following is equal to $\int (2x^3 + 5)^{-2} (6x^2\, dx)$?
    (a) $\dfrac{[(2x^4)/4 + 5x]^{-1}}{-1} \cdot \dfrac{6x^3}{3} + C$
    (b) $\dfrac{(2x^3 + 5)^{-1}}{-1} \cdot \dfrac{6x^3}{3} + C$
    (c) $\dfrac{(2x^3 + 5)^{-1}}{-1} + C$

3. True or false: Constants can be factored outside the integral sign.
4. Evaluate the following.
    (a) $\int (x^3 + 9)^5 (3x^2\, dx)$
    (b) $\int (x^3 + 9)^{15} (x^2\, dx)$
    (c) $\int (x^3 + 9)^2 (x\, dx)$

EXAMPLE 8   Revenue | APPLICATION PREVIEW |

Suppose that the marginal revenue for a product is given by

$$\overline{MR} = \frac{600}{\sqrt{3x + 1}} + 2$$

Find the total revenue function.

Solution

$$R(x) = \int \overline{MR}\, dx = \int \left[\frac{600}{(3x+1)^{1/2}} + 2 \right] dx$$

$$= \int 600(3x+1)^{-1/2}\, dx + \int 2\, dx$$

$$= 600 \left(\frac{1}{3}\right) \int (3x+1)^{-1/2}(3\, dx) + 2 \int dx$$

$$= 200 \frac{(3x+1)^{1/2}}{1/2} + 2x + K$$

$$= 400\sqrt{3x+1} + 2x + K$$

We know that $R(0) = 0$, so we have

$$0 = 400\sqrt{1} + 0 + K \quad \text{or} \quad K = -400$$

Thus the total revenue function is

$$R(x) = 400\sqrt{3x+1} + 2x - 400$$

Note in Example 8 that even though $R(0) = 0$, the constant of integration K was *not* 0. This is because $x = 0$ does not necessarily mean that $u(x)$ will also be 0.

The formulas we have stated and used in this and the previous section are all the result of "reversing" derivative formulas. We summarize in the following box.

Integration Formula		Derivative Formula
$\int dx = x + C$	because	$\frac{d}{dx}(x+C) = 1$
$\int x^n\, dx = \frac{x^{n+1}}{n+1} + C \ (n \neq -1)$	because	$\frac{d}{dx}\left(\frac{x^{n+1}}{n+1} + C\right) = x^n$
$\int [u(x) + v(x)]\, dx = \int u(x)\, dx + \int v(x)\, dx$	because	$\frac{d}{dx}[u(x)+v(x)] = \frac{du}{dx} + \frac{dv}{dx}$
$\int [u(x) - v(x)]\, dx = \int u(x)\, dx - \int v(x)\, dx$	because	$\frac{d}{dx}[u(x)-v(x)] = \frac{du}{dx} - \frac{dv}{dx}$
$\int cf(x)\, dx = c \int f(x)\, dx$	because	$\frac{d}{dx}[cf(x)] = c\left(\frac{df}{dx}\right)$
$\int u^n u'\, dx = \frac{u^{n+1}}{n+1} + C \ (n \neq -1)$	because	$\frac{d}{dx}\left(\frac{u^{n+1}}{n+1} + C\right) = u^n \cdot u'$

Note that there are no integration formulas that correspond to "reversing" the derivative formulas for a product or for a quotient. This means that functions that may be easy to differentiate can be quite difficult (or even impossible) to integrate. Hence, in general, integration is a more difficult process than differentiation. In fact, some functions whose derivatives can be readily found cannot be integrated, such as

$$f(x) = \sqrt{x^3 + 1} \quad \text{and} \quad g(x) = \frac{2x^2}{x^4 + 1}$$

In the next section, we will add to this list of basic integration formulas by "reversing" the derivative formulas for exponential and logarithmic functions.

✓ **CHECKPOINT**
ANSWERS

1. Expressions (a) and (b) can be evaluated with the Power Rule. Expressions (c) and (d) do not fit the format of the Power Rule.

2. (c) $\int (2x^3 + 5)^{-2}(6x^2)\,dx = -(2x^3 + 5)^{-1} + C$

3. True

4. (a) $\int (x^3 + 9)^5(3x^2\,dx) = \dfrac{(x^3 + 9)^6}{6} + C$

(b) $\int (x^3 + 9)^{15}(x^2\,dx) = \dfrac{(x^3 + 9)^{16}}{48} + C$

(c) $\int (x^3 + 9)^2(x\,dx) = \int (x^6 + 18x^3 + 81)x\,dx = \dfrac{x^8}{8} + \dfrac{18x^5}{5} + \dfrac{81x^2}{2} + C$

| EXERCISES | 12.2

In Problems 1 and 2, find du.

1. $u = 2x^5 + 9$

2. $u = 3x^4 - 4x^3$

In each of Problems 3 and 4, one of parts (a) and (b) can be integrated with the Power Rule and the other cannot. Integrate the part that can be done with the Power Rule, and explain why the Power Rule cannot be used to evaluate the other.

3. (a) $\int (3x^4 - 7)^{12}\,(12x\,dx)$ (b) $\int (5x^3 + 11)^7\,(15x^2\,dx)$

4. (a) $\int 5(6 + 5x)^{10}\,dx$ (b) $\int 14x^2(2x^7 + 9)^6\,dx$

Evaluate the integrals in Problems 5–34. Check your results by differentiation.

5. $\int (x^2 + 3)^3\,2x\,dx$
6. $\int (3x^3 + 1)^4\,9x^2\,dx$
7. $\int (5x^3 + 11)^4\,15x^2\,dx$
8. $\int (8x^4 + 5)^3\,(32x^3)\,dx$
9. $\int (3x - x^3)^2\,(3 - 3x^2)\,dx$
10. $\int (4x^2 - 3x)^4\,(8x - 3)\,dx$
11. $\int 4x^3(7x^4 + 12)^3\,dx$
12. $\int 9x^5(3x^6 - 4)^6\,dx$
13. $\int 7(4x - 1)^6\,dx$
14. $\int 3(5 - x)^{-3}\,dx$
15. $\int 8x^5(4x^6 + 15)^{-3}\,dx$
16. $\int 5x^3(3x^4 + 7)^{-4}\,dx$
17. $\int (x - 1)(x^2 - 2x + 5)^4\,dx$
18. $\int (2x^3 - x)(x^4 - x^2)^6\,dx$
19. $\int 2(x^3 - 1)(x^4 - 4x + 3)^{-5}\,dx$
20. $\int 3(x^5 - 2x)(x^6 - 6x^2 + 7)^{-2}\,dx$
21. $\int 7x^3\sqrt{x^4 + 6}\,dx$
22. $\int 3x\sqrt{5 - x^2}\,dx$
23. $\int (x^3 + 1)^2\,(3x\,dx)$
24. $\int (x^2 - 5)^2\,(2x^2\,dx)$
25. $\int (3x^4 - 1)^2\,12x\,dx$
26. $\int (2x^4 + 3)^2\,(8x\,dx)$
27. $\int \sqrt{x^3 - 3x}\,(x^2 - 1)\,dx$
28. $\int \sqrt[3]{x^2 + 2x}\,(x + 1)\,dx$
29. $\int \dfrac{3x^4\,dx}{(2x^5 - 5)^4}$
30. $\int \dfrac{5x^3\,dx}{(x^4 - 8)^3}$
31. $\int \dfrac{x^3 - 1}{(x^4 - 4x)^3}\,dx$
32. $\int \dfrac{3x^5 - 2x^3}{(x^6 - x^4)^5}\,dx$
33. $\int \dfrac{x^2 - 4x}{\sqrt{x^3 - 6x^2 + 2}}\,dx$
34. $\int \dfrac{x^2 + 1}{\sqrt{x^3 + 3x + 10}}\,dx$
35. If $\int f(x)\,dx = (7x - 13)^{10} + C$, find $f(x)$.
36. If $\int g(x)\,dx = (5x^2 + 2)^6 + C$, find $g(x)$.

In Problems 37 and 38, (a) evaluate each integral and (b) graph the members of the solution family for $C = -5$, $C = 0$, and $C = 5$.

37. $\int x(x^2 - 1)^3\,dx$
38. $\int (3x - 11)^{1/3}\,dx$

Each of Problems 39 and 40 has the form $\int f(x)\,dx$.
(a) Evaluate each integral to obtain a family of functions.
(b) Find and graph the family member that passes through the point $(0, 2)$. Call that function $F(x)$.
(c) Find any x-values where $f(x)$ is not defined but $F(x)$ is.
(d) At the x-values found in part (c), what kind of tangent line does $F(x)$ have?

39. $\int \dfrac{3\,dx}{(2x - 1)^{3/5}}$
40. $\int \dfrac{x^2\,dx}{(x^3 - 1)^{1/3}}$

In each of Problems 41 and 42, a family of functions is given, together with the graphs of some functions in the family. Write the indefinite integral that gives the family.

41. $F(x) = (x^2 - 1)^{4/3} + C$

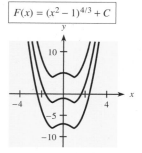

42. $F(x) = 54(4x^2 + 9)^{-1} + C$

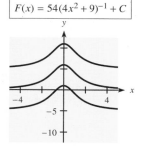

In parts (a)–(c) of Problems 43 and 44, three integrals are given. Integrate those that can be done by the methods studied so far. Additionally, as part (d), give your own example of an integral that looks as though it might use the Power Rule but that cannot be integrated by using methods studied so far.

43. (a) $\int \dfrac{7x^3 \, dx}{(x^3 + 4)^2}$ (b) $\int \dfrac{7x^2 \, dx}{(x^3 + 4)^2}$

  (c) $\int \dfrac{\sqrt{x^2 + 4}}{x} \, dx$

44. (a) $\int \dfrac{(2x^5 + 1)^{7/2}}{3x^4} \, dx$ (b) $\int 10x(2x^5 + 1)^{7/2} \, dx$

  (c) $\int \dfrac{5x^3}{(2x^4 + 1)^{7/2}} \, dx$

APPLICATIONS

45. **Revenue** Suppose that the marginal revenue for a product is given by

$$\overline{MR} = \dfrac{-30}{(2x + 1)^2} + 30$$

where x is the number of units and revenue is in dollars. Find the total revenue.

46. **Revenue** The marginal revenue for a new calculator is given by

$$\overline{MR} = 60{,}000 - \dfrac{40{,}000}{(10 + x)^2}$$

where x represents hundreds of calculators and revenue is in dollars. Find the total revenue function for these calculators.

47. **Physical productivity** The total physical output of a number of machines or workers is called *physical productivity* and is a function of the number of machines or workers. If $P = f(x)$ is the productivity, dP/dx is the marginal physical productivity. If the marginal physical productivity for bricklayers is $dP/dx = 90(x + 1)^2$, where P is the number of bricks laid per day and x is the number of bricklayers, find the physical productivity of 4 bricklayers. (*Note:* $P = 0$ when $x = 0$.)

48. **Production** The rate of production of a new line of products is given by

$$\dfrac{dx}{dt} = 200 \left[1 + \dfrac{400}{(t + 40)^2} \right]$$

where x is the number of items and t is the number of weeks the product has been in production.
  (a) Assuming that $x = 0$ when $t = 0$, find the total number of items produced as a function of time t.
  (b) How many items were produced in the fifth week?

49. **Data entry speed** The rate of change in data entry speed of the average student is $ds/dx = 5(x + 1)^{-1/2}$, where x is the number of lessons the student has had and s is in entries per minute.

  (a) Find the data entry speed as a function of the number of lessons if the average student can complete 10 entries per minute with no lessons ($x = 0$).
  (b) How many entries per minute can the average student complete after 24 lessons?

50. **Productivity** Because a new employee must learn an assigned task, production will increase with time. Suppose that for the average new employee, the rate of performance is given by

$$\dfrac{dN}{dt} = \dfrac{1}{2\sqrt{t + 1}}$$

where N is the number of units completed t hours after beginning a new task. If 2 units are completed after 3 hours, how many units are completed after 8 hours?

51. **Film attendance** An excellent film with a very small advertising budget must depend largely on word-of-mouth advertising. In this case, the rate at which weekly attendance might grow can be given by

$$\dfrac{dA}{dt} = \dfrac{-100}{(t + 10)^2} + \dfrac{2000}{(t + 10)^3}$$

where t is the time in weeks since release and A is attendance in millions.
  (a) Find the function that describes weekly attendance at this film.
  (b) Find the attendance at this film in the tenth week.

52. **Product quality and advertising** An inferior product with a large advertising budget does well when it is introduced, but sales decline as people discontinue use of the product. Suppose that the rate of weekly sales revenue is given by

$$S'(t) = \dfrac{400}{(t + 1)^3} - \dfrac{200}{(t + 1)^2}$$

where S is sales in thousands of dollars and t is time in weeks.
  (a) Find the function that describes the weekly sales.
  (b) Find the sales for the first week and the ninth week.

53. **Demographics** Because of job outsourcing, a Pennsylvania town predicts that its public school population will decrease at the rate

$$\dfrac{dN}{dx} = \dfrac{-300}{\sqrt{x + 9}}$$

where x is the number of years and N is the total school population. If the present population ($x = 0$) is 8000, what population size is expected in 7 years?

54. **Franchise growth** A new fast-food firm predicts that the number of franchises for its products will grow at the rate

$$\dfrac{dn}{dt} = 9\sqrt{t + 1}$$

where t is the number of years, $0 \le t \le 10$. If there is one franchise ($n = 1$) at present ($t = 0$), how many franchises are predicted for 8 years from now?

55. *Obesity* The rate of change of the percent of obese Americans who are severely obese can be modeled by the function

$$f'(x) = \frac{375}{(0.743x + 6.97)^2}$$

percentage points per year, where x is the number of years after 1980 (*Source: American Journal of Preventive Medicine* 42, June 2012).

(a) If 8.3% of obese Americans were severely obese in 1995, find the function $f(x)$ that gives the percent of obese Americans who are severely obese. Use three significant digits.

(b) Use the function from part (a) to predict the percent of obese American adults who will be severely obese in 2025.

56. *Social Security beneficiaries* Suppose the rate of change of the number of Social Security beneficiaries (in millions per year) can be modeled by

$$\frac{dB}{dt} = 0.07149(0.1t + 1)^2 - 0.67114(0.1t + 1) + 2.2016$$

where t is the number of years past 1950.

Year	Number of Beneficiaries (millions)	Year	Number of Beneficiaries (millions)
1950	2.9	2000	44.8
1960	14.3	2010	53.3
1970	25.2	2020	68.8
1980	35.1	2030	82.7
1990	39.5		

Source: Social Security Administration

(a) Use integration and the data point for 2000 to find the function $B(t)$ that models the millions of Social Security beneficiaries.

(b) The data in the table give the millions of Social Security beneficiaries for selected years from 1950 and projected to 2030. Graph $B(t)$ from part (a) with the data in the table; let $t = 0$ represent 1950.

(c) How well does the model fit the data?

57. *Females in the workforce* Suppose the rate of change of the percent p of total U.S. workers who are female can be modeled by

$$\frac{dp}{dt} = \frac{2154.18}{(1.38t + 64.1)^2}$$

percentage points per year, where t is the number of years past 1950.

Year	% Female	Year	% Female
1950	29.6	2010	47.9
1960	33.4	2015	48.3
1970	38.1	2020	48.1
1980	42.5	2030	48.0
1990	45.2	2040	47.9
2000	46.6	2050	47.9

Source: U.S. Census Bureau

(a) Use integration and the data point for 2040 to find the function $p(t)$ that models the percent of the workforce that is female.

(b) For selected years from 1950 and projected to 2050, the data in the table show the percent of total U.S. workers who are female. With t as the number of years past 1950, graph these data with the model found in part (a).

(c) Comment on the model's fit to the data.

58. *Energy use* Energy use per dollar of GDP in the United States indexed to 1980 means that energy use for any year is viewed as a percent of the use per dollar of GDP in 1980. The table shows the energy use per dollar of GDP, as a percent, for selected years from 1985 and projected to 2035. Suppose the rate of change of energy use per dollar of GDP can be modeled by

$$\frac{dE}{dt} = 0.00468(0.4t + 2)^2 - 0.104(0.4t + 2) - 0.56$$

percentage points per year, where t is the number of years past 1980.

Energy Use per Dollar of GDP

Year	Percent	Year	Percent
1985	83	2015	51
1990	79	2020	45
1995	75	2025	41
2000	67	2030	37
2005	60	2035	34
2010	56		

Source: U.S. Department of Energy

(a) Use integration and the data point for 1990 to find the function $E(t)$ that models the energy use per dollar of GDP. Use two significant digits.

(b) Let $t = 0$ represent 1980 and graph the model from part (a) with the data in the table.

(c) Find the model's predicted energy use per dollar of GDP in 2025.

OBJECTIVES

12.3

- To evaluate integrals of the form $\int e^u u' \, dx$ or, equivalently, $\int e^u \, du$
- To evaluate integrals of the form $\int \dfrac{u'}{u} \, dx$ or, equivalently, $\int \dfrac{1}{u} \, du$

Integrals Involving Exponential and Logarithmic Functions

■ | APPLICATION PREVIEW |

As the real estate market emerges from the crisis that began in 2008, the rate of growth of the market value of a home is expected to exceed the inflation rate. Suppose, for example, that home prices in a selected area are projected to increase at an average annual rate of 8%. Then the rate of change of the value of a house in this area that cost $200,000 can be modeled by

$$\frac{dV}{dt} = 15.4e^{0.077t}$$

where V is the value of the home in thousands of dollars and t is the time in years since the home was purchased. To find the market value of such a home 10 years after it was purchased, we would first have to integrate dV/dt. That is, we must be able to integrate an exponential. (See Example 3.)

In this section, we consider integration formulas that result in natural logarithms and formulas for integrating exponentials.

Integrals Involving Exponential Functions

We know that

$$\frac{d}{dx}(e^x) = e^x \quad \text{and} \quad \frac{d}{dx}(e^u) = e^u \cdot u'$$

The corresponding integrals are given by the following.

Exponential Formula

If u is a function of x,

$$\int e^u \cdot u' \, dx = \int e^u \, du = e^u + C$$

In particular, $\displaystyle\int e^x \, dx = e^x + C$.

EXAMPLE 1   Integral of an Exponential

Evaluate $\int 5e^x \, dx$.

Solution

$\int 5e^x \, dx = 5\int e^x \, dx = 5e^x + C$

EXAMPLE 2   Integral of $e^u \, du$

Evaluate: (a) $\displaystyle\int 2xe^{x^2} \, dx$ (b) $\displaystyle\int \frac{x^2 \, dx}{e^{x^3}}$

Solution

(a) Letting $u = x^2$ implies that $u' = 2x$, and the integral is of the form $\int e^u \cdot u' \, dx$. Thus

$$\int 2xe^{x^2} \, dx = \int e^{x^2}(2x) \, dx = \int e^u \cdot u' \, dx = e^u + C = e^{x^2} + C$$

(b) In order to use $\int e^u \cdot u' dx$, we write the exponential in the numerator. Thus

$$\int \frac{x^2 \, dx}{e^{x^3}} = \int e^{-x^3}(x^2 \, dx)$$

This is *almost* of the form $\int e^u \cdot u' \, dx$. Letting $u = -x^3$ gives $u' = -3x^2$. Thus

$$\int e^{-x^3}(x^2 \, dx) = -\frac{1}{3}\int e^{-x^3}(-3x^2 \, dx) = -\frac{1}{3}e^{-x^3} + C = \frac{-1}{3e^{x^3}} + C$$

✓ **CHECKPOINT**   1. True or false:

(a) $\int e^{x^2}(2x \, dx) = e^{x^2} \cdot x^2 + C$ (b) $\int e^{-3x} \, dx = -\frac{1}{3}e^{-3x} + C$

(c) $\int \frac{dx}{e^{3x}} = \frac{1}{3}\left(\frac{1}{e^{3x}}\right) + C$ (d) $\int e^{3x+1}(3 \, dx) = \frac{e^{3x+2}}{3x+2} + C$

EXAMPLE 3   **Real Estate Inflation** | APPLICATION PREVIEW |

Suppose the rate of change of the value of a house that cost $200,000 in 2015 can be modeled by

$$\frac{dV}{dt} = 15.4e^{0.077t}$$

where V is the market value of the home in thousands of dollars and t is the time in years since 2015.

(a) Find the function that expresses the value V in terms of t.
(b) Find the predicted value in 2025 (after 10 years).

Solution

(a) $V = \int \frac{dV}{dt} \, dt = \int 15.4e^{0.077t} \, dt$

$$V = 15.4 \int e^{0.077t} \left(\frac{1}{0.077}\right)(0.077 \, dt)$$

$$V = 15.4 \left(\frac{1}{0.077}\right) \int e^{0.077t}(0.077 \, dt)$$

$$V = 200e^{0.077t} + C$$

Using $V = 200$ (thousand) when $t = 0$, we have

$$200 = 200 + C$$
$$0 = C$$

Thus we have the value as a function of time given by

$$V = 200e^{0.077t}$$

(b) The value after 10 years is found by using $t = 10$.

$$V = 200e^{0.077(10)} = 200e^{0.77} \approx 431.95$$

Thus, in 2025, the predicted value of the home is $431,950.

EXAMPLE 4   **Graphs of Functions and Integrals**

Figure 12.5 shows the graphs of $g(x) = 5e^{-x^2}$ and $h(x) = -10xe^{-x^2}$. One of these functions is $f(x)$ and the other is $\int f(x) \, dx$ with $C = 0$.

(a) Decide which of $g(x)$ and $h(x)$ is $f(x)$ and which is $\int f(x) \, dx$.
(b) How can the graph of $f(x)$ be used to locate and classify the extrema of $\int f(x) \, dx$?

(c) What feature of the graph of $f(x)$ occurs at the same x-values as the inflection points of the graph of $\int f(x)\,dx$?

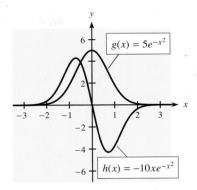

Figure 12.5

Solution

(a) The graph of $h(x)$ looks like the graph of $g'(x)$ because $h(x) > 0$ where $g(x)$ is increasing, $h(x) < 0$ where $g(x)$ is decreasing, and $h(x) = 0$ where $g(x)$ has its maximum. However, if $h(x) = g'(x)$, then, equivalently,

$$\int h(x)\,dx = \int g'(x)\,dx$$
$$= g(x) + C$$

so $h(x) = f(x)$ and $g(x) = \int f(x)\,dx$. We can verify this by noting that

$$\int -10xe^{-x^2}\,dx = 5\int e^{-x^2}(-2x\,dx)$$
$$= 5e^{-x^2} + C$$

(b) We know that $f(x)$ is the derivative of $\int f(x)\,dx$, so, as we saw in part (a), the x-intercepts of $f(x)$ locate the critical values and extrema of $\int f(x)\,dx$.

(c) The first derivative of $\int f(x)\,dx$ is $f(x)$, and its second derivative is $f'(x)$. Hence the inflection points of $\int f(x)\,dx$ occur where $f'(x) = 0$. But $f(x)$ has its extrema where $f'(x) = 0$. Thus the extrema of $f(x)$ occur at the same x-values as the inflection points of $\int f(x)\,dx$.

Integrals Involving Logarithmic Functions

Recall that the Power Rule for integrals applies only if $n \neq -1$. That is,

$$\int u^n u'\,dx = \frac{u^{n+1}}{n+1} + C \quad \text{if } n \neq -1$$

The following formula applies when $n = -1$.

Logarithmic Formula

If u is a function of x, then

$$\int u^{-1} u'\,dx = \int \frac{u'}{u}\,dx = \int \frac{1}{u}\,du = \ln|u| + C$$

In particular, $\int \frac{1}{x}\,dx = \ln|x| + C.$

We use the absolute value of u in the integral because the logarithm is defined only when the quantity is positive. This logarithmic formula is a direct result of the fact that

$$\frac{d}{dx}(\ln|u|) = \frac{1}{u} \cdot u'$$

We can see this result by considering the following.

For $u > 0$: $\dfrac{d}{dx}(\ln|u|) = \dfrac{d}{dx}(\ln u) = \dfrac{1}{u} \cdot u'$

For $u < 0$: $\dfrac{d}{dx}(\ln|u|) = \dfrac{d}{dx}[\ln(-u)] = \dfrac{1}{(-u)} \cdot (-u') = \dfrac{1}{u} \cdot u'$

In addition to this verification, we can graphically illustrate the need for the absolute value sign. Figure 12.6(a) shows that $f(x) = 1/x$ is defined for $x \ne 0$, and from Figures 12.6(b) and 12.6(c), we see that $F(x) = \int 1/x\, dx = \ln|x|$ is also defined for $x \ne 0$, but $y = \ln x$ is defined only for $x > 0$.

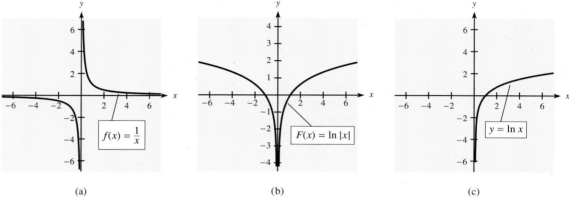

Figure 12.6   (a)   (b)   (c)

EXAMPLE 5   Integral Resulting in a Logarithmic Function

Evaluate $\displaystyle\int \dfrac{4}{4x+8}\, dx$.

Solution
This integral is of the form

$$\int \frac{u'}{u}\, dx = \ln|u| + C$$

with $u = 4x + 8$ and $u' = 4$. Thus

$$\int \frac{4}{4x+8}\, dx = \ln|4x+8| + C$$

Figure 12.7 shows several members of the family

$$F(x) = \int \frac{4\, dx}{4x+8} = \ln|4x+8| + C$$

We can choose different values for C and use a graphing utility to graph families of curves such as those in Figure 12.7.

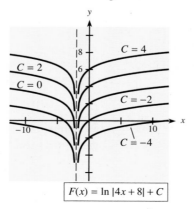

Figure 12.7

EXAMPLE **6**   **Integral of** *du/u*

Evaluate $\displaystyle\int \frac{x-3}{x^2-6x+1}\, dx$.

Solution
This integral is of the form $\int (u'/u)\, dx$, *almost*. If we let $u = x^2 - 6x + 1$, then $u' = 2x - 6$. If we multiply (and divide) the numerator by 2, we get

$$\int \frac{x-3}{x^2-6x+1}\, dx = \frac{1}{2}\int \frac{2(x-3)}{x^2-6x+1}\, dx$$

$$= \frac{1}{2}\int \frac{2x-6}{x^2-6x+1}\, dx$$

$$= \frac{1}{2}\int \frac{u'}{u}\, dx = \frac{1}{2}\ln|u| + C$$

$$= \frac{1}{2}\ln|x^2-6x+1| + C$$

EXAMPLE **7**   **Population Growth**

Because the world contains only about 10 billion acres of arable land, world population is limited. Suppose that world population is limited to 40 billion people and that the rate of population growth per year is given by

$$\frac{dP}{dt} = k(40 - P)$$

where P is the population in billions at time t and k is a positive constant. Then the relationship between the year and the population during that year is given by the integral

$$t = \frac{1}{k}\int \frac{1}{40-P}\, dP$$

where $40 - P > 0$ because 40 billion is the population's upper limit.

(a) Evaluate this integral to find the relationship.
(b) Use properties of logarithms and exponential functions to write P as a function of t.

Solution

(a) $t = \dfrac{1}{k}\displaystyle\int \dfrac{1}{40-P}\, dP = -\dfrac{1}{k}\displaystyle\int \dfrac{-dP}{40-P} = -\dfrac{1}{k}\ln|40-P| + C_1$

(b) $t = -\dfrac{1}{k}\ln(40-P) + C_1$ because $40 - P > 0$ means $|40-P| = 40 - P$.

Solving this equation for P requires converting to exponential form.

$$-k(t - C_1) = \ln(40 - P)$$
$$e^{C_1 k - kt} = 40 - P$$
$$e^{C_1 k} \cdot e^{-kt} = 40 - P$$

Because $e^{C_1 k}$ is an unknown constant, we replace it with C and solve for P.

$$P = 40 - Ce^{-kt}$$

If an integral contains a fraction in which the degree of the numerator is equal to or greater than that of the denominator, we should divide the denominator into the numerator as a first step.

EXAMPLE 8   **Integral Requiring Division**

Evaluate $\displaystyle\int \frac{x^4 - 2x^3 + 4x^2 - 7x - 1}{x^2 - 2x}\, dx.$

Solution

Because the numerator is of higher degree than the denominator, we begin by dividing $x^2 - 2x$ into the numerator.

$$
\begin{array}{r}
x^2 \qquad\quad\; + 4 \\
x^2 - 2x\overline{)x^4 - 2x^3 + 4x^2 - 7x - 1} \\
\underline{x^4 - 2x^3\qquad\qquad\qquad} \\
4x^2 - 7x - 1 \\
\underline{4x^2 - 8x\qquad} \\
x - 1
\end{array}
$$

Thus

$$
\int \frac{x^4 - 2x^3 + 4x^2 - 7x - 1}{x^2 - 2x}\, dx = \int\left(x^2 + 4 + \frac{x - 1}{x^2 - 2x}\right) dx
$$

$$
= \int(x^2 + 4)\, dx + \frac{1}{2}\int \frac{2(x - 1)\, dx}{x^2 - 2x}
$$

$$
= \frac{x^3}{3} + 4x + \frac{1}{2}\ln|x^2 - 2x| + C
$$

✓ **CHECKPOINT**

2. True or false:

(a) $\displaystyle\int \frac{3x^2\, dx}{x^3 + 4} = \ln|x^3 + 4| + C$ (b) $\displaystyle\int \frac{2x\, dx}{\sqrt{x^2 + 1}} = \ln\left|\sqrt{x^2 + 1}\right| + C$

(c) $\displaystyle\int \frac{2}{x}\, dx = 2\ln|x| + C$ (d) $\displaystyle\int \frac{x}{x + 1}\, dx = x\int \frac{1}{x + 1}\, dx = x\ln|x + 1| + C$

(e) To evaluate $\displaystyle\int \frac{4x}{4x + 1}\, dx$, our first step is to divide $4x + 1$ into $4x$.

3. (a) Divide $4x + 1$ into $4x$.   (b) Evaluate $\displaystyle\int \frac{4x}{4x + 1}\, dx$.

✓ **CHECKPOINT**
ANSWERS

1. (a) False. The correct solution is $e^{x^2} + C$ (see Example 2a).
    (b) True
    (c) False; $\displaystyle\int \frac{dx}{e^{3x}} = \frac{-1}{3e^{3x}} + C$
    (d) False; $\displaystyle\int e^{3x+1}(3\, dx) = e^{3x+1} + C$

2. (a) True
    (b) False; $\displaystyle\int \frac{2x\, dx}{\sqrt{x^2 + 1}} = 2(x^2 + 1)^{1/2} + C$
    (c) True
    (d) False. We cannot factor the variable x outside the integral sign.
    (e) True

3. (a) $\displaystyle\frac{4x}{4x + 1} = 1 - \frac{1}{4x + 1}$

    (b) $\displaystyle\int \frac{4x\, dx}{4x + 1} = \int\left(1 - \frac{1}{4x + 1}\right) dx = x - \frac{1}{4}\ln|4x + 1| + C$

| EXERCISES | 12.3

Evaluate the integrals in Problems 1–32.

1. $\int 3e^{3x}\,dx$

2. $\int 4e^{4x}\,dx$

3. $\int e^{-x}\,dx$

4. $\int e^{2x}\,dx$

5. $\int 1000e^{0.1x}\,dx$

6. $\int 1600e^{0.4x}\,dx$

7. $\int 840e^{-0.7x}\,dx$

8. $\int 250e^{-0.5x}\,dx$

9. $\int x^3 e^{3x^4}\,dx$

10. $\int xe^{2x^2}\,dx$

11. $\int \dfrac{3}{e^{2x}}\,dx$

12. $\int \dfrac{4}{e^{1-2x}}\,dx$

13. $\int \dfrac{x^5}{e^{2-3x^6}}\,dx$

14. $\int \dfrac{x^3}{e^{4x^4}}\,dx$

15. $\int \left(e^{4x} - \dfrac{3}{e^{x/2}}\right)\,dx$

16. $\int \left(xe^{3x^2} - \dfrac{5}{e^{x/3}}\right)\,dx$

17. $\int \dfrac{3x^2}{x^3 + 4}\,dx$

18. $\int \dfrac{8x^7}{x^8 - 1}\,dx$

19. $\int \dfrac{dz}{4z + 1}$

20. $\int \dfrac{y}{y^2 + 1}\,dy$

21. $\int \dfrac{6x^3}{2x^4 + 1}\,dx$

22. $\int \dfrac{7x^2}{4x^3 - 9}\,dx$

23. $\int \dfrac{4x}{5x^2 - 4}\,dx$

24. $\int \dfrac{5x^2}{3x^3 - 8}\,dx$

25. $\int \dfrac{3x^2 - 2}{x^3 - 2x}\,dx$

26. $\int \dfrac{4x^3 + 2x}{x^4 + x^2}\,dx$

27. $\int \dfrac{z^2 + 1}{z^3 + 3z + 17}\,dz$

28. $\int \dfrac{(x + 2)\,dx}{x^2 + 4x - 9}$

29. $\int \dfrac{x^3 - x^2 + 1}{x - 1}\,dx.$

30. $\int \dfrac{2x^3 + x^2 + 2x + 3}{2x + 1}\,dx$

31. $\int \dfrac{x^2 + x + 3}{x^2 + 3}\,dx$

32. $\int \dfrac{x^4 - 2x^2 + x}{x^2 - 2}\,dx$

In Problems 33 and 34, graphs of two functions labeled $g(x)$ and $h(x)$ are given. Decide which is the graph of $f(x)$ and which is one member of the family $\int f(x)\,dx$. Check your conclusions by evaluating the integral.

33.

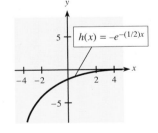
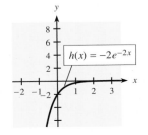

34.

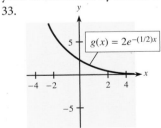
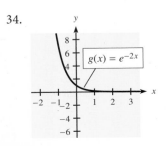

In Problems 35 and 36, a function $f(x)$ and its graph are given. Find the family $F(x) = \int f(x)\,dx$ and graph the member that satisfies $F(0) = 0$.

35.

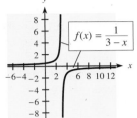

36.

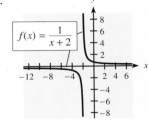

In Problems 37–40, a family of functions is given and graphs of some members are shown. Find the function $f(x)$ such that the family is given by $\int f(x)\,dx$.

37. $F(x) = x + \ln|x| + C$

38. $F(x) = -\ln(x^2 + 4) + C$

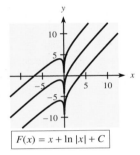
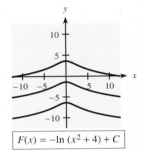

39. $F(x) = 5xe^{-x} + C$

40. $F(x) = e^{0.4x} + e^{-0.4x} + C$

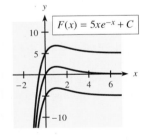
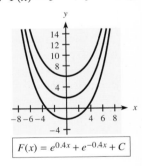

In parts (a)–(d) of Problems 41 and 42, integrate those that can be done by the methods studied so far.

41. (a) $\int xe^{x^3}\,dx$

   (b) $\int \dfrac{x + 2}{x^2 + 2x + 7}\,dx$

   (c) $\int \dfrac{x^2 + 2x}{x^3 + 3x^2 + 7}\,dx$

   (d) $\int 5x^3 e^{2x^4}\,dx$

42. (a) $\int \dfrac{3x - 1}{x^3 - x + 2}\,dx$

   (b) $\int \dfrac{3x - 1}{6x^2 - 4x + 9}\,dx$

   (c) $\int 5\sqrt{x}\,e^{\sqrt{x}}\,dx$

   (d) $\int 6xe^{-x^2/8}\,dx$

APPLICATIONS

43. *Revenue* Suppose that the marginal revenue from the sale of x units of a product is $\overline{MR} = R'(x) = 6e^{0.01x}$. What is the revenue in dollars from the sale of 100 units of the product?

44. *Concentration of a drug* Suppose that the rate at which the concentration of a drug in the blood changes with respect to time t is given by

$$C'(t) = \frac{c}{b-a}(be^{-bt} - ae^{-at}), \quad t \geq 0$$

where a, b, and c are constants depending on the drug administered, with $b > a$. Assuming that $C(t) = 0$ when $t = 0$, find the formula for the concentration of the drug in the blood at any time t.

45. *Radioactive decay* The rate of disintegration of a radioactive substance can be described by

$$\frac{dn}{dt} = n_0(-K)e^{-Kt}$$

where n_0 is the number of radioactive atoms present when time t is 0, and K is a positive constant that depends on the substance involved. Using the fact that the constant of integration is 0, integrate dn/dt to find the number of atoms n that are still radioactive after time t.

46. *Radioactive decay* Radioactive substances decay at a rate that is proportional to the amount present. Thus, if k is a constant and the amount present is x, the decay rate is

$$\frac{dx}{dt} = kx \quad (t \text{ in hours})$$

This means that the relationship between the time and the amount of substance present can be found by evaluating the integral

$$t = \int \frac{dx}{kx}$$

(a) Evaluate the integral to find the relationship.
(b) Use properties of logarithms and exponential functions to write x as a function of t.

47. *Memorization* The rate of vocabulary memorization of the average student in a foreign language course is given by

$$\frac{dv}{dt} = \frac{40}{t+1}$$

where t is the number of continuous hours of study, $0 < t \leq 4$, and v is the number of words. How many words would the average student memorize in 3 hours?

48. *Population growth* The rate of growth of world population can be modeled by

$$\frac{dN}{dt} = N_0 r e^{rt}, \quad r < 1$$

where t is the time in years from the present and N_0 and r are constants. What function describes world population if the present population is N_0?

49. *Compound interest* If $\$P$ is invested for n years at 10% compounded continuously, the rate at which the future value is growing is

$$\frac{dS}{dn} = 0.1Pe^{0.1n}$$

(a) What function describes the future value at the end of n years?
(b) In how many years will the future value double?

50. *Temperature changes* When an object is moved from one environment to another, its temperature T changes at a rate given by

$$\frac{dT}{dt} = kCe^{kt}$$

where t is the time in the new environment (in hours), C is the temperature difference (old − new) between the two environments, and k is a constant. If the temperature of the object (and the old environment) is $70°F$, and $C = -10°F$, what function describes the temperature T of the object t hours after it is moved?

51. *Blood pressure in the aorta* The rate at which blood pressure decreases in the aorta of a normal adult after a heartbeat is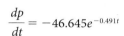

$$\frac{dp}{dt} = -46.645e^{-0.491t}$$

where t is time in seconds.
(a) What function describes the blood pressure in the aorta if $p = 95$ when $t = 0$?
(b) What is the blood pressure 0.1 second after a heartbeat?

52. *Sales and advertising* A store finds that its sales decline after the end of an advertising campaign, with its daily sales for the period declining at the rate $S'(t) = -1477.8e^{-0.2t}$, $0 \leq t \leq 35$, where t is the number of days since the end of the campaign. Suppose that $S = 7389$ units when $t = 0$.
(a) Find the function that describes the number of daily sales t days after the end of the campaign.
(b) Find the total number of sales 10 days after the end of the advertising campaign.

53. *Life expectancy* Suppose the rate of change of the expected life span l at birth of people born in the United States can be modeled by

$$\frac{dl}{dt} = \frac{14.304}{t+20}$$

where t is the number of years past 1920.

Year	Life Span (years)	Year	Life Span (years)
1920	54.1	1994	75.7
1930	59.7	1996	76.1
1940	62.9	1998	76.7
1950	68.2	2000	76.9
1960	69.7	2001	77.2
1970	70.8	2003	77.5
1975	72.6	2005	77.9
1980	73.7	2010	78.1
1985	74.7	2015	78.9
1990	75.4	2020	79.5
1992	75.5		

Source: National Center for Health Statistics

(a) Use integration and the data point for 2000 to find the function that models the life span.
(b) The data in the table give the expected life spans for people born in various years. Graph the function from part (a) with the data, with $t = 0$ representing 1920.
(c) How well does the model fit the data?

54. *U.S. households with cable/satellite TV* Suppose the rate of change of the percent P of U.S. households with cable/satellite TV can be modeled by

$$\frac{dP}{dt} = \frac{46.3}{t+5}$$

where t is the number of years past 1975.
(a) Use integration and the data point for 2010 to find the function $P(t)$ that models the percent of U.S. households with cable/satellite TV.
(b) How well does the model from part (a) fit the data in the table?
(c) If the model remains valid, use it to predict the percent of U.S. households with cable/satellite TV in 2018.

Year	Percent	Year	Percent
1980	22.6	2000	67.8
1985	46.2	2005	85.7
1990	59.0	2010	90.6
1995	65.7	2013	90.5

Source: Nielsen Media Research

55. *Consumer price index* The Social Security Administration makes projections about the consumer price index (CPI) in order to understand the effects of inflation on Social Security benefits and to plan for cost-of-living increases. Suppose the rate of change of the CPI can be modeled with the function

$$\frac{dC}{dt} = 3.087e^{0.0384t}$$

dollars per year, where C is the consumer price index and t is the number of years past 1990.
(a) Does the model for the rate reflect the fact that the Social Security Administration's data (actual and projected for selected years from 1995 to 2070) in the table show that the CPI is increasing? Explain.

(b) Use integration and the table's data point for 2005 to find the function that models the Social Security Administration's CPI figures.
(c) Find and interpret $C(35)$ and $C'(35)$.

Year	CPI	Year	CPI
1995	100.00	2035	465.98
2000	118.21	2040	566.94
2005	143.67	2045	689.77
2010	174.80	2050	839.21
2015	212.67	2055	1021.02
2020	258.74	2060	1242.23
2025	314.80	2065	1511.36
2030	383.00	2070	1838.81

Source: Social Security Administration

56. *Average annual wage* The following table shows the U.S. average annual wage in thousands of dollars for selected years from 2012 and projected to 2050. Suppose the rate of change of the U.S. average annual wage can be modeled by

$$\frac{dW}{dt} = 1.66e^{0.0395t}$$

thousand dollars per year, where t is the number of years past 2010.
(a) Use the data to find the average rates of change of the U.S. average annual wage from 2014 to 2016 and from 2016 to 2018. Which of these average rates better approximates the instantaneous rate in 2016?
(b) Use the data point from 2016 to find the function that models $W(t)$. Use three significant digits.

Year	Average Annual Wage ($ thousands)	Year	Average Annual Wage ($ thousands)
2012	44.6	2030	93.2
2014	48.6	2035	113.2
2016	53.3	2040	137.6
2018	58.7	2045	167.1
2020	63.7	2050	202.5
2025	76.8		

Source: Social Security Administration

OBJECTIVES

12.4

- To use integration to find total cost functions from information involving marginal cost
- To optimize profit, given information regarding marginal cost and marginal revenue
- To use integration to find national consumption functions from information about marginal propensity to consume and marginal propensity to save

Applications of the Indefinite Integral in Business and Economics

▊ | APPLICATION PREVIEW | ▊

If we know that the consumption of a nation is $9 trillion when income is $0 and the marginal propensity to save is 0.25, we can easily find the marginal propensity to consume and use integration to find the national consumption function. (See Example 6.)

In this section, we also use integration to derive total cost and profit functions from the marginal cost and marginal revenue functions. One of the reasons for the marginal approach in economics is that firms can observe marginal changes in real life. If they know the marginal cost and the total cost when a given quantity is sold, they can develop their total cost function.

Total Cost and Profit   We know that the marginal cost for a commodity is the derivative of the total cost function—that is, $\overline{MC} = C'(x)$, where $C(x)$ is the total cost function. Thus if we have the marginal cost function, we can integrate (or "reverse" the process of differentiation) to find the total cost. That is, $C(x) = \int \overline{MC}\, dx$.

If, for example, the marginal cost is $\overline{MC} = 4x + 3$, the total cost is given by

$$C(x) = \int \overline{MC}\, dx$$

$$= \int (4x + 3)\, dx$$

$$= 2x^2 + 3x + K$$

where K represents the constant of integration. We know that the total revenue is 0 if no items are produced, but the total cost may not be 0 if nothing is produced. The fixed costs accrue whether goods are produced or not. Thus the value of the constant of integration depends on the fixed costs FC of production.

Thus we cannot determine the total cost function from the marginal cost unless additional information is available to help us determine the fixed costs.

EXAMPLE   1   Total Cost

Suppose the marginal cost function for a month for a certain product is $\overline{MC} = 3x + 50$, where x is the number of units and cost is in dollars. If the fixed costs related to the product amount to $10,000 per month, find the total cost function for the month.

Solution
The total cost function is

$$C(x) = \int (3x + 50)\, dx$$

$$= \frac{3x^2}{2} + 50x + K$$

The constant of integration K is found by using the fact that $C(0) = FC = 10,000$. Thus

$$3(0)^2 + 50(0) + K = 10{,}000, \text{ so } K = 10{,}000$$

and the total cost for the month is given by

$$C(x) = \frac{3x^2}{2} + 50x + 10{,}000$$

EXAMPLE 2   **Cost**

Suppose monthly records show that the rate of change of the cost (that is, the marginal cost) for a product is $\overline{MC} = 3(2x + 25)^{1/2}$, where x is the number of units and cost is in dollars. If the fixed costs for the month are $11,125, what would be the total cost of producing 300 items per month?

Solution

We can integrate the marginal cost to find the total cost function.

$$
\begin{aligned}
C(x) = \int \overline{MC}\, dx &= \int 3(2x + 25)^{1/2}\, dx \\
&= 3 \cdot \left(\frac{1}{2}\right)\!\int (2x + 25)^{1/2}(2\ dx) \\
&= \left(\frac{3}{2}\right)\frac{(2x + 25)^{3/2}}{3/2} + K \\
&= (2x + 25)^{3/2} + K
\end{aligned}
$$

We can find K by using the fact that fixed costs are $11,125.

$$
\begin{aligned}
C(0) = 11{,}125 &= (25)^{3/2} + K \\
11{,}125 &= 125 + K, \ \text{ or } \ K = 11{,}000
\end{aligned}
$$

Thus the total cost function is

$$
C(x) = (2x + 25)^{3/2} + 11{,}000
$$

and the cost of producing 300 items per month is

$$
\begin{aligned}
C(300) &= (625)^{3/2} + 11{,}000 \\
&= 26{,}625 \ \text{(dollars)}
\end{aligned}
$$

It can be shown that the profit is usually maximized when $\overline{MR} = \overline{MC}$. To see that this does not always give us a maximum *positive* profit, consider the following facts concerning the manufacture of one particular product over the period of a month.

1. The marginal revenue is $\overline{MR} = 400 - 30x$.
2. The marginal cost is $\overline{MC} = 20x + 50$.
3. When 5 units are produced and sold, the total cost is $1750. The profit *should* be maximized when $\overline{MR} = \overline{MC}$, or when $400 - 30x = 20x + 50$. Solving for x gives $x = 7$. To see whether our profit is maximized when 7 units are produced and sold, let us examine the profit function.

The profit function is given by $P(x) = R(x) - C(x)$, where

$$
R(x) = \int \overline{MR}\, dx \ \text{ and } \ C(x) = \int \overline{MC}\, dx
$$

Integrating, we get

$$
R(x) = \int (400 - 30x)\, dx = 400x - 15x^2 + K
$$

but $R(0) = 0$ gives $K = 0$ for this total revenue function, so

$$
R(x) = 400x - 15x^2
$$

The total cost function is

$$
C(x) = \int (20x + 50)\, dx = 10x^2 + 50x + K
$$

The value of fixed cost can be determined by using the fact that 5 units cost $1750. This tells us that $C(5) = 1750 = 250 + 250 + K$, so $K = 1250$.

Thus the total cost is $C(x) = 10x^2 + 50x + 1250$. Thus, the profit is

$$P(x) = R(x) - C(x) = (400x - 15x^2) - (10x^2 + 50x + 1250)$$

Simplifying gives

$$P(x) = 350x - 25x^2 - 1250$$

We have found that $\overline{MR} = \overline{MC}$ if $x = 7$, and the graph of $P(x)$ is a parabola that opens downward, so profit is maximized at $x = 7$. But if $x = 7$, profit is

$$P(7) = 2450 - 1225 - 1250 = -25$$

That is, the production and sale of 7 items result in a loss of $25.

The preceding discussion indicates that even though setting $\overline{MR} = \overline{MC}$ may optimize profit, it does not indicate the level of profit or loss, as forming the profit function does.

If this firm is in a competitive market and its optimal level of production results in a loss, it has two options. It can continue to produce at the optimal level in the short run until it can lower or eliminate its fixed costs, even though it is losing money; or it can take a larger loss (its fixed cost) by stopping production. Producing 7 units causes a loss of $25 per month, and ceasing production results in a loss of $1250 (the fixed cost) per month. If this firm and many others like it cease production, the supply will be reduced, causing an eventual increase in price. The firm can resume production when the price increase indicates that it can make a profit.

EXAMPLE 3   Maximum Profit

Suppose that each week a company has a product with $\overline{MR} = 200 - 4x$, $\overline{MC} = 50 + 2x$, and the total cost of producing 10 units is $700. At what level should this company hold its weekly production in order to maximize profits?

Solution
Setting $\overline{MR} = \overline{MC}$, we can solve for the production level that maximizes profit.

$$200 - 4x = 50 + 2x$$
$$150 = 6x$$
$$25 = x$$

The level of production that should optimize profit is 25 units. To see whether 25 units maximizes profits or minimizes the losses (in the short run), we must find the total revenue and total cost functions.

$$R(x) = \int (200 - 4x)\, dx = 200x - 2x^2 + K$$
$$= 200x - 2x^2, \text{ because } K = 0$$
$$C(x) = \int (50 + 2x)\, dx = 50x + x^2 + K$$

We find K by noting that $C(x) = 700$ when $x = 10$.

$$700 = 50(10) + (10)^2 + K$$

so $K = 100$. Thus the cost is given by $C = C(x) = 50x + x^2 + 100$.

Thus the profit function is $P(x) = R(x) - C(x) = -3x^2 + 150x - 100$, whose graph is concave down, and the profit function is maximized at $x = 25$. The maximum weekly profit is $P(25) = \$1775$.

Calculator Note   If it is difficult to solve $\overline{MC} = \overline{MR}$ analytically, we can use a graphing calculator to solve this equation by finding the point of intersection of the graphs of $\overline{MC}$ and $\overline{MR}$. We may also be able to integrate $\overline{MC}$ and $\overline{MR}$ to find the functions $C(x)$ and $R(x)$ and then use a graphing calculator to graph them. From the graphs of $C(x)$ and $R(x)$ we can learn about these functions—and hence about profit.

EXAMPLE 4   **Cost, Revenue, and Profit**

Suppose that $\overline{MC} = 1.01(x + 190)^{0.01}$ and $\overline{MR} = (1/\sqrt{2x + 1}) + 2$, where x is the number of thousands of units and both revenue and cost are in thousands of dollars. Suppose further that fixed costs are $100,236 and that production is limited to at most 180 thousand units.

(a) Determine $C(x)$ and $R(x)$ and graph them to determine whether a profit can be made.

(b) Estimate the level of production that yields maximum profit, and find the maximum profit.

Solution

(a) $C(x) = \displaystyle\int \overline{MC}\ dx = \int 1.01(x + 190)^{0.01}\ dx$

$$= 1.01\frac{(x + 190)^{1.01}}{1.01} + K$$

When we say that fixed costs equal $100,236, we mean $C(0) = 100.236$.

$$100.236 = C(0) = (190)^{1.01} + K$$
$$100.236 = 200.236 + K$$
$$-100 = K$$

Thus $C(x) = (x + 190)^{1.01} - 100$.

$$R(x) = \int \overline{MR}\ dx = \int [(2x + 1)^{-1/2} + 2]dx$$

$$= \frac{1}{2}\int (2x + 1)^{-1/2}(2\ dx) + \int 2\ dx$$

$$= \frac{1}{2}\left[\frac{(2x + 1)^{1/2}}{1/2}\right] + 2x + K$$

$R(0) = 0$ means

$$0 = R(0) = (1)^{1/2} + 0 + K, \quad \text{or} \quad K = -1$$

Thus $R(x) = (2x + 1)^{1/2} + 2x - 1$.

The graphs of $C(x)$ and $R(x)$ are shown in Figure 12.8. (The x-range is chosen to include the production range from 0 to 180 (thousand) units. The y-range is chosen to extend beyond fixed costs of about 100 thousand dollars.)

From the figure we see that a profit can be made as long as the number of units sold exceeds about 95 (thousand). We could locate this break even value more precisely by using INTERSECT.

(b) From the graph we also see that $R(x) - C(x) = P(x)$ is at its maximum at the right edge of the graph. Because production is limited to at most 180 thousand units, profit will be maximized when $x = 180$ and the maximum profit is

$$P(180) = R(180) - C(180)$$
$$= [(361)^{1/2} + 360 - 1] - [(370)^{1.01} - 100]$$
$$\approx 85.46 \ \text{(thousand dollars)}$$

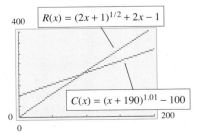

Figure 12.8

✓ CHECKPOINT

1. True or false:
   (a) If $C(x) = \int \overline{MC}\, dx$, then the constant of integration equals the fixed costs.
   (b) If $R(x) = \int \overline{MR}\, dx$, then the constant of integration equals 0.

2. Find $C(x)$ if $\overline{MC} = \dfrac{100}{\sqrt{x+1}}$ and fixed costs are $8000.

National Consumption and Savings

The consumption function is one of the basic ingredients in a larger discussion of how an economy can have persistent high unemployment or persistent high inflation. This study is often called **Keynesian analysis,** after its founder John Maynard Keynes (pronounced "canes").

If C represents national consumption (in trillions of dollars), then a **national consumption function** has the form $C = f(y)$, where y is disposable national income (also in trillions of dollars). The **marginal propensity to consume** is the derivative of the national consumption function with respect to y, or $dC/dy = f'(y)$. For example, suppose that

$$C = f(y) = 0.8y + 6$$

is a national consumption function; then the marginal propensity to consume is $f'(y) = 0.8$.

If we know the marginal propensity to consume, we can integrate with respect to y to find national consumption:

$$C = \int f'(y)\, dy = f(y) + K$$

We can find the unique national consumption function if we have additional information to help us determine the value of K, the constant of integration.

EXAMPLE 5   National Consumption

If consumption is $6 trillion when disposable income is $0, and if the marginal propensity to consume is $dC/dy = 0.3 + 0.4/\sqrt{y}$, find the national consumption function.

Solution
If

$$\frac{dC}{dy} = 0.3 + \frac{0.4}{\sqrt{y}}$$

then

$$C = \int \left(0.3 + \frac{0.4}{\sqrt{y}}\right) dy$$

$$= \int (0.3 + 0.4y^{-1/2})\, dy$$

$$= 0.3y + 0.4\,\frac{y^{1/2}}{1/2} + K = 0.3y + 0.8y^{1/2} + K$$

Now, if $C = 6$ when $y = 0$, then $6 = 0.3(0) + 0.8\sqrt{0} + K$. Thus the constant of integration is $K = 6$, and the consumption function is

$$C = 0.3y + 0.8\sqrt{y} + 6 \quad \text{(trillions of dollars)}$$

If S represents national savings, we can assume that the disposable national income is given by $y = C + S$, or $S = y - C$. Then the **marginal propensity to save** is $dS/dy = 1 - dC/dy$.

EXAMPLE 6   Consumption and Savings | APPLICATION PREVIEW |

If the consumption is $9 trillion when income is $0, and if the marginal propensity to save is 0.25, find the consumption function.

Solution

If $dS/dy = 0.25$, then $0.25 = 1 - dC/dy$, or $dC/dy = 0.75$. Thus

$$C = \int 0.75 \, dy = 0.75y + K$$

If $C = 9$ when $y = 0$, then $9 = 0.75(0) + K$, or $K = 9$. Then the consumption function is $C = 0.75y + 9$ (trillions of dollars). ∎

✓ CHECKPOINT

3. If the marginal propensity to save is

$$\frac{dS}{dy} = 0.7 - \frac{0.4}{\sqrt{y}}$$

find the marginal propensity to consume.

4. Find the national consumption function if the marginal propensity to consume is

$$\frac{dC}{dy} = \frac{1}{\sqrt{y+4}} + 0.2$$

and national consumption is $6.8 trillion when disposable income is $0.

✓ CHECKPOINT ANSWERS

1. (a) False. $C(0)$ equals the fixed costs. It may or may not be the constant of integration.
   (b) False. We use $R(0) = 0$ to determine the constant of integration, but it may be nonzero.

2. $C(x) = 200\sqrt{x+1} + 7800$

3. $\dfrac{dC}{dy} = 1 - \dfrac{dS}{dy} = 0.3 + \dfrac{0.4}{\sqrt{y}}$

4. $C(y) = 2\sqrt{y+4} + 0.2y + 2.8$.

| EXERCISES | 12.4

TOTAL COST AND PROFIT

In Problems 1–12, cost, revenue, and profit are in dollars and x is the number of units.

1. If the daily marginal cost for a product is $\overline{MC} = 2x + 100$, with fixed costs amounting to $200, find the total cost function for each day.

2. If the monthly marginal cost for a product is $\overline{MC} = x + 30$ and the related fixed costs are $5000, find the total cost function for the month.

3. If the marginal cost for a product is $\overline{MC} = 4x + 2$ and the production of 10 units results in a total cost of $300, find the total cost function.

4. If the marginal cost for a product is $\overline{MC} = 3x + 50$ and the total cost of producing 20 units is $2000, find the total cost function.

5. If the marginal cost for a product is $\overline{MC} = 4x + 40$ and the total cost of producing 25 units is $3000, find the cost of producing 30 units.

6. If the marginal cost for producing a product is $\overline{MC} = 5x + 10$, with a fixed cost of $800, find the cost of producing 20 units.

7. A firm knows that its marginal cost for a product is $\overline{MC} = 3x + 20$, that its marginal revenue is $\overline{MR} = 44 - 5x$, and that the cost of production of 80 units is $11,400.
   (a) Find the optimal level of production.
   (b) Find the profit function.
   (c) Find the profit or loss at the optimal level.

8. A certain firm's marginal cost for a product is $\overline{MC} = 6x + 60$, its marginal revenue is $\overline{MR} = 180 - 2x$, and its total cost of production of 10 items is $1000.
   (a) Find the optimal level of production.
   (b) Find the profit function.
   (c) Find the profit or loss at the optimal level of production.
   (d) Should production be continued for the short run?
   (e) Should production be continued for the long run?

9. Suppose that the marginal revenue for a product is $\overline{MR} = 900$ and the marginal cost is $\overline{MC} = 30\sqrt{x+4}$, with a fixed cost of $1000.
    (a) Find the profit or loss from the production and sale of 5 units.
    (b) How many units will result in a maximum profit?
10. Suppose that the marginal cost for a product is $\overline{MC} = 60\sqrt{x+1}$ and its fixed cost is $340.00. If the marginal revenue for the product is $\overline{MR} = 80x$, find the profit or loss from production and sale of
    (a) 3 units.   (b) 8 units.
11. The average cost of a product changes at the rate

$$\overline{C}'(x) = -6x^{-2} + 1/6$$

and the average cost of 6 units is $10.00.
    (a) Find the average cost function.
    (b) Find the average cost of 12 units.
12. The average cost of a product changes at the rate

$$\overline{C}'(x) = \frac{-10}{x^2} + \frac{1}{10}$$

and the average cost of 10 units is $20.00.
    (a) Find the average cost function.
    (b) Find the average cost of 20 units.
13. Suppose that marginal cost for a certain product is given by $\overline{MC} = 1.05(x+180)^{0.05}$ and marginal revenue is given by $\overline{MR} = (1/\sqrt{0.5x+4}) + 2.8$, where x is in thousands of units and both revenue and cost are in thousands of dollars. Fixed costs are $200,000 and production is limited to at most 200 thousand units.
    (a) Find $C(x)$ and $R(x)$.
    (b) Graph $C(x)$ and $R(x)$ to determine whether a profit can be made.
    (c) Determine the level of production that yields maximum profit, and find the maximum profit (or minimum loss).
14. Suppose that the marginal cost for a certain product is given by $\overline{MC} = 1.02(x+200)^{0.02}$ and marginal revenue is given by $\overline{MR} = (2/\sqrt{4x+1}) + 1.75$, where x is in thousands of units and revenue and cost are in thousands of dollars. Suppose further that fixed costs are $150,000 and production is limited to at most 200 thousand units.
    (a) Find $C(x)$ and $R(x)$.
    (b) Graph $C(x)$ and $R(x)$ to determine whether a profit can be made.
    (c) Determine what level of production yields maximum profit, and find the maximum profit (or minimum loss).

NATIONAL CONSUMPTION AND SAVINGS

15. If consumption is $7 trillion when disposable income is $0 and if the marginal propensity to consume is 0.80, find the national consumption function (in trillions of dollars).

16. If national consumption is $9 trillion when income is $0 and if the marginal propensity to consume is 0.30, what is consumption when disposable income is $20 trillion?
17. If consumption is $8 trillion when income is $0 and if the marginal propensity to consume is

$$\frac{dC}{dy} = 0.3 + \frac{0.2}{\sqrt{y}}$$

find the national consumption function.
18. If consumption is $5 trillion when disposable income is $0 and if the marginal propensity to consume is

$$\frac{dC}{dy} = 0.4 + \frac{0.3}{\sqrt{y}}$$

find the national consumption function.
19. If consumption is $6 trillion when disposable income is $0 and if the marginal propensity to consume is

$$\frac{dC}{dy} = \frac{1}{\sqrt{y+1}} + 0.4$$

find the national consumption function.
20. If consumption is $5.8 trillion when disposable income is $0 and if the marginal propensity to consume is

$$\frac{dC}{dy} = \frac{1}{\sqrt{2y+9}} + 0.8$$

find the national consumption function.
21. Suppose that the marginal propensity to consume is

$$\frac{dC}{dy} = 0.7 - e^{-2y}$$

and that consumption is $5.65 trillion when disposable income is $0. Find the national consumption function.
22. Suppose that the marginal propensity to consume is

$$\frac{dC}{dy} = 0.04 + \frac{\ln(y+1)}{y+1}$$

and that consumption is $6.04 trillion when disposable income is $0. Find the national consumption function.
23. Suppose that the marginal propensity to save is

$$\frac{dS}{dy} = 0.15$$

and that consumption is $5.15 trillion when disposable income is $0. Find the national consumption function.
24. Suppose that the marginal propensity to save is

$$\frac{dS}{dy} = 0.22$$

and that consumption is $8.6 trillion when disposable income is $0. Find the national consumption function.
25. Suppose that the marginal propensity to save is

$$\frac{dS}{dy} = 0.2 - \frac{1}{\sqrt{3y+7}}$$

and that consumption is $6 trillion when disposable income is $0. Find the national consumption function.

26. If consumption is $3 trillion when disposable income is $0 and if the marginal propensity to save is

$$\frac{dS}{dy} = 0.2 + e^{-1.5y}$$

find the national consumption function.

Differential Equations

- To show that a function is the solution to a differential equation
- To use integration to find the general solution to a differential equation
- To find particular solutions to differential equations using given conditions
- To solve separable differential equations
- To solve applied problems involving separable differential equations

APPLICATION PREVIEW

Carbon-14 dating, used to determine the age of fossils, is based on three facts. First, the half-life of carbon-14 is 5730 years. Second, the amount of carbon-14 in any living organism is essentially constant. Third, when an organism dies, the rate of change of carbon-14 in the organism is proportional to the amount present. If y represents the amount of carbon-14 present in the organism, then we can express the rate of change of carbon-14 by the differential equation

$$\frac{dy}{dt} = ky$$

where k is a constant and t is time in years. In this section, we study methods that allow us to find a function y that satisfies this differential equation, and then we use that function to date a fossil. (See Example 6.)

Recall that we introduced the derivative as an instantaneous rate of change and denoted the instantaneous rate of change of y with respect to time as dy/dt. For many growth or decay processes, such as carbon-14 decay, the rate of change of the amount of a substance with respect to time is proportional to the amount present. As we noted above, this can be represented by the equation

$$\frac{dy}{dt} = ky \quad (k = \text{constant})$$

An equation of this type, where y is an unknown function of x or t, is called a **differential equation** because it contains derivatives (or differentials). In this section, we restrict ourselves to differential equations where the highest derivative present in the equation is the first derivative. These differential equations are called **first-order differential equations.** Examples are

$$f'(x) = \frac{1}{x+1}, \quad \frac{dy}{dt} = 2t, \text{ and } x\,dy = (y+1)\,dx$$

Solution of Differential Equations   The solution to a differential equation is a function [say $y = f(x)$] that, when used in the differential equation, results in an identity.

EXAMPLE 1   Differential Equation

Show that $y = 4e^{-5t}$ is a solution to $dy/dt + 5y = 0$.

Solution

We must show that substituting $y = 4e^{-5t}$ into the equation $dy/dt + 5y = 0$ results in an identity:

$$\frac{d}{dt}(4e^{-5t}) + 5(4e^{-5t}) = 0$$

$$-20e^{-5t} + 20e^{-5t} = 0$$

$$0 = 0$$

Thus $y = 4e^{-5t}$ is a solution.

Now that we know what it means for a function to be a solution to a differential equation, let us consider how to find solutions.

The most elementary differential equations are of the form

$$\frac{dy}{dx} = f(x)$$

where $f(x)$ is a continuous function. These equations are elementary to solve because the solutions are found by integration:

$$y = \int f(x)\, dx$$

EXAMPLE 2   Solving a Differential Equation

Find the solution of

$$f'(x) = \frac{1}{x+1}$$

Solution

The solution is

$$f(x) = \int f'(x)\, dx = \int \frac{1}{x+1}\, dx = \ln |x+1| + C$$

The solution in Example 2, $f(x) = \ln |x+1| + C$, is called the **general solution** because every solution to the equation has this form, and different values of C give different **particular solutions**. Figure 12.9 shows the graphs of several members of the family of solutions to this differential equation. (We cannot, of course, show all of them.)

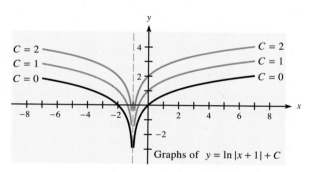

Figure 12.9

Graphs of $y = \ln |x+1| + C$

We can find a particular solution to a differential equation when we know that the solution must satisfy additional conditions, such as **initial conditions** or **boundary conditions.** For instance, to find the particular solution to

$$f'(x) = \frac{1}{x+1} \quad \text{with the condition that} \quad f(-2) = 2$$

we use $f(-2) = 2$ in the general solution, $f(x) = \ln |x+1| + C$.

$$2 = f(-2) = \ln |-2+1| + C$$
$$2 = \ln |-1| + C \text{ so } C = 2$$

Thus the particular solution is

$$f(x) = \ln |x+1| + 2$$

and is shown in Figure 12.9 with $C = 2$.

We frequently denote the value of the solution function $y = f(t)$ at the initial time $t = 0$ as $y(0)$ instead of $f(0)$.

✓ CHECKPOINT

1. Given $f'(x) = 2x - [1/(x + 1)]$, $f(0) = 4$,
   (a) find the general solution to the differential equation.
   (b) find the particular solution that satisfies $f(0) = 4$.

Just as we can find the differential of both sides of an equation, we can find the solution to a differential equation of the form

$$g(y)\, dy = f(x)\, dx$$

by integrating both sides.

EXAMPLE 3   Differential Equation with a Boundary Condition

Solve $3y^2\, dy = 2x\, dx$, if $y(1) = 2$.

Solution
We find the general solution by integrating both sides.

$$\int 3y^2\, dy = \int 2x\, dx$$
$$y^3 + C_1 = x^2 + C_2$$
$$y^3 = x^2 + C, \qquad \text{where } C = C_2 - C_1$$

By using $y(1) = 2$, we can find C.

$$2^3 = 1^2 + C$$
$$7 = C$$

Thus the particular solution is given implicitly by

$$y^3 = x^2 + 7$$

Calculator Note We can use a graphing calculator to help solve a differential equation of the form $\dfrac{dy}{dx} = f(x)$, with boundary conditions. After integrating to get $y = F(x) + C$, we can use SOLVER with the known x-value and corresponding y-value to find C. The general solution to $\dfrac{dy}{dx} = 2x - 4$ is $y = x^2 - 4x + C$. The value of C that satisfies the boundary condition $y = 8$ when $x = -1$ is found to be 3, as shown in Figure 12.10; thus the particular solution is $y = x^2 - 4x + 3$. Details can be found in Appendix A, Section 12.5.

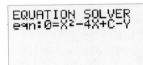

Figure 12.10

Separable Differential Equations

It is frequently necessary to change the form of a differential equation before it can be solved by integrating both sides.
For example, the equation

$$\frac{dy}{dx} = y^2$$

cannot be solved by simply integrating both sides of the equation with respect to x because we cannot evaluate $\int y^2\, dx$.

However, we can multiply both sides of $dy/dx = y^2$ by dx/y^2 to obtain an equation that has all terms containing y on one side of the equation and all terms containing x on the other side. That is, we obtain

$$\frac{dy}{y^2} = dx$$

Separable Differential Equations

When a differential equation can be equivalently expressed in the form

$$g(y)\, dy = f(x)\, dx$$

we say that the equation is **separable**.
  The solution of a separable differential equation is obtained by integrating both sides of the equation after the variables have been separated.

EXAMPLE 4 Separable Differential Equation

Solve the differential equation

$$(x^2 y + x^2)\, dy = x^3\, dx$$

Solution
To write the equation in separable form, we first factor x^2 from the left side and divide both sides by it.

$$x^2(y + 1)\, dy = x^3\, dx$$
$$(y + 1)\, dy = \frac{x^3}{x^2}\, dx$$

The equation is now separated, so we integrate both sides.

$$\int (y + 1)\, dy = \int x\, dx$$
$$\frac{y^2}{2} + y + C_1 = \frac{x^2}{2} + C_2$$

This equation, as well as the equation

$$y^2 + 2y - x^2 = C, \quad \text{where} \quad C = 2(C_2 - C_1)$$

gives the solution implicitly.
  Note that we need not write both C_1 and C_2 when we integrate because it is always possible to combine the two constants into one. ∎

EXAMPLE 5 Separable Differential Equation

Solve the differential equation

$$\frac{dy}{dt} = ky \quad (k = \text{constant})$$

Solution
To solve the equation, we write it in separated form and integrate both sides:

$$\frac{dy}{y} = k\, dt \;\Rightarrow\; \int \frac{dy}{y} = \int k\, dt \;\Rightarrow\; \ln |y| = kt + C_1$$

Assuming that $y > 0$ and writing this equation in exponential form gives

$$y = e^{kt + C_1}$$
$$y = e^{kt} \cdot e^{C_1} = Ce^{kt}, \quad \text{where } C = e^{C_1}$$

This solution,

$$y = Ce^{kt}$$

is the general solution to the differential equation $dy/dt = ky$ because all solutions have this form, with different values of C giving different particular solutions. The case of $y < 0$ is covered by values of $C < 0$. ∎

✓ CHECKPOINT

2. True or false:
   (a) The general solution to $dy = (x/y)\,dx$ can be found from
   $$\int y\,dy = \int x\,dx$$
   (b) The first step in solving $dy/dx = -2xy^2$ is to separate it.
   (c) The equation $dy/dx = -2xy^2$ separates as $y^2\,dy = -2x\,dx$.
3. Suppose that $(xy + x)(dy/dx) = x^2y + y$.
   (a) Separate this equation.   (b) Find the general solution.

In many applied problems that can be modeled with differential equations, we know conditions that allow us to obtain a particular solution.

Applications of Differential Equations   We now consider two applications that can be modeled by differential equations. These are radioactive decay and one-container mixture problems (as a model for drugs in an organ).

EXAMPLE 6   **Carbon-14 Dating | APPLICATION PREVIEW |**

When an organism dies, the rate of change of the amount of carbon-14 present is proportional to the amount present and is represented by the differential equation

$$\frac{dy}{dt} = ky$$

where y is the amount present, k is a constant, and t is time in years. If we denote the initial amount of carbon-14 in an organism as y_0, then $y = y_0$ represents the amount present at time $t = 0$ (when the organism dies). Suppose that anthropologists discover a fossil that contains 1% of the initial amount of carbon-14. Find the age of the fossil. (Recall that the half-life of carbon-14 is 5730 years.)

Solution
We must find a particular solution to

$$\frac{dy}{dt} = ky$$

subject to the fact that when $t = 0$, $y = y_0$, and we must determine the value of k on the basis of the half-life of carbon-14 ($t = 5730$ years, $y = \frac{1}{2}y_0$ units.) From Example 5, we know that the general solution to the differential equation $dy/dt = ky$ is $y = Ce^{kt}$. Using $y = y_0$ when $t = 0$, we obtain $y_0 = C$, so the equation becomes $y = y_0e^{kt}$. Then using $t = 5730$ and $y = \frac{1}{2}y_0$ in this equation gives

$$\frac{1}{2}y_0 = y_0e^{5730k} \quad \text{or} \quad 0.5 = e^{5730k}$$

Rewriting this equation in logarithmic form and then solving for k, we get

$$\ln(0.5) = 5730k$$
$$-0.69315 \approx 5730k$$
$$-0.00012097 \approx k$$

Thus the equation we seek is

$$y = y_0e^{-0.00012097t}$$

Using the fact that $y = 0.01y_0$ when the fossil was discovered, we can find its age t by solving

$$0.01y_0 = y_0 e^{-0.00012097t} \quad \text{or} \quad 0.01 = e^{-0.00012097t}$$

Rewriting this in logarithmic form and then solving give

$$\ln (0.01) = -0.00012097t$$
$$-4.6051702 = -0.00012097t$$
$$38{,}069 \approx t$$

Thus the fossil is approximately 38,069 years old.

The differential equation $dy/dt = ky$, which describes the decay of radioactive substances in Example 6, also models the rate of growth of an investment that is compounded continuously and the rate of decay of purchasing power due to inflation.

Another application of differential equations comes from a group of applications called *one-container mixture problems*. In problems of this type, there is a substance whose amount in a container is changing with time, and the goal is to determine the amount of the substance at any time t. The differential equations that model these problems are of the following form:

$$\begin{bmatrix} \text{Rate of change} \\ \text{of the amount} \\ \text{of the substance} \end{bmatrix} = \begin{bmatrix} \text{Rate at which} \\ \text{the substance} \\ \text{enters the container} \end{bmatrix} - \begin{bmatrix} \text{Rate at which} \\ \text{the substance} \\ \text{leaves the container} \end{bmatrix}$$

We consider this application as it applies to the amount of a drug in an organ.

EXAMPLE 7   Drug in an Organ

A liquid carries a drug into an organ of volume 300 cubic centimeters at a rate of 5 cubic centimeters per second, where the liquid becomes well-mixed and then leaves the organ at the same rate. If the concentration of the drug in the entering liquid is 0.1 grams per cubic centimeter, and if x represents the amount of drug in the organ at any time t, then using the fact that the rate of change of the amount of the drug in the organ, dx/dt, equals the rate at which the drug enters minus the rate at which it leaves, we have

$$\frac{dx}{dt} = \left(\frac{5 \text{ cc}}{\text{s}} \right) \left(\frac{0.1 \text{ g}}{\text{cc}} \right) - \left(\frac{5 \text{ cc}}{\text{s}} \right) \left(\frac{x \text{g}}{300 \text{ cc}} \right)$$

or

$$\frac{dx}{dt} = 0.5 - \frac{x}{60} = \frac{30}{60} - \frac{x}{60} = \frac{30 - x}{60}, \text{ in grams per second}$$

Find the amount of the drug in the organ as a function of time t.

Solution

Multiplying both sides of the equation $\dfrac{dx}{dt} = \dfrac{30 - x}{60}$ by $\dfrac{dt}{(30 - x)}$ gives

$$\frac{dx}{30 - x} = \frac{1}{60}\, dt$$

The equation is now separated, so we can integrate both sides.

$$\int \frac{dx}{30 - x} = \int \frac{1}{60}\, dt$$

$$-\ln (30 - x) = \frac{1}{60}t + C_1 \quad (30 - x > 0)$$

$$\ln (30 - x) = -\frac{1}{60}t - C_1$$

Rewriting this in exponential form gives

$$30 - x = e^{-t/60 - C_1} = e^{-t/60} \cdot e^{-C_1}$$

Letting $C = e^{-C_1}$ yields

$$30 - x = Ce^{-t/60}$$
$$x = 30 - Ce^{-t/60}$$

so

and we have the desired function.

✓ CHECKPOINT ANSWERS

1. (a) $f(x) = \int \left(2x - \dfrac{1}{x+1} \right) dx = x^2 - \ln|x+1| + C$

    (b) $f(x) = x^2 - \ln|x+1| + 4$

2. (a) True

    (b) True

    (c) False. It separates as $dy/y^2 = -2x\, dx$.

3. (a) $\dfrac{y+1}{y}\, dy = \dfrac{x^2+1}{x}\, dx$ (b) $y + \ln|y| = \dfrac{x^2}{2} + \ln|x| + C$

| EXERCISES | 12.5

In Problems 1–4, show that the given function is a solution to the differential equation.

1. $y = x^2$; $4y - 2xy' = 0$
2. $y = x^3$; $3y - xy' = 0$
3. $y = 3x^2 + 1$; $2y\, dx - x\, dy = 2\, dx$
4. $y = 4x^3 + 2$; $3y\, dx - x\, dy = 6\, dx$

In Problems 5–10, use integration to find the general solution to each differential equation.

5. $dy = xe^{x^2+1}\, dx$
6. $dy = x^2 e^{x^3-1}\, dx$
7. $2y\, dy = 4x\, dx$
8. $4y\, dy = 4x^3\, dx$
9. $3y^2\, dy = (2x - 1)\, dx$
10. $4y^3\, dy = (3x^2 + 2x)\, dx$

In Problems 11–14, find the particular solution.

11. $y' = e^{x-3}$; $y(0) = 2$
12. $y' = e^{2x+1}$; $y(0) = e$
13. $dy = \left(\dfrac{1}{x} - x \right) dx$; $y(1) = 0$
14. $dy = \left(x^2 - \dfrac{1}{x+1} \right) dx$; $y(0) = \dfrac{1}{3}$

In Problems 15–28, find the general solution to the given differential equation.

15. $\dfrac{dy}{dx} = \dfrac{x^2}{y}$

16. $y^3\, dx = \dfrac{dy}{x^3}$

17. $dx = x^3 y\, dy$

18. $dy = x^2 y^3\, dx$

19. $dx = (x^2 y^2 + x^2)\, dy$

20. $dy = (x^2 y^3 + xy^3)\, dx$

21. $y^2\, dx = x\, dy$

22. $y\, dx = x\, dy$

23. $\dfrac{dy}{dx} = \dfrac{x}{y}$

24. $\dfrac{dy}{dx} = \dfrac{x^2 + x}{y + 1}$

25. $(x + 1)\dfrac{dy}{dx} = y$

26. $x^2 y\dfrac{dy}{dx} = y^2 + 1$

27. $(x^2 + 2)e^{y^2} dx = xy\, dy$

28. $e^{4x}(y + 1)\, dx + e^{2x}y\, dy = 0$

In Problems 29–36, find the particular solution to each differential equation.

29. $\dfrac{dy}{dx} = \dfrac{x^2}{y^3}$ when $x = 1, y = 1$

30. $\dfrac{dy}{dx} = \dfrac{x+1}{xy}$ when $x = 1, y = 3$

31. $2y^2\, dx = 3x^2\, dy$ when $x = 2, y = -1$

32. $(x + 1)\, dy = y^2\, dx$ when $x = 0, y = 2$

33. $x^2 e^{2y}\, dy = (x^3 + 1)\, dx$ when $x = 1, y = 0$

34. $y' = \dfrac{1}{xy}$ when $x = 1, y = 3$

35. $2xy\dfrac{dy}{dx} = y^2 + 1$ when $x = 1, y = 2$

36. $xe^y\, dx = (x + 1)\, dy$ when $x = 0, y = 0$

APPLICATIONS

37. *Allometric growth* If x and y are measurements of certain parts of an organism, then the rate of change of y with respect to x is proportional to the ratio of y to x. That is, if k is a constant, then these measurements satisfy

$$\dfrac{dy}{dx} = k\dfrac{y}{x}$$

which is referred to as an allometric law of growth. Solve this differential equation.

38. *Bimolecular chemical reactions* A bimolecular chemical reaction is one in which two chemicals react to form another substance. Suppose that one molecule of each of the two chemicals reacts to form two molecules of a new substance. If x represents the number

of molecules of the new substance at time t, then the rate of change of x is proportional to the product of the numbers of molecules of the original chemicals available to be converted. That is, if each of the chemicals initially contained A molecules, then

$$\frac{dx}{dt} = k(A - x)^2$$

where k is a constant. If 40% of the initial amount A is converted after 1 hour, how long will it be before 90% is converted?

Compound interest **In Problems 39 and 40, use the following information.**

When interest is compounded continuously, the rate of change of the amount x of the investment is proportional to the amount present. In this case, the proportionality constant is the annual interest rate r (as a decimal); that is,

$$\frac{dx}{dt} = rx$$

39. (a) If $10,000 is invested at 6%, compounded continuously, find an equation for the future value of the investment as a function of time t in years.
    (b) What is the future value of the investment after 1 year? After 5 years?
    (c) How long will it take for the investment to double?
40. (a) If $2000 is invested at 8%, compounded continuously, find an equation for the future value of the investment as a function of time t, in years.
    (b) How long will it take for the investment to double?
    (c) What will be the future value of this investment after 35 years?
41. *Investing* When the interest on an investment is compounded continuously, the investment grows at a rate that is proportional to the amount in the account, so that if the amount present is P, then

$$\frac{dP}{dt} = kP$$

where P is in dollars, t is in years, and k is a constant. If $100,000 is invested (when $t = 0$) and the amount in the account after 15 years is $211,700, find the function that gives the value of the investment as a function of t. What is the interest rate on this investment?
42. *Investing* When the interest on an investment is compounded continuously, the investment grows at a rate that is proportional to the amount in the account. If $20,000 is invested (when $t = 0$) and the amount in the account after 22 years is $280,264, find the function that gives the value of the investment as a function of t. What is the interest rate on this investment?
43. *Bacterial growth* Suppose that the growth of a certain population of bacteria satisfies

$$\frac{dy}{dt} = ky$$

where y is the number of organisms, t is the number of hours, and k is a constant. If initially there are 10,000 organisms and the number triples after 2 hours, how long will it be before the population reaches 100 times the original population?
44. *Bacterial growth* Suppose that, for a certain population of bacteria, growth occurs according to

$$\frac{dy}{dt} = ky \quad (t \text{ in hours, } k \text{ constant})$$

If the doubling rate depends on temperature, find how long it takes for the number of bacteria to reach 50 times the original number at each given temperature in parts (a) and (b).
    (a) At 90°F, the number doubles after 30 minutes ($\frac{1}{2}$ hour).
    (b) At 40°F, the number doubles after 3 hours.
45. *Sales and pricing* Suppose that in a certain company, the relationship between the price per unit p of its product and the weekly sales volume y, in thousands of dollars, is given by

$$\frac{dy}{dp} = -\frac{2}{5}\left(\frac{y}{p+8}\right)$$

Solve this differential equation if $y = 8$ when $p = $24.
46. *Sales and pricing* Suppose that a chain of auto service stations, Quick-Oil, Inc., has found that the relationship between its price p for an oil change and its monthly sales volume y, in thousands of dollars, is

$$\frac{dy}{dp} = -\frac{1}{2}\left(\frac{y}{p+5}\right)$$

Solve this differential equation if $y = 18$ when $p = $20.
47. *Half-life* A breeder reactor converts uranium-238 into an isotope of plutonium-239 at a rate proportional to the amount present at any time. After 10 years, 0.03% of the radioactivity has dissipated (that is, 0.9997 of the initial amount remains). Suppose that initially there is 100 pounds of this substance. Find the half-life.
48. *Radioactive decay* A certain radioactive substance has a half-life of 50 hours. Find how long it will take for 90% of the radioactivity to be dissipated if the amount of material x satisfies

$$\frac{dx}{dt} = kx \quad (t \text{ in hours, } k \text{ constant})$$

49. *Drug in an organ* Suppose that a liquid carries a drug into a 100-cc organ at a rate of 5 cc/s and leaves the organ at the same rate. Suppose that the concentration of the drug entering is 0.06 g/cc. If initially there is no drug in the organ, find the amount of drug in the organ as a function of time t.
50. *Drug in an organ* Suppose that a liquid carries a drug into a 250-cc organ at a rate of 10 cc/s and leaves the organ at the same rate. Suppose that the concentration

of the drug entering is 0.15 g/cc. Find the amount of drug in the organ as a function of time t if initially there is none in the organ.

51. ***Drug in an organ*** Suppose that a liquid carries a drug with concentration 0.1 g/cc into a 200-cc organ at a rate of 5 cc/s and leaves the organ at the same rate. If initially there is 10 g of the drug in the organ, find the amount of drug in the organ as a function of time t.

52. ***Drug in an organ*** Suppose that a liquid carries a drug with concentration 0.05 g/cc into a 150-cc organ at a rate of 6 cc/s and leaves at the same rate. If initially there is 1.5 g of drug in the organ, find the amount of drug in the organ as a function of time t.

53. ***Tumor volume*** Let V denote the volume of a tumor, and suppose that the growth rate of the tumor satisfies

$$\frac{dV}{dt} = 0.2Ve^{-0.1t}$$

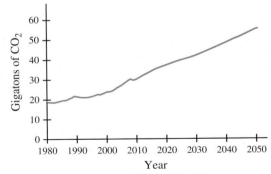

If the initial volume of the tumor is 1.86 units, find an equation for V as a function of t.

54. ***Gompertz curves*** The differential equation

$$\frac{dx}{dt} = x(a - b \ln x)$$

where x represents the number of objects at time t, and a and b are constants, is the model for Gompertz curves. Recall from Section 5.3, "Solutions of Exponential Equations," that Gompertz curves can be used to study growth or decline of populations, organizations, and revenue from sales of a product, as well as forecast equipment maintenance costs. Solve the differential equation to obtain the Gompertz curve formula

$$x = e^{a/b}e^{-ce^{-bt}}$$

55. ***Cell growth*** If V is the volume of a spherical cell, then in certain cell growth and for some fetal growth models, the rate of change of V is given by

$$\frac{dV}{dt} = kV^{2/3}$$

where k is a constant depending on the organism. If $V = 0$ when $t = 0$, find V as a function of t.

56. ***Atmospheric pressure*** The rate of change of atmospheric pressure P with respect to the altitude above sea level h is proportional to the pressure. That is,

$$\frac{dP}{dh} = kP \quad (k \text{ constant})$$

Suppose that the pressure at sea level is denoted by P_0, and at 18,000 ft the pressure is half what it is at sea level. Find the pressure, as a percent of P_0, at 25,000 ft.

57. ***Newton's law of cooling*** Newton's law of cooling (and warming) states that the rate of change of temperature $u = u(t)$ of an object is proportional to the temperature difference between the object and its surroundings, where T is the constant temperature of the surroundings. That is,

$$\frac{du}{dt} = k(u - T) \quad (k \text{ constant})$$

Suppose an object at 0°C is placed in a room where the temperature is 20°C. If the temperature of the object is 8°C after 1 hour, how long will it take for the object to reach 18°C?

58. ***Newton's law of cooling*** Newton's law of cooling can be used to estimate time of death. (Actually the estimate may be quite rough because cooling does not begin until metabolic processes have ceased.) Suppose a corpse is discovered at noon in a 70°F room and at that time the body temperature is 96.1°F. If at 1:00 P.M. the body temperature is 94.6°F, use Newton's law of cooling to estimate the time of death.

59. ***Fossil-fuel emissions*** Carbon in the atmosphere is due to carbon dioxide (CO_2) emissions from fossil-fuel burning and is considered to be a primary contributor to climate change. Using data from the Organization for Economic Cooperation and Development (OECD) for selected years from 1980 and projected to 2050, global CO_2 emissions can be modeled by the differential equation

$$\frac{dE}{dt} = 0.0164E$$

where t is the number of years past 1980 and E is global CO_2 emissions (in gigatons).
(a) Solve this differential equation and find a particular solution that satisfies $E(0) = 18.5$.
(b) Graph your solution and compare it with the following graph that shows OECD's data and projections.

Global CO₂ Emissions: 1980–2050

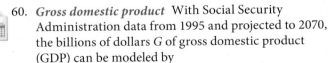

Source: OECD Environmental Outlook Baseline

60. ***Gross domestic product*** With Social Security Administration data from 1995 and projected to 2070, the billions of dollars G of gross domestic product (GDP) can be modeled by

$$\frac{dG}{dt} = 0.05317G, \quad G(15) = 12{,}145$$

where t is the number of years past 1990 (and thus $G(15)$ is the GDP in 2005).

(a) Find the particular solution to this differential equation.

(b) The Social Security Administration's forecast for the 2020 GDP is $27,683 billion. What does the model predict for the 2020 GDP?

61. ***Impact of inflation*** The impact of a 5% inflation rate on an $80,000-per-year pension can be severe. If P represents the purchasing power (in dollars) of an $80,000 pension, then the effect of a 5% inflation rate can be modeled by the differential equation

$$\frac{dP}{dt} = -0.05P, \quad P(0) = 80,000$$

where t is in years.

(a) Find the particular solution to this differential equation.

(b) Find the purchasing power after 15 years.

62. ***Alzheimer's disease*** The rate of change of the number of Americans over age 65 with Alzheimer's disease (in millions per year) for the years 2000 through 2050 can be modeled by the differential equation

$$\frac{dA}{dt} = 0.0228A$$

where t is the number of years after 2000 (*Source:* Alzheimer's Association).

(a) Given that in 2010, Alzheimer's disease affected 5.15 million Americans over age 65, find the particular solution to the differential equation. This solution models the number of Americans over age 65 with Alzheimer's disease.

(b) Use the model found in part (a) to project the number of Americans over age 65 with Alzheimer's disease in 2035.

Chapter 12 Summary & Review

KEY TERMS AND FORMULAS

Section 12.1

General antiderivative of $f'(x)$ (p. 739)
    $f(x) + C$
Indefinite integral (p. 739)
$$\int f(x)\, dx$$
Powers of x Formula (p. 740)
$$\int x^n\, dx = \frac{x^{n+1}}{n+1} + C \;(n \neq -1)$$

Integration Formulas (p. 741)
$$\int dx = x + C$$
$$\int cu(x)\, dx = c\int u(x)\, dx \quad (c = \text{a constant})$$
$$\int [u(x) \pm v(x)]\, dx = \int u(x)\, dx \pm \int v(x)\, dx$$

Section 12.2

Differentials (p. 746)
Power Rule (p. 747)

$$\int [u(x)]^n\, u'(x)\, dx = \frac{[u(x)]^{n+1}}{n+1} + C \;(n \neq -1)$$

Section 12.3

Exponential Formula (p. 755)
$$\int e^u\, u'\, dx = \int e^u\, du = e^u + C$$

Logarithmic Formula (p. 757)
$$\int \frac{u'}{u}\, dx = \int \frac{1}{u}\, du = \ln |u| + C$$

Section 12.4

Total cost (p. 764)
    $C(x) = \int \overline{MC}\, dx$
Total revenue (p. 765)
    $R(x) = \int \overline{MR}\, dx$
Profit (p. 766)
National consumption (p. 768)
$$C = \int f'(y)\, dy = \int \frac{dC}{dy}\, dy$$

Marginal propensity to consume (p. 768)
$$\frac{dC}{dy}$$
Marginal propensity to save (p. 768)
$$\frac{dS}{dy} = 1 - \frac{dC}{dy}$$

Section 12.5

Differential equations (p. 771)
    General solution
    Particular solution

First order (p. 771)
$$\frac{dy}{dx} = f(x) \Longrightarrow y = \int f(x)\, dx$$

Separable (p. 774)

$g(y)\, dy = f(x)\, dx \Rightarrow \int g(y)\, dy = \int f(x)\, dx$

Radioactive decay (p. 775)

$\dfrac{dy}{dt} = ky$

Drug in an organ (p. 776)

Rate = (rate in) − (rate out)

REVIEW EXERCISES

Sections 12.1–12.3

Evaluate the integrals in Problems 1–26.

1. $\int x^6\, dx$

2. $\int x^{1/2}\, dx$

3. $\int (12x^3 - 3x^2 + 4x + 5)\, dx$

4. $\int 7(x^2 - 1)^2\, dx$

5. $\int 7x(x^2 - 1)^2\, dx$

6. $\int (x^3 - 3x^2)^5(x^2 - 2x)\, dx$

7. $\int (x^3 + 4)^2 3x\, dx$

8. $\int 5x^2(3x^3 + 7)^6\, dx$

9. $\int \dfrac{x^2}{x^3 + 1}\, dx$

10. $\int \dfrac{x^2}{(x^3 + 1)^2}\, dx$

11. $\int \dfrac{x^2\, dx}{\sqrt[3]{x^3 - 4}}$

12. $\int \dfrac{x^2\, dx}{x^3 - 4}$

13. $\int \dfrac{x^3 + 1}{x^2}\, dx$

14. $\int \dfrac{x^3 - 3x + 1}{x - 1}\, dx$

15. $\int y^2 e^{y^3}\, dy$

16. $\int (3x - 1)^{12}\, dx$

17. $\int \dfrac{3x^2}{2x^3 - 7}\, dx$

18. $\int \dfrac{5\, dx}{e^{4x}}$

19. $\int (x^3 - e^{3x})\, dx$

20. $\int xe^{1+x^2}\, dx$

21. $\int \dfrac{6x^7}{(5x^8 + 7)^3}\, dx$

22. $\int \dfrac{7x^3}{\sqrt{1 - x^4}}\, dx$

23. $\int \left(\dfrac{e^{2x}}{2} + \dfrac{2}{e^{2x}}\right) dx$

24. $\int \left[x - \dfrac{1}{(x+1)^2}\right] dx$

25. (a) $\int (x^2 - 1)^4 x\, dx$

(b) $\int (x^2 - 1)^{10} x\, dx$

(c) $\int (x^2 - 1)^7 3x\, dx$

(d) $\int (x^2 - 1)^{-2/3} x\, dx$

26. (a) $\int \dfrac{2x\, dx}{x^2 - 1}$

(b) $\int \dfrac{2x\, dx}{(x^2 - 1)^2}$

(c) $\int \dfrac{3x\, dx}{\sqrt{x^2 - 1}}$

(d) $\int \dfrac{3x\, dx}{x^2 - 1}$

Section 12.5

In Problems 27–32, find the general solution to each differential equation.

27. $\dfrac{dy}{dt} = 4.6e^{-0.05t}$

28. $dy = (64 + 76x - 36x^2)\, dx$

29. $\dfrac{dy}{dx} = \dfrac{4x}{y - 3}$

30. $t\, dy = \dfrac{dt}{y + 1}$

31. $\dfrac{dy}{dx} = \dfrac{x}{e^y}$

32. $\dfrac{dy}{dt} = \dfrac{4y}{t}$

In Problems 33 and 34, find the particular solution to each differential equation.

33. $y' = \dfrac{x^2}{y + 1}$, $y(0) = 4$

34. $y' = \dfrac{2x}{1 + 2y}$, $y(2) = 0$

APPLICATIONS

Section 12.1

35. *Revenue* If the marginal revenue for a month for a product is $\overline{MR} = 0.06x + 12$ dollars per unit, find the total revenue from the sale of $x = 800$ units of the product.

36. *Productivity* Suppose that the rate of change of production of the average worker at a factory is given by

$$\dfrac{dp}{dt} = 27 + 24t - 3t^2, \quad 0 \le t \le 8$$

where p is the number of units the worker produces in t hours. How many units will the average worker produce in an 8-hour shift? (Assume that $p = 0$ when $t = 0$.)

Section 12.2

37. *Oxygen levels in water* The rate of change of the oxygen level (in mmol/l) per month in a body of water after an oil spill is given by

$$P'(t) = 400\left[\dfrac{5}{(t + 5)^2} - \dfrac{50}{(t + 5)^3}\right]$$

where t is the number of months after the spill. What function gives the oxygen level P at any time t if $P = 400$ mmol/l when $t = 0$?

38. *Bacterial growth* A population of bacteria grows at the rate

$$\dfrac{dp}{dt} = \dfrac{100{,}000}{(t + 100)^2}$$

where p is the population and t is time. If the population is 1000 when $t = 1$, write the equation that gives the size of the population at any time t.

Section 12.3

39. *Market share* The rate of change of the market share (as a percent) a firm expects for a new product is

$$\frac{dy}{dt} = 2.4e^{-0.04t}$$

where t is the number of months after the product is introduced.
   (a) Write the equation that gives the expected market share y at any time t. (Note that $y = 0$ when $t = 0$.)
   (b) What market share does the firm expect after 1 year?

40. *Revenue* If the marginal revenue for a product is

$$\overline{MR} = \frac{800}{x + 2}, \text{ find the total revenue function.}$$

Section 12.4

41. *Cost* The marginal cost for a product is $\overline{MC} = 6x + 4$ dollars per unit, and the cost of producing 100 items is $31,400.
   (a) Find the fixed costs.
   (b) Find the total cost function.

42. *Profit* Suppose a product has a daily marginal revenue $\overline{MR} = 46$ and a daily marginal cost $\overline{MC} = 30 + \frac{1}{5}x$, both in dollars per unit. If the daily fixed cost is $200, how many units will give maximum profit and what is the maximum profit?

43. *National consumption* If consumption is $8.5 trillion when disposable income is $0, and if the marginal propensity to consume is

$$\frac{dC}{dy} = \frac{1}{\sqrt{2y + 16}} + 0.6$$

   find the national consumption function.

44. *National consumption* Suppose that the marginal propensity to save is

$$\frac{dS}{dy} = 0.2 - 0.1e^{-2y}$$

and consumption is $7.8 trillion when disposable income is $0. Find the national consumption function.

Section 12.5

45. *Allometric growth* For many species of fish, the length L and weight W of a fish are related by

$$\frac{dW}{dL} = \frac{3W}{L}$$

The general solution to this differential equation expresses the allometric relationship between the length and weight of a fish. Find the general solution.

46. *Investment* When the interest on an investment is compounded continuously, the investment grows at a rate that is proportional to the amount in the account, so that if the amount present is P, then

$$\frac{dP}{dt} = kP \quad (k \text{ constant})$$

where P is in dollars, t is in years, and k is a constant.
   (a) Solve this differential equation to find the relationship.
   (b) Use properties of logarithms and exponential functions to write P as a function of t.
   (c) If $50,000 is invested (when $t = 0$) and the amount in the account after 10 years is $135,914, find the function that gives the value of the investment as a function of t.
   (d) In part (c), what does the value of k represent?

47. *Fossil dating* Radioactive beryllium is sometimes used to date fossils found in deep-sea sediment. The amount of radioactive material x satisfies

$$\frac{dx}{dt} = kx$$

Suppose that 10 units of beryllium are present in a living organism and that the half-life of beryllium is 4.6 million years. Find the age of a fossil if 20% of the original radioactivity is present when the fossil is discovered.

48. *Drug in an organ* Suppose that a liquid carries a drug into a 120-cc organ at a rate of 4 cc/s and leaves the organ at the same rate. If initially there is no drug in the organ and if the concentration of drug in the liquid is 3 g/cc, find the amount of drug in the organ as a function of time.

49. *Chemical mixture* A 300-gal tank initially contains a solution with 100 lb of a chemical. A mixture containing 2 lb/gal of the chemical enters the tank at 3 gal/min, and the well-stirred mixture leaves at the same rate. Find an equation that gives the amount of the chemical in the tank as a function of time. How long will it be before there is 500 lb of chemical in the tank?

Chapter 12 TEST

Evaluate the integrals in Problems 1–11.

1. $\int (6x^2 + 8x - 7)\, dx$

2. $\int (11 - 2x^3)dx$

3. $\int 5(x^2 - 1)dx$

4. $\int \left(4 + \sqrt{x} - \dfrac{1}{x^2}\right) dx$

5. $\int 6x^2(7 + 2x^3)^9 dx$

6. $\int 5x^2(4x^3 - 7)^9\, dx$

7. $\int (3x^2 - 6x + 1)^{-3}(2x - 2)\, dx$

8. $\int \left(e^x + \dfrac{5}{x} - 1\right) dx$

9. $\int \dfrac{s^3}{2s^4 - 5}\, ds$

10. $\int 100e^{-0.01x}\, dx$

11. $\int 5y^3 e^{2y^4 - 1}\, dy$

12. Evaluate $\int \dfrac{4x^2}{2x + 1}\, dx$. Use long division.

13. If $\int f(x)\, dx = 2x^3 - x + 5e^x + C$, find $f(x)$.

14. Find the general solution to $f'(x) = \dfrac{x^2}{3} - \dfrac{5}{8}$.

In Problems 15 and 16, find the particular solution to each differential equation.

15. $y' = 4x^3 + 3x^2$, if $y(0) = 4$

16. $\dfrac{dy}{dx} = e^{4x}$, if $y(0) = 2$

17. Find the general solution of the separable differential equation $\dfrac{dy}{dx} = x^3 y^2$.

18. Suppose the rate of growth of the population of a city is predicted to be

$$\frac{dp}{dt} = 2000t^{1.04}$$

where p is the population and t is the number of years past 2015. If the population in the year 2015 is 50,000, what is the predicted population in the year 2025?

19. Suppose that the marginal cost for x units of a product is $\overline{MC} = 4x + 50$, the marginal revenue is $\overline{MR} = 500$, and the cost of the production and sale of 10 units is $1000. What is the profit function for this product?

20. Suppose the marginal propensity to save is given by

$$\frac{dS}{dy} = 0.22 - \frac{0.25}{\sqrt{0.5y + 1}}$$

and national consumption is $6.6 trillion when disposable income is $0. Find the national consumption function.

21. A certain radioactive material has a half-life of 100 days. If the amount of material present, x, satisfies

$$\frac{dx}{dt} = kx$$

where t is in days and k is constant, how long will it take for 90% of the radioactivity to dissipate?

22. Suppose that a liquid carries a drug with concentration 0.1 g/cc into a 160-cc organ at the rate of 4 cc/sec and leaves at the same rate. Find the amount of drug in the organ as a function of time t, if initially there is none in the organ.

I. Employee Production Rate

The manager of a plant has been instructed to hire and train additional employees to manufacture a new product. She must hire a sufficient number of new employees so that within 30 days they will be producing 2500 units of the product each day.

Because a new employee must learn an assigned task, production will increase with training. Suppose that research on similar projects indicates that production increases with training according to the learning curve, so that for the average employee, the rate of production per day is given by

$$\frac{dN}{dt} = be^{-at}$$

where N is the number of units produced per day after t days of training and a and b are constants that depend on the project. Because of experience with a similar project, the manager expects the rate for this project to be

$$\frac{dN}{dt} = 2.5e^{-0.05t}$$

The manager tested her training program with 5 employees and learned that the average employee could produce 11 units per day after 5 days of training. On the basis of this information, she must decide how many employees to hire and begin to train so that a month from now they will be producing 2500 units of the product per day. She estimates that it will take her 10 days to hire the employees, and thus she will have 15 days remaining to train them. She also expects a 10% attrition rate during this period.

How many employees would you advise the plant manager to hire? Check your advice by answering the following questions.

1. Use the expected rate of production and the results of the manager's test to find the function relating N and t—that is, $N = N(t)$.
2. Find the number of units the average employee can produce after 15 days of training. How many such employees would be needed to maintain a production rate of 2500 units per day?
3. Explain how you would revise this last result to account for the expected 10% attrition rate. How many new employees should the manager hire?

II. Supply and Demand

If p is the price in dollars of a given commodity at time t, then we can think of price as a function of time. Similarly, the number of units demanded by consumers q_d at any time, and the number of units supplied by producers q_s at any time, may also be considered as functions of time as well as functions of price.

Both the quantity demanded and the quantity supplied depend not only on the price at the time, but also on the direction and rate of change that consumers and producers ascribe to prices. For example, even when prices are high, if consumers feel that prices are rising, the demand may rise. Similarly, if prices are low but producers feel they may go lower, the supply may rise.

If we assume that prices are determined in the marketplace by supply and demand, then the equilibrium price is the one we seek.

Suppose the supply and demand functions for a certain commodity in a competitive market are given, in hundreds of units, by

$$q_s = 30 + p + 5\frac{dp}{dt}$$

$$q_d = 51 - 2p + 4\frac{dp}{dt}$$

where dp/dt denotes the rate of change of the price with respect to time. If, at $t = 0$, the market equilibrium price is \$12, we can express the market equilibrium price as a function of time.

Our goals are as follows.

A. To express the market equilibrium price as a function of time.
B. To determine whether there is price stability in the marketplace for this item (that is, to determine whether the equilibrium price approaches a constant over time).

To achieve these goals, do the following.

1. Set the expressions for q_s and q_d equal to each other.
2. Solve this equation for $\dfrac{dp}{dt}$.
3. Write this equation in the form $f(p)\, dp = g(t)\, dt$.
4. Integrate both sides of this separated differential equation.
5. Solve the resulting equation for p in terms of t.
6. Use the fact that $p = 12$ when $t = 0$ to find C, the constant of integration, and write the market equilibrium price p as a function of time t.
7. Find $\lim\limits_{t \to \infty} p$, which gives the price we can expect this product to approach. If this limit is finite, then for this item there is price stability in the marketplace. If $p \to \infty$ as $t \to \infty$, then price will continue to increase until economic conditions change.

13

Definite Integrals: Techniques of Integration

We saw some applications of the indefinite integral in Chapter 12. In this chapter we define the definite integral and discuss a theorem and techniques that are useful in evaluating or approximating it. We will also see how it can be used in many interesting applications, such as consumer's and producer's surplus and total value, present value, and future value of continuous income streams. Improper integrals can be used to find the capital value of a continuous income stream.

The topics and some representative applications discussed in this chapter include the following.

Prerequisite Problem Type	For Section	Answer	Section for Review
Simplify: $\dfrac{1}{n^3}\left[\dfrac{n(n+1)(2n+1)}{6} - \dfrac{2n(n+1)}{2} + n\right]$	**13.1**	$\dfrac{2n^2 - 3n + 1}{6n^2}$	0.7 Fractions
(a) If $F(x) = \dfrac{x^4}{4} + 4x + C$, what is $F(4) - F(2)$? (b) If $F(x) = -\dfrac{1}{9}\ln\left(\dfrac{9 + \sqrt{81 - 9x^2}}{3x}\right)$ what is $F(3) - F(2)$?	**13.2** **13.5**	(a) 68 (b) $\dfrac{1}{9}\ln\left(\dfrac{3 + \sqrt{5}}{2}\right)$	1.2 Function notation
Find the limit: (a) $\displaystyle\lim_{n \to \infty} \dfrac{n^2 + n}{2n^2}$ (b) $\displaystyle\lim_{n \to \infty} \dfrac{2n^2 - 3n + 1}{6n^2}$ (c) $\displaystyle\lim_{b \to \infty}\left(1 - \dfrac{1}{b}\right)$ (d) $\displaystyle\lim_{b \to \infty}\left(\dfrac{-100{,}000}{e^{0.10b}} + 100{,}000\right)$	**13.1** **13.7**	(a) $\frac{1}{2}$ (b) $\frac{1}{3}$ (c) 1 (d) 100,000	9.2 Limits at infinity
Find the derivative of $y = \ln x$.	**13.6**	$\dfrac{1}{x}$	11.1 Derivatives of logarithmic functions
Integrate: (a) $\int (x^3 + 4)dx$ (b) $\int x\sqrt{x^2 - 9}\,dx$ (c) $\int e^{2x}\,dx$	**13.2–13.7**	(a) $\dfrac{x^4}{4} + 4x + C$ (b) $\frac{1}{3}(x^2 - 9)^{3/2} + C$ (c) $\frac{1}{2}e^{2x} + C$	12.1, 12.2, 12.3 Integration

OBJECTIVES

13.1

- To use the sum of areas of rectangles to approximate the area under a curve
- To use Σ notation to denote sums
- To find the exact area under a curve

Area Under a Curve

▮ | APPLICATION PREVIEW | ▮

One way to find the accumulated production (such as the production of ore from a mine) over a period of time is to graph the rate of production as a function of time and find the area under the resulting curve over a specified time interval. For example, if a coal mine produces at a rate of 30 tons per day, the production over 10 days ($30 \cdot 10 = 300$) could be represented by the area under the line $y = 30$ between $x = 0$ and $x = 10$ (see Figure 13.1).

Using area to determine the accumulated production is very useful when the rate-of-production function varies at different points in time. For example, if the rate of production (in tons per day) is represented by

$$y = 100e^{-0.1x}$$

where x represents the number of days, then the area under the curve (and above the x-axis) from $x = 0$ to $x = 10$ represents the total production over the 10-day period (see Figure 13.2(a) and Example 1). In order to determine the accumulated production and to solve other types of problems, we need a method for finding areas under curves. That is the goal of this section.

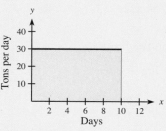

Figure 13.1

Area Under a Curve   To estimate the accumulated production for the example in the Application Preview, we approximate the area under the graph of the production rate function. We can find a rough approximation of the area under this curve by fitting two rectangles to the curve as shown in Figure 13.2(b). The area of the first rectangle is $5 \cdot 100 = 500$ square units, and the area of the second rectangle is $(10 - 5)[100e^{-0.1(5)}] \approx 303.27$ square units, so this rough approximation is 803.27 square units or 803.27 tons of ore. This approximation is clearly larger than the exact area under the curve. Why?

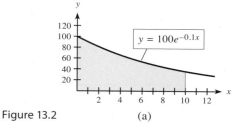
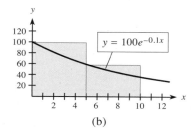
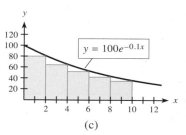

Figure 13.2   (a)   (b)   (c)

EXAMPLE 1   Ore Production | APPLICATION PREVIEW |

Find another, more accurate approximation of the tons of ore produced by approximating the area under the curve in Figure 13.2(a). Fit five rectangles with equal bases inside the area under the curve $y = 100e^{-0.1x}$, and use them to approximate the area under the curve from $x = 0$ to $x = 10$ (see Figure 13.2(c)).

Solution
Each of the five rectangles has base 2, and the height of each rectangle is the value of the function at the right-hand endpoint of the interval forming its base. Thus the areas of the rectangles are as follows.

Rectangle	Base	Height	Area = Base × Height
1	2	$100e^{-0.1(2)} \approx 81.87$	$2(81.87) = 163.74$
2	2	$100e^{-0.1(4)} \approx 67.03$	$2(67.03) = 134.06$
3	2	$100e^{-0.1(6)} \approx 54.88$	$2(54.88) = 109.76$
4	2	$100e^{-0.1(8)} \approx 44.93$	$2(44.93) = 89.86$
5	2	$100e^{-0.1(10)} \approx 36.79$	$2(36.79) = 73.58$

The area under the curve is approximately equal to

$$163.74 + 134.06 + 109.76 + 89.86 + 73.58 = 571$$

so approximately 571 tons of ore are produced in the 10-day period. The area is actually 632.12, to 2 decimal places (or 632.12 tons of ore), so the approximation 571 is smaller than the actual area but is much better than the one we obtained with just two rectangles. In general, if we use bases of equal width, the approximation of the area under a curve improves when more rectangles are used.

Suppose that we wish to find the area between the curve $y = 2x$ and the x-axis from $x = 0$ to $x = 1$ (see Figure 13.3). As we saw in Example 1, one way to approximate this area is to use the areas of rectangles whose bases are on the x-axis and whose heights are the vertical distances from points on their bases to the curve. We can divide the interval $[0, 1]$ into n equal subintervals and use them as the bases of n rectangles whose heights are determined by the curve (see Figure 13.4). The width of each of these rectangles is $1/n$. Using the function value at the right-hand endpoint of each subinterval as the height of the rectangle, we get n rectangles as shown in Figure 13.4. Because part of each rectangle lies above the curve, the sum of the areas of the rectangles will overestimate the area.

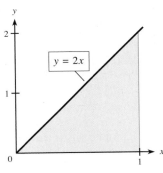

Figure 13.3

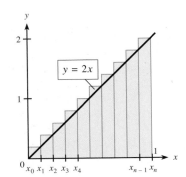

Figure 13.4

Then, with $y = f(x) = 2x$ and subinterval width $1/n$, the areas of the rectangles are as shown in the following table.

Rectangle	Base	Right Endpoint	Height	Area = Base × Height
1	$\dfrac{1}{n}$	$x_1 = \dfrac{1}{n}$	$f(x_1) = 2\left(\dfrac{1}{n}\right)$	$\dfrac{1}{n} \cdot \dfrac{2}{n} = \dfrac{2}{n^2}$
2	$\dfrac{1}{n}$	$x_2 = \dfrac{2}{n}$	$f(x_2) = 2\left(\dfrac{2}{n}\right)$	$\dfrac{1}{n} \cdot \dfrac{4}{n} = \dfrac{4}{n^2}$
3	$\dfrac{1}{n}$	$x_3 = \dfrac{3}{n}$	$f(x_3) = 2\left(\dfrac{3}{n}\right)$	$\dfrac{1}{n} \cdot \dfrac{6}{n} = \dfrac{6}{n^2}$
$\vdots$				
i	$\dfrac{1}{n}$	$x_i = \dfrac{i}{n}$	$f(x_i) = 2\left(\dfrac{i}{n}\right)$	$\dfrac{1}{n} \cdot \dfrac{2i}{n} = \dfrac{2i}{n^2}$
$\vdots$				
n	$\dfrac{1}{n}$	$x_n = \dfrac{n}{n}$	$f(x_n) = 2\left(\dfrac{n}{n}\right)$	$\dfrac{1}{n} \cdot \dfrac{2n}{n} = \dfrac{2n}{n^2}$

Note that $2i/n^2$ gives the area of the ith rectangle for *any* value of i. Thus for any value of n, this area can be approximated by the sum

$$A \approx \frac{2}{n^2} + \frac{4}{n^2} + \frac{6}{n^2} + \cdots + \frac{2i}{n^2} + \cdots + \frac{2n}{n^2}$$

In particular, we have the following approximations of this area for specific values of n (the number of rectangles).

$$n = 5: \quad A \approx \frac{2}{25} + \frac{4}{25} + \frac{6}{25} + \frac{8}{25} + \frac{10}{25} = \frac{30}{25} = 1.20$$

$$n = 10: \quad A \approx \frac{2}{100} + \frac{4}{100} + \frac{6}{100} + \cdots + \frac{20}{100} = \frac{110}{100} = 1.10$$

$$n = 100: \quad A \approx \frac{2}{10{,}000} + \frac{4}{10{,}000} + \frac{6}{10{,}000} + \cdots + \frac{200}{10{,}000}$$

$$= \frac{10{,}100}{10{,}000} = 1.01$$

Figure 13.5 shows the rectangles associated with each of these approximations ($n = 5$, 10, and 100) to the area under $y = 2x$ from $x = 0$ to $x = 1$. For larger n, the rectangles closely approximate the area under the curve.

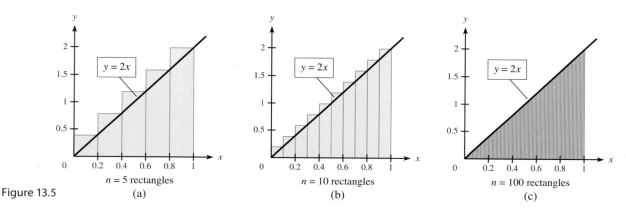

Figure 13.5

(a) $n = 5$ rectangles
(b) $n = 10$ rectangles
(c) $n = 100$ rectangles

We can find this sum for any n more easily if we observe that the common denominator is n^2 and that the numerator is twice the sum of the first n terms of an arithmetic sequence with first term 1 and last term n. As you may recall from Section 6.1, "Simple Interest; Sequences," the first n terms of this arithmetic sequence add to $n(n + 1)/2$. Thus the area is approximated by

$$A \approx \frac{2(1 + 2 + 3 + \cdots + n)}{n^2} = \frac{2[n(n + 1)/2]}{n^2} = \frac{n + 1}{n}$$

Using this formula, we see the following.

$$n = 5: \quad A \approx \frac{5 + 1}{5} = \frac{6}{5} = 1.20$$

$$n = 10: \quad A \approx \frac{10 + 1}{10} = \frac{11}{10} = 1.10$$

$$n = 100: \quad A \approx \frac{100 + 1}{100} = \frac{101}{100} = 1.01$$

As Figure 13.5 indicated, as n gets larger, the number of rectangles increases, the area of each rectangle decreases, and the approximation becomes more accurate. If we let n increase without bound, the approximation approaches the exact area.

$$A = \lim_{n \to \infty} \frac{n + 1}{n} = \lim_{n \to \infty} \left(1 + \frac{1}{n}\right) = 1$$

We can see that this area is correct, for we are computing the area of a triangle with base 1 and height 2. The formula for the area of a triangle gives

$$A = \frac{1}{2}bh = \frac{1}{2} \cdot 1 \cdot 2 = 1$$

Summation Notation

A special notation exists that uses the Greek letter Σ (capital sigma) to express the sum of numbers or expressions. (We used sigma notation informally in Chapter 8, "Further Topics in Probability; Data Description.") We may indicate the sum of the n numbers $a_1, a_2, a_3, a_4, \dots, a_n$ by

$$\sum_{i=1}^{n} a_i = a_1 + a_2 + a_3 + \cdots + a_n$$

This may be read as "The sum of a_i as i goes from 1 to n." The subscript i in a_i is replaced first by 1, then by 2, then by 3, ... , until it reaches the value above the sigma. The i is called the **index of summation,** and it starts with the lower limit, 1, and ends with the upper limit, n. For example, if $x_1 = 2$, $x_2 = 3$, $x_3 = -1$, and $x_4 = -2$, then

$$\sum_{i=1}^{4} x_i = x_1 + x_2 + x_3 + x_4 = 2 + 3 + (-1) + (-2) = 2$$

The area of the triangle under $y = 2x$ that we discussed above was approximated by

$$A \approx \frac{2}{n^2} + \frac{4}{n^2} + \frac{6}{n^2} + \cdots + \frac{2i}{n^2} + \cdots + \frac{2n}{n^2}$$

Using **sigma notation,** we can write this sum as

$$A \approx \sum_{i=1}^{n} \left(\frac{2i}{n^2} \right)$$

Sigma notation allows us to represent the sums of the areas of the rectangles in an abbreviated fashion. Some formulas that simplify computations involving sums follow.

Sum Formulas

I. $\displaystyle\sum_{i=1}^{n} 1 = n$

II. $\displaystyle\sum_{i=1}^{n} cx_i = c \sum_{i=1}^{n} x_i$ $(c = \text{constant})$

III. $\displaystyle\sum_{i=1}^{n} (x_i + y_i) = \sum_{i=1}^{n} x_i + \sum_{i=1}^{n} y_i$

IV. $\displaystyle\sum_{i=1}^{n} i = \frac{n(n+1)}{2}$

V. $\displaystyle\sum_{i=1}^{n} i^2 = \frac{n(n+1)(2n+1)}{6}$

We have found that the area of the triangle discussed above was approximated by

$$A \approx \sum_{i=1}^{n} \frac{2i}{n^2}$$

We can use formulas II and IV to simplify this sum as follows.

$$\sum_{i=1}^{n} \frac{2i}{n^2} = \frac{2}{n^2} \sum_{i=1}^{n} i = \frac{2}{n^2} \left[\frac{n(n+1)}{2} \right] = \frac{n+1}{n}$$

Note that this is the same formula we obtained previously using other methods.

We can also use these sum formulas to evaluate a particular sum. For example,

$$\sum_{i=1}^{100}(2i^2 - 3) = \sum_{i=1}^{100}2i^2 - \sum_{i=1}^{100}3(1) \qquad \text{Formula III}$$

$$= 2\sum_{i=1}^{100}i^2 - 3\sum_{i=1}^{100}1 \qquad \text{Formula II}$$

$$= 2\left[\frac{100(101)(201)}{6}\right] - 3(100) \qquad \text{Formulas I and V with } n = 100$$

$$= 676{,}400$$

Areas and Summation Notation   The following example shows that we can find the area by evaluating the function at the left-hand endpoints of the subintervals.

EXAMPLE 2   Area Under a Curve

Use rectangles to find the area under $y = x^2$ (and above the x-axis) from $x = 0$ to $x = 1$.

Solution

We again divide the interval $[0, 1]$ into n equal subintervals of length $1/n$. If we evaluate the function at the left-hand endpoints of these subintervals to determine the heights of the rectangles, the sum of the areas of the rectangles will underestimate the area (see Figure 13.6). Thus we have the information shown in the following table.

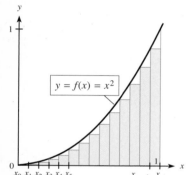

Figure 13.6

Rectangle	Base	Left Endpoint	Height	Area = Base × Height
1	$\dfrac{1}{n}$	$x_0 = 0$	$f(x_0) = 0$	$\dfrac{1}{n}\cdot 0 = 0$
2	$\dfrac{1}{n}$	$x_1 = \dfrac{1}{n}$	$f(x_1) = \dfrac{1}{n^2}$	$\dfrac{1}{n}\cdot\dfrac{1}{n^2} = \dfrac{1}{n^3}$
3	$\dfrac{1}{n}$	$x_2 = \dfrac{2}{n}$	$f(x_2) = \dfrac{4}{n^2}$	$\dfrac{1}{n}\cdot\dfrac{4}{n^2} = \dfrac{4}{n^3}$
4	$\dfrac{1}{n}$	$x_3 = \dfrac{3}{n}$	$f(x_3) = \dfrac{9}{n^2}$	$\dfrac{1}{n}\cdot\dfrac{9}{n^2} = \dfrac{9}{n^3}$
⋮				
i	$\dfrac{1}{n}$	$x_{i-1} = \dfrac{i-1}{n}$	$\dfrac{(i-1)^2}{n^2}$	$\dfrac{(i-1)^2}{n^3}$
⋮				
n	$\dfrac{1}{n}$	$x_{n-1} = \dfrac{n-1}{n}$	$\dfrac{(n-1)^2}{n^2}$	$\dfrac{(n-1)^2}{n^3}$

Thus: Area $= A \approx 0 + \dfrac{1}{n^3} + \dfrac{4}{n^3} + \dfrac{9}{n^3} + \cdots + \dfrac{(i-1)^2}{n^3} + \cdots + \dfrac{(n-1)^2}{n^3}$.

Note that $(i - 1)^2/n^3 = (i^2 - 2i + 1)/n^3$ gives the area of the ith rectangle for *any* value of i. The sum of these areas may be written as

$$S = \sum_{i=1}^{n}\frac{i^2 - 2i + 1}{n^3} = \frac{1}{n^3}\left(\sum_{i=1}^{n}i^2 - 2\sum_{i=1}^{n}i + \sum_{i=1}^{n}1\right) \qquad \text{Formulas II and III}$$

$$= \frac{1}{n^3}\left[\frac{n(n+1)(2n+1)}{6} - \frac{2n(n+1)}{2} + n\right] \qquad \text{Formulas V, IV, and I}$$

$$= \frac{2n^3 + 3n^2 + n}{6n^3} - \frac{n^2 + n}{n^3} + \frac{n}{n^3} = \frac{2n^2 - 3n + 1}{6n^2}$$

We can use this formula to find the approximate area (value of S) for different values of n.

$$\text{If } n = 10: \quad \text{Area} \approx S(10) = \frac{200 - 30 + 1}{600} = 0.285$$

$$\text{If } n = 100: \quad \text{Area} \approx S(100) = \frac{20{,}000 - 300 + 1}{60{,}000} = 0.328$$

Figure 13.7 shows the rectangles associated with each of these approximations.

As Figure 13.7 shows, the larger the value of n, the better the value of the sum approximates the exact area under the curve. If we let n increase without bound, we find the exact area.

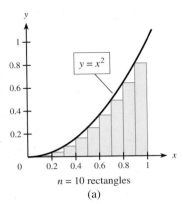

$n = 10$ rectangles
(a)

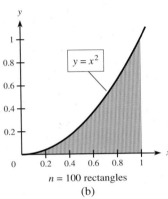

$n = 100$ rectangles
(b)

Figure 13.7

$$A = \lim_{n \to \infty}\left(\frac{2n^2 - 3n + 1}{6n^2}\right) = \lim_{n \to \infty}\left(\frac{2 - \dfrac{3}{n} + \dfrac{1}{n^2}}{6}\right) = \frac{1}{3}$$

Note that the approximations with $n = 10$ and $n = 100$ are less than $\frac{1}{3}$. This is because all the rectangles are *under* the curve (see Figure 13.7).

Thus we see that we can determine the area under a curve $y = f(x)$ from $x = a$ to $x = b$ by dividing the interval $[a, b]$ into n equal subintervals of width $(b - a)/n$ and evaluating

$$A = \lim_{n \to \infty} S_R = \lim_{n \to \infty} \sum_{i=1}^{n} f(x_i)\left(\frac{b - a}{n}\right) \qquad \text{(using right-hand endpoints)}$$

or

$$A = \lim_{n \to \infty} S_L = \lim_{n \to \infty} \sum_{i=1}^{n} f(x_{i-1})\left(\frac{b - a}{n}\right) \qquad \text{(using left-hand endpoints)}$$

✓ **CHECKPOINT**

1. For the interval $[0, 2]$, determine whether the following statements are true or false.

(a) For 4 subintervals, each subinterval has width $\dfrac{1}{2}$.

(b) For 200 subintervals, each subinterval has width $\dfrac{1}{100}$.

(c) For n subintervals, each subinterval has width $\dfrac{2}{n}$.

(d) For n subintervals, $x_0 = 0$, $x_1 = \dfrac{2}{n}$, $x_2 = 2\left(\dfrac{2}{n}\right)$, ..., $x_i = i\left(\dfrac{2}{n}\right)$, ..., $x_n = 2$.

2. Find the area under $y = f(x) = 3x - x^2$ from $x = 0$ to $x = 2$ using right-hand endpoints (see the figure). To accomplish this, use $\dfrac{b - a}{n} = \dfrac{2}{n}$, $x_i = \dfrac{2i}{n}$, and $f(x) = 3x - x^2$; find and simplify the following.

(a) $f(x_i)$

(b) $f(x_i)\left(\dfrac{b - a}{n}\right)$

(c) $S_R = \displaystyle\sum_{i=1}^{n} f(x_i)\left(\dfrac{b - a}{n}\right)$

(d) $A = \lim_{n \to \infty} S_R = \lim_{n \to \infty} \displaystyle\sum_{i=1}^{n} f(x_i)\left(\dfrac{b - a}{n}\right)$

Technology Note   Graphing calculators and Excel can be used to approximate the area under a curve. These technologies are especially useful when summations approximating the area do not simplify easily. Example 3 shows steps for using both a graphing calculator and Excel to approximate an area. See Appendices A and B, Section 13.1, for additional details.

EXAMPLE 3   Estimating an Area with Technology

Approximate the area under the graph of $f(x) = \sqrt{x}$ on the interval $[0, 4]$ by using $n = 8$ rectangles with:

(a) a graphing calculator and both left-hand and right-hand endpoints.
(b) Excel and left-hand endpoints.

Solution

Figure 13.8(a) shows the graph of $y = \sqrt{x}$ with 8 rectangles whose heights are determined by evaluating the function at the left-hand endpoint of each interval (the first of these rectangles has height 0). Figure 13.8(b) shows the same graph with 8 rectangles whose heights are determined at the right-hand endpoints.

(a) To approximate the area with a graphing calculator, first enter the function as Y1. With $n = 8$, each rectangle has base width $(4 - 0)/8 = 0.5$. The subdivision values are $x_0 = 0$, $x_1 = 0.5$, $x_2 = 1$, ... $x_7 = 3.5$, $x_8 = 4$.
Because Y1(x_i) on a graphing calculator gives $\sqrt{x_i}$, the height of a rectangle at x_i, the left approximation of the area is

$$S_L = \sum_{i=1}^{8} f(x_{i-1})\Delta x = \left[Y1(x_0) + Y1(x_1) + \cdots + Y1(x_{8-1}) \right]\Delta x$$
$$= [Y1(0) + Y1(0.5) + Y1(1) + Y1(1.5) + Y1(2) + Y1(2.5) + Y1(3) + Y1(3.5)](0.5) \approx 4.765$$

Figure 13.8(c) shows the right approximation of the area to be $S_R \approx 5.765$.

(b) To find the approximate area with Excel using the left-hand endpoints of rectangles with base width 0.5, we proceed as follows.
1. Enter "x" and the eight x-values of the left-hand endpoints of each rectangle in Column B, starting with 0.
2. Enter the formula for the function, =SQRT(B2), in C2 and fill down column C to get the function values that are the heights of the rectangles.
3. Enter the rectangle width, 0.5, in each cell of Column D.
4. Enter the formula for the area of each rectangle, =C2*D2, in E2 and fill down to get the area of each rectangle.
5. Enter "Total" in A10 and the formula =SUM(E2:E9) in E10 to get the approximate area, $S_L \approx 4.765$.

The following Excel output shows this S_L calculation. Note that S_R can be found by removing Row 2, adding a new row with $x = 4$, and proceeding as above.

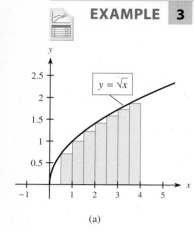

(a)

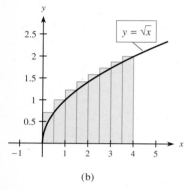

(b)

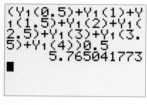

(c)

Figure 13.8

	A	B	C	D	E
1	Rectangle	x	y	Width	Area
2	1	0	0	0.5	0
3	2	0.5	0.707107	0.5	0.353553
4	3	1	1	0.5	0.5
5	4	1.5	1.224745	0.5	0.612372
6	5	2	1.414214	0.5	0.707107
7	6	2.5	1.581139	0.5	0.790569
8	7	3	1.732051	0.5	0.866025
9	8	3.5	1.870829	0.5	0.935414
10	Total				4.765042

✓ CHECKPOINT
ANSWERS

1. All parts are true.

2. (a) $f(x_i) = \dfrac{6i}{n} - \dfrac{4i^2}{n^2}$

(b) $f(x_i)\dfrac{b-a}{n} = \dfrac{12i}{n^2} - \dfrac{8i^2}{n^3}$

(c) $S_R = \dfrac{12}{n^2}\left[\dfrac{n(n+1)}{2}\right] - \dfrac{8}{n^3}\left[\dfrac{n(n+1)(2n+1)}{6}\right]$

$= \dfrac{6(n+1)}{n} - \dfrac{4(n+1)(2n+1)}{3n^2}$

(d) $A = \lim\limits_{n\to\infty}\sum\limits_{i=1}^{n} f(x_i)\dfrac{b-a}{n} = 6 - \dfrac{8}{3} = \dfrac{10}{3}$

| EXERCISES | 13.1

In Problems 1–4, approximate the area under each curve over the specified interval by using the indicated number of subintervals (or rectangles) and evaluating the function at the *right-hand* endpoints of the subintervals. (See Example 1.)

1. $f(x) = 4x - x^2$ from $x = 0$ to $x = 2$; 2 subintervals
2. $f(x) = x^3$ from $x = 0$ to $x = 3$; 3 subintervals
3. $f(x) = 9 - x^2$ from $x = 1$ to $x = 3$; 4 subintervals
4. $f(x) = x^2 + x + 1$ from $x = -1$ to $x = 1$; 4 subintervals

In Problems 5–8, approximate the area under each curve by evaluating the function at the *left-hand* endpoints of the subintervals.

5. $f(x) = 4x - x^2$ from $x = 0$ to $x = 2$; 2 subintervals
6. $f(x) = x^3$ from $x = 0$ to $x = 3$; 3 subintervals
7. $f(x) = 9 - x^2$ from $x = 1$ to $x = 3$; 4 subintervals
8. $f(x) = x^2 + x + 1$ from $x = -1$ to $x = 1$; 4 subintervals

When the area under $f(x) = x^2 + x$ from $x = 0$ to $x = 2$ is approximated, the formulas for the sum of n rectangles using *left-hand* endpoints and *right-hand* endpoints are

Left-hand endpoints: $S_L = \dfrac{14}{3} - \dfrac{6}{n} + \dfrac{4}{3n^2}$

Right-hand endpoints: $S_R = \dfrac{14n^2 + 18n + 4}{3n^2}$

Use these formulas to answer Problems 9–13.

9. Find $S_L(10)$ and $S_R(10)$.
10. Find $S_L(100)$ and $S_R(100)$.
11. Find $\lim\limits_{n\to\infty} S_L$ and $\lim\limits_{n\to\infty} S_R$.
12. Compare the right-hand and left-hand values by finding $S_R - S_L$ for $n = 10$, for $n = 100$, and as $n \to \infty$. (Use Problems 9–11.)
13. Because $f(x) = x^2 + x$ is increasing over the interval from $x = 0$ to $x = 2$, function values at the right-hand endpoints are maximum values for each subinterval, and function values at the left-hand endpoints are minimum values for each subinterval. How would

the approximate area using $n = 10$ and *any* other point within each subinterval compare with $S_L(10)$ and $S_R(10)$? What would happen to the area result as $n \to \infty$ if any other point in each subinterval were used?

In Problems 14–19, find the value of each sum.

14. $\sum\limits_{k=1}^{3} x_k$, if $x_1 = 1, x_2 = 3, x_3 = -1, x_4 = 5$

15. $\sum\limits_{i=1}^{4} x_i$, if $x_1 = 3, x_2 = -1, x_3 = 3, x_4 = -2$

16. $\sum\limits_{i=3}^{5} (i^2 + 1)$

17. $\sum\limits_{j=2}^{5} (j^2 - 3)$

18. $\sum\limits_{i=4}^{7} \left(\dfrac{i-3}{i^2}\right)$

19. $\sum\limits_{j=0}^{4} (j^2 - 4j + 1)$

In Problems 20–25, use the sum formulas I–V to express each of the following without the summation symbol. In Problems 20–23, find the numerical value.

20. $\sum\limits_{k=1}^{50} 1$

21. $\sum\limits_{j=1}^{60} 3$

22. $\sum\limits_{k=1}^{50} (6k^2 + 5)$

23. $\sum\limits_{k=1}^{30} (k^2 + 4k)$

24. $\sum\limits_{i=1}^{n} \left(1 - \dfrac{i^2}{n^2}\right)\left(\dfrac{2}{n}\right)$

25. $\sum\limits_{i=1}^{n} \left(1 - \dfrac{2i}{n} + \dfrac{i^2}{n^2}\right)\left(\dfrac{3}{n}\right)$

Use the function $y = 2x$ from $x = 0$ to $x = 1$ and n equal subintervals with the function evaluated at the *left-hand* endpoint of each subinterval for Problems 26 and 27.

26. What is the area of the
    (a) first rectangle?   (b) second rectangle?
    (c) ith rectangle?

27. (a) Find a formula for the sum of the areas of the n rectangles (call this S). Then find
    (b) $S(10)$.   (c) $S(100)$.
    (d) $S(1000)$.   (e) $\lim\limits_{n\to\infty} S$.

28. How do your answers to Problems 27(a)–(e) compare with the corresponding calculations in the discussion (after Example 1) of the area under $y = 2x$ using *right-hand* endpoints?

29. For parts (a)–(e), use the function $y = x^2$ from $x = 0$ to $x = 1$ with n equal subintervals and the function evaluated at the *right-hand* endpoints.
   (a) Find a formula for the sum of the areas of the n rectangles (call this S). Then find
   (b) $S(10)$.   (c) $S(100)$.
   (d) $S(1000)$.   (e) $\lim_{n \to \infty} S$.

30. How do your answers to Problems 29(a)–(e) compare with the corresponding calculations in Example 2?

31. Use rectangles to find the area between $y = x^2 - 6x + 8$ and the x-axis from $x = 0$ to $x = 2$. Divide the interval $[0, 2]$ into n equal subintervals so that each subinterval has length $2/n$.

32. Use rectangles to find the area between $y = 4x - x^2$ and the x-axis from $x = 0$ to $x = 4$. Divide the interval $[0, 4]$ into n equal subintervals so that each subinterval has length $4/n$.

APPLICATIONS

33. **Per capita health care expenses** The annual per capita out-of-pocket expenses (to the nearest dollar) for U.S. health care for selected years from 2013 and projected to 2021 are shown in the table and figure.
   (a) Use $n = 4$ equal subdivisions and left-hand endpoints to estimate the area under the graph from 2013 to 2021.
   (b) What does this area represent in terms of per capita out-of-pocket expenses for U.S. health care?

Year	Dollars
2013	1020
2015	1022
2017	1097
2019	1209
2021	1325

Source: U.S. Centers for Medicare and Medicaid Services

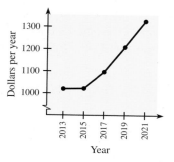

34. **Oil imports** Crude oil and petroleum products are imported continuously by the United States. The following table and figure show the net expenditures for U.S. oil imports for selected years (in billions of dollars per year) (*Source:* Energy Information Administration).
   (a) Use $n = 5$ equal subdivisions and left-hand endpoints to estimate the area under the graph from 2014 to 2024.
   (b) What does this area represent in terms of U.S. oil imports?

Year	Billions of Dollars
2014	219.5
2016	192.0
2018	191.0
2020	198.9
2022	214.5
2024	228.4

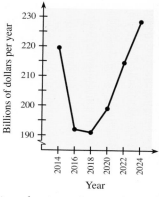

35. **Speed trials** The figure gives the times that it takes a Porsche 911 to reach speeds from 0 mph to 100 mph, in increments of 10 mph, with a curve connecting them. The area under this curve from $t = 0$ seconds to $t = 14$ seconds represents the total amount of distance traveled over the 14-second period. Count the squares under the curve to estimate this distance. This car will travel 1/4 mile in 14 seconds, to a speed of 100.2 mph. Is your estimate close to this result? (Be careful with time units.)

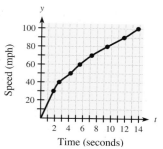

Source: *Motor Trend*

36. **Speed trials** The figure gives the times that it takes a Mitsubishi Eclipse GSX to reach speeds from 0 mph to 100 mph, in increments of 10 mph, with a curve connecting them. The area under this curve from $t = 0$ seconds to $t = 21.1$ seconds represents the total amount of distance traveled over the 21.1-second period. Count the squares under the curve to estimate this distance. This car will travel 1/4 mile in 15.4 seconds, to a speed of 89.0 mph, so your estimate should be more than 1/4 mile. Is it? (Be careful with time units.)

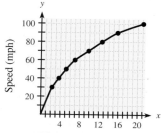

Source: *Road & Track*

37. *Pollution monitoring* Suppose the presence of phosphates in certain waste products dumped into a lake promotes the growth of algae. Rampant growth of algae affects the oxygen supply in the water, so an environmental group wishes to estimate the area of algae growth. The group measures the length across the algae growth (see the figure) and obtains the data (in feet) in the table.

x	Length	x	Length
0	0	50	27
10	15	60	24
20	18	70	23
30	18	80	0
40	30		

Use 8 rectangles with bases of 10 feet and lengths measured at the left-hand endpoints to approximate the area of the algae growth.

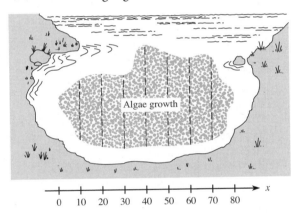

38. *Drug levels in the blood* The manufacturer of a medicine wants to test how a new 300-milligram capsule is released into the bloodstream. After a volunteer is given a capsule, blood samples are drawn every half-hour, and the number of milligrams of the drug in the bloodstream is calculated. The results obtained are shown in the table.

Time t (hr)	$N(t)$ (mg)	Time t (hr)	$N(t)$ (mg)
0	0	2.0	178.3
0.5	247.3	2.5	113.9
1.0	270.0	3.0	56.2
1.5	236.4	3.5	19.3

Use 7 rectangles, each with height $N(t)$ at the left endpoint and with width 0.5 hr, to estimate the area under the graph representing these data. Divide this area by 3.5 hr to estimate the average drug level over this time period.

39. *Emissions* With U.S. Department of Energy data for selected years from 2000 and projected to 2030, sulphur dioxide emissions from electricity generation (in millions of short tons per year) can be modeled by

$$E(x) = 0.0112x^2 + 0.612x + 11.9$$

where x is the number of years past 2000. Use $n = 10$ equal subdivisions and right-hand endpoints to approximate the area under the graph of $E(x)$ between $x = 10$ and $x = 15$. What does this area represent?

40. *Per capita income* The per capita personal income (in dollars per year) in the United States for selected years from 1960 and projected to 2018 can be modeled by

$$I(t) = 13.93t^2 + 136.8t + 1971$$

where t is the number of years past 1960 (*Source*: U.S. Bureau of Labor Statistics). Use $n = 10$ equal subdivisions with right-hand endpoints to approximate the area under the graph of $I(t)$ between $t = 50$ and $t = 55$. What does this area represent?

OBJECTIVES   **13.2**

- To evaluate definite integrals using the Fundamental Theorem of Calculus
- To use definite integrals to find the area under a curve

The Definite Integral: The Fundamental Theorem of Calculus

■| APPLICATION PREVIEW |■

Suppose that money flows continuously into a slot machine at a casino and grows at a rate given by $A'(t) = 100e^{0.1t}$, where t is the time in hours and $0 \le t \le 10$. Then the definite integral

$$\int_0^{10} 100\, e^{0.1t}\, dt$$

gives the total amount of money that accumulates over the 10-hour period, if no money is paid out. (See Example 6.)

(*continued*)

In the previous section, we used the sums of areas of rectangles to approximate the areas under curves. In this section, we will see how such sums are related to the definite integral and how to evaluate definite integrals. In addition, we will see how definite integrals can be used to solve several types of applied problems.

Riemann Sums and the Definite Integral

In the previous section, we saw that we could determine the area under a curve $y = f(x)$ over a closed interval $[a, b]$ by using equal subintervals and the function values at either the left-hand endpoints or the right-hand endpoints of the subintervals. In fact, we can use subintervals that are not of equal length, and we can use any point within each subinterval, denoted by x_i^*, to determine the height of each rectangle. For the ith rectangle (for any i), if we denote the width as Δx_i then the height is $f(x_i^*)$ and the area is $f(x_i^*)\Delta x_i$. Then, if $[a, b]$ is divided into n subintervals, the sum of the areas of the n rectangles is

$$S = \sum_{i=1}^{n} f(x_i^*)\,\Delta x_i$$

Such a sum is called a **Riemann sum** of f on $[a, b]$. Increasing the number of subintervals and making sure that every interval becomes smaller will in the long run improve the estimation. Thus for any subdivision of $[a, b]$ and any x_i^*, the exact area is given by

$$A = \lim_{\substack{\max \Delta x_i \to 0 \\ (n \to \infty)}} \sum_{i=1}^{n} f(x_i^*)\,\Delta x_i \qquad \text{provided that this limit exists}$$

In addition to giving the exact area, this limit of the Riemann sum has other important applications and is called the **definite integral** of $f(x)$ over interval $[a, b]$.

Definite Integral

If f is a function on the interval $[a, b]$, then, for any subdivision of $[a, b]$ and any choice of x_i^* in the ith subinterval, the **definite integral** of f from a to b is

$$\int_a^b f(x)dx = \lim_{\substack{\max \Delta x_i \to 0 \\ (n \to \infty)}} \sum_{i=1}^{n} f(x_i^*)\,\Delta x_i$$

If f is a continuous function, and $\Delta x_i \to 0$ as $n \to \infty$, then the limit exists and we say that f is integrable on $[a, b]$.

Note that for some intervals, values of f may be negative. In this case, the product $f(x_i^*)\Delta x_i$ will be negative and can be thought of geometrically as a "signed area." (Remember that area is a positive number.) Thus a definite integral can be thought of geometrically as the sum of signed areas, just as a derivative can be thought of geometrically as the slope of a tangent line. In the case where $f(x)$ is positive for all x from a to b, the definite integral equals the area between the graph of $y = f(x)$ and the x-axis.

Fundamental Theorem of Calculus

The obvious question is how this definite integral is related to the indefinite integral (the antiderivative) discussed in Chapter 12. The connection between these two concepts is the most important result in calculus, because it connects derivatives, indefinite integrals, and definite integrals.

To help see the connection, consider the marginal revenue function

$$R'(x) = 300 - 0.2x$$

and the revenue function

$$R(x) = \int (300 - 0.2x)\,dx = 300x - 0.1x^2$$

that is the indefinite integral of the marginal revenue function. (See Figure 13.9(a).)

Using this revenue function, we can find the revenue from the sale of 1000 units to be

$$R(1000) = 300(1000) - 0.1(1000)^2 = 200,000 \text{ dollars}$$

and the revenue from the sale of 500 units to be

$$R(500) = 300(500) - 0.1(500)^2 = 125,000 \text{ dollars}$$

Thus the additional revenue received from the sale of 500 units to 1000 units is

$$200,000 - 125,000 = 75,000 \text{ dollars}$$

If we used the definition of the definite integral (or geometry) to find the area under the graph of the marginal revenue function from $x = 500$ to $x = 1000$, we would find that the area is 75,000 (see Figure 13.9(b)). Note in Figure 13.9(b) that the shaded area is given by

Area = Area (Δ with base from 500 to 1500) $-$ Area (Δ with base from 1000 to 1500)

Recall that the area of a triangle is $\frac{1}{2}$(base)(height) so we have

$$\text{Area} = \tfrac{1}{2}(1000)(200) - \tfrac{1}{2}(500)(100) = 75,000$$

Because the area under $R'(x)$ is also given by the definite integral, we can find this additional revenue when sales are increased from 500 to 1000 by evaluating

$$\int_{500}^{1000} (300 - 0.2x)\, dx$$

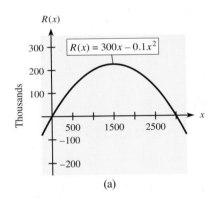

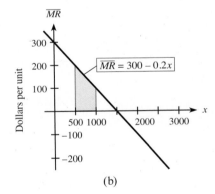

Figure 13.9   (a)   (b)

In general, the definite integral

$$\int_a^b f(x)\, dx$$

can be used to find the change in the function $F(x)$ when x changes from a to b, where $f(x)$ is the derivative of $F(x)$. This result is the **Fundamental Theorem of Calculus.**

Fundamental Theorem of Calculus

Let f be a continuous function on the closed interval $[a, b]$; then the definite integral of f exists on this interval, and

$$\int_a^b f(x)\, dx = F(b) - F(a)$$

where F is any function such that $F'(x) = f(x)$ for all x in $[a, b]$.

Stated differently, this theorem says that if the function F is an indefinite integral of a function f that is continuous on the interval $[a, b]$, then

$$\int_a^b f(x)\, dx = F(b) - F(a)$$

Thus, we apply the Fundamental Theorem of Calculus by using the following two steps.

1. Integration of $f(x)$: $\displaystyle\int_a^b f(x)\,dx = F(x)\,\Big|_a^b$

2. Evaluation of $F(x)$: $F(x)\,\Big|_a^b = F(b) - F(a)$

EXAMPLE 1   Definite Integral

Evaluate $\displaystyle\int_2^4 (x^3 + 4)\,dx$.

Solution

1. $\displaystyle\int_2^4 (x^3 + 4)\,dx = \frac{x^4}{4} + 4x + C\,\Big|_2^4$

2. $\displaystyle\qquad\qquad = \left[\frac{(4)^4}{4} + 4(4) + C\right] - \left[\frac{(2)^4}{4} + 4(2) + C\right]$

$\qquad\qquad = (64 + 16 + C) - (4 + 8 + C)$

$\qquad\qquad = 68 \text{ (Note that the } C\text{'s subtract out.)}$

Note that the Fundamental Theorem states that F can be *any* indefinite integral of f, so we need not add the constant of integration to the integral.

EXAMPLE 2   Fundamental Theorem

Evaluate $\displaystyle\int_1^3 (3x^2 + 6x)\,dx$.

Solution

$$\int_1^3 (3x^2 + 6x)\,dx = x^3 + 3x^2\,\Big|_1^3$$

$$= (3^3 + 3\cdot 3^2) - (1^3 + 3\cdot 1^2)$$

$$= 54 - 4 = 50$$

Properties   The properties of definite integrals given next follow from properties of summations.

1. $\displaystyle\int_a^b [f(x) \pm g(x)]\,dx = \int_a^b f(x)\,dx \pm \int_a^b g(x)\,dx$

2. $\displaystyle\int_a^b kf(x)\,dx = k\int_a^b f(x)\,dx,$ where k is a constant

The following example uses both of these properties.

EXAMPLE 3   Definite Integral

Evaluate $\displaystyle\int_3^5 (\sqrt{x^2 - 9} + 2)x\,dx$.

Solution

$$\int_3^5 (\sqrt{x^2 - 9} + 2)x\,dx = \int_3^5 \sqrt{x^2 - 9}(x\,dx) + \int_3^5 2x\,dx$$

$$= \frac{1}{2}\int_3^5 (x^2 - 9)^{1/2}(2x\,dx) + \int_3^5 2x\,dx$$

$$= \frac{1}{2}\left[\frac{2}{3}(x^2 - 9)^{3/2}\right]_3^5 + x^2\,\Big|_3^5$$

$$= \frac{1}{3}[(16)^{3/2} - (0)^{3/2}] + (25 - 9)$$

$$= \frac{64}{3} + 16 = \frac{64}{3} + \frac{48}{3} = \frac{112}{3}$$

In the integral $\int_a^b f(x)\,dx$, we call a the *lower limit* and b the *upper limit* of integration. Although we developed the definite integral with the assumption that the lower limit was less than the upper limit, the following properties permit us to evaluate the definite integral even when that is not the case.

3. $\int_a^a f(x)\,dx = 0$

4. If f is integrable on $[a, b]$, then

$$\int_b^a f(x)\,dx = -\int_a^b f(x)\,dx$$

The following examples illustrate these properties.

EXAMPLE 4   Properties of Definite Integrals

(a) Evaluate $\int_4^4 x^2\,dx.$ (b) Compare $\int_2^4 3x^2\,dx$ and $\int_4^2 3x^2\,dx.$

Solution

(a) $\int_4^4 x^2\,dx = \dfrac{x^3}{3}\Big|_4^4 = \dfrac{4^3}{3} - \dfrac{4^3}{3} = 0$

This illustrates Property 3.

(b) $\int_2^4 3x^2\,dx = x^3\Big|_2^4 = 4^3 - 2^3 = 56$ and $\int_4^2 3x^2\,dx = x^3\Big|_4^2 = 2^3 - 4^3 = -56$

This illustrates Property 4.

Another property of definite integrals is called the additive property.

5. If f is continuous on some interval containing a, b, and c,* then

$$\int_a^c f(x)\,dx + \int_c^b f(x)\,dx = \int_a^b f(x)\,dx$$

EXAMPLE 5   Properties of Definite Integrals

Show that $\int_2^3 4x\,dx + \int_3^5 4x\,dx = \int_2^5 4x\,dx.$

Solution

$$\int_2^3 4x\,dx = 2x^2\Big|_2^3 = 18 - 8 = 10 \quad \text{and} \quad \int_3^5 4x\,dx = 2x^2\Big|_3^5 = 50 - 18 = 32$$

Thus $\int_2^5 4x\,dx = 2x^2\Big|_2^5 = 50 - 8 = 42 = \int_2^3 4x\,dx + \int_3^5 4x\,dx$

The Definite Integral and Areas   Let us now return to area problems, to see the relationship between the definite integral and the area under a curve. By the formula for the area of a triangle or by using rectangles and the limit definition of area, the area under the curve (line) $y = x$ from $x = 0$

*Note that c need not be between a and b.

to $x = 1$ can be shown to be $\frac{1}{2}$ (see Figure 13.10(a)). Using the definite integral to find the area gives

$$A = \int_0^1 x \, dx = \frac{x^2}{2} \bigg|_0^1 = \frac{1}{2} - 0 = \frac{1}{2}$$

In the previous section, we used rectangles to find that the area under $y = x^2$ from $x = 0$ to $x = 1$ was $\frac{1}{3}$ (see Figure 13.10(b)). Using the definite integral, we get

$$A = \int_0^1 x^2 \, dx = \frac{x^3}{3} \bigg|_0^1 = \frac{1}{3} - 0 = \frac{1}{3}$$

which agrees with the answer obtained previously.

However, not every definite integral represents the area between the curve and the x-axis over an interval. For example,

$$\int_0^2 (x - 2) \, dx = \frac{x^2}{2} - 2x \bigg|_0^2 = (2 - 4) - (0) = -2$$

This would indicate that the area between the curve and the x-axis is negative, but area must be positive. A look at the graph of $y = x - 2$ (see Figure 13.10(c)) shows us what is happening.

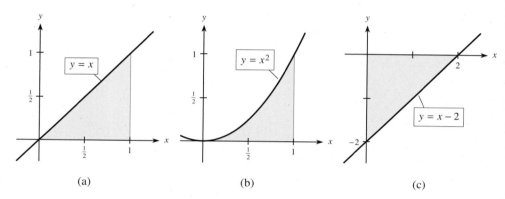

(a)	(b)	(c)

Figure 13.10

The region bounded by $y = x - 2$ and the x-axis between $x = 0$ and $x = 2$ is a triangle whose base is 2 and whose height is 2, so its area is $\frac{1}{2}bh = \frac{1}{2}(2)(2) = 2$. The integral has value -2 because $y = x - 2$ lies below the x-axis from $x = 0$ to $x = 2$, and the function values over the interval $[0, 2]$ are negative. Thus the value of the definite integral over *this* interval does not represent the area between the curve and the x-axis but, rather, represents the "signed" area as mentioned previously.

In general, the definite integral will give the **area under the curve** and above the x-axis only when $f(x) \geq 0$ for all x in $[a, b]$.

Area Under a Curve

If f is a continuous function on $[a, b]$ and $f(x) \geq 0$ on $[a, b]$, then the exact area between $y = f(x)$ and the x-axis from $x = a$ to $x = b$ is given by

$$\text{Area} \atop \text{(shaded)} = \int_a^b f(x) \, dx$$

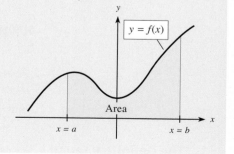

Note also that if $f(x) \leq 0$ for all x in $[a, b]$, then

$$\int_a^b f(x) \, dx = -\text{Area (between } f(x) \text{ and the } x\text{-axis)}$$

Calculator Note   The approximate area under the graph of $y = f(x)$ and above the x-axis can be found with a calculator. After we enter the function in the $Y =$ menu and graph it, we choose $\int f(x)dx$ under 2nd CALC, press ENTER, and select the lower and upper x-values for the interval on which we seek the area. Figure 13.11 shows the steps in finding the area under the graph of $f(x) = x^2 + 1$ from $x = 0$ to $x = 3$ after the function is graphed. See Appendix A, Section 13.2, for details.

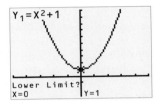
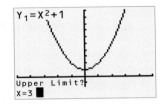
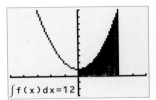

Figure 13.11

✓ CHECKPOINT

1. True or false:
   (a) For any integral, we can omit the constant of integration (the $+C$).
   (b) $-\displaystyle\int_{-1}^{3} f(x)\,dx = \int_{3}^{-1} f(x)\,dx$, if f is integrable on $[-1, 3]$.

   (c) The area between $f(x)$ and the x-axis on the interval $[a, b]$ is given by $\displaystyle\int_{a}^{b} f(x)\,dx$.

2. Evaluate:
   (a) $\displaystyle\int_{0}^{3} (x^2 + 1)\,dx$
   (b) $\displaystyle\int_{0}^{3} (x^2 + 1)^4 x\,dx$

If the rate of growth of some function with respect to time t is $f'(t)$, then the total growth of the function during the period from $t = 0$ to $t = k$ can be found by evaluating the definite integral

$$\int_{0}^{k} f'(t)\,dt = f(t)\Big|_{0}^{k} = f(k) - f(0)$$

For nonnegative rates of growth, this definite integral (and thus growth) is the same as the area under the graph of $f'(t)$ from $t = 0$ to $t = k$.

EXAMPLE 6   **Income Stream | APPLICATION PREVIEW |**

Suppose that money flows continuously into a slot machine at a casino and grows at a rate given by

$$A'(t) = 100e^{0.1t}$$

where t is time in hours and $0 \le t \le 10$. Find the total amount that accumulates in the machine during the 10-hour period, if no money is paid out.

Solution
The total dollar amount is given by

$$A = \int_{0}^{10} 100e^{0.1t}\,dt = \frac{100}{0.1}\int_{0}^{10} e^{0.1t}(0.1)\,dt = 1000e^{0.1t}\Big|_{0}^{10} = 1000e - 1000 \approx 1718.28$$

Probability Density Functions   In Section 8.4, "Normal Probability Distribution," we stated that the total area under the normal curve is 1 and that the area under the curve from value x_1 to value x_2 represents the probability that a score chosen at random will lie between x_1 and x_2.

   The normal distribution is an example of a **continuous probability distribution** because the values of the random variable are considered over intervals rather than at discrete values. The statements above relating probability and area under the graph apply to other continuous probability distributions determined by **probability density functions.** In fact, if x is a continuous random variable with probability density function $f(x)$, then the probability that x is between a and b is

$$\Pr(a \le x \le b) = \int_a^b f(x)\, dx$$

EXAMPLE 7   Product Life

Suppose the probability density function for the life of a computer component is $f(x) = 0.10e^{-0.10x}$, where $x \ge 0$ is the number of years the component is in use. Find the probability that the component will last between 3 and 5 years.

```
fnInt(0.10*e^(⁻0
.10X),X,3,5)
        .134287561
■
```

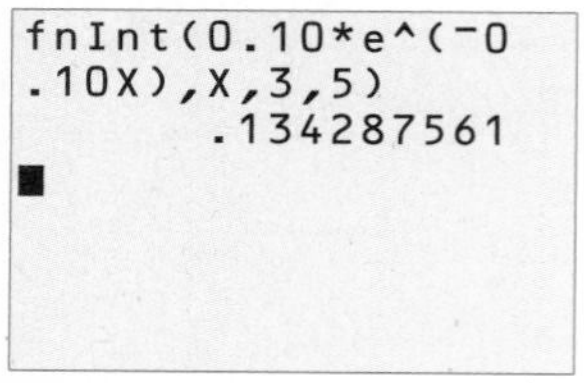

Figure 13.12

Solution
The probability that the component will last between 3 and 5 years is the area under the graph of the function between $x = 3$ and $x = 5$. The probability is given by

$$\Pr(3 \le x \le 5) = \int_3^5 0.10e^{-0.10x}\, dx = -e^{-0.10x}\Big|_3^5 = -e^{-0.5} + e^{-0.3}$$

$$\approx -0.6065 + 0.7408 = 0.1343 \qquad ■$$

Calculator Note   Using $\text{fnInt}(f(x), x, a, b)$ under MATH on a graphing calculator gives the definite integral of the function $y = f(x)$ from $x = a$ to $x = b$. This feature can be used to evaluate definite integrals directly or to check those done with the Fundamental Theorem of Calculus. Figure 13.12 shows the numerical integration feature applied to the integral in Example 7. Note that when this answer is rounded to 4 decimal places, the results agree. See Appendix A, Section 13.2 for details. ■

✓ **CHECKPOINT ANSWERS**

1. (a) False
   (b) True   (c) False; this is true only if $f(x) \ge 0$ on $[a, b]$

2. (a) $\int_0^3 (x^2 + 1)\, dx = \dfrac{x^3}{3} + x\Big|_0^3 = 12$

   (b) $\int_0^3 (x^2 + 1)^4 x\, dx = \dfrac{1}{2} \cdot \dfrac{(x^2 + 1)^5}{5}\Big|_0^3 = \dfrac{1}{10}(10^5 - 1) = 9999.9$

| EXERCISES | 13.2

Evaluate the definite integrals in Problems 1–30.

1. $\displaystyle\int_0^3 4x\, dx$

2. $\displaystyle\int_0^1 8x\, dx$

3. $\displaystyle\int_2^4 dx$

4. $\displaystyle\int_1^5 2\, dy$

5. $\displaystyle\int_2^4 x^3\, dx$

6. $\displaystyle\int_0^5 x^2\, dx$

7. $\displaystyle\int_0^5 4\sqrt[3]{x^2}\, dx$

8. $\displaystyle\int_2^4 3\sqrt{x}\, dx$

9. $\displaystyle\int_1^4 (10 - 4x)\, dx$

10. $\displaystyle\int_{-1}^4 (6x - 9)\, dx$

11. $\displaystyle\int_2^4 (4x^3 - 6x^2 - 5x)\, dx$

12. $\displaystyle\int_0^2 (x^4 - 5x^3 + 2x)\, dx$

13. $\displaystyle\int_3^4 (x - 4)^9\, dx$

14. $\displaystyle\int_{-1}^0 (x + 2)^{13}\, dx$

15. $\displaystyle\int_2^4 (x^2 + 2)^3 x\, dx$

16. $\displaystyle\int_0^1 5x^2\,(4x^3 - 2)^4\, dx$

17. $\displaystyle\int_{-1}^2 (x^3 - 3x^2)^3 (x^2 - 2x)\, dx$

18. $\displaystyle\int_0^3 (2x - x^2)^4 (1 - x)\, dx$

19. $\displaystyle\int_{-2}^2 15x^3\,(x^4 - 6)^6\, dx$

20. $\displaystyle\int_0^4 (3x^2 - 2)^4 x\, dx$

21. $\displaystyle\int_0^4 \sqrt{4x + 9}\, dx$

22. $\displaystyle\int_0^2 \sqrt[3]{2x^3 - 8}\, x^2\, dx$

23. $\displaystyle\int_1^3 \dfrac{3}{y^2}\, dy$

24. $\displaystyle\int_1^2 \dfrac{5}{z^3}\, dz$

25. $\displaystyle\int_0^1 e^{3x}\, dx$

26. $\displaystyle\int_0^2 e^{4x-3}\, dx$

27. $\displaystyle\int_1^e \dfrac{4}{z}\, dz$

28. $\displaystyle\int_1^{5e} 3y^{-1}\, dy$

29. $\displaystyle\int_0^2 8x^2 e^{-x^3}\,dx$

30. $\displaystyle\int_0^1 \frac{3x^3\,dx}{4x^4+9}$

In Problems 31–34, evaluate each integral (a) with the Fundamental Theorem of Calculus and (b) with a graphing calculator (as a check).

31. $\displaystyle\int_3^6 \frac{x}{3x^2+4}\,dx$

32. $\displaystyle\int_0^2 \frac{x}{x^2+4}\,dx$

33. $\displaystyle\int_1^2 \frac{x^2+3}{x}\,dx$

34. $\displaystyle\int_1^4 \frac{4\sqrt{x}+5}{\sqrt{x}}\,dx$

35. In the figures, which of the shaded regions (A, B, C, or D) has the area given by

(a) $\displaystyle\int_a^b f(x)\,dx$?   (b) $-\displaystyle\int_a^b f(x)\,dx$?

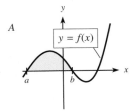
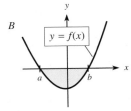
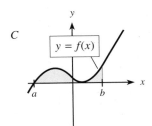
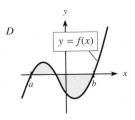

36. For which of the following functions $f(x)$ does

$$\int_0^2 f(x)\,dx$$

give the area between the graph of $f(x)$ and the x-axis from $x=0$ to $x=2$?

(a) $f(x)=x^2+1$ (b) $f(x)=-x^2$
(c) $f(x)=x-1$

In Problems 37–40, (a) write the integral that describes the area of the shaded region and (b) find the area.

37.
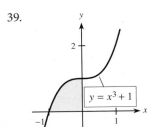

38.
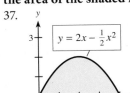

39.
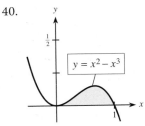

40.

41. Find the area between the curve $y=-x^2+3x-2$ and the x-axis from $x=1$ to $x=2$.
42. Find the area between the curve $y=x^2+3x+2$ and the x-axis from $x=-1$ to $x=3$.
43. Find the area between the curve $y=xe^{x^2}$ and the x-axis from $x=1$ to $x=3$.
44. Find the area between the curve $y=e^{-x}$ and the x-axis from $x=-1$ to $x=1$.

In Problems 45 and 46, use the figures to decide which of $\displaystyle\int_0^a f(x)\,dx$ or $\displaystyle\int_0^a g(x)\,dx$ is larger or if they are equal. Explain your choices.

45.
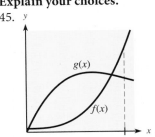

46.
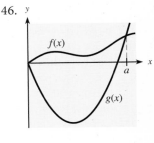

In Problems 47–52, use properties of definite integrals.

47. How does $\displaystyle\int_{-1}^{-3} x\sqrt{x^2+1}\,dx$ compare with

$$\int_{-3}^{-1} x\sqrt{x^2+1}\,dx?$$

48. If $\displaystyle\int_{-1}^0 x^3\,dx=-\frac14$ and $\displaystyle\int_0^1 x^3\,dx=\frac14$, what does $\displaystyle\int_{-1}^1 x^3\,dx$ equal?

49. If $\displaystyle\int_1^2 (2x-x^2)\,dx=\frac23$ and $\displaystyle\int_2^4 (2x-x^2)\,dx=-\frac{20}{3}$, what does $\displaystyle\int_1^4 (x^2-2x)\,dx$ equal?

50. If $\displaystyle\int_1^2 (2x-x^2)\,dx=\frac23$, what does $\displaystyle\int_1^2 6(2x-x^2)\,dx$ equal?

51. Evaluate $\displaystyle\int_4^4 \sqrt{x^2-2}\,dx$.

52. Evaluate $\displaystyle\int_2^2 (x^3+4x)^{-6}\,dx$.

APPLICATIONS

53. *Depreciation* The rate of depreciation of a building is given by $D'(t)=3000(20-t)$ dollars per year, $0\le t\le 20$; see the figure on the next page.
(a) Use the graph to find the total depreciation of the building over the first 10 years ($t=0$ to $t=10$).
(b) Use a definite integral to find the total depreciation over the first 10 years.

$D'(t)$

60,000

30,000

5   10   15   20

t

54. **Depreciation** The rate of depreciation of a build-ing is given by $D'(t) = 3000(20 - t)$ dollars per year, $0 \le t \le 20$; see the figure in Problem 53.
  (a) Use the graph to find the total depreciation of the building over the first 20 years.
  (b) Use a definite integral to find the total deprecia-tion over the first 20 years.
  (c) Use the graph to find the total depreciation between 10 years and 20 years and check it with a definite integral.

55. **Sales and advertising** A store finds that its sales revenue changes at a rate given by

$$S'(t) = -30t^2 + 360t \quad \text{dollars per day}$$

where t is the number of days after an advertising campaign ends and $0 \le t \le 30$.
  (a) Find the total sales for the first week after the campaign ends ($t = 0$ to $t = 7$).
  (b) Find the total sales for the second week after the campaign ends ($t = 7$ to $t = 14$).

56. **Health care costs** The total annual health care costs in the United States (actual and projected, in billions of dollars) for selected years are given in the table. The equation

$$y = 4.447x^2 - 9.108x + 1055.4$$

models the annual health care costs, y (in billions of dollars per year), as a function of the number of years past 1990, x. Use a definite integral and this model to find the total cost of health care over the period 2005–2015.

Year	Cost	Year	Cost
2000	1353	2012	2931
2003	1735	2015	3541
2006	2113	2018	4353
2009	2509		

Source: U.S. Department of Health and Human Services

57. **Total income** The income from an oil change service chain can be considered as flowing continuously at an annual rate given by

$$f(t) = 10,000e^{0.02t} \quad \text{(dollars/year)}$$

Find the total income for this chain over the first 2 years (from $t = 0$ to $t = 2$).

58. **Total income** Suppose that a vending machine service company models its income by assuming that money flows continuously into the machines, with the annual rate of flow given by

$$f(t) = 120e^{0.01t}$$

in thousands of dollars per year. Find the total income from the machines over the first 3 years.

59. **CO_2 Emissions** Using U.S. Energy Information Administration data from 2010 and projected to 2030, the carbon dioxide emissions from biomass energy combustion (in millions of metric tons per year) can be modeled by

$$C(t) = 19.12t + 319.0$$

where t is the number of years past 2010. Evaluate $\int_0^{10} C(t)\, dt$ and tell what it represents.

60. **Health services and supplies expenditures** The per capita expenditures for U.S. health services and sup-plies (in dollars per year) for selected years from 2000 and projected to 2018 can be modeled by

$$H(t) = 4676e^{0.053t}$$

where t is the number of years past 2000 (*Source:* U.S. Centers for Medicare and Medicaid Services). Assuming the model remains valid, evaluate $\int_{10}^{20} H(t)\, dt$ and tell what it represents.

Velocity of blood In Problems 61 and 62, the velocity of blood through a vessel is given by $v = K(R^2 - r^2)$, where K is a constant, R is the (constant) radius of the vessel, and r is the distance of the particular corpuscle from the center of the vessel. The rate of flow can be found by measuring the volume of blood that flows past a point in a given time period. This volume, V, is given by

$$V = \int_0^R v\,(2\pi r\, dr)$$

61. If $R = 0.30$ cm and $v = (0.30 - 3.33r^2)$ cm/s, find the volume.

62. Develop a general formula for V by evaluating

$$V = \int_0^R v(2\pi r\, dr)$$

using $v = K(R^2 - r^2)$.

Production In Problems 63 and 64, the rate of produc-tion of a new line of products is given by

$$\frac{dx}{dt} = 200\left[1 + \frac{400}{(t + 40)^2}\right]$$

where x is the number of items produced and t is the number of weeks the products have been in production.
63. How many units were produced in the first 5 weeks?
64. How many units were produced in the sixth week?
65. **Testing** The time t (in minutes) needed to read an article appearing on a foreign-language placement test is given by the probability density function

$$f(t) = 0.012t^2 - 0.0012t^3, \qquad 0 \le t \le 10$$

For a test taker chosen at random, find the probability that this person takes 8 minutes or more to read the article.

66. *Response time* In a small city the response time t (in minutes) of the fire company is given by the probability density function

$$f(t) = \frac{60t^2 - 4t^3}{16{,}875}, \qquad 0 \le t \le 15$$

For a fire chosen at random, find the probability that the response time is 10 minutes or less.

67. *Customer service* The duration t (in minutes) of customer service calls received by a certain company is given by the probability density function

$$f(t) = 0.3e^{-0.3t}, \qquad t \ge 0$$

Find the probability that a call selected at random lasts
(a) 3 minutes or less.   (b) between 5 and 10 minutes.

68. *Product life* The useful life of a car battery t (in years) is given by the probability density function

$$f(t) = 0.2e^{-0.2t}, \qquad t \ge 0$$

Find the probability that a battery chosen at random lasts
(a) 2 years or less.   (b) between 4 and 6 years.

69. **Modeling** *Gasoline usage* In the United States, gasoline for motor vehicles is used continuously, and that usage, in billions of gallons per year, is shown in the table for selected years from 2014 and projected to 2024.
(a) Find a quadratic function that models these data, with t as the number of years past 2014. Report the model as $G(t)$ with three significant digits.

(b) Evaluate $\int_0^{10} G(t)\,dt$ and tell what it represents.

Year	2014	2016	2018	2020	2022	2024
Gasoline Usage (billions of gallons)	132.8	133.5	130.4	126.1	121.2	116.3

Source: U.S. Department of Energy

70. **Modeling** *SRT Viper acceleration* Table 13.1(a) shows the time in seconds that an SRT Viper requires to reach various speeds up to 100 mph. Table 13.1(b) shows the same data, but with speeds in miles per second.
(a) Fit a power model to the data in Table 13.1(b).
(b) Use a definite integral from 0 to 9.2 of the function you found in part (a) to find the distance traveled by the Viper as it went from 0 mph to 100 mph in 9.2 seconds.

| TABLE 13.1 |

(a)		(b)	
Time (seconds)	Speed (mph)	Time (seconds)	Speed (mi/s)
1.7	30	1.7	0.00833
2.4	40	2.4	0.01111
3.2	50	3.2	0.01389
4.1	60	4.1	0.01667
5.8	70	5.8	0.01944
6.2	80	6.2	0.02222
7.8	90	7.8	0.02500
9.2	100	9.2	0.02778

Source: Motor Trend

(continued)

OBJECTIVES

13.3

- To find the area between two curves
- To find the average value of a function

Area Between Two Curves

| APPLICATION PREVIEW |

In economics, the **Lorenz curve** is used to represent the inequality of income distribution among different groups in the population of a country. The curve is constructed by plotting the cumulative percent of families at or below a given income level and the cumulative percent of total personal income received by these families. For example, the table on the next page shows the coordinates of some points on the Lorenz curve $y = L(x)$ that divide the income (for the United States in 2012) into 5 equal income levels (quintiles). The point (0.40, 0.115) is on the Lorenz curve because the families with incomes in the bottom 40% of the country received 11.5% of the total income in 2012. The graph of the Lorenz curve $y = L(x)$ is shown in Figure 13.13.

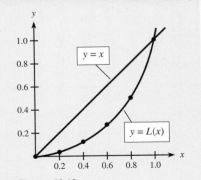

Figure 13.13

U.S. Income Distribution for 2012 (Points on the Lorenz Curve)	
x, Cumulative Proportion of Families Below Income Level	y = L(x), Cumulative Proportion of Total Income
0	0
0.20	0.032
0.40	0.115
0.60	0.259
0.80	0.489
1	1

Source: U.S. Bureau of the Census

Equality of income would result if each family received an equal proportion of the total income, so that the bottom 20% would receive 20% of the total income, the bottom 40% would receive 40%, and so on. The Lorenz curve representing this would have the equation $y = x$.

The inequality of income distribution is measured by the Gini coefficient of income, which measures how far the Lorenz curve falls below $y = x$. It is defined as

$$\frac{\text{Area between } y = x \text{ and } y = L(x)}{\text{Area below } y = x}$$

Because the area of the triangle below $y = x$ and above the x-axis from $x = 0$ to $x = 1$ is $1/2$, the Gini coefficient of income is

$$\frac{\text{Area between } y = x \text{ and } y = L(x)}{1/2} = 2 \cdot [\text{area between } y = x \text{ and } y = L(x)]$$

In this section we will use the definite integral to find the area between two curves. We will use the area between two curves to find the Gini coefficient of income (see Example 4) and to find average cost, average revenue, average profit, and average inventory.

Area Between Two Curves

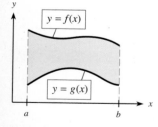

Figure 13.14

We have used the definite integral to find the area of the region between a curve and the x-axis over an interval where the curve lies above the x-axis. We can easily extend this technique to finding the area between two curves over an interval.

Suppose that the graphs of both $y = f(x)$ and $y = g(x)$ lie above the x-axis and that the graph of $y = f(x)$ lies above $y = g(x)$ throughout the interval from $x = a$ to $x = b$; that is, $f(x) \geq g(x)$ on $[a, b]$. (See Figure 13.14.)

Then Figures 13.15(a) and 13.15(b) show the areas under $y = f(x)$ and $y = g(x)$. Figure 13.15(c) shows how the difference of these two areas can be used to find the area of the region between the graphs of $y = f(x)$ and $y = g(x)$. That is,

$$\text{Area between the curves} = \int_a^b f(x)\, dx - \int_a^b g(x)\, dx$$

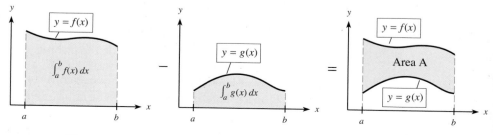

Figure 13.15   (a)   (b)   (c)

Although Figure 13.15(c) shows the graphs of both $y = f(x)$ and $y = g(x)$ lying above the x-axis, this difference of their integrals will always give the area between their graphs if both functions are continuous and if $f(x) \geq g(x)$ on the interval $[a, b]$. Using the fact that

$$\int_a^b f(x)\,dx - \int_a^b g(x)\,dx = \int_a^b [f(x) - g(x)]\,dx$$

we have the following result for the **area between two curves.**

Area Between Two Curves	If f and g are continuous functions on $[a, b]$ and if $f(x) \geq g(x)$ on $[a, b]$, then the area of the region bounded by $y = f(x)$, $y = g(x)$, $x = a$, and $x = b$ is $$A = \int_a^b [f(x) - g(x)]\,dx$$

EXAMPLE 1   Area Between Two Curves

Find the area of the region bounded by $y = x^2 + 4$, $y = x$, $x = 0$, and $x = 3$.

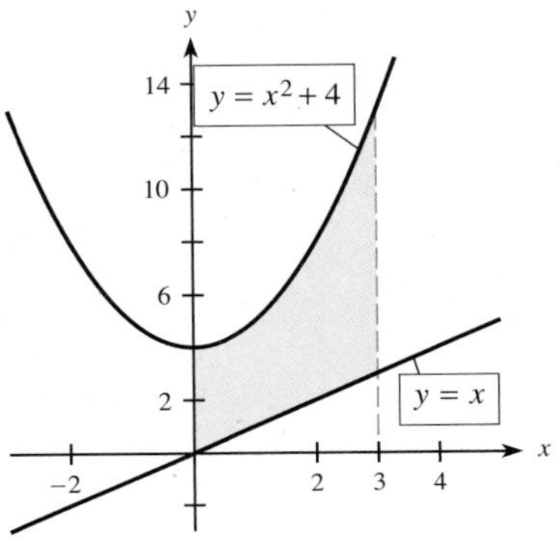

Figure 13.16

Solution
We first sketch the graphs of the functions on the same set of axes. The graph of the region is shown in Figure 13.16. Because $y = x^2 + 4$ lies above $y = x$ in the interval from $x = 0$ to $x = 3$, the area is

$$A = \int (\text{top curve} - \text{bottom curve})\,dx$$

$$A = \int_0^3 [(x^2 + 4) - x]\,dx = \frac{x^3}{3} + 4x - \frac{x^2}{2}\bigg|_0^3$$

$$= \left(9 + 12 - \frac{9}{2}\right) - (0 + 0 - 0) = 16\tfrac{1}{2} \text{ square units}$$

We are sometimes asked to find the area enclosed by two curves. In this case, we find the points of intersection of the curves to determine a and b.

EXAMPLE 2   Area Enclosed by Two Curves

Find the area enclosed by $y = x^2$ and $y = 2x + 3$.

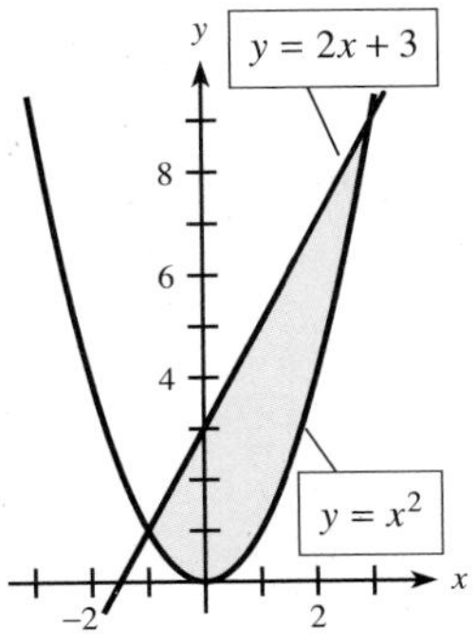

Figure 13.17

Solution
We first find a and b by finding the x-coordinates of the points of intersection of the graphs. Setting the y-values equal gives

$$x^2 = 2x + 3$$
$$x^2 - 2x - 3 = 0$$
$$(x - 3)(x + 1) = 0$$
$$x = 3, \quad x = -1$$

Thus with $a = -1$ and $b = 3$, we sketch the graphs of these functions on the same set of axes. Because the graphs do not intersect on the interval $(-1, 3)$, we can determine which function is larger on this interval by evaluating $2x + 3$ and x^2 at any value c where $-1 < c < 3$. Figure 13.17 shows the region between the graphs, with $2x + 3 \geq x^2$ from $x = -1$ to $x = 3$. The area of the enclosed region is

$$A = \int_{-1}^3 [(2x + 3) - x^2]\,dx = x^2 + 3x - \frac{x^3}{3}\bigg|_{-1}^3$$

$$= (9 + 9 - 9) - \left(1 - 3 + \frac{1}{3}\right) = 10\tfrac{2}{3} \text{ square units}$$

Some graphs enclose two or more regions because they have more than two points of intersection.

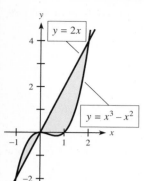

Figure 13.18

EXAMPLE 3   A Region with Two Sections

Find the area of the region enclosed by the graphs of

$$y = f(x) = x^3 - x^2 \quad \text{and} \quad y = g(x) = 2x.$$

Solution

To find the points of intersection of the graphs, we solve $f(x) = g(x)$, or $x^3 - x^2 = 2x$.

$$x^3 - x^2 - 2x = 0$$
$$x(x - 2)(x + 1) = 0$$
$$x = 0, x = 2, x = -1$$

Graphing these functions between $x = -1$ and $x = 2$, we see that for any x-value in the interval $(-1, 0)$, $f(x) \geq g(x)$, so $f(x) \geq g(x)$ for the region enclosed by the curves from $x = -1$ to $x = 0$. But evaluating the functions for any x-value in the interval $(0, 2)$ shows that $f(x) \leq g(x)$ for the region enclosed by the curves from $x = 0$ to $x = 2$. See Figure 13.18.

Thus we need one integral to find the area of the region from $x = -1$ to $x = 0$ and a second integral to find the area from $x = 0$ to $x = 2$. The area is found by summing these two integrals.

$$A = \int_{-1}^{0} [(x^3 - x^2) - (2x)] \, dx + \int_{0}^{2} [(2x) - (x^3 - x^2)] \, dx$$

$$= \int_{-1}^{0} (x^3 - x^2 - 2x) \, dx + \int_{0}^{2} (2x - x^3 + x^2) \, dx$$

$$= \left(\frac{x^4}{4} - \frac{x^3}{3} - x^2 \right) \Big|_{-1}^{0} + \left(x^2 - \frac{x^4}{4} + \frac{x^3}{3} \right) \Big|_{0}^{2}$$

$$= \left[(0) - \left(\frac{1}{4} - \frac{-1}{3} - 1 \right) \right] + \left[\left(4 - \frac{16}{4} + \frac{8}{3} \right) - (0) \right] = \frac{37}{12}$$

The area between the curves is $\frac{37}{12}$ square units.

Calculator Note   We've seen how to perform numerical integration with a graphing calculator. Appendix A, Section 13.3, shows two methods of approximating the area between two curves with a graphing calculator.

✓ CHECKPOINT

1. True or false:
    (a) Over the interval $[a, b]$, the area between the continuous functions $f(x)$ and $g(x)$ is

    $$\int_{a}^{b} [f(x) - g(x)] \, dx$$

    (b) If $f(x) \geq g(x)$ and the area between $f(x)$ and $g(x)$ is given by

    $$\int_{a}^{b} [f(x) - g(x)] \, dx$$

    then $x = a$ and $x = b$ represent the left and right boundaries, respectively, of the region.
    (c) To find points of intersection of $f(x)$ and $g(x)$, solve $f(x) = g(x)$.

2. Consider the functions $f(x) = x^2 + 3x - 9$ and $g(x) = \frac{1}{4}x^2$.

    (a) Find the points of intersection of $f(x)$ and $g(x)$.
    (b) Determine which function is greater than the other between the points found in part (a).
    (c) Set up the integral used to find the area between the curves in the interval between the points found in part (a).
    (d) Find the area.

EXAMPLE 4 | **Income Distribution** | **APPLICATION PREVIEW** |

The inequality of income distribution is measured by the **Gini coefficient** of income, which is defined as

$$\frac{\text{Area between } y = x \text{ and } y = L(x)}{\text{Area below } y = x} = \frac{\int_0^1 [x - L(x)]\, dx}{1/2}$$

$$= 2\int_0^1 [x - L(x)]\, dx$$

The function $y = L(x) = 2.409x^4 - 3.400x^3 + 2.164x^2 - 0.1746x$ models the 2012 income distribution data in the Application Preview.

(a) Use this $L(x)$ to find the Gini coefficient of income for 2012.
(b) If the Census Bureau Gini coefficient of income for 1991 is 0.428, during which year is the distribution of income more nearly equal?

Solution
(a) The Gini coefficient of income for 2012 is

$$2\int_0^1 [x - L(x)]\, dx = 2\int_0^1 [x - (2.409x^4 - 3.400x^3 + 2.164x^2 - 0.1746x)]\, dx$$

$$= 2[-0.4818x^5 + 0.8500x^4 - 0.7213x^3 + 0.5873x^2]_0^1 \approx 0.468$$

(b) Absolute equality of income would occur if the Gini coefficient of income were 0; and smaller coefficients indicate more nearly equal incomes. Thus the distribution of income was more nearly equal in 1991 than in 2012. ∎

Average Value If the graph of $y = f(x)$ lies on or above the x-axis from $x = a$ to $x = b$, then the area between the graph and the x-axis is

$$A = \int_a^b f(x)\, dx \quad \text{(See Figure 13.19(a))}$$

The area A is also the area of a rectangle with base equal to $b - a$ and height equal to the **average value** (or average height) of the function $y = f(x)$ (see Figure 13.19(b)).

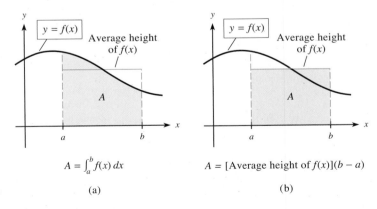

$$A = \int_a^b f(x)\, dx \qquad\qquad A = [\text{Average height of } f(x)](b - a)$$

Figure 13.19   (a)   (b)

Thus the average value of the function in Figure 13.19 is

$$\frac{A}{b - a} = \frac{1}{b - a}\int_a^b f(x)\, dx$$

Even if $f(x) \le 0$ on all or part of the interval $[a, b]$, we can find the average value by using the integral. Thus we have the following.

Average Value	The **average value** of a continuous function $y = f(x)$ over the interval $[a, b]$ is
	$$\text{Average value} = \frac{1}{b-a}\int_a^b f(x)\, dx$$

EXAMPLE 5   Average Cost

Suppose that the cost in dollars for x table lamps is given by $C(x) = 400 + x + 0.3x^2$.

(a)   What is the average value of $C(x)$ for 10 to 20 lamps?
(b)   Find the average cost per unit if 40 lamps are produced.

Solution

(a)   The average value of $C(x)$ from $x = 10$ to $x = 20$ is

$$\frac{1}{20-10}\int_{10}^{20}(400 + x + 0.3x^2)\, dx = \frac{1}{10}\left(400x + \frac{x^2}{2} + 0.1x^3\right)\Big|_{10}^{20}$$

$$= \frac{1}{10}[(8000 + 200 + 800) - (4000 + 50 + 100)]$$

$$= 485 \quad \text{(dollars)}$$

Thus for any number of lamps between 10 and 20 the *average total cost* for that number of lamps is $485.

(b)   The average cost per unit if 40 units are produced is the average cost function evaluated at $x = 40$. The average cost function is

$$\overline{C}(x) = \frac{C(x)}{x} = \frac{400}{x} + 1 + 0.3x$$

Thus the *average cost per unit* if 40 units are produced is

$$\overline{C}(40) = \frac{400}{40} + 1 + 0.3(40) = 23 \quad \text{[dollars per unit (i.e., lamp)]}$$

✓ **CHECKPOINT**   3.   Find the average value of $f(x) = x^2 - 4$ over $[-1, 3]$.

EXAMPLE 6   Average Value of a Function

Consider the functions $f(x) = x^2 - 4$ and $g(x) = x^3 - 4x$. For each function, do the following.

(a)   Graph the function on the interval $[-3, 3]$.
(b)   On the graph, "eyeball" the average value (height) of each function on $[-2, 2]$.
(c)   Compute the average value of the function over the interval $[-2, 2]$.

Solution

For $f(x) = x^2 - 4$:

(a)   The graph of $f(x) = x^2 - 4$ is shown in Figure 13.20(a).
(b)   The average height of $f(x)$ over $[-2, 2]$ appears to be near -2.
(c)   The average value of $f(x)$ over the interval is given by

$$\frac{1}{2-(-2)}\int_{-2}^{2}(x^2 - 4)\, dx = \frac{1}{4}\left(\frac{x^3}{3} - 4x\right)\Big|_{-2}^{2}$$

$$= \left(\frac{8}{12} - 2\right) - \left(-\frac{8}{12} + 2\right) = \frac{4}{3} - 4 = -\frac{8}{3} = -2\tfrac{2}{3}$$

For $g(x) = x^3 - 4x$:

(a) The graph of $g(x) = x^3 - 4x$ is shown in Figure 13.20(b).

(b) The average height of $g(x)$ over $[-2, 2]$ appears to be approximately 0.

(c) The average value of $g(x)$ is given by

$$\frac{1}{2 - (-2)}\int_{-2}^{2} (x^3 - 4x)\, dx = \frac{1}{4}\left(\frac{x^4}{4} - \frac{4x^2}{2}\right)\Big|_{-2}^{2}$$

$$= \left(\frac{16}{16} - \frac{16}{8}\right) - \left(\frac{16}{16} - \frac{16}{8}\right) = 0$$

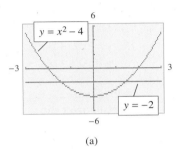

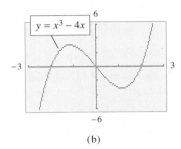

Figure 13.20   (a)   (b)

✓ CHECKPOINT ANSWERS

1. (a) False. This is true only if $f(x) \geq g(x)$ over $[a, b]$.

   (b) True   (c) True

2. (a) Solve $f(x) = g(x)$, or $x^2 + 3x - 9 = \frac{1}{4}x^2$. The solutions are $x = -6$ and $x = 2$.

   The points of intersection are $(-6, 9)$ and $(2, 1)$.

   (b) $g(x) \geq f(x)$ on the interval $[-6, 2]$.

   (c) $A = \int_{-6}^{2}\left[\frac{1}{4}x^2 - (x^2 + 3x - 9)\right] dx$

   (d) $A = \frac{x^3}{12} - \frac{x^3}{3} - \frac{3x^2}{2} + 9x\Big|_{-6}^{2} = 64$ square units

3. $\frac{1}{3 - (-1)}\int_{-1}^{3} (x^2 - 4)\, dx = -\frac{5}{3}$

| EXERCISES | 13.3

For each shaded region in Problems 1–6, (a) form the integral that represents the area of the shaded region and (b) find the area of the region.

1.

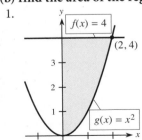

2.

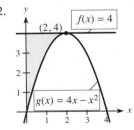

3.

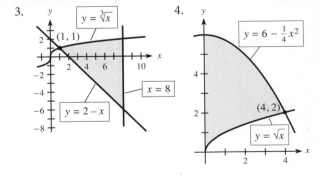

4.

5.

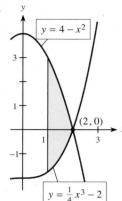

6.

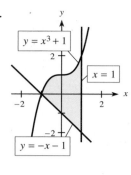

15. $y = x^3 - 1;$ $y = x - 1;$ to the right of the y-axis
16. $y = x^2 - 2x + 1;$ $y = x^2 - 5x + 4;$ $x = 2$
17. $y = \frac{1}{2}x^2;$ $y = x^2 - 2x$
18. $y = x^2;$ $y = 4x - x^2$
19. $h(x) = x^2;$ $k(x) = \sqrt{x}$
20. $g(x) = 1 - x^2;$ $h(x) = x^2 + x$
21. $f(x) = x^3;$ $g(x) = x^2 + 2x$
22. $f(x) = x^3;$ $g(x) = 2x - x^2$
23. $f(x) = \dfrac{3}{x};$ $g(x) = 4 - x$

24. $f(x) = \dfrac{6}{x};$ $g(x) = -x - 5$

25. $y = \sqrt{x + 3};$ $x = -3;$ $y = 2$
26. $y = \sqrt{4 - x};$ $x = 4;$ $y = 3$

For each shaded region in Problems 7–12, (a) find the points of intersection of the curves, (b) form the integral that represents the area of the shaded region, and (c) find the area of the shaded region.

In Problems 27–32, find the average value of each function over the given interval.

27. $f(x) = 9 - x^2$ over $[0, 3]$
28. $f(x) = 2x - x^2$ over $[0, 2]$
29. $f(x) = x^3 - x$ over $[-1, 1]$
30. $f(x) = \frac{1}{2}x^3 + 1$ over $[-2, 0]$
31. $f(x) = \sqrt{x} - 2$ over $[1, 4]$
32. $f(x) = \sqrt[3]{x}$ over $[-8, -1]$

7.

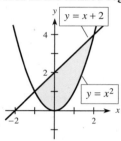

8.

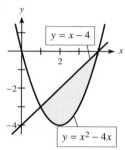

33. Use a graphing calculator or computer to find the area between the curves $y = f(x) = x^3 - 4x$ and $y = g(x) = x^2 - 4$.
34. Use a graphing calculator or computer to find the area between the curves $f(x) = \sqrt[3]{x}$ and $g(x) = x^3 - x$.

9.

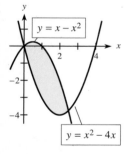

10.

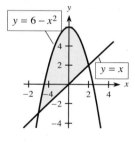

APPLICATIONS

35. *Average profit* For the product whose total cost and total revenue are shown in the figure, represent total revenue by $R(x)$ and total cost by $C(x)$ and write an integral that gives the average profit for the product over the interval from x_0 to x_1.

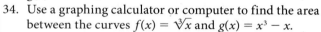

11.

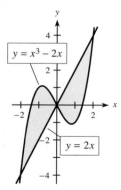

12.

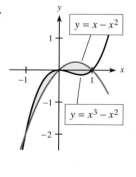

36. *Sales and advertising* The figure shows the sales growth rates under different levels of distribution and advertising from a to b. Set up an integral to determine the extra sales growth if $4 million is used in advertising rather than $2 million.

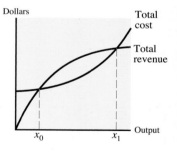

In Problems 13–26, equations are given whose graphs enclose a region. In each problem, find the area of the region.

13. $f(x) = x^2 + 2;$ $g(x) = -x^2;$ $x = 0;$ $x = 2$
14. $f(x) = x^2;$ $g(x) = -\frac{1}{10}(10 + x);$ $x = 0;$ $x = 3$

37. *Cost* The cost of producing x smart phones is $C(x) = x^2 + 400x + 2000.$

(a) Use $C(x)$ to find the average cost of producing 1000 smart phones.

(b) Find the average value of the cost function $C(x)$ over the interval from 0 to 1000.

38. *Inventory management* The figure shows how an inventory of a product is depleted each quarter of a given year. What is the average inventory per month for the first 3 months for this product? (Assume that the graph is a line joining (0, 1300) and (3, 100).)

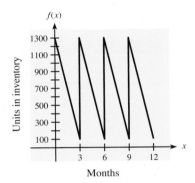

39. *Sales and advertising* The number of daily sales of a product was found to be given by

$$S = 100xe^{-x^2} + 100$$

x days after the start of an advertising campaign for this product.

(a) Find the average daily sales during the first 20 days of the campaign—that is, from $x = 0$ to $x = 20$.

(b) If no new advertising campaign is begun, what is the average number of sales per day for the next 10 days (from $x = 20$ to $x = 30$)?

40. *Demand* The demand function for a certain product is given by

$$p = 500 + \frac{1000}{q + 1}$$

where p is the price and q is the number of units demanded. Find the average price as demand ranges from 49 to 99 units.

41. *Social Security beneficiaries* With data from the Social Security Trustees Report for selected years from 1950 and projected to 2030, the number of Social Security beneficiaries (in millions) can be modeled by

$$B(t) = 0.00024t^3 - 0.026t^2 + 1.6t + 2.2$$

where t is the number of years past 1950. Use the model to find the average number of Social Security beneficiaries per year (actual and predicted) between
(a) 1980 and 2000.   (b) 2010 and 2030.

42. *Total income* Suppose that the income from a slot machine in a casino flows continuously at a rate of

$$f(t) = 100e^{0.1t}$$

where t is the time in hours since the casino opened. Then the total income during the first 10 hours is given by

$$\int_0^{10} 100e^{0.1t}\, dt$$

Find the average income over the first 10 hours.

43. *Drug levels in the blood* A drug manufacturer has developed a time-release capsule with the number of milligrams of the drug in the bloodstream given by

$$S = 30x^{18/7} - 240x^{11/7} + 480x^{4/7}$$

where x is in hours and $0 \le x \le 4$. Find the average number of milligrams of the drug in the bloodstream for the first 4 hours after a capsule is taken.

44. *Income distribution* With data from the U.S. Census Bureau, the Lorenz curves for the income distribution for 2012 in the United States for White non-Hispanic households and for Asian households are given below. Find the Gini coefficient of income for both groups, and compare the distribution of income for these groups.

White non-Hispanic:

$$y = 2.344x^4 - 3.340x^3 + 2.154x^2 - 0.1588x + 0.0005952$$

Asian:

$$y = 2.240x^4 - 3.222x^3 + 2.169x^2 - 0.1871x + 0.0004762$$

45. *Income distribution* With U.S. Census Bureau data, the Lorenz curves for the 2012 income distribution in the United States for Black households and for Hispanic households (of any race) are given below. Find the Gini coefficient of income for both groups, and compare the distribution of income for these groups.

Black:

$$y = 2.292x^4 - 3.127x^3 + 2.006x^2 - 0.1710x + 0.0005556$$

Hispanic:

$$y = 1.830x^4 - 2.564x^3 + 1.806x^2 - 0.1137x + 0.0003512$$

46. *Income distribution* In an effort to make the distribution of income more nearly equal, the government of a country passes a tax law that changes the Lorenz curve from $y = 0.99x^{2.1}$ for one year to $y = 0.32x^2 + 0.68x$ for the next year. Find the Gini coefficient of income for both years, and compare the distributions of income before and after the tax law was passed. Interpret the result.

47. *Income distribution* The Lorenz curves for the income distribution in the United States for all races for 2012 and for 2004 are given below (*Source:* U.S. Census Bureau). Find the Gini coefficient of income for both groups, and compare the distribution of income for these groups.

2012: $y = x^{2.760}$ 2004: $y = x^{2.671}$

48. *Income distribution* Suppose the Gini coefficient of income for a certain country is $2/5$. Find the value of p if the Lorenz curve for this country is

$$L(x) = \frac{1}{3}x + \frac{2}{3}x^p.$$

49. *Gini coefficient* If the Lorenz curve for the income distribution for a given year is $L(x) = x^p$, use integration to find a simple formula for the corresponding Gini coefficient.

50. *Lorenz curve* If the Lorenz curve for the income distribution for a given year has the form $L(x) = x^p$ and the Gini coefficient is G, find a formula for p.

OBJECTIVES

13.4

- To use definite integrals to find total income, present value, and future value of continuous income streams
- To use definite integrals to find the consumer's surplus
- To use definite integrals to find the producer's surplus

Applications of Definite Integrals in Business and Economics

| APPLICATION PREVIEW |

Suppose the oil pumped from a well is considered as a continuous income stream with annual rate of flow (in thousands of dollars per year) at time t years given by

$$f(t) = 600e^{-0.2(t+5)}$$

The company can use a definite integral involving $f(t)$ to estimate the well's present value over the next 10 years (see Example 2).

The definite integral can be used in a number of applications in business and economics. In addition to the present value, the definite integral can be used to find the total income over a fixed number of years from a continuous income stream.

Definite integrals also can be used to determine the savings realized in the marketplace by some consumers (called consumer's surplus) and some producers (called producer's surplus).

Continuous Income Streams

An oil company's profits depend on the amount of oil that can be pumped from a well. Thus we can consider a pump at an oil field as producing a **continuous stream of income** for the owner. Because both the pump and the oil field "wear out" with time, the continuous stream of income is a function of time. Suppose $f(t)$ is the (annual) *rate* of flow of income from this pump; then we can find the total income from the rate of income by using integration. In particular, the total income for k years is given by

$$\text{Total income} = \int_0^k f(t)\, dt$$

EXAMPLE 1   Oil Revenue

Now ——→ 10 Years From Now

$2,594,000 = Total Income

© Wade H. Massie/Shutterstock.com

A small oil company considers the continuous pumping of oil from a well as a continuous income stream with its annual rate of flow at time t given by

$$f(t) = 600e^{-0.2t}$$

in thousands of dollars per year. Find an estimate of the total income from this well over the next 10 years.

Solution

$$\text{Total income} = \int_0^{10} f(t)\, dt = \int_0^{10} 600e^{-0.2t}\, dt$$

$$= \left. \frac{600}{-0.2}e^{-0.2t} \right|_0^{10} \approx 2594 \quad \text{(to the nearest integer)}$$

Thus the total income is approximately $2,594,000.

In addition to the total income from a continuous income stream, the **present value** of the stream is also important. The present value is the value today of a continuous income stream that will be providing income in the future. The present value is useful in deciding when to replace machinery or what new equipment to select.

To find the present value of a continuous stream of income with rate of flow $f(t)$, we first graph the function $f(t)$ and divide the time interval from 0 to k into n subintervals of width Δt_i, $i = 1$ to n.

The total amount of income is the area under this curve between $t = 0$ and $t = k$. We can approximate the amount of income in each subinterval by finding the area of the rectangle in that subinterval. (See Figure 13.21.)

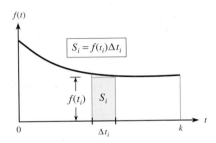

Figure 13.21

We have shown that the future value S that accrues if P is invested for t years at an annual rate r, compounded continuously, is $S = Pe^{rt}$. Thus the present value of the investment that yields the single payment of S after t years is

$$P = \frac{S}{e^{rt}} = Se^{-rt}$$

The contribution to S in the ith subinterval is $S_i = f(t_i)\,\Delta t_i$, and the present value of this amount is $P_i = f(t_i)\,\Delta t_i e^{-rt_i}$. Thus the total present value of S can be approximated by

$$\sum_{i=1}^{n} f(t_i)\,\Delta t_i e^{-rt_i}$$

This approximation improves as $\Delta t_i \to 0$ with the present value given by

$$\lim_{\Delta t_i \to 0} \sum_{i=1}^{n} f(t_i)\,\Delta t_i e^{-rt_i}$$

This limit gives the **present value** as a definite integral.

Present Value of a Continuous Income Stream

If $f(t)$ is the rate of continuous income flow earning interest at rate r, compounded continuously, then the **present value of the continuous income stream** is

$$\text{Present value} = \int_0^k f(t)e^{-rt}\,dt$$

where $t = 0$ to $t = k$ is the time interval.

EXAMPLE 2   **Present Value | APPLICATION PREVIEW |**

Suppose that the oil company in Example 1 is planning to sell one of its wells because of its remote location. Suppose further that the company wants to use the present value of this well over the next 10 years to help establish its selling price. If the company determines that the annual rate of flow is

$$f(t) = 600e^{-0.2(t+5)}$$

in thousands of dollars per year, and if money is worth 10%, compounded continuously, find this present value.

Solution

$$\text{Present value} = \int_0^{10} f(t)e^{-rt}\,dt$$

$$= \int_0^{10} 600e^{-0.2(t+5)}e^{-0.1t}\,dt = \int_0^{10} 600e^{-0.3t-1}\,dt$$

If $u = -0.3t - 1$, then $u' = -0.3$ and we get

$$\frac{1}{-0.3}\int 600e^{-0.3t-1}(-0.3\,dt) = \frac{600}{-0.3}e^{-0.3t-1}\Big|_0^{10}$$

$$= -2000(e^{-4} - e^{-1}) \approx 699 \quad \text{(to the nearest integer)}$$

Thus the present value is $699,000.

Recall that the future value of a continuously compounded investment at rate r after k years is Pe^{rk}, where P is the amount invested (or the present value). Thus, for a continuous income stream, the **future value** is found as follows.

Future Value of a Continuous Income Stream

If $f(t)$ is the rate of continuous income flow for k years earning interest at rate r, compounded continuously, then the **future value of the continuous income stream** is

$$FV = e^{rk}\int_0^k f(t)e^{-rt}\,dt$$

EXAMPLE 3   Future Value

If the rate of flow of income from an asset is $1000e^{0.02t}$, in millions of dollars per year, and if the income is invested at 6% compounded continuously, find the future value of the asset 4 years from now.

Solution
The future value is given by

$$FV = e^{rk}\int_0^k f(t)e^{-rt}\,dt$$

$$= e^{(0.06)4}\int_0^4 1000e^{0.02t}e^{-0.06t}\,dt = e^{0.24}\int_0^4 1000e^{-0.04t}\,dt$$

$$= e^{0.24}(-25{,}000e^{-0.04t})\Big|_0^4 = -25{,}000e^{0.24}(e^{-0.16} - 1)$$

$$\approx 4699.05 \quad \text{(millions of dollars)}$$

✓ CHECKPOINT

1. Suppose that a continuous income stream has an annual rate of flow given by $f(t) = 5000e^{-0.01t}$, and suppose that money is worth 7% compounded continuously. Create the integral used to find
   (a) the total income for the next 5 years.
   (b) the present value for the next 5 years.
   (c) the future value 5 years from now.

Consumer's Surplus

Suppose that the demand for a product is given by $p = f(x)$ and that the supply of the product is described by $p = g(x)$. The price p_1 where the graphs of these functions intersect is the **equilibrium price** (see Figure 13.22(a)). As the demand curve shows, some consumers (but not all) would be willing to pay more than $$p_1$ for the product.

For example, some consumers would be willing to buy x_3 units if the price were $\$p_3$. Those consumers willing to pay more than $\$p_1$ are benefiting from the lower price. The total gain for all those consumers willing to pay more than $\$p_1$ is called the **consumer's surplus,** and under proper assumptions the area of the shaded region in Figure 13.22(a) represents this consumer's surplus.

Looking at Figure 13.22(b), we see that if the demand curve has equation $p = f(x)$, the consumer's surplus is given by the area between $f(x)$ and the x-axis from 0 to x_1, *minus* the area of the rectangle denoted TR:

$$CS = \int_0^{x_1} f(x)\, dx - p_1 x_1$$

Note that with equilibrium price p_1 and equilibrium quantity x_1, the product $p_1 x_1$ is the area of the rectangle that represents the total dollars spent by consumers and received as revenue by producers (see Figure 13.22(b)).

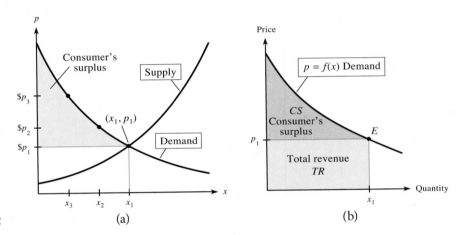

Figure 13.22   (a)   (b)

EXAMPLE 4 Consumer's Surplus

The demand function for x units of a product is $p = f(x) = 1020/(x + 1)$ dollars. If the equilibrium price is $20, what is the consumer's surplus?

Solution
We must first find the quantity that will be purchased at this price. Letting $p = 20$ and solving for x, we get

$$20 = \frac{1020}{x + 1} \quad \text{so} \quad 20(x + 1) = 1020$$

Thus $20x + 20 = 1020$ or $20x = 1000$ so $x = 50$

Thus the equilibrium point is $(x_1, p_1) = (50, 20)$. The consumer's surplus is given by

$$CS = \int_0^{x_1} f(x)\, dx - p_1 x_1 = \int_0^{50} \frac{1020}{x + 1}\, dx - 20 \cdot 50$$

$$= 1020 \ln |x + 1| \Big|_0^{50} - 1000$$

$$= 1020(\ln 51 - \ln 1) - 1000$$

$$\approx 4010.46 - 1000 = 3010.46$$

The consumer's surplus is $3010.46.

EXAMPLE 5   Consumer's Surplus

A product's demand function is $p = f(x) = \sqrt{49 - 6x}$ and its supply function is $p = g(x) = x + 1$, where p is the price per unit in dollars and x is the number of units. Find the equilibrium point and the consumer's surplus there.

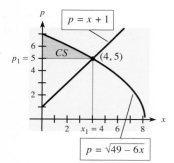

Figure 13.23

Solution

We can determine the equilibrium point by solving the two equations simultaneously.

$$\sqrt{49 - 6x} = x + 1$$
$$49 - 6x = (x + 1)^2$$
$$0 = x^2 + 8x - 48$$
$$0 = (x + 12)(x - 4)$$
$$x = 4 \quad \text{or} \quad x = -12$$

Thus the equilibrium quantity is $x_1 = 4$ and the equilibrium price is $p_1 = \$5$ ($x = -12$ is not a solution). The graphs of the supply and demand functions are shown in Figure 13.23. The consumer's surplus is given by

$$CS = \int_0^4 f(x)\,dx - p_1 x_1 = \int_0^4 \sqrt{49 - 6x}\,dx - 5 \cdot 4$$

$$= -\frac{1}{6}\int_0^4 \sqrt{49 - 6x}\,(-6\,dx) - 20 = -\frac{1}{9}(49 - 6x)^{3/2}\Big|_0^4 - 20$$

$$= -\frac{1}{9}[(25)^{3/2} - (49)^{3/2}] - 20 = -\frac{1}{9}(125 - 343) - 20 \approx 4.22$$

The consumer's surplus is $4.22.

In a monopoly market there is no market equilibrium point, and we find consumer's surplus at the point where the monopoly has maximum profit.

EXAMPLE 6   Monopoly Market

Suppose a monopoly has its total cost (in dollars) for a product given by $C(x) = 6000 + 0.2x^3$. Suppose also that demand is given by $p = f(x) = 300 - 0.1x$, where p is in dollars and x is the number of units. Find the consumer's surplus at the point where the monopoly has maximum profit.

Solution

We must first find the point where the profit function is maximized. Because the demand for x units is $p = 300 - 0.1x$, the total revenue is

$$R(x) = (300 - 0.1x)x = 300x - 0.1x^2$$

Thus the profit function is

$$P(x) = R(x) - C(x)$$
$$P(x) = 300x - 0.1x^2 - (6000 + 0.2x^2)$$
$$P(x) = 300x - 6000 - 0.3x^2$$

Then $P'(x) = 300 - 0.6x$. So $0 = 300 - 0.6x$ has the solution $x = 500$.

Because $P''(500) = -0.6 < 0$, the profit for the monopoly is maximized when $x = 500$ units are sold at price $p = 300 - 0.1(500) = 250$ dollars per unit.

The consumer's surplus at $x_1 = 500$, $p_1 = 250$ is given by

$$CS = \int_0^{500} f(x)\,dx - 500 \cdot 250 = \int_0^{500} (300 - 0.1x)\,dx - 125{,}000$$

$$= 300x - \frac{0.1x^2}{2}\Big|_0^{500} - 125{,}000 = (150{,}000 - 12{,}500) - 125{,}000 = 12{,}500$$

The consumer's surplus is $12,500.

MONEY ON THE TABLE

Another way to understand consumer surplus is through the popular concept of "money on the table." Imagine you have $500 to spend on an iPad. When you get to the Apple store, the model you want costs only $450. You're delighted to spend only $450, but you **would** have spent all your money if the iPad had been priced at $500. In this example, Apple left money—$50 to be exact—on the table (or in your pocket). That's a consumer's surplus.

GRAVY

Now think of the iPad example in another way. Suppose Apple meets all its profit targets at a price of $400 per iPad. The fact that you pay $450 means that there is a producer surplus. Apple would sell that iPad at the $400 price point, but because you were willing to part with $450, the company receives an extra $50—or gravy—for its bottom line. That is, a producer's surplus.

Producer's Surplus

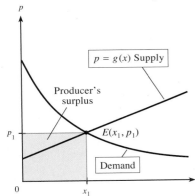

Figure 13.24

When a product is sold at the equilibrium price, p_1, some producers will also benefit, for they would have sold the product at a lower price. The area between the line $p = p_1$ and the supply curve (from $x = 0$ to $x = x_1$) gives the producer's surplus (see Figure 13.24).

If the supply function is $p = g(x)$, the **producer's surplus** is given by the area between the graph of $p = g(x)$ and the x-axis from 0 to x_1 *subtracted from* $p_1 x_1$, the area of the rectangle shown in Figure 13.24.

$$PS = p_1 x_1 - \int_0^{x_1} g(x)\, dx$$

Note that $p_1 x_1$ represents the total revenue at the equilibrium point.

EXAMPLE 7   Producer's Surplus

Suppose that the supply function for x million units of a product is $p = x^2 + x$ dollars per unit. If the equilibrium price is $20 per unit, what is the producer's surplus?

Solution

Because $p = 20$, we can find the equilibrium quantity x as follows:

$$20 = x^2 + x$$
$$0 = x^2 + x - 20$$
$$0 = (x + 5)(x - 4)$$
$$x = -5, \quad x = 4$$

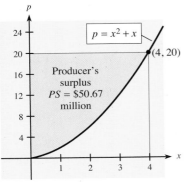

Figure 13.25

The equilibrium point is $x_1 = 4$ million units, $p_1 = \$20$. The producer's surplus is given by

$$PS = 20 \cdot 4 - \int_0^4 (x^2 + x)\, dx$$

$$= 80 - \left(\frac{x^3}{3} + \frac{x^2}{2}\right)\Big|_0^4$$

$$= 80 - \left(\frac{64}{3} + 8\right)$$

$$\approx 50.67$$

The producer's surplus is $50.67 million. See Figure 13.25.

EXAMPLE 8 Producer's Surplus

The demand function for a product is $p = \sqrt{49 - 6x}$ and the supply function is $p = x + 1$. Find the producer's surplus.

Solution

We found the equilibrium point for these functions to be (4, 5) in Example 5 (see Figure 13.23 earlier in this section). The producer's surplus is

$$PS = 5 \cdot 4 - \int_0^4 (x + 1) \, dx = 20 - \left(\frac{x^2}{2} + x \right) \Big|_0^4$$

$$= 20 - (8 + 4) = 8$$

The producer's surplus is $8.

✓ **CHECKPOINT**

2. Suppose that for a certain product, the supply function is $p = f(x)$, the demand function is $p = g(x)$, and the equilibrium point is (x_1, p_1). Decide whether the following are true or false.

(a) $CS = \int_0^{x_1} f(x) \, dx - p_1 x_1$ (b) $PS = \int_0^{x_1} f(x) \, dx - p_1 x_1$

3. If demand is $p = \dfrac{100}{x + 1}$, supply is $p = x + 1$, and the market equilibrium is (9, 10), create the integral used to find the
   (a) consumer's surplus.   (b) producer's surplus.

EXAMPLE 9 Consumer's Surplus and Producer's Surplus

Suppose that for x units of a certain product, the demand function is $p = 200e^{-0.01x}$ dollars and the supply function is $p = \sqrt{200x + 49}$ dollars.

(a) Use a graphing calculator to find the market equilibrium point.
(b) Find the consumer's surplus.
(c) Find the producer's surplus.

Solution

(a) Solving $200e^{-0.01x} = \sqrt{200x + 49}$ is very difficult using algebraic techniques. Using SOLVER or INTERSECT on a graphing calculator gives $x = 60$, to the nearest unit, with a price of $109.76. (See Figure 13.26(a).)

(b) The consumer's surplus, shown in Figure 13.26(b), is

$$\int_0^{60} 200e^{-0.01x} \, dx - 109.76(60) = (-20{,}000e^{-0.01x}) \Big|_0^{60} - 6585.60$$

$$= -20{,}000e^{-0.6} + 20{,}000 - 6585.60$$

$$\approx 2438.17 \text{ dollars}$$

(c) The producer's surplus, shown in Figure 13.26(b), is

$$60(109.76) - \int_0^{60} \sqrt{200x + 49} \, dx = 6585.60 - \frac{1}{200} \left[\frac{(200x + 49)^{3/2}}{3/2} \right]_0^{60}$$

$$= 6585.60 - \frac{1}{300} [(12{,}049^{3/2} - 49^{3/2})] \approx 2178.10 \text{ dollars}$$

Note that we also could have evaluated these definite integrals with the numerical integration feature of a graphing calculator, and we would have obtained the same results.

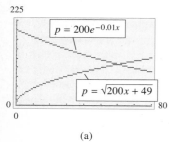

(a)

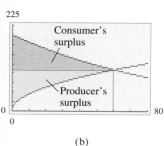

(b)

Figure 13.26

✓ CHECKPOINT ANSWERS

1. (a) $\int_0^5 5000e^{-0.01t}\,dt$

   (b) $\int_0^5 (5000e^{-0.01t})(e^{-0.07t})\,dt = \int_0^5 5000e^{-0.08t}\,dt$

   (c) $e^{(0.07)(5)}\int_0^5 (5000e^{-0.01t})(e^{-0.07t})\,dt = e^{0.35}\int_0^5 5000e^{-0.08t}\,dt$

2. (a) False. Consumer's surplus uses the demand function, so

   $$CS = \int_0^{x_1} g(x)\,dx - p_1x_1$$

   (b) False. Producer's surplus uses the supply function, but the formula is

   $$PS = p_1x_1 - \int_0^{x_1} f(x)\,dx$$

3. (a) $CS = \int_0^9 \dfrac{100}{x+1}\,dx - 90$ (b) $PS = 90 - \int_0^9 (x+1)\,dx$

| EXERCISES | 13.4

CONTINUOUS INCOME STREAMS

1. Find the total income over the next 10 years from a continuous income stream that has an annual rate of flow at time t given by $f(t) = 12{,}000e^{0.01t}$ (dollars per year).

2. Find the total income over the next 8 years from a continuous income stream with an annual rate of flow at time t given by $f(t) = 8500e^{-0.2t}$ (dollars per year).

3. Suppose that a steel company views the production of its continuous caster as a continuous income stream with a monthly rate of flow at time t given by

   $$f(t) = 24{,}000e^{0.03t}\quad\text{(dollars per month)}$$

   Find the total income from this caster in the first year.

4. Suppose that the Quick-Fix Car Service franchise finds that the income generated by its stores can be modeled by assuming that the income is a continuous stream with a monthly rate of flow at time t given by

   $$f(t) = 10{,}000e^{0.02t}\quad\text{(dollars per month)}$$

   Find the total income from a Quick-Fix store for the first 2 years of operation.

5. A small brewery considers the output of its bottling machine as a continuous income stream with an annual rate of flow at time t given by

   $$f(t) = 80e^{-0.1t}$$

   in thousands of dollars per year. Find the income from this stream for the next 10 years.

6. A company that services a number of vending machines considers its income as a continuous stream with an annual rate of flow at time t given by

   $$f(t) = 120e^{-0.4t}$$

   in thousands of dollars per year. Find the income from this stream over the next 5 years.

7. A franchise models the profit from its store as a continuous income stream with a monthly rate of flow at time t given by

   $$f(t) = 3000e^{0.004t}\quad\text{(dollars per month)}$$

   When a new store opens, its manager is judged against the model, with special emphasis on the second half of the first year. Find the total profit for the second 6-month period ($t = 6$ to $t = 12$).

8. The Medi Spa franchise has a continuous income stream with a monthly rate of flow modeled by $f(t) = 20{,}000e^{0.03t}$ (dollars per month). Find the total income for years 2 through 5.

9. A continuous income stream has an annual rate of flow at time t given by

   $$f(t) = 12{,}000e^{0.04t}\quad\text{(dollars per year)}$$

   If money is worth 8% compounded continuously, find the present value of this stream for the next 8 years.

10. A continuous income stream has an annual rate of flow at time t given by

    $$f(t) = 9000e^{0.12t}\quad\text{(dollars per year)}$$

    Find the present value of this income stream for the next 10 years, if money is worth 6% compounded continuously.

11. The income from an established chain of laundromats is a continuous stream with its annual rate of flow at time t given by $f(t) = 630{,}000$ (dollars per year). If money is worth 7% compounded continuously, find the present value and future value of this chain over the next 5 years.

12. The profit from an insurance agency can be considered as a continuous income stream with an annual rate of flow at time t given by $f(t) = 840{,}000$ (dollars per year). Find the present value and future value of this agency

over the next 12 years, if money is worth 8% compounded continuously.

13. Suppose that a printing firm considers its production as a continuous income stream. If the annual rate of flow at time t is given by

$$f(t) = 97.5e^{-0.2(t+3)}$$

in thousands of dollars per year, and if money is worth 6% compounded continuously, find the present value and future value of the presses over the next 10 years.

14. Suppose that a vending machine company is considering selling some of its machines. Suppose further that the income from these particular machines is a continuous stream with an annual rate of flow at time t given by

$$f(t) = 12e^{-0.4(t+3)}$$

in thousands of dollars per year. Find the present value and future value of the machines over the next 5 years if money is worth 10% compounded continuously.

15. A 58-year-old couple are considering opening a business of their own. They will either purchase an established Gift and Card Shoppe or open a new Wine Boutique. The Gift Shoppe has a continuous income stream with an annual rate of flow at time t given by

$$G(t) = 30,000 \qquad \text{(dollars per year)}$$

and the Wine Boutique has a continuous income stream with a projected annual rate of flow at time t given by

$$W(t) = 21,600e^{0.08t} \qquad \text{(dollars per year)}$$

The initial investment is the same for both businesses, and money is worth 10% compounded continuously. Find the present value of each business over the next 7 years (until the couple reach age 65) to see which is the better buy.

16. If the couple in Problem 15 plan to keep the business until age 70 (for the next 12 years), find each present value to see which business is the better buy in this case.

CONSUMER'S SURPLUS

In Problems 17–26, p and C are in dollars and x is the number of units.

17. The demand function for a product is $p = 34 - x^2$. If the equilibrium price is $9 per unit, what is the consumer's surplus?

18. The demand function for a product is $p = 100 - 4x$. If the equilibrium price is $40 per unit, what is the consumer's surplus?

19. The demand function for a product is $p = 200/(x + 2)$. If the equilibrium quantity is 8 units, what is the consumer's surplus?

20. The demand function for a certain product is $p = 100/(1 + 2x)$. If the equilibrium quantity is 12 units, what is the consumer's surplus?

21. The demand function for a certain product is $p = 81 - x^2$ and the supply function is $p = x^2 + 4x + 11$. Find the equilibrium point and the consumer's surplus there.

22. The demand function for a product is $p = 49 - x^2$ and the supply function is $p = 4x + 4$. Find the equilibrium point and the consumer's surplus there.

23. If the demand function for a product is $p = 12/(x + 1)$ and the supply function is $p = 1 + 0.2x$, find the consumer's surplus under pure competition.

24. If the demand function for a good is $p = 110 - x^2$ and the supply function for it is $p = 2 - \frac{6}{5}x + \frac{1}{5}x^2$, find the consumer's surplus under pure competition.

25. A monopoly has a total cost function $C = 1000 + 120x + 6x^2$ for its product, which has demand function $p = 360 - 3x - 2x^2$. Find the consumer's surplus at the point where the monopoly has maximum profit.

26. A monopoly has a total cost function $C = 500 + 2x^2 + 10x$ for its product, which has demand function $p = -\frac{1}{3}x^2 - 2x + 30$. Find the consumer's surplus at the point where the monopoly has maximum profit.

PRODUCER'S SURPLUS

In Problems 27–36, p is in dollars and x is the number of units.

27. Suppose that the supply function for a good is $p = 4x^2 + 2x + 2$. If the equilibrium price is $422 per unit, what is the producer's surplus there?

28. Suppose that the supply function for a good is $p = 0.1x^2 + 3x + 20$. If the equilibrium price is $36 per unit, what is the producer's surplus there?

29. If the supply function for a commodity is $p = 10e^{x/3}$, what is the producer's surplus when 15 units are sold?

30. If the supply function for a commodity is $p = 40 + 100(x + 1)^2$, what is the producer's surplus at $x = 20$?

31. Find the producer's surplus at market equilibrium for a product if its demand function is $p = 81 - x^2$ and its supply function is $p = x^2 + 4x + 11$.

32. Find the producer's surplus at market equilibrium for a product if its demand function is $p = 49 - x^2$ and its supply function is $p = 4x + 4$.

33. Find the producer's surplus at market equilibrium for a product with demand function $p = 12/(x + 1)$ and supply function $p = 1 + 0.2x$.

34. Find the producer's surplus at market equilibrium for a product with demand function $p = 110 - x^2$ and supply function $p = 2 - \frac{6}{5}x + \frac{1}{5}x^2$.

35. The demand function for a certain product is $p = 144 - 2x^2$ and the supply function is $p = x^2 + 33x + 48$. Find the producer's surplus at the equilibrium point.

36. The demand function for a product is $p = 280 - 4x - x^2$ and the supply function for it is $p = 160 + 4x + x^2$. Find the producer's surplus at the equilibrium point.

13.5

Using Tables of Integrals

■| **APPLICATION PREVIEW** |■

The rate of change of worldwide sales (in billions of dollars per year) of Hepatitis C treatments, from 2012 and projected to 2016, is given by

$$\frac{dS}{dt} = 0.575(1.234^t)$$

where t equals the number of years after 2010 and S is projected to be $9.7 billion in 2016 (*Source:* Evaluate Pharma). Finding the function that models the worldwide sales of Hepatitis C treatments requires evaluating the integral

$$S(t) = \int 0.575(1.234^t)dt$$

Evaluating this integral is made easier by using a formula such as those given in Table 13.2. (See Example 4.) The examples in this section illustrate how some of these formulas are used.

The formulas in Table 13.2, and others listed in other resources, extend the number of integrals that can be evaluated. Using the formulas is not quite as easy as it may sound because finding the correct formula and using it properly may present problems.

■| **TABLE 13.2** |■

INTEGRATION FORMULAS

1. $\int u^n\, du = \dfrac{u^{n+1}}{n+1} + C,\ \text{for } n \neq -1$

2. $\int \dfrac{du}{u} = \int u^{-1}\, du = \ln|u| + C$

3. $\int a^u\, du = a^u \log_a e + C = \dfrac{a^u}{\ln a} + C$

4. $\int e^u\, du = e^u + C$

5. $\int \dfrac{du}{a^2 - u^2} = \dfrac{1}{2a} \ln\left|\dfrac{a+u}{a-u}\right| + C$

6. $\int \sqrt{u^2 + a^2}\, du = \dfrac{1}{2}(u\sqrt{u^2+a^2} + a^2 \ln|u + \sqrt{u^2+a^2}|) + C$

7. $\int \sqrt{u^2 - a^2}\, du = \dfrac{1}{2}(u\sqrt{u^2-a^2} - a^2 \ln|u + \sqrt{u^2-a^2}|) + C$

8. $\int \dfrac{du}{\sqrt{u^2+a^2}} = \ln|u + \sqrt{u^2+a^2}| + C$

9. $\int \dfrac{du}{u\sqrt{a^2-u^2}} = -\dfrac{1}{a} \ln\left|\dfrac{a+\sqrt{a^2-u^2}}{u}\right| + C$

10. $\int \dfrac{du}{\sqrt{u^2-a^2}} = \ln|u + \sqrt{u^2-a^2}| + C$

11. $\int \dfrac{du}{u\sqrt{a^2+u^2}} = -\dfrac{1}{a} \ln\left|\dfrac{a+\sqrt{a^2+u^2}}{u}\right| + C$

12. $\int \dfrac{u\, du}{au+b} = \dfrac{u}{a} - \dfrac{b}{a^2} \ln|au+b| + C$

(continued)

■| TABLE 13.2 |■

INTEGRATION FORMULAS (*continued*)

13. $\int \dfrac{du}{u(au + b)} = \dfrac{1}{b} \ln \left| \dfrac{u}{au + b} \right| + C$

14. $\int \ln u \, du = u(\ln u - 1) + C$

15. $\int \dfrac{u \, du}{(au + b)^2} = \dfrac{1}{a^2} \left(\ln|au + b| + \dfrac{b}{au + b} \right) + C$

16. $\int u \sqrt{au + b} \, du = \dfrac{2(3au - 2b)(au + b)^{3/2}}{15a^2} + C$

EXAMPLE 1   Using an Integration Formula

Evaluate $\displaystyle\int \dfrac{dx}{\sqrt{x^2 + 4}}$.

Solution
We must find a formula in Table 13.2 that is of the same form as this integral. We see that formula 8 has the desired form, *if* we let $u = x$ and $a = 2$. Thus

$$\int \dfrac{dx}{\sqrt{x^2 + 4}} = \ln\left|x + \sqrt{x^2 + 4}\right| + C$$

EXAMPLE 2   Fitting Integration Formulas

Evaluate (a) $\displaystyle\int_1^2 \dfrac{dx}{x^2 + 2x}$ and   (b) $\displaystyle\int \ln(2x + 1)\,dx$.

Solution
(a) There does not appear to be any formula that has exactly the same form as this integral. But if we rewrite the integral as

$$\int_1^2 \dfrac{dx}{x(x + 2)}$$

we see that formula 13 will work. Letting $u = x$, $a = 1$, and $b = 2$, we get

$$\int_1^2 \dfrac{dx}{x(x + 2)} = \dfrac{1}{2} \ln\left|\dfrac{x}{x + 2}\right|\Big|_1^2 = \dfrac{1}{2} \ln\left|\dfrac{2}{4}\right| - \dfrac{1}{2} \ln\left|\dfrac{1}{3}\right|$$

$$= \dfrac{1}{2}\left(\ln\dfrac{1}{2} - \ln\dfrac{1}{3}\right)$$

$$= \dfrac{1}{2} \ln \dfrac{3}{2} \approx 0.2027$$

(b) This integral has the form of formula 14, with $u = 2x + 1$. But if $u = 2x + 1$, du must be represented by the differential of $2x + 1$ (that is, $2\,dx$). Thus

$$\int \ln(2x + 1)\,dx = \dfrac{1}{2}\int \ln(2x + 1)(2\,dx)$$

$$= \dfrac{1}{2}\int \ln(u)\,du = \dfrac{1}{2} u[\ln(u) - 1] + C$$

$$= \dfrac{1}{2}(2x + 1)[\ln(2x + 1) - 1] + C$$

✓ CHECKPOINT

1. Can both $\displaystyle\int \frac{dx}{\sqrt{x^2 - 4}}$ and $\displaystyle -\int \frac{dx}{\sqrt{4 - x^2}}$ be evaluated with formula 10 in Table 13.2?

2. Determine the formula used to evaluate $\displaystyle\int \frac{3x}{4x - 5}\, dx$, and show how the formula would be applied.

3. True or false: In order for us to use a formula, the given integral must correspond exactly to the formula, including du.

4. True or false: $\displaystyle\int \frac{dx}{x^2(3x^2 - 7)}$ can be evaluated with formula 13.

5. True or false: $\displaystyle\int \frac{dx}{(6x + 1)^2}$ can be evaluated with either formula 1 or formula 15.

6. True or false: $\displaystyle\int \sqrt{x^2 + 4}\, dx$ can be evaluated with formula 1, formula 6, or formula 16.

EXAMPLE 3   Fitting an Integration Formula

Evaluate $\displaystyle\int_1^2 \frac{dx}{x\sqrt{81 - 9x^2}}$.

Solution

This integral is similar to that of formula 9 in Table 13.2. Letting $a = 9$, letting $u = 3x$, and multiplying the numerator and denominator by 3 give the proper form.

$$\int_1^2 \frac{dx}{x\sqrt{81 - 9x^2}} = \int_1^2 \frac{3\, dx}{3x\sqrt{81 - 9x^2}}$$

$$= -\frac{1}{9} \ln \left| \frac{9 + \sqrt{81 - 9x^2}}{3x} \right| \Bigg|_1^2$$

$$= \left[-\frac{1}{9} \ln \left(\frac{9 + \sqrt{45}}{6} \right) \right] - \left[-\frac{1}{9} \ln \left(\frac{9 + \sqrt{72}}{3} \right) \right]$$

$$\approx 0.088924836$$

Remember that the formulas given in Table 13.2 represent only a very small sample of all possible integration formulas. Additional formulas may be found in books of mathematical tables or online.

EXAMPLE 4   Hepatitis C | APPLICATION PREVIEW |

The rate of change of worldwide sales (in billions of dollars per year) of Hepatitis C treatments, from 2012 and projected to 2016, is given by

$$\frac{dS}{dt} = 0.575(1.234^t)$$

where t equals the number of years after 2010 and S is projected to be $9.7 billion in 2016 (*Source:* Evaluate Pharma).

(a) Find the function that models the worldwide sales of Hepatitis C treatments.
(b) Find the predicted worldwide sales in 2020.

Solution

(a) To find $S(t)$, we integrate $\dfrac{dS}{dt}$ by using formula 3, with $a = 1.234$ and $u = t$.

$$S(t) = \int 0.575(1.234^t)dt = 0.575\int (1.234^t)dt = 0.575\frac{1.234^t}{\ln 1.234} + C \approx 2.735(1.234^t) + C$$

We use the projected sales of \$9.7 billion for 2016 (when $t = 6$) to find the value of C.

$$9.7 = 2.735(1.234^6) + C \Rightarrow 9.7 \approx 9.7 + C \Rightarrow C \approx 0$$

Thus $S(t) = 2.735(1.234^t)$.

(b) The projected sales in 2020 (when $t = 10$) are $S(10) = 2.735(1.234^{10}) \approx \$22.4$ billion. ■

Calculator Note Numerical integration with a graphing calculator is especially useful in evaluating definite integrals when the formulas for the integrals are difficult to use or are not available. For example, evaluating the definite integral in Example 3 with the numerical integration feature of a graphing calculator gives 0.08892484. The decimal approximation of the answer found in Example 3 is 0.088924836, so the numerical approximation of the answer agrees for the first 8 decimal places. ■

✓ **CHECKPOINT ANSWERS**

1. No; $\sqrt{4 - x^2}$ cannot be written in the form $\sqrt{u^2 - a^2}$.
2. Use formula 12: $\dfrac{3x}{4} + \dfrac{15}{16} \ln|4x - 5| + C$
3. True.
4. False. With $u = x^2$, we must have $du = 2x\,dx$.
5. False. The integral can be evaluated with formula 1, but not with formula 15.
6. False. The integral can be evaluated only with formula 6.

| EXERCISES | 13.5

Evaluate the integrals in Problems 1–32. Identify the formula used.

1. $\displaystyle\int \frac{dx}{16 - x^2}$

2. $\displaystyle\int \frac{dx}{x(3x + 5)}$

3. $\displaystyle\int_1^4 \frac{dx}{x\sqrt{9 + x^2}}$

4. $\displaystyle\int \frac{dx}{x\sqrt{9 - x^2}}$

5. $\displaystyle\int \ln w\, dw$

6. $\displaystyle\int 4(3^x)\, dx$

7. $\displaystyle\int_0^2 \frac{q\, dq}{6q + 9}$

8. $\displaystyle\int_1^5 \frac{dq}{q\sqrt{25 + q^2}}$

9. $\displaystyle\int \frac{dv}{v(3v + 8)}$

10. $\displaystyle\int_0^3 \sqrt{x^2 + 16}\, dx$

11. $\displaystyle\int_5^7 \sqrt{x^2 - 25}\, dx$

12. $\displaystyle\int \frac{x\, dx}{(3x + 2)^2}$

13. $\displaystyle\int w\sqrt{4w + 5}\, dw$

14. $\displaystyle\int \frac{dy}{\sqrt{9 + y^2}}$

15. $\displaystyle\int x\, 5^{x^2}\, dx$

16. $\displaystyle\int \sqrt{9x^2 + 4}\, dx$

17. $\displaystyle\int_0^3 x\sqrt{x^2 + 4}\, dx$

18. $\displaystyle\int x\sqrt{x^4 - 36}\, dx$

19. $\displaystyle\int \frac{5\, dx}{x\sqrt{4 - 9x^2}}$

20. $\displaystyle\int x\, e^{x^2}\, dx$

21. $\displaystyle\int \frac{dx}{\sqrt{9x^2 - 4}}$

22. $\displaystyle\int \frac{dx}{25 - 4x^2}$

23. $\displaystyle\int \frac{3x\, dx}{(2x - 5)^2}$

24. $\displaystyle\int_0^1 \frac{x\, dx}{6 - 5x}$

25. $\displaystyle\int \frac{dx}{\sqrt{(3x + 1)^2 + 1}}$

26. $\displaystyle\int \frac{dx}{9 - (2x + 3)^2}$

27. $\displaystyle\int_0^3 x\sqrt{(x^2 + 1)^2 + 9}\, dx$

28. $\displaystyle\int_1^e x \ln x^2\, dx$

29. $\displaystyle\int \frac{x\, dx}{7 - 3x^2}$

30. $\displaystyle\int_0^1 \frac{e^x}{1 + e^x}\, dx$

31. $\displaystyle\int \frac{dx}{\sqrt{4x^2 + 7}}$

32. $\displaystyle\int e^{2x}\sqrt{3e^x + 1}\, dx$

 Use formulas or numerical integration with a graphing calculator or computer to evaluate the definite integrals in Problems 33–36.

33. $\displaystyle\int_2^3 \frac{e^{\sqrt{x-1}}}{\sqrt{x - 1}}\, dx$

34. $\displaystyle\int_2^4 \frac{3x}{\sqrt{x^4 - 9}}\, dx$

35. $\displaystyle\int_0^1 \frac{x^3\, dx}{(4x^2 + 5)^2}$

36. $\displaystyle\int_0^1 (e^x + 1)^3 e^x\, dx$

APPLICATIONS

37. *Producer's surplus* If the supply function for x units of a commodity is $p = 40 + 100 \ln (x + 1)^2$ dollars, what is the producer's surplus at $x = 20$?

38. *Consumer's surplus* If the demand function for wheat is $p = \dfrac{1500}{\sqrt{x^2 + 1}} + 4$ dollars, where x is the number of hundreds of bushels of wheat, what is the consumer's surplus at $x = 7$, $p = 216.13$?

39. *Cost* (a) If the marginal cost for x units of a good is $MC = \sqrt{x^2 + 9}$ (dollars per unit) and if the fixed cost is \$300, what is the total cost function of the good?
(b) What is the total cost of producing 4 units of this good?

40. *Consumer's surplus* Suppose that the demand function for an appliance is

$$p = \frac{400q + 400}{(q + 2)^2}$$

where q is the number of units and p is in dollars. What is the consumer's surplus if the equilibrium price is $19 and the equilibrium quantity is 18?

41. *Income streams* Suppose that when a new oil well is opened, its production is viewed as a continuous income stream with monthly rate of flow

$$f(t) = 10 \ln (t + 1) - 0.1t$$

where t is time in months and $f(t)$ is in thousands of dollars per month. Find the total income over the next 10 years (120 months).

42. *Spread of disease* An isolated community of 1000 people susceptible to a certain disease is exposed when one member returns carrying the disease. If x represents the number infected with the disease at time t (in days), then the rate of change of x is proportional to the product of the number infected, x, and the number still susceptible, $1000 - x$. That is,

$$\frac{dx}{dt} = kx(1000 - x) \ \text{ or } \ \frac{dx}{x(1000 - x)} = k \, dt$$

(a) If $k = 0.001$, integrate both sides to solve this differential equation.
(b) Find how long it will be before half the population of the community is affected.
(c) Find the rate of new cases, dx/dt, every other day for the first 13 days.

OBJECTIVE

13.6

- To evaluate integrals using the method of integration by parts

Integration by Parts

▌| APPLICATION PREVIEW |▌

If the value of oil produced by a piece of oil extraction equipment is considered a continuous income stream with an annual rate of flow (in dollars per year) at time t in years given by

$$f(t) = 300{,}000 - 2500t, \quad 0 \le t \le 10$$

and if money can be invested at 8%, compounded continuously, then the present value of the piece of equipment is

$$\int_0^{10} (300{,}000 - 2500t)e^{-0.08t} \, dt$$

$$= 300{,}000 \int_0^{10} e^{-0.08t} \, dt - 2500 \int_0^{10} te^{-0.08t} \, dt$$

The first integral can be evaluated with the formula for the integral of $e^u \, du$. Evaluating the second integral can be done by using integration by parts, which is a special technique that involves rewriting an integral in a form that can be evaluated. (See Example 6.)

Integration by parts is an integration technique that uses a formula that follows from the Product Rule for derivatives (actually differentials) as follows:

$$\frac{d}{dx} (uv) = u \frac{dv}{dx} + v \frac{du}{dx} \quad \text{so} \quad d(uv) = u \, dv + v \, du$$

Rearranging the differential form and integrating both sides give the following.

$$u \, dv = d(uv) - v \, du$$
$$\int u \, dv = \int d(uv) - \int v \, du$$
$$\int u \, dv = uv - \int v \, du$$

Integration by Parts Formula

$$\int u \, dv = uv - \int v \, du$$

Integration by parts is very useful if the integral we seek to evaluate can be treated as the product of one function, u, and the differential dv of a second function, so that the two integrals $\int dv$ and $\int v\, du$ can be found. Let us consider an example using this method.

EXAMPLE 1 **Integration by Parts**

Evaluate $\int xe^x\, dx$.

Solution
We cannot evaluate this integral using methods we have learned. But we can "split" the integrand into two parts, setting one part equal to u and the other part equal to dv. This "split" must be done in such a way that $\int dv$ and $\int v\, du$ can be evaluated. Letting $u = x$ and letting $dv = e^x dx$ are possible choices. If we make these choices, we have

$$u = x \quad dv = e^x\, dx$$
$$du = 1\, dx \quad v = \int e^x\, dx = e^x$$

Then

$$\int xe^x\, dx = uv - \int v\, du$$
$$= xe^x - \int e^x\, dx = xe^x - e^x + C$$

We see that choosing $u = x$ and $dv = e^x dx$ worked in evaluating $\int xe^x dx$ in Example 1. If we had chosen $u = e^x$ and $dv = x\, dx$, the results would not have been so successful.

How can we select u and dv to make integration by parts work? As a general guideline, we do the following.

First identify the types of functions occurring in the problem in the order

Logarithm, Polynomial (or Power of x), Radical, Exponential*

Thus, in Example 1, we had x and e^x, a polynomial and an exponential.

Second, choose u to equal the function whose type occurs first on the list; hence in Example 1 we chose $u = x$. Then dv equals the rest of the integrand (and always includes dx) so that $u\, dv$ equals the original integrand. A helpful way to remember the order of the function types that help us choose u is the sentence

"Lazy People Rarely Excel."

in which the first letters, LPRE, coordinate with the order and types of functions. Consider the following examples.

EXAMPLE 2 **Integration by Parts**

Evaluate $\int x \ln x\, dx$.

Solution
The integral contains a logarithm ($\ln x$) and a polynomial (x). Thus, choose $u = \ln x$ and $dv = x\, dx$. Then

$$du = \frac{1}{x}\, dx \quad \text{and} \quad v = \frac{x^2}{2}$$

so $\int x \ln x\, dx = u \cdot v - \int v\, du = (\ln x)\frac{x^2}{2} - \int \frac{x^2}{2} \cdot \frac{1}{x}\, dx$

$$= \frac{x^2}{2} \ln x - \int \frac{x}{2}\, dx = \frac{x^2}{2} \ln x - \frac{x^2}{4} + C$$

---

*This order is related to the ease with which the function types can be integrated.

Note that letting $dv = \ln x\, dx$ is contrary to our guidelines and would lead to great difficulty in evaluating $\int dv$ and $\int v\, du$. ■

EXAMPLE 3   Integration by Parts

Evaluate $\int \ln x^2\, dx$.

Solution

The only function in this problem is a logarithm, the first function type on our list for choosing u. Thus

$$\text{Choose:} \qquad u = \ln x^2 \qquad\qquad dv = dx$$

$$\text{Calculate:} \qquad du = \frac{2x}{x^2}\, dx = \frac{2}{x}\, dx \qquad v = x$$

Then

$$\int \ln x^2\, dx = x \ln x^2 - \int x \cdot \frac{2}{x}\, dx = x \ln x^2 - 2x + C$$

Note that if we write $\ln x^2$ as $2 \ln x$, we can also evaluate this integral using formula 14 in Table 13.2 in the previous section, so integration by parts would not be needed. ■

✓ CHECKPOINT

1. True or false: In evaluating $\int u\, dv$ by parts,
   (a) the parts u and dv are selected and the parts du and v are calculated.
   (b) the differential (often dx) is always chosen as part of dv.
   (c) the parts du and v are found from u and dv as follows:

   $$du = u'\, dx \quad \text{and} \quad v = \int dv$$

   (d) For $\int \frac{3x}{e^{2x}}\, dx$, we could choose $u = 3x$ and $dv = e^{2x}\, dx$.

2. For $\int \frac{\ln x}{x^4}\, dx$,
   (a) identify u and dv.
   (b) find du and v.
   (c) complete the evaluation of the integral.

Sometimes it is necessary to repeat integration by parts to complete the evaluation. When this occurs, at each use of integration by parts it is important to choose u and dv consistently according to our guidelines.

EXAMPLE 4   Repeated Integration by Parts

Evaluate $\int x^2 e^{2x}\, dx$.

Solution

Choose $u = x^2$ and $dv = e^{2x}\, dx$. Then we calculate $du = 2x\, dx$ and $v = \frac{1}{2}e^{2x}$. Thus

$$\int x^2 e^{2x}\, dx = \frac{1}{2}x^2 e^{2x} - \int x e^{2x}\, dx$$

We cannot evaluate $\int x e^{2x}\, dx$ directly, but this new integral is simpler than the original, and a second integration by parts will be successful. Choosing $u = x$ and $dv = e^{2x}\, dx$, we calculate $du = dx$ and $v = \frac{1}{2}e^{2x}$. Thus

$$\int x^2 e^{2x}\, dx = \frac{1}{2}x^2 e^{2x} - \left(\frac{1}{2}x e^{2x} - \int \frac{1}{2} e^{2x}\, dx \right)$$

$$= \frac{1}{2}x^2 e^{2x} - \frac{1}{2}x e^{2x} + \frac{1}{4}e^{2x} + C$$

$$= \frac{1}{4}e^{2x}(2x^2 - 2x + 1) + C$$ ■

The most obvious choices for u and dv are not always the correct ones, as the following example shows. Integration by parts may still involve some trial and error.

EXAMPLE 5   A Tricky Integration by Parts

Evaluate $\int x^3\sqrt{x^2+1}\, dx$.

Solution

Here we have a polynomial (x^3) and a radical. However, if we choose $u = x^3$, then the resulting $dv = \sqrt{x^2+1}\, dx$ cannot be integrated easily. But we can use $\sqrt{x^2+1}$ as part of dv, and we can evaluate $\int dv$ if we let $dv = x\sqrt{x^2+1}\, dx$. Then

$$u = x^2 \qquad dv = (x^2+1)^{1/2} x\, dx$$

$$du = 2x\, dx \qquad v = \int (x^2+1)^{1/2}(x\, dx) = \frac{1}{2}\int (x^2+1)^{1/2}(2x\, dx)$$

$$v = \frac{1}{2}\frac{(x^2+1)^{3/2}}{3/2} = \frac{1}{3}(x^2+1)^{3/2}$$

Then $\int x^3\sqrt{x^2+1}\, dx = \dfrac{x^2}{3}(x^2+1)^{3/2} - \int \dfrac{1}{3}(x^2+1)^{3/2}(2x\, dx)$

$$= \frac{x^2}{3}(x^2+1)^{3/2} - \frac{1}{3}\frac{(x^2+1)^{5/2}}{5/2} + C$$

$$= \frac{x^2}{3}(x^2+1)^{3/2} - \frac{2}{15}(x^2+1)^{5/2} + C \qquad \blacksquare$$

EXAMPLE 6   Income Stream | APPLICATION PREVIEW |

Suppose that the value of oil produced by a piece of oil extraction equipment is considered a continuous income stream with an annual rate of flow (in dollars per year) at time t in years given by

$$f(t) = 300{,}000 - 2500t, \qquad 0 \le t \le 10$$

and that money is worth 8%, compounded continuously. Find the present value of the piece of equipment.

Solution

The present value of the piece of equipment is given by

$$\int_0^{10} (300{,}000 - 2500t)e^{-0.08t}\, dt = 300{,}000\int_0^{10} e^{-0.08t}\, dt - 2500\int_0^{10} te^{-0.08t}\, dt$$

$$= \frac{300{,}000}{-0.08}e^{-0.08t}\Big|_0^{10} - 2500\int_0^{10} te^{-0.08t}\, dt$$

The value of the first integral is

$$\frac{300{,}000}{-0.08}e^{-0.08t}\Big|_0^{10} = \frac{300{,}000}{-0.08}e^{-0.8} - \frac{300{,}000}{-0.08}$$

$$\approx -1{,}684{,}983.615 + 3{,}750{,}000 = 2{,}065{,}016.385$$

The second of these integrals can be evaluated by using integration by parts, with $u = t$ and $dv = e^{-0.08t}\, dt$. Then $du = 1\, dt$ and $v = \dfrac{e^{-0.08t}}{-0.08}$, and this integral is

$$-2500\int_0^{10} te^{-0.08t}\, dt = -2500\frac{te^{-0.08t}}{-0.08}\Big|_0^{10} + 2500\int_0^{10} \frac{e^{-0.08t}}{-0.08}\, dt$$

$$= \frac{2500}{0.08}te^{-0.08t}\Big|_0^{10} + \frac{2500}{0.0064}e^{-0.08t}\Big|_0^{10}$$

$$= \frac{2500}{0.08}10e^{-0.8} + \frac{2500}{0.0064}e^{-0.8} - \frac{2500}{0.0064} \approx -74{,}690.572$$

Thus the sum of the integrals is

$$2,065,016.385 + (-74,690.572) = 1,990,325.813$$

so the present value of this piece of equipment is $1,990,325.81.

One further note about integration by parts. It can be very useful on certain types of problems, but not on all types. Don't attempt to use integration by parts when easier methods are available.

Calculator Note   Using the numerical integration feature of a graphing calculator to evaluate the integral in Example 6 gives the present value of $1,990,325.81, so this answer is the same as that found in Example 6.

✓ **CHECKPOINT ANSWERS**

1. (a) True   (b) True   (c) True
    (d) False. The *product* of u and dv must equal the original integrand.
2. (a) $u = \ln x$ and $dv = x^{-4}\, dx$

    (b) $du = \dfrac{1}{x}\, dx$ and $v = \displaystyle\int x^{-4}\, dx = \dfrac{x^{-3}}{-3}$

    (c) $-\dfrac{\ln x}{3x^3} - \dfrac{1}{9x^3} + C$

| EXERCISES | 13.6

In Problems 1–16, use integration by parts to evaluate the integral.

1. $\displaystyle\int xe^{2x}\, dx$

2. $\displaystyle\int xe^{-x}\, dx$

3. $\displaystyle\int x^2 \ln x\, dx$

4. $\displaystyle\int x^3 \ln x\, dx$

5. $\displaystyle\int_4^6 q\sqrt{q-4}\, dq$

6. $\displaystyle\int_0^1 y(1-y)^{3/2}\, dy$

7. $\displaystyle\int \frac{\ln x}{x^2}\, dx$

8. $\displaystyle\int \frac{\ln (x-1)}{\sqrt{x-1}}\, dx$

9. $\displaystyle\int_1^e \ln x\, dx$

10. $\displaystyle\int \frac{x}{\sqrt{x-3}}\, dx$

11. $\displaystyle\int x \ln (2x-3)\, dx$

12. $\displaystyle\int x \ln (4x)\, dx$

13. $\displaystyle\int q^3 \sqrt{q^2-3}\, dq$

14. $\displaystyle\int \frac{x^3}{\sqrt{9-x^2}}\, dx$

15. $\displaystyle\int_0^4 x^3 \sqrt{x^2+9}\, dx$

16. $\displaystyle\int \sqrt{x} \ln x\, dx$

In Problems 17–24, use integration by parts to evaluate the integral. Note that evaluation may require integration by parts more than once.

17. $\displaystyle\int x^2 e^{-x}\, dx$

18. $\displaystyle\int_0^1 4x^2 e^x\, dx$

19. $\displaystyle\int_0^2 3x^3 e^{x^2}\, dx$

20. $\displaystyle\int x^3 e^x\, dx$

21. $\displaystyle\int x^3 \ln^2 x\, dx$

22. $\displaystyle\int \frac{x^2}{\sqrt{x-3}}\, dx$

23. $\displaystyle\int e^{2x} \sqrt{e^x+1}\, dx$

24. $\displaystyle\int_1^2 (\ln x)^2\, dx$

In Problems 25–30, match each of the integrals with the formula or method (I–IV) that should be used to evaluate it. Then evaluate the integral.

   I. Integration by parts

  II. $\displaystyle\int e^u\, du$

 III. $\displaystyle\int \frac{du}{u}$

  IV. $\displaystyle\int u^n\, du$

25. $\displaystyle\int xe^{x^2}\, dx$

26. $\displaystyle\int \frac{x}{9-4x^2}\, dx$

27. $\displaystyle\int e^x \sqrt{e^x+1}\, dx$

28. $\displaystyle\int 4x^2 e^{x^3}\, dx$

29. $\displaystyle\int_0^4 \frac{t}{e^t}\, dt$

30. $\displaystyle\int x^2 \sqrt{x-1}\, dx$

APPLICATIONS

31. **Producer's surplus** If the supply function for x units of a commodity is $p = 30 + 50 \ln (2x+1)^2$ dollars, what is the producer's surplus at $x = 30$?

32. **Cost** If the marginal cost function for x units of a product is $\overline{MC} = 1 + 3 \ln (x+1)$ dollars per unit and if the fixed cost is $100, find the total cost function.

33. **Present value** Suppose that a machine's production can be considered as a continuous income stream with annual rate of flow at time t given by

$$f(t) = 10,000 - 500t \quad \text{(dollars per year)}$$

If money is worth 10%, compounded continuously, find the present value of the machine over the next 5 years.

34. *Present value* Suppose that the production of a machine used to mine coal is considered as a continuous income stream with annual rate of flow at time t given by

$$f(t) = 280{,}000 - 14{,}000t \quad \text{(dollars per year)}$$

If money is worth 7%, compounded continuously, find the present value of this machine over the next 8 years.

35. *Income distribution* Suppose the Lorenz curve for the distribution of income of a certain country is given by

$$y = xe^{x-1}$$

Find the Gini coefficient of income.

36. *Income streams* Suppose the income from an Internet access business is a continuous income stream with annual rate of flow given by

$$f(t) = 100te^{-0.1t}$$

in thousands of dollars per year. Find the total income over the next 10 years.

37. *Demographics* The number of millions of White non-Hispanic individuals in the U.S. civilian non-institutional population age 16 and older for selected years from 1980 and projected to 2050 can be modeled by

$$P(x) = 96.1 + 17.4 \ln x$$

with x equal to the number of years past 1970 (*Source:* U.S. Census Bureau). Find the projected average population over the years 2020 through 2030.

38. *Natural gas* The percent of natural gas in the United States extracted from shale rock from 2012 and projected to 2040 is given by the function $y = -0.843 + 13.8 \ln x$, where x is the is the number of years after 2010 (*Source:* Energy Information Administration). What does this model project the average percent to be for the years 2015 through 2030?

- To evaluate improper integrals
- To apply improper integrals to continuous income streams and to probability density functions

Improper Integrals and Their Applications

▮| APPLICATION PREVIEW |▮

We saw in Section 13.4, "Applications of Definite Integrals in Business and Economics," that the present value of a continuous income stream over a fixed number of years can be found by using a definite integral. When this notion is extended to an infinite time interval, the result is called the capital value of the income stream and is given by

$$\text{Capital value} = \int_0^\infty f(t)e^{-rt}\, dt$$

where $f(t)$ is the annual rate of flow at time t, and r is the annual interest rate, compounded continuously. This is called an improper integral. For example, the capital value of a trust that provides $f(t) = \$10{,}000$ per year indefinitely (when interest is 10% compounded continuously) is found by evaluating an improper integral. (See Example 2.)

Improper Integral   Some applications of calculus to statistics or business (such as capital value) involve definite integrals over intervals of infinite length (**improper integrals**). The area of a region that extends infinitely to the left or right along the x-axis (see Figure 13.27) could be described by an improper integral.

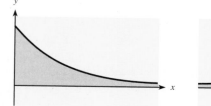 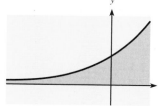 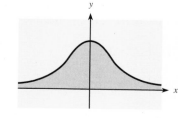

Figure 13.27

To see how to find such an area and hence evaluate an improper integral, let us consider how to find the area between the curve $y = 1/x^2$ and the x-axis to the right of $x = 1$.

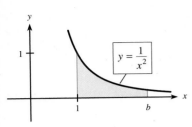

Figure 13.28

To find the area under this curve from $x = 1$ to $x = b$, where b is any number greater than 1 (see Figure 13.28), we evaluate

$$A = \int_1^b \frac{1}{x^2}\, dx = \frac{-1}{x}\Big|_1^b = \frac{-1}{b} - \left(\frac{-1}{1}\right) = 1 - \frac{1}{b}$$

Note that the larger b is, the closer the area is to 1. If $b = 100$, $A = 0.99$; if $b = 1000$, $A = 0.999$; and if $b = 1,000,000$, $A = 0.999999$.

We can represent the area of the region under $1/x^2$ to the right of 1 using the notation

$$\lim_{b \to \infty} \int_1^b \frac{1}{x^2}\, dx = \lim_{b \to \infty}\left(1 - \frac{1}{b}\right)$$

where $\lim_{b \to \infty}$ represents the limit as b gets larger without bound. Note that $\frac{1}{b} \to 0$ as $b \to \infty$, so

$$\lim_{b \to \infty}\left(1 - \frac{1}{b}\right) = 1 - 0 = 1$$

Thus the area under the curve $y = 1/x^2$ to the right of $x = 1$ is 1.

In general, we define the area under a curve $y = f(x)$ to the right of $x = a$, with $f(x) \geq 0$, to be

$$\text{Area} = \lim_{b \to \infty}(\text{area from } a \text{ to } b) = \lim_{b \to \infty}\int_a^b f(x)\, dx$$

This motivates the definition that follows.

Improper Integral

$$\int_a^\infty f(x)\, dx = \lim_{b \to \infty}\int_a^b f(x)\, dx$$

If the limit defining the **improper integral** is a unique finite number, we say that the integral *converges*; otherwise, we say that the integral *diverges*.

EXAMPLE 1   Improper Integrals

Evaluate the following improper integrals, if they converge.

(a) $\displaystyle\int_1^\infty \frac{1}{x^3}\, dx$ (b) $\displaystyle\int_1^\infty \frac{1}{x}\, dx$

Solution

(a) $\displaystyle\int_1^\infty \frac{1}{x^3}\, dx = \lim_{b \to \infty}\int_1^b x^{-3}\, dx = \lim_{b \to \infty}\left(\frac{x^{-2}}{-2}\right)\Big|_1^b$

$$= \lim_{b \to \infty}\left[\frac{-1}{2b^2} - \left(\frac{-1}{2(1)^2}\right)\right] = \lim_{b \to \infty}\left(\frac{-1}{2b^2} + \frac{1}{2}\right)$$

Notice that $1/(2b^2) \to 0$ as $b \to \infty$, so the limit converges to $0 + \frac{1}{2} = \frac{1}{2}$. That is,

$$\int_1^\infty \frac{1}{x^3}\, dx = \frac{1}{2}$$

(b) $\displaystyle\int_1^\infty \frac{1}{x}\, dx = \lim_{b \to \infty}\int_1^b \frac{1}{x}\, dx = \lim_{b \to \infty}\left(\ln |x|\right)\Big|_1^b = \lim_{b \to \infty}(\ln b - \ln 1)$

Here, $\ln b$ increases without bound as $b \to \infty$, so the limit diverges and we write

$$\int_1^\infty \frac{1}{x}\, dx = \infty$$

From Example 1 we can conclude that the area under the curve $y = 1/x^3$ to the right of $x = 1$ is $\frac{1}{2}$ whereas the corresponding area under the curve $y = 1/x$ is infinite. (We have already seen that the corresponding area under $y = 1/x^2$ is 1.)

As Figure 13.29 shows, the graphs of $y = 1/x^2$ and $y = 1/x$ look similar, but the graph of $y = 1/x^2$ gets "close" to the x-axis much more rapidly than the graph of $y = 1/x$. The area under $y = 1/x$ does not converge to a finite number because as $x \rightarrow \infty$ the graph of $1/x$ does not approach the x-axis rapidly enough.

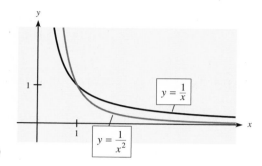

Figure 13.29

EXAMPLE 2   Capital Value | APPLICATION PREVIEW |

Suppose that an organization wants to establish a trust fund that will provide a continuous income stream with an annual rate of flow at time t given by $f(t) = 10,000$ dollars per year. If the interest rate remains at 10% compounded continuously, find the capital value of the fund.

Solution
The capital value of the fund uses the formula

$$\text{Capital value} = \int_0^\infty f(t)\, e^{-rt}\, dt$$

where $f(t)$ is the annual rate of flow at time t, and r is the annual interest rate, compounded continuously.

$$\int_0^\infty 10,000 e^{-0.10t}\, dt = \lim_{b\to\infty} \int_0^b 10,000 e^{-0.10t}\, dt = \lim_{b\to\infty} \left(-100,000 e^{-0.10t} \right)\Big|_0^b$$

$$= \lim_{b\to\infty} \left(\frac{-100,000}{e^{0.10b}} + 100,000 \right) = 100,000$$

Thus the capital value of the fund is $100,000.

Another term for a fund such as the one in Example 2 is a **perpetuity.** Usually the rate of flow of a perpetuity is a constant. If the rate of flow is a constant A, it can be shown that the capital value is given by A/r (see Problem 37 in the 13.7 Exercises).

✓ CHECKPOINT

1. True or false:

(a) $\lim\limits_{b\to\infty} \dfrac{1}{b^p} = 0$ if $p > 0$ (b) If $p > 0$, $b^p \rightarrow \infty$ as $b \rightarrow \infty$

(c) $\lim\limits_{b\to\infty} e^{-pb} = 0$ if $p > 0$

2. Evaluate the following (if they exist).

(a) $\displaystyle\int_1^\infty \dfrac{1}{x^{4/3}}\, dx = \lim_{b\to\infty} \int_1^b x^{-4/3}\, dx$ (b) $\displaystyle\int_0^\infty \dfrac{dx}{\sqrt{x+1}}$

Two **additional improper integrals** involving infinite limits are defined as follows:

Additional Improper Integrals

$$\int_{-\infty}^{b} f(x)\, dx = \lim_{a\to\infty} \int_{-a}^{b} f(x)\, dx$$

The integral converges if the limit is finite. Otherwise it diverges.

$$\int_{-\infty}^{\infty} f(x)\, dx = \lim_{a\to\infty} \int_{-a}^{c} f(x)\, dx + \lim_{b\to\infty} \int_{c}^{b} f(x)\, dx$$

for any finite constant c. (Often, c is chosen to be 0.) If both limits are finite, the improper integral converges; otherwise, it diverges.

EXAMPLE 3 Improper Integrals

Evaluate the following integrals.

(a) $\displaystyle\int_{-\infty}^{4} e^{3x}\, dx$ 　　　 (b) $\displaystyle\int_{-\infty}^{\infty} \frac{x^3}{(x^4+3)^2}\, dx$

Solution

(a) $\displaystyle\int_{-\infty}^{4} e^{3x}\, dx = \lim_{a\to\infty} \int_{-a}^{4} e^{3x}\, dx = \lim_{a\to\infty}\left[\left(\frac{1}{3}\right)e^{3x}\right]_{-a}^{4}$

$= \lim_{a\to\infty}\left[\left(\frac{1}{3}\right)e^{12} - \left(\frac{1}{3}\right)e^{-3a}\right] = \lim_{a\to\infty}\left[\left(\frac{1}{3}\right)e^{12} - \left(\frac{1}{3}\right)\left(\frac{1}{e^{3a}}\right)\right]$

$= \frac{1}{3}e^{12}$　　(because $1/e^{3a} \to 0$ as $a \to \infty$)

(b) $\displaystyle\int_{-\infty}^{\infty} \frac{x^3}{(x^4+3)^2}\, dx = \lim_{a\to\infty}\int_{-a}^{0}\frac{x^3}{(x^4+3)^2}\, dx + \lim_{b\to\infty}\int_{0}^{b}\frac{x^3}{(x^4+3)^2}\, dx$

$= \lim_{a\to\infty}\left[\frac{1}{4}\frac{(x^4+3)^{-1}}{-1}\right]_{-a}^{0} + \lim_{b\to\infty}\left[\frac{1}{4}\frac{(x^4+3)^{-1}}{-1}\right]_{0}^{b}$

$= \lim_{a\to\infty}\left[-\frac{1}{4}\left(\frac{1}{3} - \frac{1}{a^4+3}\right)\right] + \lim_{b\to\infty}\left[-\frac{1}{4}\left(\frac{1}{b^4+3} - \frac{1}{3}\right)\right]$

$= -\frac{1}{12} + 0 + 0 + \frac{1}{12} = 0\ \left(\text{since } \lim_{a\to\infty}\frac{1}{a^4+3} = 0 \text{ and } \lim_{b\to\infty}\frac{1}{b^4+3} = 0\right)$ ▪

Probability　We noted in Chapter 8, "Further Topics in Probability; Data Description," that the sum of the probabilities for a probability distribution (a **probability density function**) equals 1. In particular, we stated that the area under the normal probability curve is 1. The normal distribution is an example of a continuous probability distribution because the values of the random variable are considered over intervals rather than at discrete values. There are many important continuous probability distributions besides the normal distribution, but all such distributions satisfy the following definition.

Probability Density Function

If $f(x) \geq 0$ for all x, then f is a **probability density function** for a continuous random variable x if and only if

$$\int_{-\infty}^{\infty} f(x)\, dx = 1$$

We have noted previously that when $f(x)$ is a continuous probability density function, then

$$Pr(a \leq x \leq b) = \int_{a}^{b} f(x)\, dx$$

EXAMPLE 4   Product Life

Suppose the probability density function for the life span of a computer component is given by

$$f(x) = \begin{cases} 0.10e^{-0.10x} & \text{if } x \geq 0 \\ 0 & \text{if } x < 0 \end{cases}$$

(a) Verify that $f(x)$ is a probability density function.
(b) Find the probability that such a component lasts more than 3 years.

Solution

(a) To verify that $f(x)$ is a probability density function, we show $\int_{-\infty}^{\infty} f(x)\, dx = 1$:

$$\int_{-\infty}^{\infty} f(x)\, dx = \int_{-\infty}^{0} f(x)\, dx + \int_{0}^{\infty} f(x)\, dx = \int_{-\infty}^{0} 0\, dx + \int_{0}^{\infty} 0.10e^{-0.10x}\, dx$$

$$= 0 + \lim_{b\to\infty} \int_{0}^{b} 0.10e^{-0.10x}\, dx$$

$$= \lim_{b\to\infty}(-e^{-0.10x})\big|_{0}^{b} = \lim_{b\to\infty}(-e^{-0.10b} + 1) = 1$$

(b) The probability that the component lasts more than 3 years is given by

$$\Pr(x \geq 3) = \int_{3}^{\infty} 0.10e^{-0.10x}\, dx$$

$$= \lim_{b\to\infty} \int_{3}^{b} 0.10e^{-0.10x}\, dx = \lim_{b\to\infty}(-e^{-0.10x})\big|_{3}^{b}$$

$$= \lim_{b\to\infty}(-e^{-0.10b} + e^{-0.3}) = e^{-0.3} \approx 0.7408$$

In Section 8.3, "Discrete Probability Distributions; The Binomial Distribution," we found the expected value (mean) of a discrete probability distribution using the formula

$$E(x) = \sum x \Pr(x)$$

For continuous probability distributions, such as the normal probability distribution, the **expected value**, or **mean**, can be found by evaluating the improper integral

$$\int_{-\infty}^{\infty} xf(x)\, dx$$

Mean (Expected Value)

If x is a continuous random variable with probability density function f, then the **mean (expected value)** of the probability distribution is

$$\mu = \int_{-\infty}^{\infty} xf(x)\, dx$$

The normal distribution density function, in standard form, is

$$f(x) = \frac{1}{\sqrt{2\pi}} e^{-x^2/2}$$

so the mean of the normal probability distribution is given by

$$\mu = \int_{-\infty}^{\infty} x\left(\frac{1}{\sqrt{2\pi}} e^{-x^2/2}\right) dx$$

$$= \lim_{a\to\infty} \int_{-a}^{0} \frac{1}{\sqrt{2\pi}} xe^{-x^2/2}\, dx + \lim_{b\to\infty} \int_{0}^{b} \frac{1}{\sqrt{2\pi}} xe^{-x^2/2}\, dx$$

$$= \lim_{a \to \infty} \frac{1}{\sqrt{2\pi}} \left(-e^{-x^2/2} \right) \Big|_{-a}^{0} + \lim_{b \to \infty} \frac{1}{\sqrt{2\pi}} \left(-e^{-x^2/2} \right) \Big|_{0}^{b}$$

$$= \frac{1}{\sqrt{2\pi}} (-1 + 0) + \frac{1}{\sqrt{2\pi}} (0 + 1) = 0$$

This verifies the statement in Chapter 8 that the mean of the standard normal distribution is 0.

✓ **CHECKPOINT ANSWERS**

1. (a) True   (b) True   (c) True

2. (a) $\displaystyle\int_{1}^{\infty} \frac{1}{x^{4/3}} \, dx = 3$

   (b) $\displaystyle\lim_{b \to \infty} \int_{0}^{b} (x + 1)^{-1/2} \, dx = \lim_{b \to \infty} (2\sqrt{b+1} - 2)$; diverges

---

| **EXERCISES** | **13.7**

In Problems 1–20, evaluate the improper integrals that converge.

1. $\displaystyle\int_{1}^{\infty} \frac{dx}{x^6}$

2. $\displaystyle\int_{1}^{\infty} \frac{1}{x^4} \, dx$

3. $\displaystyle\int_{1}^{\infty} \frac{dt}{t^{3/2}}$

4. $\displaystyle\int_{5}^{\infty} \frac{dx}{(x-1)^3}$

5. $\displaystyle\int_{1}^{\infty} e^{-x} \, dx$

6. $\displaystyle\int_{0}^{\infty} x^2 e^{-x^3} \, dx$

7. $\displaystyle\int_{1}^{\infty} \frac{dt}{t^{1/3}}$

8. $\displaystyle\int_{1}^{\infty} \frac{1}{\sqrt{x}} \, dx$

9. $\displaystyle\int_{0}^{\infty} e^{3x} \, dx$

10. $\displaystyle\int_{1}^{\infty} xe^{x^2} \, dx$

11. $\displaystyle\int_{-\infty}^{-1} \frac{10}{x^2} \, dx$

12. $\displaystyle\int_{-\infty}^{-2} \frac{x}{\sqrt{(x^2 - 1)^3}} \, dx$

13. $\displaystyle\int_{-\infty}^{0} x^2 e^{-x^3} \, dx$

14. $\displaystyle\int_{-\infty}^{0} \frac{x}{(x^2 + 1)^2} \, dx$

15. $\displaystyle\int_{-\infty}^{-1} \frac{6}{x} \, dx$

16. $\displaystyle\int_{-\infty}^{-2} \frac{5}{3x + 5} \, dx$

17. $\displaystyle\int_{-\infty}^{\infty} \frac{2x}{(x^2 + 1)^2} \, dx$

18. $\displaystyle\int_{-\infty}^{\infty} \frac{9x^5}{(3x^6 + 7)^2} \, dx$

19. $\displaystyle\int_{-\infty}^{\infty} x^3 e^{-x^4} \, dx$

20. $\displaystyle\int_{-\infty}^{\infty} x^4 e^{-x^5} \, dx$

21. For what value of c does $\displaystyle\int_{0}^{\infty} \frac{c}{e^{0.5t}} \, dt = 1$?

22. For what value of c does $\displaystyle\int_{10}^{\infty} \frac{c}{x^3} \, dx = 1$?

In Problems 23–26, find the area, if it exists, of the region under the graph of $y = f(x)$ and to the right of $x = 1$.

23. $f(x) = \dfrac{x}{e^{x^2}}$

24. $f(x) = \dfrac{1}{\sqrt[5]{x^3}}$

25. $f(x) = \dfrac{1}{\sqrt[3]{x^5}}$

26. $f(x) = \dfrac{1}{x\sqrt{x}}$

27. Show that the function

$$f(x) = \begin{cases} \dfrac{200}{x^3} & \text{if } x \geq 10 \\ 0 & \text{otherwise} \end{cases}$$

is a probability density function.

28. Show that

$$f(t) = \begin{cases} 3e^{-3t} & \text{if } t \geq 0 \\ 0 & \text{if } t < 0 \end{cases}$$

is a probability density function.

29. For what value of c is the function

$$f(x) = \begin{cases} c/x^2 & \text{if } x \geq 1 \\ 0 & \text{otherwise} \end{cases}$$

a probability density function?

30. For what value of c is the function

$$f(x) = \begin{cases} c/x^3 & \text{if } x \geq 100 \\ 0 & \text{otherwise} \end{cases}$$

a probability density function?

31. Find the value of c so that

$$f(x) = \begin{cases} ce^{-x/4} & x \geq 0 \\ 0 & x < 0 \end{cases}$$

is a probability density function.

32. Find the value of c (in terms of k) so that

$$f(x) = \begin{cases} ce^{-kx} & \text{if } x \geq 0 \\ 0 & \text{if } x < 0 \end{cases}$$

is a probability density function.

33. Find the mean of the probability distribution if the probability density function is

$$f(x) = \begin{cases} \dfrac{200}{x^3} & \text{if } x \geq 10 \\ 0 & \text{otherwise} \end{cases}$$

34. Find the mean of the probability distribution if the probability density function is

$$f(x) = \begin{cases} c/x^4 & \text{if } x \geq 10 \\ 0 & \text{otherwise} \end{cases}$$

35. Find the area below the graph of $y = f(x)$ and above the x-axis for $f(x) = 24xe^{-3x}$. Use the graph of $y = f(x)$ to find the interval for which $f(x) \geq 0$ and the graph of the integral of $f(x)$ over this interval to find the area.

36. Find the area below the graph of $y = f(x)$ and above the x-axis for $f(x) = x^2e^{-x}$ and $x \geq 0$. Use the graph of the integral of $f(x)$ over this interval to find the area.

APPLICATIONS

37. *Capital value* Suppose that a continuous income stream has an annual rate of flow at time t given by $f(t) = A$, where A is a constant. If the interest rate is r (as a decimal, $r > 0$), compounded continuously, show that the capital value of the stream is A/r.

38. *Capital value* Suppose that a donor wishes to provide a cash gift to a hospital that will generate a continuous income stream with an annual rate of flow at time t given by $f(t) = \$20{,}000$ per year. If the annual interest rate is 12% compounded continuously, find the capital value of this perpetuity.

39. *Capital value* Suppose that a business provides a continuous income stream with an annual rate of flow at time t given by $f(t) = 120e^{0.04t}$ in thousands of dollars per year. If the interest rate is 9% compounded continuously, find the capital value of the business.

40. *Capital value* Suppose that the output of the machinery in a factory can be considered as a continuous income stream with annual rate of flow at time t given by $f(t) = 450e^{-0.09t}$ (in thousands of dollars per year). If the annual interest rate is 6% compounded continuously, find the capital value of the machinery.

41. *Capital value* A business has a continuous income stream with an annual rate of flow at time t given by $f(t) = 56{,}000e^{0.02t}$ (dollars per year). If the interest rate is 10% compounded continuously, find the capital value of the business.

42. *Capital value* Suppose that a business provides a continuous income stream with an annual rate of flow at time t given by $f(t) = 10{,}800e^{0.06t}$ (dollars per year).

If money is worth 12% compounded continuously, find the capital value of the business.

43. *Repair time* In a manufacturing process involving several machines, the average down time t (in hours) for a machine that needs repair has the probability density function

$$f(t) = 0.5e^{-0.5t} \quad t \geq 0$$

Find the probability that a failed machine's down time is

(a) 2 hours or more.   (b) 8 hours or more.

44. *Customer service* The duration t (in minutes) of customer service calls received by a certain company is given by the probability density function

$$f(t) = 0.4e^{-0.4t} \quad t \geq 0$$

Find the probability that a call selected at random lasts

(a) 4 minutes or more.

(b) 10 minutes or more.

45. *Quality control* The probability density function for the life span of an electronics part is $f(t) = 0.08e^{-0.08t}$, where t is the number of months in service. Find the probability that any given part of this type lasts longer than 24 months.

46. *Warranties* A transmission repair firm that wants to offer a lifetime warranty on its repairs has determined that the probability density function for transmission failure after repair is $f(t) = 0.3e^{-0.3t}$, where t is the number of months after repair. What is the probability that a transmission chosen at random will last

(a) 3 months or less?

(b) more than 3 months?

47. *Radioactive waste* Suppose that the rate at which a nuclear power plant produces radioactive waste is proportional to the number of years it has been operating, according to $f(t) = 500t$ (in pounds per year). Suppose also that the waste decays exponentially at a rate of 3% per year. Then the amount of radioactive waste that will accumulate in b years is given by

$$\int_0^b 500te^{-0.03(b-t)} \, dt$$

(a) Evaluate this integral.

(b) How much waste will accumulate in the long run? Take the limit as $b \to \infty$ in part (a).

OBJECTIVES

13.8

- To approximate definite integrals by using the Trapezoidal Rule
- To approximate definite integrals by using Simpson's Rule

Numerical Integration Methods: The Trapezoidal Rule and Simpson's Rule

■| APPLICATION PREVIEW |■

A pharmaceutical company tests the body's assimilation of a new drug by administering a 200-milligram dose and collecting the following data from blood samples (t is time in hours, and $R(t)$ gives the assimilation of the drug in milligrams per hour).

t	0	0.5	1.0	1.5	2.0	2.5	3.0
$R(t)$	0.0	15.3	32.3	51.0	74.8	102.0	130.9

The company would like to find the amount of drug assimilated in 3 hours, which is given by

$$\int_0^3 R(t)\, dt$$

In this section we develop straightforward and quite accurate methods for evaluating integrals such as this, even when, as with $R(t)$, only function data, rather than a formula, are given. (See Example 4.)

We have studied several techniques for integration and have even used tables to evaluate some integrals. Yet some functions that arise in practical problems cannot be integrated by using any formula. For any function $f(x) \geq 0$ on an interval $[a, b]$, however, we have seen that a definite integral can be viewed as an area and that we can usually approximate the area and hence the integral (see Figure 13.30). One such approximation method uses rectangles, as we saw when we defined the definite integral. In this section, we consider two other **numerical integration methods** to approximate a definite integral: the **Trapezoidal Rule** and **Simpson's Rule.**

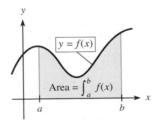

Figure 13.30

Trapezoidal Rule To develop the Trapezoidal Rule formula, we assume that $f(x) \geq 0$ on $[a, b]$ and subdivide the interval $[a, b]$ into n equal pieces, each of length $(b - a)/n = h$. Then, within each subdivision, we can approximate the area by using a trapezoid. As shown in Figure 13.31 on the next page, we can use the formula for the area of a trapezoid to approximate the area of the first subdivision. Continuing in this way for each trapezoid, we have

$$\int_a^b f(x)\, dx \approx A_1 + A_2 + A_3 + \cdots + A_{n-1} + A_n$$

$$= \left[\frac{f(x_0) + f(x_1)}{2}\right] h + \left[\frac{f(x_1) + f(x_2)}{2}\right] h +$$

$$\left[\frac{f(x_2) + f(x_3)}{2}\right] h + \cdots + \left[\frac{f(x_{n-1}) + f(x_n)}{2}\right] h$$

$$= \frac{h}{2} [f(x_0) + f(x_1) + f(x_1) + f(x_2) + f(x_2) + \cdots + f(x_{n-1}) + f(x_{n-1}) + f(x_n)]$$

This can be simplified to obtain the **Trapezoidal Rule**.

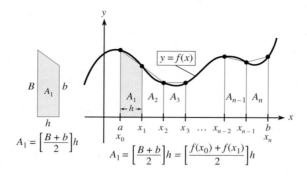

Figure 13.31

$$A_1 = \left[\frac{B+b}{2}\right]h$$

$$A_1 = \left[\frac{B+b}{2}\right]h = \left[\frac{f(x_0)+f(x_1)}{2}\right]h$$

Trapezoidal Rule

If f is continuous on $[a, b]$, then

$$\int_a^b f(x)\, dx \approx \frac{h}{2}[f(x_0) + 2f(x_1) + 2f(x_2) + \cdots + 2f(x_{n-1}) + f(x_n)]$$

where $h = \dfrac{b-a}{n}$ and n is the number of equal subdivisions of $[a, b]$.

Despite the fact that we used areas to develop the Trapezoidal Rule, we can use this rule to evaluate definite integrals even if $f(x) < 0$ on all or part of $[a, b]$.

EXAMPLE   1   Trapezoidal Rule

Use the Trapezoidal Rule to approximate $\displaystyle\int_1^3 \frac{1}{x}\, dx$ with

(a) $n = 4$.
(b) $n = 8$.

Solution

First, we note that this integral can be evaluated directly:

$$\int_1^3 \frac{1}{x}\, dx = \ln|x|\ \Big|_1^3 = \ln 3 - \ln 1 = \ln 3 \approx 1.099$$

(a)   The interval $[1, 3]$ must be divided into 4 equal subintervals of width $h = \frac{3-1}{4} = \frac{2}{4} = \frac{1}{2}$ as follows:

```
1        1.5     2     2.5      3
├─────────┼───────┼──────┼───────┤
x_0       x_1     x_2    x_3     x_4
```

Thus, from the Trapezoidal Rule, we have

$$\int_1^3 \frac{1}{x}\, dx \approx \frac{h}{2}[f(x_0) + 2f(x_1) + 2f(x_2) + 2f(x_3) + f(x_4)]$$

$$= \frac{1/2}{2}[f(1) + 2f(1.5) + 2f(2) + 2f(2.5) + f(3)]$$

$$= \frac{1}{4}\left[1 + 2\left(\frac{1}{1.5}\right) + 2\left(\frac{1}{2}\right) + 2\left(\frac{1}{2.5}\right) + \frac{1}{3}\right] \approx 1.117$$

(b)   In this case, the interval $[1, 3]$ is divided into 8 equal subintervals of width $h = \frac{3-1}{8} = \frac{2}{8} = \frac{1}{4}$ as follows.

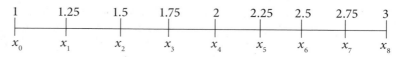

Thus, from the Trapezoidal Rule, we have

$$\int_1^3 \frac{1}{x}\, dx \approx \frac{h}{2}[f(x_0) + 2f(x_1) + 2f(x_2) + 2f(x_3) + 2f(x_4) + 2f(x_5)$$
$$+ 2f(x_6) + 2f(x_7) + f(x_8)]$$
$$= \frac{1/4}{2}\left[\frac{1}{1} + 2\left(\frac{1}{1.25}\right) + 2\left(\frac{1}{1.5}\right) + 2\left(\frac{1}{1.75}\right) + 2\left(\frac{1}{2}\right) + 2\left(\frac{1}{2.25}\right)\right.$$
$$\left. + 2\left(\frac{1}{2.5}\right) + 2\left(\frac{1}{2.75}\right) + \frac{1}{3}\right]$$
$$\approx 1.103$$

In Example 1, because we know that the value of the integral is $\ln 3 \approx 1.099$, we can measure the accuracy of each approximation. We can see that a larger value of n (namely, $n = 8$) produced a more accurate approximation to $\ln 3$. In general, larger values of n produce more accurate approximations, but they also make computations more difficult.

Technology Note   The TABLE feature of a graphing calculator can be used to find the values of $f(x_0), f(x_1), f(x_2)$, etc. needed for the Trapezoidal Rule. Figure 13.32(a) shows the TABLE set up for Example 1(b), and Figures 13.32(b) and 13.32(c) show the TABLE values.

TABLE SETUP
TblStart=1
ΔTbl=.25
Indpnt: **Auto** Ask
Depend: **Auto** Ask

X	Y₁
1	1
1.25	.8
1.5	.66667
1.75	.57143
2	.5
2.25	.44444
2.5	.4
X=1	

X	Y₁
1.5	.66667
1.75	.57143
2	.5
2.25	.44444
2.5	.4
2.75	.36364
3	.33333
Y₁=.5	

Figure 13.32   (a)   (b)   (c)

Thus for the Trapezoidal Rule, we get

$$\int_1^3 \frac{1}{x}\, dx \approx \frac{0.25}{2}\left[\begin{array}{l}1(1) + 2(0.8) + 2(0.66667) + 2(0.57143) + 2(0.5) \\ + 2(0.44444) + 2(0.4) + 2(0.36364) + 1(0.33333)\end{array}\right] \approx 1.103$$

just as we did in Example 1.

An Excel spreadsheet also can be very useful in finding the numerical integral with the Trapezoidal Rule. A discussion of the use of Excel in finding numerical integrals is given in the Online Excel Guide that accompanies this text.

Because the exact value of an integral is rarely available when an approximation is used, it is important to have some way to judge the accuracy of an answer. The following formula, which we state without proof, can be used to bound the error that results from using the Trapezoidal Rule.

Trapezoidal Rule Error

The error E in using the Trapezoidal Rule to approximate $\int_a^b f(x)\, dx$ satisfies

$$|E| \le \frac{(b-a)^3}{12n^2}\left[\max_{a \le x \le b}|f''(x)|\right]$$

where n is the number of equal subdivisions of $[a, b]$.

For a numerical method to be worthwhile, there must be some way of assessing its accuracy. Hence, this formula is important. We leave its application, however, to more advanced courses.

Simpson's Rule   The Trapezoidal Rule was developed by using a line segment to approximate the function over each subinterval and then using the areas under the line segments to approximate the area under the curve. Another numerical method, **Simpson's Rule,** uses a parabola to approximate the function over each pair of subintervals (see Figure 13.33) and then uses the areas under the parabolas to approximate the area under the curve. Because Simpson's Rule is based on pairs of subintervals, n must be even.

Simpson's Rule (n Even)	If $f(x)$ is continuous on $[a, b]$, and if $[a, b]$ is divided into an *even* number n of equal subdivisions, then

$$\int_a^b f(x)\, dx \approx \frac{h}{3}[f(x_0) + 4f(x_1) + 2f(x_2) + 4f(x_3) + \cdots + 2f(x_{n-2}) + 4f(x_{n-1}) + f(x_n)]$$

where $h = \dfrac{b-a}{n}$.

We leave the derivation of Simpson's Rule to more advanced courses.

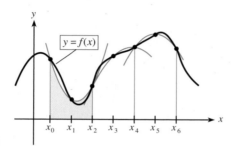

Figure 13.33

EXAMPLE 2   Simpson's Rule

Use Simpson's Rule with $n = 4$ to approximate $\displaystyle\int_1^3 \frac{1}{x}\, dx$.

Solution

Because $n = 4$ is even, Simpson's Rule can be used, and the interval is divided into four subintervals of length $h = \frac{3-1}{4} = \frac{1}{2}$ as follows:

$$\int_1^3 \frac{1}{x}\, dx \approx \frac{1/2}{3}[f(1) + 4f(1.5) + 2f(2) + 4f(2.5) + f(3)]$$

$$= \frac{1}{6}\left[\frac{1}{1} + 4\left(\frac{1}{1.5}\right) + 2\left(\frac{1}{2}\right) + 4\left(\frac{1}{2.5}\right) + \frac{1}{3}\right]$$

$$= 1.100$$

Note that the result of Example 2 is better than both the $n = 4$ and the $n = 8$ Trapezoidal Rule approximations done in Example 1. In general, Simpson's Rule is more accurate than the Trapezoidal Rule for a given number of subdivisions. We can determine the accuracy of Simpson's Rule approximations by using the following formula.

Simpson's Rule Error Formula	The error E in using Simpson's Rule to approximate $\displaystyle\int_a^b f(x)\, dx$ satisfies

$$|E| \le \frac{(b-a)^5}{180n^4}\left[\max_{a \le x \le b}|f^{(4)}(x)|\right]$$

where n is the number of equal subdivisions of $[a, b]$ and $f^{(4)}(x)$ is the fourth derivative of $f(x)$.

The presence of the factor $180n^4$ in the denominator indicates that the error will often be quite small for even a modest value of n. Although Simpson's Rule often leads to more accurate results than the Trapezoidal Rule for a fixed choice of n, the Trapezoidal Rule is sometimes used because its error is more easily determined than that of Simpson's Rule or, more important, because the number of subdivisions is odd.

✓ CHECKPOINT

1. Suppose [1, 4] is divided into 6 equal subintervals.
   (a) Find the width h of each subinterval.
   (b) Find the subdivision points.
2. True or false:
   (a) When the Trapezoidal Rule is used, the number of subdivisions, n, must be even.
   (b) When Simpson's Rule is used, the number of subdivisions, n, must be even.
3. We can show that $\int_{0}^{2} 4x^3 \, dx = 16$. Use $n = 4$ subdivisions to find

   (a) the Trapezoidal Rule approximation of this integral.
   (b) the Simpson's Rule approximation of this integral.

Technology Note   As mentioned previously for the Trapezoidal Rule, the TABLE feature of a graphing calculator can be used in exactly the same way with Simpson's Rule. An Excel spreadsheet also can be very useful with Simpson's Rule. ■

 EXAMPLE **3**   **Simpson's Rule**

Use Simpson's Rule with $n = 10$ subdivisions to approximate

$$\int_{1}^{6} [\ln(x)]^2 \, dx$$

Solution

With $y_1 = [\ln(x)]^2$ and $h = \dfrac{b-a}{n} = \dfrac{6-1}{10} = 0.5$, we can use a graphing calculator with $\Delta\text{Tbl} = 0.5$ to find the following table of values.

x	y_1	x	y_1
1	0	4	1.9218
1.5	0.1644	4.5	2.2622
2	0.48045	5	2.5903
2.5	0.83959	5.5	2.9062
3	1.2069	6	3.2104
3.5	1.5694		

Thus Simpson's Rule yields

$$\int_{1}^{6} [\ln(x)]^2 \, dx$$

$$\approx \frac{0.5}{3} \left[\begin{array}{l} 1(0) + 4(0.1644) + 2(0.48045) + 4(0.83959) + 2(1.2069) + 4(1.5694) \\ \quad + 2(1.9218) + 4(2.2622) + 2(2.5903) + 4(2.9062) + 1(3.2104) \end{array} \right]$$

$$\approx 7.7627$$

One advantage that both the Trapezoidal Rule and Simpson's Rule offer is that they may be used when only function values at the subdivision points are known and the function formula itself is not known. This can be especially useful in applied problems.

EXAMPLE 4   **Pharmaceutical Testing** | APPLICATION PREVIEW |

A pharmaceutical company tests the body's ability to assimilate a drug. The test is done by administering a 200-milligram dose and then, every half-hour, monitoring the rate of assimilation. The following table gives the data; t is time in hours, and $R(t)$ is the rate of assimilation in milligrams per hour.

t	0	0.5	1.0	1.5	2.0	2.5	3.0
$R(t)$	0.0	15.3	32.3	51.0	74.8	102.0	130.9

To find the total amount of the drug (in milligrams) that is assimilated in the first 3 hours, the company must find

$$\int_0^3 R(t)\, dt$$

Use Simpson's Rule to approximate this definite integral.

Solution
The values of t correspond to the endpoints of the subintervals, and the values of $R(t)$ correspond to function values at those endpoints. From the table we see that $h = \frac{1}{2}$ and $n = 6$ (even); thus Simpson's Rule is applied as follows:

$$\int_0^3 R(t)\, dt \approx \frac{h}{3}[R(t_0) + 4R(t_1) + 2R(t_2) + 4R(t_3) + 2R(t_4) + 4R(t_5) + R(t_6)]$$

$$= \frac{1}{6}[0 + 4(15.3) + 2(32.3) + 4(51.0) + 2(74.8) + 4(102.0) + 130.9]$$

$$\approx 169.7 \text{ mg}$$

Thus at the end of 3 hours, the body has assimilated approximately 169.7 milligrams of the 200-milligram dose.   ■

Note in Example 4 that the Trapezoidal Rule could also be used, because it relies only on the values of $R(t)$ at the subdivision endpoints.

In practice, these kinds of approximations are usually done with a computer, where the computations can be done quickly, even for large values of n. In addition, numerical methods (and hence computer programs) exist that approximate the errors, even in cases such as Example 4 where the function is not known. We leave any further discussion of error approximation formulas and additional numerical techniques for a more advanced course.

✓ CHECKPOINT
ANSWERS

1. (a) $h = \frac{1}{2} = 0.5$

   (b) $x_0 = 1, x_1 = 1.5, x_2 = 2, x_3 = 2.5, x_4 = 3, x_5 = 3.5, x_6 = 4$
2. (a) False. With the Trapezoidal Rule, n can be even or odd.
   (b) True
3. (a) 17
   (b) 16

| EXERCISES | 13.8

For each interval $[a, b]$ and value of n given in Problems 1–6, find h and the values of $x_0, x_1, \ldots x_n$.

1. $[0, 2]\ n = 4$
2. $[0, 4]\ n = 8$
3. $[1, 4]\ n = 6$
4. $[2, 5]\ n = 9$
5. $[-1, 4]\ n = 5$
6. $[-1, 2]\ n = 6$

For each integral in Problems 7–12, do the following.
(a) Approximate its value by using the Trapezoidal Rule.
(b) Approximate its value by using Simpson's Rule.
(c) Find its exact value by integration.

(d) State which approximation is more accurate. (Round each result to 2 decimal places.)

7. $\int_0^3 x^2\, dx;\quad n = 6$

8. $\int_0^1 x^3\, dx;\quad n = 4$

9. $\int_1^2 \frac{1}{x^2}\, dx;\quad n = 4$

10. $\int_1^4 \frac{1}{x}\, dx;\quad n = 6$

11. $\int_0^4 x^{1/2}\, dx;\quad n = 8$

12. $\int_0^2 x^{3/2}\, dx;\quad n = 8$

In Problems 13–18, approximate each integral by
(a) the Trapezoidal Rule.
(b) Simpson's Rule.
Use $n = 4$ and round answers to 3 decimal places.

13. $\int_0^2 \sqrt{x^3 + 1}\, dx$

14. $\int_0^2 \frac{dx}{\sqrt{4x^3 + 1}}$

15. $\int_0^1 e^{-x^2}\, dx$

16. $\int_0^1 e^{x^2}\, dx$

17. $\int_1^5 \ln(x^2 - x + 1)\, dx$

18. $\int_1^5 \ln(x^2 + x + 2)\, dx$

Use the table of values given in each of Problems 19–22 to approximate $\int_a^b f(x)\, dx$. Use Simpson's Rule whenever n is even; otherwise, use the Trapezoidal Rule. Round answers to 1 decimal place.

19. Find $\int_1^4 f(x)\, dx$.

20. Find $\int_1^2 f(x)\, dx$.

x	f(x)
1	1
1.6	2.2
2.2	1.8
2.8	2.9
3.4	4.6
4.0	2.1

x	f(x)
1	1
1.2	0.5
1.4	0.3
1.6	0.1
1.8	0.8
2.0	0.1

21. Find $\int_{1.2}^{3.6} f(x)\, dx$.

22. Find $\int_0^{1.8} f(x)\, dx$.

x	f(x)
1.2	6.1
1.6	4.8
2.0	3.1
2.4	2.0
2.8	2.8
3.2	5.6
3.6	9.7

x	f(x)
0	8.8
0.3	4.6
0.6	1.5
0.9	0
1.2	0.7
1.5	2.8
1.8	7.6

APPLICATIONS

In Problems 23–30, round all calculations to 2 decimal places.

23. *Total income* Suppose that the production from an assembly line can be considered as a continuous income stream with annual rate of flow given by

$$f(t) = 100\frac{e^{0.1t}}{t + 1}\quad \text{(in thousands of dollars per year)}$$

Use Simpson's Rule with $n = 4$ to approximate the total income over the first 2 years, given by

$$\text{Total income} = \int_0^2 \frac{100e^{0.1t}}{t + 1}\, dt$$

24. *Present value* Suppose that the rate of flow of a continuous income stream is given by $f(t) = 500t$ (in thousands of dollars per year). If money is worth 7% compounded continuously, then the present value of this stream over the next 5 years is given by

$$\text{Present value} = \int_0^5 500t\, e^{-0.07t}\, dt$$

Use the Trapezoidal Rule with $n = 5$ to approximate this present value.

25. *Cost* Suppose that a company's total cost (in dollars) of producing x items is given by $C(x) = (x^2 + 1)^{3/2} + 1000$. Use the Trapezoidal Rule with $n = 3$ to approximate the average total cost for the production of $x = 30$ to $x = 33$ items.

26. *Demand* Suppose that the demand for q units of a certain product at $\$p$ per unit is given by

$$p = 850 + \frac{100}{q^2 + 1}$$

Use Simpson's Rule with $n = 6$ to approximate the average price as demand ranges from 3 to 9 items.

Supply and demand **Use the supply and demand schedules in Problems 27 and 28, with p in dollars and x as the number of units.**

Supply Schedule		Demand Schedule	
x	p	x	p
0	120	0	2400
10	260	10	1500
20	380	20	1200
30	450	30	950
40	540	40	800
50	630	50	730
60	680	60	680
70	720	70	640

27. Use Simpson's Rule to approximate the producer's surplus at market equilibrium. Note that market equilibrium can be found from the tables.

28. Use Simpson's Rule to approximate the consumer's surplus at market equilibrium.

29. *Production* Suppose that the rate of production of a product (in units per week) is measured at the end of each of the first 5 weeks after start-up, and the data in the table are obtained.

Weeks t	Rate $R(t)$	Weeks t	Rate $R(t)$
0	250.0	3	243.3
1	247.6	4	241.3
2	245.4	5	239.5

Approximate the total number of units produced in the first 5 weeks.

30. **Drug levels in the blood** The manufacturer of a medicine wants to test how a new 300-milligram capsule is released into the bloodstream. After a volunteer is given a capsule, blood samples are drawn every half-hour, and the number of milligrams of the drug in the bloodstream is calculated. The results obtained are as follows.

Time t (hr)	$N(t)$ (mg)	Time t (hr)	$N(t)$ (mg)
0	0	2.0	178.3
0.5	247.3	2.5	113.9
1.0	270	3.0	56.2
1.5	236.4	3.5	19.3

Approximate the *average* number of milligrams in the bloodstream during the first $3\frac{1}{2}$ hours.

Income distribution **If the Lorenz curves for years a and b are given by $L_a(x)$ and $L_b(x)$, respectively, then from year a to year b, the change in the Gini coefficient $(G_b - G_a)$ is given by**

$$2\int_0^1 [L_a(x) - L_b(x)]\, dx$$

In Problems 31 and 32, complete the following.
(a) **Use the data in the table and make a new table for x and the corresponding values of $[L_a(x) - L_b(x)]$ for the given years, where year b is 2012.**
(b) **Use the table from part (a) in the Trapezoidal Rule to approximate**

$$2\int_0^1 [L_a(x) - L_b(x)]\, dx$$

which gives $G_b - G_a$, the difference of the Gini coefficients for the two years.
(c) **Is the value of the integral positive or negative? In which year was the income more equally distributed?**

x	0.0	0.2	0.4	0.6	0.8	1.0
			$L(x)$ for Blacks			
2012	0.0	0.028	0.106	0.247	0.482	1.0
1990	0.0	0.031	0.111	0.260	0.511	1.0

x	0.0	0.2	0.4	0.6	0.8	1.0
			$L(x)$ for Asians			
2012	0.0	0.030	0.119	0.269	0.506	1.0
2009	0.0	0.027	0.109	0.253	0.483	1.0

Source: U.S. Bureau of the Census

31. Complete parts (a)–(c) above for Blacks in 1990 and 2012.
32. Complete parts (a)–(c) above for Asians in 2009 and 2012.
33. **Pollution monitoring** Suppose that the presence of phosphates in certain waste products dumped into a lake promotes the growth of algae. Rampant growth of algae affects the oxygen supply in the water, so an environmental group wishes to estimate the area of algae growth. Group members measure across the algae growth (see Figure 13.34) and obtain the data (in feet) in the table.

x	Width w	x	Width w
0	0	50	27
10	15	60	24
20	18	70	23
30	18	80	0
40	30		

(a) Can either the Trapezoidal Rule or Simpson's Rule be used to calculate the area of the algae growth?
(b) When either the Trapezoidal Rule or Simpson's Rule can be used, which is usually more accurate?
(c) Use Simpson's Rule to approximate the area of the algae growth.

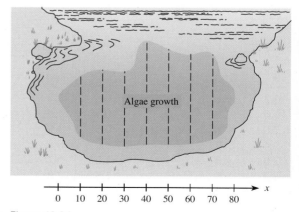

Figure 13.34

34. **Development costs** A land developer is planning to dig a small lake and build a group of homes around it. To estimate the cost of the project, the area of the lake

must be calculated from the proposed measurements (in feet) given in Figure 13.35 and in the data in the table. Use Simpson's Rule to approximate the area of the lake.

x	Width $w(x)$
0	0
100	300
200	200
300	400
400	0

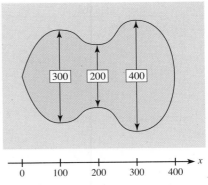

Figure 13.35

Chapter 13 Summary & Review

KEY TERMS AND FORMULAS

Section 13.1

Sigma (summation) notation (p. 791)

$$\sum_{i=1}^{n} a_i = a_1 + a_2 + \cdots + a_n$$

Formulas (p. 791)

$$\sum_{i=1}^{n} 1 = n; \quad \sum_{i=1}^{n} i = \frac{n(n+1)}{2}$$

$$\sum_{i=1}^{n} i^2 = \frac{n(n+1)(2n+1)}{6}$$

Area (p. 792)

Right-hand endpoints

$$\lim_{n \to \infty} \sum_{i=1}^{n} f(x_i) \frac{b-a}{n}; \quad x_i = a + i\left(\frac{b-a}{n}\right)$$

Left-hand endpoints

$$\lim_{n \to \infty} \sum_{i=1}^{n} f(x_{i-1}) \frac{b-a}{n}$$

Section 13.2

Riemann sum (p. 798)

$$\sum_{i=1}^{n} f(x_i^*) \Delta x_i$$

Definite integral (p. 798)

$$\int_a^b f(x)\,dx = \lim_{\substack{\max \Delta x_i \to 0 \\ (n \to \infty)}} \sum_{i=1}^{n} f(x_i^*) \Delta x_i$$

Fundamental Theorem of Calculus (p. 799)

$$\int_a^b f(x)\,dx = F(b) - F(a), \text{ where } F'(x) = f(x)$$

Definite integral properties (pp. 800–801)

$$\int_a^a f(x)\,dx = 0$$

$$\int_b^a f(x)\,dx = -\int_a^b f(x)\,dx$$

$$\int_a^b [f(x) \pm g(x)]\,dx = \int_a^b f(x)\,dx \pm \int_a^b g(x)\,dx$$

$$\int_a^b kf(x)\,dx = k\int_a^b f(x)\,dx$$

$$\int_a^c f(x)\,dx + \int_c^b f(x)\,dx = \int_a^b f(x)\,dx$$

Area under $f(x)$, where $f(x) \geq 0$ (p. 802)

$$A = \int_a^b f(x)\,dx$$

$f(x)$ is a probability density function (p. 803)

$$\Pr(a \leq x \leq b) = \int_a^b f(x)\,dx$$

Section 13.3

Lorenz curve, $L(x)$ (p. 807)
Area between $f(x)$ and $g(x)$, where $f(x) \geq g(x)$ (p. 808)

$$A = \int_a^b [f(x) - g(x)]\,dx$$

Gini coefficient (p. 811)

$$2\int_0^1 [x - L(x)]\,dx$$

Average value of f over $[a, b]$ (p. 811)

$$\frac{1}{b-a} \int_a^b f(x)\,dx$$

Section 13.4

Continuous income streams (p. 816)

Total income

$$\int_0^k f(t)\, dt \quad \text{(for } k \text{ years)}$$

Present value

$$\int_0^k f(t)e^{-rt}\, dt, \quad \text{where } r \text{ is the interest rate}$$

Future value

$$e^{rk}\int_0^k f(t)e^{-rt}\, dt$$

Consumer's surplus [demand is $f(x)$] (p. 818)

$$CS = \int_0^{x_1} f(x)\, dx - p_1 x_1$$

Producer's surplus [supply is $g(x)$] (p. 821)

$$PS = p_1 x_1 - \int_0^{x_1} g(x)\, dx$$

Section 13.5

Integration by formulas (p. 825)

See Table 13.2.

Section 13.6

Integration by parts (p. 829)

$$\int u\, dv = uv - \int v\, du$$

Section 13.7

Improper integrals (p. 834)

$$\int_a^\infty f(x)\, dx = \lim_{b\to\infty}\int_a^b f(x)\, dx$$

$$\int_{-\infty}^b f(x)\, dx = \lim_{a\to\infty}\int_{-a}^b f(x)\, dx$$

$$\int_{-\infty}^\infty f(x)\, dx = \int_{-\infty}^c f(x)\, dx + \int_c^\infty f(x)\, dx$$

Capital value of a continuous income stream (p. 836)

$$\int_0^\infty f(t)e^{-rt}dt$$

Probability density function, $f(x)$ (p. 837)

$$f(x) \geq 0 \ \text{ and } \int_{-\infty}^\infty f(x)\, dx = 1$$

Mean

$$u = \int_{-\infty}^\infty xf(x)dx$$

Section 13.8

Trapezoidal Rule (p. 841)

$$\int_a^b f(x)dx \approx \frac{h}{2}[f(x_0) + 2f(x_1) + \cdots + 2f(x_{n-1}) + f(x_n)]$$

where $h = \dfrac{b-a}{n}$

Error formula

$$|E| \leq \frac{(b-a)^3}{12n^2}\left[\max_{a\leq x\leq b}|f''(x)|\right]$$

Simpson's Rule (p. 843)

$$\int_a^b f(x)\, dx \approx \frac{h}{3}[f(x_0) + 4f(x_1) + 2f(x_2) + 4f(x_3)$$
$$+ \cdots + 2f(x_{n-2}) + 4f(x_{n-1}) + f(x_n)],$$

where n is even and $h = \dfrac{b-a}{n}$

Error formula

$$|E| \leq \frac{(b-a)^5}{180n^4}\left[\max_{a\leq x\leq b}|f^{(4)}(x)|\right]$$

REVIEW EXERCISES

Section 13.1

1. Calculate $\displaystyle\sum_{k=1}^{8}(k^2 + 1)$.

2. Use formulas to simplify

$$\sum_{i=1}^{n}\frac{3i}{n^3}$$

3. Use 6 subintervals of the same size to approximate the area under the graph of $y = 3x^2$ from $x = 0$ to $x = 1$.

Use the right-hand endpoints of the subintervals to find the heights of the rectangles.

4. Use rectangles to find the exact area under the graph of $y = 3x^2$ from $x = 0$ to $x = 1$. Use n equal subintervals.

Section 13.2

5. Use a definite integral to find the area under the graph of $y = 3x^2$ from $x = 0$ to $x = 1$.

II. Retirement Planning

A 52-year-old client asks an accountant how to plan for his future retirement at age 62. He expects income from Social Security in the amount of $21,600 per year and a retirement pension of $40,500 per year from his employer. He wants to make monthly contributions to an investment plan that pays 8%, compounded monthly, for 10 years so that he will have a total income of $83,700 per year for 30 years. What will the size of the monthly contributions have to be to accomplish this goal, if it is assumed that money will be worth 8%, compounded continuously, throughout the period after he is 62?

To help you answer this question, complete the following.

1. How much money must the client withdraw annually from his investment plan during his retirement so that his total income goal is met?
2. How much money S must the client's account contain when he is 62 so that it will generate this annual amount for 30 years? (*Hint:* S can be considered the present value over 30 years of a continuous income stream with the amount you found in Question 1 as its annual rate of flow.)
3. The monthly contribution R that would, after 10 years, amount to the present value S found in Question 2 can be obtained from the formula

$$R = S\left[\frac{i}{(1 + i)^n - 1}\right]$$

where i represents the monthly interest rate and n the number of months. Find the client's monthly contribution, R.

Graphing Calculator Guide

Operating the TI-83 and TI-84 Plus Calculators

Turning the Calculator On and Off

| ON | Turns the calculator on. |
| 2nd ON | Turns the calculator off. |

Adjusting the Display Contrast

| 2nd ▲ | Increases the contrast (darkens the screen). |
| 2nd ▼ | Decreases the contrast (lightens the screen). |

Note: If the display begins to dim (especially during calculations) and you must adjust the contrast to 8 or 9 in order to see the screen, then batteries are low and you should replace them soon.

The TI-83 and TI-84 Plus keyboards are divided into four zones: graphing keys, editing keys, advanced function keys, and scientific calculator keys (Figure 1).

Courtesy of Texas Instruments

Home screen

Graphing keys

Editing keys (Allow you to edit expressions and variables)

Advanced function keys (Display menus that access advanced functions)

Scientific calculator keys

Figure 1

Chapter 1
Section 1.4 Graphing Equations

Entering Equations for Graphing

To graph an equation in the variables x and y, first solve the equation for y in terms of x. If the equation has variables other than x and y, solve for the dependent variable and replace the independent variable with x. Press the Y = key to access the function entry screen and enter the equation. To erase an equation, press CLEAR. To return to the home-screen, press 2nd MODE (QUIT).

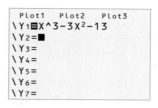

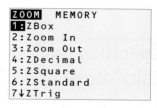

Setting Windows

The window defines the highest and lowest values of x and y on the graph of the function that will be shown on the screen. The values that define the viewing window can be set by using ZOOM keys. The standard window (ZOOM 6) is often appropriate. The standard window gives x- and y-values between -10 and 10.

To set the window manually, press the WINDOW key and enter the values that you want.

The Xscl (x scale) is the distance between tic marks on the x-axis, going in both directions from the origin, and the Yscl (y scale) is the distance between tic marks on the y-axis, going in both directions from the origin. The scales can be set individually, and are useful in visually determining x- and y-intercepts of graphs.

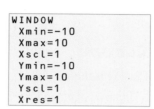

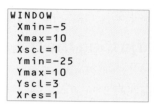

Graphing Equations

Determine an appropriate viewing window. The window should be set so that the important parts of the graph are shown and the unseen parts are suggested. Such a graph is called **complete**. Using the displayed coordinates from TRACE helps to determine an appropriate window. Pressing GRAPH or a ZOOM key will activate the graph.

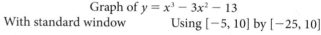

Graph of $y = x^3 - 3x^2 - 13$

With standard window   Using $[-5, 10]$ by $[-25, 10]$

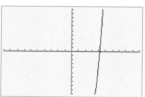

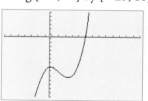

Section 1.4 Finding Function Values

Using TRACE on the Graph

Enter the function to be evaluated in Y_1. Choose a window so that it contains the x-value whose y-value you seek. Press TRACE and then enter the selected x-value followed by ENTER. The cursor will move to the selected value and give the resulting y-value if the selected x-value is in the window. If the selected x-value is not in the window, Err: INVALID occurs. If the x-value is in the window, the y-value will occur even if it is not visible in the window.

To evaluate $y = -x^2 + 8x + 9$ when $x = -5$ and when $x = 3$, graph the function using the window $[-10, 10]$ by $[-10, 30]$.

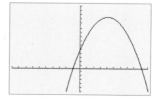

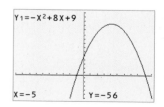

Using the TABLE ASK Feature

Enter the function with the Y = key. {Note: The = sign must be highlighted.) Press 2nd WINDOW (TBLSET), move the cursor to Ask opposite Indpnt:, and press ENTER. This allows you to input specific values for x. Then press 2nd TABLE and enter the specific values. Pressing DEL clears an entry. The table on the right evaluates $y = -x^2 + 8x + 9$ at -5 and at 3.

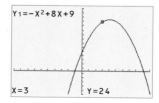

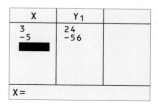

Making a Table of Values

If the Indpnt variable is on Auto, enter an initial x-value for the table in TblStart, and enter the desired change in the x-value as ΔTbl.

Enter 2nd TABLE to get a list of x-values and the corresponding y-values. The value of the function at the given value of x can be read from the table. Use the up or down arrows to find the x-values where the function is to be evaluated. The table on the right evaluates $y = -x^2 + 8x + 9$ for integer x-values from -3 to 3.

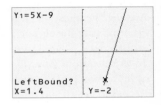

Section 1.4 Solving Linear Equations by the x-Intercept Method

To find the solution to $f(x) = 0$ (the x-value where the graph crosses the x-axis):

1. Set one side of the equation to 0 and enter the other side as Y_1 in the Y = menu.
2. Set the window so that the x-intercept to be located can be seen.
3. Press 2nd TRACE to access the CALC menu and select 2:zero.
4. Answer the question "*Left Bound?*" with ENTER after moving the cursor close to and to the left of an x-intercept.
5. Answer the question "*Right Bound?*" with ENTER after moving the cursor close to and to the right of this x-intercept.
6. To the question "*Guess?*" press ENTER. The coordinates of the x-intercept are displayed. The x-value is a solution.

The solution to $5x - 9 = 0$ is found to be $x = 1.8$.

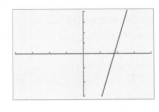

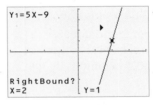

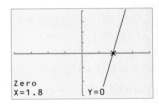

Section 1.5 Solving Systems of Equations in Two Variables

To solve a system of linear equations in two variables graphically:

1. Solve both equations for y.
2. Graph the first equation as Y_1 and the second as Y_2.
3. To find the point of intersection of the graphs:
   (a) Press 2nd TRACE to access the CALC menu and select 5:intersect.
   (b) Answer the question "*First curve?*" by pressing ENTER and "*Second curve?*" by pressing ENTER.
   (c) To the question "*Guess?*" press ENTER. The solution is shown on the right.

If the two lines intersect in one point, the coordinates give the x- and y-values of the solution.

The solution of the system at the right is $x = 2$, $y = 1$.

To solve $\begin{cases} 4x + 3y = 11 \\ 2x - 5y = -1 \end{cases}$ graphically, graph

$y_1 = -\dfrac{4}{3}x + \dfrac{11}{3}$ and $y_2 = \dfrac{2}{5}x + \dfrac{1}{5}$, then use Intersect.

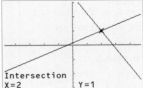

Chapter 2

Section 2.1 Solving Nonlinear Equations by the x-Intercept Method

To find the solutions to $f(x) = 0$ (the x-values where the graph crosses the x-axis):

1. Set one side of the equation to 0 and enter the other side as Y_1 in the Y = menu.
2. Set the window so that the x-intercepts to be located can be seen.
3. Press 2nd TRACE to access the CALC menu and select 2:zero.
4. Answer the question "*Left Bound?*" with ENTER after moving the cursor close to and to the left of an x-intercept.
5. Answer the question "*Right Bound?*" with ENTER after moving the cursor close to and to the right of this x-intercept.
6. To the question "*Guess?*" press ENTER. The coordinates of the x-intercept are displayed. The x-value is a solution.
7. Repeat to get all x-intercepts. The graph of a linear equation will cross the x-axis at most 1 time; the graph of quadratic equation will cross the x-axis at most 2 times, etc.

The solutions to $0 = -x^2 + 8x + 9$ are found to be 9 and -1.

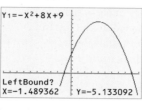

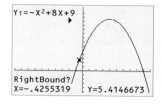

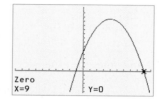

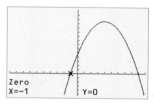

Section 2.1 Solving Nonlinear Equations by the Intersection Method

To solve nonlinear equations by the intersection method:

1. Graph the left side of the equation as Y_1 and the right side as Y_2.
2. Find a point of intersection of the graphs as shown in Section 1.5.
3. To find another point of intersection, repeat while keeping the cursor near the second point.

The solutions to $7x^2 = 16x - 4$ are found at the right.

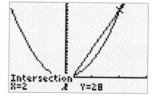

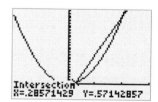

Section 2.2 Graphing Quadratic Functions

To graph a quadratic function:

1. Solve for y in terms of x and enter it in the Y = menu.
2. Find the coordinates of its vertex, with $x = -b/a$.
3. Set the window so the x-coordinate of its vertex is near its center and the y-coordinate is visible.
4. Press Graph.

To graph $P(x) = -0.1x^2 + 300x - 1200$, enter $y_1 = -0.1x^2 + 300x - 1200$ on a window with its center near $x = (-300)/[2(-0.1)] = 1500$ and with $y = P(1500) = 223{,}800$ visible, and graph.

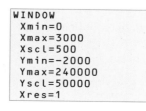

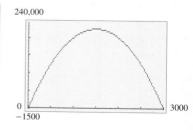

Section 2.4 Graphing Polynomial Functions

To graph a polynomial function:

1. See Table 2.1 in the text to determine possible shapes for the graph.
   (The graph of the function $y = x^3 - 16x$ has one of four shapes in the table.)
2. Graph the function in a window large enough to see the shape of the complete graph. This graph is like the graph of Degree 3(b) in the table in Section 2.4.
3. If necessary, adjust the window for a better view of the graph.

$[-40, 40]$ by $[-100, 100]$ $[-6, 6]$ by $[-30, 30]$

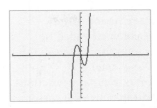   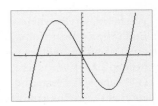

$y = x^3 - 16x$ $y = x^3 - 16x$
                          (Better view)

Section 2.4 Graphing Rational Functions

To graph a rational function:

1. Determine the vertical and horizontal asymptotes.
2. Set the window so that the x range is centered near the x-value of the vertical asymptote.
3. Set the window so that the horizontal asymptote is near the center of the y range.
4. Graph the function in a window large enough to see the shape of the complete graph.
5. If necessary, adjust the window for a better view of the graph.

To graph $y = \dfrac{12x + 8}{3x - 9}$, set the center of the window near the vertical asymptote $x = 3$ and near the horizontal asymptote $y = 4$.

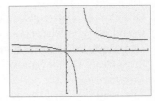

```
WINDOW
 Xmin=-12
 Xmax=18
 Xscl=3
 Ymin=-18
 Ymax=22
 Yscl=2
 Xres=1
```

Section 2.4 Graphing Piecewise Defined Functions

A piecewise defined function is defined differently over two or more intervals.

To graph a piecewise defined function $y = \begin{cases} f(x) \text{ if } x \le a \\ g(x) \text{ if } x > a \end{cases}$

1. Go to the Y = key and enter

   $Y_1 = f(x)/(x \le a)$ and $Y_2 = g(x)/(x > a)$

   (The inequality symbols are found under the TEST menu.)
2. Graph the function using an appropriate window.
3. Evaluating a piecewise defined function at a given value of x requires that the correct equation ("piece") be selected.

To graph $y = \begin{cases} x + 7 \text{ if } x \le -5 \\ -x + 2 \text{ if } x > -5 \end{cases}$

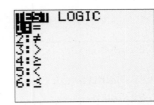

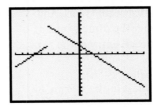

Section 2.5 Modeling

A. To Create a Scatter Plot

1. Press STAT and under EDIT press 1:Edit. This brings you to the screen where you enter data into lists.
2. Enter the x-values (input) in the column headed L1 and the corresponding y-values (output) in the column headed L2.
3. Go to the Y = menu and turn off or clear any functions entered there. To turn off a function, move the cursor over the = sign and press ENTER.
4. Press 2nd STAT PLOT, 1:Plot 1. Highlight ON, and then highlight the first graph type (Scatter Plot), Enter Xlist:L1, Ylist:L2, and pick the point plot mark you want.
5. Choose an appropriate WINDOW for the graph and press GRAPH, or press ZOOM, 9:ZoomStat to plot the data points.

B. To Find an Equation That Models a Set of Data Points

1. Observe the scatter plot to determine what type function would best model the data. Press STAT, move to CALC, and select the function type to be used to model the data.
2. Press the VARS key, move to Y-VARS, and select 1:Function and 1:Y$_1$. Press ENTER.
   The coefficients of the equation will appear on the screen and the regression equation will appear as Y$_1$ on the Y = screen.

Pressing ZOOM 9 shows how well the model fits the data.

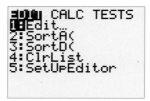

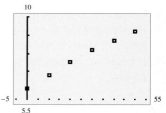

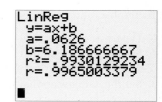

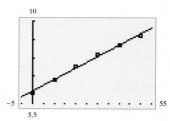

The Model is $y = 0.0626x + 6.19$.

Chapter 3

Section 3.1 Entering Data into Matrices

To enter data into matrices, press the MATRIX key. Move the cursor to EDIT. Enter the number of the matrix into which the data is to be entered. Enter the dimensions of the matrix, and enter the value for each entry of the matrix. Press ENTER after each entry.

For example, we enter the matrix below as [A].

$$\begin{bmatrix} 1 & 2 & 3 \\ 2 & -2 & 1 \\ 3 & 1 & -2 \end{bmatrix}$$

1. Enter 3's to set the dimension, and enter the numbers.
2. To perform operations with the matrix or leave the editor, first press 2nd QUIT.
3. To view the matrix, press MATRIX, the number of the matrix, and ENTER.

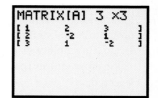

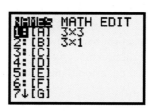

Section 3.1 Operations with Matrices

To find the sum of two matrices, [A] and [D], enter
[A] + [D], and press ENTER. For example, the sum

$$\begin{bmatrix} 1 & 2 & 3 \\ 2 & -2 & 1 \\ 3 & 1 & -2 \end{bmatrix} + \begin{bmatrix} 7 & -3 & 2 \\ 4 & -5 & 3 \\ 0 & 2 & 1 \end{bmatrix}$$ is shown at right.

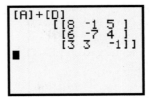

To find the difference, enter [A] − [D] and press ENTER.
We can multiply a matrix [D] by a real number (scalar) k by
entering k [D].

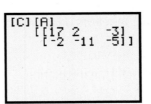

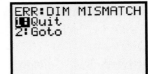

Section 3.2 Multiplying Two Matrices

To find the product of two matrices, [C] times [A], enter
[C][A] and press ENTER. For example, we compute the
product

$$\begin{bmatrix} 1 & 2 & 4 \\ -3 & 2 & -1 \end{bmatrix} \begin{bmatrix} 1 & 2 & 3 \\ 2 & -2 & 1 \\ 3 & 1 & -2 \end{bmatrix}$$ at right.

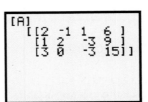

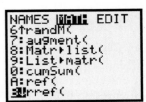

Note that entering [A][C] gives an error message. [A][C]
cannot be computed because the dimensions do not match
in this order.

Section 3.3 Solution of Systems—
Reduced Echelon Form

To solve a 3 × 3 system:
1. Enter the coefficients and the constants in an
    augmented matrix.
2. Under the MATRIX menu, choose MATH and B:rref,
    then enter the matrix to be reduced followed by “)”, and
    press ENTER.
3. (a) If each row in the coefficient matrix (first 3 columns)
        contains a 1 with the other elements 0's, the solution
        is unique and the number in column 4 of a row is the
        value of the variable corresponding to a 1 in that row.

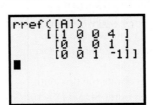

For example, the system $\begin{cases} 2x - y + z = 6 \\ x + 2y - 3z = 9 \\ 3x \quad\quad - 3z = 15 \end{cases}$ is solved at right.

The solution to the system above is unique: $x = 4$, $y = 1$,
and $z = -1$.
(b) If the reduced matrix has all zeros in the third row,
    the solution is nonunique.
(c) If the reduced matrix has 3 zeros in a row and a
    nonzero element in the fourth column in that row,
    there is no solution.

Section 3.4 Finding the Inverse of a Matrix

To find the inverse of a matrix:
1. Enter the elements of the matrix using MATRIX and EDIT. Press 2nd QUIT.
2. Press MATRIX, the number of the matrix, and ENTER, then press the x^{-1} key and ENTER.

For example, the inverse of $E = \begin{bmatrix} 2 & 0 & 2 \\ -1 & 0 & 1 \\ 4 & 2 & 0 \end{bmatrix}$

   is shown at right.
3. To see the entries as fractions, press MATH, press 1:Frac, and press ENTER.

Not all matrices have inverses. Matrices that do not have inverses are called singular matrices. See matrix F at the right.

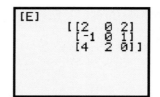

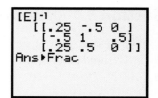

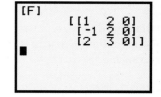

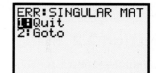

Section 3.4 Solving Systems of Linear Equations with Matrix Inverses

The matrix equation $AX = B$ can be solved by computing $X = A^{-1}B$ if a unique solution exists.

The solution to $\begin{cases} 25x + 20y + 50z = 15{,}000 \\ 25x + 50y + 100z = 27{,}500 \\ 250x + 50y + 500z = 92{,}250 \end{cases}$

is found at the right to be $x = 254$, $y = 385$, $z = 19$.

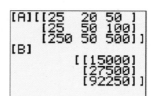

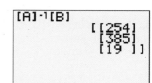

Chapter 4
Section 4.1 Graphing Solution Regions of Linear Inequalities

To graph the solution of a linear inequality in two variables, first solve the inequality for the dependent variable and enter the other side of the inequality in Y_1, so that $Y_1 = f(x)$. If the inequality has the form $y \le f(x)$, shade the region below the graphed line and if the inequality has the form $y \ge f(x)$, shade the region above the line.

In this example, we shade the region above the line with SHADE under the DRAW menu and enter Shade $(Y_1, 10)$ on the home screen. See Section 4.1 on the next page for an alternate method of shading.

To solve $4x - 2y \le 6$, convert it to $y \ge 2x - 3$ and graph $Y_1 = 2x - 3$.

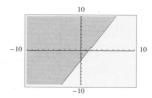

Section 4.1 Graphing Solutions of Systems of Linear Inequalities

To graph the solution region for a system of linear inequalities in two variables, write the inequalities as equations solved for y, and graph the equations.

For example, to find the region defined by the inequalities

$$\begin{cases} 5x + 2y \le 54 \\ 2x + 4y \le 60 \\ x \ge 0, y \ge 0 \end{cases}$$

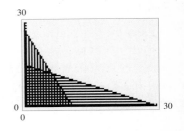

1. Choose a window with x min $= 0$ and y min $= 0$ because the inequalities $x \ge 0, y \ge 0$ limit the graph to Quadrant I.
2. Solve the equations for y getting $y = 27 - 5x/2$ and $y = 15 - x/2$. Enter these equations as Y_1 and Y_2.
3. Because both inequalities have "$y \le$," we move our cursor to the left of Y_1 and press ENTER until a triangle shaded like that in the figure appears and then repeat this with Y_2. Pressing GRAPH then shows the solution to the system.
4. Using TRACE or INTERSECT with the pair of equations and finding the intercepts give the corners of the solution region, where the borders intersect. These corners of the region are $(0, 0)$ $(0, 15)$, $(6, 12)$, and $(10.8, 0)$.

Section 4.2 Linear Programming

To solve a linear programming problem involving constraints in two variables:

1. Graph the constraint inequalities as equations, solved for y.
2. Test points to determine the region and use TRACE or INTERSECT to find each of the corners of the region, where the borders intersect.
3. Then evaluate the objective function at each of the corners.

   For example, to maximize $f = 5x + 11y$ subject to the constraints

$$\begin{cases} 5x + 2y \le 54 \\ 2x + 4y \le 60 \\ x \ge 0, y \ge 0 \end{cases}$$

we graphically find the constraint region (as shown above), and evaluate the objective function at the coordinates of each of the corners of the region. Evaluating $f = 5x + 11y$ at each of the corners determines where this objective function is maximized or minimized.

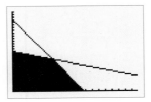

The corners of the region determined by the inequalities are $(0, 0)$ $(0, 15)$, $(6, 12)$, and $(10.8, 0)$.

At $(0, 0)$, $f = 0$ At $(0, 15)$, $f = 165$
At $(6, 12)$, $f = 162$ At $(10.8, 0)$, $f = 54$

The maximum value of f is 165 at $x = 0$, $y = 15$.

Chapter 5
Section 5.1 Graphing Exponential Functions

1. Enter the function as Y_1 in the $Y =$ menu.
2. Set the x-range centered at $x = 0$.
3. Set the y-range to reflect the function's range of $y > 0$.

Note that some graphs (such as the graph of $y = 4^x$ shown here) appear to eventually merge with the negative x-axis. Adjusting the window can show that these graphs never touch the x-axis. For more complicated exponential functions, it may be helpful to use TABLE to find a useful window.

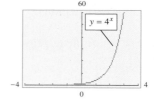

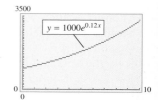

Section 5.1 Modeling with Exponential Functions

1. Create a scatter plot for the data.
2. Choose STAT, then CALC. Scroll down to 0:ExpReg and press ENTER, then VARS, Y-VARS, FUNCTION, Y_1, and ENTER.

    (Recall that this both calculates the requested exponential model and enters its equation as Y_1 in the $Y =$ menu.)

The last screen shows how well the model fits the data.

Find the exponential model for the following data.

x	1	2	3	4	5	6	7	8	9	10
y	43	38	33	29	25	22	19	15	14	12

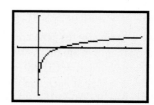

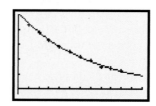

Section 5.2 Graphing Base e and Base 10 Logarithmic Functions

Enter the function as Y_1 in the $Y =$ menu.

1. For $y = \ln(x)$ use the LN key.
2. For $y = \log(x)$ use the LOG key.
3. Set the window x-range to reflect that the function's domain is $x > 0$.
4. Center the window y-range at $y = 0$.

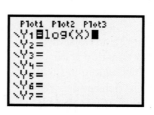

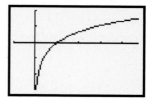

Section 5.2 Modeling with Logarithmic Functions

1. Create a scatter plot for the data.
2. Choose STAT, then CALC. Scroll down to 9:LnReg and press ENTER, then VARS, Y-VARS, FUNCTION, Y1, and ENTER.

The last figure on the right shows how well the model fits the data.

Find the logarithmic model for the following data.

x	10	20	30	38
y	2.21	3.79	4.92	5.77

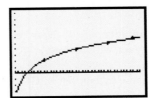

Section 5.2 Graphing Logarithmic Functions with Other Bases

1. Use a change of base formula to rewrite the logarithmic function with base 10 or base e.

$$\log_b x = \frac{\log x}{\log b} \quad \text{or} \quad \log_b x = \frac{\ln x}{\ln b}$$

2. Proceed as described above for graphing base e and base 10 logarithms.

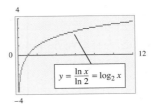

Chapter 6
Section 6.2 Future Value of a Lump Sum

To find the future value of a lump-sum investment:

1. Press the APPS key and select Finance, press ENTER.
2. Select TVM Solver, press ENTER.
3. Set N = the total number of periods, set I% = the annual percentage rate.
4. Set the PV = the lump sum preceded by a "−" to indicate the lump sum is leaving your possession.
5. Set PMT = 0 and set both P/Y and C/Y = the number of compounding periods per year.
6. Put the cursor on FV and press ALPHA ENTER to get the future value.

The future value of $10,000 invested at 9.8% compounded quarterly for 17 years is shown at the right.

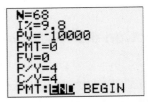

Section 6.3   Future Value of an Annuity

To find the future value of an ordinary annuity:

1. Press the APPS key and select Finance, press ENTER.
2. Select TVM Solver, press ENTER.
3. Set N = the total number of periods, set I% = the annual percentage rate.
4. Set the PV = 0 and set both P/Y and C/Y = the number of compounding periods per year. END should be highlighted.
5. Set PMT = the periodic payment preceded by a " − " to indicate the lump sum is leaving your possession.
6. Put the cursor on FV and press ALPHA ENTER to get the future value.
   The future value of an ordinary annuity of $200 deposited at the end of each quarter for $2\frac{1}{4}$ years, with interest at 4% compounded quarterly, is shown.

For annuities due, all steps are the same except that BEGIN is highlighted.

Ordinary annuity   Annuity due

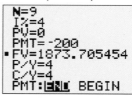

Section 6.4   Present Value of an Annuity

To find the present value of an ordinary annuity:

1. Press the APPS key and select Finance, press ENTER.
2. Select TVM Solver, press ENTER.
3. Set N = the total number of periods, set I% = the annual percentage rate.
4. Set the FV = 0 and set both P/Y and C/Y = the number of compounding periods per year. END should be highlighted.
5. Set PMT = the periodic payment.
6. Put the cursor on PV and press ALPHA ENTER to get the present value.

The lump sum that needs to be deposited to receive $1000 at the end of each month for 16 years if the annuity pays 9%, compounded monthly is shown at the right.
For annuities due, BEGIN is highlighted.

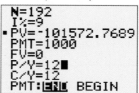

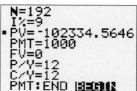

Ordinary annuity   Annuity due

Section 6.5   Finding Payments to Amortize a Loan

To find the size of periodic payments to amortize a loan:

1. Press the APPS key and select Finance, press ENTER.
2. Select TVM Solver, press ENTER.
3. Set N = the total number of periods, set I% = the APR.
4. Set the PV = loan value and set both P/Y and C/Y = the number of periods per year. END should be highlighted.
5. Set FV = 0.
6. Put the cursor on PMT and press ALPHA ENTER to get the payment.

To repay a loan of $10,000 in 5 annual payments with annual interest at 10%, each payment must be $2637.97.

Section 6.5 Finding the Number of Payments to Amortize a Loan

To find the number of payments needed to amortize a loan:

1. Press the APPS key and select Finance, press ENTER.
2. Select TVM Solver, press ENTER.
3. Set the PV = loan value, set both P/Y and C/Y = the number of periods per year, set I% = the APR.
4. Set PMT = required payment and set FV = 0.
5. Put the cursor on N and press ALPHA ENTER to get the number of payments.

The number of monthly payments to pay a $2500 credit card loan with $55 payments and 18% interest is 76.9 months, or 6 years, 5 months.

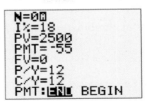
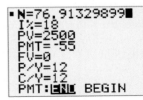

Chapter 7

Section 7.5 Evaluating Factorials

To evaluate factorials:

1. Enter the number whose factorial is to be calculated.
2. Choose MATH, then PRB. Scroll to 4: ! and press ENTER.

Press ENTER again to find the factorial.
7! is shown on the right.

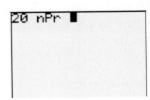

Section 7.5 Evaluating Permutations

To evaluate permutations:

1. For a "permutation of n objects taken r at a time" (such as $_{20}P_4$), first enter the value of n (such as $n = 20$).
2. Choose MATH, then PRB. Scroll to 2: nPr and press ENTER.
3. Enter the value of r (such as $r = 4$), and press ENTER to find the value of nPr.
   $_{20}P_4$ is shown on the right.

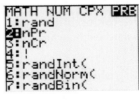
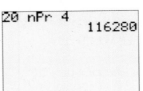

Section 7.5 Evaluating Combinations

To evaluate combinations:

1. For a "combination of n objects taken r at a time" (such as $_{20}C_4$), first enter the value of n (such as $n = 20$).
2. Choose MATH, then PRB. Scroll to 3:nCr and press ENTER.
3. Enter the value of r (such as $r = 4$), and press ENTER to find the value of nCr.

Note that nCr = nC(n − r), as the figure on the right shows for $_{20}C_4$ and $_{20}C_{16}$.

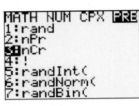
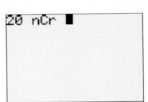
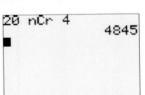
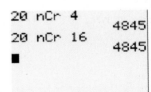

Section 7.6 Finding Probabilities Using Permutations and Combinations

To solve a probability problem that involves permutations or combinations:

1. Determine if permutations or combinations should be used.
2. Enter the ratios of permutations or combinations to find the probability.
3. If desired, use MATH, then 1:Frac to get the probability as a fraction.

If there are 5 defective computer chips in a box of 10, the probability that 2 chips drawn together from the box will both be defective is

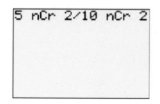 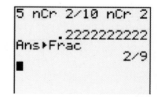

Section 7.7 Evaluating Markov Chains

To evaluate a Markov chain:

1. Enter the initial probability vector as matrix A and the transition matrix as matrix B.
2. To find the probabilities for the nth state, calculate $[A][B]^n$. The 3rd state, $[A][B]^3$, is shown on the right.

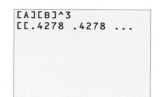

Section 7.7 Finding Steady-State Vectors for Markov Chains

If the transition matrix contains only positive entries, the probabilities will approach a steady-state vector, which is found as follows.

1. Calculate and store $[C] = [B] - [I]$, where $[B]$ is the regular transition matrix and $[I]$ is the appropriately sized identity matrix.
2. Solve $[C]^T = [0]$ as follows:
   (a) Find $[C]^T$ with MATRIX, then MATH, 2:^{T}.
   (b) Find rref$[C]^T$.
3. Choose the solutions that add to 1 because they are probabilities.

```
identity(3)→[I]
           [[1 0 0]
            [0 1 0]
            [0 0 1]]
■
```

```
[B]-[I]
      [[-.5  .4   .1 ]
       [.4  -.5  .1 ]
       [.3   .3  -.6]]
Ans→[C]■
```

```
rref([C]ᵀ)
       [[1 0 -3]
        [0 1 -3]
        [0 0  0]]
```

Thus $x = 3z$ and $y = 3z$, and $3z + 3z + z = 1$ gives $z = 1/7$, so the probabilities are given in the steady-state vector $\begin{bmatrix} \dfrac{3}{7} & \dfrac{3}{7} & \dfrac{1}{7} \end{bmatrix}$.

Chapter 8
Section 8.1 Binomial Probabilities

To find binomial probabilities:

1. 2nd DISTR A:binompdf(n,p,x) computes the probability of x success in n trials of a binomial experiment with probability of success p. Using MATH 1:Frac gives the probabilities as fractions.
   The probability of 3 heads in 6 tosses of a fair coin is found using 2nd DISTR, binompdf(6,.5,3).
2. The probabilities can be computed for more than one number in one command, using 2nd DISTR, binompdf($n,p,\{x_1,x_2,\ldots\}$).
   The probabilities of 4, 5, or 6 heads in 6 tosses of a fair coin are found using 2nd DISTR, binompdf(6,.5,{4,5,6}).
3. 2nd DISTR, binomcdf(n,p,x) computes the probability that the number of successes is less than or equal to x for the binomial distribution with n trials and probability of success p.

   The probability of 4 or fewer heads in 6 tosses of a fair coin is found using 2nd DISTR, binomcdf(6,.5,4).

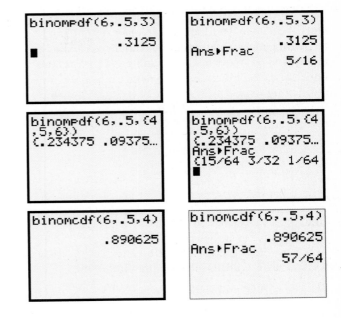

Section 8.2 Histograms

To find a frequency histogram for a set of data:

1. Press STAT, EDIT, 1:edit to enter each number in a column headed by L1 and the corresponding frequency of each number in L2.
2. Press 2nd STAT PLOT, 1:Plot 1. Highlight ON, and then press ENTER on the histogram icon. Enter L1 in xlist and L2 in Feq.
3. Press ZOOM, 9:ZoomStat or press Graph with an appropriate window.
4. If the data is given in interval form, a histogram can be created using the steps above with the class marks used to represent the intervals.

The frequency histogram for the scores 38, 37, 36, 40, 35, 40, 38, 37, 36, 37, 39, 38 is shown.

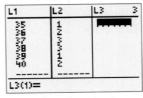

Section 8.2 Finding the Mean and Standard Deviation of Raw Data

To find descriptive statistics for a set of data:

1. Enter the data in list L1.
2. To find the mean and standard deviation of the data in L1, press STAT, move to CALC, and press 1:1-Var Stats, and ENTER.

The mean and sample standard deviation of the data 1, 2, 3, 3, 4, 4, 4, 4, 5, 5, 6, 7 are $\bar{x} = 4$ and $s \approx 1.65$.

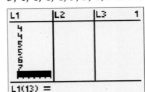
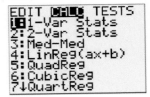

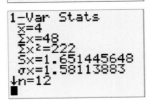

Section 8.2 Finding the Mean and Standard Deviation of Grouped Data

To find descriptive statistics for a set of data:

1. Enter the data in list L1 and the frequencies in L2.
2. To find the mean and standard deviation of the data in L1, press STAT, move to CALC, and press 1:1-Var Stats L1, L2, and ENTER.

The mean and standard deviation for the data in the table are shown on the right.

Salary	Number	Salary	Number
$59,000	1	$31,000	1
30,000	2	75,000	1
26,000	7	35,000	1
34,000	2		

The mean is $34,000 and the sample standard deviation is $14,132.84.

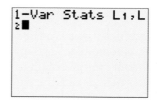

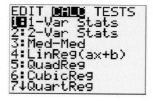

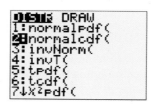

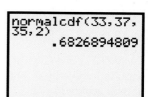

Section 8.4 Calculating Normal Probabilites

To calculate normal probabilities:

The command 2nd DISTR, 2:normalcdf(lowerbound, upperbound, μ, σ) gives the probability that x lies between the lower bound and the upper bound when the mean is μ and the standard deviation is σ.

The probability that a score lies between 33 and 37 when the mean is 35 and the standard deviation is 2 is found below.

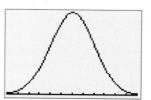

Section 8.4 Graphing Normal Distributions

To graph the normal distribution, press Y = and enter 2nd DIST 1:normalpdf(x, μ, σ) into Y_1.

Then set the window values xmin and xmax so the mean μ falls between them and press ZOOM, 0:Zoomfit.

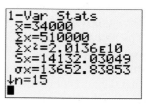

Chapter 9
Section 9.1 Evaluating Limits

To evaluate $\lim\limits_{x \to c} f(x)$

1. Enter the function as Y_1 in the $Y =$ menu.
2. Set the x-range so it contains $x = c$.
3. Evaluate $f(x)$ for several x-values near $x = c$ and on each side by c by using one of the following methods.
    (a) Graphical Evaluation
    TRACE and ZOOM near $x = c$. If the values of y approach the same number L as x approaches c from the left and the right, there is evidence that the limit is L.
    (b) Numerical Evaluation
    Use TBLSET with Indpnt set to *Ask*. Enter values very close to and on both sides of c. The y-values will approach the same limit as above.

Evaluate $\lim\limits_{x \to 3} \dfrac{x^2 - 9}{x - 3}$.

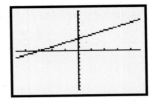
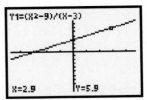
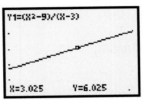
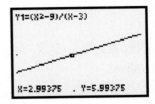

The y-values seem to approach 6.

The limit as x approaches 3 of $f(x)$ appears to be 6.

X	Y₁	
2.998	5.998	
2.999	5.999	
3	ERROR	
3.001	6.001	
3.002	6.002	
3.003	6.003	
3.004	6.004	

Y₁=ERROR

Section 9.1 Limits of Piecewise Functions

Enter the function, then use one of the methods for evaluating limits discussed above.

Find $\lim\limits_{x \to -5} f(x)$ where $f(x) = \begin{cases} x + 7 & \text{if } x \leq -5 \\ -x + 2 & \text{if } x > -5 \end{cases}$

First enter $Y_1 = (x + 7)/(x \leq -5)$ and $Y_2 = (-x + 2)/(x > -5)$.

Both methods indicate that the limit does not exist (DNE).

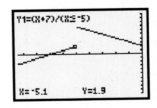
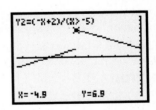

TABLE SETUP
TblStart=-5.003
ΔTbl=1
Indpnt: **Auto** Ask
Depend: **Auto** Ask

X	Y₁	Y₂
-5.003	1.997	ERROR
-5.001	1.999	ERROR
-4.999	ERROR	6.999
-4.98	ERROR	6.98

X=

Section 9.2 Limits as $x \rightarrow \infty$

Enter the function as Y_1, then use large values of x with one of the methods for evaluating limits discussed above. Note: limits as $x \rightarrow -\infty$ are done similarly.

Evaluate $\lim\limits_{x \to \infty} \dfrac{3x - 2}{1 - 5x}$.

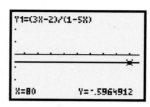

Both methods suggest that the limit is -0.6.

Sections 9.3–9.7 Approximating Derivatives

To find the numerical derivative (approximate derivative) of $f(x)$ at $x = c$, use Method 1 or Method 2.

Method 1
1. Choose MATH, then 8:nDeriv(and press ENTER.
2. Enter the function, x, and the value of c, so the display shows nDeriv($f(x)$, x, c) then press ENTER. The approximate derivative at the specified value will be displayed.

Method 2
1. Enter the function as Y_1 in the Y = menu, and graph in a window that contains both c and $f(c)$.
2. Choose CALC by using 2nd TRACE, then 6:dy/dx, enter the x-value, c, and press ENTER. Then approximate derivative at the specified value will be displayed.

Warning: Both approximation methods above require that the derivative exists at $x = c$ and will give incorrect information when $f'(c)$ does not exist.

Find the numerical derivative of $f(x) = x^3 - 2x^2$ at $x = 2$.

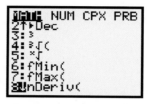 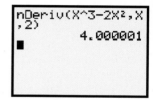

The numerical derivative is approximately 4.

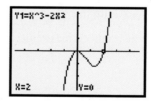 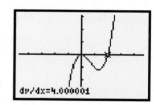

The value of the derivative is approximately 4.

Sections 9.3–9.7 Checking Derivatives

To check the correctness of the derivative function $f(x)$:

1. In the Y = menu, enter as Y_1 the derivative $f'(x)$ that you found, and graph it in a convenient window.
2. Enter the following as Y_2:nDeriv(f(x), x, x).
3. If the second graph lies on top of the first, the derivative is correct.

Verify the derivative of $f(x) = x^3 - 2x^2$ is $f'(x) = 3x^2 - 4x$.

 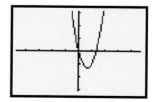

 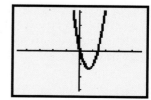

Section 9.8 Approximating the Second Derivative

To approximate $f''(c)$:

1. Enter $f(x)$ as Y_1 in the Y = menu.
2. Enter nDeriv(Y_1,x,x) as Y_2.
3. Estimate $f''(c)$ by using nDeriv(Y_2,x,c).

Find the second derivative of $f(x) = x^3 - 2x^2$ at $x = 2$.

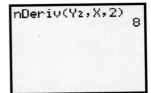

Thus $f''(2) = 8$.

Chapter 10
Section 10.1 Finding Critical Values

To find or approximate critical values of $f(x)$, that is x-values that make the derivative equal to 0 or undefined:

I. Find the derivative of $f(x)$.

II. Use Method 1 or Method 2 to find the critical values.

Method 1

1. Enter the derivative in the Y = menu as Y_1 and graph it in a convenient window.
2. Find where $Y_1 = 0$ by one of the following:
   (a) Using TRACE to find the x-intercepts of Y_1.
   (b) Using 2nd CALC then 2:zero.
   (c) Using TBLSET then TABLE to find the values of x that give $Y_1 = 0$.
3. Use the graph of Y_1 (and TRACE or TABLE) to find the values of x that make the derivative undefined.

Method 2

1. Enter the derivative in the Y = menu as Y_1.
2. Press MATH and select Solver. Press the up arrow revealing EQUATION SOLVER equ:0 =, and enter Y_1 (the derivative).
3. Press the down arrow or ENTER and the variable x appears with a value (not the solution). Move the cursor to the line containing the variable whose value is sought.
4. Press ALPHA SOLVE (ENTER). The value of the variable changes to the solution that is closest to that value originally shown.
5. To find additional solutions (if they exist), change the value of the variable and press ALPHA SOLVE (ENTER). The value of the variable changes to the solution of $Y_1 = 0$ that is closest to that value.
6. If appropriate, use 0:Solver to solve (Denominator of Y_1) = 0 to find the critical values for which the derivative is undefined.

Methods 1 and 2 show how to find the critical values of $f(x) = \frac{1}{3}x^3 - 4x$. Note that the derivative is $f'(x) = x^2 - 4$.

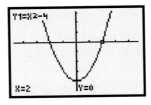
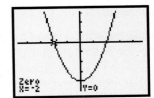

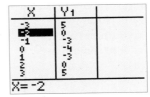

The only critical values are $x = 2$ and $x = -2$.

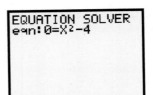
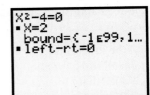

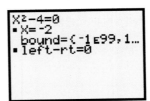

The only critical values are $x = 2$ and $x = -2$.

Section 10.1 Relative Maxima and Minima

To find relative maxima and minima:

1. In the Y = menu enter the function as Y_1 and the derivative as Y_2.
2. Use TBLSET and TABLE to evaluate the derivative to the left and to the right of each critical value.
3. Use the signs of the values of the derivative to determine whether f is increasing or decreasing around the critical values, and thus to classify the critical values as relative maxima, relative minima, or horizontal points of inflection.
4. Graph the function to confirm your conclusions.

Find the relative maxima and minima of $f(x) = \dfrac{1}{3}x^3 - 4x$. Note that the derivative is $f'(x) = x^2 - 4$.

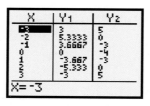 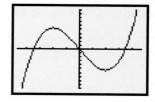

The relative max is at $(-2, 16/3)$, and the relative min is at $(2, -16/3)$.

Section 10.1 Critical Values and Viewing Windows

To use critical values to set a viewing window that shows a complete graph:

1. Once the critical values for a function have been found,
   (a) Enter the function as Y_1 and the derivative as Y_2. Use TABLE to determine where the function is increasing and where it is decreasing.
   (b) In WINDOW menu set x-min so that it is smaller than the smallest critical value and set x-max so that it is larger than the largest critical value.
2. Use TABLE to determine the y-coordinates of the critical values. Set y-min and y-max to contain the y-coordinates of the critical points.
3. Graph the function.

Let $f(x) = 0.0001x^3 + 0.003x^2 - 3.6x + 5$. Given that the critical values for $f(x)$ are $x = -120$ and $x = 100$, set a window that shows a complete graph and graph the function.

X	Y1	Y2
-150	275	2.25
-120	307.4	0
0	5	-3.6
100	-225	0
150	-130	4.05

X=0

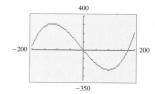

Section 10.2 Exploring f, f', and f" Relationships

To explore relationships among the graphs of a function and its derivatives:

1. Find the functions for f' and f''.
2. Graph all three functions in the same window.
   - Notice that f increases when f' is above the x-axis $(+)$ and decreases when f' is below the x-axis $(-)$.
   - Notice that f is concave up when f'' is above the x-axis $(+)$ and is concave down when f'' is below the x-axis $(-)$.

Let $f(x) = x^3 - 9x^2 + 24x$. Graph f', f'', and f'' on the interval $[0, 5]$ to explore the relationships among these functions.

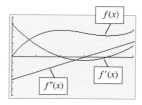

Sections 10.3–10.4 Finding Optimal Values

To find the optimal values of a function when the goal is not to produce a graph:

1. Enter the function as Y_1 in the Y = menu.
2. Select a window that includes the x-values of interest and graph the function.
3. While looking at the graph of the function, choose the CALC menu, scroll to 3:minimum or 4:maximum depending on which one is to be found, and press ENTER. This will result in a "*Left Bound?*" prompt.
   (a) Move the cursor to a point to the left of the point of interest. Press ENTER to select the left bound.
   (b) Move the cursor to the right of the point of interest. Press ENTER to select the right bound.
   (c) Press ENTER at the "*Guess?*" prompt. The resulting point is an approximation of the desired optimum value.

Let $f(x) = 100\sqrt{2304 + x^2} + 50(100 - x)$. Find the minimum value of $f(x)$ on the interval $[0, 100]$ for x. Note: the following screens use the window x: $[-10, 110]$ and y: $[-2500, 12500]$

The minimum value is $y \approx 9157$ and occurs when $x \approx 27.7$.

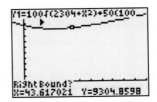 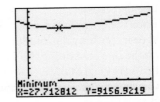

Note: Finding a maximum value works similarly.

Section 10.5 Asymptotes and Window Setting

To use asymptotes and critical values to set a viewing window that shows a complete graph:

1. Once the asymptotes and critical values for a function have been found,
   (a) Determine where the function is increasing and where it is decreasing (by using TABLE and with Y_1 as the function and Y_2 as the derivative).
   (b) Under WINDOW, set x-min so that it is smaller than the smallest x-value that is either a vertical asymptote or a critical value and set x-max so that it is larger than the largest of these important x-values.
2. Use TABLE or VALUE to determine the y-coordinates of the critical values. Set y-min and y-max so they contain the y-coordinates of any horizontal asymptotes and critical points.
3. Graph the function.

Let $f(x) = \dfrac{x^2}{x - 2}$. Given that $f(x)$ has the line $x = 2$ as a vertical asymptote, has no horizontal asymptote, and has critical values $x = 0$ and $x = 4$. Set the window and graph $y = f(x)$.

The critical points for $f(x)$ are $(0, 0)$ and $(4, 8)$. The window needs an x-range that contains 0, 2, and 4 and a y-range that contains 0 and 8.

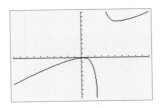

Chapter 11
Section 11.1 Derivatives of Logarithmic Functions

To check that the derivative of $y = \ln(2x^6 - 3x + 2)$

is $Y_1 = \dfrac{12x^5 - 3}{2x^6 - 3x + 2}$, we show that the graph of

$Y_2 = $ nDeriv($\ln(2x^6 - 3x + 2)$, x, x) lies on the graph of

$$y_1 = \dfrac{12x^5 - 3}{2x^6 - 3x + 2}.$$

 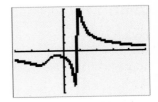

Section 11.1 Finding Critical Values

To find the critical values of a function $y = f(x)$:

1. Enter the function as Y_1 in the $Y =$ menu and the derivative as Y_2.
2. Press MATH and select Solver. Press the up arrow revealing EQUATION SOLVER equ:0 = , and enter Y_2 (the derivative).
3. Press the down arrow or ENTER, and the variable x appears with a value (not the solution). Place the cursor on the line containing the variable whose value is sought.
4. Press ALPHA SOLVE (ENTER). The value of the variable changes to the solution of the equation that is closest to that value.
5. To find additional solutions (if they exist), change the value of the variable and press ALPHA SOLVE (ENTER). The value of the variable gives the solution of $Y_2 = 0$ that is closest to that value.

To find the critical values of $y = x^2 - 8 \ln x$, we solve

$$0 = 2x - \frac{8}{x}.$$

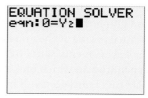

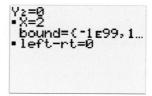
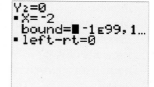

The two critical values are $x = 2$ and $x = -2$.

Section 11.1 Finding Optimal Values

To find the optimal values of a function $y = f(x)$:

1. Find the critical values of a function $y = f(x)$. (Use the steps for finding critical values discussed above.)
2. Graph $y = f(x)$ on a window containing the critical values.
3. The y-values at the critical values (if they exist) are the optimal values of the function.

To find the optimal values of $y = x^2 - 8 \ln x$, we solve

$0 = 2x - \dfrac{8}{x}$ and evaluate $y = x^2 - 8 \ln x$ at the solutions.

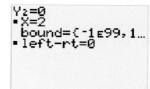

The two critical values are $x = 2$ and $x = -2$.

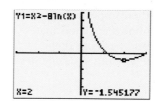
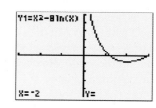

The minimum of $y = x^2 - 8 \ln x$ is -1.545 at $x = 2$. The function $y = x^2 - 8 \ln x$ is undefined for all negative values because $\ln x$ is undefined for all negative values. Thus, there is no optimum value of the function at $x = -2$.

Section 11.2 Derivatives of Exponential Functions

To check that the derivative of $y = 5^{x^2+x}$ is $y' = 5^{x^2+x}(2x + 1) \ln 5$, we show that the graph of $Y_2 = \text{nDeriv}(5^{x^2+x}, x, x)$ lies on the graph of $Y_1 = 5^{x^2+x}(2x + 1) \ln 5$.

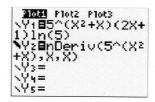
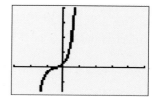

Section 11.2 Finding Critical Values

To find the critical values of a function $y = f(x)$:

1. Enter the function as Y_1 in the Y = menu and the derivative as Y_2.
2. Press MATH and select Solver. Press the up arrow revealing EQUATION SOLVER equ:0 =, and enter Y_2 (the derivative).
3. Press the down arrow or ENTER and the variable appears with a value (not the solution). Place the cursor on the variable whose value is sought.
4. Press ALPHA SOLVE (ENTER). The value of the variable changes to the solution of the equation that is closest to that value.
5. To find additional solutions (if they exist), change the value of the variable and press ALPHA SOLVE (ENTER). The value of the variable gives the solution of $Y_2 = 0$ that is closest to that value.

To find the critical values of $y = e^x - 3x^2$, we solve $0 = e^x - 6x$.

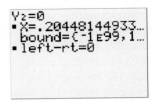

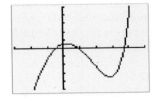

A relative maximum of $y = e^x - 3x^2$ occurs at $x \approx 0.204$, and a relative minimum occurs at $x \approx 2.833$.

Chapter 12
Section 12.1 Checking Powers of x Integrals

To check a computed indefinite integral with the command fnInt:

1. Enter the integral of $f(x)$ (without the $+ C$) as Y_1 in Y = menu.
2. Move the cursor to Y_2, press MATH, 9:fnInt(and enter $f(x)$, x, 0, x) so the equation is $Y_2 = $ fnInt $(f(x), x, 0, x)$.
3. Pressing ENTER with the cursor to the left of Y_2 changes the thickness of the second graph, making it more evident that the second lies on top of the first.
4. Press GRAPH with an appropriate window. If the second graph lies on top of the first, the graphs agree and the computed integral checks.

Checking that the integral of $f(x) = x^2$ is $\int x^2 \, dx = \dfrac{x^3}{3} + C$:

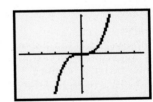

Sections 12.1–12.2 Families of Functions

To graph some functions in the family of indefinite integrals of $f(x)$:

1. Integrate $f(x)$.
2. Enter equations of the form $\int f(x) \, dx + C$ for different values of C.
3. Press GRAPH with an appropriate window. The graphs will be shifted up or down, depending on C.

The graphs of members of the family $y = \int (2x - 4) dx + C$ with $C = 0, 1, -2,$ and 3.

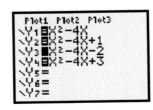

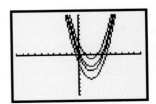

Section 12.5 Differential Equations

To solve initial value problems in differential equations:

1. Integrate $f(x)$, getting $y = F(x) + C$. If a value of x and a corresponding value of y in the integral $y = F(x) + C$ are known, this initial value can be used to find one function that satisfies the given conditions.
2. Press MATH and select Solver. Press the up arrow to see EQUATION SOLVER.
3. Set 0 equal the integral minus y, getting $0 = F(x) + C - y$, and press the down arrow.
4. Enter the given values of x and y, place the cursor on C, and press ALPHA, SOLVE. Replace C with this value to find the function satisfying the conditions.

To solve $\dfrac{dy}{dx} = 2x - 4$, we note that the integral of both sides is $y = x^2 - 4x + C$. If $y = 8$ when $x = -1$ in this integral, we can find C, and thus a unique solution, shown below.

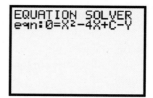
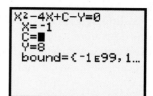

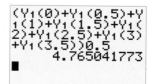

The unique solution is $y = x^2 - 4x + 3$.

Chapter 13
Section 13.1 Approximating Areas Under Curves Using Rectangles

To find the area under $y = f(x)$ and above the x-axis over a given interval using rectangles of equal width:

1. Enter $f(x)$ in Y_1 of the Y = menu and calculate the width of the base of each of the n rectangles.
2. Compute the area using left-hand endpoints.

$$S_L = \sum_{i=1}^{n} f(x_{i-1})\Delta x$$
$$= \left[Y_1(x_0) + Y_1(x_1) + \cdots + Y_1(x_{n-1})\right]\Delta x$$

3. Use a similar formula to compute the area using right-hand endpoints.

$$S_R = \sum_{i=1}^{n} f(x_i)\Delta x$$
$$= \left[Y_1(x_1) + Y_1(x_2) + \cdots + Y_1(x_n)\right]\Delta x$$

To find the left and right approximations for the area under $f(x) = \sqrt{x}$ from $x = 0$ to $x = 4$ using $n = 8$ equal subdivisions:

1. Each rectangle has base width $(4 - 0)/8 = 0.5$. The subdivision values are
   $x_0 = 0, x_1 = 0.5, x_2 = 1, \cdots x_7 = 3.5, x_8 = 4$.
2. Calculate the left approximation of the area as follows.
   $S_L = 0.5[Y_1(0) + Y_1(0.5) + Y_1(1) + Y_1(1.5) + Y_1(2)$
   $\qquad + Y_1(2.5) + Y_1(3) + Y_1(3.5)] \approx 4.765$
   (See the screen below.)
3. Calculate the right approximation of the area as follows.
   $S_R = [Y_1(0.5) + Y_1(1) + Y_1(1.5) + Y_1(2) + Y_1(2.5)$
   $\qquad + Y_1(3) + Y_1(3.5) + Y_1(4)]0.5 \approx 5.765$

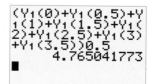
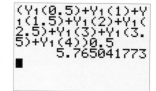

Section 13.2 Approximating Definite Integrals—Areas Under Curves

To approximate the area under the graph of $y = f(x)$ and above the x-axis:

1. Enter $f(x)$ under the Y = menu and graph the function with an appropriate window.

2. Press 2nd CALC and 7: $\int f(x)\,dx$.

3. Press ENTER. Move the cursor to, or enter, the lower limit (the left x-value).
4. Press ENTER. Move the cursor to, or enter, the upper limit (the right x-value).
5. Press ENTER. The area will be displayed.

The approximate area under the graph of $f(x) = x^2 + 1$ from $x = 0$ to $x = 3$ is found below.

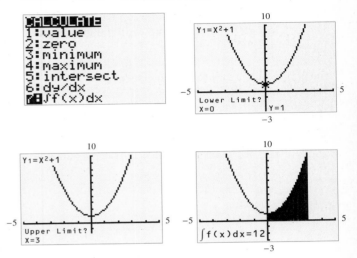

Section 13.2 Approximating Definite Integrals—Alternative Method

To approximate the definite integral of $f(x)$ from $x = a$ to $x = b$:

1. Press MATH, 9: fnInt(. Enter $f(x)$, x, a, b) so the display shows fnInt($f(x)$, x, a, b).
2. Press ENTER to find the approximation of the integral.
3. The approximation may be made closer than that in Step 2 by adding a fifth argument with a number (tolerance) smaller than 0.00001.

The approximation of $\displaystyle\int_{-1}^{3}(4x^2 - 2x)\,dx$ is found as follows.

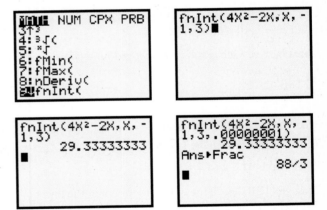

Section 13.3 Approximating the Area Between Two Curves

To approximate the area between the graphs of two functions:

1. Enter one function as Y_1 and the second as Y_2. Press GRAPH using a window that shows all points of intersection of the graphs.
2. Find the x-coordinates of the points of intersection of the graphs, using 2nd CALC: intersect.
3. Determine visually which graph is above the other over the interval between the points of intersection.
4. Press MATH, 9: fnInt(. Enter $f(x)$, x, a, b so the display shows fnInt($f(x)$, x, a, b) where $f(x)$ is $Y_2 - Y_1$ if the graph of Y_2 is above the graph of Y_1 between a and b, or $Y_1 - Y_2$ if Y_1 is above Y_2.

The area enclosed by the graphs of $y = 4x^2$ and $y = 8x$ is found as follows.

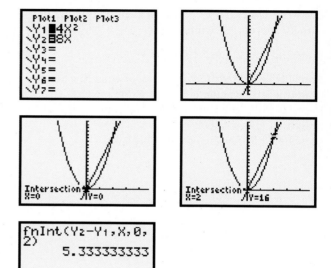

The area between the curves is $16/3$.

Section 13.3 Approximating the Area Between Two Curves—Alternate Method

The area between the graphs can also be found by using 2nd CALC, $\int f(x)\, dx$.

1. Enter $Y_3 = Y_2 - Y_1$ where Y_2 is above Y_1.
2. Turn off the graphs of Y_1 and Y_2 and graph Y_3 with a window showing where $Y_3 > 0$.
3. Press 2nd CALC and $\int f(x)\, dx$.
4. Press ENTER. Move the cursor to, or enter, the lower limit (the left x-value).
5. Press ENTER. Move the cursor to, or enter, the upper limit (the right x-value).
6. Press ENTER. The area will be displayed.

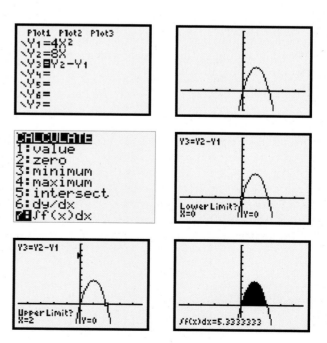

Excel Guide Part 1
Excel 2003

Excel Worksheet

When you start up Excel by using the instructions for your software and computer, the following screen will appear.

The components of the **spreadsheet** are shown, and the grid shown is called a **worksheet.** You can move to other worksheets by clicking on the tabs at the bottom.

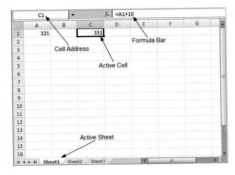

Addresses and Operations

Notice the letters at the top of the columns and the numbers identifying the rows. The cell addresses are given by the column and row; for example, the first cell has address A1. You can move from one cell to another with arrow keys, or you can select a cell by clicking on it. After you type an entry in a cell, press enter to accept it. To edit the contents of a cell, click on the cell and edit the contents in the formula bar at the top. To delete the contents, press the delete key.

The file operations such as "open a new file," "saving a file," and "printing a file" are similar to those in Word. For example, <CTRL>S saves a file. You can also format a cell entry by selecting it and using menus similar to those in Word.

Working with Cells

Cell entries, rows containing entries, and columns containing entries can be copied and pasted with the same commands as in Word. For example, a highlighted cell can be copied with <CTRL>C. Sometimes entries exceed the width of the cells containing them, especially if they are text. To widen the cells in a column, place the cursor at the right side of the column heading until you see the symbol ↔, then move the cursor to the right (moving it to the left makes the column more narrow). If entering a number results in ####, the number is too long for the cell, and the cell should be widened.

Chapter 1

Section 1.4 Entering Data and Evaluating Functions

The cells are identified by the column and the row. For example, the cell B3 is in the second column and the third row.

1. Put headings on the two columns.
2. Fill the inputs in Column A by hand or with a formula for them. The formula $=A2+1$ gives 2 in A3 when ENTER is pressed.
3. Moving the mouse to the lower right corner of A3 until there is a thin "+" sign and dragging the mouse down "fills down" all required entries in column A.
4. Enter the function formula for the function in B2. Use $= 1000*(1.1)\wedge A2$ to represent $S = 1000(1.1)^t$. Pressing ENTER gives the value when $t = 1$.
5. Using Fill Down gives the output for all inputs.

	A	B
1	Year	Future Value
2	1	=1000*(1.1)^(A2)
3	=A2+1	

	A	B
1	Year	Future Value
2	1	1100
3	2	1210
4	3	1331

Section 1.4 Graphing a Function

1. Put headings on the two columns (x and $f(x)$, for example).
2. Fill the inputs (x-values) in Column A by hand or with a formula for them.
3. Enter the formula for the function in B2. Use $= 6*A2 - 3$ to represent $f(x) = 6x - 3$.
4. Select the cell containing the formula for the function (B2, for example).
5. Move the mouse to the lower right corner until there is a thin "+" sign.
6. Drag the mouse down to the last cell where formula is required, and press ENTER.
7. Highlight the two columns containing the values of x and $f(x)$.
8. Click the *Chart Wizard* icon and then select the *XY(Scatter)* chart with smooth curve option.
9. Click the Next button to get the *Chart Source Data* box. Then click Next to get the *Chart Options* box, and enter your chart title and labels for the x- and y-axes.
10. Click Next, select whether the graph should be within the current worksheet or on another, and click Finish.

	A	B
1	x	$f(x) = 6x - 3$
2	−5	−33
3	−2	−15
4	−1	−9
5	0	−3
6	1	3
7	3	15
8	5	27

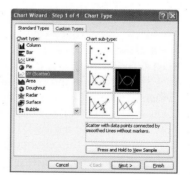

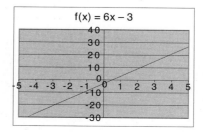

Section 1.5 Solving Systems of Two Equations in Two Variables

1. Write the two equations as linear functions in the form $y = mx + b$.
2. Enter the input variable x in cell A2 and the formula for each of the two equations in cells B2 and C2, respectively.
3. Enter $= B2 - C2$ in cell D2.
4. Use *Tools > Goal Seek*.
5. In the dialog box:
   a. Click the *Set Cell* box and click on the D2 cell.
   b. Enter 0 in the *To Value* box.
   c. Click the *By Changing Cell* box and click on the A2 cell.
6. Click OK in the *Goal Seek* dialog box, getting 0.
7. The x-value of the solution is in cell A2, and the y-value is in both B2 and C2.

The solution of the system

$$\begin{cases} 3x + 2y = 12 \\ 4x - 3y = -1 \end{cases}$$

is found to be $x = 2$, $y = 3$ using *Goal Seek* as follows.

	A	B	C	D
1	x	= 6 − 1.5x	= 1/3 + 4x/3	= y1 − y2
2	1	= 6 − 1.5*A2	= 1/3 + 4*A2/3	= B2 − C2

	A	B	C	D
1	x	= 6 − 1.5x	= 1/3 + 4x/3	= y1 − y2
2	2	3	3	0

Chapter 2
Section 2.1 Solving Quadratic Equations

To solve a quadratic equation of the form $f(x) = ax^2 + bx + c = 0$:

1. Enter x-values centered around the x-coordinate $x = \dfrac{-b}{2a}$ in column A and use the function formula to find the values of $f(x)$ in column B.

2. Graph the function, $f(x) = 2x^2 - 9x + 4$ in this case, and observe where the graph crosses the x-axis ($f(x)$ near 0).

3. Use *Tools > Goal Seek*, entering a cell address with a function value in column B at or near 0, enter the set cell to the value 0, and enter the changing cell.

4. Click OK to find the x-value of the solution in cell A2. The solution may be approximate. The spreadsheet shows $x = 0.5001$, which is an approximation of the exact solution $x = 0.5$.

5. After finding the first solution, repeat the process using a second function value at or near 0. The second solution is $x = 4$ in this case.

	A	B	C	D	E	F
1	x	f(x)=2x^2−9x+4				
2	−1	15				
3	0	4				
4	1	−3				
5	2	−6				
6	3	−5				
7	4	0				
8	5	9				
9						

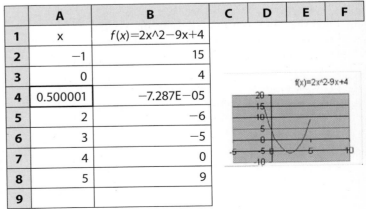

	A	B	C	D	E	F
1	x	f(x)=2x^2−9x+4				
2	−1	15				
3	0	4				
4	0.500001	−7.287E−05				
5	2	−6				
6	3	−5				
7	4	0				
8	5	9				
9						

Sections 2.2 and 2.4 Graphing Polynomial Functions

To graph a polynomial function:

1. Use the function to create a table containing values for x and $f(x)$. (See Graphing a Function on page AP-28.)
2. Highlight the two columns containing the values of x and $f(x)$.
3. Click the *Chart Wizard* icon and then select the *XY(Scatter)* chart with smooth curve option.
4. Click the Next button to get the *Chart Source Data* box. Then click Next to get the *Chart Options* box, and enter your chart title and labels for the x- and y-axes.
5. Click Next, select whether the graph should be within the current worksheet or on another, and click Finish.

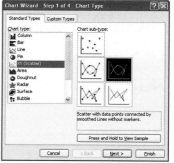

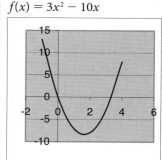

$f(x) = 3x^2 - 10x$

Section 2.4 Graphing Rational Functions

An Excel graph will connect all points corresponding to values in the table, so if the function you are graphing is undefined for some x-value a, enter x-values near this value and leave (or make) the corresponding $f(a)$ cell blank.

To graph $f(x) = \dfrac{1}{1-x}$, which is undefined at $x = 1$:

1. Generate a table for x-values from -1 to 3, with extra values near $x = 1$.
2. Generate the values of $f(x)$, and leave a blank cell for the $f(x)$ value for $x = 1$.
3. Select the table and plot the graph using *Chart Wizard*.

x	$f(x)$
-1	-0.5
-0.5	-0.6667
0	-1
0.5	-2
0.75	-4
0.9	-10
1	
1.1	10
1.25	4
1.5	2
2	1
2.5	0.666667
3	0.5

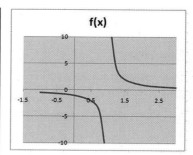

Section 2.5 Modeling

To create a scatter plot of data:

1. Enter the inputs (x-values) in Column A and the outputs (y-values) in Column B.
2. Highlight the two columns and use *Chart Wizard* to plot the points.
3. In Step 3 of the *Chart Wizard*, you can add the title and x- and y-axis labels.

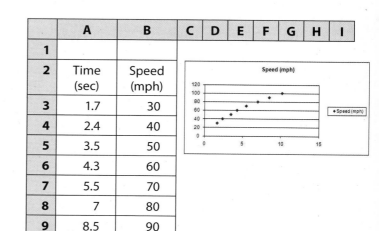

	A	B	C	D	E	F	G	H	I
1									
2	Time (sec)	Speed (mph)							
3	1.7	30							
4	2.4	40							
5	3.5	50							
6	4.3	60							
7	5.5	70							
8	7	80							
9	8.5	90							
10	10.2	100							
11									

To find the equation of a line or curve that best fits a given set of data points:

1. Place the scatter plot of the data in the worksheet.
2. Single-click on the scatter plot in the workbook.
3. From the *Chart* menu select *Add Trendline*.
4. Select the regression type that appears to be the best function fit for the scatter plot. [Note: If *Polynomial* is selected, choose the appropriate Order (degree).]
5. Click the *Options* tab and check the *Display equation on chart* box.
6. Click OK and the graph of the selected best-fit function will appear along with its equation.

The power function that models Corvette acceleration follows.

	A	B	C	D	E	F	G	H	I
1									
2	Time (sec)	Speed (mph)		**Corvette Acceleration**					
3	1.7	30							
4	2.4	40							
5	3.5	50							
6	4.3	60							
7	5.5	70							
8	7	80							
9	8.5	90							
10	10.2	100							
11									

The speed of the Corvette is given by $y = 21.875x^{0.6663}$ where x is the time in seconds.

Chapter 3
Section 3.1 Operations with Matrices

Operations for 3×3 matrices can be used for other orders.

1. Type a name A in A1 to identify the first matrix.
2. Enter the matrix elements of matrix A in the cells B1:D3.
3. Type a name B in A5 to identify the second matrix.
4. Enter the matrix elements of matrix B in the cells B5:D7.
5. Type a name A + B in A9 to indicate the matrix sum.
6. Type the formula "=B1 + B5" in B9 and press ENTER.
7. Use Fill Across to copy this formula across the row to C9 and D9.
8. Use Fill Down to copy the row B9:D9 to B11:D11, which gives the sum.
9. To subtract the matrices, change the formula in B9 to "=B1 − B5" and proceed as with addition.

	A	B	C	D
1	A	1	2	3
2		4	5	6
3		7	8	9
4				
5	B	−2	−4	3
6		1	4	−5
7		3	6	−1
8				
9	A+B	−1	−2	6
10		5	9	1
11		10	14	8

Section 3.2 Multiplying Two Matrices

Steps for two 3×3 matrices:

1. Enter the names and elements of the matrices.
2. Enter the name AxB in A9 to indicate the matrix product.
3. Select a range of cells that is the correct size to contain the product (B9:D11 in this case).
4. Type "=mmult(" in the formula bar, and then select the cells containing the elements of matrix A (B1:D3).
5. Stay in the formula bar, type a comma and select the matrix B elements (B5:D7), and close the parentheses.
6. Hold the CTRL and SHIFT keys down and press ENTER, giving the product.

	A	B	C	D
1	A	1	2	3
2		4	5	6
3		7	8	9
4				
5	B	−2	−4	3
6		1	4	−5
7		3	6	−1
8				
9	AxB	=mmult(B1:D3		
10		MMULT(**array1**,		
11		array2)		

B9	fx	{(=MMULT(B1:D3,B5:D7)}			
	A	B	C	D	E
1	A	1	2	3	
2		4	5	6	
3		7	8	9	
4					
5	B	−2	−4	3	
6		1	4	−5	
7		3	6	−1	
8					
9	AxB	9	22	−10	
10		15	40	−19	
11		21	58	−28	

Section 3.4 Finding the Inverse of a Matrix

Steps for a 3 × 3 matrix:

1. Enter the name A in A1 and the elements of the matrix in B1:D3 as above.
2. Enter the name "Inverse(A)" in A5 and select a range of cells that is the correct size to contain the inverse [(B5:D7) in this case].
3. Enter "=minverse(", select matrix A (B1:D3), and close the parentheses.
4. Hold the CTRL and SHIFT keys down and press ENTER, getting the inverse.

SUM	fx	=minverse(B1:D3)		
	A	B	C	D
1	A	2	1	1
2		1	2	0
3		2	0	1
4				
5	inverse(A)	=minverse(B1:D3)		
6				
7				

Section 3.4 Solving Systems of Linear Equations with Matrix Inverses

A system of linear equations can be solved by multiplying the matrix containing the augment by the inverse of the coefficient matrix. The steps used to solve a 3 × 3 system follow.

1. Enter the coefficient matrix A in B1:D3.
2. Enter the name "inverse(A)" in A5 and compute the inverse of A in B5:D7.
3. Enter B in cell A9 and enter the augment matrix in B9:B11.
4. Enter X in A13 and select the cells B13:B15.
5. In the formula bar, type "=mmult(", then select matrix inverse(A) in B5:D7, type a comma, select matrix B in B9:B11, and close the parentheses.
6. Hold the CTRL and SHIFT keys down and press ENTER, getting the solution.
7. Matrix X gives the solution.

The system $\begin{cases} 2x + y + z = 8 \\ x + 2y = 6 \\ 2x + z = 5 \end{cases}$ is solved as follows.

B5	fx	{=MINVERSE(B1:D3)}		
	A	B	C	D
1	A	2	1	1
2		1	2	0
3		2	0	1
4				
5	inverse(A)	−2	1	2
6		1	0	−1
7		4	−2	−3

SUM	fx	=mmult(B5:D7,B9:B11)		
	A	B	C	D	E
1	A	2	1	1	
2		1	2	0	
3		2	0	1	
4					
5	inverse(A)	−2	1	2	
6		1	0	−1	
7		4	−2	−3	
8					
9	B	8			
10		6			
11		5			
12					
13	X	=mmult(B5:D7,B9:B11)			
14					
15					

The solution is $x = 0$, $y = 3$, $z = 5$.

B13	fx	{(=MMULT(B5:D7,B9:B11)}		
	A	B	C	D	E
1	A	2	1	1	
2		1	2	0	
3		2	0	1	
4					
5	inverse(A)	−2	1	2	
6		1	0	−1	
7		4	−2	−3	
8					
9	B	8			
10		6			
11		5			
12					
13	X	0			
14		3			
15		5			

Chapter 4
Sections 4.3–4.5 Linear Programming

Maximize $f = 12x + 26y + 40z$ subject to the constraints

$$\begin{cases} 5x + 7y + 10z \leq 90{,}000 \\ x + 3y + 4z \leq 30{,}000 \\ x + y + z \leq 9000 \\ x \geq 0, y \geq 0, z \geq 0 \end{cases}$$

1. On a blank spreadsheet, type a heading in cell A1, followed by the variable descriptions in cells A3–A5 and the initial values (zeros) in cells B3–B5.
2. a. Enter the heading "Objective" in cell A7.
   b. Enter a description of the objective in cell A9 and the formula for the objective function in B9. The formula is $=12*B3 + 26*B4 + 40*B5$.
3. a. Type in the heading "Constraints" in A11 and descriptive labels in A13–A15.
   b. Enter the left side of the constraint inequalities in B13–B15 and the maximums from the right side in C13–C15.
4. Select *Solver* under the *Tools* menu. A dialog box will appear.*
5. a. Click the *Set Target Cell* box and B9 (containing the formula for the objective function).
   b. Check the button *Max* for maximization.
   c. Click the *By Changing Cells* box and select cells B3–B5.
6. a. Click the *Subject to Constraints* entry box. Press the Add button to add the first constraint.
   b. Click the left entry box and click cell B13 (containing the formula for the first constraint).
   c. Set the middle entry box to $<=$.
   d. Click the right entry box and C13 to enter the constraint.
   e. Click Add and repeat the Steps 6b–6d for the remaining constraints.
   f. Click in the left entry box for the constraints and select the variables in B3–B5. Set the middle entry to $>=$, and type 0 in the right entry box.
7. Click Solve in the *Solver* dialog box. A dialog box states that *Solver* found a solution. To see the *Solver* results, click *Keep Solver Solution* and also select Answer.
8. Go back to the spreadsheet. The new values in B3–B5 are the values of the variables that give the maximum, and the value in B9 is the maximum value of the objective function.

In *Solver*, minimization of an objective function is handled exactly the same as maximization, except min is checked and the inequality signs are $\geq$.

When mixed constraints are used, simply enter them with "mixed" inequalities.

*You may need to use an "Add-In" to access *Solver*.

	A	B	C
1	**Variables**		
2			
3	# small calculators (x)	0	
4	# medium calculators (y)	0	
5	# large calculators (z)	0	
6			
7	**Objective**		
8			
9	Maximize profit	=12*B3+26*B4+40*B5	
10			
11	**Constraints**		
12		Amount used	Maximum
13	Circuit components	=5*B3+7*B4+10*B5	90000
14	Labor	=B3+3*B4+4*B5	30000
15	Cases	=B3+B4+B5	9000

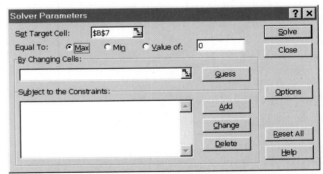

	A	B	C
1	Variables		
2			
3	# small calculators (x)	2000	
4	# medium calculators (y)	0	
5	# large calculators (z)	7000	
6			
7	Objective		
8			
9	Maximize profit	304000	
10			
11	Constraints		
12		Amount used	Maximum
13	Circuit components	80000	90000
14	Labor	30000	30000
15	Cases	9000	9000

Chapter 5

Section 5.1 Graphing Exponential Functions

Exponential functions are entered into Excel differently for base e than for bases other than e.

A. To graph $y = a^x$, use the formula =a^x.
B. To graph $y = e^x$, use the formula =exp(x).

To graph $f(x) = 1.5^x$ and $g(x) = e^x$ on the same axes:
 1. Type x in cell A1 and numbers centered at 0 in Column A.
 2. Type $f(x)$ in cell B1, enter the formula =1.5^A2 in cell B2 and fill down.
 3. Type $g(x)$ in cell C1, enter the formula =exp(A2) in cell C2 and fill down.
 4. Select the entire table and use *Chart Wizard* to graph as described in Section 1.4.

	A	B	C
	x	$f(x)$	$g(x)$
1			
2	−2	0.444444	0.135335
3	−1.5	0.544433	0.22313
4	−1	0.666667	0.367879
5	−0.5	0.816497	0.606531
6	0	1	1
7	0.5	1.224745	1.648721
8	1	1.5	2.718282
9	1.5	1.837117	4.481689
10	2	2.25	7.389056
11	2.5	2.755676	12.18249
12	3	3.375	20.08554

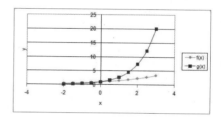

Section 5.1 Modeling with Exponential Functions

To model data with an exponential function:

 1. Create a scatter plot for the data.
 2. From the *Chart* menu, choose *Add Trendline*.
 3. Check *exponential regression* type since that function type appears to be the best fit for the scatter plot.
 4. Click the *Options* tab on this box and select *Display equation* on chart box.
 5. Click Next and Finish to see the equation and graph.

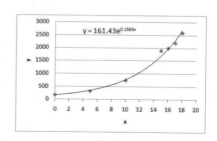

The exponential model for the following data is shown.

x	0	5	10	15	16	17	18
y	170	325	750	1900	2000	2200	2600

Section 5.2 Graphing Base *e* and Base 10
Logarithmic Functions

1. Create a table of values for *x*-values with $x > 0$ to reflect the function's domain.
2. For $y = \ln(x)$, use the formula $=\ln(x)$.
3. For $y = \log(x)$, use the formula $=\log 10(x)$.
4. Select the entire table and use *Chart Wizard* to graph.

	A	B
1	*x*	$f(x)=\ln(x)$
2	0.5	−0.6931472
3	0.9	−0.1053605
4	1	0
5	2	0.6931472
6	3	1.0986123
7	4	1.3862944
8	5	1.6094379
9	6	1.7917595
10	7	1.9459101
11	8	2.0894415
12	9	2.1972246
13	10	2.3025851
14	11	2.3978953

	A	B
1	*x*	$f(x)=\log(x)$
2	0.5	−0.30103
3	0.9	−0.0457575
4	1	0
5	2	0.30103
6	3	0.47712125
7	4	0.60205999
8	5	0.69897
9	6	0.77815125
10	7	0.84509804
11	8	0.90308999
12	9	0.95424251
13	10	1
14	11	1.04139269

f(x)=ln(x)

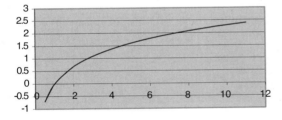

f(x)=log(x)

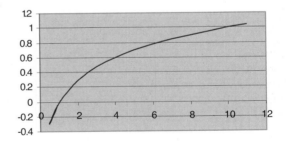

Section 5.2 Modeling Logarithmic Functions

1. Create a scatter plot for the data.
2. In the *Chart* menu, choose *Add Trendline* and click logarithmic regression.
3. Click the *options* tab, select *Display equation* and click Next and Finish.

x	*y*
10	2.207
20	3.972
30	5.004
40	5.737

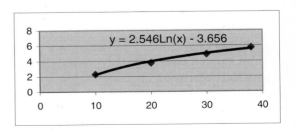

y = 2.546Ln(x) - 3.656

Section 5.2 Graphing Logarithmic Functions with Other Bases

1. The graph of a logarithm with any base b can be created by entering the formula =log(x, b).
2. Proceed as described above for graphing base e and base 10 logarithms.

	A	B
1	x	$f(x)=\log(x,7)$
2	0.5	−0.356207187
3	0.9	−0.054144594
4	1	0
5	2	0.356207187
6	3	0.564575034
7	4	0.712414374
8	5	0.827087475
9	6	0.920782221
10	7	1
11	8	1.068621561
12	9	1.129150068
13	10	1.183294662
14	11	1.1232274406

The graph of $f(x) = \log_7 x$ is shown below.

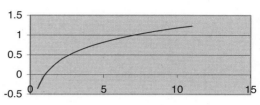

Chapter 6

Section 6.2 Finding the Future Value of a Lump Sum

To find the future value of a lump-sum investment:

1. Type the headings in Row 1, and enter their values (with the interest rate as a decimal) in Row 2. Enter the investment as a negative number.
2. Type the formula =D2/E2 in F2 to compute the rate per period.
3. Type the heading Future Value in A4.
4. In cell B4, type the formula =fv(F2,B2,C2,A2,0) to compute the future value.

This spreadsheet gives the future value of an investment of $10,000 for 17 years at 9.8%, compounded quarterly.

Principal	Number of Periods	Payment	Annual Rate	Periods per year	Periodic Rate
−10,000	68	0	0.098	4	0.0245
Future Value	$51,857.73				

Section 6.3 Finding the Future Value of an Annuity

To find the future value of an ordinary annuity:

1. Type the headings in Row 1, and enter their values (with the interest rate as a decimal) in Row 2. Enter the deposit as a negative payment.
2. Type the formula =D2/E2 in F2 to compute the rate per period.
3. Type the heading Future Value in A4.
4. In cell B4, type the formula =fv(F2,B2,C2,A2,0) to compute the future value.
   (The 0 indicates that the payments are made at the end of each period.)

For annuities due, use =fv(F2,B2,C2,A2,1).
The payments are made at the beginning of each period.

This spreadsheet gives the future value of an ordinary annuity of $200 deposited at the end of each quarter for $2\frac{1}{4}$ years, with interest at 4%, compounded quarterly.

Principal	Number of Periods	Payment	Annual Rate	Periods per year	Periodic Rate
0	9	−200	0.04	4	0.01
Ordinary annuity					
Future Value	$1,873.71				
Annui- ties due					
Future Value	$1,892.44				

Section 6.4 Finding the Present Value of an Annuity

To find the present value of an ordinary annuity:

1. Type the headings in Row 1, and enter their values (with the interest rate as a decimal) in Row 2.
2. Enter the formula =D2/E2 in F2 to compute the rate per period.
3. Type the heading Present Value in A4.
4. In cell B4, type the formula =pv(F2,B2,C2,A2,0) to compute the present value. (The 0 indicates that the payments are made at the end of each period.) The parentheses on the present value in cell B4 mean that it is negative (the money leaves the investor to start the annuity).

For annuities due, use =pv(F2,B2,C2,A2,1). The payments are made at the beginning of each period.

This spreadsheet gives the lump sum deposit (present value) necessary to receive $1000 per month for 16 years, with interest at 9%, compounded monthly, for both an ordinary annuity and an annuity due.

Future Value	Number of Periods	Payment	Annual Rate	Periods per year	Periodic Rate
0	192	1000	0.09	12	0.0075
Ordinary annuity					
Present Value	($101,572.77)				
Annui-ties due					
Present value	($102,334.56)				

Section 6.5 Finding Payments to Amortize a Loan

To find the periodic payment to pay off a loan:

1. Type the headings in Row 1 and their values (with the interest rate as a decimal) in Row 2.
2. Enter the formula =D2/E2 in F2 to compute the rate per period.
3. Type the heading Payment in A4.
4. In cell B4, type the formula =Pmt(F2,B2,A2,C2,0) to compute the payment.

This spreadsheet gives the annual payment of a loan of $10,000 over 5 years when interest is 10% per year.

The parentheses indicates a payment out.

Loan Amount	Number of Periods	Future Value	Annual Rate	Periods per year	Periodic Rate
10000	5	0	0.1	1	0.1
Payment	($2,637.97)				

Chapter 8

Section 8.1 Binomial Probabilities

1. Type headings in cells A1:A3 and their respective values in cells B1:B3.
2. Use the function =binomdist(B1,B2,B3,cumulative) where
   - B1 is the number of successes.
   - B2 is the number of independent trials.
   - B3 is the probability of success in each trial.
   - True replaces cumulative if a cumulative probability is sought; it is replaced by false otherwise.
   - The probability of exactly 3 heads in 6 tosses is found by evaluating =binomdist(B1,B2,B3,false) in B4.
   - The probability of 3 or fewer heads in 6 tosses is found by evaluating =binomdist(B1,B2,B3,true) in B5.

This spreadsheet gives the probability of 3 heads in 6 tosses of a fair coin and the probability of 3 or fewer heads in 6 tosses.

	A	B
1	Number of successes	3
2	Number of trials	6
3	Probability of success	.5
4	Probability of 3 successes	.3125
5	Probability of 3 or fewer successes	.65625

Section 8.2 Bar Graphs

To construct a bar graph for the given table of test scores:

1. Copy the entries of the table to cells A2:B6.
2. Select the range A2:B6.
3. Click the *Chart Wizard* icon.
4. Select the graph option with the first sub-type.
5. Click Next.
6. Click Next through Steps 2–4. Note that you can add a title in Step 3.

	A	B
1	Grade Range	Frequency
2	90–100	2
3	80–89	5
4	70–79	3
5	60–69	3
6	0–59	2

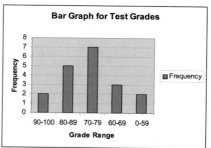

Section 8.2 Finding the Mean, Standard Deviation, and Median of Raw Data

To find the mean, standard deviation, and median of a raw data set:

1. Enter the data in Row 1 (cells A1:L1).
2. Type the heading Mean in cell A3.
3. Type the formula =average(A1:L1) in cell B4.
4. Type the heading Standard Deviation in cell A4.
5. In cell B4, type the formula =stdev(A1:L1).
6. In cell A5, type the heading Median.
7. In cell B5, type the formula =median(A1:L1).

The mean, standard deviation, and median for the data 1, 1, 1, 3, 3, 4, 4, 5, 6, 6, 7, 7 is shown below.

	A	B	C	D	E	F	G	H	I	J	K	L
1	1	1	1	3	3	4	4	5	6	6	7	7
2												
3	Mean	4										
4	Standard Deviation	2.2563										
5	Median	4										

Section 8.2 Finding the Mean and Standard Deviation of Grouped Data

To find the mean:

1. Enter the data and headings in the cells A1:C6.
2. In D1, type the heading Class mark*frequency.
3. In D2, type the formula =B2*C2.
4. Copy the formula in D2 to D3:D6.
5. In B7, type the heading Total.
6. In cell C7, type the formula for the total frequencies, =sum(C2:C6).
7. In cell D7, type the formula for the total, =sum(D2:D6).
8. In cell A8, type the heading Mean.
9. In cell A9, type in the formula =D7/C7.

To find the standard deviation:

10. In cell E1, type in the heading freq *(x − x_mean)^2.
11. In cell E2, type the formula =C2*(B2-A9)^2. (The A9 gives the value in A9; the reference doesn't change as we fill down.)
12. Copy the formula in E2 to E3:E6.
13. In cell E7, type the formula =sum(E2:E6).
14. In cell A10 type the heading Standard Deviation.
15. In cell A11, type the formula =sqrt(E7/(C7-1)).

Grade Range	Class Marks	Frequency
90–100	95	3
80–89	84.5	4
70–79	74.5	7
60–69	64.5	0
50–59	54.5	2

	A	B	C	D	E
1	Grade Range	Class Marks	Frequency	Class mark*frequency	Freq*(x-x_mean)^2
2	90-100	95	3	285	832.2919922
3	80-89	84.5	4	338	151.5976563
4	70-79	74.5	7	521.5	103.4208984
5	60-69	64.5	0	0	0
6	50-59	54.5	2	109	1137.048828
7		Total	16	1253.5	2224.359375
8	Mean				
9	78.344				
10	Standard Deviation				
11	12.177				

Section 8.4 Calculating Normal Probabilities

To calculate normal probabilities:

1. Type headings in A1:A4 and their respective values in cells B1:B4.
2. To find the probability that a score X is less than the x1 value in B3, enter the formula =normdist(B3,B1,B2,true) in cell B5.
3. To find the probability that X is less than the x2 value in B4, enter the formula =normdist(B4,B1,B2,true) in cell B6.
4. To find the probability that a score X is more than the value in B3 and less than the x2 value in B4, enter the formula =B6-B5 in cell B7.

Entries in B5, B6, and B7 give the probabilities of a score X being less than 100, less than 115, and between 100 and 115, respectively, when the mean is 100 and the standard deviation is 15.

	A	B
1	Mean	100
2	Standard Deviation	15
3	x1	100
4	x2	115
5	Pr(X<x1)	0.5
6	Pr(X<x2)	0.841345
7	Pr(x1<X<x2)	0.341345

Chapter 9

Sections 9.1–9.2 Evaluating Limits

To evaluate $\lim_{x \to c} f(x)$:

1. Make a table of values for $f(x)$ near $x = c$. Include values on both sides of $x = c$.
2. Use the table of values to predict the limit (or that the limit does not exist).

   Note: All limit evaluations with Excel use appropriate tables of values of $f(x)$. This is true when $f(x)$ is piecewise defined and for limits as $\to \infty$.

Find $\lim_{x \to 2} \dfrac{x^2 - 4}{x - 2}$.

	A	B	C	D
	x	**f(x)**	**x**	**f(x)**
1				
2	2.1	4.1	1.9	3.9
3	2.05	4.05	1.95	3.95
4	2.01	4.01	1.99	3.99
5	2.001	4.001	1.999	3.999

The tables suggest that $\lim_{x \to 2} \dfrac{x^2 - 4}{x - 2} = 4$.

Sections 9.3–9.7 Approximating Derivatives

To approximate $f'(c)$:

1. Numerically investigate the limit in the definition of derivative:
$$f'(x) = \lim_{h \to 0} \frac{f(x + h) - f(x)}{h}$$

2. Use the given $f(x)$ and $x = c$ to create a table of values for h near 0 (and on both sides of $h = 0$).

Note that rows 5 and 6 have the values of h closest to 0.

Investigate $f'(1)$ for $f(x) = x^3$.

	A	B	C	D	E
	h	**1+h**	**f(1)**	**f(1+h)**	**(f(1+h)-f(1))/h**
1					
2	0.1	1.1	1	1.331	3.31
3	0.01	1.01	1	1.030301	3.0301
4	0.001	1.001	1	1.003003	3.003001
5	0.0001	1.0001	1	1.0003	3.00030001
6	−0.0001	0.9999	1	0.9997	2.99970001
7	−0.001	0.999	1	0.997003	2.997001
8	−0.01	0.99	1	0.970299	2.9701
9	−0.1	0.9	1	0.729	2.71

The table suggests that $f'(1) = 3$, which is the actual value. Note: Excel has no built-in derivative approximation tool.

Chapter 10

Section 10.1 Relative Maxima and Minima

1. Make a table with columns for x-values, the function, and the derivative.
2. Extend the table to include x-values to the left and to the right of all critical values.
3. Use the signs of the values of the derivative to determine whether f is increasing or decreasing around the critical values, and thus to classify the critical values as relative maxima, relative minima, or horizontal points of inflection. You may want to graph the function to confirm your conclusions.

The spreadsheet shows that the relative maxima or minima of $f(x) = x^2$ is 0 at $x = 0$. Note that the derivative is $f'(x) = 2x$.

	A	B	C
1	x	f(x)	f'(x)
2	−2	4	−4
3	−1.5	2.25	−3
4	−1	1	−2
5	−0.5	0.25	−1
6	0	0	0
7	0.5	0.25	1
8	1	1	2
9	1.5	2.25	3
10	2	4	4

Section 10.2 Exploring f, f', f'' Relationships

To explore relationships among the graphs of a function and its derivatives:

1. Find functions for f' and f''.
2. Graph all three functions on the same plot.
   - Notice that f increases when f' is above the x-axis ($+$) and decreases when f' is below the x-axis ($-$).
   - Notice that f is concave up when f'' is above the x-axis ($+$) and is concave down when f'' is below the x-axis ($-$).

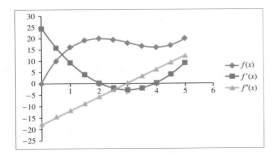

Let $f(x) = x^3 - 9x^2 + 24x$. Graph f, f', and f'' on the interval $[0, 5]$ to explore the relationships among these functions.

	A	B	C	D
	x	f(x)	f'(x)	f''(x)
1				
2	0	0	24	−18
3	0.5	9.875	15.75	−15
4	1	16	9	−12
5	1.5	19.125	3.75	−9
6	2	20	0	−6
7	2.5	19.375	−2.25	−3
8	3	18	−3	0
9	3.5	16.625	−2.25	3
10	4	16	0	6
11	4.5	16.875	3.75	9
12	5	20	9	12

Sections 10.3–10.4 Finding Optimal Values

To find the optimal value of a function when the goal is not to produce a graph:

1. Set up a spreadsheet that identifies the variable and the function whose optimal value is sought.
2. Choose *Tools > Solver*. Then, in the *Solver* dialog box,
   a. Set the *Target Cell* as that of the objective function.
   b. Check *Max* or *Min* according to your goal.
   c. Set the *Changing Cells* to reference the variable.
3. Click on the *Options* box. Make sure "Assume Linear Model" is not checked. Then click OK.
4. Click *Solve* in the *Solver* dialog box. You will get a dialog box stating that Solver found a solution. Save the solution if desired, then click OK.
5. The cells containing the variable and the function should now contain the optimal values.

Minimize area $A = x^2 + \dfrac{160}{x}$ for $x > 0$.

	A	B
1	**Variable**	
2		
3	x length of base	1
4		
5	**Objective**	
6		
7	Minimize Area	=B3^2+160/B3

	A	B
1	**Variable**	
2		
3	x length of base	4.3089
4		
5	**Objective**	
6		
7	Minimize Area	55.699

The function is minimized for $x = 4.3089$ and the minimum value is $A = 55.699$.

Chapter 13
Section 13.1 Approximating Definite Integrals
Using Rectangles

To find the approximate area between $y = f(x)$ and the x-axis over an interval by using the right-hand endpoints of rectangles with equal base width:

1. Enter "x" and the x-values of the right-hand endpoints of each rectangle in Column B. Fill down can be used if the number of rectangles is large.
2. Enter the formula for the function, using cell addresses, in C2 and fill down column C to get the heights of the rectangles.
3. Enter the width of the rectangles in Column D.
4. Enter the formula for the area of each rectangle, =C2*D2, in E2 and fill down to get the area of each rectangle.
5. Enter "Total" in A10 and the formula =SUM(E2:E9) in E10 to get the approximate area.

To find the approximation for the area under $y = \sqrt{x}$ from $x = 0$ to $x = 4$ using $n = 8$ equal subdivisions (with base width 0.5) and right-hand endpoints:

1. Enter "x" and the eight x-values of the right-hand endpoints (starting with 0.5) in Column B.
2. Enter "y" in C1 and =SQRT(B2) in C2 and fill down column C.
3. Enter "width" in D1 and 0.5 below in Column D.
4. Enter "Area" in E1, =C2*D2 in E2, and fill down to get the area of each rectangle.
5. Enter "Total" in A10 and the formula =SUM(E2:E9) in E10 to get the approximate area, $S_R \approx 5.765$.

	A	B	C	D	E
1	Rectangle	x	y	Width	Area
2	1	0.5	0.707107	0.5	0.353553
3	2	1	1	0.5	0.5
4	3	1.5	1.224745	0.5	0.612372
5	4	2	1.414214	0.5	0.707107
6	5	2.5	1.581139	0.5	0.790569
7	6	3	1.732051	0.5	0.866025
8	7	3.5	1.870829	0.5	0.935414
9	8	4	2	0.5	1
10	Total				5.765042

Chapter 14
Section 14.1   Graphs of Functions of Two Variables

To create a surface plot for a function of two variables:

1. a. Generate appropriate *x*-values beginning in B1 and continuing *across*.
   b. Generate appropriate *y*-values beginning in A2 and continuing *down*.
2. Generate values for the function that correspond to the points (x, y) from Step 1 as follows:
   In cell B2, enter the function formula with B$1 used to represent *x* and $A2 to represent *y*. (See the online Excel Guide for additional information about the role and use of the $ in this step.) Then use fill down and fill across to complete the table.
3. Select the entire table of values. Click the *Chart Wizard* and choose *Surface in the Chart* menu.
4. Annotate the graph and click *Finish* to create the surface plot. You can move and view the surface from a different perspective by clicking into the resulting graph.

Let $f(x, y) = 10 - x^2 - y^2$. Plot the graph of this function for both *x* and *y* in the interval $[-2, 2]$.

	A	B	C	D	E	F	G	H	I	J
1		−2	−1.5	−1	−0.5	0	0.5	1	1.5	2
2	−2									
3	−1.5									
4	−1									
5	−0.5									
6	0									
7	0.5									
8	1									
9	1.5									
10	2									

	A	B	C	D	E	F	G	H	I	J
1		−2	−1.5	−1	−0.5	0	0.5	1	1.5	2
2	−2	2	3.75	5	5.75	6	5.75	5	3.75	2
3	−1.5	3.75	5.5	6.75	7.5	7.75	7.5	6.75	5.5	3.75
4	−1	5	6.75	8	8.75	9	8.75	8	6.75	5
5	−0.5	5.75	7.5	8.75	9.5	9.75	9.5	8.75	7.5	5.75
6	0	6	7.75	9	9.75	10	9.75	9	7.75	6
7	0.5	5.75	7.5	8.75	9.5	9.75	9.5	8.75	7.5	5.75
8	1	5	6.75	8	8.75	9	8.75	8	6.75	5
9	1.5	3.75	5.5	6.75	7.5	7.75	7.5	6.75	5.5	3.75
10	2	2	3.75	5	5.75	6	5.75	5	3.75	2

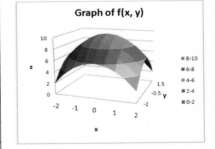

Graph of f(x, y)

Section 14.5 Constrained Optimization and Lagrange Multipliers

To solve a constrained optimization problem:

1. Set up the problem in Excel.
2. Choose *Tolls > Solver* and do the following:
   - Choose the objective function as the *Target Cell*.
   - Check *Max* or *Min* depending on the problem.
   - Choose the cells representing the variables for the *By Changing Cells* box.
   - Click on the *Constraints* box and press Add. Then enter the constraint equations.
3. Click on the *Options* box and make sure that "Assume Linear Model" is *not* checked. Then click OK.
4. Click *Solve* in the *Solver* dialog box. Then click OK to solve.

Maximize $P = 600l^{2/3}k^{1/3}$ subject to $40l + 100k = 3000$.

	A	B	C
1	**Variables**		
2			
3	units labor (l)	0	
4	units capital (k)	0	
5			
6			
7	**Objective**		
8			
9	Maximize production	=600*B3^(2/3)*B4^(1/3)	
10			
11	Constraint		
12		Amount used	Available
13	Cost	=40*B3+100*B4	3000

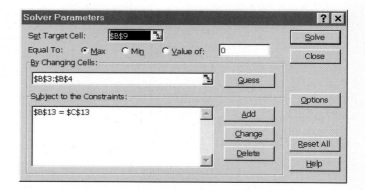

	A	B	C
1	**Variables**		
2			
3	units labor (l)	50.00000002	
4	units capital (k)	10	
5			
6			
7	**Objective**		
8			
9	Maximize product	17544.10644	
10			
11	**Constraint**		
12		Amount used	Available
13	Cost	3000.000001	3000

Excel Guide Part 2
Excel 2007 and 2010

Except where noted, the directions given will work in both Excel 2007 and Excel 2010.

Excel Worksheet

When you start up Excel by using the instructions for your software and computer, the following screen will appear.

The components of the **spreadsheet** are shown, and the grid shown is called a **worksheet.** You can move to other worksheets by clicking on the tabs at the bottom.

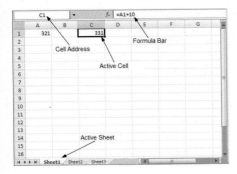

Addresses and Operations

Notice the letters at the top of the columns and the numbers identifying the rows. The cell addresses are given by the column and row; for example, the first cell has address A1. You can move from one cell to another with arrow keys, or you can select a cell by clicking on it. After you type an entry in a cell, press enter to accept it. To edit the contents of a cell, click on the cell and edit the contents in the formula bar at the top. To delete the contents, press the delete key.

The file operations such as "open a new file," "saving a file," and "printing a file" are similar to those in Word. For example, <CTRL>S saves a file. You can also format a cell entry by selecting it and using menus similar to those in Word.

Working with Cells

Cell entries, rows containing entries, and columns containing entries can be copied and pasted with the same commands as in Word. For example, a highlighted cell can be copied with <CTRL>C. Sometimes entries exceed the width of the cells containing them, especially if they are text. To widen the cells in a column, place the cursor at the right side of the column heading until you see the symbol ↔, then move the cursor to the right (moving it to the left makes the column more narrow). If entering a number results in #####, the number is too long for the cell, and the cell should be widened.

Chapter 1

Section 1.4 Entering Data and Evaluating Functions

The cells are identified by the column and the row. For example, the cell B3 is in the second column and the third row.

1. Put headings on the two columns.
2. Fill the inputs in Column A by hand or with a formula for them. The formula =A2+1 gives 2 in A3 when ENTER is pressed.
3. Moving the mouse to the lower right corner of A3 until there is a thin "+" sign and dragging the mouse down "fills down" all required entries in column A.
4. Enter the function formula for the function in B2. Use = 1000*(1.1)^A2 to represent $S = 1000(1.1)^t$. Pressing ENTER gives the value when $t = 1$.
5. Using Fill Down gives the output for all inputs.

	A	B
1	Year	Future Value
2	1	=1000*(1.1)^(A2)
3	=A2+1	

	A	B
1	Year	Future Value
2		1	1100
3		2	1210
4		3	1331

Section 1.4 Graphing a Function

1. Put headings on the two columns (x and $f(x)$, for example).
2. Fill the inputs (x-values) in Column A by hand or with a formula for them.
3. Enter the formula for the function in B2. Use = 6*A2 − 3 to represent $f(x) = 6x − 3$.
4. Select the cell containing the formula for the function (B2, for example).
5. Move the mouse to the lower right corner until there is a thin "+" sign.
6. Drag the mouse down to the last cell where formula is required, and press ENTER.
7. Highlight the two columns containing the values of x and $f(x)$.
8. Click the Insert tab and then select the *Scatter* chart type with the smooth curve option.
9. Once the smooth curve option is selected, the chart will appear within the worksheet. The worksheet is now in design mode, where you can change the chart options.
10. Click on the Home tab to get back to the original view of the spreadsheet.

	A	B
1	x	$f(x) = 6x − 3$
2	−5	−33
3	−2	−15
4	−1	−9
5	0	−3
6	1	3
7	3	15
8	5	27

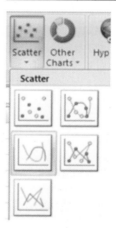

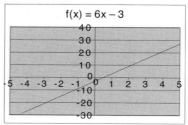

Section 1.5 Solving Systems of Two Equations in Two Variables

1. Write the two equations as linear functions in the form $y = mx + b$.
2. Enter the input variable x in cell A2 and the formula for each of the two equations in cells B2 and C2, respectively.
3. Enter = B2 − C2 in cell D2.
4. Start *Goal Seek* by clicking on the Data tab. Then select *What-If Analysis* in the Data Tools group, and then *Goal Seek*.
5. In the dialog box:
   a. Click the *Set Cell* box and click on the D2 cell.
   b. Enter 0 in the *To Value* box.
   c. Click the *By Changing Cell* box and click on the A2 cell.
6. Click OK in the *Goal Seek* dialog box, getting 0.
7. The x-value of the solution is in cell A2, and the y-value is in both B2 and C2.

The solution of the system
$$\begin{cases} 3x + 2y = 12 \\ 4x - 3y = -1 \end{cases}$$
is found to be $x = 2$, $y = 3$ using *Goal Seek* as follows.

	A	B	C	D
1	x	= 6 − 1.5x	= 1/3 + 4x/3	= y1 − y2
2	1	= 6 − 1.5*A2	= 1/3 + 4*A2/3	= B2 − C2

	A	B	C	D
1	x	= 6 − 1.5x	= 1/3 + 4x/3	= y1 − y2
2	2	3	3	0

Chapter 2
Section 2.1 Solving Quadratic Equations

To solve a quadratic equation of the form
$f(x) = ax^2 + bx + c = 0$

1. Enter x-values centered around the x-coordinate $x = \dfrac{-b}{2a}$ in column A and use the function formula to find the values of $f(x)$ in column B.

2. Graph the function, $f(x) = 2x^2 - 9x + 4$ in this case, and observe where the graph crosses the x-axis ($f(x)$ near 0). Insert the graph by selecting *Insert>Scatter>Smooth curve* option.

3. Use *Data>What-If>Goal Seek*, entering a cell address with a function value in column B at or near 0, enter the set cell to the value 0, and enter the changing cell.

4. Click OK to find the x-value of the solution in cell A2. The solution may be approximate. The spreadsheet shows $x = 0.5001$, which is an approximation of the exact solution $x = 0.5$.

5. After finding the first solution, repeat the process using a second function value at or near 0. The second solution is $x = 4$ in this case.

	A	B	C	D	E	F
1	x	$f(x)=2x^2-9x+4$				
2	−1	15				
3	0	4				
4	1	−3				
5	2	−6				
6	3	−5				
7	4	0				
8	5	9				
9						

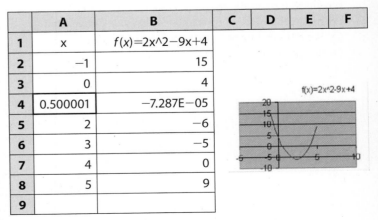

	A	B	C	D	E	F
1	x	$f(x)=2x^2-9x+4$				
2	−1	15				
3	0	4				
4	0.500001	−7.287E−05				
5	2	−6				
6	3	−5				
7	4	0				
8	5	9				
9						

Sections 2.2 and 2.4 Graphing Polynomial Functions

To graph a polynomial function:

1. Use the function to create a table containing values for x and $f(x)$. (See Graphing a Function on page AP-46.)
2. Highlight the two columns containing the values of x and $f(x)$.
3. Insert the graph by selecting *Insert > Scatter > Smooth curve* option.
4. Click on the Home tab to get back to the original view of the spreadsheet.

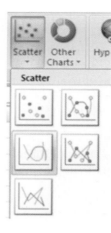

$f(x) = 3x^2 - 10x$

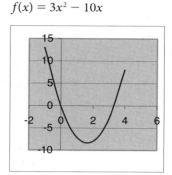

Section 2.4 Graphing Rational Functions

An Excel graph will connect all points corresponding to values in the table, so if the function you are graphing is undefined for some x-value a, enter x-values near this value and leave (or make) the corresponding $f(a)$ cell blank.

To graph $f(x) = \dfrac{1}{1-x}$, which is undefined at $x = 1$:

1. Generate a table for x-values from -1 to 3, with extra values near $x = 1$.
2. Generate the values of $f(x)$, and leave a blank cell for the $f(x)$ value for $x = 1$.
3. Select the table and plot the graph using *Insert > Scatter > Smooth curve* option.

x	f(x)
−1	−0.5
−0.5	−0.6666667
0	−1
0.5	−2
0.75	−4
0.9	−10
1	
1.1	10
1.25	4
1.5	2
2	1
2.5	0.66666667
3	0.5

Section 2.5 Modeling

To create a scatter plot of data:

1. Enter the inputs (x-values) in Column A and the outputs (y-values) in Column B.
2. Highlight the two columns and use *Insert > Scatter* and choose the points only option to plot the points.
3. To add titles, click on the icons in the *Charts Layout* group.

	A	B	C	D	E	F	G	H	I
1									
2	Time (sec)	Speed (mph)							
3	1.7	30							
4	2.4	40							
5	3.5	50							
6	4.3	60							
7	5.5	70							
8	7	80							
9	8.5	90							
10	10.2	100							
11									

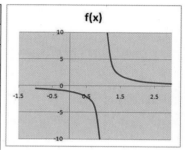

To find the equation of a line or curve that best fits a given set of data points:

1. Single-click on the scatter plot of the data in the worksheet.
2. Right-click on one of the data points.
3. Select *Add Trendline*.
4. Select the function type that appears to best fit and check the box that says *Display Equation on chart*. [Note: If *Polynomial* is selected, choose the appropriate Order (degree).]
5. Close the dialog box and you will see the graph of the selected function that is best fit along with its equation.

The power function that models Corvette acceleration follows.

	A	B	C	D	E	F	G	H	I
1									
2	Time (sec)	Speed (mph)			Corvette Acceleration				
3	1.7	30							
4	2.4	40							
5	3.5	50							
6	4.3	60							
7	5.5	70							
8	7	80							
9	8.5	90							
10	10.2	100							
11									

Corvette Acceleration chart: Speed (mph), $y = 21.875x^{0.6663}$

The speed of the Corvette is given by $y = 21.875x^{0.6663}$ where x is the time in seconds.

Chapter 3
Section 3.1 Operations with Matrices

Operations for 3×3 matrices can be used for other orders.

1. Type a name A in A1 to identify the first matrix.
2. Enter the matrix elements of matrix A in the cells B1:D3.
3. Type a name B in A5 to identify the second matrix.
4. Enter the matrix elements of matrix B in the cells B5:D7.
5. Type a name A + B in A9 to indicate the matrix sum.
6. Type the formula "=B1 + B5" in B9 and press ENTER.
7. Use Fill Across to copy this formula across the row to C9 and D9.
8. Use Fill Down to copy the row B9:D9 to B11:D11, which gives the sum.
9. To subtract the matrices, change the formula in B9 to "=B1 − B5" and proceed as with addition.

	A	B	C	D
1	A	1	2	3
2		4	5	6
3		7	8	9
4				
5	B	−2	−4	3
6		1	4	−5
7		3	6	−1
8				
9	A+B	−1	−2	6
10		5	9	1
11		10	14	8

Section 3.2 Multiplying Two Matrices

Steps for two 3×3 matrices:

1. Enter the names and elements of the matrices.
2. Enter the name AxB in A9 to indicate the matrix product.
3. Select a range of cells that is the correct size to contain the product (B9:D11 in this case).
4. Type "=mmult(" in the formula bar, and then select the cells containing the elements of matrix A (B1:D3).
5. Stay in the formula bar, type a comma and select the matrix B elements (B5:D7), and close the parentheses.
6. Hold the CTRL and SHIFT keys down and press ENTER, giving the product.

	A	B	C	D
1	A	1	2	3
2		4	5	6
3		7	8	9
4				
5	B	−2	−4	3
6		1	4	−5
7		3	6	−1
8				
9	AxB	=mmult(B1:D3)		
10		MMULT(**array1,**		
11		array2)		

B9	fx	{(=MMULT(B1:D3,B5:D7)}			
	A	B	C	D	E
1	A	1	2	3	
2		4	5	6	
3		7	8	9	
4					
5	B	−2	−4	3	
6		1	4	−5	
7		3	6	−1	
8					
9	AxB	9	22	−10	
10		15	40	−19	
11		21	58	−28	

Section 3.4 Finding the Inverse of a Matrix

Steps for a 3 × 3 matrix:

1. Enter the name A in A1 and the elements of the matrix in B1:D3 as above.
2. Enter the name "Inverse(A)" in A5 and select a range of cells that is the correct size to contain the inverse [(B5:D7) in this case].
3. Enter "=minverse(", select matrix A(B1:D3), and close the parentheses.
4. Hold the CTRL and SHIFT keys down and press ENTER, getting the inverse.

SUM	fx	=minverse(B1:D3)		
	A	B	C	D
1	A	2	1	1
2		1	2	0
3		2	0	1
4				
5	inverse(A)	=minverse(B1:D3)		
6				
7				

Section 3.4 Solving Systems of Linear Equations with Matrix Inverses

A system of linear equations can be solved by multiplying the matrix containing the augment by the inverse of the coefficient matrix. The steps used to solve a 3 × 3 system follow.

1. Enter the coefficient matrix A in B1:D3.
2. Enter the name "inverse(A)" in A5 and compute the inverse of A in B5:D7.
3. Enter B in cell A9 and enter the augment matrix in B9:B11.
4. Enter X in A13 and select the cells B13:B15.
5. In the formula bar, type "=mmult(", then select matrix inverse(A) in B5:D7, type a comma, select matrix B in B9:B11, and close the parentheses.
6. Hold the CTRL and SHIFT keys down and press ENTER, getting the solution.
7. Matrix X gives the solution.

The system $\begin{cases} 2x + y + z = 8 \\ x + 2y \quad\;\; = 6 \\ 2x + \quad\;\; z = 5 \end{cases}$ is solved as follows.

B5	fx	{=MINVERSE(B1:D3)}		
	A	B	C	D
1	A	2	1	1
2		1	2	0
3		2	0	1
4				
5	inverse(A)	−2	1	2
6		1	0	−1
7		4	−2	−3

	SUM	fx	=mmult(B5:D7,B9:B11)		
		A	B	C	D	E
1	A	2	1	1	
2		1	2	0	
3		2	0	1	
4					
5	inverse(A)	−2	1	2	
6		1	0	−1	
7		4	−2	−3	
8					
9	B	8			
10		6			
11		5			
12					
13	X	=mmult(B5:D7,B9:B11)			
14					
15					

	B13	fx	{(=MMULT(B5:D7,B9:B11)}		
		A	B	C	D	E
1	A	2	1	1	
2		1	2	0	
3		2	0	1	
4					
5	inverse(A)	−2	1	2	
6		1	0	−1	
7		4	−2	−3	
8					
9	B	8			
10		6			
11		5			
12					
13	X	0			
14		3			
15		5			

The solution is $x = 0, y = 3, z = 5$.

Section 5.2 Graphing Logarithmic Functions with Other Bases

1. The graph of a logarithm with any base b can be created by entering the formula $=\log(x, b)$.
2. Proceed as described above for graphing base e and base 10 logarithms.

	A	B
1	x	f(x)=log(x,7)
2	0.5	−0.356207187
3	0.9	−0.054144594
4	1	0
5	2	0.356207187
6	3	0.564575034
7	4	0.712414374
8	5	0.827087475
9	6	0.920782221
10	7	1
11	8	1.068621561
12	9	1.129150068
13	10	1.183294662
14	11	1.1232274406

The graph of $f(x) =\log_7 x$ is shown below.

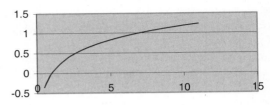

Chapter 6
Section 6.2 Finding the Future Value of a Lump Sum

To find the future value of a lump-sum investment:

1. Type the headings in Row 1, and enter their values (with the interest rate as a decimal) in Row 2. Enter the investment as a negative number.
2. Type the formula $=D2/E2$ in F2 to compute the rate per period.
3. Type the heading Future Value in A4.
4. In cell B4, type the formula $=fv(F2,B2,C2,A2,0)$ to compute the future value.

This spreadsheet gives the future value of an investment of $10,000 for 17 years at 9.8%, compounded quarterly.

Principal	Number of Periods	Payment	Annual Rate	Periods per year	Periodic Rate
−10,000	68	0	0.098	4	0.0245
Future Value	$51,857.73				

Section 6.3 Finding the Future Value of an Annuity

To find the future value of an ordinary annuity:

1. Type the headings in Row 1, and enter their values (with the interest rate as a decimal) in Row 2. Enter the deposit as a negative payment.
2. Type the formula $=D2/E2$ in F2 to compute the rate per period.
3. Type the heading Future Value in A4.
4. In cell B4, type the formula $=fv(F2,B2,C2,A2,0)$ to compute the future value.
   (The 0 indicates that the payments are made at the end of each period.)

For annuities due, use $=fv(F2,B2,C2,A2,1)$.
The payments are made at the beginning of each period.

This spreadsheet gives the future value of an ordinary annuity of $200 deposited at the end of each quarter for $2\frac{1}{4}$ years, with interest at 4%, compounded quarterly.

Principal	Number of Periods	Payment	Annual Rate	Periods per year	Periodic Rate
0	9	−200	0.04	4	0.01
Ordinary annuity					
Future Value	$1,873.71				
Annuities due					
Future Value	$1,892.44				

Section 6.4 Finding the Present Value of an Annuity

To find the present value of an ordinary annuity:

1. Type the headings in Row 1, and enter their values (with the interest rate as a decimal) in Row 2.
2. Enter the formula =D2/E2 in F2 to compute the rate per period.
3. Type the heading Present Value in A4.
4. In cell B4, type the formula =pv(F2,B2,C2,A2,0) to compute the present value. (The 0 indicates that the payments are made at the end of each period.) The parentheses on the present value in cell B4 mean that it is negative (the money leaves the investor to start the annuity).

For annuities due, use =pv(F2,B2,C2,A2,1).
The payments are made at the beginning of each period.

This spreadsheet gives the lump sum deposit (present value) necessary to receive $1000 per month for 16 years, with interest at 9%, compounded monthly, for both an ordinary annuity and an annuity due.

Future Value	Number of Periods	Payment	Annual Rate	Periods per year	Periodic Rate
0	192	1000	0.09	12	0.0075
Ordinary annuity					
Present Value	($101,572.77)				
Annuities due					
Present value	($102,334.56)				

Section 6.5 Finding Payments to Amortize a Loan

To find the periodic payment to pay off a loan:

1. Type the headings in Row 1 and their values (with the interest rate as a decimal) in Row 2.
2. Enter the formula =D2/E2 in F2 to compute the rate per period.
3. Type the heading Payment in A4.
4. In cell B4, type the formula =Pmt(F2,B2,A2,C2,0) to compute the payment.

This spreadsheet gives the annual payment of a loan of $10,000 over 5 years when interest is 10% per year.

The parentheses indicates a payment out.

Loan Amount	Number of Periods	Future Value	Annual Rate	Periods per year	Periodic Rate
10000	5	0	0.1	1	0.1
Payment	($2,637.97)				

Chapter 8
Section 8.1 Binomial Probabilities

1. Type headings in cells A1:A3 and their respective values in cells B1:B3.
2. Use the function =binomdist(B1,B2,B3,cumulative) where
   - B1 is the number of successes.
   - B2 is the number of independent trials.
   - B3 is the probability of success in each trial.
   - True replaces cumulative if a cumulative probability is sought; it is replaced by false otherwise.
   - The probability of exactly 3 heads in 6 tosses is found by evaluating =binomdist(B1,B2,B3,false) in B4.
   - The probability of 3 or fewer heads in 6 tosses is found by evaluating =binomdist(B1,B2,B3,true) in B5.

This spreadsheet gives the probability of 3 heads in 6 tosses of a fair coin and the probability of 3 or fewer heads in 6 tosses.

	A	B
1	Number of successes	3
2	Number of trials	6
3	Probability of success	.5
4	Probability of 3 successes	.3125
5	Probability of 3 or fewer successes	.65625

Section 8.2 Bar Graphs

To construct a bar graph for the given table of test scores:

1. Copy the entries of the table to cells A2:B6.
2. Select the range A2:B6.
3. Click on the *Insert* tab. Then select *Column > Clustered Column* (first option), and the graph appears.
4. Single-click on the chart. You can add labels and change the title of the graph by clicking *Layout* under *Chart Tools*, and choosing the appropriate options.

	A	B
1	Grade Range	Frequency
2	90–100	2
3	80–89	5
4	70–79	3
5	60–69	3
6	0–59	2

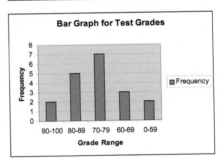

Section 8.2 Finding the Mean, Standard Deviation, and Median of Raw Data

To find the mean, standard deviation, and median of a raw data set:

1. Enter the data in Row 1 (cells A1:L1).
2. Type the heading Mean in cell A3.
3. Type the formula =average(A1:L1) in cell B4.
4. Type the heading Standard Deviation in cell A4.
5. In cell B4, type the formula =stdev(A1:L1).
6. In cell A5, type the heading Median.
7. In cell B5, type the formula =median(A1:L1).

The mean, standard deviation, and median for the data 1, 1, 1, 3, 3, 4, 4, 5, 6, 6, 7, 7 is shown below.

	A	B	C	D	E	F	G	H	I	J	K	L
1	1	1	1	3	3	4	4	5	6	6	7	7
2												
3	Mean	4										
4	Standard Deviation	2.2563										
5	Median	4										

Section 8.2 Finding the Mean and Standard Deviation of Grouped Data

To find the mean:

1. Enter the data and headings in the cells A1:C6.
2. In D1, type the heading Class mark*frequency.
3. In D2, type the formula =B2*C2.
4. Copy the formula in D2 to D3:D6.
5. In B7, type the heading Total.
6. In cell C7, type the formula for the total frequencies, =sum(C2:C6).
7. In cell D7, type the formula for the total, =sum(D2:D6).
8. In cell A8, type the heading Mean.
9. In cell A9, type in the formula =D7/C7.

To find the standard deviation:

10. In cell E1, type in the heading freq *(x − x_mean)^2.
11. In cell E2, type the formula =C2*(B2-A9)^2. (The A9 gives the value in A9; the reference doesn't change as we fill down.)
12. Copy the formula in E2 to E3:E6.
13. In cell E7, type the formula =sum(E2:E6).
14. In cell A10 type the heading Standard Deviation.
15. In cell A11, type the formula =sqrt(E7/(C7-1)).

Grade Range	Class Marks	Frequency
90–100	95	3
80–89	84.5	4
70–79	74.5	7
60–69	64.5	0
50–59	54.5	2

	A	B	C	D	E
1	Grade Range	Class Marks	Frequency	Class mark*frequency	Freq*(x-x_mean)^2
2	90-100	95	3	285	832.2919922
3	80-89	84.5	4	338	151.5976563
4	70-79	74.5	7	521.5	103.4208984
5	60-69	64.5	0	0	0
6	50-59	54.5	2	109	1137.048828
7		Total	16	1253.5	2224.359375
8	Mean				
9	78.344				
10	Standard Deviation				
11	12.177				

Section 8.4 Calculating Normal Probabilities

To calculate normal probabilities:

1. Type headings in A1:A4 and their respective values in cells B1:B4.
2. To find the probability that a score X is less than the x1 value in B3, enter the formula =normdist(B3,B1,B2,true) in cell B5.
3. To find the probability that X is less than the x2 value in B4, enter the formula =normdist(B4,B1,B2,true) in cell B6.
4. To find the probability that a score X is more than the value in B3 and less than the x2 value in B4, enter the formula =B6-B5 in cell B7.

Entries in B5, B6, and B7 give the probabilities of a score X being less than 100, less than 115, and between 100 and 115, respectively, when the mean is 100 and the standard deviation is 15.

	A	B
1	Mean	100
2	Standard Deviation	15
3	x1	100
4	x2	115
5	Pr(X<x1)	0.5
6	Pr(X<x2)	0.841345
7	Pr(x1<X<x2)	0.341345

Chapter 9
Sections 9.1–9.2 Evaluating Limits

To evaluate $\lim\limits_{x \to c} f(x)$:

1. Make a table of values for $f(x)$ near $x = c$. Include values on both sides of $x = c$.
2. Use the table of values to predict the limit (or that the limit does not exist).

Note: All limit evaluations with Excel use appropriate tables of values of $f(x)$. This is true when $f(x)$ is piecewise defined and for limits as $\to \infty$.

Find $\lim\limits_{x \to 2} \dfrac{x^2 - 4}{x - 2}$.

	A	B	C	D
	x	**f(x)**	**x**	**f(x)**
1				
2	2.1	4.1	1.9	3.9
3	2.05	4.05	1.95	3.95
4	2.01	4.01	1.99	3.99
5	2.001	4.001	1.999	3.999

The tables suggest that $\lim\limits_{x \to 2} \dfrac{x^2 - 4}{x - 2} = 4$.

Sections 9.3–9.7 Approximating Derivatives

To approximate $f'(c)$:

1. Numerically investigate the limit in the definition of derivative:
$$f'(x) = \lim_{h \to 0} \frac{f(x + h) - f(x)}{h}$$
2. Use the given $f(x)$ and $x = c$ to create a table of values for h near 0 (and on both sides of $h = 0$).

Note that rows 5 and 6 have the values of h closest to 0.

Investigate $f'(1)$ for $f(x) = x^3$.

	A	B	C	D	E
1	**h**	**1+h**	**f(1)**	**f(1+h)**	**(f(1+h)-f(1))/h**
2	0.1	1.1	1	1.331	3.31
3	0.01	1.01	1	1.030301	3.0301
4	0.001	1.001	1	1.003003	3.003001
5	0.0001	1.0001	1	1.0003	3.00030001
6	−0.0001	0.9999	1	0.9997	2.99970001
7	−0.001	0.999	1	0.997003	2.997001
8	−0.01	0.99	1	0.970299	2.9701
9	−0.1	0.9	1	0.729	2.71

The table suggests that $f'(1) = 3$, which is the actual value.
Note: Excel has no built-in derivative approximation tool.

Chapter 10
Section 10.1 Relative Maxima and Minima

1. Make a table with columns for x-values, the function, and the derivative.
2. Extend the table to include x-values to the left and to the right of all critical values.
3. Use the signs of the values of the derivative to determine whether f is increasing or decreasing around the critical values, and thus to classify the critical values as relative maxima, relative minima, or horizontal points of inflection. You may want to graph the function to confirm your conclusions.

The spreadsheet shows that the relative minima of $f(x) = x^2$ is 0 at $x = 0$. Note that the derivative is $f'(x) = 2x$.

	A	B	C
1	x	f(x)	f'(x)
2	−2	4	−4
3	−1.5	2.25	−3
4	−1	1	−2
5	−0.5	0.25	−1
6	0	0	0
7	0.5	0.25	1
8	1	1	2
9	1.5	2.25	3
10	2	4	4

Section 10.2 Exploring f, f', f'' Relationships

To explore relationships among the graphs of a function and its derivatives:

1. Find functions for f' and f''.
2. Graph all three functions on the same plot.
   - Notice that f increases when f' is above the x-axis ($+$) and decreases when f' is below the x-axis ($-$).
   - Notice that f is concave up when f'' is above the x-axis ($+$) and is concave down when f'' is below the x-axis ($-$).

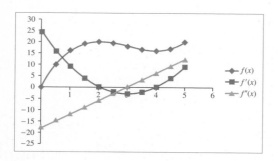

Let $f(x) = x^3 - 9x^2 + 24x$. Graph f, f', and f'' on the interval $[0, 5]$ to explore the relationships among these functions.

	A	B	C	D
1	x	$f(x)$	$f'(x)$	$f''(x)$
2	0	0	24	−18
3	0.5	9.875	15.75	−15
4	1	16	9	−12
5	1.5	19.125	3.75	−9
6	2	20	0	−6
7	2.5	19.375	−2.25	−3
8	3	18	−3	0
9	3.5	16.625	−2.25	−3
10	4	16	0	6
11	4.5	16.875	3.75	9
12	5	20	9	12

Sections 10.3–10.4 Finding Optimal Values

To find the optimal value of a function when the goal is not to produce a graph:

1. Set up a spreadsheet that identifies the variable and the function whose optimal value is sought.
2. Choose *Data* > *Analysis* > *Solver*. Then, in the Dialog Box
   a. Set the *Target Cell* as that of the objective function.
   b. Check *Max* or *Min* according to your goal.
   c. Set the *Changing Cells* to reference the variable.
3. Click on the *Options* box. Make sure "Assume Linear Model" is *not* checked. Then click OK.
4. Click *Solve* in the *Solver* dialog box. You will get a dialog box stating that *Solver* found a solution. Save the solution if desired, then click OK.
5. The cells containing the variable and the function should now contain the optimal values.

Minimize area $A = x^2 + \dfrac{160}{x}$ for $x > 0$.

	A	B
1	**Variable**	
2		
3	x length of base	1
4		
5	**Objective**	
6		
7	Minimize Area	=B3^2+160/B3

	A	B
1	**Variable**	
2		
3	x length of base	4.3089
4		
5	**Objective**	
6		
7	Minimize Area	55.699

The function is minimized for $x = 4.3089$ and the minimum value is $A = 55.699$.

Chapter 13
Section 13.1 Approximating Definite Integrals

Using Rectangles

To find the approximate area between $y = f(x)$ and the x-axis over an interval by using the right-hand endpoints of rectangles with equal base width:

1. Enter "x" and the x- values of the right-hand endpoints of each rectangle in Column B. Fill down can be used if the number of rectangles is large.
2. Enter the formula for the function, using cell addresses, in C2 and fill down column C to get the heights of the rectangles.
3. Enter the width of the rectangles in Column D.
4. Enter the formula for the area of each rectangle, =C2*D2, in E2 and fill down to get the area of each rectangle.
5. Enter "Total" in A10 and the formula =SUM(E2:E9) in E10 to get the approximate area.

To find the approximation for the area under $y = \sqrt{x}$ from $x = 0$ to $x = 4$ using $n = 8$ equal subdivisions (with base width 0.5) and right-hand endpoints:

1. Enter "x" and the eight x- values of the right-hand endpoints (starting with 0.5) in Column B.
2. Enter "y" in C1 and =SQRT(B2) in C2 and fill down column C.
3. Enter "width" in D1 and 0.5 below in Column D.
4. Enter "Area" in E1, =C2*D2 in E2, and fill down to get the area of each rectangle.
5. Enter "Total" in A10 and the formula =SUM(E2:E9) in E10 to get the approximate area, $S_R \approx 5.765$.

	A	B	C	D	E
1	Rectangle	x	y	Width	Area
2	1	0.5	0.707107	0.5	0.353553
3	2	1	1	0.5	0.5
4	3	1.5	1.224745	0.5	0.612372
5	4	2	1.414214	0.5	0.707107
6	5	2.5	1.581139	0.5	0.790569
7	6	3	1.732051	0.5	0.866025
8	7	3.5	1.870829	0.5	0.935414
9	8	4	2	0.5	1
10	Total				5.765042

Chapter 14
Section 14.1 Graphs of Functions of Two Variables

To create a surface plot for a function of two variables:

1. a. Generate appropriate *x*-values beginning in B1 and continuing *across*.
   b. Generate appropriate *y*-values beginning in A2 and continuing *down*.
2. Generate values for the function that correspond to the points (*x*, *y*) from Step 1 as follows:
   In cell B2, enter the function formula with B$1 used to represent *x* and $A2 to represent *y*. (See the online Excel Guide for additional information about the role and use of the $ in this step.) Then use fill down and fill across to complete the table.
3. Select the entire table of values. Click on *Insert > Other Charts > 3-D Surface* option, the first option in the Surface group.
4. To rotate the graph, click on the chart and click on *3-D rotation*. You can click on the various options present in the dialog box.

Let $f(x,y) = 10 - x^2 - y^2$. Plot the graph of this function for both *x* and *y* in the interval $[-2, 2]$.

	A	B	C	D	E	F	G	H	I	J
1		-2	-1.5	-1	-0.5	0	0.5	1	1.5	2
2	-2									
3	-1.5									
4	-1									
5	-0.5									
6	0									
7	0.5									
8	1									
9	1.5									
10	2									

	A	B	C	D	E	F	G	H	I	J
1		-2	-1.5	-1	-0.5	0	0.5	1	1.5	2
2	-2	2	3.75	5	5.75	6	5,75	5	3.75	2
3	-1.5	3.75	5.5	6.75	7.5	7.75	7.5	6.75	5.5	3.75
4	-1	5	6.75	8	8.75	9	8.75	8	6.75	5
5	-0.5	5.75	7.5	8.75	9.5	9.75	9.5	8.75	7.5	5.75
6	0	6	7.75	9	9.75	10	9.75	9	7.75	6
7	0.5	5.75	7.5	8.75	9.5	9.75	9.5	8.75	7.5	5.75
8	1	5	6.75	8	8.75	9	8.75	8	6.75	5
9	1.5	3.75	5.5	6.75	7.5	7.75	7.5	6.75	5.5	3.75
10	2	2	3.75	5	5.75	6	5.75	5	3.75	2

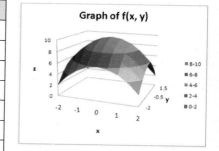

Graph of f(x, y)

Section 14.5 Constrained Optimization and Lagrange Multipliers (Excel 2007)

To solve a constrained optimization problem:

1. Set up the problem in Excel.
2. Choose *Data > Analysis > Solver* and do the following:
   - Choose the objective function as the *Target Cell*.
   - Check *Max* or *Min* depending on the problem.
   - Choose the cells representing the variables for the *By Changing Cells* box.
   - Click on the *Constraints* box and press Add. Then enter the constraint equations.
3. Click on the *Options* box and make sure that "Assume Linear Model" is *not* checked. Then click OK.
4. Click *Solve* in the *Solver* dialog box. Then click OK to solve.

Maximize $P = 600l^{2/3}k^{1/3}$ subject to $40l + 100k = 3000$.

	A	B	C
1	**Variables**		
2			
3	units labor (l)	0	
4	units capital (k)	0	
5			
6			
7	**Objective**		
8			
9	Maximize production	=600*B3^(2/3)*B4^(1/3)	
10			
11	**Constraint**		
12		Amount used	Available
13	Cost	=40*B3+100*B4	3000

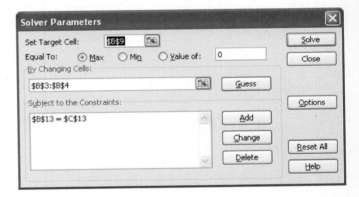

	A	B	C
1	**Variables**		
2			
3	units labor (l)	50.00000002	
4	units capital (k)	10	
5			
6			
7	**Objective**		
8			
9	Maximize product	17544.10644	
10			
11	**Constraint**		
12		Amount used	Available
13	Cost	3000.000001	3000

Section 14.5 Constrained Optimization and Lagrange Multipliers (Excel 2010)

To solve a constrained optimization problem:

1. Set up the problem in Excel.
2. Choose *Data > Analysis > Solver* and do the following:
   - Choose the objective function as the *Target Cell*.
   - Check *Max* or *Min* depending on the problem.
   - Choose the cells representing the variables for the *By Changing Cells* box.
   - Click on the *Constraints* box and press Add. Then enter the constraint equations.
3. Check the box making the variables nonnegative.
4. Select "GRG Nonlinear" as the solving method.
5. Click *Solve* in the *Solver* dialog box. Then click OK to solve.

Maximize $P = 600l^{2/3}k^{1/3}$ subject to $40l + 100k = 3000$.

	A	B	C
1	**Variables**		
2			
3	units labor (l)	0	
4	units capital (k)	0	
5			
6			
7	**Objective**		
8			
9	Maximize production	=600*B3^(2/3)*B4^(1/3)	
10			
11	**Constraint**		
12		Amount used	Available
13	Cost	=40*B3+100*B4	3000

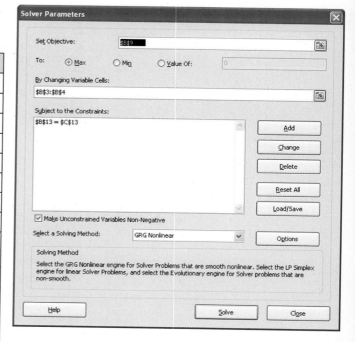

	A	B	C
1	**Variables**		
2			
3	units labor (l)	50.00000002	
4	units capital (k)	10	
5			
6			
7	**Objective**		
8			
9	Maximize product	17544.10644	
10			
11	**Constraint**		
12		Amount used	Available
13	Cost	3000.000001	3000

Areas Under the Standard Normal Curve

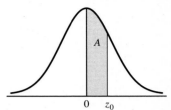

The value of A is the area under the standard normal curve between $z = 0$ and $z = z_0$, for $z_0 \geq 0$. Areas for negative values of z_0 are obtained by symmetry.

z_0	A	z_0	A	z_0	A	z_0	A
0.00	0.0000	0.43	0.1664	0.86	0.3051	1.29	0.4015
0.01	0.0040	0.44	0.1700	0.87	0.3078	1.30	0.4032
0.02	0.0080	0.45	0.1736	0.88	0.3106	1.31	0.4049
0.03	0.0120	0.46	0.1772	0.89	0.3133	1.32	0.4066
0.04	0.0160	0.47	0.1808	0.90	0.3159	1.33	0.4082
0.05	0.0199	0.48	0.1844	0.91	0.3186	1.34	0.4099
0.06	0.0239	0.49	0.1879	0.92	0.3212	1.35	0.4115
0.07	0.0279	0.50	0.1915	0.93	0.3238	1.36	0.4131
0.08	0.0319	0.51	0.1950	0.94	0.3264	1.37	0.4147
0.09	0.0359	0.52	0.1985	0.95	0.3289	1.38	0.4162
0.10	0.0398	0.53	0.2019	0.96	0.3315	1.39	0.4177
0.11	0.0438	0.54	0.2054	0.97	0.3340	1.40	0.4192
0.12	0.0478	0.55	0.2088	0.98	0.3365	1.41	0.4207
0.13	0.0517	0.56	0.2123	0.99	0.3389	1.42	0.4222
0.14	0.0557	0.57	0.2157	1.00	0.3413	1.43	0.4236
0.15	0.0596	0.58	0.2190	1.01	0.3438	1.44	0.4251
0.16	0.0636	0.59	0.2224	1.02	0.3461	1.45	0.4265
0.17	0.0675	0.60	0.2257	1.03	0.3485	1.46	0.4279
0.18	0.0714	0.61	0.2291	1.04	0.3508	1.47	0.4292
0.19	0.0754	0.62	0.2324	1.05	0.3531	1.48	0.4306
0.20	0.0793	0.63	0.2357	1.06	0.3554	1.49	0.4319
0.21	0.0832	0.64	0.2389	1.07	0.3577	1.50	0.4332
0.22	0.0871	0.65	0.2422	1.08	0.3599	1.51	0.4345
0.23	0.0910	0.66	0.2454	1.09	0.3621	1.52	0.4357
0.24	0.0948	0.67	0.2486	1.10	0.3643	1.53	0.4370
0.25	0.0987	0.68	0.2517	1.11	0.3665	1.54	0.4382
0.26	0.1026	0.69	0.2549	1.12	0.3686	1.55	0.4394
0.27	0.1064	0.70	0.2580	1.13	0.3708	1.56	0.4406
0.28	0.1103	0.71	0.2611	1.14	0.3729	1.57	0.4418
0.29	0.1141	0.72	0.2642	1.15	0.3749	1.58	0.4429
0.30	0.1179	0.73	0.2673	1.16	0.3770	1.59	0.4441
0.31	0.1217	0.74	0.2704	1.17	0.3790	1.60	0.4452
0.32	0.1255	0.75	0.2734	1.18	0.3810	1.61	0.4463
0.33	0.1293	0.76	0.2764	1.19	0.3830	1.62	0.4474
0.34	0.1331	0.77	0.2794	1.20	0.3849	1.63	0.4484
0.35	0.1368	0.78	0.2823	1.21	0.3869	1.64	0.4495
0.36	0.1406	0.79	0.2852	1.22	0.3888	1.65	0.4505
0.37	0.1443	0.80	0.2881	1.23	0.3907	1.66	0.4515
0.38	0.1480	0.81	0.2910	1.24	0.3925	1.67	0.4525
0.39	0.1517	0.82	0.2939	1.25	0.3944	1.68	0.4535
0.40	0.1554	0.83	0.2967	1.26	0.3962	1.69	0.4545
0.41	0.1591	0.84	0.2995	1.27	0.3980	1.70	0.4554
0.42	0.1628	0.85	0.3023	1.28	0.3997	1.71	0.4564

(continued)

z_0	A	z_0	A	z_0	A	z_0	A
1.72	0.4573	2.26	0.4881	2.80	0.4974	3.34	0.4996
1.73	0.4582	2.27	0.4884	2.81	0.4975	3.35	0.4996
1.74	0.4591	2.28	0.4887	2.82	0.4976	3.36	0.4996
1.75	0.4599	2.29	0.4890	2.83	0.4977	3.37	0.4996
1.76	0.4608	2.30	0.4893	2.84	0.4977	3.38	0.4996
1.77	0.4616	2.31	0.4896	2.85	0.4978	3.39	0.4997
1.78	0.4625	2.32	0.4898	2.86	0.4979	3.40	0.4997
1.79	0.4633	2.33	0.4901	2.87	0.4979	3.41	0.4997
1.80	0.4641	2.34	0.4904	2.88	0.4980	3.42	0.4997
1.81	0.4649	2.35	0.4906	2.89	0.4981	3.43	0.4997
1.82	0.4656	2.36	0.4909	2.90	0.4981	3.44	0.4997
1.83	0.4664	2.37	0.4911	2.91	0.4982	3.45	0.4997
1.84	0.4671	2.38	0.4913	2.92	0.4982	3.46	0.4997
1.85	0.4678	2.39	0.4916	2.93	0.4983	3.47	0.4997
1.86	0.4686	2.40	0.4918	2.94	0.4984	3.48	0.4997
1.87	0.4693	2.41	0.4920	2.95	0.4984	3.49	0.4998
1.88	0.4699	2.42	0.4922	2.96	0.4985	3.50	0.4998
1.89	0.4706	2.43	0.4925	2.97	0.4985	3.51	0.4998
1.90	0.4713	2.44	0.4927	2.98	0.4986	3.52	0.4998
1.91	0.4719	2.45	0.4929	2.99	0.4986	3.53	0.4998
1.92	0.4726	2.46	0.4931	3.00	0.4987	3.54	0.4998
1.93	0.4732	2.47	0.4932	3.01	0.4987	3.55	0.4998
1.94	0.4738	2.48	0.4934	3.02	0.4987	3.56	0.4998
1.95	0.4744	2.49	0.4936	3.03	0.4988	3.57	0.4998
1.96	0.4750	2.50	0.4938	3.04	0.4988	3.58	0.4998
1.97	0.4756	2.51	0.4940	3.05	0.4989	3.59	0.4998
1.98	0.4761	2.52	0.4941	3.06	0.4989	3.60	0.4998
1.99	0.4767	2.53	0.4943	3.07	0.4989	3.61	0.4998
2.00	0.4772	2.54	0.4945	3.08	0.4990	3.62	0.4999
2.01	0.4778	2.55	0.4946	3.09	0.4990	3.63	0.4999
2.02	0.4783	2.56	0.4948	3.10	0.4990	3.64	0.4999
2.03	0.4788	2.57	0.4949	3.11	0.4991	3.65	0.4999
2.04	0.4793	2.58	0.4951	3.12	0.4991	3.66	0.4999
2.05	0.4798	2.59	0.4952	3.13	0.4991	3.67	0.4999
2.06	0.4803	2.60	0.4953	3.14	0.4992	3.68	0.4999
2.07	0.4808	2.61	0.4955	3.15	0.4992	3.69	0.4999
2.08	0.4812	2.62	0.4956	3.16	0.4992	3.70	0.4999
2.09	0.4817	2.63	0.4957	3.17	0.4992	3.71	0.4999
2.10	0.4821	2.64	0.4959	3.18	0.4993	3.72	0.4999
2.11	0.4826	2.65	0.4960	3.19	0.4993	3.73	0.4999
2.12	0.4830	2.66	0.4961	3.20	0.4993	3.74	0.4999
2.13	0.4834	2.67	0.4962	3.21	0.4993	3.75	0.4999
2.14	0.4838	2.68	0.4963	3.22	0.4994	3.76	0.4999
2.15	0.4842	2.69	0.4964	3.23	0.4994	3.77	0.4999
2.16	0.4846	2.70	0.4965	3.24	0.4994	3.78	0.4999
2.17	0.4850	2.71	0.4966	3.25	0.4994	3.79	0.4999
2.18	0.4854	2.72	0.4967	3.26	0.4994	3.80	0.4999
2.19	0.4857	2.73	0.4968	3.27	0.4995	3.81	0.4999
2.20	0.4861	2.74	0.4969	3.28	0.4995	3.82	0.4999
2.21	0.4864	2.75	0.4970	3.29	0.4995	3.83	0.4999
2.22	0.4868	2.76	0.4971	3.30	0.4995	3.84	0.4999
2.23	0.4871	2.77	0.4972	3.31	0.4995	3.85	0.4999
2.24	0.4875	2.78	0.4973	3.32	0.4995	3.86	0.4999
2.25	0.4878	2.79	0.4974	3.33	0.4996		

Answers

Below are the answers to odd-numbered Section Exercises and all the Chapter Review and Chapter Test problems.

0.1 EXERCISES

1. $\in$ 3. $\notin$ 5. $\{1, 2, 3, 4, 5, 6, 7\}$
7. $\{x : x$ is a natural number greater than 2 and less than 8$\}$
9. $\varnothing, A, B$ 11. no   13. $D \subseteq C$
15. $A \subseteq B$ or $B \subseteq A$ 17. yes   19. no
21. A and B, B and D, C and D
23. $A \cap B = \{4, 6\}$ 25. $A \cap B = \varnothing$
27. $A \cup B = \{1, 2, 3, 4, 5\}$
29. $A \cup B = \{1, 2, 3, 4\} = B$
31. $A' = \{4, 6, 9, 10\}$
33. $A \cap B' = \{1, 2, 5, 7\}$
35. $(A \cup B)' = \{6, 9\}$
37. $A' \cup B' = \{1, 2, 4, 5, 6, 7, 9, 10\}$
39. $\{1, 2, 3, 5, 7, 9\}$ 41. $\{4, 6, 8, 10\}$
43. $A - B = \{1, 7\}$
45. $A - B = \varnothing$ or $\{\ \}$
47. (a) $L = \{00, 01, 04, 05, 06, 07, 10, 11, 12\}$
         $H = \{00, 01, 06, 07, 08, 10, 11, 12\}$
         $C = \{01, 02, 03, 08, 09\}$
   (b)   no
   (c) C' is the set of years when the percent change from low to high was 35% or less.
   (d) $\{00, 02, 03, 04, 05, 06, 07, 09, 10, 11, 12\}$ = the set of years when the high was 11,000 or less or the percent change was 35% or less.
   (e) $\{02, 03, 08, 09\}$ = the set of years when the low was 8000 or less and the percent change exceeded 35%.
49. (a)   130   (b)   840   (c)   520
51. (a)

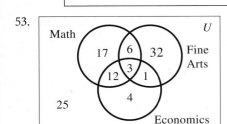

   (b)   40
   (c)   85
   (d)   25

53.

Math, Fine Arts, Economics Venn diagram with values 17, 6, 32, 12, 3, 1, 4, 25

(a)   25
(b)   43
(c)   53

55. (a) and (b)

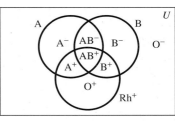

   (c) A^+: 34%; B^+: 9%; O^+: 38%; AB^+: 3%; O^-: 7%; A^-: 6%; B^-: 2%; AB^-: 1%

0.2 EXERCISES

1. (a)   irrational   (b)   rational, integer
   (c)   rational, integer, natural   (d)   meaningless
3. (a)   Commutative   (b)   Distributive
   (c)   Associative   (d)   Additive identity
5. $<$ 7. $<$ 9. $<$ 11. $>$
13. 11   15. 4   17. 2   19. $\frac{-4}{3}$ 21. 3   23. $\frac{17}{11}$
25. entire line
27. (1, 3]; half open
29. (2, 10); open
31. $-3 \le x < 5$
33. $x > 4$
35. $(-3, 4)$
37. $(4, \infty)$
39. $[-1, \infty)$
41. $(-\infty, 0) \cup (7, \infty)$
43. -0.000038585
45. 9122.387471   47. 3240.184509
49. (a) $1088.91   (b) $258.62   (c) $627.20
51. (a)   Eq. (1) = 2.69 billion
         Eq. (2) = 2.68 billion
         Eq. (1) is more accurate
   (b)   Eq. (1) = 3.73 billion
         Eq. (2) = 4.01 billion
53. (a) $82,401 \le I \le 171,850$; $171,851 \le I \le 373,650$; $I > 373,650$
   (b) $T = 4681.25 for $I = $34,000$
         $T = $16,781.25$ for $I = $82,400$
   (c)   [4681.25, 16,781.25]

0.3 EXERCISES

1. 256   3. -64 5. $\frac{1}{9}$ 7. $-\frac{9}{4}$
9. 2.0736   11. 0.1316872428   13. 6^8 15. $\frac{1}{10}$
17. $9^0 = 1$ 19. 3^9 21. $\left(\frac{3}{2}\right)^2 = \frac{9}{4}$

23. $-1/x^3$ 25. x/y^2 27. x^7

29. $x^{-2} = 1/x^2$ 31. x^4 33. y^{12} 35. x^{12}

37. x^2y^2 39. $16/x^{20}$ 41. $x^8/(16y^4)$

43. $-16a^2/b^2$ 45. $2/(xy^2)$ 47. $1/(x^9y^6)$

49. $(a^{18}c^{12})/b^6$

51. (a) $1/(2x^4)$ (b) $1/(16x^4)$ (c) $1/x^4$ (d) 8

53. x^{-1} 55. $8x^3$ 57. $\frac{1}{4}x^{-2}$ 59. $-\frac{1}{8}x^3$

61. $S = \$2114.81; I = \$914.81$

63. $S = \$9607.70; I = \$4607.70$

65. $\$7806.24$

67. (a) 20, 40, 48
    (b) $1905, $7373, $12,669 billion
    (c) $24,922 billion

69. (a) 442, 976, 1072
    (b) In 2020, 1090; 53 more
    (c) Two possibilities might be more environmental protections and the fact that there are only a limited number of species.
    (d) There are only a limited number of species. Also, below some threshold level the ecological balance might be lost, perhaps resulting in an environmental catastrophe (which the equation could not predict). Upper limit = 1095

71. (a) 10   (b) $1385.5 billion
    (c) $2600.8 billion   (d) $4304.3 billion

0.4 EXERCISES

1. (a) $\frac{16}{3} \approx 5.33$ (b) 1.2

3. (a) 8   (b) not real   5. $\frac{9}{4}$

7. (a) 16   (b) 1/16

9. $(6.12)^{4/9} \approx 2.237$

11. $m^{3/2}$ 13. $(m^2n^5)^{1/4}$ 15. $2\sqrt{x}$

17. $\sqrt[6]{x^7}$ 19. $-1/(4\sqrt[4]{x^5})$ 21. $y^{3/4}$

23. $z^{19/4}$ 25. $1/y^{5/2}$ 27. x

29. $1/y^{21/10}$ 31. $x^{1/2}$ 33. $1/x$

35. $8x^2$ 37. $8x^2y^2\sqrt{2y}$ 39. $2x^2y\sqrt[3]{5x^2y^2}$

41. $6x^2y\sqrt{x}$ 43. $42x^3y^2\sqrt{x}$ 45. $2xy^5/3$

47. $2b\sqrt[4]{b}/(3a^2)$ 49. $1/9$ 51. 7

53. $\sqrt{6}/3$ 55. $\sqrt{mx}/x$ 57. $\sqrt[3]{mx^2}/x^2$

59. $-\frac{2}{3}x^{-2/3}$ 61. $3x^{3/2}$ 63. $(3\sqrt{x})/2$

65. $1/(2\sqrt{x})$

67. (a) $10^{8.5} = 10^{17/2} = \sqrt{10^{17}}$
    (b) $10^{9.0} = 1,000,000,000$ (c) $10^{2.1} \approx 125.9$

69. (a) $S = 1000\sqrt{\left(1 + \dfrac{r}{100}\right)^5}$
    (b) $1173.26 (nearest cent)

71. (a) $P = 0.924\sqrt[100]{t^{13}}$
    (b) 2005 to 2010; 0.1074 billion vs. 0.0209 billion. By 2045 and 2050 the population will be much larger than earlier in the 21st century, and there is a limited number of people that any land can support—in terms of both space and food.

73. 74 kg   75. 39,491

77. (a) 10   (b) 259

0.5 EXERCISES

1. (a) 2   (b) -1 (c) 10   (d) one

3. (a) 5   (b) -14 (c) 0   (d) several

5. (a) 5   (b) 0   (c) 2   (d) -5

7. -12 9. -296 11. $\frac{-7}{31}$

13. 87.4654   15. $21pq - 2p^2$ 17. $m^2 - 7n^2 - 3$

19. $3q + 12$ 21. $x^2 - 1$ 23. $35x^5$

25. $3rs$ 27. $2ax^4 + a^2x^3 + a^2bx^2$

29. $6y^2 - y - 12$ 31. $12 - 30x^2 + 12x^4$

33. $16x^2 + 24x + 9$ 35. $0.01 - 16x^2$

37. $36x^2 - 9$ 39. $x^4 - x^2 + \frac{1}{4}$

41. $0.1x^2 - 1.995x - 0.1$

43. $x^3 - 8$ 45. $x^8 + 3x^6 - 10x^4 + 5x^3 + 25x$

47. $3 + m + 2m^2n$ 49. $8x^3y^2/3 + 5/(3y) - 2x^2/(3y)$

51. $x^3 + 3x^2 + 3x + 1$

53. $8x^3 - 36x^2 + 54x - 27$

55. $x^2 - 2x + 5 - 11/(x + 2)$

57. $x^2 + 3x - 1 + (-4x + 2)/(x^2 + 1)$

59. (a) $9x^2 - 21x + 13$ (b) 5

61. $x + 2x^2$ 63. $x - x^{1/2} - 2$ 65. $x - 9$

67. $4x^2 + 4x$ 69. $55x$

71. (a) $49.95 + 0.49x$ (b) $114.63

73. (a) $4000 - x$ (b) $0.10x$
    (c) $0.08(4000 - x)$ (d) $0.10x + 0.08(4000 - x)$

75. $(15 - 2x)(10 - 2x)x$

0.6 EXERCISES

1. $3b(3a - 4a^2 + 6b)$ 3. $2x(2x + 4y^2 + y^3)$

5. $(7x^2 + 2)(x - 2)$ 7. $(6 + y)(x - m)$

9. $(x + 2)(x + 6)$ 11. $(x - 16)(x + 1)$

13. $(7x + 4)(x - 2)$ 15. $(x - 5)^2$

17. $(7a + 12b)(7a - 12b)$

19. (a) $(3x - 1)(3x + 8)$ (b) $(9x + 4)(x + 2)$

21. $x(4x - 1)$ 23. $(x^2 - 5)(x + 4)$

25. $(x - 3)(x + 2)$ 27. $2(x - 7)(x + 3)$

29. $2x(x - 2)^2$ 31. $(2x - 3)(x + 2)$

33. $3(x + 4)(x - 3)$ 35. $2x(x + 2)(x - 2)$

37. $(5x + 2)(2x + 3)$ 39. $(5x - 1)(2x - 9)$

41. $(y^2 + 4x^2)(y + 2x)(y - 2x)$

43. $(x + 2)^2(x - 2)^2$

45. $(2x + 1)(2x - 1)(x + 1)(x - 1)$

47. $x + 1$ 49. $1 + x$ 51. $(x + 1)^3$

53. $(x - 4)^3$ 55. $(x - 4)(x^2 + 4x + 16)$

57. $(3 + 2x)(9 - 6x + 4x^2)$

59. $P(1 + rt)$ 61. $m(c - m)$

63. (a) $p(10,000 - 100p); x = 10,000 - 100p$ (b) 6200

65. (a) $R = x(300 - x)$ (b) $300 - x$

0.7 EXERCISES

1. $2y^3/z$ 3. $\frac{1}{3}$ 5. $(x - 1)/(x - 3)$

7. $20x/y$ 9. $\frac{32}{3}$ 11. $3x + 9$

13. $\dfrac{-(x + 1)(x + 3)}{(x - 1)(x - 3)}$ 15. $15bc^2/2$ 17. $5y/(y - 3)$

19. $\dfrac{-x(x-3)(x+2)}{x+3}$

21. $\dfrac{1}{x+1}$

23. $\dfrac{4a-4}{a(a-2)}$

25. $\dfrac{-x^2+x+1}{x+1}$

27. $\dfrac{16a+15a^2}{12(x+2)}$

29. $\dfrac{79x+9}{30(x-2)}$

31. $\dfrac{9x+4}{(x-2)(x+2)(x+1)}$

33. $(7x-3x^3)/\sqrt{3-x^2}$

35. $\frac{1}{6}$

37. xy

39. $\dfrac{x+1}{x^2}$

41. $\dfrac{1}{\sqrt{a}}=\dfrac{\sqrt{a}}{a}$

43. (a) -12 (b) $\frac{25}{36}$

45. $2b^2-a$

47. $(1-2\sqrt{x}+x)/(1-x)$

49. $1/(\sqrt{x+h}+\sqrt{x})$

51. $(bc+ac+ab)/abc$

53. (a) $\dfrac{0.1x^2+55x+4000}{x}$

   (b) $0.1x^2+55x+4000$

55. $\dfrac{t^2+9t}{(t+3)^2}$

CHAPTER 0 REVIEW EXERCISES

1. yes   2. no   3. no
4. $\{1,2,3,4,9\}$ 5. $\{5,6,7,8,10\}$ 6. $\{1,2,3,4,9\}$
7. yes, $(A'\cup B')'=\{1,3\}=A\cap B$
8. (a) Commutative Property of Addition
   (b) Associative Property of Multiplication
   (c) Distributive Law
9. (a) irrational   (b) rational, integer
   (c) undefined
10. (a) $>$ (b) $<$ (c) $>$
11. 6   12. 142   13. 10
14. 5/4   15. 9   16. -29
17. 13/4   18. -10.62857888
19. (a) $[0,5]$, closed

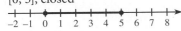

   (b) $[-3,7)$, half-open

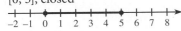

   (c) $(-4,0)$, open

20. (a) $-1<x<16$ (b) $-12\le x\le 8$
    (c) $x<-1$
21. (a) 1   (b) $2^{-2}=1/4$ (c) 4^6 (d) 7
22. (a) $1/x^2$ (b) x^{10} (c) x^9 (d) $1/y^8$
    (e) y^6
23. $-x^2y^2/36$ 24. $9y^8/(4x^4)$ 25. $y^2/(4x^4)$
26. $-x^8z^4/y^4$ 27. $3x/(y^7z)$ 28. $x^5/(2y^3)$
29. (a) 4   (b) 2/7   (c) 1.1
30. (a) $x^{1/2}$ (b) $x^{2/3}$ (c) $x^{-1/4}$

31. (a) $\sqrt[7]{x^3}$ (b) $1/\sqrt{x}=\sqrt{x}/x$ (c) $-x\sqrt{x}$
32. (a) $5y\sqrt{2x}/2$ (b) $\sqrt[3]{x^2y}/x^2$
33. $x^{5/6}$ 34. y 35. $x^{17/4}$
36. $x^{11/3}$ 37. $x^{2/5}$ 38. x^2y^8
39. $2xy^2\sqrt{3xy}$ 40. $25x^3y^4\sqrt{2y}$
41. $6x^2y^4\sqrt[3]{5x^2y^2}$ 42. $8a^2b^4\sqrt{2a}$
43. $2xy$ 44. $4x\sqrt{3xy}/(3y^4)$
45. $-x-2$ 46. $-x^2-x$
47. $4x^3+xy+4y-4$ 48. $24x^5y^5$
49. $3x^2-7x+4$ 50. $3x^2+5x-2$
51. $4x^2-7x-2$ 52. $6x^2-11x-7$
53. $4x^2-12x+9$ 54. $16x^2-9$
55. $2x^4+2x^3-5x^2+x-3$ 56. $8x^3-12x^2+6x-1$
57. x^3-y^3 58. $(2/y)-(3xy/2)-3x^2$
59. $3x^2+2x-3+(-3x+7)/(x^2+1)$
60. $x^3-x^2+2x+7+21/(x-3)$
61. x^2-x 62. $2x-a$
63. $x^3(2x-1)$
64. $2(x^2+1)^2(1+x)(1-x)$
65. $(2x-1)^2$ 66. $(4+3x)(4-3x)$
67. $2x^2(x+2)(x-2)$ 68. $(x-7)(x+3)$
69. $(3x+2)(x-1)$ 70. $(x-3)(x-2)$
71. $(x-12)(x+2)$ 72. $(4x+3)(3x-8)$
73. $(2x+3)^2(2x-3)^2$ 74. $x^{2/3}+1$
75. (a) $\dfrac{x}{(x+2)}$ (b) $\dfrac{2xy(2-3xy)}{2x-3y}$
76. $\dfrac{x^2-4}{x(x+4)}$ 77. $\dfrac{(x+3)}{(x-3)}$
78. $\dfrac{x^2(3x-2)}{(x-1)(x+2)}$ 79. $(6x^2+9x-1)/(6x^2)$
80. $\dfrac{4x-x^2}{4(x-2)}$ 81. $-\dfrac{x^2+2x+2}{x(x-1)^2}$
82. $\dfrac{x(x-4)}{(x-2)(x+1)(x-3)}$ 83. $\dfrac{(x-1)^3}{x^2}$
84. $\dfrac{1-x}{1+x}$ 85. $3(\sqrt{x}+1)$
86. $2/(\sqrt{x}+\sqrt{x-4})$
87. (a)

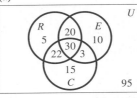

R: recognized
E: exercise
C: community involvement

    (b) 10   (c) 100
88. 52.55%   89. 16
90. (a) \$4115.27   (b) \$66,788.69
91. (a) 16   (b) \$820.40   (c) \$3281.60
92. (a) 1.1 inch, about quarter-sized
    (b) 104 mph
93. (a) $10{,}000\left[\dfrac{(0.0065)(1.0065)^n}{(1.0065)^n-1}\right]$ (b) \$243.19 (for both)
94. (a) $S=k\sqrt[3]{A}$ (b) $\sqrt[3]{2.25}\approx 1.31$

95. $26x - 300 - 0.001x^2$

96. $1,450,000 - 3625x$

97. $(50 + x)(12 - 0.5x)$

98. (a) $\dfrac{12,000p}{100 - p}$

(b) $0. It costs nothing if no effort is made to remove pollution.

(c) $588,000

(d) Undefined. Removing 100% would be impossible, and the cost of getting close would be enormous.

99. $\dfrac{56x^2 + 1200x + 8000}{x}$

CHAPTER 0 TEST

1. (a) {3, 4, 6, 8} (b) {3, 4}; {3, 6}; or {4, 6}
(c) {6} or {8}

2. 21

3. (a) 8 (b) 1 (c) $\frac{1}{2}$ (d) -10
(e) 30 (f) $\frac{5}{6}$ (g) $\frac{2}{3}$ (h) -3

4. (a) $\sqrt[5]{x}$ (b) $1/\sqrt[4]{x^3}$

5. (a) $1/x^5$ (b) x^{21}/y^6

6. (a) $\dfrac{\sqrt{5x}}{5}$ (b) $2a^2b^2\sqrt{6ab}$ (c) $\dfrac{1 - 2\sqrt{x} + x}{1 - x}$

7. (a) 5 (b) -8 (c) -5

8. $(-2, 3]$

9. (a) $2x^2(4x - 1)$ (b) $(x - 4)(x - 6)$
(c) $(3x - 2)(2x - 3)$ (d) $2x^3(1 + 4x)(1 - 4x)$

10. (c); -2

11. $2x + 1 + \dfrac{2x - 6}{x^2 - 1}$

12. (a) $19y - 45$ (b) $-6t^6 + 9t^9$
(c) $4x^3 - 21x^2 + 13x - 2$ (d) $-18x^2 + 15x - 2$
(e) $4m^2 - 28m + 49$ (f) $\dfrac{x^4}{3x + 9}$
(g) $\dfrac{x^7}{81}$ (h) $\dfrac{6 - x}{x - 8}$
(i) $\dfrac{x^2 - 4x - 3}{x(x - 3)(x + 1)}$

13. $\dfrac{y - x}{y + xy^2}$

14. (a)
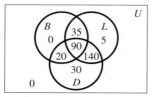

(b) 0
(c) 175

15. $4875.44 (nearest cent)

1.1 EXERCISES

1. $x = -9/4$ **3.** $x = 0$ **5.** $x = -32$
7. $x = -29/2$ **9.** $x = -5$ **11.** $x = 17/13$
13. $x = -1/3$ **15.** $x = 3$ **17.** $x = 5/4$

19. no solution **21.** $x \approx -0.279$

23. $x \approx -1147.362$ **25.** $y = \frac{3}{4}x - \frac{15}{4}$

27. $y = -6x + \frac{22}{3}$ **29.** $t = \dfrac{S - P}{Pr}$

31. $x < 2$ **33.** $x < -4$ **35.** $x \leq -1$
37. $x < -3$

39. $x < -6$

41. $x < 2$

43. 145 months

45. $3356.50 **47.** 440 packs, or 220,000 CDs

49. $29,600

51. (a) 82.3% (b) $t \approx 25.6$, during 2016

53. 96

55. $90,000 at 9%; $30,000 at 13%

57. $2160/month; 8% increase

59. $x > 80$

61. $695 + 5.75x \leq 900$; 35 or fewer

63. (a) $t = 38$ (b) $t \approx 47.6$ (c) in 2028

65. (a) $0.479 \leq h \leq 1$; $h = 1$ means 100% humidity
(b) $0 \leq h \leq 0.237$

1.2 EXERCISES

1. (a) To each x-value there corresponds exactly one y-value.
(b) domain: $\{-7, -1, 0, 3, 4.2, 9, 11, 14, 18, 22\}$
range: $\{0, 1, 5, 9, 11, 22, 35, 60\}$
(c) $f(0) = 1, f(11) = 35$

3. yes; to each x-value there corresponds exactly one y-value; domain = $\{1, 2, 3, 8, 9\}$, range = $\{-4, 5, 16\}$

5. The vertical-line test shows the graph represents a function of x.

7. The vertical line test shows the graph is not a function of x.

9. yes **11.** no

13. (a) -10 (b) 6 (c) -34 (d) 2.8
15. (a) -3 (b) 1 (c) 13 (d) 6
17. (a) -251 (b) -128 (c) 22 (d) -4.25
19. (a) $63/8$ (b) 6 (c) -6
21. (a) no, $f(2 + 1) = f(3) = 13$ but $f(2) + f(1) = 10$
(b) $1 + x + h + x^2 + 2xh + h^2$
(c) no, $f(x) + f(h) = 2 + x + h + x^2 + h^2$
(d) no, $f(x) + h = 1 + x + x^2 + h$
(e) $1 + 2x + h$
23. (a) $-2x^2 - 4xh - 2h^2 + x + h$
(b) $-4x - 2h + 1$
25. (a) 10 (b) 6
27. (a) $(1, -3)$, yes (b) $(3, -3)$, yes
(c) $b = a^2 - 4a$ (d) $x = 0, x = 4$, yes
29. domain: all reals; range: reals $y \geq 4$
31. domain: reals $x \geq -4$; range: reals $y \geq 0$
33. $x \geq 1, x \neq 2$ **35.** $-7 \leq x \leq 7$
37. (a) $3x + x^3$ (b) $3x - x^3$ (c) $3x^4$ (d) $\dfrac{3}{x^2}$

39. (a) $\sqrt{2x} + x^2$ (b) $\sqrt{2x} - x^2$

    (c) $x^2\sqrt{2x}$ (d) $\dfrac{\sqrt{2x}}{x^2}$

41. (a) $-8x^3$ (b) $1 - 2(x-1)^3$
    (c) $[(x-1)^3 - 1]^3$ (d) $(x-1)^6$

43. (a) $2\sqrt{x^4 + 5}$ (b) $16x^2 + 5$
    (c) $2\sqrt{2}\sqrt{x}$ (d) $4x$

45. (a) $f(20) = 103{,}000$ means that if $103,000
    is borrowed, it can be repaid in 20 years
    (of $800-per-month payments).
    (b) no; $f(5+5) = f(10) = 69{,}000$, but
    $f(5) + f(5) = 40{,}000 + 40{,}000 = 80{,}000$
    (c) 15 years; $f(15) = 89{,}000$

47. (a) $866; $1080
    (b) $1160; starting benefits at age 68 provides $1160
    per month.
    (c) $250; starting benefits at age 66 gives $250 more
    per month than starting at age 62.

49. (a) $W(100) \approx 155$ million; $O(140) \approx 120$ million
    (b) 166.3; in 2020 there are expected to be 166.3 mil-
    lion White, non-Hispanics in the civilian non-
    institutional labor force (CN-ILF).
    (c) 42.6; in 1990 there were 42.6 million non-Whites
    or Hispanics in the CN-ILF.
    (d) 79.5; in 2020 there are expected to be 79.5 million
    more White non-Hispanics in the CN-ILF than
    others.
    (e) 312.4; in 2050 the total size of the CN-ILF is
    expected to be 312.4 million.
    (f) $(W-O)(100)$ is greater; the graphs are further
    apart at $t = 100$ than at $t = 140$.

51. (a) Yes
    (b) All reals for F
    (c) Domain: $32 < F < 212$
    Range: $0 < C < 100$
    (d) $C = \left(\dfrac{40}{9}\right)^{\circ}$

53. (a) $C(10) = \$4210$
    (b) $C(100) = \$32{,}200$
    (c) The total cost of producing 100 items is $32,200.

55. (a) $0 \le p < 100$
    (b) $5972.73; to remove 45% of the particulate
    pollution would cost $5972.73.
    (c) $65,700; to remove 90% of the particulate
    pollution would cost $65,700.
    (d) $722,700; to remove 99% of the particulate
    pollution would cost $722,700.
    (e) $1,817,700; to remove 99.6% of the particulate
    pollution would cost $1,817,700.

57. (a) $(P \circ q)(t) = 180(1000 + 10t)$
    $-\dfrac{(1000 + 10t)^2}{100} - 200$
    (b) $x = 1150, P = \$193{,}575$

59. (a) yes; the output of g (customers) is the input for f.
    (b) no; the output of f is revenue, and this is not the
    input for g.

    (c) $f \circ g$: input (independent variable) is advertising
    dollars.
    output (dependent variable) is revenue dollars.
    $f \circ g$ shows how advertising dollars result in rev-
    enue dollars.

61. $L = 2x + 3200/x$

63. $R = (30 + x)(100 - 2x)$

1.3 EXERCISES

1. x-intercept 4
    y-intercept 3

3. x-intercept 12
    y-intercept -7.5

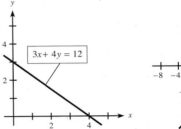

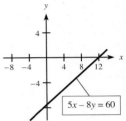

5. $m = 4$ **7.** $m = -1/2$ **9.** $m = 0$ **11.** 0
13. 0   **15.** (a) negative   (b) undefined
17. $m = 7/3, b = -1/4$ **19.** $m = 0, b = 3$

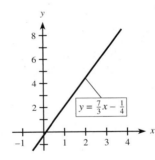

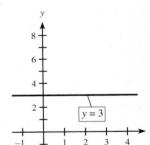

21. undefined slope,
    no y-intercept

23. $m = -2/3, b = 2$

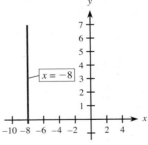

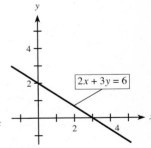

25.

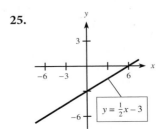

27.

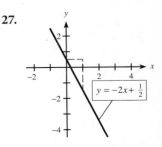

29.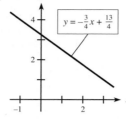

31.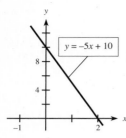

33.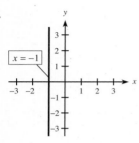

35. $y = 2x - 4$ **37.** $-x + 13y = 32$ **39.** $y = -3x - 12$
41. perpendicular **43.** neither; same line
45. $y = -\frac{3}{5}x - \frac{41}{5}$ **47.** $y = -\frac{6}{5}x + \frac{23}{5}$
49. (a)

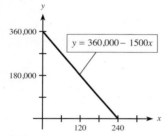

(b) 240 months
(c) After 60 months, the value of the building is $270,000.
51. (a) $m = 1.36; b = 55.98$
(b) The percent of the U.S. population with Internet service is changing at the rate of 1.36 percentage points per year.
(c)

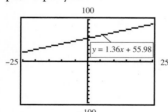

53. (a) $m = -0.065; b = 31.39$
(b) The F-intercept represents the percent of the world's land that was forest in 1990.
(c) -0.065 percentage points per year. This means that after 1990, the world forest area as a percent of land area changes by -0.065 percentage points per year.

55. (a) $m = 0.78$
(b) This means that the average annual earnings of females increases $0.78 for each $1 increase in the average annual earnings of males.
(c) $45,484
57. $y = 0.0838x + 16.37$
59. (a) $y = 1.296x - 2465$
(b) The U.S. civilian workforce changes at the rate of 1.296 million workers per years.
61. (a) $y = 5.183x - 10{,}349.10$
(b) The CPI is changing at the rate of about $5.18/year.
63. $p = 85{,}000 - 1700x$ **65.** $R = 3.2t - 0.2$
67. $y = 0.48x - 71$

1.4 EXERCISES

1.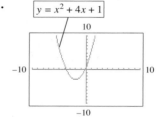

3.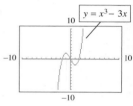

5.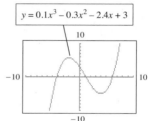

7.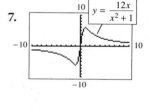

9.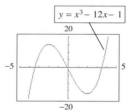

11. $y = (3x + 7)/(x^2 + 4)$
13. (a) $y = 0.01x^3 + 0.3x^2 - 72x + 150$

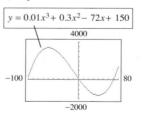

(b) standard window

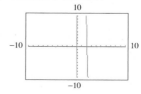

15. (a) $y = \dfrac{x + 15}{x^2 + 400}$

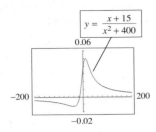

(b) standard window

17. (a) x-intercept 30, y-intercept -0.03

(b)

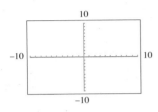

19.

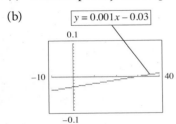

21.

23.

25.

Not linear

27.

Not linear

29. $f(-2) = -18; f\left(\tfrac{3}{4}\right) = 0.734375$

31.

33.

35. $x = 3.5$

37. either $x = 5$ or $x = -2$

39. (a) $-1.1098, 8.1098$ (b) $-1.1098, 8.1098$

41. (a)

(b) When average annual earnings for males is $50,000, average annual earnings for females is $37,684.   (c) $47,434

43. (a)

(b) $E \ge 0$ when $0 \le p \le 100$

45. (a)

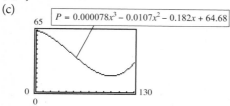

(b) decreasing; as more people become aware of the product, there are fewer to learn about it, so the rate will decrease.

47. (a) x-min $= 0$, x-max $= 130$
(b) y-max $= 65$
(c)

$P = 0.000078x^3 - 0.0107x^2 - 0.182x + 64.68$

(d) The percent decreases from 57.4% in 1920 to 17.5% in 2000, and then it increases to 31.6% in 2030.

49. (a)

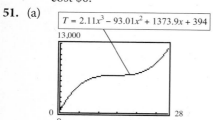

$C = \dfrac{285{,}000}{p} - 2850$

(b) Near $p = 0$, cost grows without bound.
(c) The coordinates of the point mean that obtaining stream water with 1% of the current pollution levels would cost $282,150.
(d) The p-intercept means that stream water with 100% of the current pollution levels would cost $0.

51. (a)

$T = 2.11x^3 - 93.01x^2 + 1373.9x + 394$

13,000

0 ⌐   28
  0

(b) increasing; the per capita tax burden is increasing

1.5 EXERCISES

1. one solution; $(-1, -2)$
3. infinitely many solutions (each point on the line)
5. $x = 2, y = 2$ **7.** no solution
9. $x = 10/3, y = 2$ **11.** $x = 14/11, y = 6/11$
13. $x = 4, y = -1$ **15.** $x = 3, y = -2$
17. $x = 2, y = 1$ **19.** $x = -52/7, y = -128/7$
21. $x = 1, y = 1$ **23.** dependent
25. $x = 4, y = 2$ **27.** $x = -1, y = 1$
29. $x = -17, y = 7, z = 5$
31. $x = 4, y = 12, z = -1$
33. $x = 44, y = -9, z = -1/2$

35. (a) $C = 10, F = 50$
(b) The tourist formula overestimates the F temperature—it adds 2°F to the estimate for each 1°C, but actual change is 1.8°C.
37. (a) $x + y = 1800$ (b) $20x$ (c) $30y$
(d) $20x + 30y = 42{,}000$
(e) 1200 tickets at $20; 600 tickets at $30
39. $68,000 at 18%; $77,600 at 10%
41. 10%: $27,000; 12%: $24,000
43. 4 oz of A, $6\frac{2}{3}$ oz of B
45. 4550 of species A, 1500 of species B
47. 7 cc of 20%; 3 cc of 5%
49. 10,000 at $40; 6000 at $60
51. 80 cc   **53.** 5 oz of A, 1 oz of B, 5 oz of C
55. 200 type A, 100 type B, 200 type C

1.6 EXERCISES

1. (a) $P(x) = 34x - 6800$ (b) $95,200
3. (a) $P(x) = 37x - 1850$
(b) $-$740$, loss of $740   (c) 50
5. (a) $m = 5, b = 250$
(b) $\overline{MC} = 5$ means each additional unit produced costs $5.
(c) slope $=$ marginal cost; C-intercept $=$ fixed costs
(d) 5, 5
7. (a) 27
(b) $\overline{MR} = 27$ means each additional unit sold brings in $27.
(c) 27, 27
9. (a) $P(x) = 22x - 250$ (b) 22   (c) $\overline{MP} = 22$
(d) Each unit sold adds $22 to profits at all levels of production, so produce and sell as much as possible.
11. $P = 58x - 8500, \overline{MP} = 58$
13. (a) $C(x) = 35x + 6600$ (b) $R(x) = 60x$
(c) $P(x) = 25x - 6600$
(d) $C(200) = 13{,}600$ dollars is the cost of producing 200 helmets.
$R(200) = 12{,}000$ dollars is the revenue from sale of 200 helmets.
$P(200) = -1600$ dollars; will lose $1600 from production and sale of 200 helmets.
(e) $C(300) = 17{,}100$ dollars is the cost of producing 300 helmets.
$R(300) = 18{,}000$ dollars is the revenue from sale of 300 helmets.
$P(300) = 900$ dollars; will profit $900 from production and sale of 300 helmets.
(f) $\overline{MP} = 25$ dollars per unit; each additional unit produced and sold increases profit by $25.
15. (a) Revenue passes through the origin.
(b) $2000   (c) 400 units
(d) $\overline{MC} = 2.5$; $\overline{MR} = 7.5$
17. 33
19. (a) $R(x) = 12x$; $C(x) = 8x + 1600$
(b) 400 units

21. (a) $P(x) = 4x - 1600$
(b) $x = 400$ units to break even
23. (a) $C(x) = 4.5x + 1045$
(b) $R(x) = 10x$
(c) $P(x) = 5.5x - 1045$
(d) 190 surge protectors
25. (a) $R(x) = 54.90x$ (b) $C(x) = 14.90x + 20{,}200$
(c) 505
27. (a) R starts at origin and is the steeper line.
FC is a horizontal line.
VC starts at origin and is not as steep as R.
(See figure.)

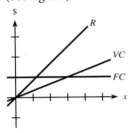

(b) C starts where FC meets the \$-axis and is parallel to VC. Where C meets R is the break-even point (BE). P starts on the \$-axis at the negative of FC and crosses the x-axis at BE. (See figure.)

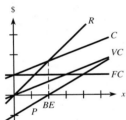

29. Demand decreases.
31. (a) 600   (b) 300   (c) shortage
33. 16 demanded, 25 supplied; surplus
35. $p = -2q/3 + 1060$
37. $p = 0.001q + 5$
39. (a) demand falls; supply rises   (b) (30, \$25)
41. (a) $q = 20$ (b) $q = 40$
(c) shortage, 20 units short
43. shortage   **45.** $q = 20, p = \$18$
47. $q = 10, p = \$180$ **49.** $q = 100, p = \$325$
51. (a) \$15   (b) $q = 100, p = \$100$
(c) $q = 50, p = \$110$ (d) yes
53. $q = 8; p = \$188$
55. $q = 500; p = \$40$
57. $q = 1200; p = \$15$

CHAPTER 1 REVIEW EXERCISES

1. $x = \frac{31}{3}$ **2.** $x = -13$ **3.** $x = -\frac{29}{8}$
4. $x = -\frac{1}{9}$ **5.** $x = 8$
6. no solution   **7.** $y = -\frac{2}{3}x - \frac{4}{3}$
8. $x \le 3$

9. $x \ge -20/3$

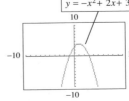

10. $x \ge -15/13$

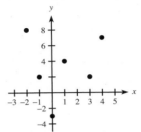

11. yes   **12.** no   **13.** yes
14. domain: reals $x \le 9$; range: reals $y \ge 0$
15. (a) 2   (b) 37   (c) 29/4
16. (a) 0   (b) 9/4   (c) 10.01
17. $9 - 2x - h$ **18.** yes   **19.** no
20. 4   **21.** $x = 0, x = 4$
22. (a) domain: $\{-2, -1, 0, 1, 3, 4\}$
range: $\{-3, 2, 4, 7, 8\}$
(b) 7   (c) $x = -1, x = 3$
(d)

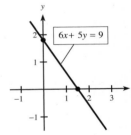

(e) no; for $y = 2$, there are two different x-values, -1 and 3.
23. (a) $x^2 + 3x + 5$ (b) $(3x + 5)/x^2$
(c) $3x^2 + 5$ (d) $9x + 20$
24. x: 2, y: 5   **25.** x: 3/2, y: 9/5

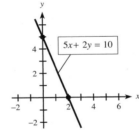
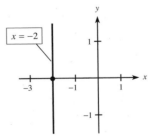

26. x: -2, y: none

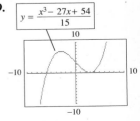

27. $m = 1$ **28.** undefined   **29.** $m = -\frac{2}{5}, b = 2$
30. $m = -\frac{4}{3}, b = 2$ **31.** $y = 4x + 2$ **32.** $y = -\frac{1}{2}x + 3$
33. $y = \frac{2}{5}x + \frac{9}{5}$ **34.** $y = -\frac{11}{8}x + \frac{17}{4}$ **35.** $x = -1$
36. $y = 4x + 2$ **37.** $y = \frac{4}{3}x + \frac{10}{3}$
38.

39.

40. (a)

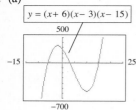

(b)

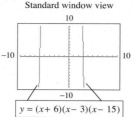

Standard window view

(c) The graph in (a) shows a complete graph. The graph in (b) shows a piece that rises toward the high point and a piece between the high and low points.

41. (a)

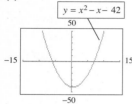

(b)

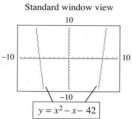

Standard window view

(c) The graph in (a) shows a complete graph. The one in (b) shows pieces that fall toward the minimum point and rise from it.

42. reals $x \geq -3$ with $x \neq 0$

43. $0.2857 \approx 2/7$

44. $x = 2, y = 1$

45. $x = 10, y = -1$

46. $x = 3, y = -2$

47. no solution

48. $x = 10, y = -71$

49. $x = 1, y = -1, z = 2$

50. $x = 11, y = 10, z = 9$

51. (a) 2020

(b) 21.5 years, to age 86.5

(c) $x = 80.5$; in 2031

52. 95%

53. 40,000 miles. He probably would drive more than 40,000 miles in 7 years, so he should buy diesel.

54. (a) yes   (b) no   (c) 4

55. (a) $565.44

(b) The monthly payment on a $70,000 loan is $494.75.

56. (a) $(P \circ q)(t) = 330(100 + 10t)$
$- 0.05(100 + 10t)^2 - 5000$

(b) $x = 250, P = \$74,375$

57. $(W \circ L)(t) = 0.03[65 - 0.1(t - 25)^2]^3$

58. (a)

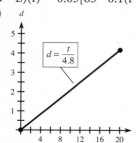

(b) When the time between seeing lightning and hearing thunder is 9.6 seconds, the storm is 2 miles away.

59.

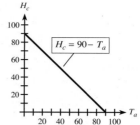

60. (a) $P = 58x - 8500$

(b) The profit increases by $58 for each unit sold.

61. (a) yes

(b) $m = 427, b = 4541$

(c) In 2000, average annual health care costs were $4541 per consumer.

(d) Average annual health care costs are changing at the rate of $427 per year.

62. $F = \frac{9}{5}C + 32$ or $C = \frac{5}{9}(F - 32)$

63. (a)

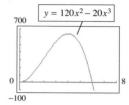

(b) $0 \leq x \leq 6$

64. (a) $v^2 = 1960(h + 10)$

$\frac{v^2}{1960} = h + 10$

$h = \frac{1}{1960}v^2 - 10$

(b) 12.5 cm

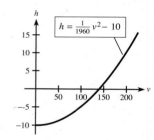

65. $100,000 at 9.5%; $50,000 at 11%

66. 2.8 liters of 20%; 1.2 liters of 70%

67. (a) 12 supplied; 14 demanded   (b) shortfall

(c) increase

68.

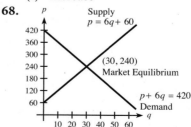

69. (a) 38.80   (b) 61.30   (c) 22.50   (d) 200

70. (a) $C(x) = 22x + 1500$ (b) $R(x) = 52x$

(c) $P(x) = 30x - 1500$ (d) $\overline{MC} = 22$

(e) $\overline{MR} = 52$ (f) $\overline{MP} = 30$ (g) $x = 50$

71. (a) S: $p = 4q - 400$
D: $p = -4q + 1520$

(b) $q = 240; p = \$560$

72. $q = 700, p = \$80$

CHAPTER 1 TEST

1. $x = -6$ **2.** $x = 18/7$ **3.** $x = -3/7$
4. $x = -38$ **5.** $5 - 4x - 2h$
6. $x \geq -9$

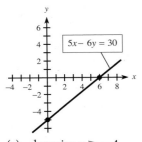

7. x: 6; y: -5 **8.** x: 3; y: $21/5$

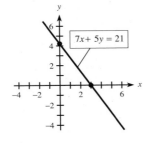

9. (a) domain: $x \geq -4$
        range: $f(x) \geq 0$
    (b) $2\sqrt{7}$ (c) 6
10. $y = -\frac{3}{2}x + \frac{1}{2}$ **11.** $m = -\frac{5}{4}; b = \frac{15}{4}$
12. (a) $x = -3$ (b) $y = -4x - 13$
13. (a) no; a vertical line intersects the curve twice.
    (b) yes; there is exactly one y-value for each x-value.
    (c) no; one value of x gives two y-values.
14. (a)

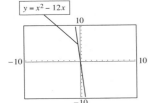

    (b)

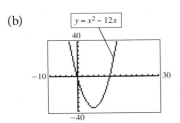

15. $x = -2$, $y = 2$
16. (a) $5x^3 + 2x^2 - 3x$ (b) $x + 2$
    (c) $5x^2 + 7x + 2$
17. (a)

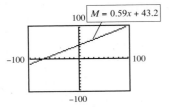

    (b) The model predicts that there will be 90.4 million
        men in the U.S. workforce in 2030.
    (c) 102.2 million
18. (a) 30   (b) $P = 8x - 1200$ (c) 150
    (d) $\overline{MP} = 8$; the sale of each additional unit gives
        $8 more profit.

19. (a) $R = 50x$
    (b) 19,000; it costs $19,000 to produce 100 units.
    (c) 450
20. $q = 200$, $p = \$2500$
21. (a) 720,000; original value of the building
    (b) -2000; building depreciates $2000 per month.
22. 400
23. 12,000 at 9%, 8000 at 6%

2.1 EXERCISES

1. $x^2 + 2x - 1 = 0$ **3.** $y^2 + 3y - 2 = 0$
5. $-2, 6$ **7.** $\frac{3}{2}, -\frac{3}{2}$ **9.** $0, 1$ **11.** $\frac{1}{2}$
13. (a) $2 + 2\sqrt{2}, 2 - 2\sqrt{2}$ (b) $4.83, -0.83$
15. no real solutions   **17.** $\sqrt{7}, -\sqrt{7}$ **19.** $4, -4$
21. $1, -9$ **23.** $-7, 3$ **25.** $8, -4$ **27.** $-\frac{7}{4}, \frac{3}{4}$
29. $-6, 2$ **31.** $(1 + \sqrt{31})/5, (1 - \sqrt{31})/5$
33. $-2, 5$ **35.** $-300, 100$ **37.** $0.69, -0.06$
39. $8, 1$ **41.** $1/2$ **43.** $-9, -10$
45. $x = 20$ or $x = 70$
47. (a) $x = 10$ or $x = 345\frac{5}{9}$
    (b) Yes; for any $x > 10$ and $x < 345\frac{5}{9}$
49. 6 seconds
51. (a) ± 50
    (b) $s = 50$; there is no particulate pollution in the air
        above the plant.
53. 97.0 mph   **55.** $t \approx 16.2$; in 2017   **57.** $80
59. $x \approx 16.8$; in 2022
61. (a) 18   (b) ≈ 31
    (c) Speed triples, but K changes only by a factor of
        1.72.

2.2 EXERCISES

1. (a) $(-1, -\frac{1}{2})$ (b) minimum
    (c) -1 (d) $-\frac{1}{2}$
3. (a) $(1, 9)$ (b) maximum   (c) 1   (d) 9
5. (a) $(3, 9)$ (b) maximum   (c) 3   (d) 9
7. maximum, $(2, 1)$; zeros $(0, 0)$, $(4, 0)$; y-intercept $= 0$

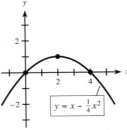

9. minimum, $(-2, 0)$; zero $(-2, 0)$; y-intercept $= 4$

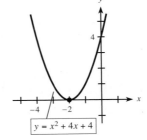

11. minimum, $(-1, -3\frac{1}{2})$; zeros $(-1 + \sqrt{7}, 0)$, $(-1 - \sqrt{7}, 0)$; y-intercept $= -3$

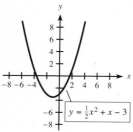

13. (a)   3 units to the right and 1 unit up

(b)

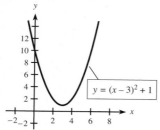

15. $y = (x + 2)^2 - 2$

(a)   2 units to the left and 2 units down

(b)

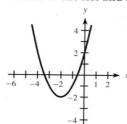

17. vertex $(1, -8)$; zeros $(-3, 0), (5, 0)$

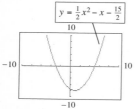

19. vertex $(-6, 3)$; no real zeros

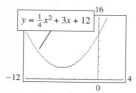

21. -5

23. vertex $(10, 64)$; zeros $(90, 0), (-70, 0)$

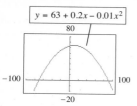

25. vertex $(0, -0.01)$; zeros $(10, 0), (-10, 0)$

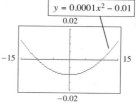

27. (a) $(1, -24)$ (b) $x \approx -0.732, 2.732$

29. (a) $x = 2$ (b) $x - 2$
(c) $(x - 2)(3x - 2)$ (d) $x = 2, \frac{2}{3}$

31. (a)   80 units   (b)   \$540

33. 400 trees

35. dosage $= 500$ mg   **37.** intensity $= 1.5$ lumens

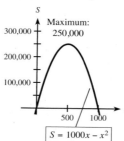
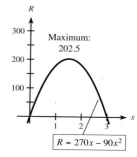

39. equation (a) $(384.62, 202.31)$ (b) $(54, 46)$
Projectile (a) goes higher.

41. (a)   From b to c. The average rate is the same as the slope of the segment. Segment b to c is steeper.
(b) $d > b$ to make segment a to d be steeper (have greater slope).

43. (a)

Rent	Number Rented	Revenue
600	50	\$30,000
620	49	\$30,380
640	48	\$30,720

(b)   increase
(c) $R = (50 - x)(600 + 20x)$
(d)   \$800

45. (a)   quadratic
(b) $a < 0$ because the graph opens downward.
(c)   The vertex occurs after 2004 (when $x > 0$). Hence $-b/2a > 0$ and $a < 0$ means $b > 0$. The value $c = f(0)$, or the y-value in 2004. Hence $c > 0$.

47. 2010–2015: \$399/year
2015–2020: \$605/year

49.

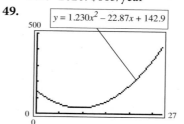

2.3 EXERCISES

1. $x = 40$ units, $x = 50$ units
3. $x = 50$ units, $x = 300$ units
5. $x = 15$ units; reject $x = 100$
7. \$41,173.61
9. \$87.50
11. $x = 55$, $P(55) = \$2025$
13. (a)

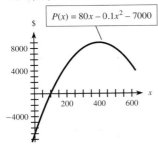

$P(x) = 80x - 0.1x^2 - 7000$

(b) $(400, 9000)$; maximum point   (c) positive
(d) negative   (e) closer to 0 as a gets closer to 400
15. (a) $P(x) = -x^2 + 350x - 15{,}000$; maximum profit is
    \$15,625
    (b) no   (c) x-values agree
17. (a) $x = 28$ units, $x = 1000$ units
    (b) \$651,041.67
    (c) $P(x) = -x^2 + 1028x - 28{,}000$; maximum profit is
    \$236,196
    (d) \$941.60
19. (a) $t \approx 5.1$, in 2012; $R \approx \$60.79$ billion
    (b) The data show a smaller revenue,
        $R = \$60.27$ billion, in 2011.
    (c)

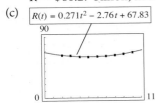

$R(t) = 0.271t^2 - 2.76t + 67.83$

    (d) The model fits the data quite well.
21. (a) $P(t) = -0.019t^2 + 0.284t - 0.546$
    (b) 2011
    (c)

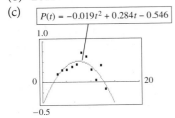

$P(t) = -0.019t^2 + 0.284t - 0.546$

    (d) The model projects decreasing profits, and except
        for 2015, the data support this.
    (e) Management would be interested in increasing
        revenues or reducing costs (or both) to improve
        profits.

23. (a)

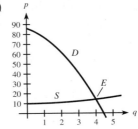

    (b) See E on graph.   (c) $q = 4$, $p = \$14$
25. $q = 10$, $p = \$196$
27. $q = 216\frac{2}{3}$, $p = \$27.08$
29. $p = \$40$, $q = 30$
31. $q = 90$, $p = \$50$
33. $q = 70$, $p = \$62$

2.4 EXERCISES

1. b   3. f   5. j   7. k   9. a
11. c   13. (a) cubic   (b) quartic
15. e   17. b   19. d   21. g
23.

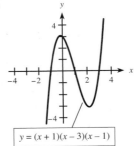

$y = (x + 1)(x - 3)(x - 1)$

25.

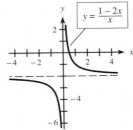

$y = \dfrac{1 - 2x}{x}$

27.

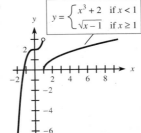

$y = \begin{cases} x^3 + 2 & \text{if } x < 1 \\ \sqrt{x-1} & \text{if } x \geq 1 \end{cases}$

29. (a) $8/3$ (b) 9.9   (c) -999.999 (d) no
31. (a) 64   (b) 1   (c) 1000   (d) 0.027
33. (a) 2   (b) 4   (c) 0   (d) 2

35. (a)

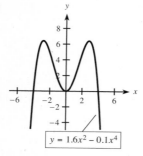

$y = 1.6x^2 - 0.1x^4$

(b) polynomial   (c) no asymptotes
(d) turning points at $x = 0$ and approximately $x = -2.8$ and $x = 2.8$

37. (a)

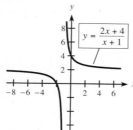

$y = \dfrac{2x + 4}{x + 1}$

(b) rational
(c) vertical: $x = -1$, horizontal: $y = 2$
(d) no turning points

39. (a)

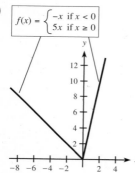

$f(x) = \begin{cases} -x & \text{if } x < 0 \\ 5x & \text{if } x \geq 0 \end{cases}$

(b) piecewise defined
(c) no asymptotes
(d) turning point at $x = 0$

41. (a) 6800; 11,200   (b) $0 < x < 27$
43. (a) upward   (b)

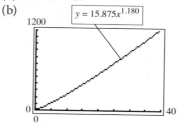

$y = 15.875x^{1.180}$

(c) $x \approx 37.7$; in 2018
45. (a) yes; $p = 100$
(b) $p \neq 100$
(c) $0 \leq p < 100$
(d) It increases without bound.
47. (a) $A(2) = 96$; $A(30) = 600$
(b) $0 < x < 50$
49. (a)

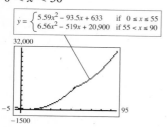

$y = \begin{cases} 5.59x^2 - 93.5x + 633 & \text{if } 0 \leq x \leq 55 \\ 6.56x^2 - 519x + 20{,}900 & \text{if } 55 < x \leq 90 \end{cases}$

(b) \$9933 billion (\$9.933 trillion)
(c) \$18,875 billion (\$18.875 trillion)

51. (a) $P = \begin{cases} 49 & \text{if } 0 < x \leq 1 \\ 70 & \text{if } 1 < x \leq 2 \\ 91 & \text{if } 2 < x \leq 3 \\ 112 & \text{if } 3 < x \leq 4 \end{cases}$

(b) 70; it costs 70 cents to mail a 1.2 oz letter.
(c) Domain $0 < x \leq 4$; Range $\{49, 70, 91, 112\}$
(d) 70 cents and 91 cents

53. (a) $p = \dfrac{200}{2 + 0.1x}$
(b) yes, when $p = \$100$

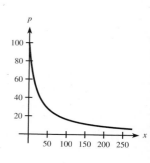

55. $C(x) = 30(x - 1) + \dfrac{3000}{x + 10}$

(a)

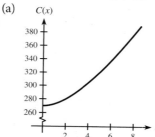

(b) Any turning point would indicate the minimum or the maximum cost. In this case, $x = 0$ gives a minimum.
(c) The y-intercept is the fixed cost of production.

2.5 EXERCISES

1. linear   **3.** quadratic   **5.** quartic
7. quadratic or power
9. $y = 2x - 3$ **11.** $y = 2x^2 - 1.5x - 4$

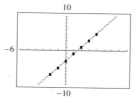

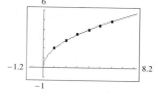

13. $y = x^3 - x^2 - 3x - 4$ **15.** $y = 2x^{0.5}$

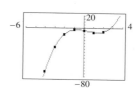

17. (a)
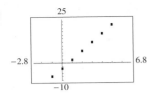
(b) linear
(c) $y = 5x - 3$

19. (a)
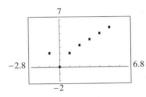
(b) quadratic
(c) $y = 0.09595x^2 + 0.4656x + 1.4758$

21. (a)
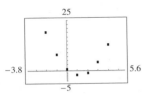
(b) quadratic
(c) $y = 2x^2 - 5x + 1$

23. (a)
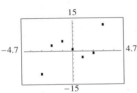
(b) cubic
(c) $y = x^3 - 5x + 1$

25. (a) $y = 154.0x + 35,860$ (b) $40,018,000$ (c) 2070

27. (a) A linear function is best; $y = 327.6x + 9591$
(b) $15,160$ billion
(c) $m = 327.6$ means the U.S. disposable income is increasing at the rate of about \$327.6 billion per year.

29. (a) $y = 0.0052x^2 - 0.62x + 15$ (b) $x \approx 59.6$
(c) No, it is unreasonable to feel warmer for winds greater than 60 mph.

31. (a)
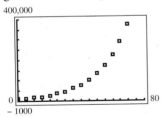
(b) $y = 106x^2 - 2870x + 28,500$
(c) $y = 1.70x^3 - 72.9x^2 + 1970x + 5270$
(d)
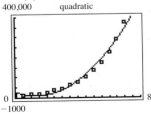

Cubic model fits better

33. (a) $y = 0.0157x + 2.01$
(b) $y = -0.00105x^2 + 0.0367x + 1.94$
(c)
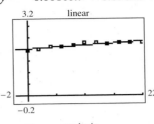
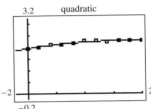
(d) The quadratic model is a slightly better fit.

35. (a) A cubic models looks best because of the two bends.
(b) $y = 0.864x^3 - 128x^2 + 6610x - 62,600$
(c)
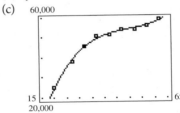
(d) 57

37. (a) $y = 0.0514x^{2.73}$
(b)
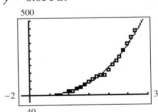
(c) \$546 billion

CHAPTER 2 REVIEW EXERCISES

1. $x = 0, x = -\frac{5}{3}$ **2.** $x = 0, x = \frac{4}{3}$
3. $x = -2, x = -3$
4. $x = (-5 + \sqrt{47})/2, x = (-5 - \sqrt{47})/2$
5. no real solutions   **6.** $x = \sqrt{3}/2, x = -\sqrt{3}/2$
7. $\frac{5}{7}, -\frac{4}{5}$ **8.** $(-1 + \sqrt{2})/4, (-1 - \sqrt{2})/4$
9. $7/2, 100$ **10.** $13/5, 90$
11. no real solutions   **12.** $z = -9, z = 3$
13. $x = 8, x = -2$ **14.** $x = 3, x = -1$
15. $x = (-a \pm \sqrt{a^2 - 4b})/2$
16. $r = (2a \pm \sqrt{4a^2 + x^3c})/x$
17. $1.64, -7051.64$ **18.** $0.41, -2.38$

19. vertex $(-2, -2)$;
zeros $(0, 0)$, $(-4, 0)$

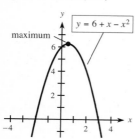

20. vertex $(0, 4)$;
zeros $(4, 0)$, $(-4, 0)$

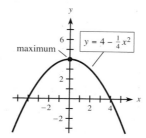

21. vertex $\left(\frac{1}{2}, \frac{25}{4}\right)$;
zeros $(-2, 0)$, $(3, 0)$

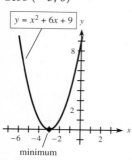

22. vertex $(2, 1)$;
no real zeros

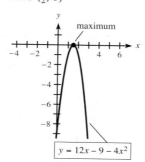

23. vertex $(-3, 0)$;
zero $(-3, 0)$

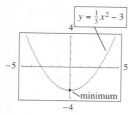

24. vertex $\left(\frac{3}{2}, 0\right)$;
zero $\left(\frac{3}{2}, 0\right)$

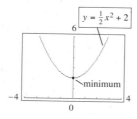

25. vertex $(0, -3)$;
zeros $(-3, 0)$, $(3, 0)$

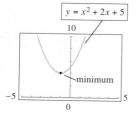

26. vertex $(0, 2)$;
no real zeros

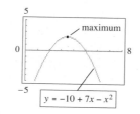

27. vertex $(-1, 4)$;
no real zeros

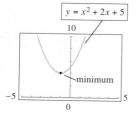

28. vertex $\left(\frac{7}{2}, \frac{9}{4}\right)$;
zeros $(2, 0)$, $(5, 0)$

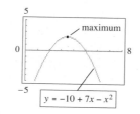

29. vertex $(100, 1000)$;
zeros $(0, 0)$, $(200, 0)$

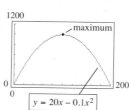

30. vertex $(75, -6.25)$;
zeros $(50, 0)$, $(100, 0)$

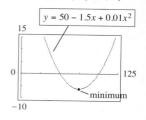

31. 20   **32.** 30

33. (a) $\left(1, -4\frac{1}{2}\right)$ (b) $x = -2, x = 4$ (c) B

34. (a) $(0, 49)$ (b) $x = -7, x = 7$ (c) D

35. (a) $(7, 25)$ approximately, actual is $\left(7, 24\frac{1}{2}\right)$
(b) $x = 0, x = 14$ (c) A

36. (a) $(-1, 9)$ (b) $x = -4, x = 2$ (c) C

37. (a)

(b)

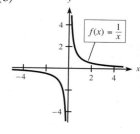

(c)

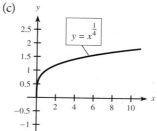

38. (a) 0   (b) 10,000   (c) -25 (d) 0.1

39. (a) -2 (b) 0   (c) 1   (d) 4

40.

$$y = \begin{cases} x & \text{if } x \le 1 \\ 3x - 2 & \text{if } x > 1 \end{cases}$$

41. (a)

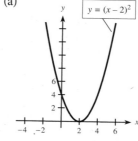

(b)

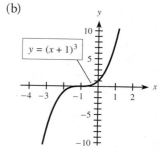

42. Turns: $(1, -5), (-3, 27)$

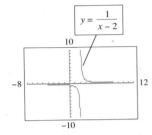

43. Turns: $(1.7, -10.4)$, $(-1.7, 10.4)$

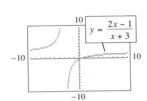

44. VA: $x = 2$; HA: $y = 0$

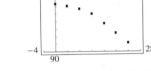

45. VA: $x = -3$; HA: $y = 2$

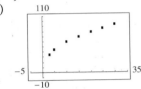

46. (a)

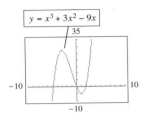

(b) $y = -2.1786x + 159.8571$
(c) $y = -0.0818x^2 - 0.2143x + 153.3095$

47. (a)

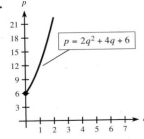

(b) $y = 2.1413x + 34.3913$
(c) $y = 22.2766x^{0.4259}$

48. (a) $t = -1.65, t = 3.65$ (b) Just $t = 3.65$
(c) at 3.65 seconds

49. $x = 20, x = 800$

50. (a) $t \approx 7.69$, in 2018; $E \approx 12.3$ million
(b) $t \approx 20.2$, in 2031

51. (a) $x = 200$
(b) $A = 30{,}000$ square feet

52.

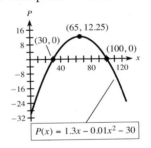

53.

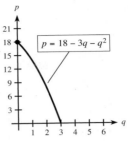

54. (a)

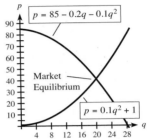

(b) $p = 41, q = 20$

55. $p = 400, q = 10$ **56.** $p = 10, q = 20$
57. $x = 46 + 2\sqrt{89} \approx 64.9, x = 46 - 2\sqrt{89} \approx 27.1$
58. $x = 15, x = 60$
59. max revenue $= \$2500$; max profit $= \$506.25$
60. max profit $= 12.25$; break-even at $x = 100, x = 30$

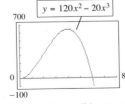

61. $x = 50, P(50) = 640$
62. (a) $C = 15{,}000 + 140x + 0.04x^2$;
$R = 300x - 0.06x^2$
(b) $100, 1500$ (c) 2500
(d) $P = 160x - 15{,}000 - 0.1x^2$; max at 800
(e) at 2500: $P = -240{,}000$; at 800: $P = 49{,}000$

63. (a) power   (b) 21.8%
(c) 24.4; in 2025 about 24.4% of U.S. adults are expected to have diabetes.

64. (a) (b) $0 \le x \le 6$

65. (a) rational   (b) $0 \le p < 100$
(c) 0; it costs $\$0$ to remove no pollution.
(d) $\$475{,}200$

66. (a) $x = 12; C(12) = \$30.68$
(b) $x = 825; C(825) = \$1734.70$

67. (a)   linear, quadratic, cubic, power
(b) and (c)

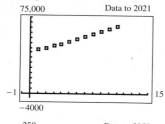

$y = 23.779x^{0.525}$

(d)   55 mph   (e)   9.9 seconds

68. (a)

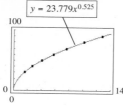

Data to 2021

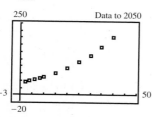

Data to 2050

(b)   Quadratic: $a(x) = 47.70x^2 + 1802x + 40{,}870$;
$A(x) = 0.07294x^2 + 0.9815x + 44.45$

(c)   2020 Data: \$63,676; $a(10) \approx \$63{,}664$–closer;
$A(10) \approx \$61.564$ (\$61,564)
2050 Data: 202.5 (\$202,500); $a(40) \approx \$189{,}292$;
$A(40) \approx 200.413$ (\$200,413–closer)

(d) $a = 150{,}000$ when $x \approx 32.5$, in 2043;
$A = 150$ thousand when $x \approx 31.9$, in 2042

69. (a) $y = O(x) = 0.743x + 6.97$
(b) $y = S(x) = 0.264x - 2.57$

(c) $F(x) = \dfrac{0.264x - 2.57}{0.743x + 6.97}$. This is called a rational

function and measures the fraction of obese
adults who are severely obese.

(d)   Horizontal asymptote: $y \approx 0.355$ means that if
this model remains valid far into the future, then
the long-term projection is that about 0.355, or
35.5%, of obese adults will be severely obese.

70. (a)   Quadratic: $W(x) = -0.00903x^2 + 1.28x + 124$
$O(x) = 0.00645x^2 + 1.02x + 20.0$

(b) $x \approx 91.1$, in 2162

CHAPTER 2 TEST

1. (a)

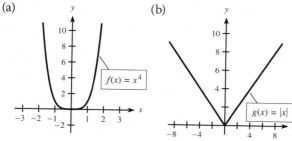

$f(x) = x^4$

(b)

$g(x) = |x|$

(c)

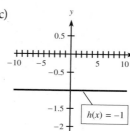

$h(x) = -1$

(d)

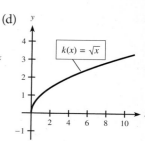

$k(x) = \sqrt{x}$

2.   b; a

3.

4. (a)

$y = (x + 1)^2 - 1$

(b)

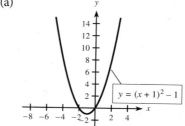

$y = (x - 2)^3 + 1$

5.   b; the function is cubic, $f(1) < 0$

6. (a) -10 (b) $-16\frac{1}{2}$ (c) -7

7.

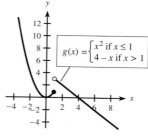

$g(x) = \begin{cases} x^2 \text{ if } x \le 1 \\ 4 - x \text{ if } x > 1 \end{cases}$

8.   vertex $(-2, 25)$;
zeros $-7, 3$

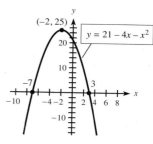

$(-2, 25)$

$y = 21 - 4x - x^2$

9. $x = 2, x = 1/3$

10. $x = \dfrac{-3 + 3\sqrt{3}}{2}, x = \dfrac{-3 - 3\sqrt{3}}{2}$

11. $x = 2/3$

12. c; $g(x)$ has a vertical asymptote at $x = -2$, as does graph c.

13. HA: $y = 0$; VA: $x = 5$

14. 42

15. (a) quartic   (b) cubic

16. (a)

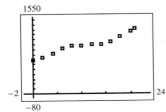

model: $y = -0.3577x + 19.9227$
(b) $f(x) = 5.6$
(c) at $x = 55.7$

17. $q = 300$, $p = \$80$

18. (a) $P(x) = -x^2 + 250x - 15{,}000$
(b) 125 units, \$625   (c) 100 units, 150 units

19. (a) $f(15) = -19.5$ means that when the air temperature is $0°F$ and the wind speed is 15 mph, the air temperature feels like $-19.5°F$.
(b) $-31.4°F$

20. (a)

model: 1550 ... −2 ... 24 ... −80

(b) Linear: $y = 26.8x + 695$;
Cubic: $y = 0.175x^3 - 5.27x^2 + 65.7x + 654$
(c) Linear: \$1258; Cubic: \$1326. The cubic model is quite accurate, but both models are fairly close.
(d) The linear model increases steadily, but the cubic model rises rapidly for years past 2021.

3.1 EXERCISES

1. 3   **3.** A, F, Z **5.** $\begin{bmatrix} -1 & -2 & -3 \\ 1 & 0 & -1 \\ -2 & 3 & 4 \end{bmatrix}$

7. A, C, D, F, G, Z

9. 1   **11.** $\begin{bmatrix} 1 & 3 & 4 \\ 0 & 2 & 0 \\ -2 & 1 & 3 \end{bmatrix}$ **13.** $\begin{bmatrix} 0 & 0 & 0 \\ 0 & 0 & 0 \\ 0 & 0 & 0 \end{bmatrix}$

15. $\begin{bmatrix} 9 & 5 \\ 4 & 7 \end{bmatrix}$ **17.** $\begin{bmatrix} 0 & -2 & -5 \\ 4 & 2 & 0 \\ 2 & 3 & 7 \end{bmatrix}$ **19.** $\begin{bmatrix} 2 & 3 & 2 \\ 3 & 4 & 1 \\ 2 & 1 & 6 \end{bmatrix}$

21. impossible   **23.** $\begin{bmatrix} 3 & 3 & 9 & 0 \\ 12 & 6 & 3 & 3 \\ 9 & 6 & 0 & 3 \end{bmatrix}$

25. $\begin{bmatrix} 28 & 16 \\ 10 & 18 \end{bmatrix}$ **27.** impossible

29. $x = 3, y = 2, z = 3, w = 4$

31. $x = 4, y = 1, z = 3, w = 3$

33. $x = 2, y = 2, z = -3$

35. (a) $A = \begin{bmatrix} 70 & 78 & 14 & 15 & 82 \\ 14 & 13 & 20 & 9 & 65 \end{bmatrix}$

$B = \begin{bmatrix} 256 & 208 & 69 & 8 & 11 \\ 16 & 15 & 17 & 1 & 1 \end{bmatrix}$

(b) $A + B = \begin{bmatrix} 326 & 286 & 83 & 23 & 93 \\ 30 & 28 & 37 & 10 & 66 \end{bmatrix}$

(c) $\begin{bmatrix} 186 & 130 & 55 & -7 & -71 \\ 2 & 2 & -3 & -8 & -64 \end{bmatrix}$
more species in the United States

37. (a) $\begin{bmatrix} 11{,}041.7 & 8978.4 & 6461 \\ 8739.8 & 9159.6 & 6877.3 \\ 9798.1 & 9086.7 & 6448.4 \\ 9696.6 & 8926.7 & 6109.5 \end{bmatrix}$

(b) air pollution

39. (a) $\begin{bmatrix} 825 & 580 & 1560 \\ 810 & 650 & 350 \end{bmatrix}$ (b) $\begin{bmatrix} -75 & 20 & -140 \\ 10 & -50 & 50 \end{bmatrix}$

41. (a) $A = \begin{bmatrix} 74.7 & 79.9 \\ 75.7 & 80.6 \\ 76.5 & 81.3 \\ 77.1 & 81.8 \\ 77.7 & 82.4 \end{bmatrix}$ $B = \begin{bmatrix} 67.8 & 74.7 \\ 69.7 & 76.5 \\ 70.2 & 77.2 \\ 71.4 & 78.2 \\ 72.6 & 79.2 \end{bmatrix}$

(b) $A - B = \begin{bmatrix} 6.9 & 5.2 \\ 6 & 4.1 \\ 6.3 & 4.1 \\ 5.7 & 3.6 \\ 5.1 & 3.2 \end{bmatrix}$ (c) 2000

43. All answers are in quadrillion BTUs.

(a) $E - M = \begin{bmatrix} 0.41 & -0.18 & -0.33 \\ -1.49 & 0.09 & 1.56 \\ -13.29 & -12.05 & -12.56 \end{bmatrix}$
This represents the U.S. balance of trade for various energy types for selected years.

(b) $\frac{1}{12}C \approx \begin{bmatrix} 3.09 & 3.13 & 3.07 \\ 2.16 & 2.23 & 2.27 \\ 2.90 & 3.06 & 3.18 \end{bmatrix}$
This represents the average monthly U.S. consumption of various energy types for selected years.

(c) $C + E - M = \begin{bmatrix} 37.45 & 37.36 & 36.54 \\ 24.37 & 26.86 & 28.84 \\ 21.53 & 24.68 & 25.63 \end{bmatrix}$
This represents the total U.S production of various energy types for selected years.

45. (a) $\begin{bmatrix} 46.20 & 84.00 & 210.00 & 10.50 \\ 42.00 & 84.00 & 42.00 & 0.00 \\ 58.80 & 147.00 & 94.50 & 0.00 \\ 31.50 & 147.00 & 42.00 & 21.00 \\ 42.00 & 0.00 & 210.00 & 10.50 \end{bmatrix}$

(b) $\begin{bmatrix} 48.40 & 88.00 & 220.00 & 11.00 \\ 44.00 & 88.00 & 44.00 & 0.00 \\ 61.60 & 154.00 & 99.00 & 0.00 \\ 33.00 & 154.00 & 44.00 & 22.00 \\ 44.00 & 0.00 & 220.00 & 11.00 \end{bmatrix}$

47. (a) $A = \begin{bmatrix} 0 & 1 & 1 & 0 \\ 1 & 0 & 1 & 1 \\ 0 & 0 & 0 & 1 \\ 0 & 1 & 1 & 0 \end{bmatrix}$

(b) $B = \begin{bmatrix} 0 & 1 & 1 & 1 \\ 1 & 0 & 1 & 1 \\ 0 & 1 & 0 & 1 \\ 1 & 1 & 1 & 0 \end{bmatrix}$　　(c) person 2

49. (a) $\begin{bmatrix} 80 & 75 \\ 58 & 106 \end{bmatrix}$　(b) $\begin{bmatrix} 176 & 127 \\ 139 & 143 \end{bmatrix}$

(c) $\begin{bmatrix} 10 & 4 \\ 7 & 2 \end{bmatrix}$　(d) $\begin{bmatrix} -10 & 19 \\ -7 & 20 \end{bmatrix}$ shortage, taken from inventory.

51. (a) 3, 4, 5, 6　(b) 1

53. Worker 1: 0.9625　Worker 2: 0.9375

Worker 3: 0.9125　Worker 4: 0.8875

Worker 5: 0.85　Worker 6: 0.875

Worker 7: 0.90　Worker 8: 0.925

Worker 9: 0.95

Worker 5 is least efficient; performs best at center 5

3.2 EXERCISES

1. (a) $[32]$　(b) $[11 \quad 17]$　**3.** $\begin{bmatrix} 29 & 25 \\ 10 & 12 \end{bmatrix}$

5. $\begin{bmatrix} 14 & 2 & 16 \\ 28 & 5 & 12 \end{bmatrix}$

7. $\begin{bmatrix} 7 & 5 & 3 & 2 \\ 14 & 9 & 11 & 3 \\ 13 & 10 & 12 & 3 \end{bmatrix}$　**9.** impossible

11. $\begin{bmatrix} 13 & 9 & 3 & 4 \\ 9 & 7 & 16 & 1 \end{bmatrix}$　**13.** $\begin{bmatrix} 9 & 7 & 16 \\ 5 & 17 & 20 \end{bmatrix}$

15. $\begin{bmatrix} 9 & 0 & 8 \\ 13 & 4 & 11 \\ 16 & 0 & 17 \end{bmatrix}$　**17.** $\begin{bmatrix} 161 & 126 \\ 42 & 35 \end{bmatrix}$　**19.** no

21. no　**23.** $\begin{bmatrix} -55 & 88 & 0 \\ -42 & 67 & 0 \\ 28 & -44 & 1 \end{bmatrix}$　**25.** $\begin{bmatrix} 0 & 0 & 0 \\ 0 & 0 & 0 \\ 0 & 0 & 0 \end{bmatrix}$

27. $\begin{bmatrix} 0 & 0 & 0 \\ 0 & 0 & 0 \\ 0 & 0 & 0 \end{bmatrix}$　**29.** A　**31.** Z

33. no (see Problem 25)

35. (a) $AB = \begin{bmatrix} 1 & 0 \\ 0 & 1 \end{bmatrix}$, $BA = \begin{bmatrix} 1 & 0 \\ 0 & 1 \end{bmatrix}$

(b) $ad - bc \neq 0$

37. $\begin{bmatrix} 2 - 2 + 2 \\ 6 - 4 - 4 \\ 4 + 0 - 2 \end{bmatrix} = \begin{bmatrix} 2 \\ -2 \\ 2 \end{bmatrix}$; solution

39. $\begin{bmatrix} 1 + 2 + 2 \\ 4 + 0 + 1 \\ 2 + 2 + 1 \end{bmatrix} = \begin{bmatrix} 5 \\ 5 \\ 5 \end{bmatrix}$; solution

41. $\begin{bmatrix} 1 & 0 & 0 & 0 & 0 \\ 0 & 1 & 0 & 0 & 0 \\ 0 & 0 & 1 & 0 & 0 \\ 0 & 0 & 0 & 1 & 0 \\ 0 & 0 & 0 & 0 & 1 \end{bmatrix}$　(Some entries may appear as decimal approximations of 0.)

43. $\begin{bmatrix} 31,680 & 36,960 \\ 42,500 & 47,600 \end{bmatrix}$

The entries represent the dealer's cost for each car.

45. (a) $A = \begin{bmatrix} 86.86 & 91.25 & 95.37 \\ 27.57 & 29.82 & 32.05 \\ 6.36 & 6.45 & 6.60 \end{bmatrix}$ and

$B = \begin{bmatrix} 91.1 & 0 & 0 \\ 0 & 86.0 & 0 \\ 0 & 0 & 82.5 \end{bmatrix}$

(b) $AB \approx \begin{bmatrix} 7913 & 7848 & 7868 \\ 2512 & 2565 & 2644 \\ 579.4 & 554.7 & 544.5 \end{bmatrix}$

(c) The 1–1 entry is the trillions of BTUs used in single-family households in 2015. The 2–3 entry is the trillions of BTUs predicted to be used in multi-family households in 2025.

(d) Using AB as stored in a calculator,
$[1 \quad 1 \quad 1] AB \approx [11,004.0 \quad 10,966.7 \quad 11,056.7]$
Left to right, each entry gives the trillions of BTUs of delivered energy consumed by all households in 2015, 2020, and 2025.

47. (a) $[0.55 \quad 0.45]$ After 5 years, M has 55% and S has 45% of the population.

(b) 10 years: $(PD)D = PD^2$; 15 years: PD^3

(c) 60% in M and 40% in S. Population proportions are stable.

49. 124, 149, 275, 334, 268, 327, 205, 249, 343, 417, 124, 149, 250, 304, 261, 316, 255, 310

51. (a)

$B = \begin{bmatrix} \frac{3}{4} & \frac{2}{5} & \frac{1}{4} \\ \frac{1}{4} & \frac{3}{5} & \frac{3}{4} \end{bmatrix}$; $D = \begin{bmatrix} 22 & 30 \\ 12 & 20 \\ 8 & 11 \end{bmatrix}$; $BD = \begin{bmatrix} 23.3 & 33.25 \\ 18.7 & 27.75 \end{bmatrix}$

Houston's need for black crude is 23,300 gal and for gold crude is 18,700 gal. Gulfport needs 33,250 gal of black and 27,750 gal of gold.

(b) $PBD = [135.945 \quad 197.5325]$; Houston's cost = $135,945; Gulfport's cost = $197,532.50

53. (a) $B =$
$$\begin{bmatrix} 0.7 & 8.5 & 10.2 & 1.1 & 5.6 & 3.6 \\ 0.5 & 0.2 & 6.1 & 1.3 & 0.2 & 1.0 \\ 2.2 & 0.4 & 8.8 & 1.2 & 1.2 & 4.8 \\ 251.8 & 63.4 & 81.6 & 35.2 & 54.3 & 144.2 \\ 30.0 & 1.0 & 1.0 & 1.0 & 1.0 & 1.0 \\ 788.9 & 0 & 0 & 0 & 0 & 0 \end{bmatrix}$$

(b) $A =$
$$\begin{bmatrix} 1.11 & 0 & 0 & 0 & 0 & 0 \\ 0 & 0.95 & 0 & 0 & 0 & 0 \\ 0 & 0 & 1.11 & 0 & 0 & 0 \\ 0 & 0 & 0 & 1.11 & 0 & 0 \\ 0 & 0 & 0 & 0 & 0.95 & 0 \\ 0 & 0 & 0 & 0 & 0 & 0.95 \end{bmatrix}$$

3.3 EXERCISES

1. $\begin{bmatrix} 1 & -2 & -1 & -7 \\ 0 & 7 & 5 & 21 \\ 4 & 2 & 2 & 1 \end{bmatrix}$

3. $\begin{bmatrix} 1 & -3 & 4 & 2 \\ 2 & 0 & 2 & 1 \\ 1 & 2 & 1 & 1 \end{bmatrix}$ **5.** $x = 2, y = 1/2, z = -5$

7. $x = -5, y = 2, z = 1$
9. $x = 4, y = 1, z = -2$ **11.** $x = 15, y = -13, z = 2$
13. $x = 15, y = 0, z = 2$
15. $x = 1, y = 3, z = 1, w = 0$
17. no solution
19. (a) $x = (11 + 2z)/3, y = (-1 - z)/3$,
    $z = $ any real number
   (b) many possibilities, including $x = 11/3, y = -\frac{1}{3}$,
    $z = 0$ and $x = 13/3, y = -2/3, z = 1$
21. If a row of the matrix has all 0's in the coefficient
    matrix and a nonzero number in the augment, there is
    no solution.
23. $x = 0, y = -z, z = $ any real number
25. no solution
27. $x = 1 - z, y = \frac{1}{2}z, z = $ any real number
29. $x = 1, y = -1, z = 1$
31. $x = 2z - 2, y = 1 + z, z = $ any real number
33. $x = \frac{7}{2} - z, y = -\frac{1}{2}, z = $ any real number
35. $x = \frac{26}{5} - \frac{7}{5}z, y = \frac{4}{5} + \frac{2}{5}z, z = $ any real number
37. $x_1 = 20, x_2 = 60, x_3 = 40$
39. $x_1 = 1, x_2 = 0, x_3 = 1, x_4 = 0$
41. $x = 7/5, y = -3/5, z = w, w = $ any real number
43. no solution
45. $x_1 = 1 - 2x_4 - 3x_5, x_2 = 4 + 5x_4 + 7x_5$,
    $x_3 = -3 - 3x_4 - 5x_5, x_4 = $ any real number,
    $x_5 = $ any real number
47. $x = (b_2c_1 - b_1c_2)/(a_1b_2 - a_2b_1)$
49. beef: 2 cups; sirloin: 8 cups
51. (a) $50,000 at 12%, $85,000 at 10%, $100,000 at 8%
   (b) $6000 at 12%, $8500 at 10%, $8000 at 8%
53. AP = 1100, DT = 440, CA = 660
55. AF: 2 oz, FP: 2 oz, NMG: 1 oz
57. 2 of portfolio I, 2 of portfolio II

59. $\frac{3}{8}$ pound of red meat, 6 slices of bread, 4 glasses of milk
61. type I = 3(type IV), type II = 1000 − 2(type IV),
    type III = 500 − type IV, type IV = any integer
    satisfying $0 \le$ type IV ≤ 500
63. bacteria III = any amount satisfying
    $1800 \le$ bacteria III ≤ 2300
    bacteria I = 6900 − 3 (bacteria III)
    bacteria II = $\frac{1}{2}$(bacteria III) − 900
65. (a) $C = 2800 + 0.6R$
      $U = 7000 - R$
      $R = $ any integer satisfying $0 \le R \le 7000$
   (b) $R = 1000: C = 3400$
          $U = 6000$
      $R = 2000: C = 4000$
          $U = 5000$
   (c) Min $C = 2800$ when $R = 0$ and $U = 7000$
   (d) Max $C = 7000$ when $R = 7000$ and $U = 0$
67. There are three possibilities:
   (1) 4 of I and 2 of II
   (2) 5 of I, 1 of II, and 1 of III
   (3) 6 of I and 2 of III

3.4 EXERCISES

1. $\begin{bmatrix} 1 & 0 & 0 \\ 0 & 1 & 0 \\ 0 & 0 & 1 \end{bmatrix}$ **3.** Yes   **5.** $\begin{bmatrix} 2 & -7 \\ -1 & 4 \end{bmatrix}$

7. no inverse   **9.** $\begin{bmatrix} -\frac{1}{10} & \frac{7}{10} \\ \frac{1}{5} & -\frac{2}{5} \end{bmatrix}$

11. $\begin{bmatrix} \frac{1}{3} & 0 & 0 \\ 0 & \frac{1}{3} & -\frac{2}{3} \\ 0 & 0 & 1 \end{bmatrix}$ **13.** $\begin{bmatrix} -1 & 1 & 0 \\ 1 & 0 & 0 \\ -1 & 0 & 1 \end{bmatrix}$

15. $\begin{bmatrix} \frac{1}{3} & -\frac{1}{3} & \frac{1}{3} \\ -\frac{2}{3} & -\frac{1}{3} & \frac{7}{3} \\ \frac{1}{3} & \frac{2}{3} & -\frac{5}{3} \end{bmatrix}$

17. no inverse   **19.** no inverse

21. $\begin{bmatrix} 1 & 1 & 0 & 0 & -1 \\ -3 & 0 & -3 & 1 & 4 \\ 1 & -2 & 0 & 0 & 1 \\ -3 & 1 & -3 & 1 & 3 \\ -8 & 5 & -8 & 2 & 7 \end{bmatrix}$ **23.** $\begin{bmatrix} 13 \\ 5 \end{bmatrix}$ **25.** $\begin{bmatrix} 9 \\ 6 \\ 3 \end{bmatrix}$

27. $\begin{bmatrix} x \\ y \\ z \end{bmatrix} = \begin{bmatrix} 1 \\ 1 \\ 2 \end{bmatrix}$ **29.** $x = 2, y = 1$

31. $x = 1, y = 2$ **33.** $x = 1, y = 1, z = 1$
35. $x = 1, y = 3, z = 2$
37. $x_1 = 5.6, x_2 = 5.4, x_3 = 3.25, x_4 = 6.1, x_5 = 0.4$
39. (a) -2 (b) inverse exists
41. (a) 0 (b) no inverse
43. (a) -5 (b) inverse exists
45. (a) -19 (b) inverse exists
47. Hang on   **49.** Answers in back
51. $x_0 = 2400, y_0 = 1200$

53. (a) A = 5.5 mg and B = 8.8 mg for patient I
   (b) A = 10 mg and B = 16 mg for patient II
55. $68,000 at 18%, $77,600 at 10%
57. (a) 2 Deluxe, 8 Premium, 32 Ultimate
   (b) 22 Deluxe, 8 Premium, 22 Ultimate
   [New] = [Old] + 8[Col. 1 of A^{-1}]
59. $200,000 at 6%, $300,000 at 8%, $500,000 at 10%
61. (a) $\begin{bmatrix} 0 & 1 & 0 \\ 0 & 0 & 1 \\ 1 & 1 & 1 \end{bmatrix}$ (b) 108

63. (a) $M = \begin{bmatrix} 0 & 1 & 0 \\ 0 & 0 & 1 \\ 1 & 1 & 1 \end{bmatrix}$ (b) 30

3.5 EXERCISES

1. (a) 15   (b) 4   **3.** 8   **5.** 40
7. most: raw materials; least: fuels
9. raw materials, manufacturing, service
11. farm products = 200; machinery = 40
13. utilities = 200; manufacturing = 400
15. (a) agricultural products = 244; oil products = 732
   (b) agricultural products = 0.4; oil products = 1.2
17. (a) mining = 106; manufacturing = 488
   (b) mining = 1.4; manufacturing = 1.2
19. (a)

$$A = \begin{bmatrix} 0.3 & 0.6 \\ 0.2 & 0.2 \end{bmatrix} \begin{matrix} \text{Electronic components} \\ \text{Computers} \end{matrix}$$

with column headings EC and C

   (b) electronic components = 1200; computers = 320
21. (a)

$$A = \begin{bmatrix} 0.30 & 0.04 \\ 0.35 & 0.10 \end{bmatrix} \begin{matrix} \text{Fishing} \\ \text{Oil} \end{matrix}$$

with column headings F and O

   (b) fishing = 100; oil = 1250
23. development = $21,000; promotional = $12,000
25. engineering = $15,000; computer = $13,000
27. fishing = 400; agriculture = 500; mining = 400
29. electronics = 1240; steel = 1260; autos = 720
31. service = 90; manufacturing = 200; agriculture = 100
33. products = $\frac{7}{17}$ households;
   machinery = $\frac{1}{17}$ households
35. government = $\frac{10}{19}$ households;
   industry = $\frac{11}{19}$ households
37. (a)

$$A = \begin{bmatrix} 0.5 & 0.4 & 0.3 \\ 0.4 & 0.5 & 0.3 \\ 0.1 & 0.1 & 0.4 \end{bmatrix} \begin{matrix} \text{Manufacturing} \\ \text{Utilities} \\ \text{Households} \end{matrix}$$

with column headings M, U, H

   (b) manufacturing = 3 households;
   utilities = 3 households
39. $\begin{bmatrix} 24 \\ 96 \\ 24 \\ 120 \\ 492 \\ 3456 \end{bmatrix}$ 3456 bolts, 492 braces, 120 panels

41. $\begin{bmatrix} 10 \\ 10 \\ 20 \\ 56 \\ 20 \\ 26 \\ 300 \end{bmatrix}$ 56 2 × 4s, 20 braces, 26 clamps, 300 nails

CHAPTER 3 REVIEW EXERCISES

1. 4   **2.** 0   **3.** A, B   **4.** none   **5.** D, F, G, I
6. $\begin{bmatrix} -2 & 5 & 11 & -8 \\ -4 & 0 & 0 & -4 \\ 2 & 2 & -1 & -9 \end{bmatrix}$
7. zero matrix   **8.** order
9. $\begin{bmatrix} 6 & -1 & -9 & 3 \\ 10 & 3 & -1 & 4 \\ -2 & -2 & -2 & 14 \end{bmatrix}$ **10.** $\begin{bmatrix} 3 & -3 \\ 4 & -1 \\ 2 & -6 \\ 1 & -2 \end{bmatrix}$
11. $\begin{bmatrix} 2 & 1 \\ 5 & 1 \end{bmatrix}$ **12.** $\begin{bmatrix} 12 & -6 \\ 15 & 0 \\ 18 & 0 \\ 3 & 9 \end{bmatrix}$ **13.** $\begin{bmatrix} 4 & 0 \\ 0 & 4 \end{bmatrix}$
14. $\begin{bmatrix} 2 & -12 \\ -8 & -22 \end{bmatrix}$ **15.** $\begin{bmatrix} 9 & 20 \\ 4 & 5 \end{bmatrix}$ **16.** $\begin{bmatrix} 5 & 16 \\ 6 & 15 \end{bmatrix}$
17. $\begin{bmatrix} 2 & 37 & 61 & -55 \\ -2 & 9 & -3 & -20 \\ 10 & 10 & -14 & -30 \end{bmatrix}$ **18.** $\begin{bmatrix} 43 & -23 \\ 33 & -12 \\ -13 & 15 \end{bmatrix}$
19. $\begin{bmatrix} 10 & 16 \\ 15 & 25 \\ 18 & 30 \\ 6 & 11 \end{bmatrix}$ **20.** $\begin{bmatrix} 17 & 73 \\ 7 & 28 \end{bmatrix}$ **21.** $\begin{bmatrix} 3 & 7 \\ 23 & 42 \end{bmatrix}$
22. F   **23.** F   **24.** $\begin{bmatrix} -19 & 12 \\ -8 & 5 \end{bmatrix}$ **25.** F
26. (a) infinitely many solutions (bottom row of 0s)
   (b) $x = 6 + 2z$
   $y = 7 - 3z$
   z = any real number
   Two specific solutions:
   If $z = 0$, then $x = 6$, $y = 7$.
   If $z = 1$, then $x = 8$, $y = 4$.
27. (a) no solution (last row says 0 = 1)
   (b) no solution
28. (a) Unique (coefficient matrix is I_3)
   (b) $x = 0, y = -10, z = 14$
29. (1, 2, 1)   **30.** $x = 22, y = 9$
31. $x = -3, y = 3, z = 4$
32. $x = -\frac{3}{2}, y = 7, z = -\frac{11}{2}$ **33.** no solution
34. $x = 2 - 2z, y = -1 - 2z, z$ = any real number
35. $x = -2 + 8z$
   $y = -2 + 3z$
   z = any real number

36. $x_1 = 1, x_2 = 11, x_3 = -4, x_4 = -5$ **37.** yes

38. $\begin{bmatrix} \frac{1}{2} & \frac{1}{4} \\ \frac{5}{2} & \frac{7}{4} \end{bmatrix}$ **39.** $\begin{bmatrix} -1 & -2 & 8 \\ 1 & 2 & -7 \\ 1 & 1 & -4 \end{bmatrix}$

40. $\begin{bmatrix} 2 & 1 & -2 \\ 7 & 5 & -8 \\ -13 & -9 & 15 \end{bmatrix}$

41. $x = -33, y = 30, z = 19$

42. $x = 4, y = 5, z = -13$

43. $A^{-1} = \begin{bmatrix} -41 & 32 & 5 \\ 17 & -13 & -2 \\ -9 & 7 & 1 \end{bmatrix}; x = 4, y = -2, z = 2$

44. no   **45.** (a) 16   (b) yes, det $\neq$ 0

46. (a) 0   (b) no, det $= 0$

47. $\begin{bmatrix} 250 & 140 \\ 480 & 700 \end{bmatrix}$ **48.** $\begin{bmatrix} 1030 & 800 \\ 700 & 1200 \end{bmatrix}$

49. (a) higher in June
(b) higher in July

50. $\begin{array}{cc} \text{Men} & \text{Women} \end{array}$
$\begin{bmatrix} 865 & 885 \\ 210 & 270 \end{bmatrix} \begin{array}{l} \text{Robes} \\ \text{Hoods} \end{array}$ **51.** $\begin{bmatrix} 1750 \\ 480 \end{bmatrix} \begin{array}{l} \text{Robes} \\ \text{Hoods} \end{array}$

52. (a) $\begin{bmatrix} 13,500 & 12,400 \\ 10,500 & 10,600 \end{bmatrix}$

(b) Department A should buy from Kink;
Department B should buy from Ace.

53. (a) [0.20   0.30   0.50]

(b) $\begin{bmatrix} 0.013469 \\ 0.013543 \\ 0.006504 \end{bmatrix}$

(c) $[0.20\ 0.30\ 0.50]\begin{bmatrix} 0.013469 \\ 0.013543 \\ 0.006504 \end{bmatrix} = 0.20(0.013469) +$

$0.30(0.013543) + 0.50(0.006504) = 0.0100087$

(d) The historical return of the portfolio, 0.0100087, is the estimated expected monthly return of the portfolio. This is roughly 1% per month.

54. 400 fast food, 700 software, 200 pharmaceutical

55. (a) $A = 2C, B = 2000 - 4C$,
$C =$ any integer satisfying $0 \le C \le 500$
(b) yes; $A = 500, B = 1000, C = 250$
(c) max $A = 1000$ when $B = 0, C = 500$

56. (a) 3 passenger, 4 transport, 4 jumbo
(b) 1 passenger, 3 transport, 7 jumbo
(c) column 2

57. (a) shipping $= 5680$; agriculture $= 1960$
(b) shipping $= 0.4$; agriculture $= 1.8$

58. (a) $\begin{array}{cc} & \text{S} \quad\ \ \text{C} \end{array}$
$A = \begin{bmatrix} 0.1 & 0.1 \\ 0.2 & 0.05 \end{bmatrix} \begin{array}{l} \text{Shoes} \\ \text{Cattle} \end{array}$

(b) shoes $= 1000$; cattle $= 500$

59. mining $= 360$; manufacturing $= 320$; fuels $= 400$
60. government $= \frac{64}{93}$ households;
agriculture $= \frac{59}{93}$ households;
manufacturing $= \frac{40}{93}$ households

CHAPTER 3 TEST

1. $\begin{bmatrix} 3 & 1 & 5 \\ 1 & 3 & 6 \end{bmatrix}$ **2.** $\begin{bmatrix} -1 & 2 & 2 \\ 1 & -1 & 6 \end{bmatrix}$

3. $\begin{bmatrix} -12 & -16 & -155 \\ 5 & 12 & 87 \end{bmatrix}$ **4.** $\begin{bmatrix} 23 & 6 \\ 182 & 45 \\ 21 & 1 \end{bmatrix}$

5. $\begin{bmatrix} 0 & -7 \\ 26 & 1 \end{bmatrix}$ **6.** $\begin{bmatrix} -43 & -46 & -207 \\ 39 & 30 & -77 \\ 17 & 5 & -216 \end{bmatrix}$

7. $\begin{bmatrix} -2 & 3/2 \\ 1 & -1/2 \end{bmatrix}$ **8.** $\begin{bmatrix} -3 & 2 & 2 \\ 1 & 0 & -1 \\ 1/2 & -1/2 & 0 \end{bmatrix}$

9. $\begin{bmatrix} 5 \\ 14 \\ 15 \end{bmatrix}$ **10.** $x = -0.5, y = 0.5, z = 2.5$

11. $x = 4 - 1.8z, y = 0.2z, z =$ any real number
12. no solution
13. $x = 2, y = 2, z = 0, w = -2$
14. $x = 6w - 0.5, y = 0.5 - w, z = 2.5 - 3w, w =$ any real number

15. (a) $B = \$45,000, E = \$40,000$
(b) $\$0 \le H \le \$25,000$ (so $B \ge 0$)
(c) min $E = \$20,000$ when $H = \$0$ and $B = \$75,000$

16. (a) $\begin{bmatrix} 0.08 & 0.22 & 0.12 \\ 0.10 & 0.08 & 0.19 \\ 0.05 & 0.07 & 0.09 \\ 0.10 & 0.26 & 0.15 \\ 0.12 & 0.04 & 0.24 \end{bmatrix}$
(b) 0.08, 0.22, 0.12 consumed by carnivores 1, 2, 3
(c) plant 5 by 1, plant 4 by 2, plant 5 by 3

17. (a) [1000   4000   2000   1000]
(b) [45,000   55,000   90,000   70,000]

(c) $\begin{bmatrix} 5 \\ 3 \\ 4 \\ 4 \end{bmatrix}$ (d) [$1,030,000]   (e) $\begin{array}{c} \\ A \\ B \\ C \\ D \end{array} \begin{bmatrix} \$ \\ 65 \\ 145 \\ 125 \\ 135 \end{bmatrix}$

18. (a) 121, 46, 247, 95, 261, 99, 287, 111, 179, 69, 169, 64
(b) Frodo lives
19. growth, 2000; blue-chip, 400; utility, 400
20. (a) agriculture $= 245$; minerals $= 235$
(b) agriculture $= 7$; minerals $= 1$
(c) agriculture $= 0.5$; minerals $= 1.5$
21. profit $=$ households
nonprofit $= \frac{2}{3}$ households

22.
$$\begin{array}{c c c c} \text{Ag} & \text{M} & \text{F} & \text{S} \\ \end{array}$$
$$\begin{bmatrix} 0.2 & 0.1 & 0.1 & 0.1 \\ 0.3 & 0.2 & 0.2 & 0.2 \\ 0.2 & 0.2 & 0.3 & 0.3 \\ 0.1 & 0.4 & 0.2 & 0.2 \end{bmatrix} \begin{array}{l} \text{Agriculture} \\ \text{Machinery} \\ \text{Fuel} \\ \text{Steel} \end{array}$$

23. agriculture: 5000; machinery: 8000; fuel: 8000; steel: 7000

24. agriculture: $\frac{520}{699}$ households; steel: $\frac{236}{233}$ households; fuel: $\frac{159}{233}$ households

4.1 EXERCISES

1.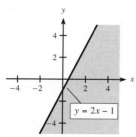

3.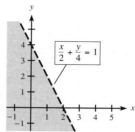

5.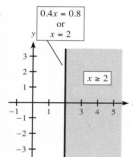

7. $(0, 0), (20, 10), (0, 15), (25, 0)$
9. $(5, 0), (15, 0), (6, 9), (2, 6)$
11. $(0, 5), (1, 2), (3, 1), (6, 0)$

13.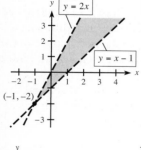

15.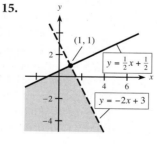

17.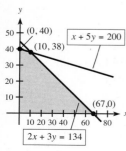

19.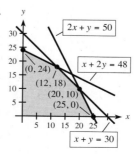

21.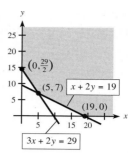

23.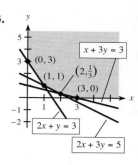

25.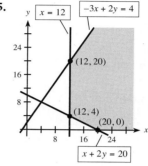

27. (a) Let $x =$ the number of deluxe models and $y =$ the number of economy models.
$$3x + 2y \leq 24$$
$$\tfrac{1}{2}x + y \leq 8$$
$$x \geq 0, y \geq 0$$

(b)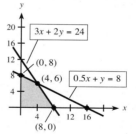

Corners: $(0, 0)$, $(8, 0), (4, 6)$, $(0, 8)$

29. (a) Let $x =$ the number of cord-type trimmers and $y =$ the number of cordless trimmers. Constraints are
$$x + y \leq 300$$
$$2x + 4y \leq 800$$
$$x \geq 0, y \geq 0$$

(b)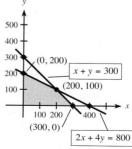

31. (a) Let x = the number of minutes on finance programs and y = the number of minutes on sports programs.
$$7x + 2y \geq 30$$
$$4x + 12y \geq 28$$
$$x \geq 0, y \geq 0$$

(b)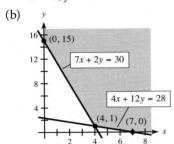

33. (a) Let x = the number of minutes of radio and y = the number of minutes of television. Constraints are
$$x + y \geq 80$$
$$0.006x + 0.09y \geq 2.16$$
$$x \geq 0, y \geq 0$$

(b)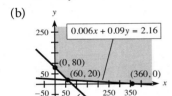

35. (a) Let x = the number of pounds of regular hot dogs and y = the number of pounds of all-beef hot dogs.
$$0.18x + 0.75y \leq 1020$$
$$0.2x + 0.2y \geq 500$$
$$0.3x \leq 600$$

(b)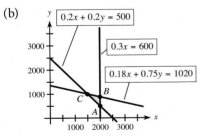

Solution region is triangle ABC, with
$A = (2000, 500)$
$B = (2000, 880)$
$C = (1500, 1000)$

4.2 EXERCISES

1. max = 76 at (4, 4); min = 0 at (0, 0)
3. no max; min = 11 at (1, 3)
5. (0, 0), (0, 20), (10, 18), (15, 10), (20, 0);
max = 66 at (10, 18); min = 0 at (0, 0)
7. (0, 60), (10, 30), (20, 20), (70, 0); min = 100 at (20, 20); no max

9. max = 1260 at $x = 12, y = 18$
11. min = 66 at $x = 0, y = 3$
13. max = 22 at (2, 4)
15. max = 30 on line between (0, 5) and (3, 4)
17. min = 32 at (2, 3)
19. min = 9 at (2, 3)
21. max = 10 at (2, 4)
23. min = 3100 at (40, 60)
25. If x = the number of deluxe models and y = the number of economy models, then max = \$792 at (4, 6).
27. If x = the number of cord-type trimmers and y = the number of cordless trimmers, then max = \$9000 at any point with integer coordinates on the segment joining (0, 200) and (200, 100), such as (20, 190).
29. radio = 60, TV = 20, min C = \$16,000
31. inkjet = 45, laser = 25, max P = \$3300
33. 250 fish: 150 bass and 100 trout
35. (a) Max P = \$1,260,120 when corn = 3749.5 acres and soybeans = 2251.5 acres
(b) Max P = \$1,260,960 when corn = 3746 acres and soybeans = 2262 acres
(c) \$120/acre
37. 30 days for factory 1 and 20 days for factory 2; minimum cost = \$700,000
39. 60 days for location I and 70 days for location II; minimum cost = \$86,000
41. reg = 2000 lb; all-beef = 880 lb; maximum profit = \$3320
43. From Pittsburgh: 20 to Blairsville, 40 to Youngstown; From Erie: 15 to Blairsville, 0 to Youngstown; minimum cost = \$1540
45. (a) R = \$366,000 with 6 satellite and 17 full-service branches
(b) Branches: used 23 of 25 possible; 2 not used (slack)
New employees: hired 120 of 120 possible; 0 not hired (slack)
Budget: used all \$2.98 million; \$0 not used (slack)
(c) Additional new employees and additional budget. These items are completely used in the current optimal solution; more could change and improve the optimal solution.
(d) Additional branches. The current optimal solution does not use all those allotted; more would just add to the extras.

4.3 EXERCISES

1. $3x + 5y + s_1 = 15, 3x + 6y + s_2 = 20$

3.
$$\begin{bmatrix} 2 & 5 & 1 & 0 & 0 & | & 400 \\ 1 & 2 & 0 & 1 & 0 & | & 175 \\ -3 & -7 & 0 & 0 & 1 & | & 0 \end{bmatrix}$$

5.
$$\begin{bmatrix} 2 & 7 & 9 & 1 & 0 & 0 & 0 & | & 100 \\ 6 & 5 & 1 & 0 & 1 & 0 & 0 & | & 145 \\ 1 & 2 & 7 & 0 & 0 & 1 & 0 & | & 90 \\ -2 & -5 & -2 & 0 & 0 & 0 & 1 & | & 0 \end{bmatrix}$$

7. $x = 11, y = 9; f = 20$

9. $x = 0, y = 14, z = 11; f = 525$

11. (a) $x_1 = 0, x_2 = 45, s_1 = 14, s_2 = 0, f = 75$

   (b) not complete

   (c) $$\begin{bmatrix} ② & 0 & 1 & -\frac{3}{4} & 0 & | & 14 \\ 3 & 1 & 0 & \frac{1}{3} & 0 & | & 45 \\ \hline -6 & 0 & 0 & 3 & 1 & | & 75 \end{bmatrix}$$

   $\frac{1}{2}R_1 \rightarrow R_1$, then $-3R_1 + R_2 \rightarrow R_2, 6R_1 + R_3 \rightarrow R_3$

13. (a) $x_1 = 0, x_2 = 0, s_1 = 200, s_2 = 400, s_3 = 350, f = 0$

   (b) not complete

   (c) $$\begin{bmatrix} ⑩ & 27 & 1 & 0 & 0 & 0 & | & 200 \\ 4 & 51 & 0 & 1 & 0 & 0 & | & 400 \\ 15 & 27 & 0 & 0 & 1 & 0 & | & 350 \\ \hline -8 & -7 & 0 & 0 & 0 & 1 & | & 0 \end{bmatrix}$$

   $\frac{1}{10}R_1 \rightarrow R_1$, then $-4R_1 + R_2 \rightarrow R_2$,
   $-15R_1 + R_3 \rightarrow R_3, 8R_1 + R_4 \rightarrow R_4$

15. (a) $x_1 = 24, x_2 = 0, x_3 = 21,$
      $s_1 = 16, s_2 = 0, s_3 = 0, f = 780$

   (b) complete (no part (c))

17. (a) $x_1 = 0, x_2 = 0, x_3 = 12,$
      $s_1 = 4, s_2 = 6, s_3 = 0, f = 150$

   (b) not complete

   (c) $$\begin{bmatrix} 4 & 4 & 1 & 0 & 0 & 2 & 0 & | & 12 \\ ② & ④ & 0 & 1 & 0 & 1 & 0 & | & 4 \\ -3 & -11 & 0 & 0 & 1 & -1 & 0 & | & 6 \\ \hline -3 & -3 & 0 & 0 & 0 & 4 & 1 & | & 150 \end{bmatrix}$$

   Either circled number may act as the next pivot entry,
   but only one of them. If 4 is used,
   $\frac{1}{4}R_2 \rightarrow R_2$, then $-4R_2 + R_1 \rightarrow R_1$,
   $11R_2 + R_3 \rightarrow R_3, 3R_2 + R_4 \rightarrow R_4$. If 2 is used,
   $\frac{1}{2}R_2 \rightarrow R_2$, then $-4R_2 + R_1 \rightarrow R_1$,
   $3R_2 + R_3 \rightarrow R_3, 3R_2 + R_4 \rightarrow R_4$.

19. $x = 0, y = 5; f = 50$

21. $x = 4, y = 3; f = 17$

23. $x = 4, y = 3; f = 11$

25. $x = 0, y = 2, z = 5; f = 40$

27. $x = 4, y = 2, z = 6; f = 16$

29. $x_1 = 36, x_2 = 24; x_3 = 0, x_4 = 8; f = 1728$

31. No solution; a new pivot cannot be found in column 2.

33. $x = 50, y = 10; f = 100$. Multiple solutions are possible;
   pivot with the 3-5 entry.

35. no solution

37. $x = 0, y = 50$ or $x = 40, y = 40; f = 600$

39. (a) $$\begin{bmatrix} 1 & 1 & 1 & 0 & 0 & | & 60 \\ 1 & 3 & 0 & 1 & 0 & | & 120 \\ \hline -40 & -60 & 0 & 0 & 1 & | & 0 \end{bmatrix}$$

   (b) Maximum profit is $3000 with 30 inkjet and
      30 laser printers.

41. 300 style-891, 450 style-917, maximum $P = \$15,525$

43. premium and light = 175 each; maximum
   $P = \$35,000$

45. Aries = 3, Belfair = 5, Wexford = 4; maximum
   $P = \$305,000$

47. (a) 26 one-bedroom; 40 two-bedroom;
      48 three-bedroom

   (b) $100,200 per month

49. 21 newspapers, 13 radio; 230,000 exposures

51. $1650 profit with 46 A, 20 B, 6 C

53. 20-in. LCDs = 40, 42-in. LCDs = 115, 42-in.
   plasma = 0, 50-in. plasma = 38; max $P = \$12,540$

4.4 EXERCISES

1. (a) $$\begin{bmatrix} 5 & 2 & | & 16 \\ 1 & 2 & | & 8 \\ 4 & 5 & | & g \end{bmatrix} \text{ transpose} = \begin{bmatrix} 5 & 1 & | & 4 \\ 2 & 2 & | & 5 \\ 16 & 8 & | & g \end{bmatrix}$$

   (b) maximize $f = 16x_1 + 8x_2$ subject to
      $5x_1 + x_2 \leq 4, 2x_1 + 2x_2 \leq 5, x_1 \geq 0, x_2 \geq 0.$

3. (a) $$\begin{bmatrix} 1 & 2 & | & 30 \\ 1 & 4 & | & 50 \\ 7 & 3 & | & g \end{bmatrix} \text{ transpose} = \begin{bmatrix} 1 & 1 & | & 7 \\ 2 & 4 & | & 3 \\ 30 & 50 & | & g \end{bmatrix}$$

   (b) maximize $f = 30x_1 + 50x_2$ subject to
      $x_1 + x_2 \leq 7, 2x_1 + 4x_2 \leq 3, x_1 \geq 0, x_2 \geq 0$

5. (a) $y_1 = 7, y_2 = 4, y_3 = 0$; min $g = 452$

   (b) $x_1 = 15, x_2 = 0, x_3 = 29$; max $f = 452$

7. maximize $f = 11x_1 + 11x_2 + 16x_3$ subject to
   $2x_1 + x_2 + x_3 \leq 2$
   $x_1 + 3x_2 + 4x_3 \leq 10$
   primal: $y_1 = 16, y_2 = 0; g = 32$ (min)
   dual: $x_1 = 0, x_2 = 0, x_3 = 2; f = 32$ (max)

9. maximize $f = 11x_1 + 12x_2 + 6x_3$ subject to
   $4x_1 + 3x_2 + 3x_3 \leq 3$
   $x_1 + 2x_2 + x_3 \leq 1$
   primal: $y_1 = 2, y_2 = 3; g = 9$ (min)
   dual: $x_1 = 3/5, x_2 = 1/5, x_3 = 0; f = 9$ (max)

11. min $= 28$ at $x = 2, y = 0, z = 1$

13. $y_1 = 2/5, y_2 = 1/5, y_3 = 1/5; g = 16$ (min)

15. (a) minimize $g = 120y_1 + 50y_2$ subject to
      $3y_1 + y_2 \geq 40$
      $2y_1 + y_2 \geq 20$

   (b) primal: $x_1 = 40, x_2 = 0, f = 1600$ (max)
      dual: $y_1 = 40/3, y_2 = 0, g = 1600$ (min)

17. min $= 480$ at $y_1 = 0, y_2 = 0, y_3 = 16$

19. min $= 90$ at $y_1 = 0, y_2 = 3, y_3 = 1, y_4 = 0$

21. Atlanta = 150 hr, Fort Worth = 50 hr;
   min C = $210,000

23. line 1 for 4 hours, line 2 for 1 hour; $1200

25. A = 12 weeks, B = 0 weeks, C = 0 weeks;
   cost = $12,000

27. factory 1: 50 days, factory 2: 0 days; min cost $500,000

29. 105 minutes on radio, nothing on TV; min cost $10,500

31. (a) Georgia package = 10
      Union package = 20
      Pacific package = 5

   (b) $4630

33. (a) min cost = $16

   (b) Many solutions are possible; two are: 16 oz of food I,
      0 oz of food II, 0 oz of food III and 11 oz of food I,
      1 oz of food II, 0 oz of food III.

35. Mon. = 8, Tues. = 0, Wed. = 5, Thurs. = 4,
Fri. = 5, Sat. = 0, Sun. = 3; min = 25

4.5 EXERCISES

1. $-3x + y \le -5$

3. $-6x - y \le -40$

5. (a) maximize $f = 2x + 3y$ subject to
$$7x + 4y \le 28$$
$$3x - y \le -2$$
$$x \ge 0, y \ge 0$$

(b) $\begin{bmatrix} 7 & 4 & 1 & 0 & 0 & | & 28 \\ 3 & \boxed{-1} & 0 & 1 & 0 & | & -2 \\ \hline -2 & -3 & 0 & 0 & 1 & | & 0 \end{bmatrix}$

7. (a) Maximize $-g = -3x - 8y$ subject to
$$4x - 5y \le 50$$
$$x + y \le 80$$
$$x - 2y \le -4$$
$$x \ge 0, y \ge 0$$

(b) $\begin{bmatrix} 4 & -5 & 1 & 0 & 0 & 0 & | & 50 \\ 1 & 1 & 0 & 1 & 0 & 0 & | & 80 \\ 1 & \boxed{-2} & 0 & 0 & 1 & 0 & | & -4 \\ \hline 3 & 8 & 0 & 0 & 0 & 1 & | & 0 \end{bmatrix}$

9. $x = 6, y = 8, z = 12; f = 120$

11. $x = 10, y = 17; f = 57$

13. $x = 5, y = 7; f = 31$

15. $x = 5, y = 15; f = 45$

17. $x = 10, y = 20; f = 120$

19. $x = 20, y = 10, z = 0; f = 40$

21. $x = 5, y = 0, z = 3; f = 22$

23. $x = 70, y = 0, z = 40; f = 2100$

25. $x_1 = 20, x_2 = 10, x_3 = 20, x_4 = 80,$
$x_5 = 10, x_6 = 10; f = 3250$

27. regular = 2000 lb; beef = 880 lb; profit = $3320

29. Produce 200 of each at Monaca; produce 300
commercial components and 550 domestic furnaces
at Hamburg; profit = $355,250

31. 400 filters, 300 housing units; min cost = $5145

33. Produce 200 of each at Monaca; produce 300
commercial components and 550 domestic furnaces
at Hamburg; cost = $337,750

35. I = 3 million, II = 0, III = 3 million;
cost = $180,000

37. 2000 footballs, 0 soccer balls, 0 volleyballs; $60,000

CHAPTER 4 REVIEW EXERCISES

1.
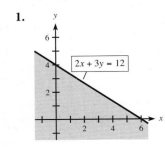

2.
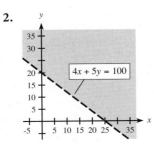

3.
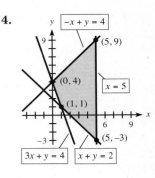

4.

5. max = 25 at (5, 10); min = −12 at (12, 0)

6. max = 194 at (17, 23); min = 104 at (8, 14)

7. max = 140 at (20, 0); min = −52 at (20, 32)

8. min = 115 at (5, 7); no max exists, f can be made arbitrarily large

9. $f = 66$ at (6, 6)

10. $f = 43$ at (7, 9)

11. $f = 300$ at any point on the segment joining (0, 60) and (50, 40)

12. $g = 24$ at (3, 3)   **13.** $g = 84$ at (64, 4)

14. $f = 76$ at (12, 8)   **15.** $f = 75$ at (15, 15)

16. $f = 168$ at (12, 7)   **17.** $f = 260$ at (60, 20)

18. $f = 360$ at (40, 30)   **19.** $f = 80$ at (20, 10)

20. $f = 640$ on the line between (160, 0) and (90, 70)

21. no solution

22. $g = 32$ at $y_1 = 2, y_2 = 3$

23. $g = 20$ at $y_1 = 4, y_2 = 2$

24. $g = 7$ at $y_1 = 1, y_2 = 5$

25. $g = 1180$ at $y_1 = 80, y_2 = 20$

26. $f = 165$ at $x = 20, y = 21$

27. $f = 54$ at $x = 6, y = 5$

28. $f = 270$ at (5, 3, 2)

29. $g = 140$ at $y_1 = 0, y_2 = 20, y_3 = 20$

30. $g = 1400$ at $y_1 = 0, y_2 = 100, y_3 = 100$

31. $f = 156$ at $x = 15, y = 2$

32. $f = 31$ at $x = 4, y = 5$

33. $f = 4380$ at (40, 10, 0, 0)

34. $f = 900$ at $x_1 = 25, x_2 = 50, x_3 = 25, x_4 = 0$

35. $g = 2020$ at $x_1 = 0, x_2 = 100, x_3 = 80, x_4 = 20$

36. $P = \$29,500$ when 110 large and 75 small swing sets
are made

37. $C = \$300,000$ when factory 1 operates 30 days, factory
2 operates 25 days

38. $P = \$10,680$ at any pair of integer values on the segment joining (120, 0) and (90, 20)

39. $P = \$960$; I = 40, II = 20

40. $P = \$1260$; Jacob's ladders = 90,
locomotive engines = 30

41. (a) Let x_1 = the number of 27-in LCD sets,
x_2 = the number of 32-in LCD sets,
x_3 = the number of 42-in LCD sets,
x_4 = the number of 42-in plasma sets.

(b) Maximize $P = 80x_1 + 120x_2 + 160x_3 + 200x_4$
subject to
$$8x_1 + 10x_2 + 12x_3 + 15x_4 \leq 1870$$
$$2x_1 + 4x_2 + 4x_3 + 4x_4 \leq 530$$
$$x_1 + x_2 + x_3 + x_4 \leq 200$$
$$x_3 + x_4 \leq 100$$
$$x_2 \leq 120$$

(c) $x_1 = 15, x_2 = 25, x_3 = 0, x_4 = 100;$
max profit = \$24,200

42. food I = 0 oz, food II = 3 oz; $C = \$0.60$ (min)
43. cost = \$5.60; $A = 40$ lb, $B = 0$ lb
44. cost = \$85,000; $A = 20$ days, $B = 15$ days, $C = 0$ days
45. pancake mix = 8000 lb; cake mix = 3000 lb;
profit = \$3550
46. Texas: 55 desks, 65 computer tables; Louisiana:
75 desks, 65 computer tables; cost = \$12,735
47. Midland: grade 1 = 486.5 tons, grade 2 = 0 tons;
Donora: grade 1 = 13.5 tons, grade 2 = 450 tons;
Cost = \$271,905

CHAPTER 4 TEST

1. max = 120 at (0, 24)
2. (a)

$$C;\begin{bmatrix} 1 & 2 & 0 & 1 & 0 & -3/2 & 0 & 40 \\ 0 & \boxed{1} & 0 & -2 & 1 & 1/2 & 0 & 15 \\ 0 & 3 & 1 & -1 & 0 & 1/4 & 0 & 60 \\ 0 & 0 & 0 & 4 & 0 & 6 & 1 & 220 \end{bmatrix}$$

$-2R_2 + R_1 \rightarrow R_1 \quad -3R_2 + R_3 \rightarrow R_3$

(b) A; pivot column is column 3, but new pivot is undefined.

(c) B; $x_1 = 40, x_2 = 12, x_3 = 0, s_1 = 0,$
$s_2 = 20, s_3 = 0; f = 170;$ This solution is not optimal; the next pivot is the 3-6 entry.

3. (a)

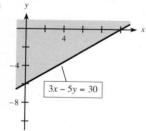

(b)

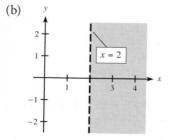

(c)

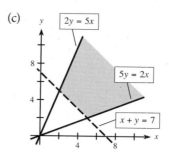

4. maximize $f = 100x_1 + 120x_2$ subject to
$$3x_1 + 4x_2 \leq 2$$
$$5x_1 + 6x_2 \leq 3$$
$$x_1 + 3x_2 \leq 5$$
$$x_1 \geq 0, x_2 \geq 0$$

5. min = 21 at (1, 8); no max exists, f can be made arbitrarily large
6. min = 136 at (28, 52)
7. maximize $-g = -7x - 3y$ subject to
$$x - 4y \leq -4$$
$$x - y \leq 5$$
$$2x + 3y \leq 30$$
8. max: $x_1 = 17, x_2 = 15, x_3 = 0; f = 658$ (max)
min: $y_1 = 4, y_2 = 18, y_3 = 0; g = 658$ (min)
9. max: = 6300 at $x = 90, y = 0$
10. max $f = 6000$ at any point on the segment joining (250, 150) and (350, 90)
11. max = 1188 at $x = 0, y = 16, z = 12$
12. If $x =$ the number of barrels of lager and $y =$ the number of barrels of ale, then maximize $P = 35x + 30y$ subject to
$$3x + 2y \leq 1200$$
$$2x + 2y \leq 1000$$
$P = \$16,000$ (max) at $x = 200, y = 300$
13. If $x =$ the number of day calls and $y =$ the number of evening calls, then minimize $C = 3x + 4y$ subject to
$$0.3x + 0.3y \geq 150$$
$$0.1x + 0.3y \geq 120$$
$$x \leq 0.5(x + y)$$
$C = \$1850$ (min) at $x = 150, y = 350$
14. max profit = \$15,000 when product 1 = 25 tons, product 2 = 62.5 tons, product 3 = 0 tons, product 4 = 12.5 tons

5.1 EXERCISES

1. (a) 3.162278   (b) 0.01296525
3. (a) 1.44225   (b) 7.3891
5.

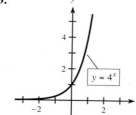

7.

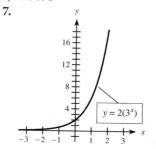

9.

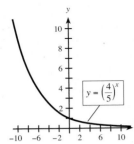

11.

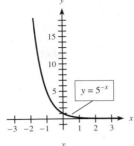

13.

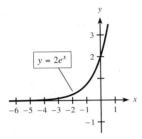

15.

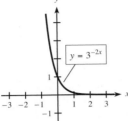

17. (a) $y = 3(2.5)^{-x}$
  (b) Decay. They have the form $y = C \cdot b^x$ for $0 < b < 1$
      or $y = C \cdot a^{-x}$ for $a > 1$.
  (c) The graphs are identical.

19. (a) and (b)

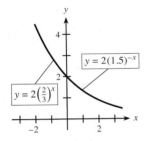

  (c) $(1.5)^{-x} = \left(\dfrac{3}{2}\right)^{-x} = \left(\dfrac{2}{3}\right)^{x}$

21. $y = \left(\dfrac{5}{4}\right)^{-x}$

23. All graphs have the same basic shape. For larger
positive values of k, the graphs fall more sharply.
For positive values of k nearer 0, the graphs fall
more slowly.

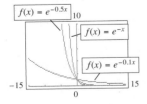

25. $y = f(x) + C$ is the same graph as $y = f(x)$ but shifted
C units on the y-axis.

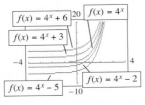

27. (a)

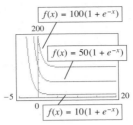

(b) As c changes, the
y-intercept and the
asymptote change.

29. $1884.54

31.

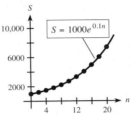

33. At time 0, the concentration is 0. The concentration
rises rapidly for the first 4 minutes and then tends
toward 100% as time nears 10 minutes.

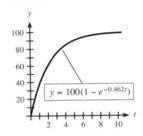

35.

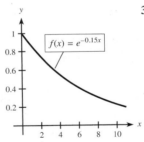

As the TV sets age
(x increases), the fraction
of sets still in service
declines.

37.

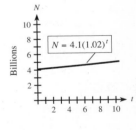

39.

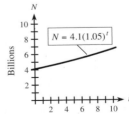

41. (a) Growth; $e > 1$ and the exponent is positive for
$t > 0$.
(b)

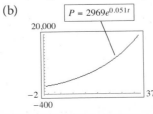

43. (a)

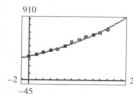

(b) $y = 342.8(1.037^x)$

(c)

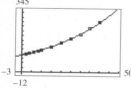

The model is an excellent fit to the data.

45. (a) $y = 492.4(1.070^x)$
(b) $24,608 billion is an overestimate   **(c)** 2021
47. (a) $y = 92.750(1.0275^x)$
(b)

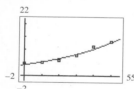

(c) $198.23
(d) $x \approx 36.6$, during 2047
49. (a) $y = 4.10(1.02^x)$ **(b)** growth
(c)   **(d)** 16.1 million

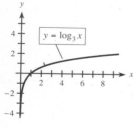

5.2 EXERCISES

1. $2^4 = 16$ **3.** $4^{1/2} = 2$ **5.** $x = 81$ **7.** $x = \frac{1}{4}$
9. $x = 16$ **11.** $x = 26.75$ **13.** $x \approx 2.013$
15. $\log_2 32 = 5$
17. $\log_4\left(\frac{1}{4}\right) = -1$
19. $3x + 5 = \ln(0.55); x \approx -1.866$
21.   **23.**

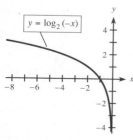
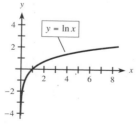

25.

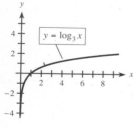

27. (a) 3   **(b)** -1 **29.** x **31.** -7 **33.** 3
35. (a) 4.9   **(b)** 0.4   **(c)** 12.4   **(d)** 0.9
37. $\log x - \log(x + 1)$ **39.** $\log_7 x + \frac{1}{3}\log_7(x + 4)$
41. $\ln(x/y)$ **43.** $\log_5[x^{1/2}(x + 1)]$
45. equivalent; Properties V and III
47. not equivalent; $\log(\sqrt[3]{8}/5)$
49. (a)

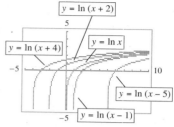

(b) For each c, the domain is $x > c$ and the vertical
asymptote is at $x = c$.
(c) Each x-intercept is at $x = c + 1$.
(d) The graph of $y = f(x - c)$ is the graph of $y = f(x)$
shifted c units on the x-axis.
51. (a) 4.0875   **(b)** -0.1544
53.   **55.**

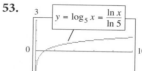
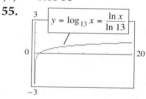

57. If $\log_a M = u$ and $\log_a N = v$, then $a^u = M$ and
$a^v = N$. Therefore, $\log_a(M/N) = \log_a(a^u/a^v) = \log_a(a^{u-v}) = u - v = \log_a M - \log_a N$.
59. 63.1 times as severe   **61.** 3.2 times as severe
63. 40
65. $L = 10 \log(I/I_0)$

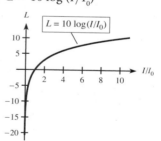

67. 0.1 and 1×10^{-14}
69. $\text{pH} = \log\dfrac{1}{[\text{H}^+]} = \log 1 - \log[\text{H}^+] = -\log[\text{H}^+]$
71. $\log_{1.02} 2 = 4t; t \approx 8.75$ years
73. (a)

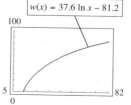

(b) 83.6 million   **(c)** 2023

75. (a) $y = -13.0 + 11.9 \ln x$

(b)

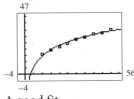

A good fit.

(c) 26.1%

77. $y = 20.0 + 20.8 \ln x$

(b) A good fit.   (c) 91%

5.3 EXERCISES

1. $\frac{5}{3}$ **3.** 2.943   **5.** 9.390   **7.** 18.971   **9.** 151.413

11. 6.679   **13.** $10^5 = 100{,}000$ **15.** 7

17. $5e^{10}$ **19.** $\dfrac{10^6}{2} = 5 \cdot 10^5$ **21.** 3

23. (a)

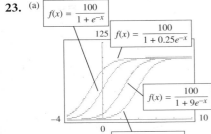

(b) Different c-values change the y-intercept and how the graph approaches the asymptote.

25. (a) 2038   (b) 4.9 months

27. (a) 13.86 years   (b) $105{,}850.00

29. 24.5 years   **31.** 128,402

33. $t \approx 13.3$, in 2019

35. (a) $4.98   (b) 8   **37.** $502

39. (a) $14,203.51   (b) $x \approx 164.6$

41. $x \approx 56.7$, in 2027

43. (a) $10,100.31   (b) 6.03 years

45. (a) $5469.03

(b) 7 years, 9 months (approximately)

47. (a) $142.5 million   (b) 35.3 years, in 2026

49. (a) $P(18) \approx 0.66$ means that in 2028, $1.00 is expected to purchase 66% of what it did in 2012.

(b) $x \approx 29.3$, in 2040

51. $x \approx 993.3$; about 993 units

53. (a) 600   (b) 2119   (c) 3000

(d)

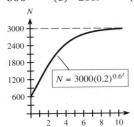

55. (a) 10   (b) 2.5 years

57. (a) 37   (b) 1.5 hours

59. (a) 52   (b) the 10th day

61. (a) 2%   (b) 20 months ($x = 19.6$)

63. (a) 0.23 km³   (b) 5.9 years

65. (a) 160.48 million

(b) $t \approx 84.7$; in 2025

67. (a) $y = \dfrac{120}{1 + 5.25e^{-0.0637x}}$

(b) 63.9 million

(c) 120 million

(d) $x \approx 36.8$, in 2037

CHAPTER 5 REVIEW EXERCISES

1. (a) $\log_2 y = x$ (b) $\log_3 2x = y$

2. (a) $7^{-2} = \frac{1}{49}$ (b) $4^{-1} = x$

3.

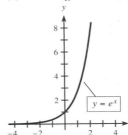

4.

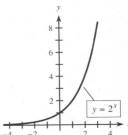

5.

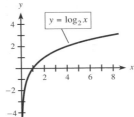

6.

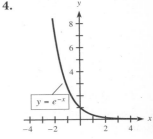

7.

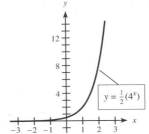

8.

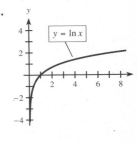

9.

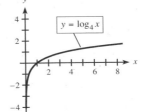

10.

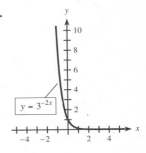

11.

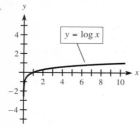

12.

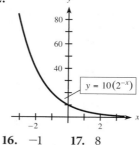

13. 0   **14.** 3   **15.** $\frac{1}{2}$ **16.** -1 **17.** 8
18. 1   **19.** 5   **20.** 3.15   **21.** -2.7
22. 0.6   **23.** 5.1   **24.** 15.6   **25.** $\log y + \log z$
26. $\frac{1}{2}\ln(x+1) - \frac{1}{2}\ln x$ **27.** no   **28.** -2
29. 5   **30.** 1   **31.** 0   **32.** 3.4939   **33.** -1.5845

34.

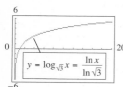

35.

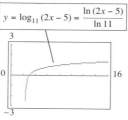

36. $x = 1.5$ **37.** $x \approx 51.224$
38. $x \approx 28.175$ **39.** $x \approx 40.236$
40. $x = 8$ **41.** $x = 14$ **42.** $x = 6$
43. Growth exponential, because the general outline has the same shape as a growth exponential.
44. (a) $C(15) \approx 139.19$ means that in 2025 goods that cost $100.00 in 2012 are expected to cost $139.19.
   (b)

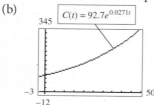

45. (a) $32,627.66
   (b)

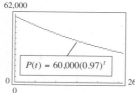

46. (a) $y = 42.1(1.04^x)$ (b)

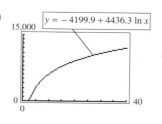

   (c) $239.2 thousand
47. (a) $11,938   (b)

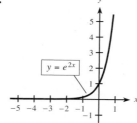

48. (a) $y = -363.3 + 166.9\ln x$
   (b)   341.1 million
   (c) $x \approx 96.9$, in 2047
49. (a) -3.9 (b) $0.14B_0$ (c) $0.004B_0$ (d)   yes
50. (a)   27,441   (b)   12 weeks
51. 1366   **52.** 5.8 years
53. (a) $5532.77   (b)   5.13 years
54. logistic, because the graph begins like an exponential function but then grows at a slower rate
55. (a)   3000   (b)   8603   (c)   10,000
56. (a)

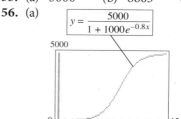

   (b)   5   (c)   4969   (d)   10 days

CHAPTER 5 TEST

1.

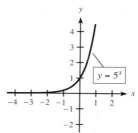

2.

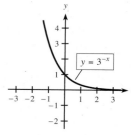

3.

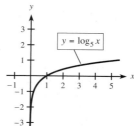

4.

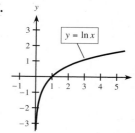

5.

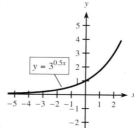

6.

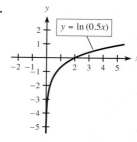

7.

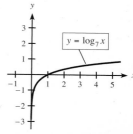

8.

9. 54.598   10. 0.100   11. 1.386
12. 1.322   13. $x = 7^{3.1}, x \approx 416.681$
14. $\log_3(27) = 2x; x = 1.5$ 15. $x \approx 0.203$
16. $x = 8$ 17. 3   18. x^4 19. 3   20. x^2
21. $\ln M + \ln N$ 22. $\ln(x^3 - 1) - \ln(x + 2)$
23. $\dfrac{\ln(x^3 + 1)}{\ln 4} \approx 0.721 \ln(x^3 + 1)$
24. $x \approx 38.679$
25. Decay exponential
26. (a) Decay exponential
    (b) In 2030, the expected tons of CO_2 emissions per person is 14.8 tons.
27. (a) $11,943.51
    (b) $t \approx 16.0$, in 2034
28. about 6.2 months
29. (a) about $16,716 billion
    (b) $x \approx 39.8$; in 2025
30. (a) $y = 63.31(1.048^x)$
    (b) 461,000
    (c) $x \approx 59.0$, in 2069

6.1 EXERCISES

1. $r = 0.0625, I = 250, P = 1000, t = 4$
3. $P = 8000, S = 9600, I = 1600, r = 0.05, t = 4$
5. (a) $9600   (b) $19,600
7. (a) $30   (b) $1030
9. $864   11. $3850   13. 13%
15. (a) 5.13%   (b) 4.29%   17. $1631.07
19. $12,000   21. 10 years   23. pay on time
25. (a) $2120   (b) $2068.29 (nearest cent)
27. 3, 6, 9, 12, 15, 18, 21, 24, 27, 30
29. $-\frac{1}{3}, \frac{1}{5}, -\frac{1}{7}, \frac{1}{9}, -\frac{1}{11}, \frac{1}{13}$ 31. $-1, -\frac{1}{4}, -\frac{1}{15}, 0; a_{10} = \frac{1}{20}$
33. (a) $d = 3, a_1 = 2$ (b) 11, 14, 17
35. (a) $d = \frac{3}{2}, a_1 = 3$ (b) $\frac{15}{2}, 9, \frac{21}{2}$
37. -35 39. 203   41. 2185   43. 1907.5
45. $-15,862.5$ 47. 21, 34, 55   49. $4800
51. the job starting at $40,000 ($58,000 versus $57,600)
53. (a) $6000   (b) $9000   (c) plan II, by $3000
    (d) $20,000   (e) $27,000   (f) plan II, by $7000
    (g) plan II

6.2 EXERCISES

(Minor differences may occur because of rounding.)
1. $S = 3216.87$ = future value; principal = 2000; rate = 0.02; periods = 24

3. $P = 6049.97$ = principal; future value = 25,000; rate = 0.03; periods = 48
5. (a) 8%   (b) 7   (c) 2% = 0.02   (d) 28
7. (a) 9%   (b) 5   (c) $\left(\frac{9}{12}\right)\% = 0.0075$ (d) 60
9. $24,846.79   11. $S = $4755.03; I = $1555.03
13. $13,322.91   15. $5583.95
17. $7309.98   19. $502.47
21. (a) $12,245.64   (b) $11,080.32
    (c) A $\frac{1}{2}$% increase in the interest rate reduces the amount required by $1165.32.
23. $50.26 more at 8%   25. (a) 7.55%   (b) 6.18%
27. 8% compounded monthly, 8% compounded quarterly, 8% compounded annually
29. 8.2% continuously yields 8.55%. 8.4% compounded quarterly yields 8.67% and so is better.
31. The higher graph is for continuous compounding because its yield (its effective annual rate) is higher.
33. 37.02%   35. 3 years   37. 4%   39. $3996.02
41. (a) $2,124,876.38   (b) $480,087.44 more
43. $n \approx 20.5$; 21 quarters   45. $13,916.24
47.

	A	B	C
1		Future Value	(Yearly)
2	End of Year	Quarterly	Monthly
3	0	$5000.00	$5000.00
4	1	$5322.52	$5324.26
5	2	$5665.84	$5669.54
6	3	$6031.31	$6037.22
7	4	$6420.36	$6428.74
8	5	$6834.50	$6845.65
9	6	$7275.35	$7289.60
10	7	$7744.64	$7762.34
11	8	$8244.20	$8265.74
12	9	$8775.99	$8801.79
13	10	$9342.07	$9372.59

(a) from quarterly and monthly spreadsheets: after $6\frac{1}{2}$ years (26 quarters or 78 months)
(b) See the spreadsheet.
49. (a) 24, 48, 96   (b) 24, 16, $\frac{32}{3}$

51. $10(2^{12})$ **53.** $4 \cdot \left(\frac{3}{2}\right)^{15}$ **55.** $\dfrac{6(1 - 3^{17})}{-2}$

57. $\dfrac{3^{35} - 1}{2}$ **59.** $18\left[1-\left(\frac{2}{3}\right)^{18}\right]$

61. \$350,580 (approx.)   **63.** 24.4 million (approx.)

65. 35 years   **67.** 40.5 ft   **69.** \$4096

71. 320,000   **73.** \$7,231,366   **75.** $6; 5^6 = 15,625$

77. 305,175,780

6.3 EXERCISES

1. $S = \$285,129$ = future value; $R = 2500$; $i = 0.02$; $n = 60$

3. $R = \$1426$ = payment; $S = 80,000$; $i = 0.04$; $n = 30$

5. (a) The higher graph is \$1120 per year.
   (b) $R = \$1000$: $S = \$73,105.94$;
       $R = \$1120$: $S = \$81,878.65$;
       Difference = \$8772.71

7. \$7328.22   **9.** \$1072.97   **11.** \$1482.94

13. $n \approx 27.1$; 28 quarters   **15.** \$4651.61

17. \$1180.78   **19.** \$4152.32   **21.** \$3787.92

23. $n \approx 17.7$; 18 quarters

25. (a) ordinary annuity   (b) \$4774.55

27. (a) annuity due   (b) \$3974.73

29. (a) ordinary annuity   (b) \$1083.40

31. (a) ordinary annuity   (b) \$1130.51

33. (a) annuity due   (b) \$290,976.81

35. (a) ordinary annuity   (b) $n \approx 108.5$; 109 months

37. (a) annuity due   (b) \$235.16

39. (a) annuity due   (b) \$26,517.13

41. (a) ordinary annuity   (b) \$795.75

43. \$53,677.40

45. (a) $n \approx 35$ quarters   (b) \$1,062,412 (nearest dollar)

6.4 EXERCISES

1. $A_n = \$22,480$ = present value; $R = 1300$; $i = 0.04$; $n = 30$

3. $R = \$809$ = payment; $A_n = 135,000$; $i = 0.005$; $n = 360$

5. \$69,913.77   **7.** \$2,128,391   **9.** \$4595.46

11. $n \approx 73.8$; 74 quarters   **13.** \$1141.81; premium

15. (a) The higher graph corresponds to 8%.
   (b) \$1500 (approximately)
   (c) With an interest rate of 10%, a present value of about \$9000 is needed to purchase an annuity of \$1000 for 25 years. If the interest rate is 8%, about \$10,500 is needed.

17. Ordinary annuity—payments at the end of each period Annuity due—payments at the beginning of each period

19. \$69,632.02   **21.** \$445,962.23   **23.** \$2145.59

25. (a) ordinary annuity   (b) \$10,882.46

27. (a) annuity due   (b) \$316,803.61

29. (a) ordinary annuity
   (b) Taking \$500,000 and \$140,000 payments for the next 10 years has a slightly higher present value: \$1,506,436.24.

31. (a) annuity due   (b) \$146,235.06

33. (a) ordinary annuity
   (b) $n \approx 1025.7$; 1026 months; about 85.5 yrs.

35. (a) annuity due   (b) \$22,663.74

37. (a) ordinary annuity   (b) \$11,810.24

39. (a) ordinary annuity   (b) \$27,590.62

41. (a) \$8629.16   (b) \$9883.48

43. (a) \$30,078.99   (b) \$16,900   (c) \$607.02
   (d) \$36,421.20

45. (a) \$4504.85   (b) $n \approx 21.9$; 22 withdrawals

47. \$25,785.99   **49.** \$74,993.20   **51.** \$59,768.91

53. \$1317.98   **55.** \$1,290,673.16

57. (a) The spreadsheet below shows the payments for the first 12 months and the last 12 months. Full payments for $13\frac{1}{2}$ years.

(b) The spreadsheet below shows the payments for the first 12 months and the last 12 months. Full payments for almost 4 years.

	A	B	C	D
1	End of Month	Acct. Value	Payment	New Balance
2	0	$100000.00	$0.00	$100000.00
3	1	$100650.00	$1000.00	$99650.00
4	2	$100297.73	$1000.00	$99297.73
5	3	$99943.16	$1000.00	$98943.16
6	4	$99586.29	$1000.00	$98586.29
7	5	$99227.10	$1000.00	$98227.10
8	6	$98865.58	$1000.00	$97865.58
9	7	$98501.70	$1000.00	$97501.70
10	8	$98135.47	$1000.00	$97135.47
11	9	$97766.85	$1000.00	$96766.85
12	10	$97395.83	$1000.00	$96395.83
13	11	$97022.40	$1000.00	$96022.40
14	12	$96646.55	$1000.00	$95646.55
⋮	⋮	⋮	⋮	⋮
154	152	$10684.71	$1000.00	$9684.71
155	153	$9747.66	$1000.00	$8747.66
156	154	$8804.52	$1000.00	$7804.52
157	155	$7855.25	$1000.00	$6855.25
158	156	$6899.81	$1000.00	$5899.81
159	157	$5938.16	$1000.00	$4938.16
160	158	$4970.25	$1000.00	$3970.25
161	159	$3996.06	$1000.00	$2996.06
162	160	$3015.53	$1000.00	$2015.53
163	161	$2028.64	$1000.00	$1028.64
164	162	$1035.32	$1000.00	$35.32
165	163	$35.55	$35.55	$0.00

	A	B	C	D
1	End of Month	Acct. Value	Payment	New Balance
2	0	$100000.00	$0.00	$100000.00
3	1	$100650.00	$2500.00	$98150.00
4	2	$98787.98	$2500.00	$96287.98
5	3	$96913.85	$2500.00	$94413.85
6	4	$95027.54	$2500.00	$92527.54
7	5	$93128.97	$2500.00	$90628.97
8	6	$91218.05	$2500.00	$88718.05
9	7	$89294.72	$2500.00	$86794.72
10	8	$87358.89	$2500.00	$84858.89
11	9	$85410.47	$2500.00	$82910.47
12	10	$83449.39	$2500.00	$80949.39
13	11	$81475.56	$2500.00	$78975.56
14	12	$79488.90	$2500.00	$76988.90
⋮	⋮	⋮	⋮	⋮
38	36	$27734.95	$2500.00	$25234.95
39	37	$25398.98	$2500.00	$22898.98
40	38	$23047.83	$2500.00	$20547.83
41	39	$20681.39	$2500.00	$18181.39
42	40	$18299.57	$2500.00	$15799.57
43	41	$15902.26	$2500.00	$13402.26
44	42	$13489.38	$2500.00	$10989.38
45	43	$11060.81	$2500.00	$8560.81
46	44	$8616.45	$2500.00	$6116.45
47	45	$6156.21	$2500.00	$3656.21
48	46	$3679.98	$2500.00	$1179.98
49	47	$1187.65	$1187.65	$0.00

6.5 EXERCISES

1. (a) the 10-year loan, because the loan must be paid more quickly
   (b) the 25-year loan, because the loan is paid more slowly
3. $1288.29
5. $553.42
7. $31,035.34

9.
Period	Payment	Interest
1	$39,505.48	$9000.00
2	39,505.48	6254.51
3	39,505.47	3261.92
	118,516.43	18,516.43

Period	Balance Reduction	Unpaid Balance
		$100,000.00
1	$30,505.48	69,494.52
2	33,250.97	36,243.55
3	36,243.55	0.00
	100,000.00	

11.
Period	Payment	Interest
1	$5380.54	$600.00
2	5380.54	456.58
3	5380.54	308.87
4	5380.54	156.71
	21,522.16	1,522.16

Period	Balance Reduction	Unpaid Balance
		$20,000.00
1	$4780.54	15,219.46
2	4923.96	10,295.50
3	5071.67	5,223.83
4	5223.83	0.00
	20,000.00	

13. $8852.05
15. $11,571.67
17. (a) $17,436.92
   (b) $348,738.40 + $150,000 = $498,738.40
   (c) $148,738.40
19. (a) $11,714.19
   (b) $1,405,702.80 + $250,000 = $1,655,702.80
   (c) $405,702.80

21. $8903.25
23. (a) $276,991.32
   (b) $263,575.30
25. (a) $89,120.53
   (b) $6451.45
27. (a) $168,121.30
   (b) $1286.12
   (c) $56,282.40
29. (a) $368.43; $383.43
   (b) $n \approx 57$
   (c) $211.95
31. (a) $12,007,827.36
   (b) $246,017.20
   (c) $n \approx 86.9$; 87 payments (rather than 100)
33. (a) The line is the total amount paid ($644.30 per month × the number of months). The curve is the total amount paid toward the principal.
   (b)

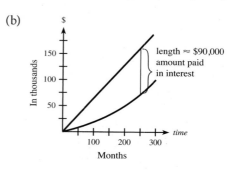

35.
	Rate	Payment	Total Interest
(a)	8%	$366.19	$2577.12
	8.5%	$369.72	$2746.56
(b)	6.75%	$518.88	$106,796.80
	7.25%	$545.74	$116,466.40

   (c) The duration of the loan seems to have the greatest effect. It greatly influences payment size (for a $15,000 loan versus one for $80,000), and it also affects total interest paid.

37.
		Payment	Points	Total Paid
(a)	(i)	$738.99	–	$221,697
	(ii)	$722.81	$1000	$217,843
	(iii)	$706.78	$2000	$214,034

   (b) The 7% loan with 2 points.
39. (a) $17,525.20
   (b) $508.76
   (c) $n \approx 33.2$; 34 quarters
   (d) $471.57

41. The spreadsheet shows the amortization schedule for the first 12 and the last 12 payments.

	A	B	C	D	E
1	Period	Payment	Interest	Bal. Reduction	Unpaid Bal.
2	0				$16700.00
3	1	$409.27	$114.12	$295.15	$16404.85
4	2	$409.27	$112.10	$297.17	$16107.68
5	3	$409.27	$110.07	$299.20	$15808.48
6	4	$409.27	$108.02	$301.25	$15507.23
7	5	$409.27	$105.97	$303.30	$15203.93
8	6	$409.27	$103.89	$305.38	$14898.55
9	7	$409.27	$101.81	$307.46	$14591.09
10	8	$409.27	$99.71	$309.56	$14281.52
11	9	$409.27	$97.59	$311.68	$13969.84
12	10	$409.27	$95.46	$313.81	$13656.03
13	11	$409.27	$93.32	$315.95	$13340.08
14	12	$409.27	$91.16	$318.11	$13021.97
⋮	⋮	⋮	⋮	⋮	⋮
39	37	$409.27	$32.11	$377.16	$4322.49
40	38	$409.27	$29.54	$379.73	$3942.75
41	39	$409.27	$26.94	$382.33	$3560.43
42	40	$409.27	$24.33	$384.94	$3175.49
43	41	$409.27	$21.70	$387.57	$2787.91
44	42	$409.27	$19.05	$390.22	$2397.70
45	43	$409.27	$16.38	$392.89	$2004.81
46	44	$409.27	$13.70	$395.57	$1609.24
47	45	$409.27	$11.00	$398.27	$1210.97
48	46	$409.27	$8.27	$401.00	$809.97
49	47	$409.27	$5.53	$403.74	$406.24
50	48	$409.02	$2.78	$406.24	$0.00

CHAPTER 6 REVIEW EXERCISES

1. $1, \frac{1}{4}, \frac{1}{9}, \frac{1}{16}$
2. Arithmetic: (a) and (c)   (a) $d = -5$ (c) $d = \frac{1}{6}$
3. 235   4. 109   5. 315
6. Geometric: (a) and (b)   (a) $r = 8$ (b) $r = -\frac{3}{4}$
7. 8   8. 2, 391, $484\frac{4}{9}$
9. $10,880   10. $6\frac{2}{3}$%   11. $2941.18   12. $4650
13. the $40,000 job ($490,000 versus $472,500)

14. (a) 40   (b) 2% = 0.02
15. (a) $S = P(1 + i)^n$ (b) $S = Pe^{rt}$
16. (b) monthly   17. $372.79   18. $14,510.26
19. $1616.07   20. $21,299.21
21. $n \approx 34.3$; 35 quarters
22. (a) 13.29%   (b) 14.21%
23. (a) 7.40%   (b) 7.47%
24. 2^{63} 25. $2^{32} - 1$ 26. $29,428.47
27. $6069.44   28. $31,194.18   29. $10,841.24
30. $n \approx 36$ quarters   31. $130,079.36   32. $12,007.09
33. (a) $11.828 million   (b) $161.5 million
34. $1726.85   35. $5390.77
36. $4053.54; discount   37. $n \approx 16$ half-years (8 years)
38. $88.85   39. $3443.61   40. $163,792.21

41.

Payment Number	Payment Amount	Interest	Balance Reduction	Unpaid Balance
57	$699.22	$594.01	$105.21	$94,936.99
58	$699.22	$593.36	$105.86	$94,831.13

42. (a) $401,134.67   (b) $45,596.63
    (c) $22,376.50
43. $S = R\left[\dfrac{(1 + i)^n - 1}{i}\right]$ 44. $I = Prt$
45. $A_n = R\left[\dfrac{1 - (1 + i)^{-n}}{i}\right]$ 46. $S = P(1 + i)^n$
47. $A_n = R\left[\dfrac{1 - (1 + i)^{-n}}{i}\right]$, solved for R
48. $S = Pe^{rt}$ 49. 16.32%   50. $213.81
51. (a) $1480   (b) $1601.03
52. $9319.64   53. 14.5 years   54. 79.4%
55. $381,195
56. (a) $4728.19   (b) $5398.07   (c) $1749.88
    (d) 10.78%
57. $21,474.08   58. $12,162.06
59. Quarterly APY = 6.68%. This rate is better for the bank; it pays less interest. Continuous APY = 6.69%. This rate is better for the consumer, who earns more interest.
60. (a) $243,429.20
    (b) $1825.11
    (c) $n \approx 158.9$; 159 payments (rather than 180)
    (d) $62,438.30
61. $32,834.69   62. $3,466.64
63. (a) $1185.51   (b) $355,653   (c) $171,653
    (d) $\approx$ $156,366
64. (a) $95,164.21   (b) $1300.14
65. $994.08
66. Future value of IRA = $172,971.32
    Present value needed = $2,321,520.10
    Future value needed from deposits = $2,148,548.78
    Deposits = $711.60
67. Regular payment = $64,337.43
    Unpaid balance = $2,365,237.24
    Number of $70,000 payments = $n \approx 46.1$
    Savings $\approx$ $118,546

CHAPTER 6 TEST

1. 25.3 years (approximately) **2.** $7999.41
3. 6.87% **4.** $158,524.90 **5.** 33.53%
6. (a) $698.00 (b) $112,400
7. $2625 **8.** $815.47 **9.** 8.73%
10. $119,912.92 **11.** $40,552.00 **12.** $22,439.01
13. $6781.17 **14.** $n \approx 66.8$; 67 half-years
15. $116,909.12 **16.** $29,716.47
17. (a) $161,270.52 (b) $924.08 (c) $5788.80
18. $12,975.49; premium
19. (a) The difference between successive terms is always -5.5.
    (b) 23.8 (c) 8226.3
20. 1000 mg (approximately)
21. (a) $145,585.54 (with the $2000);
        $147,585.54 (without the $2000)
    (b) $n \approx 318.8$; 319 months
        Total interest = $243,738.13
    (c) $n \approx 317.2$; 318 months
        Total interest = $245,378.24
    (d) Paying the $2000 is slightly better; it saves about $1640 in interest.
22. $1688.02
23. (a) $279,841.35 (b) $13,124.75

7.1 EXERCISES

1. (a) $\frac{2}{5}$ (b) 0 (c) 1 **3.** $\frac{1}{4}$ **5.** 1
7. (a) $\frac{3}{10}$ (b) $\frac{1}{2}$ (c) $\frac{1}{5}$ (d) $\frac{3}{5}$ (e) $\frac{7}{10}$
9. (a) $\frac{1}{13}$ (b) $\frac{1}{2}$ (c) $\frac{1}{4}$
11. {HH, HT, TH, TT}; (a) $\frac{1}{4}$ (b) $\frac{1}{2}$ (c) $\frac{1}{4}$
13. (a) $\frac{1}{12}$ (b) $\frac{1}{12}$ (c) $\frac{1}{36}$ **15.** (a) $\frac{1}{2}$ (b) $\frac{5}{12}$
17. (a) 431/1200
    (b) If fair, $\Pr(6) = \frac{1}{6}$; 431/1200 not close to $\frac{1}{6}$, so not a fair die
19. (a) 2:3 (b) 3:2 **21.** (a) $\frac{1}{21}$ (b) $\frac{20}{21}$
23. 0.46 **25.** (a) 63/425 (b) 32/425
27. (a) R: 0.63 D: 0.41 I: 0.51
    (b) Republican
29. (a) 1/3601 (b) 100/3601 (c) 3500/3601
    (d) 30%
31. (a) 0.402 (b) 0.491 (c) 100%; yes
33. $S = \{$A+, A−, B+, B−, AB+, AB−, O+, O−$\}$; No.
    Type O+ is the most frequently occurring blood type.
35. (a) 0.04 (b) 0.96 **37.** (a) 0.13 (b) 0.87
39. 0.03 **41.** 0.75 **43.** $\frac{1}{3}$ **45.** $\frac{1}{3}$
47. 0.22; yes, 0.39 is much higher than 0.22 **49.** $\frac{3}{8}$
51. (a) no (b) {BB, BG, GB, GG} (c) $\frac{1}{2}$
53. $\frac{1}{8}$ **55.** $\frac{3}{125}$
57. $\Pr(A) = 0.000019554$, or about 2.0 accidents per 100,000
    $\Pr(B) = 0.000035919$, or about 3.6 accidents per 100,000
    $\Pr(C) = 0.000037679$, or about 3.8 accidents per 100,000
    Intersection C is the most dangerous.

59. (a) 557/1200 (b) 11/120
61. (a) boy: 1/5; girl: 4/5
    (b) boy: 0.4946; girl: 0.5054 (c) part (b)
63. 3/4 **65.** $3/3995 \approx 0.00075$ **67.** 3 to 1

7.2 EXERCISES

1. $\frac{1}{6}$ **3.** $\frac{2}{3}$ **5.** $\frac{2}{5}$ **7.** (a) $\frac{1}{7}$ (b) $\frac{5}{7}$
9. $\frac{3}{4}$ **11.** $\frac{2}{3}$ **13.** $\frac{10}{17}$ **15.** $\frac{2}{3}$
17. (a) $\frac{1}{2}$ (b) $\frac{1}{3}$ (c) $\frac{8}{9}$ (d) $\frac{1}{9}$
19. 0.54 **21.** (a) 362/425 (b) $\frac{66}{85}$
23. $\frac{17}{50}$ **25.** (a) $\frac{5}{6}$ (b) $\frac{1}{6}$
27. (a) 0.35 (b) 0.08 (c) 0.83
29. (a) 0.508 (b) 0.633 (c) 0.761
31. (a) 0.210 (b) 0.015 (c) 0.879
33. (a) $\frac{11}{12}$ (b) $\frac{5}{6}$ **35.** (a) $\frac{1}{2}$ (b) $\frac{7}{8}$ (c) $\frac{3}{4}$
37. 0.56 **39.** 0.965
41. (a) 0.72 (b) 0.84 (c) 0.61
43. $\frac{31}{40}$ **45.** 0.13

7.3 EXERCISES

1. (a) $\frac{1}{2}$ (b) $\frac{1}{13}$ **3.** (a) $\frac{1}{3}$ (b) $\frac{1}{3}$ **5.** $\frac{4}{7}$
7. (a) $\frac{2}{3}$ (b) $\frac{4}{9}$ (c) $\frac{3}{5}$ **9.** (a) $\frac{1}{4}$ (b) $\frac{1}{2}$
11. $\frac{1}{36}$ **13.** (a) $\frac{1}{8}$ (b) $\frac{7}{8}$
15. (a) $\frac{3}{50}$ (b) $\frac{1}{15}$
    (c) The events in part (a) are independent because the result of the first draw does not affect the probability for the second draw.
17. (a) $\frac{4}{25}$ (b) $\frac{9}{25}$ (c) $\frac{6}{25}$ (d) 0 **19.** $\frac{5}{68}$
21. (a) $\frac{1}{5}$ (b) $\frac{3}{5}$ (c) 0 **23.** (a) $\frac{1}{17}$ (b) 13/204
25. (a) $\frac{13}{17}$ (b) $\frac{4}{17}$ (c) $\frac{8}{51}$ **27.** $\frac{31}{52}$ **29.** $\frac{25}{96}$
31. $\frac{43}{50}$ **33.** $\frac{65}{87}$ **35.** $35/435 = \frac{7}{87}$ **37.** $\frac{1}{10}$
39. 1/144,000,000 **41.** 0.004292 **43.** 0.06
45. 0.045 **47.** $(0.95)^5 = 0.774$ **49.** 0.06
51. (a) 0.366 (b) 0.634
53. (a) 0.4565 (b) 0.5435
55. (a) $\left(\frac{1}{3}\right)^3 \left(\frac{1}{5}\right)^4 = 1/16,875$
    (b) $\left(\frac{2}{3}\right)^3 \left(\frac{4}{5}\right)^4 = 2048/16,875$ (c) 14,827/16,875
57. 4/11; 4:7
59. (a) 364/365 (b) $\frac{1}{365}$
61. (a) 0.59 (b) 0.41

7.4 EXERCISES

1. $\frac{2}{5}$ **3.** (a) $\frac{2}{21}$ (b) $\frac{4}{21}$ (c) $\frac{23}{35}$
5. (a) $\frac{5}{42}$ (b) $\frac{10}{21}$ (c) $\frac{4}{9}$
7. (a) $\frac{1}{30}$ (b) $\frac{1}{2}$ (c) $\frac{5}{6}$ **9.** $\frac{3}{5}$
11. (a) $\frac{6}{25}$ (b) $\frac{9}{25}$ (c) $\frac{12}{25}$ (d) $\frac{19}{25}$
13. $\frac{2}{3}$ **15.** $\frac{2}{3}$ **17.** 0.3095
19. (a) 81/10,000 (b) 1323/5000
21. (a) $\frac{6}{35}$ (b) $\frac{6}{35}$ (c) $\frac{12}{35}$
23. (a) $\frac{4}{7}$ (b) $\frac{5}{14}$ (c) $\frac{7}{10}$ (d) $\frac{16}{25}$ **25.** $\frac{17}{45}$
27. 0.079 **29.** (a) 49/100 (b) $\frac{12}{49}$

7.5 EXERCISES

1. 360   **3.** 151,200   **5.** 1
7. (a) $6 \cdot 5 \cdot 4 \cdot 3 = 360$ (b) $6^4 = 1296$ **9.** $n!$
11. $n + 1$ **13.** 16   **15.** 4950   **17.** 1   **19.** 1
21. 10   **23.** (a) 8 (b) 240   **25.** 604,800
27. 120   **29.** 24   **31.** 64   **33.** 720
35. $2^{10} = 1024$ **37.** $4(_{13}C_5) = 5148$
39. 10,816,000   **41.** 30,045,015   **43.** 792
45. 210   **47.** 2,891,999,880   **49.** 3,700,000

7.6 EXERCISES

1. $\frac{1}{120}$ **3.** (a) 120 (b) $\frac{1}{120}$
5. 0.639   **7.** (a) 1/10,000 (b) 1/5040
9. $1/10^6$ **11.** 0.000048   **13.** $1/10! = 1/3,628,800$
15. (a) $\frac{1}{22}$ (b) $\frac{6}{11}$ (c) $\frac{9}{22}$
17. 0.098   **19.** $\dfrac{_{90}C_{28} \cdot {_{10}}C_2}{_{100}C_{30}}$
21. (a) 0.119 (b) 0.0476 (c) 0.476
23. 0.0238   **25.** (a) 0.721   (b) 0.262   (c) 0.279
27. (a) $\frac{1}{3}$ (b) $\frac{1}{6}$ **29.** $\dfrac{_{20}C_{10}}{_{80}C_{10}} = 0.00000011$
31. (a) 0.033 (b) 0.633
33. (a) 0.0005 (b) 0.011   **35.** 0.00198
37. (a) $1/1000 = 0.001$
   (b) 444, 446, 464, 644, 466, 646, 664, 666
   (b) $1/8 = 0.125$

7.7 EXERCISES

1. can   **3.** cannot, sum $\neq 1$
5. cannot, not square   **7.** can
9. [0.248 0.752]   **11.** [0.228 0.236 0.536]
13. [0.25 0.75]   **15.** [0.249 0.249 0.502]
17. $\left[\frac{1}{4} \quad \frac{3}{4}\right]$ **19.** $\left[\frac{1}{4} \quad \frac{1}{4} \quad \frac{1}{2}\right]$
21. [0.5 0.4 0.1]; [0.44 0.43 0.13];
   [0.431 0.43 0.139]; [0.4292 0.4291 0.1417]
23. $\begin{array}{c} \\ R \\ N \end{array} \overset{\begin{array}{cc} R & N \end{array}}{\begin{bmatrix} 0.8 & 0.2 \\ 0.3 & 0.7 \end{bmatrix}}$ **25.** 0.45
27. $\begin{array}{c} \\ A \\ F \\ V \end{array} \overset{\begin{array}{ccc} A & F & V \end{array}}{\begin{bmatrix} 0 & 0.7 & 0.3 \\ 0.6 & 0 & 0.4 \\ 0.8 & 0.2 & 0 \end{bmatrix}}$
29. [0.3928 0.37 0.2372]
31. [46/113 38/113 29/113]
33. $\begin{array}{c} \\ r \\ u \end{array} \overset{\begin{array}{cc} r & u \end{array}}{\begin{bmatrix} 0.7 & 0.3 \\ 0.1 & 0.9 \end{bmatrix}}$; [1/4 3/4]
35. $\left[\frac{1}{14} \quad \frac{3}{14} \quad \frac{5}{7}\right]$ **37.** $\left[\frac{4}{7} \quad \frac{2}{7} \quad \frac{1}{7}\right]$
39. [49/100 42/100 9/100]

CHAPTER 7 REVIEW EXERCISES

1. (a) $\frac{5}{9}$ (b) $\frac{1}{3}$ (c) $\frac{2}{9}$
2. (a) S_1 (b) $\frac{3}{4}$ (c) $\frac{1}{2}$ (d) $\frac{1}{6}$ (e) $\frac{2}{3}$
3. (a) 3:4 (b) 4:3   **4.** (a) $\frac{1}{4}$ (b) $\frac{1}{2}$ (c) $\frac{1}{4}$
5. (a) $\frac{3}{8}$ (b) $\frac{1}{8}$ (c) $\frac{3}{8}$ **6.** $\frac{2}{13}$ **7.** 16/169
8. $\frac{3}{4}$ **9.** $\frac{2}{13}$ **10.** $\frac{7}{13}$ **11.** (a) $\frac{2}{9}$ (b) $\frac{2}{3}$ (c) $\frac{7}{9}$
12. $\frac{2}{7}$ **13.** $\frac{1}{2}$ **14.** 7/320
15. 7/342   **16.** 3/14   **17.** $\frac{8}{15}$
18. (a) $\frac{3}{14}$ (b) $\frac{4}{7}$ (c) $\frac{3}{8}$ **19.** 49/89
20. 30   **21.** 35   **22.** 26^3 **23.** 56
24. (a) Not square (b) The row sums are not 1.
25. [0.76 0.24], [0.496 0.504]
26. [0.2 0.8]
27. $\frac{5}{8}$ **28.** $\frac{1}{4}$ **29.** $\frac{29}{50}$
30. $\frac{5}{56}$ **31.** $\frac{33}{56}$ **32.** $\frac{15}{22}$ **33.** 0.72
34. (a) 63/2000 (b) $\frac{60}{63}$ **35.** 39/116   **36.** $4! = 24$
37. $_8P_4 = 1680$ **38.** $_{12}C_4 = 495$ **39.** $_8C_4 = 70$
40. (a) $_{12}C_2 = 66$ (b) $_{12}C_3 = 220$ **41.** 1,544,760
42. If her assumption about blood groups is accurate, there would be $4 \cdot 2 \cdot 4 \cdot 8 = 256$, not 288, unique groups.
43. $\frac{1}{24}$ **44.** $\frac{3}{500}$ **45.** $\frac{3}{1250}$
46. (a) 0.3398 (b) 0.1975   **47.** $\frac{1}{10}$
48. (a) $(_{10}C_5)(_2C_1)/_{12}C_6$
   (b) $\dfrac{(_{10}C_5)(_2C_1) + (_{10}C_4)(_2C_2)}{_{12}C_6}$
49. [0.135 0.51 0.355], [0.09675 0.3305 0.57275], [0.0640875 0.288275 0.6476375]
50. [12/265 68/265 37/53]

CHAPTER 7 TEST

1. (a) $\frac{4}{7}$ (b) $\frac{3}{7}$ **2.** (a) $\frac{2}{7}$ (b) $\frac{5}{7}$
3. (a) 0 (b) 1   **4.** $\frac{1}{7}$ **5.** $\frac{1}{7}$
6. (a) $\frac{2}{7}$ (b) $\frac{4}{7}$ **7.** $\frac{2}{7}$ **8.** $\frac{3}{7}$ **9.** $\frac{2}{3}$
10. 1/17,576   **11.** 0.2389   **12.** (a) $\frac{1}{5}$ (b) $\frac{1}{20}$
13. (a) $\frac{3}{95}$ (b) $\frac{6}{19}$ (c) $\frac{21}{38}$ (d) 0
14. (a) 5,245,786 (b) 1/5,245,786
15. (a) 2,118,760 (b) 1/2,118,760
16. 0.064   **17.** (a) 0.633 (b) 0.962   **18.** 0.229
19. (a) $\frac{1}{5}$ (b) $\frac{1}{14}$ (c) $\frac{13}{14}$ **20.** $\frac{3}{14}$
21. (a) 2^{10} (b) $\dfrac{1}{2^{10}}$ (c) $\frac{1}{3}$ (d) Change the code.
22. (a) $A = \begin{bmatrix} 0.80 & 0.20 \\ 0.07 & 0.93 \end{bmatrix}$ (b) [0.25566 0.74434]; about 25.6%   (c) $\frac{7}{27}$; 25.9% of market

8.1 EXERCISES

1. (a) 1/6 (b) 5/6 (c) 18 (d) 0.045
3. 0.0595
5. (a) $\frac{1}{64}$ (b) $\frac{5}{16}$ (c) $\frac{15}{64}$ **7.** 0.0284
9. (a) 0.2304 (b) 0.0102 (c) 0.3174
11. 0.0585   **13.** 0.2759
15. (a) 0.375 (b) 0.0625

17. (a) 0.035   (b) 0.706
19. (a) $\frac{27}{64}$ (b) $\frac{27}{128}$ (c) $\frac{81}{256}$
21. (a) 0.0729   (b) 0.5905   (c) 0.9914
23. 0.2457   **25.** 0.0007
27. (a) 0.1323   (b) 0.0308
29. (a) 0.9044   (b) 0.0914   (c) 0.0043
31. (a) 0.8683   (b) 0.2099   **33.** 0.740

8.2 EXERCISES

1. 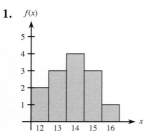   **3.**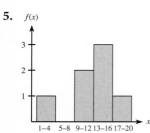

5.   **7.**

9. 3   **11.** 13   **13.** 5   **15.** 10.5
17. mode = 2, median = 4.5, mean = 6
19. mode = 17, median = 18.5, mean = 23.5
21. mode = 5.3, median = 5.3, mean = 5.32
23. 12.21, 14.5, 14.5   **25.** 9   **27.** 14
29. 4, 8.5714, 2.9277   **31.** 14, 4.6667, 2.1602
33. 2.73, 1.35   **35.** 6.75, 2.96
37. (a)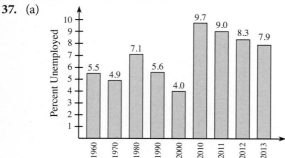

(b) $\bar{x} = 6.9$, $s = 1.98$
39.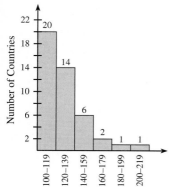

41. The mean will give the highest measure.
43. The median will give the most representative average.
45. (a) $\bar{x} \approx 63.4\%$; $s \approx 19.3\%$ (b) Yes
47.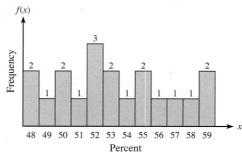

49. $\bar{x} = 3.32$ kg; $s = 0.677$ kg
51. (a) $60,000   (b) $36,000   (c) $32,000
53. (a) $23.33   (b) $5.14
55. (a) 35,434,000   (b) 13,312,000
57. (a)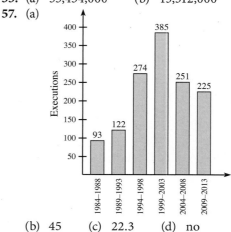

(b) 45   (c) 22.3   (d) no

8.3 EXERCISES

1. no; $\Pr(x) \neq 0$ **3.** yes; both conditions satisfied
5. yes; both conditions satisfied
7. no; $\Sigma\Pr(x) > 1$ **9.** $\frac{15}{8}$ **11.** 5
13. $\mu = \frac{13}{8}, \sigma^2 = 1.48, \sigma = 1.22$
15. $\mu = \frac{13}{3}, \sigma^2 = 2.22, \sigma = 1.49$
17. 3   **19.** 2
21. (a)

x	$\Pr(x)$
0	125/216
1	25/72
2	5/72
3	1/216

(b) $3\left(\frac{1}{6}\right) = \frac{1}{2}$ (c) $\sqrt{3\left(\frac{1}{6}\right)\left(\frac{5}{6}\right)} = \left(\frac{1}{6}\right)\sqrt{15}$
23. (a) 42   (b) 3.55
25. (a) 30   (b) 3.464
27. 125
29. $a^6 + 6a^5b + 15a^4b^2 + 20a^3b^3 + 15a^2b^4 + 6ab^5 + b^6$
31. $x^4 + 4x^3h + 6x^2h^2 + 4xh^3 + h^4$
33. 1.85
35. TV: 37,500; personal appearances: 35,300
37. $-$67.33

39. Expect to lose $2 per game in the long run.
41. 100
43. E(cost with policy) = $108,
E(cost without policy) = $80;
save $28 by "taking the chance"
45. no; some pipes may be more than 0.01 in. from 2 in.
even if average is 2 in.
47. (a) 100(0.10) = 10   (b) $\sqrt{100(0.10)(0.90)} = 3$
49. (a) 60,000   (b) $\sqrt{24,000} = 154.919$
51. 59,690   **53.** (a) 4   (b) 1.79
55. 2, 1.41   **57.** 300

8.4 EXERCISES

1. 0.4641   **3.** 0.2257   **5.** 0.9153   **7.** 0.1070
9. 0.0166   **11.** 0.0228   **13.** 0.8849   **15.** 0.1915
17. 0.3944   **19.** 0.3830   **21.** 0.7745   **23.** 0.9772
25. 0.0668   **27.** −1.645   **29.** −0.3
31. (a) 0.3413   (b) 0.3944   **33.** 0.9876
35. (a) 0.4192   (b) 0.0228   (c) 0.0580   (d) 0.8965
37. (a) 0.0668   (b) 0.3085   (c) 0.3830
39. (a) 0.0475   (b) 0.2033   (c) 0.5934
41. (a) 0.0228   (b) 0.1587   (c) 0.8186
43. 86   **45.** 128.7 oz.   **47.** 1.544

8.5 EXERCISES

1. yes   **3.** no   **5.** 0.0668   **7.** 0.0001
9. 0.0521   **11.** 0.0110   **13.** 0.9890
15. 0.7324   **17.** 0.3520   **19.** 0.0443
21. 0.5398   **23.** 0.7852   **25.** 0.0129
27. 0.2514   **29.** 0.0011   **31.** 0.9990
33. 0.1272; 0.4364
35. (a) 0.0038   (b) yes; students were smarter or
questions were leaked   **37.** 0.0166

CHAPTER 8 REVIEW EXERCISES

1. 0.0774   **2.** (a) 0.3545   (b) 0.5534
3. 0.407
4.

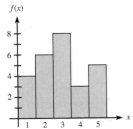

5. 3
6. $\frac{77}{26} \approx 2.96$
7. 3

8.

9. 14
10. 14
11. 14.3

12. $\bar{x} = 3.86$; $s^2 = 6.81$; $s = 2.61$
13. $\bar{x} = 2$; $s^2 = 2.44$; $s = 1.56$
14. 2.4   **15.** yes   **16.** no; $\Sigma Pr(x) \neq 1$
17. yes   **18.** no; $Pr(x) \neq 0$ **19.** 2

20. (a) 4.125   (b) 2.7344   (c) 1.654
21. (a) $\frac{37}{12}$ (b) 0.9097   (c) 0.9538
22. $\mu = 4$, $\sigma = (2\sqrt{3})/3$ **23.** 3
24. $x^5 + 5x^4y + 10x^3y^2 + 10x^2y^3 + 5xy^4 + y^5$
25. 0.9165   **26.** 0.1498   **27.** 0.1039   **28.** 0.3413
29. 0.6826   **30.** 0.1359   **31.** 2.33   **32.** not good
33. good   **34.** 0.0151   **35.** 0.9625   **36.** 0.8475
37. 0.0119   **38.** 0.297   **39.** 0.16308   **40.** 0.2048
41. (a) $(99,999/100,000)^{99,999} \approx 0.37$
(b) $1 - (99,999/100,000)^{100,000} \approx 0.63$

42.

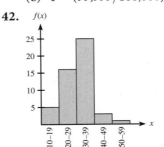

43. 30.3%
44. 8.35%
45. 455
46. 3
47. $18.00
48. −$0.50

49. (a) 1   (b) $\left(\frac{4}{5}\right)^4$
50. (a) 0.4772   (b) 0.1359   (c) 0.0228
51. 15%   **52.** 47 minutes   **53.** 0.3821
54. 0.4090   **55.** 0.0262   **56.** 0.1788

CHAPTER 8 TEST

1. (a) $\frac{40}{243}$ (b) $\frac{51}{243} = \frac{17}{81}$
2. (a) 4   (b) $\mu = 4$, $\sigma^2 = \frac{8}{3}$, $\sigma = \frac{2}{3}\sqrt{6}$
3. (i) For each x, $0 \leq Pr(x) \leq 1$ (ii) $\Sigma Pr(x) = 1$
4. 5.1
5. $\mu = 16.7$, $\sigma^2 = 26.61$, $\sigma = 5.16$
6. $\bar{x} = 21.57$, median $= 21$, mode $= 21$
7. (a) 0.4706   (b) 0.8413   (c) 0.0669
8. (a) 0.3891   (b) 0.5418   (c) 0.1210
9. 38.4   **10.** 0.9554   **11.** 0.6331
12.

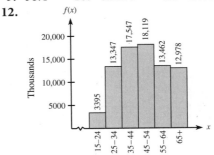

13. $\bar{x} = 48.3$, $s = 15.6$
14. (a) 38.5   (b) under 30; it would be lower
15. (a) 109.5   (b) Increase, unless a new technology
replaces mobile phones.
16. (a) 0.00003   (b) 30
17. 2 (1.8)   **18.** 5 (5.4)
19. 0 (0.054) with correct use
20. (a) 0.0158   (b) 0.0901   (c) 0.5383
21. 0.1814

9.1 EXERCISES

1. (a) -8 (b) -8
3. (a) 10   (b) does not exist
5. (a) 0   (b) -6
7. (a) does not exist (∞) (b) does not exist (∞)
   (c) does not exist (∞) (d) does not exist
9. (a) 3   (b) -6 (c) does not exist
   (d) -6

11.

x	$f(x)$
0.9	-2.9
0.99	-2.99
0.999	-2.999
1.001	-3.001
1.01	-3.01
1.1	-3.1

$\lim\limits_{x\to 1} f(x) = -3$

13.

x	$f(x)$
0.9	3.5
0.99	3.95
0.999	3.995
1.001	4.995999
1.01	4.9599
1.1	4.59

$\lim\limits_{x\to 1^-} f(x) = 4$ and $\lim\limits_{x\to 1^+} f(x) = 5$. These limits differ so $\lim\limits_{x\to 1} f(x)$ does not exist

15. -1 17. -4 19. -2 21. 6
23. $3/4$ 25. $3/2$ 27. 0   29. does not exist
31. -3 33. does not exist   35. does not exist
37. $3x^2$ 39. $\frac{1}{30}$ 41. does not exist
43. -4 45. 9
47.

a	$(1+a)^{1/a}$
0.1	2.5937
0.01	2.7048
0.001	2.7169
0.0001	2.7181
0.00001	2.71827
$\downarrow$	$\downarrow$
0	≈ 2.718

49. (a) 2   (b) 6   (c) -8 (d) $-\frac{1}{2}$
51. (a) -6 (b) -85 (c) $-33/17$
53. $150,000
55. (a) $32 (thousands)   (b) $55.04 (thousands)
57. (a) $2800   (b) $700   (c) $560
59. (a) 1.52 units/hr   (b) 0.85 units/hr   (c) lunch
61. (a) $0; p \to 100^-$ means the water approaches not being treated (containing 100% or all of its impurities); the associated costs of nontreatment approach zero.
   (b) ∞ (c) no, because $C(0)$ is undefined
63. (a) $5081.25   (b) $5081.25   (c) $5081.25
65. $C(x) = \begin{cases} 12.76 + 15.96x & 0 \le x \le 10 \\ 172.36 + 13.56(x-10) & 10 < x \le 120 \\ 1675 & x > 120 \end{cases}$
   $\lim\limits_{x\to 10} C(x) = 172.36$

67. 11,228.00. This corresponds to the Dow Jones opening average.
69. (a) 33.7
   (b) This predicts the percent of obese Americans who are severely obese as the year approaches 2040.
   (c) Yes. The table shows increases of 3% to 6% per decade, and severe obesity is expected to get worse.

9.2 EXERCISES

1. (a) continuous
   (b) discontinuous; $f(1)$ does not exist
   (c) discontinuous; $\lim\limits_{x\to 3} f(x)$ does not exist
   (d) discontinuous; $f(0)$ does not exist and $\lim\limits_{x\to 0} f(x)$ does not exist
3. continuous
5. discontinuous; $f(-3)$ does not exist
7. discontinuous; $\lim\limits_{x\to 2} f(x)$ does not exist
9. continuous
11. discontinuity at $x = -2$; $g(-2)$ and $\lim\limits_{x\to -2} g(x)$ do not exist
13. continuous   15. continuous
17. discontinuity at $x = -1$; $f(-1)$ does not exist
19. discontinuity at $x = 3$; $\lim\limits_{x\to 3} f(x)$ does not exist
21. vertical asymptote: $x = -2$;
   $\lim\limits_{x\to\infty} f(x) = 0$; $\lim\limits_{x\to -\infty} f(x) = 0$; $y = 0$
23. vertical asymptotes: $x = -2$, $x = 3$;
   $\lim\limits_{x\to\infty} f(x) = 2$; $\lim\limits_{x\to -\infty} f(x) = 2$; $y = 2$
25. (a) 0   (b) $y = 0$ is a horizontal asymptote.
27. (a) 1   (b) $y = 1$ is a horizontal asymptote.
29. (a) $5/3$ (b) $y = 5/3$ is a horizontal asymptote.
31. (a) does not exist (∞)
   (b) no horizontal asymptotes
33. (a)

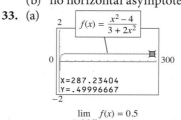

$\lim\limits_{x\to +\infty} f(x) = 0.5$

   (b) The table indicates $\lim\limits_{x\to\infty} f(x) = 0.5$.
35. (a) $x = -1000$ (b) 1000
   (c) These values are so large that experimenting with windows may never locate them.
37. $\lim\limits_{x\to\infty} \dfrac{a_n + \dfrac{a_{n-1}}{x} + \cdots + \dfrac{a_1}{x^{n-1}} + \dfrac{a_0}{x^n}}{b_n + \dfrac{b_{n-1}}{x} + \cdots + \dfrac{b_1}{x^{n-1}} + \dfrac{b_0}{x^n}}$
   $= \dfrac{a_n + 0 + \cdots + 0 + 0}{b_n + 0 + \cdots + 0 + 0} = \dfrac{a_n}{b_n}$
39. (a) no, not at $p = -8$ (b) yes   (c) yes
   (d) $p > 0$
41. (a) yes, $q = -1$ (b) yes
43. (a) R/i (b) $10,000   45. yes, $0 \le p \le 100$

47. 100%; No, for p to approach 100% (as a limit) requires spending to increase without bound, which is impossible.

49. $R(x)$ is discontinuous at $x = 18,150$; $x = 73,800$; $x = 148,850$; $x = 226,850$; $x = 405,100$; and $x = 457,600$

51. (a) \$158.80
(b) $\lim\limits_{x \to 100} C(x) = 38.80$; $\lim\limits_{x \to 500} C(x) = 98.80$
(c) yes

53. (a) $m(x) = 0.591x + 43.2$; $w(x) = 0.787x + 20.9$
(b) $r(x) = \dfrac{0.591x + 43.2}{0.787x + 20.9}$
(c) $\lim\limits_{x \to 0} r(x) \approx 2.07$ means that for years approaching 1950 there were about 2.07 men per woman in the U.S. workforce.
$\lim\limits_{x \to 100} r(x) \approx 1.03$ means that for years approaching 2050 it is projected that there will be 1.03 men per woman in the U.S. workforce.
(d) $\lim\limits_{x \to \infty} r(x) \approx 0.751 \approx 3/4$ means that the long-term projection is for about 3 men per 4 women in the U.S. workforce.

9.3 EXERCISES

1. (a) 6   (b) 8   **3.** (a) $\frac{10}{3}$ (b) -5
5. (a) $-3.9, -3.99$ (b) $-4.1, -4.01$ (c) -4
7. (a) 32   (b) 32   (c) $(4, 64)$
9. (a) verification   (b) -8 (c) -8
(d) $(-1, 5)$
11. (a) $P(1, 1), A(3, 0)$ (b) $-\frac{1}{2}$ (c) $-\frac{1}{2}$ (d) $-\frac{1}{2}$
13. (a) $P(1, 3), A(0, 3)$ (b) 0   (c) 0   (d) 0
15. (a) $f'(x) = 10x + 6$ (b) $10x + 6; -14$
(c) -14
17. (a) $p'(q) = 4q + 1$ (b) $4q + 1; 41$ (c) 41
19. (a) 89.000024   (b) 89.0072   (c) ≈ 89
21. (a) 294.000008   (b) 294.0084   (c) ≈ 294
23. -31
25. (a) At A the slope is positive; at B it is negative.
(b) $-1/3$
27. $f'(4) = 7/3$; $f(4) = -11$ **29.** $y = 5x - 14$
31. (a) a, b, d (b) c (c) A, C, E
33. (a) A, B, C, D (b) A, D
35. (a) $f'(x) = 2x + 1$ (b) $f'(2) = 5$
(c) $y = 5x - 4$ (d)

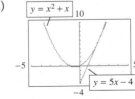

37. (a) $f'(x) = 3x^2$ (b) $f'(1) = 3$
(c) $y = 3x + 1$
(d)

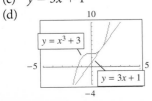

39. (a) 43 dollars per unit   (b) 95.50 dollars per unit
(c) The average cost per printer when 100 to 300 are produced (a) is \$43 per printer, and the average cost when 300 to 600 are produced (b) is \$95.50 per printer.

41. (a) $-100/3$ (b) $-4/3$
43. AB, AC, BC. Average rate is found from the slope of a segment; AB rises most slowly; BC is steepest.
45. (a) $R'(x) = \overline{MR} = 300 - 2x$
(b) 200; the predicted change in revenue from selling the 51st unit is about \$200.
(c) -100; the predicted change in revenue from the 201st unit is about -100 dollars.
(d) 0   (e) It changes from increasing to decreasing.
47. 200
49. (a) 100; the expected profit from the sale of the 201st car is \$100.
(b) -100; the expected profit from the sale of the 301st car is a loss of \$100.
51. (a) 1.039
(b) If humidity changes by 1%, the heat index will change by about 1.039°F.
53. (a) Marginal revenue is given by the slope of the tangent line, which is steeper at 300 cell phones. Hence marginal revenue is greater for 300 cell phones.
(b) Marginal revenue predicts the revenue from the next unit sold. Hence, the 301st item brings in more revenue because the marginal revenue for 300 cell phones is greater than for 700.

9.4 EXERCISES

1. $y' = 0$ **3.** $f'(t) = 1$
5. $y' = -8 + 4x = 4x - 8$ **7.** $f'(x) = 12x^3 - 6x^5$
9. $y' = 50x^4 - 9x^2 + 5$ **11.** $w'(z) = 7z^6 - 18z^5$
13. $g'(x) = 24x^{11} - 30x^5 + 36x^3 + 1$
15. (a) 30   (b) 30   **17.** (a) 6   (b) 6
19. $y' = -5x^{-6} - 8x^{-9} = -5/x^6 - 8/x^9$
21. $\dfrac{dz}{dt} = 11t^{8/3} - \frac{7}{2}t^{3/4} - \frac{1}{2}t^{-1/2}$
$= 11\sqrt[3]{t^8} - \frac{7}{2}\sqrt[4]{t^3} - \dfrac{1}{2\sqrt{t}}$
23. $f'(x) = -4x^{-9/5} - \frac{8}{3}x^{-7/3}$
$= \dfrac{-4}{\sqrt[5]{x^9}} - \dfrac{8}{3\sqrt[3]{x^7}}$
25. $g'(x) = \dfrac{-15}{x^6} - \dfrac{8}{x^5} + \dfrac{2}{\sqrt[3]{x^2}}$
27. $y = -7x + 10$ **29.** $y = 3$
31. $(1, -1), (5, 31)$ **33.** $(0, 9), (3, -18)$
35. (a) $-1/2$ (b) -0.5000 (to four decimal places)
37. (a) $f'(x) = 6x^2 + 5$
(b)

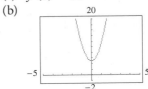

Graph of $f'(x)$ and numerical derivative of $f(x)$

39. (a) $h'(x) = -30x^{-4} + 4x^{-7/5} + 2x$

$$= \frac{-30}{x^4} + \frac{4}{\sqrt[5]{x^7}} + 2x$$

(b)

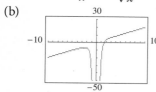

Graph of $h'(x)$ and numerical derivative of $h(x)$

41. (a) $y = 8x - 3$

(b)   (c) Yes

$y = 3x^2 + 2x$ $y = 8x - 3$

43. (a) $f'(x) = -2 - 2x$

(b)

$f(x) = 8 - 2x - x^2$

$f'(x) = -2 - 2x$

(c) $f'(x) = 0$ at $x = -1$; $f'(x) > 0$ for $x < -1$; $f'(x) < 0$ for $x > -1$

(d) $f(x)$ has a maximum when $x = -1$. $f(x)$ rises for $x < -1$. $f(x)$ falls for $x > -1$.

45. (a) $f'(x) = 3x^2 - 12$

(b)

$f'(x) = 3x^2 - 12$

$f(x) = x^3 - 12x - 5$

(c) $f'(x) = 0$ at $x = -2$ and $x = 2$ $f'(x) > 0$ for $x < -2$ and $x > 2$ $f'(x) < 0$ for $-2 < x < 2$

(d) $f(x)$ has a maximum when $x = -2$, a minimum when $x = 2$ $f(x)$ rises when $x < -2$ and when $x > 2$ $f(x)$ falls when $-2 < x < 2$

47. (a) 40; the expected change in revenue from the 301st unit is about $40

(b) -20; the expected change in revenue from the 601st unit is about -20 dollars

49. $\dfrac{dq}{dM} = \dfrac{3k}{4M^{1/4}}$

51. (a) -4; if the price changes to $26, the quantity demanded will change by approximately -4 units

(b) $-\frac{1}{2}$; if the price changes to $101, the quantity demanded will change by approximately $-\frac{1}{2}$ unit

53. (a) $\overline{C}'(x) = (-4000/x^2) + 0.1$ (b) 200

(c) $C'(200) = \overline{C}(200) = 95$

55. (a) -1200

(b) If the impurities change from 10% to 11%, then the cost decreases by about $1200.

57. (a) $WC = 45.0625 - 29.3375s^{0.16}$

(b) -0.31

(c) At 15° F, if the wind speed changes by $+1$ mph (to 26 mph), then the wind chill will change by approximately -0.31°F.

59. (a) $y = 0.0682x^2 + 1.76x + 96.0$

(b) $2.57 per year

(c) $\dfrac{dy}{dx} = 0.1364x + 1.76$

(d) $\dfrac{dy}{dx}\Big|_{x=10} = 3.124$; about $3.12 per year

(e) $126.81

61. (a) $P(t) = -0.0000738t^3 + 0.0102t^2 + 2.20t + 163$

(b) $P'(t) = -0.0002214t^2 + 0.0204t + 2.20$

(c) 2000: $P'(50) \approx 2.67$ means that for 2001, the U.S. population will rise by about 2.67 million people. 2025: $P'(75) \approx 2.48$ means that for 2026, the U.S. population is expected to rise by about 2.48 million people.

9.5 EXERCISES

1. $y' = 15x^2 - 14x - 6$

3. $f'(x) = (x^{12} + 3x^4 + 4)(6x^2) + (2x^3 - 1)(12x^{11} + 12x^3)$ $= 30x^{14} - 12x^{11} + 42x^6 - 12x^3 + 24x^2$

5. $y' = (7x^6 - 5x^4 + 2x^2 - 1)(36x^8 + 21x^6 - 10x + 3)$ $+ (4x^9 + 3x^7 - 5x^2 + 3)(42x^5 - 20x^3 + 4x)$

7. $y' = (x^2 + x + 1)(\frac{1}{3}x^{-2/3} - x^{-1/2}) +$ $(x^{1/3} - 2x^{1/2} + 5)(2x + 1)$

9. (a) 40   (b) 40

11. $\dfrac{dp}{dq} = \dfrac{2q^2 - 2q - 6}{(2q - 1)^2}$

13. $\dfrac{dy}{dx} = \dfrac{4x^5 - 4x^3 - 16x}{(x^4 - 2x^2 + 5)^2}$

15. $\dfrac{dz}{dx} = 2x + \dfrac{2x - x^2}{(1 - x - 2x^2)^2}$

17. $\dfrac{dp}{dq} = \dfrac{2q + 1}{\sqrt[3]{q^2}(1 - q)^2}$

19. $y' = \dfrac{2x^3 - 6x^2 - 8}{(x - 2)^2}$

21. (a) $\frac{3}{5}$ (b) $\frac{3}{5}$ **23.** $y = 44x - 32$

25. $y = \frac{10}{3}x - \frac{10}{3}$ **27.** 104

29. 1.3333 (to four decimal places)

31. (a) $f'(x) = 3x^2 - 6x - 24$

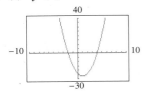

Graph of both $f'(x)$ and numerical derivative of $f(x)$

(b) Horizontal tangents where $f'(x) = 0$; at $x = -2$ and $x = 4$

(c)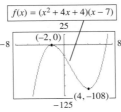

$f(x) = (x^2 + 4x + 4)(x - 7)$

33. (a) $y' = \dfrac{x^2 - 4x}{(x - 2)^2}$

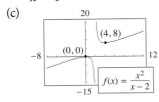

Graph of both y' and the numerical derivative of y

(b) Horizontal tangents where $y' = 0$; at $x = 0$ and $x = 4$

(c)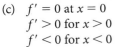

$f(x) = \dfrac{x^2}{x - 2}$

35. (a) $f'(x) = \dfrac{20x}{(x^2 + 1)^2}$

(b)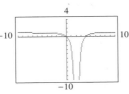

$f(x) = \dfrac{10x^2}{x^2 + 1}$

$f'(x) = \dfrac{20x}{(x^2 + 1)^2}$

(c) $f' = 0$ at $x = 0$
$f' > 0$ for $x > 0$
$f' < 0$ for $x < 0$

(d) f has a minimum at $x = 0$.
f is increasing for $x > 0$.
f is decreasing for $x < 0$.

37. $f'(x) = \lim\limits_{h \to 0} \dfrac{\dfrac{u(x+h)}{v(x+h)} - \dfrac{u(x)}{v(x)}}{h}$

$= \lim\limits_{h \to 0} \dfrac{u(x+h)v(x) - u(x)v(x+h)}{h \cdot v(x)v(x+h)}$

$= \lim\limits_{h \to 0} \dfrac{u(x+h)v(x) - u(x)v(x) + u(x)v(x) - u(x)v(x+h)}{h \cdot v(x)v(x+h)}$

$= \lim\limits_{h \to 0} \dfrac{v(x)\left[\dfrac{u(x+h) - u(x)}{h}\right] - u(x)\left[\dfrac{v(x+h) - v(x)}{h}\right]}{v(x)v(x+h)}$

$= \dfrac{v(x)u'(x) - u(x)v'(x)}{[v(x)]^2}$

39. $C'(p) = 810{,}000/(100 - p)^2$

41. $R'(49) \approx 30.00$ The expected revenue from the sale of the next unit (the 50th) is about $30.00.

43. $R'(5) = -50$ As the group changes by 1 person (to 31), the revenue will drop by about $50.

45. $S = 1000x - x^2$

47. $\dfrac{dR}{dn} = \dfrac{r(1 - r)}{[1 + (n - 1)r]^2}$

49. (a) $P'(6) \approx 0.045$ During the next (7th) month of the campaign, the proportion of voters who recognize the candidate will change by about 0.045, or 4.5%.

(b) $P'(12) \approx -0.010$ During the next (13th) month of the campaign, the proportion of voters who recognize the candidate will drop by about 0.010, or 1%.

(c) It is better for $P'(t)$ to be positive—that is, to have increasing recognition.

51. (a) $f'(20) \approx -0.79$

(b) At 0°F, if the wind speed changes by 1 mph (to 21 mph), the wind chill will change by about -0.79°F.

53. (a) $B'(t) = (0.01t + 3)(0.0476t - 9.79)$ $+ (0.01)(0.0238t^2 - 9.79t + 3100)$

(b) $B'(70) \approx 1.42$ means that in 2020 the number of beneficiaries will be changing at the rate of about 1.42 million per year.

(c) [2010, 2020]: 1.55
[2020, 2030]: 1.39
[2010, 2030]: 1.47
The average rate over [2020, 2030] is best but is still off by almost 0.03 million per year.

55. (a) $p'(t) = \dfrac{2154.06}{(1.38t + 64.1)^2}$

(b) 2005: $p'(55) \approx 0.110$; 2020: $p'(70) \approx 0.083$

(c) $p'(55)$ means that in 2005, the percent of women in the workforce was changing about 0.110 percentage points per year. $p'(70)$ predicts the rate in 2020 will be about 0.083 percentage points per year.

9.6 EXERCISES

1. $\dfrac{dy}{du} = 3u^2,\ \dfrac{du}{dx} = 2x,\ \dfrac{dy}{dx} = 3u^2 \cdot 2x = 6x(x^2 + 1)^2$

3. $\dfrac{dy}{du} = 4u^3,\ \dfrac{du}{dx} = 8x - 1,\ \dfrac{dy}{dx} = 4u^3(8x - 1)$
$= 4(8x - 1)(4x^2 - x + 8)^3$

5. $f'(x) = 20(3x^5 - 2)^{19}(15x^4) = 300x^4(3x^5 - 2)^{19}$

7. $h'(x) = 6(x^5 - 2x^3 + 5)^7(5x^4 - 6x^2)$
$= 6x^2(5x^2 - 6)(x^5 - 2x^3 + 5)^7$

9. $s'(t) = 5 - 9(2t^4 + 7)^2(8t^3) = 5 - 72t^3(2t^4 + 7)^2$

11. $g'(x) = -2(x^4 - 5x)^{-3}(4x^3 - 5) = \dfrac{-2(4x^3 - 5)}{(x^4 - 5x)^3}$

13. $f'(s) = -12(2s^5 + 1)^{-5}(10s^4) = \dfrac{-120s^4}{(2s^5 + 1)^5}$

15. $g'(x) = -\dfrac{3}{4}(2x^3 + 3x + 5)^{-7/4}(6x^2 + 3)$
$= \dfrac{-3(6x^2 + 3)}{4(2x^3 + 3x + 5)^{7/4}}$

17. $y' = \dfrac{1}{2}(3x^2 + 4x + 9)^{-1/2}(6x + 4)$

$= \dfrac{3x + 2}{\sqrt{3x^2 + 4x + 9}}$

19. $y' = \dfrac{66}{9}(x^3 - 7)^5(3x^2) = 22x^2(x^3 - 7)^5$

21. $\dfrac{dz}{dw} = \dfrac{15(3w + 1)^4 - 3}{7}$

23. (a) and (b) 96,768

25. (a) and (b) 2

27. $y = 3x - 5$ **29.** $9x - 5y = 2$

31. (a) $f'(x) = 6x(x^2 - 4)^2$

(b)

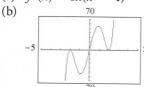

(c) $x = 0, x = 2,$
$x = -2$

(d) $(0, -52),$
$(2, 12),$
$(-2, 12)$

Graph of both $f'(x)$ and numerical derivative of $f(x)$

(e)

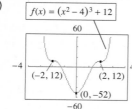

33. (a) $f'(x) = 8x(1 - x^2)^{1/3}$

(b)

$f(x) = 12 - 3(1 - x^2)^{4/3}$

$f'(x) = 8x(1 - x^2)^{1/3}$

(c) $f'(x) = 0$ at $x = -1, x = 0, x = 1$
$f'(x) > 0$ for $x < -1$ and $0 < x < 1$
$f'(x) < 0$ for $-1 < x < 0$ and $x > 1$

(d) $f(x)$ has a maximum at $x = -1$ and $x = 1$, a
minimum at $x = 0$.
$f(x)$ is increasing for $x < -1$ and $0 < x < 1$.
$f(x)$ is decreasing for $-1 < x < 0$ and $x > 1$.

35. (a) $y' = 2x^2$ (b) $y' = -2/x^4$

(c) $y' = 2(2x)^2$ (d) $y' = \dfrac{-18}{(3x)^4}$

37. 120 in./sec

39. $1499.85 (approximately); if a 101st unit is sold,
revenue will change by about $1499.85

41. (a) -0.114 (approximately)

(b) If the price changes by $1, to $22, the weekly sales
volume will change by approximately -0.114
thousand units.

43. (a) $-$3.20 per unit

(b) If the quantity demanded changes from 49 to 50
units, the change in price will be about $-$3.20.

45. $\dfrac{dy}{dx} = \left(\dfrac{8k}{5}\right)(x - x_0)^{3/5}$

47. $\dfrac{dp}{dq} = -100(2q + 1)^{-3/2} = \dfrac{-100}{(2q + 1)^{3/2}}$

49. $\dfrac{dK_c}{dv} = 8(4v + 1)^{-1/2} = \dfrac{8}{\sqrt{4v + 1}}$

51. (a) $658.75. If the interest changed from 6% to 7%,
the amount of the investment would change by
about $658.75.

(b) $2156.94. If the interest rate changed from 12% to
13%, the amount of the investment would change
by about $2156.94.

53. (a) 2008: $A'(8) \approx 126.3$; 2015: $A'(15) \approx 231.4$
These mean that the total national expendi-
tures for health are predicted to change by about
$126.3 billion from 2008 to 2009 and about
$231.4 billion from 2015 to 2016.

(b) The average rate for 2014 to 2015 is best: $228 bil-
lion/year.

55. (a) 2005: $G'(5) \approx 1370.64$; 2015: $G'(15) \approx 934.56$
These mean that the rate of change of the GDP
was about $1370.64 billion per year in 2005 and
about $934.5 billion per year in 2015.

(b) 912.5 (billion per year)

(c) 2010: $G'(10) \approx 1024.86$. The answer from part (b)
is not a good approximation to $G'(10)$.

9.7 EXERCISES

1. 0   **3.** $4(-4x^{-5}); -16/x^5$

5. $15x^2 + 4(-x^{-2}); 15x^2 - 4/x^2$

7. $(x^2 - 2)1 + (x + 4)(2x); 3x^2 + 8x - 2$

9. $\dfrac{u^2(3u^2) - (u^3 + 1)(2u)}{(u^2)^2}; (u^3 - 2)/u^3$

11. $(3x^2 - 4)(x^3 - 4x)^9$

13. $\frac{5}{3}x^3[3(4x^5 - 5)^2(20x^4)] + (4x^5 - 5)^3(5x^2)$;
$5x^2(4x^5 - 5)^2(24x^5 - 5)$

15. $(x - 1)^2(2x) + (x^2 + 1)2(x - 1)$;
$2(x - 1)(2x^2 - x + 1)$

17. $\dfrac{(x^2 + 1)3(x^2 - 4)^2(2x) - (x^2 - 4)^3(2x)}{(x^2 + 1)^2}$;
$\dfrac{2x(x^2 - 4)^2(2x^2 + 7)}{(x^2 + 1)^2}$

19. $3[(q + 1)(q^3 - 3)]^2[(q + 1)3q^2 + (q^3 - 3)1]$;
$3(4q^3 + 3q^2 - 3)[(q + 1)(q^3 - 3)]^2$

21. $4[x^2(x^2 + 3x)]^3[x^2(2x + 3) + (x^2 + 3x)(2x)]$;
$4x^2(4x + 9)[x^2(x^2 + 3x)]^3 = 4x^{11}(4x + 9)(x + 3)^3$

23. $4\left(\dfrac{2x - 1}{x^2 + x}\right)^3\left[\dfrac{(x^2 + x)2 - (2x - 1)(2x + 1)}{(x^2 + x)^2}\right]$;
$\dfrac{4(-2x^2 + 2x + 1)(2x - 1)^3}{(x^2 + x)^5}$

25. $(8x^4 + 3)^2 3(x^3 - 4x)^2(3x^2 - 4) +$
$(x^3 - 4x)^3 2(8x^4 + 3)(32x^3)$;
$(8x^4 + 3)(x^3 - 4x)^2(136x^6 - 352x^4 + 27x^2 - 36)$

27. $\dfrac{(4 - x^2)\frac{1}{3}(x^2 + 5)^{-2/3}(2x) - (x^2 + 5)^{1/3}(-2x)}{(4 - x^2)^2}$;

$\dfrac{2x(2x^2 + 19)}{3\sqrt[3]{(x^2 + 5)^2}(4 - x^2)^2}$

29. $(x^2)\frac{1}{4}(4x - 3)^{-3/4}(4) + (4x - 3)^{1/4}(2x)$;
$(9x^2 - 6x)/\sqrt[4]{(4x - 3)^3}$

31. $(2x)\frac{1}{2}(x^3 + 1)^{-1/2}(3x^2) + (x^3 - 1)^{1/2}(2)$;
$(5x^3 + 2)/\sqrt{x^3 + 1}$

33. (a) $F_1'(x) = 12x^3(x^4 + 1)^4$

(b) $F_2'(x) = \dfrac{-12x^3}{(x^4 + 1)^6}$

(c) $F_3'(x) = 12x^3(3x^4 + 1)^4$

(d) $F_4'(x) = \dfrac{-300x^3}{(5x^4 + 1)^6}$

35. $dP/dx = 90(3x + 1)^2$

37. (a) $59,900 per camper
(b) An 11th camper sold would change revenue by about $59,900.

39. $dC/dy = 1/\sqrt{y + 1} + 0.4$

41. $dV/dx = 144 - 96x + 12x^2$

43. -1.6; This means that from the 9th to the 10th week, sales are expected to decrease by about $1600.

45. (a) 2005: $350/year; 2015: $549/year
(b) In 2015, the per capita expenditures for health care are predicted to be changing at a rate of about $549 per year.
(c) Average rate = 380; This approximates the instantaneous rate in 2005 quite well.

9.8 EXERCISES

1. $f''(x) = 180x^8 - 360x^3 - 72x$ 3. $g''(x) = 6x - 2x^{-3}$

5. $d^2y/dx^2 = 6x + \frac{1}{4}x^{-3/2}$ 7. $d^3y/dx^3 = 60x^2 - 96$

9. $f'''(x) = 1008x^6 - 720x^3$ 11. $d^3y/dx^3 = -6/x^4$

13. $d^2y/dx^2 = 20x^3 + \frac{1}{4}x^{-3/2}$ 15. $f'''(x) = \frac{3}{8}(x + 1)^{-5/2}$

17. $d^4y/dx^4 = 0$ 19. $f^{(4)}(x) = -15/(16x^{7/2})$

21. $y^{(4)} = 24(4x - 1)^{-5/2}$ 23. $f^{(6)}(x) = -2(x + 1)^{-3}$

25. 26   27. 16.0000 (to four decimal places)

29. 0.0004261

31. (a) $f'(x) = 3x^2 - 6x$ $f''(x) = 6x - 6$
(b)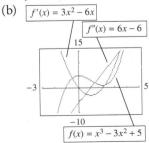
(c) $f''(x) = 0$ at $x = 1$
$f''(x) > 0$ for $x > 1$
$f''(x) < 0$ for $x < 1$

(d) $f'(x)$ has a minimum at $x = 1$.
$f'(x)$ is increasing for $x > 1$.
$f'(x)$ is decreasing for $x < 1$.
(e) $f''(x) < 0$ (f) $f''(x) > 0$.

33. $a = 0.12$ m/sec^2

35. -0.02 $/unit per unit

37. (a) $\dfrac{dR}{dm} = mc - m^2$ (b) $\dfrac{d^2R}{dm^2} = c - 2m$
(c) second

39. (a) 0.0009 (approximately)
(b) When 1 more unit is sold (beyond 25), the marginal revenue will change by about 0.0009 thousand dollars per unit, or $0.90 per unit.

41. (a) $S' = \dfrac{-3}{(t + 3)^2} + \dfrac{36}{(t + 3)^3}$ (b) $S''(15) = 0$
(c) After 15 weeks, the rate of change of the rate of sales is zero because the rate of sales reaches a minimum value.

43. (a) $W'(t) \approx 0.0447t^{1.11}$ (b) $W''(t) \approx 0.0497t^{0.11}$
(c) $W(50) \approx 81.5$, $W'(50) \approx 3.44$, and $W''(50) \approx 0.0764$. These mean that in 2025 the average annual wage is expected to be $81,500 and changing at a rate of about $3440 per year. Also that rate is expected to be changing about $76.40 per year per year.

45. (a) $R(x) = -0.000190x^3 + 0.0519x^2 - 4.06x + 192$
(b) $R'(x) = -0.000570x^2 + 0.1038x - 4.06$
(c) $R''(x) = -0.00114x + 0.1038$
(d) $R'(90) \approx 0.665$; $R''(90) \approx 0.0012$
In 2040, the economic dependency ratio is expected to be changing at a rate of about 0.665 per year, and this rate is expected to be changing about 0.0012 per year per year.

47. (a) $f'(x) = 0.002592x^2 - 0.256x + 6.61$
(b) At age 25: about $1830 per year and at age 55: about $371 per year
(c) $f''(x) = 0.005184x - 0.256$
(d) At age 25: about $-$126 per year per year of age and at age 55: about $29 per year per year of age
(e) The rate of change in the median income of 55-year-old workers is about $371 per year of age, and it is increasing at a rate of about $29 per year per year of age.

9.9 EXERCISES

1. (a) $\overline{MR} = 4$
(b) The sale of each additional item brings in $4 revenue at all levels of production.

3. (a) $3500; this is revenue from the sale of 100 units.
(b) $\overline{MR} = 36 - 0.02x$
(c) $34; Revenue will increase by about $34 if a 101st item is sold and by about $102 if 3 additional units past 100 units are sold.
(d) Actual revenue from the sale of the 101st item is $33.99.

5. (a) $R(x) = 80x - 0.4x^2$ (in hundreds of dollars)
(b) 7500 subscribers $(x = 75)$; $R = \$375{,}000$
(c) Lower the price per month.
(d) $\overline{MR} = R'(x) = 80 - 0.8x$; when $p = 50$, $x = 75$
$\overline{MR}(75) = 20$ means that if the number of customers increased from 75 to 76 (hundred), the revenue would increase by about 20 (hundred dollars), or $2000. This means the company should try to increase subscribers by lowering its monthly charge.

7. (a)

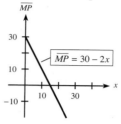

(b) $x = 1800$
(c) $\$32{,}400$

9. $\overline{MC} = 8$
11. $\overline{MC} = 13 + 2x$
13. $\overline{MC} = 3x^2 - 12x + 24$
15. $\overline{MC} = 27 + 3x^2$
17. (a) $10; the cost will increase by about $10.
(b) $11
19. $46; the cost will increase by about $46. For 3 additional units, the cost will increase by about $138.
21.

MC

$\overline{MC} = 2x + 4$

23. (a) The 101st item costs more. The tangent line slope is greater at $x = 100$ than at $x = 500$, and the slope of the tangent line gives the marginal cost and predicts the cost of the next item.
(b) More efficient. As x increases, the slopes of the tangents decrease. This means that the costs of additional items decrease as x increases.
25. $\overline{MP} = 5$; This means that for each additional unit sold, profit changes by $5.
27. (a) $5600   (b) $\overline{MP} = 20 - 0.02x$
(c) 10; profit will increase by about $10 if a 501st unit is sold.
(d) 9.99; the sale of the 501st item results in a profit of $9.99.
29. (a) $P(x) = R(x) - C(x)$, so profit is the distance between $R(x)$ and $C(x)$ (when $R(x)$ is above $C(x)$). $P(100) < P(700) < P(400)$; $P(100) < 0$, so there is a loss when 100 units are sold.
(b) This asks us to rank $\overline{MP}(100)$, $\overline{MP}(400)$, and $\overline{MP}(700)$. Because $\overline{MP} = \overline{MR} - \overline{MC}$, compare the slopes of the tangents to $R(x)$ and $C(x)$ at the three x-values. Thus $\overline{MP}(700) < \overline{MP}(400) < \overline{MP}(100)$. $\overline{MP}(700) < 0$ because $C(x)$ is steeper than $R(x)$ at $x = 700$. At $x = 100$, $R(x)$ is much steeper than $C(x)$.

31. (a) $A < B < C$. Amount of profit is the height of the graph. There is a loss at A.
(b) $C < B < A$. Marginal profit is the slope of the tangent to the graph. Marginals (slopes) are positive at all three points.
33. (a)

$\overline{MP}$

$\overline{MP} = 30 - 2x$

(b) 15 hundred units
(c) 15 hundred units
(d) $25 thousand

35. 700   **37.** $9000

CHAPTER 9 REVIEW EXERCISES

1. (a) 2   (b) 2   **2.** (a) 0   (b) 0
3. (a) 2   (b) 1   **4.** (a) 2   (b) does not exist
5. (a) does not exist   (b) 2
6. (a) does not exist   (b) does not exist
7. 55   **8.** 0   **9.** -2 **10.** 4/5   **11.** $\frac{1}{2}$
12. $\frac{1}{5}$ **13.** no limit   **14.** 0   **15.** 4
16. no limit   **17.** 3   **18.** no limit   **19.** $6x$
20. $1 - 4x$ **21.** -14 **22.** 5
23. (a) yes   (b) no   **24.** (a) yes   (b) no
25. 2   **26.** no limit   **27.** 1   **28.** no   **29.** yes
30. yes   **31.** discontinuity at $x = 5$
32. discontinuity at $x = 2$ **33.** continuous
34. discontinuity at $x = 1$
35. (a) $x = 0$, $x = 1$ (b) 0   (c) 0
36. (a) $x = -1$, $x = 0$ (b) $\frac{1}{2}$ (c) $\frac{1}{2}$
37. -2; $y = -2$ is a horizontal asymptote.
38. 0; $y = 0$ is a horizontal asymptote.
39. 7   **40.** true   **41.** false
42. $f'(x) = 6x + 2$ **43.** $f'(x) = 1 - 2x$
44. $[-1, 0]$; the segment over this interval is steeper.
45. (a) no   (b) no   **46.** (a) yes   (b) no
47. (a) -5.9171 (to four decimal places)   (b) -5.9
48. (a) 4.9/3   (b) 7   **49.** about $-1/4$
50. B, C, A: $B < 0$ and $C < 0$; the tangent line at $x = 6$ falls more steeply than the segment over $[2, 10]$.
51. $20x^4 - 18x^2$ **52.** $90x^8 - 30x^5 + 4$
53. 1   **54.** $1/(2\sqrt{x})$ **55.** 0   **56.** $-4/(3\sqrt[3]{x^4})$
57. $\dfrac{-1}{x^2} + \dfrac{1}{2\sqrt{x^3}}$ **58.** $\dfrac{-3}{x^3} - \dfrac{1}{3\sqrt[3]{x^2}}$
59. $y = 15x - 18$ **60.** $y = 34x - 48$
61. (a) $x = 0$, $x = 2$ (b) $(0, 1)$ $(2, -3)$
(c)

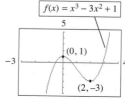

62. (a) $x = 0$, $x = 2$, $x = -2$
(b) $(0, 8)$ $(2, -24)$ $(-2, -24)$

(c)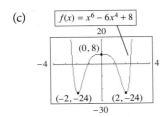

$f(x) = x^6 - 6x^4 + 8$

$(0, 8)$

$(-2, -24)$ $(2, -24)$

63. $9x^2 - 26x + 4$ 64. $21x^6 + 4x^3 + 27x^2$

65. $\dfrac{15q^2}{(2q^3 + 1)^2}$ 66. $\dfrac{1 - 3t}{[2\sqrt{t}(3t + 1)^2]}$ 67. $\dfrac{9x + 2}{2\sqrt{x}}$

68. $\dfrac{5x^6 + 2x^4 + 20x^3 - 3x^2 - 4x}{(x^3 + 1)^2}$

69. $(9x^2 - 24x)(x^3 - 4x^2)^2$

70. $6(30x^5 + 24x^3)(5x^6 + 6x^4 + 5)^5$

71. $72x^3(2x^4 - 9)^8$ 72. $\dfrac{-(3x^2 - 4)}{2\sqrt{(x^3 - 4x)^3}}$

73. $2x(2x^4 + 5)^7(34x^4 + 5)$ 74. $\dfrac{-2(3x + 1)(x + 12)}{(x^2 - 4)^2}$

75. $36[(3x + 1)(2x^3 - 1)]^{11}(8x^3 + 2x^2 - 1)$

76. $\dfrac{3}{(1 - x)^4}$ 77. $\dfrac{(2x^2 - 4)}{\sqrt{x^2 - 4}}$ 78. $\dfrac{2x - 1}{(3x - 1)^{4/3}}$

79. $y'' = \dfrac{-1}{4}x^{-3/2} - 2$ 80. $y'' = 12x^2 - 2/x^3$

81. $\dfrac{d^5y}{dx^5} = 0$ 82. $\dfrac{d^5y}{dx^5} = -30(1 - x)$

83. $\dfrac{d^3y}{dx^3} = -4[(x^2 - 4)^{-3/2}]$ 84. $\dfrac{d^4y}{dx^4} = \dfrac{2x(x^2 - 3)}{(x^2 + 1)^3}$

85. (a) $400,000   (b) $310,000   (c) $90,000

86. (a) $70,000; this is fixed costs.
   (b) $0; $x = 1000$ is break-even.

87. (a) $140 per unit
   (b) $\overline{C}(x) \to \infty$; the limit does not exist.

88. (a) $C(x) \to \infty$; the limit does not exist. As the number of units produced increases without bound, so does the total cost.
   (b) $60 per unit. As more units are produced, the average cost of each unit approaches $60.

89. The average annual percent change of (a) elderly men in the workforce is 0.0825 percentage points per year and of (b) elderly women in the workforce is 0.0775 percentage points per year.

90. (a) Annual average rate of change of percent of elderly men in the workforce:
   1970–1980: −0.78 percentage points per year
   2030–2040: −0.23 percentage points per year
   (b) Annual average rate of change of percent of elderly women in the workforce
   1970–1980: −0.16 percentage points per year
   2030–2040: −0.16 percentage points per year

91. (a) $x'(10) = -1$ means that if price changes from $10 to $11, the number of units demanded will change by about −1.
   (b) $x'(20) = -\frac{1}{4}$ means that if price changes from $20 to $21, the number of units demanded will change by about $-\frac{1}{4}$.

92. $h(100) \approx 4.15$; $h'(100) \approx 0.08$ means that when the updraft speed is 100 mph, the hail diameter is about 4.15 inches (softball-sized) and changing at the rate of 0.08 inch per mph of updraft.

93. The slope of the tangent at A gives $\overline{MR}(A)$. The tangent line at A is steeper (so has greater slope) than the tangent line at B. Hence, $\overline{MR}(A) > \overline{MR}(B)$, so the $(A + 1)$st unit will bring more revenue.

94. $R'(10) = 1570$. Raised. An 11th rent increase of $30 (and hence an 11th vacancy) would change revenue by about $1570.

95. (a) $P(20) = 23$ means productivity is 23 units per hour after 20 hours of training and experience.
   (b) $P'(20) \approx 1.4$ means that the 21st hour of training or experience will change productivity by about 1.4 units per hour.

96. $\dfrac{dq}{dp} = \dfrac{-p}{\sqrt{0.02p^2 + 500}}$

97. $x'(10) = \frac{1}{6}$ means if price changes from $10 to $11, the number of units supplied will change by about $\frac{1}{6}$.

98. $s''(t) = a = -2t^{-3/2}$; $s''(4) = -0.25$ ft/sec/sec

99. $P'(x) = 70 - 0.2x$; $P''(x) = -0.2$
   $P'(300) = 10$ means that the 301st unit brings in about $10 in profit.
   $P''(300) = -0.2$ means that marginal profit ($P'(x)$) is changing at the rate of −0.2 dollars per unit, per unit.

100. (a) $\overline{MC} = 6x + 6$ (b) 186
   (c) If a 31st unit is produced, costs will change by about $186.

101. $C'(4) = 53$ means that a 5th unit produced would change total costs by about $53.

102. (a) $\overline{MR} = 40 - 0.04x$ (b) $x = 1000$ units

103. $\overline{MP}(10) = 48$ means that if an 11th unit is sold, profit will change by about $48.

104. (a) $\overline{MR} = 80 - 0.08x$ (b) 72
   (c) If a 101st unit is sold, revenue will change by about $72.

105. $\dfrac{120x(x + 1)}{(2x + 1)^2}$ 106. $\overline{MP} = 4500 - 3x^2$

107. $\overline{MP} = 16 - 0.2x$

108. (a) C: Tangent line to $R(x)$ has smallest slope at C, so $\overline{MR}(C)$ is smallest and the next item at C will earn the least revenue.
   (b) B: $R(x) > C(x)$ at both B and C. Distance between $R(x)$ and $C(x)$ gives the amount of profit and is greatest at B.
   (c) A: $\overline{MR}$ greatest at A and $\overline{MC}$ least at A, as seen from the slopes of the tangents. Hence $\overline{MP}(A)$ is greatest, so the next item at A will give the greatest profit.
   (d) C: $\overline{MC}(C) > \overline{MR}(C)$, as seen from the slopes of the tangents. Hence $\overline{MP}(C) < 0$, so the next unit sold reduces profit.

CHAPTER 9 TEST

1. (a) $\frac{3}{4}$ (b) $-8/5$ (c) $9/8$ (d) does not exist

2. (a) $f'(x) = \lim\limits_{h \to 0} \dfrac{f(x + h) - f(x)}{h}$

   (b) $f'(x) = 6x - 1$

3. $x = 0, x = 8$

4. (a) $\dfrac{dB}{dW} = 0.523$ (b) $p'(t) = 90t^9 - 42t^6 - 17$

   (c) $\dfrac{dy}{dx} = \dfrac{99x^2 - 24x^9}{(2x^7 + 11)^2}$

   (d) $f'(x) = (3x^5 - 2x + 3)(40x^9 + 40x^3) +$
       $(4x^{10} + 10x^4 - 17)(15x^4 - 2)$

   (e) $g'(x) = 9(10x^4 + 21x^2)(2x^5 + 7x^3 - 5)^{11}$

   (f) $y' = 2(8x^2 + 5x + 18)(2x + 5)^5$

   (g) $f'(x) = \dfrac{6}{\sqrt{x}} + \dfrac{20}{x^3}$

5. $\dfrac{d^3y}{dx^3} = 6 + 60x^{-6}$

6. (a) $y = -15x - 5$ (b) $(4, -90), (-2, 18)$

7. -15 8. (a) 2   (b) does not exist   (c) -4

9. $g(-2) = 8$; $\lim\limits_{x \to -2^-} g(x) = 8$, $\lim\limits_{x \to -2^+} g(x) = -8$

   $\therefore \lim\limits_{x \to -2} g(x)$ does not exist and $g(x)$ is not continuous at $x = -2$.

10. (a) $\overline{MR} = R'(x) = 250 - 0.02x$

    (b) $R(72) = 17{,}948.16$ means that when 72 units are sold, revenue is \$17,948.16.
        $R'(72) = 248.56$ means that the expected revenue from the 73rd unit is about \$248.56.

11. (a) $P(x) = 50x - 0.01x^2 - 10{,}000$

    (b) $\overline{MP} = 50 - 0.02x$

    (c) $\overline{MP}(1000) = 30$ means that the predicted profit from the sale of the 1001st unit is approximately \$30.

12. 104

13. (a) -5 (b) -1 (c) 4   (d) does not exist

    (e) 2   (f) $3/2$ (g) $-4, 1, 3, 6$

    (h) $-4, 3, 6$

    (i) $f'(-2) <$ average rate over $[-2, 2] < f'(2)$

14. (a) $2/3$ (b) -4 (c) $2/3$

15. (a) B: $R(x) > C(x)$ at B, so there is profit. Distance between $R(x)$ and $C(x)$ gives the amount of profit.

    (b) A: $C(x) > R(x)$

    (c) A and B: slope of $R(x)$ is greater than the slope of $C(x)$. Hence $\overline{MR} > \overline{MC}$ and $\overline{MP} > 0$.

    (d) C: Slope of $C(x)$ is greater than the slope of $R(x)$. Hence $\overline{MC} > \overline{MR}$ and $\overline{MP} < 0$.

10.1 EXERCISES

1. (a) $(1, 5)$ (b) $(4, 1)$ (c) $(-1, 2)$

3. (a) $(1, 5)$ (b) $(4, 1)$ (c) $(-1, 2)$

5. (a) $3, 7$ (b) $3 < x < 7$ (c) $x < 3, x > 7$

   (d) 7   (e) 3

7. (a) $x = 0, x = 4$

   (b)

   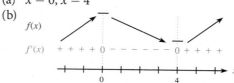

   min: $(4, -58)$; max: $(0, 6)$

9. (a) $x = -2, x = 0$

   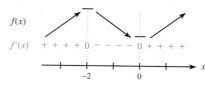

   (b) max: $(-2, 5)$; min: $(0, -11)$

11. (a) max: $(-1, 6)$; min: $(1, 2)$

    (b) $dy/dx = 3x^2 - 3$; $x = 1, x = -1$

    (c) $(1, 2), (-1, 6)$

    (d) yes

13. (a) HPI: $(-1, -3)$

    (b) $dy/dx = 3x^2 + 6x + 3$; $x = -1$

    (c) $(-1, -3)$

    (d) yes

15. (a) $\dfrac{dy}{dx} = x - 1$

    (b) $x = 1$

    (c) $\left(1, -\frac{1}{2}\right)$

    (d) decreasing: $x < 1$
        increasing: $x > 1$

    (e)

    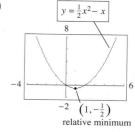

    relative minimum

17. (a) $dy/dx = x^2 + x - 2$

    (b) $x = -2, x = 1$ (c) $\left(-2, \frac{13}{3}\right), \left(1, -\frac{1}{6}\right)$

    (d) increasing: $x < -2$ and $x > 1$
        decreasing: $-2 < x < 1$

    (e)

    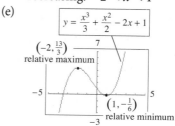

19. (a) $\dfrac{dy}{dx} = \dfrac{2}{3x^{1/3}}$ (b) $x = 0$ (c) $(0, 0)$

    (d) decreasing: $x < 0$
        increasing: $x > 0$

    (e)

    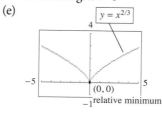

21. (a) $f'(x) = 0$ at $x = -\frac{1}{2}$
       $f'(x) > 0$ for $x < -\frac{1}{2}$
       $f'(x) < 0$ for $x > -\frac{1}{2}$
   (b) $f'(x) = -1 - 2x$ verifies these conclusions.

23. (a) $f'(x) = 0$ at $x = 0, x = -3, x = 3$
       $f'(x) > 0$ for $-3 < x < 3, x \neq 0$
       $f'(x) < 0$ for $x < -3$ and $x > 3$
   (b) $f'(x) = \frac{1}{3}x^2(9 - x^2)$ verifies these conclusions.

25. HPI $\left(1, \frac{4}{3}\right)$
   no max or min

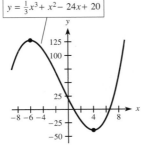

$y = \frac{1}{3}x^3 - x^2 + x + 1$

27. $(-6, 128)$ rel max;
   $\left(4, -38\frac{2}{3}\right)$ rel min

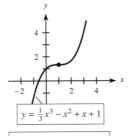

$y = \frac{1}{3}x^3 + x^2 - 24x + 20$

29. $(-1, 3)$ rel max;
   $(1, -1)$ rel min;
   HPI $(0, 1)$

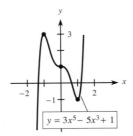

$y = 3x^5 - 5x^3 + 1$

31. $(1, 1)$ rel max;
   $(0, 0), (2, 0)$ rel min

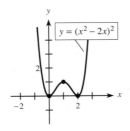

$y = (x^2 - 2x)^2$

33. $(3, 4)$ rel max;
   $(5, 0)$ rel min; HPI $(0, 0)$

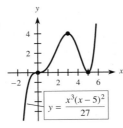

$y = \frac{x^3(x - 5)^2}{27}$

35. $(0, 0)$ rel max;
   $(2, -4.8)$ rel min

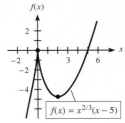

$f(x) = x^{2/3}(x - 5)$

37. $(50, 300{,}500), (100, 238{,}000)$
   $0 \leq x \leq 150, 0 \leq y \leq 301{,}000$

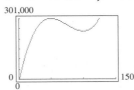

39. $(0, -40{,}000), (60, 4{,}280{,}000)$
   $-20 \leq x \leq 90, \quad -500{,}000 \leq y \leq 5{,}000{,}000$

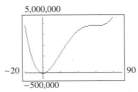

41. $(0, 2)$
   $(0.1, 1.99975)$
   $-0.1 \leq x \leq 0.2$
   $1.9997 \leq y \leq 2.0007$

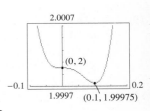

43. critical values: $x = -1, x = 2$
   $f(x)$ increasing for $x < -1$ and $x > 2$
   $f(x)$ decreasing for $-1 < x < 2$
   rel max at $x = -1$; rel min at $x = 2$
   possible graph of $f(x)$

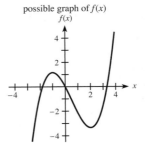

45. critical values: $x = 0, x = 3$
   $f(x)$ increasing for $x > 3$
   $f(x)$ decreasing for $x < 3, x \neq 0$
   rel min at $x = 3$; HPI at $x = 0$
   possible graph of $f(x)$

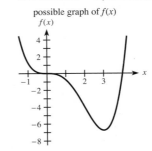

47. Graph on left is $f(x)$; on right is $f'(x)$ because $f(x)$ is increasing when $f'(x) > 0$ (i.e., above the x-axis) and $f(x)$ is decreasing when $f'(x) < 0$ (i.e., below the x-axis).

49. decreasing for $t \geq 0$

51. (a) $2 \pm \sqrt{13}$
(b) $2 + \sqrt{13} \approx 5.6$
(c) $0 \leq t < 2 + \sqrt{13}$
(d)

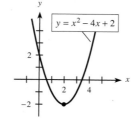

53. (a) $x = 5$ (b) $0 < x < 5$
(c) increasing for $x > 5$

55. (a) at $x = 150$, increasing; at $x = 250$, changing from increasing to decreasing; at $x = 350$, decreasing
(b) increasing for $x < 250$ (c) 250 units

57. (a) $t = 6$ (b) 6 weeks

59. (a) 10 (b) January 1

61. $x \approx 21.1$; in 2022 the model will achieve a maximum of 9.04 billion subscriberships

63. (a) $y = -0.000487x^3 - 0.162x^2 + 19.8x + 388$
(b) 912 million in 2020 (at $x \approx 49.9$)

65. (a) $M(t) = 0.0000889t^3 - 0.0111t^2 + 0.237t + 11.5$
(b) relative maximum at $(12.6, 12.9)$; relative minimum at $(70.7, 4.2)$
(c) No. The years corresponding to the critical points are 2023 and 2081. Despite the fact that the model is an excellent fit to the data given, it is unrealistic for the model to be accurate for more than 40 years beyond the data set.

10.2 EXERCISES

1. (a) concave down (b) concave up

3. (a, c) and (d, e) **5.** (c, d) and (e, f) **7.** c, d, e

9. concave up when $x > 2$; concave down when $x < 2$; POI at $x = 2$

11. concave up when $x < -2$ and $x > 1$
concave down when $-2 < x < 1$
points of inflection at $x = -2$ and $x = 1$

13. no points of inflection;
$(2, -2)$ min

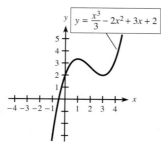

15. $\left(1, \frac{10}{3}\right)$ max; $(3, 2)$ min;
$\left(2, \frac{8}{3}\right)$ point of inflection

17. $(0, 0)$ rel max; $(2\sqrt{2}, -64)$, $(-2\sqrt{2}, -64)$ min;
points of inflection: $(2\sqrt{6}/3, -320/9)$ and
$(-2\sqrt{6}/3, -320/9)$

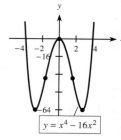

19. $(-2, 64)$ rel max; $(2, -64)$
rel min; points of inflection:
$(-\sqrt{2}, 39.6)$, $(0, 0)$, and
$(\sqrt{2}, -39.6)$

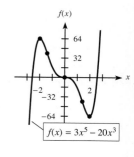

21. $(1, -3)$ min; points of
inflection: $(-2, 7.6)$
and $(0, 0)$

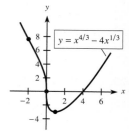

23. (a) $f''(x) = 0$ when $x = 1$
$f''(x) > 0$ when $x < 1$
$f''(x) < 0$ when $x > 1$
(b) rel max for $f'(x)$ at $x = 1$; no rel min
(c)

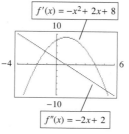

25. (a) concave up when $x < 2$; concave down when $x > 2$
(b) point of inflection at $x = 2$
(c)

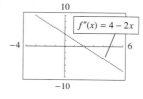

(d) possible graph of $f(x)$

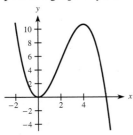

27. (a) G (b) C (c) F (d) H (e) I
29. (a) concave up when $x < 0$
              concave down when $x > 0$
              point of inflection at $x = 0$
       (b) concave up when $-1 < x < 1$
              concave down when $x < -1$ and $x > 1$
              POI at $x = -1$ and $x = 1$
       (c) concave up when $x > 0$
              concave down when $x < 0$
              point of inflection at $x = 0$
31. (a) $P'(t)$ (b) B (c) C
33. (a) C (b) right   (c) yes
35. (a) in an 8-hour shift, max when $t = 8$ (b) 4 hr
37. (a) 9 days   (b) 15 days
39. (a) (15.9, 100.3), (49.7, 85.3)
       (b) max = 100.3 at $t = 15.9$; min = 85.3 at $t = 49.7$.
              These mean that over the years 1985 to 2035,
              the energy use per capita reached a maximum
              of 100.3% of the 1995 use during 1996 and is
              expected to reach a minimum of 85.3% of the
              1995 use during 2030.
41. (a) $y = -0.000102x^3 + 0.00884x^2 + 1.43x + 57.9$
       (b) $x = 28.9$, during 1979
43. (a) $C(t) = 0.342t^3 - 6.83t^2 + 105t + 1330$
       (b) POI at $t = 6.66$, $C(t) = 1827$. These costs increase
              at a decreasing rate until $t = 6.66$ (in 2012) and
              increase at an increasing rate afterward.

10.3 EXERCISES

1. min -6 at $x = 2$, max $3.\overline{481}$ at $x = -2/3$
3. min -1 at $x = -2$, max 2 at $x = -1$
5. (a) $x = 1800$ units, $R = \$32,400$
       (b) $x = 1500$ units, $R = \$31,500$
7. $x = 20$ units, $R = \$24,000$ **9.** 85 people
11. $p = \$95$, $R = \$451,250$
13. (a) max = $\$2100$ at $x = 10$
       (b) $\overline{R}(x) = \overline{MR}$ at $x = 10$
15. $x = 50$ units, $\overline{C} = \$43$
17. $x = 90$ units, $\overline{C} = \$18$
19. 10,000 units ($x = 100$), $\overline{C} = \$216$ per 100 units
21. $\overline{C}(x)$ has its minimum and $\overline{C}(x) = \overline{MC}$ at $x = 5$.
23. (a) A line from $(0, 0)$ to $(x, C(x))$ has slope
              $C(x)/x = \overline{C}(x)$; this is minimized when the line
              has the least rise—that is, when the line is tangent
              to $C(x)$.
       (b) $x = 600$ units

25. $x = 80$ units, $P = \$280,000$
27. $x = 10\sqrt{15} \approx 39$ units, $P \approx \$71,181$ (using $x = 39$)
29. $x = 1000$ units, $P = \$39,700$
31. (a) B (b) B (c) B (d) $\overline{MR} = \overline{MC}$
33. $\$860$ **35.** $x = 600$ units, $P = \$495,000$
37. (a) 60   (b) $\$570$ (c) $\$9000$
39. (a) 1000 units   (b) $\$8066.67$ (approximately)
41. 2000 units priced at 90/unit; max profit is $90,000$/wk
43. (a) $R(x) = 2x - 0.0004x^2$
              $P(x) = 1.8x - 0.0005x^2 - 800$
       (b) $p = \$1.28$, $x = 1800$, $P(1800) = \$820$
       (c) $p = \$1.25$, $x = 1875$, $P(1875) = \$817.19$
              Coastal would still provide sodas; profits almost
              the same.
45. (a) $y = 0.000252x^3 - 0.0279x^2 + 1.63x + 2.16$
       (b) (36.9, 37.0)
       (c)

The *rate* of change of the number of beneficiaries was
decreasing until 1987, after which the rate has been
increasing. Hence, since 1987 the number of beneficiaries has been increasing at an increasing rate.
47. (a) about mid-May
       (b) just after September 11, when the terrorists' planes
              crashed into the World Trade Center and the
              Pentagon
49. (a) 16.5
       (b) 1.9
       (c) Rise. As the number of workers per beneficiary
              drops, either the amount contributed by each
              worker must rise or support must diminish.

10.4 EXERCISES

1. (a) $x_1 = \$25$ million, $x_2 = \$13.846$ million
       (b) $\$38.846$ million
3. 100 trees   **5.** (a) 5   (b) 237.5   **7.** $\$50$
9. $m = c$ **11.** 1 week   **13.** $t = 8$, $p = 45\%$
15. 240 ft   **17.** 300 ft $\times$ 150 ft
19. 20 ft long, $6\frac{2}{3}$ ft across (dividers run across)
21. 4 in. $\times$ 8 in. $\times$ 8 in. high   **23.** 30,000
25. 12,000   **27.** $x = 2$ **29.** 3 weeks from now
31. 25 plates
33. (a) 2034 (at $t = 23.3$); max $R = 27.8$ billion barrels.
              This is the absolute maximum.
       (b) absolute min: (1, 19.5)
       (c) $t = 3.2$. The rate reaches its maximum at $t = 3.2$
              (in 2014); $R''(t)$ changes from positive to negative
              at $t = 3.2$. After this $R(t)$ increases at a decreasing
              rate until its maximum.

10.5 EXERCISES

1. (a) $x = 2$ (b) 1 (c) 1 (d) $y = 1$

3. (a) $x = 2, x = -2$ (b) 3 (c) 3 (d) $y = 3$

5. HA: $y = 2$; VA: $x = 3$

7. HA: $y = 0$; VA: $x = -2, x = 2$

9. HA: none; VA: none

11. HA: $y = 2$; VA: $x = 3$
no max, min, or points
of inflection

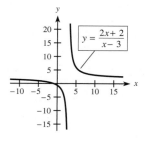

13. VA: $x = 0$;
$(-2, -4)$ rel max;
$(2, 4)$ rel min

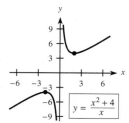

15. VA: $x = -1$; HA: $y = 0$;
$(0, 0)$ rel min; $(2, 4)$ rel max;

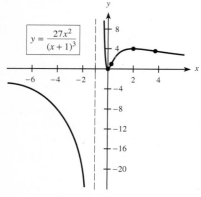

17. HA: $y = 0$; $(1, 8)$ rel max;
$(-1, -8)$ rel min

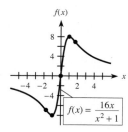

19. HA: $y = 0$; VA: $x = 1$;
$\left(-1, -\frac{1}{4}\right)$ rel min;
point of inflection: $(-2, -2/9)$

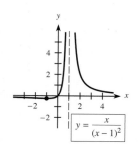

21. VA: $x = 3$;
$(2, -1)$ rel max;
$(4, 7)$ rel min

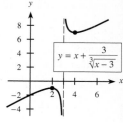

23. HA: $y = 0$;
VA: $x = 0$;
$(2, 0)$ rel min;
$(3, 1)$ rel max;
points of inflection:
$(1.87, 0.66)$,
$(4.13, 0.87)$

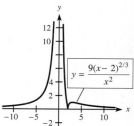

25. (a) HA: approx. $y = -2$; VA: approx. $x = 4$
(b) HA: $y = -\frac{9}{4}$, VA: $x = \frac{17}{4}$

27. (a) HA: approx. $y = 2$;
VA: approx. $x = 2.5, x = -2.5$
(b) HA: $y = \frac{20}{9}$, VA: $x = \frac{7}{3}, x = -\frac{7}{3}$

29. $f(x) = \dfrac{x + 25}{x^2 + 1400}$

(a)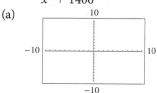

(b) HA: $y = 0$; rel min $(-70, -0.0071)$;
rel max $(20, 0.025)$

(c) x: -500 to 400
y: -0.01 to 0.03

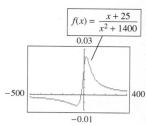

31. $f(x) = \dfrac{100(9 - x^2)}{x^2 + 100}$

(a)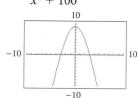

(b) HA: $y = -100$;
rel max $(0, 9)$

(c) x: -75 to 75
y: -120 to 20

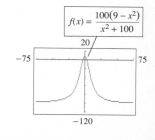

33. $f(x) = \dfrac{1000x - 4000}{x^2 - 10x - 2000}$

(a)
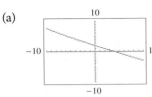

(b) HA: $y = 0$;
VA: $x = -40$,
$x = 50$; no max or min

(c) x: -200 to 200
y: -200 to 200

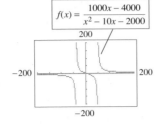

35. (a) none   (b) $C \geq 0$ (c) $p = 100$ (d) no

37. (a)
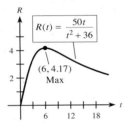

(b) 6 weeks
(c) 22 weeks after its release

39. (a) yes, $x = -1$
(b) no; domain is $x \geq 5$
(c) yes, $y = -58.5731$
(d) At $0°$F, as the wind speed increases, there is a limiting wind chill of about $-58.6°$F. This is meaningful because at high wind speeds, additional wind probably has little noticeable effect.

41. (a) $P = C$ (b) C (c) $P' = 0$ (d) 0

43. (a) 57.0
(b) The model predicts that in the long run, 57% of workers will be female.
(c) No. Vertical asymptote is only at $t \approx -46.4$.
(d) $p(t) > 0$ for $t > 0$ and $p(t)$ never exceeds 100, so the model is never inappropriate.

45. (a) No. Barometric pressure can drop off the scale (as shown), but it cannot decrease without bound. In fact, it must always be positive.
(b) See your library with regard to the "storm of the century" in March 1993.

CHAPTER 10 REVIEW EXERCISES

1. $(0, 0)$ max   **2.** $(2, -9)$ min   **3.** HPI $(1, 0)$
4. $\left(1, \frac{3}{2}\right)$ max, $\left(-1, -\frac{3}{2}\right)$ min

5. (a) $\frac{1}{3}, -1$
(b) $(-1, 0)$ rel max, $\left(\frac{1}{3}, -\frac{32}{27}\right)$ rel min
(c) none   (d)

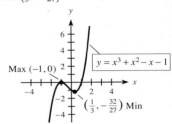

6. (a) $3, 0$ (b) $(3, 27)$ max   (c) $(0, 0)$
(d)

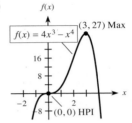

7. (a) $-1, 6$
(b) $(-1, 11)$ rel max, $(6, -160.5)$ rel min
(c) none
(d)

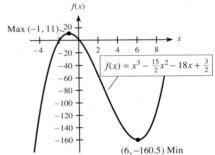

8. (a) $0, \pm 1$ (b) $(-1, 1)$ rel max, $(1, -3)$ rel min
(c) $(0, -1)$ (d)

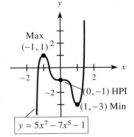

9. (a) 0 (b) $(0, -1)$ min   (c) none
(d)

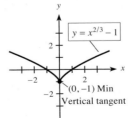

10. (a) 0, 1, 4
(b) (0, 0) rel min, (1, 9) rel max, (4, 0) rel min
(c) none (d)

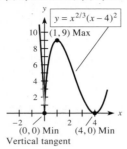

11. concave up
12. concave up when $x < -1$ and $x > 2$; concave down when $-1 < x < 2$; points of inflection at $(-1, -3)$ and $(2, -42)$
13. $(-1, 15)$ rel max; $(3, -17)$ rel min; point of inflection $(1, -1)$
14. $(-2, 16)$ rel max; $(2, -16)$ rel min; point of inflection $(0, 0)$

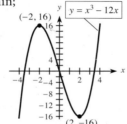

15. $(1, 4)$ rel max; $(-1, 0)$ rel min; points of inflection: $\left(\dfrac{1}{\sqrt{2}}, 2 + \dfrac{7}{4\sqrt{2}}\right)$, $(0, 2)$, and $\left(-\dfrac{1}{\sqrt{2}}, 2 - \dfrac{7}{4\sqrt{2}}\right)$

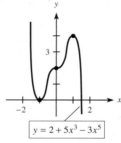

16. (a) (0, 0) absolute min; (140, 19,600) absolute max
(b) (0, 0) absolute min; (100, 18,000) absolute max
17. (a) (50, 233,333) absolute max; (0, 0) absolute min
(b) (64, 248,491) absolute max; (0, 0) absolute min
18. (a) $x = 1$ (b) $y = 0$ (c) 0 (d) 0
19. (a) $x = -1$ (b) $y = \frac{1}{2}$ (c) $\frac{1}{2}$ (d) $\frac{1}{2}$
20. HA: $y = \frac{3}{2}$, VA: $x = 2$
21. HA: $y = -1$; VA: $x = 1$, $x = -1$
22. (a) HA: $y = 3$; VA: $x = -2$
(b) no max or min (c)

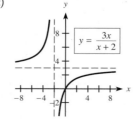

23. (a) HA: $y = 0$; VA: $x = 0$
(b) (4, 1) max (c)

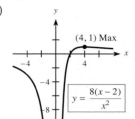

24. (a) HA: none; VA: $x = 1$
(b) (0, 0) rel max; (2, 4) rel min
(c)

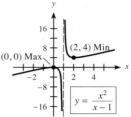

25. (a) $f'(x) > 0$ for $x < \frac{2}{3}$ (approximately) and $x > 2$
$f'(x) < 0$ for about $\frac{2}{3} < x < 2$
$f'(x) = 0$ at about $x = \frac{2}{3}$ and $x = 2$
(b) $f''(x) > 0$ for $x > \frac{4}{3}$
$f''(x) < 0$ for $x < \frac{4}{3}$
$f''(x) = 0$ at $x = \frac{4}{3}$
(c)

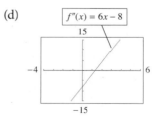

(d)

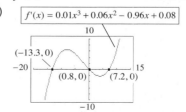

26. (a) $f'(x) > 0$ for about $-13 < x < 0$ and $x > 7$
$f'(x) < 0$ for about $x < -13$ and $0 < x < 7$
$f'(x) = 0$ at about $x = 0$, $x = -13$, $x = 7$
(b) $f''(x) > 0$ for about $x < -8$ and $x > 4$
$f''(x) < 0$ for about $-8 < x < 4$
$f''(x) = 0$ at about $x = -8$ and $x = 4$
(c)

(d)

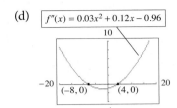

$$f''(x) = 0.03x^2 + 0.12x - 0.96$$

10

−20 $(-8, 0)$ $(4, 0)$ 20

−4

27. (a) $f(x)$ increasing for $x < -5$ and $x > 1$
    $f(x)$ decreasing for $-5 < x < 1$
    $f(x)$ has rel max at $x = -5$, rel min at $x = 1$
  (b) $f''(x) > 0$ for $x > -2$ (where $f'(x)$ increases)
    $f''(x) < 0$ for $x < -2$ (where $f'(x)$ decreases)
    $f''(x) = 0$ for $x = -2$
  (c)

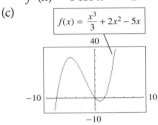

$$f(x) = \frac{x^3}{3} + 2x^2 - 5x$$

40

−10   10

−10

  (d)

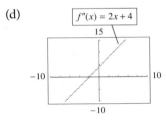

$$f''(x) = 2x + 4$$

15

−10   10

−10

28. (a) $f(x)$ increasing for $x < 6$, $x \neq 0$
    $f(x)$ decreasing for $x > 6$
    $f(x)$ has rel max at $x = 6$, point of inflection at $x = 0$
  (b) $f''(x) > 0$ for $0 < x < 4$
    $f''(x) < 0$ for $x < 0$ and $x > 4$
    $f''(x) = 0$ at $x = 0$ and $x = 4$
  (c)

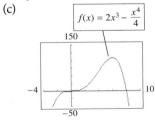

$$f(x) = 2x^3 - \frac{x^4}{4}$$

150

−4   10

−50

  (d)

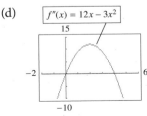

$$f''(x) = 12x - 3x^2$$

15

−2   6

−10

29. (a) $f(x)$ is concave up for $x < 4$.
    $f(x)$ is concave down for $x > 4$.
    $f(x)$ has point of inflection at $x = 4$.

(b)

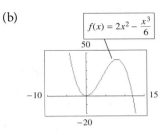

$$f(x) = 2x^2 - \frac{x^3}{6}$$

50

−10   15

−20

30. (a) $f(x)$ is concave up for $-3 < x < 2$.
    $f(x)$ is concave down for $x < -3$ and $x > 2$.
    $f(x)$ has points of inflection at $x = -3$ and $x = 2$.
  (b)

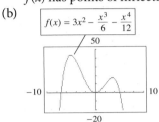

$$f(x) = 3x^2 - \frac{x^3}{6} - \frac{x^4}{12}$$

50

−10   10

−20

31. $x = 5$ units, $\overline{C} = \$45$ per unit
32. (a) $x = 1600$ units, $R = \$25,600$
    (b) $x = 1500$ units, $R = \$25,500$
33. $P = \$54,000$ at $x = 100$ units   34. $x = 300$ units
35. $x = 150$ units   36. $x = 7$ units
37. $x = 500$ units, when $\overline{MP} = 0$ and changes from positive to negative.
38. 30 hours
39. (a) $I = 60$. The point of diminishing returns is located at the point of inflection (where bending changes).
    (b) $m = f(I)/I =$ the average output
    (c) The segment from $(0, 0)$ to $y = f(I)$ has maximum slope when it is tangent to $y = f(I)$, close to $I = 70$.
40. $\$1040$ per bike
41. $\$1380$ per bike
42. $\$93,625$ at 325 units
43. (a) 150   (b) $\$650$
44. $\$208,490.67$ at 64 units
45. $x = 1000$ mg   46. 10:00 A.M.
47. 325 in 2020   48. 20 mi from A, 10 mi from B
49. 4 ft × 4 ft   50. $8\frac{3}{4}$ in. × 10. in.
51. 500 mg
52. (a) $x \approx 7.09$; during 2008
    (b) point of inflection
53. 24,000
54. (a) vertical asymptote at $x = 0$
    (d) $\overline{C}(x)$

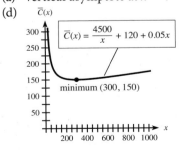

$$\overline{C}(x) = \frac{4500}{x} + 120 + 0.05x$$

300
250
200
150
100
50

minimum $(300, 150)$

200   400   600   800   1000 x

55. (a) 3%
(b) $y = 38$. The long-term market share approaches 38%.

CHAPTER 10 TEST

1. max $(-3, 3)$; min $(-1, -1)$; POI $(-2, 1)$

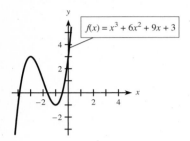

2. max $(3, 17)$; HPI $(0, -10)$; POI $(2, 6)$

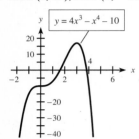

3. max $(0, -3)$;
min $(4, 5)$;
vertical asymptote $x = 2$

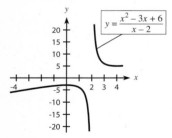

4. $\left(-\dfrac{1}{\sqrt{2}}, 0\right)$ and $\left(\dfrac{1}{\sqrt{2}}, \infty\right)$

5. $(0, 2)$, HPI; $\left(-\dfrac{1}{\sqrt{2}}, 3.237\right)$, $\left(\dfrac{1}{\sqrt{2}}, 0.763\right)$

6. max $(-1, 4)$; min $(1, 0)$

7. max 67 at $x = 8$; min -122 at $x = 5$

8. horizontal asymptote $y = 200$; vertical asymptote $x = -300$

9.

Point	f	f'	f''
A	$-$	$+$	$-$
B	$+$	$-$	0
C	$+$	0	$+$

10. (a) 2   (b) $x = -3$
(c) $y = 2$

11. local max at $(6, 10)$

12. (a) relative minimum: $(8.7, 19.6)$; relative maximum: $(51.5, 39.0)$

(b) The point $(8.7, 19.6)$ means that when $t = 8.7$ (during 1999), the aged dependency ratio reached a minimum of 19.6 aged individuals per 100 individuals ages 20–64. The point $(51.5, 39.0)$ means that when $t = 51.5$ (during 2042), the aged dependency ratio is expected to reach a maximum of 39.0 aged individuals per 100 individuals ages 20–64.

13. (a) $x = 7200$ (b) \$518,100   **14.** 100 units
15. \$250   **16.** $\frac{10}{3}$ centimeter   **17.** 28,000 units
18. (a) $y = -0.0000700x^3 + 0.00567x^2 + 0.863x + 16.0$
(b) $x \approx 27.0$; during 1977
(c) x-coordinate of the point of inflection

11.1 EXERCISES

1. $f'(x) = 4/x$

3. $y' = 1/x$

5. $y' = 4/x$

7. $f'(x) = \dfrac{4}{4x + 9}$

9. $y' = \dfrac{4x - 1}{2x^2 - x} + 3$

11. $dp/dq = 2q/(q^2 + 1)$

13. (a) $y' = \dfrac{1}{x} - \dfrac{1}{x - 1} = \dfrac{-1}{x(x - 1)}$

(b) $y' = \dfrac{-1}{x(x - 1)}$; $\ln\left(\dfrac{x}{x - 1}\right) = \ln (x) - \ln (x - 1)$

15. (a) $y' = \dfrac{2x}{3(x^2 - 1)}$

(b) $y' = \dfrac{2x}{3(x^2 - 1)}$; $\ln (x^2 - 1)^{1/3} = \frac{1}{3} \ln (x^2 - 1)$

17. (a) $y' = \dfrac{4}{4x - 1} - \dfrac{3}{x} = \dfrac{-8x + 3}{x(4x - 1)}$

(b) $y' = \dfrac{-8x + 3}{x(4x - 1)}$;

$\ln\left(\dfrac{4x - 1}{x^3}\right) = \ln (4x - 1) - 3 \ln (x)$

19. $\dfrac{dp}{dq} = \dfrac{2q}{q^2 - 1} - \dfrac{1}{q} = \dfrac{q^2 + 1}{q(q^2 - 1)}$

21. $\dfrac{dy}{dt} = \dfrac{2t}{t^2 + 3} - \dfrac{1}{2}\left(\dfrac{-1}{1 - t}\right) = \dfrac{3 + 4t - 3t^2}{2(1 - t)(t^2 + 3)}$

23. $\dfrac{dy}{dx} = \dfrac{3}{x} + \dfrac{1}{2(x + 1)} = \dfrac{7x + 6}{2x(x + 1)}$

25. $y' = 1 - \dfrac{1}{x}$

27. $y' = (1 - \ln x)/x^2$

29. $y' = 8x^3/(x^4 + 3)$

31. $y' = \dfrac{4 (\ln x)^3}{x}$

33. $y' = \dfrac{8x^3 \ln (x^4 + 3)}{x^4 + 3}$

35. $y' = \dfrac{1}{x \ln 4}$

37. $y' = \dfrac{4x^3 - 12x^2}{(x^4 - 4x^3 + 1) \ln 6}$

39. rel min $(e^{-1}, -e^{-1})$

41. rel min $(2, 4 - 8 \ln 2)$

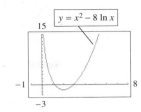

$y = x^2 - 8 \ln x$

43. (a) $\overline{MC} = \dfrac{400}{2x + 1}$

(b) $\overline{MC} = \dfrac{400}{401} \approx 1.0$; the approximate cost of the 201st unit is $1.00

(c) $\overline{MC} > 0$. Yes

45. (a) $\overline{MR} = \dfrac{2500[(x + 1) \ln (10x + 10) - x]}{(x + 1) \ln^2(10x + 10)}$

(b) 309.67; at 100 units, selling 1 additional unit yields about $309.67.

47. (a) -5.23 (b) -1.89 (c) increasing

49. A/B **51.** $dR/dI = 1/(I \ln 10)$

53. (a) $y = -31.7 + 18.7 \ln (x)$

(b) $y' = \dfrac{18.7}{x}$ (c) 0.47 percentage points per year

11.2 EXERCISES

1. $y' = 5e^x - 1$

3. $f'(x) = e^x - exe^{-1}$

5. $g'(x) = 50e^{-0.1x}$

7. $y' = 3x^2 e^{x^3}$

9. $y' = 36xe^{3x^2}$

11. $y' = 12x(x^2 + 1)^2 e^{(x^2 + 1)^3}$

13. $y' = 3x^2$

15. $y' = e^{-1/x}/x^2$

17. $y' = \dfrac{2}{x^3} e^{-1/x^2} - 2xe^{-x^2}$

19. $ds/dt = te^t(t + 2)$

21. $y' = 4x^3 e^{x^4} - 4e^{4x}$

23. $y' = \dfrac{4e^{4x}}{e^{4x} + 2}$

25. $y' = e^{-3x}/x - 3e^{-3x} \ln (2x)$

27. $y' = (2e^{5x} - 3)/e^{3x} = 2e^{2x} - 3e^{-3x}$

29. $y' = 30e^{3x}(e^{3x} + 4)^9$

31. $y' = 6^x \ln 6$

33. $y' = 4^{x^2}(2x \ln 4)$

35. (a) $y'(1) = 0$ (b) $y = e^{-1}$

37. (a) $z = 0$ (b)

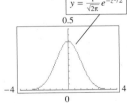

$y = \dfrac{1}{\sqrt{2\pi}} e^{-z^2/2}$

39. rel min at $x = 1, y = e$

41. rel max at $x = 0, y = -1$

43. (a) $(0.1) Pe^{0.1n}$ (b) $(0.1) Pe^{0.1}$

(c) Yes, because $e^{0.1n} > 1$ for any $n \geq 1$.

45. (a) $\dfrac{dS}{dt} = -50{,}000e^{-0.5t}$

(b) The function is a decay exponential. The derivative is always negative.

47. $40e \approx 108.73$ dollars per unit

49. (a) $\dfrac{dy}{dt} = 46.2e^{-0.462t}$

(b) 29.107 percent per hour

51. $\dfrac{dx}{dt} = -0.0684e^{-0.38t}$

53. 177.1 ($billion/year)   **55.** $\dfrac{dI}{dR} = 10^R \ln 10$

57. (a) $d'(t) = 0.1328e^{0.083t}$

(b) $d'(50) \approx 8.42$ billion dollars per year; $d'(125) \approx 4256$ billion dollars per year

59. $y' = \dfrac{98{,}990{,}100e^{-0.99t}}{(1 + 9999e^{-0.99t})^2}$

61. (a) 1.60; the rate of increase in this population was approximately 1.60 million per year in 1995.

(b) 0.808 million (808 thousand) per year

(c) The rate of increase in this population in 2040 is approximately half of the rate of increase in 1995.

63. (a) $y = 0.544(1.07^x)$

(b) $y' = 0.0368(1.07^x)$

(c) 0.55 percentage points per year

65. (a) $y' = 8.864(1.055^x)$

(b) $y'(35) \approx \$57.7$ billion

67. (a) $y = 42.1(1.04^x)$

(b) $y' = 1.65(1.04^x)$

(c) $y'(30) \approx 5.35$ thousand dollars per year

11.3 EXERCISES

1. $\frac{1}{2}$ **3.** $-\frac{1}{2}$ **5.** $-\frac{5}{3}$ **7.** $-x/(2y)$

9. $-(2x + 4)/(2y - 3)$ **11.** $y' = -x/y$

13. $y' = \dfrac{-y}{2x - 3y}$ **15.** $\dfrac{dp}{dq} = \dfrac{p^2}{4 - 2pq}$

17. $\dfrac{dy}{dx} = \dfrac{x(3x^3 - 2)}{3y^2(1 + y^2)}$ **19.** $\dfrac{dy}{dx} = \dfrac{4x^3 + 6x^2y^2 - 1}{-4x^3y - 3y^2}$

21. $\dfrac{dy}{dx} = \dfrac{(4x^3 + 9x^2y^2 - 8x - 12y)}{(18y + 12x - 6x^3y + 10y^4)}$ **23.** undefined

25. 1   **27.** $y = \frac{1}{2}x + 1$ **29.** $y = 4x + 5$

31. $\dfrac{dy}{dx} = \dfrac{1}{2xy}$ **33.** $\dfrac{dy}{dx} = \dfrac{-y}{2x \ln x}$ **35.** -15

37. $-1/x$ **39.** $\dfrac{-xy - 1}{x^2}$

41. $ye^x/(1 - e^x)$ **43.** $\frac{1}{3}$ **45.** $y = 3 - x$

47. (a) $(2, \sqrt{2}), (2, -\sqrt{2})$

(b) $(2 + 2\sqrt{2}, 0), (2 - 2\sqrt{2}, 0)$

49. (a) and (b) are verifications

(c) yes, because $x^2 + y^2 = 4$

51. $1/(2x\sqrt{x})$

53. max at $(0, 3)$; min at $(0, -3)$

55. $\frac{1}{2}$, so an additional 1 (thousand dollars) of advertising yields about $\frac{1}{2}$ (thousand) additional units

57. $-\frac{243}{128}$ hours of skilled labor per hour of unskilled labor

59. At $p = \$80, q = 49$ and $dq/dp = -\frac{5}{16}$, which means that if the price is increased to $81, quantity demanded will decrease by approximately $\frac{5}{16}$ unit.

61. $-0.000436y$ **63.** $\dfrac{dh}{dt} = -\dfrac{3}{44} - \dfrac{h}{12}$

11.4 EXERCISES

1. 36   **3.** $\frac{1}{8}$ **5.** $-\frac{24}{5}$ **7.** $\frac{7}{6}$
9. -5 if $z = 5$, -10 if $z = -5$
11. -80 units/sec   **13.** 12π ft^2/min
15. $\frac{16}{27}$ in/sec   **17.** \$1798/day
19. \$0.42/day
21. 430 units/month   **23.** 36π mm^3/month
25. $\dfrac{\frac{dW}{dt}}{W} = 3\left(\dfrac{\frac{dL}{dt}}{L}\right)$ **27.** $\dfrac{\frac{dC}{dt}}{C} = 1.54\left(\dfrac{\frac{dW}{dt}}{W}\right)$
29. $\frac{1}{4\pi}$ micrometer/day   **31.** $1/(20\pi)$ in/min
33. 0.75 ft/sec   **35.** $-120\sqrt{6}$ mph ≈ -294 mph
37. approaching at 61.18 mph   **39.** $\frac{1}{25}$ ft/hr

11.5 EXERCISES

1. (a) 1   (b) no change
3. (a) 84   (b) Revenue will decrease.
5. (a) $\frac{100}{99}$ (b) elastic   (c) decrease
7. (a) 0.81   (b) inelastic   (c) increase
9. (a) $\eta = 11.1$ (approximately)   (b) elastic
11. (a) $\eta = \dfrac{375 - 3q}{q}$
    (b) unitary: $q = 93.75$; inelastic: $q > 93.75$; elastic: $q < 93.75$
    (c) As q increases over $0 < q < 93.75$, p decreases, so elastic demand means R increases. Similarly, R decreases for $q > 93.75$.
    (d) maximum for R when $q = 93.75$; yes.

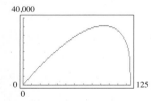

13. (a) $p = 250 - 0.125q$
    (b) $\eta = \frac{2000}{q} - 1$
    (c) $\eta \approx 2.33$; elastic. no
    (d) $q = 1000$; $p = \$125$; max $R = \$125,000$
15. \$12/item   **17.** $t = \$350$ **19.** \$115/item
21. \$483 per item; \$40,100   **23.** \$1100/item

CHAPTER 11 REVIEW EXERCISES

1. $dy/dx = 10(6x - 1)e^{3x^2 - x}$ **2.** $y' = 12/(4x + 11)$
3. $\dfrac{dp}{dq} = \dfrac{1}{q} - \dfrac{2q}{q^2 - 1}$ **4.** $dy/dx = e^{x^2}(2x^2 + 1)$
5. $f'(x) = 10e^{2x} + 4e^{-0.1x}$
6. $g'(x) = 18e^{3x+1}(2e^{3x+1} - 5)^2$
7. $\dfrac{ds}{dx} = \dfrac{9x^{11} - 6x^3}{x^{12} - 2x^4 + 5}$ **8.** $dw/dt = 2t \ln(t^2 + 1)$
9. $dy/dx = 3^{3x-3} \ln 3$ **10.** $dy/dx = \dfrac{1}{\ln 8}\left(\dfrac{10}{x}\right)$

11. $\dfrac{dy}{dx} = \dfrac{1 - \ln x}{x^2}$ **12.** $dy/dx = -2e^{-x}/(1 - e^{-x})^2$
13. $y = 12ex - 8e$, or $y \approx 32.62x - 21.75$
14. $y = 3x + 5$ **15.** $\dfrac{dy}{dx} = \dfrac{y}{x(10y - \ln x)}$
16. $dy/dx = ye^{xy}/(1 - xe^{xy})$ **17.** $dy/dx = 2/y$
18. $\dfrac{dy}{dx} = \dfrac{2(x + 1)}{3(1 - 2y)}$ **19.** $\dfrac{dy}{dx} = \dfrac{6x(1 + xy^2)}{y(5y^3 - 4x^3)}$
20. $d^2y/dx^2 = -(x^2 + y^2)/y^3 = -1/y^3$ **21.** $5/9$
22. $\left(-2, \pm\sqrt{\frac{2}{3}}\right)$ **23.** $3/4$ **24.** 11 square units/min
25. (a) $P'(t) = \dfrac{17.4}{t}$
    (b) $P(58) \approx 166.8$; $P'(58) \approx 0.3$. These mean that in 2028 this population is projected to be about 166.8 million and growing about 0.3 million (300,000) per year.
26. (a) $L'(y) = \dfrac{7.10}{y}$
    (b) $L(50) \approx 13.2$ and $L(80) \approx 16.5$. These mean that the expected number of additional years of life expectancy at age 65 is about 13.2 in 2000 and 16.5 in 2030.
    (c) $L'(50) \approx 0.14$ and $L'(80) \approx 0.09$. These mean that the number of additional years of life expectancy at age 65 is expected to change at the rate of about 0.14 years of life per year in 2000 and 0.09 years of life per year in 2030.
27. (a) $S'(n) = 120e^{0.12n}$
    (b) after 1 year: about \$135.30 per year; after 10 years: about \$398.41 per year
28. (a) $D'(t) \approx 229.7e^{0.02292t}$
    (b) $D(20) \approx 15,850$ and $D'(20) \approx 363$. These mean that in 2030 total U.S. disposable income is expected to be about \$15,850 billion and changing at the rate of about \$363 billion per year.
29. (a) $-0.00001438A_0$ units/year
    (b) $-0.00002876A_0$ units/year   (c) less
30. $\$1200e \approx \$3261.94$ per unit
31. $-\$1797.36$ per year   **32.** $-1/(25\pi)$ mm/min
33. $\frac{48}{25}$ ft/min   **34.** $\dfrac{dS/dt}{S} = \dfrac{1}{3}\left(\dfrac{dA/dt}{A}\right)$ **35.** yes
36. $t = \$1466.67$, $T \approx \$58,667$
37. $t = \$880$, $T = \$3520$
38. (a) 1   (b) no change
39. (a) $\frac{25}{12}$, elastic   (b) revenue decreases
40. (a) 1   (b) no change
41. (a) [graph: 20, 0, 500, -2, $\eta(q) = \dfrac{2(100 - 0.5q)}{q}$]   (b) $q = 100$

(c) max revenue at $q = 100$

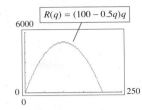

(d) Revenue is maximized where elasticity is unitary.

CHAPTER 11 TEST

1. $y' = 15x^2 e^{x^3} + 2x$

2. $y' = \dfrac{12x^2}{x^3 + 1}$

3. $y' = \dfrac{12x^3}{x^4 + 1}$

4. $f'(x) = 20(3^{2x}) \ln 3$

5. $\dfrac{dS}{dt} = e^{t^4}(4t^4 + 1)$

6. $y' = \dfrac{e^{x^3+1}(3x^3 - 1)}{x^2}$

7. $y' = \dfrac{3 - 12 \ln x}{x^5}$

8. $g'(x) = \dfrac{8}{(4x + 7) \ln 5}$

9. $y' = \dfrac{-3x^3}{y}$

10. $-\frac{3}{2}$

11. $y' = \dfrac{-e^y}{xe^y - 10}$

12. \$1349.50 per week

13. $\eta = 3.71$; decreases

14. -0.05 unit per dollar

15. 586 units per day

16. (a) $y' = 81.778e^{0.062t}$
     (b) 2005: $y'(5) \approx 111.5$ (billion dollars per year)
         2020: $y'(20) \approx 282.6$ (billion dollars per year)

17. \$540

18. (a) $y = -12.97 + 11.85 \ln x$
     (b) $y' = \dfrac{11.85}{x}$
     (c) $y(25) \approx 25.2$ means the model estimates that about 25.2% of the U.S. population will have diabetes in 2025.
         $y'(25) \approx 0.474$ predicts that in 2025 the percent of the U.S. population with diabetes will be changing by about 0.474 percentage points per year.

19. (a) $P'(t) = 1.078(0.9732^t) \cdot \ln(0.9732) \approx -0.02928(0.9732^t)$
     (b) $P(18) \approx 0.661$ and $P'(18) \approx -0.018$. These mean that in 2028 the purchasing power of \$1 is about 66.1% of what it was in 2012 and is expected to be decreasing about 1.8% per year.

12.1 EXERCISES

1. $x^4 + C$

3. $\frac{1}{7}x^7 + C$

5. $\frac{1}{8}x^8 + C$

7. $2x^4 + C$

9. $27x + \frac{1}{14}x^{14} + C$

11. $3x - \frac{2}{5}x^{5/2} + C$

13. $\frac{1}{5}x^5 - 3x^3 + 3x + C$

15. $13x - 3x^2 + 3x^7 + C$

17. $2x + \frac{4}{3}x\sqrt{x} + C$

19. $\frac{24}{5}x\sqrt[4]{x} + C$

21. $-5/(3x^3) + C$

23. $\frac{3}{2}\sqrt[3]{x} + C$

25. $\dfrac{1}{4}x^4 - 4x - \dfrac{1}{x^5} + C$

27. $\dfrac{1}{10}x^{10} + \dfrac{1}{2x^2} + 3x^{2/3} + C$

29. $2x^8 - \frac{4}{3}x^6 + \frac{1}{4}x^4 + C$

31. $-1/x - 1/(2x^2) + C$

33.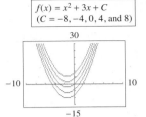

35. $f(x) = 18x^8 - 35x^4$

37. $\int (5 - \frac{1}{2}x) dx$

39. $\int (3x^2 - 6x) dx$

41. $R(x) = 30x - 0.2x^2$

43. $R(50) = \$22{,}125$

45. $P(t) = \frac{1}{4}t^4 + \frac{4}{3}t^3 + 6t$

47. (a) $x = t^{7/4}/1050$ (b) 0.96 ton

49. (a) $\overline{C}(x) = x/4 + 100/x + 30$ (b) \$56 per unit

51. (a) $E(t) = 20.61t^2 - 116.4t + 7398$
     (b) \$13,314 per person

53. (a) The wind chill temperature decreases because $\dfrac{dt}{dw} < 0$ for $w > 0$.
         The rate increases because $\dfrac{d^2t}{dw^2} > 0$ for $w > 0$.
     (b) $t = 48.12 - 27.2w^{0.16}$

55. (a) $t \approx 63.1$; in 2024
     (b) $P(t) = -0.0000729t^3 + 0.0138t^2 + 1.98t + 181$
     (c) 348 million

12.2 EXERCISES

1. $du = 10x^4 \, dx$

3. (a) Power Rule cannot be used; need x^3 as a factor of du
     (b) $\dfrac{1}{8}(5x^3 + 11)^8 + C$

5. $\frac{1}{4}(x^2 + 3)^4 + C$

7. $\frac{1}{5}(5x^3 + 11)^5 + C$

9. $\frac{1}{3}(3x - x^3)^3 + C$

11. $\frac{1}{28}(7x^4 + 12)^4 + C$

13. $\frac{1}{4}(4x - 1)^7 + C$

15. $-\frac{1}{6}(4x^6 + 15)^{-2} + C$

17. $\frac{1}{10}(x^2 - 2x + 5)^5 + C$

19. $-\frac{1}{8}(x^4 - 4x + 3)^{-4} + C$

21. $\frac{7}{6}(x^4 + 6)^{3/2} + C$

23. $\frac{3}{8}x^8 + \frac{6}{5}x^5 + \frac{3}{2}x^2 + C$

25. $10.8x^{10} - 12x^6 + 6x^2 + C$

27. $\frac{2}{9}(x^3 - 3x)^{3/2} + C$

29. $\dfrac{-1}{[10(2x^5 - 5)^3]} + C$

31. $\dfrac{-1}{[8(x^4 - 4x)^2]} + C$

33. $\frac{2}{3}\sqrt{x^3 - 6x^2 + 2} + C$

35. $f(x) = 70(7x - 13)^9$

37. (a) $f(x) = \frac{1}{8}(x^2 - 1)^4 + C$
     (b)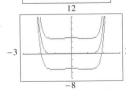

39. (a) $F(x) = \frac{15}{4}(2x-1)^{2/5} + C$

(b)

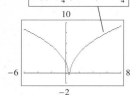

$F(x) = \frac{15}{4}(2x-1)^{2/5} - \frac{7}{4}$

(c) $x = \frac{1}{2}$

(d) vertical

41. $\int \frac{8x(x^2-1)^{1/3}}{3} \, dx$

43. (b) $\dfrac{-7}{3(x^3+4)} + C$

(d) $\int (x^2+5)^{-4} \, dx$ (Many answers are possible.)

45. $R(x) = \dfrac{15}{2x+1} + 30x - 15$

47. 3720 bricks

49. (a) $s = 10\sqrt{x+1}$ (b) 50

51. (a) $A(t) = 100/(t+10) - 1000/(t+10)^2$

(b) 2.5 million

53. 7400

55. (a) $f(x) = \dfrac{-505}{0.743x+6.97} + 36.2$

(b) 23.7%

57. (a) $p(t) = 56.19 - \dfrac{1561}{1.38t+64.1}$

(b)

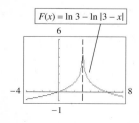

(c) The model is a good fit to the data.

12.3 EXERCISES

1. $e^{3x} + C$ **3.** $-e^{-x} + C$ **5.** $10{,}000e^{0.1x} + C$

7. $-1200e^{-0.7x} + C$ **9.** $\frac{1}{12}e^{3x^4} + C$

11. $-\frac{3}{2}e^{-2x} + C$ **13.** $\frac{1}{18}e^{3x^6-2} + C$

15. $\frac{1}{4}e^{4x} + 6/e^{x/2} + C$

17. $\ln|x^3+4| + C$ **19.** $\frac{1}{4}\ln|4z+1| + C$

21. $\frac{3}{4}\ln|2x^4+1| + C$ **23.** $\frac{2}{5}\ln|5x^2-4| + C$

25. $\ln|x^3-2x| + C$ **27.** $\frac{1}{3}\ln|z^3+3z+17| + C$

29. $\frac{1}{3}x^3 + \ln|x-1| + C$ **31.** $x + \frac{1}{2}\ln|x^2+3| + C$

33. $f(x) = h(x), \int f(x)\,dx = g(x)$

35. $F(x) = -\ln|3-x| + C$

$F(x) = \ln 3 - \ln|3-x|$

37. $f(x) = 1 + \dfrac{1}{x}; \int \left(1 + \dfrac{1}{x}\right) dx$

39. $f(x) = 5e^{-x} - 5xe^{-x}; \int (5e^{-x} - 5xe^{-x})\,dx$

41. (c) $\frac{1}{3}\ln|x^3+3x^2+7| + C$;   (d) $\frac{5}{8}e^{2x^4} + C$

43. \$1030.97   **45.** $n = n_0 e^{-Kt}$ **47.** 55

49. (a) $S = Pe^{0.1n}$ (b) $\approx$ 7 years

51. (a) $p = 95e^{-0.491t}$ (b) $\approx$ 90.45

53. (a) $l(t) = 11.028 + 14.304 \ln(t+20)$

(b)

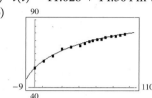

(c) The model is a very good fit to the data.

55. (a) Yes. The rate is an exponential that is always positive. Hence the function is always increasing.

(b) $C(t) = 80.39e^{0.0384t} + 0.6635$

(c) $C(35) \approx 308.91; C'(35) \approx 11.84$
For 2025, the model predicts that the CPI will be \$308.91 and will be changing at a rate of about \$11.84 per year.

12.4 EXERCISES

1. $C(x) = x^2 + 100x + 200$

3. $C(x) = 2x^2 + 2x + 80$ **5.** \$3750

7. (a) $x = 3$ units is optimal level

(b) $P(x) = -4x^2 + 24x - 200$

(c) loss of \$164

9. (a) profit of \$3120   (b) 896 units

11. (a) $\overline{C}(x) = \frac{6}{x} + \frac{x}{6} + 8$ (b) \$10.50

13. (a) and (b)

$R(x) = 4\sqrt{0.5x+4} + 2.8x - 8$

$C(x) = (x+180)^{1.05} - 33.365$

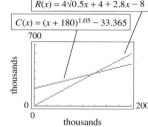

(c) Maximum profit is \$114.743 thousand at $x = 200$ thousand units.

15. $C(y) = 0.80y + 7$

17. $C(y) = 0.3y + 0.4\sqrt{y} + 8$

19. $C(y) = 2\sqrt{y+1} + 0.4y + 4$

21. $C(y) = 0.7y + 0.5e^{-2y} + 5.15$

23. $C(y) = 0.85y + 5.15$

25. $C(y) = 0.8y + \dfrac{2\sqrt{3y+7}}{3} + 4.24$

12.5 EXERCISES

1. $4y - 2xy' = 4x^2 - 2x(2x) = 0$ ✔

3. $2y\,dx - x\,dy = 2(3x^2+1)\,dx - x(6x\,dx) = 2\,dx$ ✔

5. $y = \frac{1}{2}e^{x^2+1} + C$

7. $y^2 = 2x^2 + C$

9. $y^3 = x^2 - x + C$

11. $y = e^{x-3} - e^{-3} + 2$

13. $y = \ln|x| - \dfrac{x^2}{2} + \dfrac{1}{2}$

15. $\dfrac{y^2}{2} = \dfrac{x^3}{3} + C$

17. $\dfrac{1}{2x^2} + \dfrac{y^2}{2} = C$

19. $\dfrac{1}{x} + y + \dfrac{y^3}{3} = C$

21. $\dfrac{1}{y} + \ln|x| = C$

23. $x^2 - y^2 = C$

25. $y = C(x + 1)$

27. $x^2 + 4\ln|x| + e^{-y^2} = C$

29. $3y^4 = 4x^3 - 1$

31. $2y = 3x + 4xy$ or $y = \dfrac{3x}{2 - 4x}$

33. $e^{2y} = x^2 - \dfrac{2}{x} + 2$

35. $y^2 + 1 = 5x$

37. $y = Cx^k$

39. (a) $x = 10,000e^{0.06t}$ (b) $10,618.37; $13,498.59

(c) 11.55 years

41. $P = 100,000e^{0.05t}$; 5% **43.** ≈ 8.4 hours

45. $y = \dfrac{32}{(p + 8)^{2/5}}$ **47.** $\approx 23,100$ years

49. $x = 6(1 - e^{-0.05t})$ **51.** $x = 20 - 10e^{-0.025t}$

53. $V = 1.86e^{2 - 2e^{-0.1t}}$ **55.** $V = \dfrac{k^3t^3}{27}$

57. $t \approx 4.5$ hours

59. (a) $E(t) = 18.5e^{0.0164t}$

(b)

The model looks similar, except at the right end, where it rises more sharply than the graph of the data.

61. (a) $P(t) = 80,000e^{-0.05t}$ (b) $37,789.32

CHAPTER 12 REVIEW EXERCISES

1. $\frac{1}{7}x^7 + C$

2. $\frac{2}{3}x^{3/2} + C$

3. $3x^4 - x^3 + 2x^2 + 5x + C$ **4.** $\frac{7}{5}x^5 - \frac{14}{3}x^3 + 7x + C$

5. $\frac{7}{6}(x^2 - 1)^3 + C$ **6.** $\frac{1}{18}(x^3 - 3x^2)^6 + C$

7. $\frac{3}{8}x^8 + \frac{24}{5}x^5 + 24x^2 + C$ **8.** $\frac{5}{63}(3x^3 + 7)^7 + C$

9. $\frac{1}{3}\ln|x^3 + 1| + C$ **10.** $\dfrac{-1}{3(x^3 + 1)} + C$

11. $\frac{1}{2}(x^3 - 4)^{2/3} + C$ **12.** $\frac{1}{3}\ln|x^3 - 4| + C$

13. $\dfrac{1}{2}x^2 - \dfrac{1}{x} + C$

14. $\frac{1}{3}x^3 + \frac{1}{2}x^2 - 2x - \ln|x - 1| + C$

15. $\frac{1}{3}e^{y^3} + C$ **16.** $\frac{1}{39}(3x - 1)^{13} + C$

17. $\frac{1}{2}\ln|2x^3 - 7| + C$ **18.** $\dfrac{-5}{4e^{4x}} + C$

19. $x^4/4 - e^{3x}/3 + C$ **20.** $\frac{1}{2}e^{x^2+1} + C$

21. $\dfrac{-3}{40(5x^8 + 7)^2} + C$ **22.** $-\frac{7}{2}\sqrt{1 - x^4} + C$

23. $\frac{1}{4}e^{2x} - e^{-2x} + C$ **24.** $x^2/2 + 1/(x + 1) + C$

25. (a) $\frac{1}{10}(x^2 - 1)^5 + C$ (b) $\frac{1}{22}(x^2 - 1)^{11} + C$

(c) $\frac{3}{16}(x^2 - 1)^8 + C$ (d) $\frac{3}{2}(x^2 - 1)^{1/3} + C$

26. (a) $\ln|x^2 - 1| + C$ (b) $\dfrac{-1}{x^2 - 1} + C$

(c) $3\sqrt{x^2 - 1} + C$ (d) $\frac{3}{2}\ln|x^2 - 1| + C$

27. $y = C - 92e^{-0.05t}$

28. $y = 64x + 38x^2 - 12x^3 + C$

29. $(y - 3)^2 = 4x^2 + C$ **30.** $(y + 1)^2 = 2\ln|t| + C$

31. $e^y = \dfrac{x^2}{2} + C$ **32.** $y = Ct^4$

33. $3(y + 1)^2 = 2x^3 + 75$

34. $x^2 = y + y^2 + 4$ **35.** $28,800 **36.** 472

37. $P(t) = 400[1 - 5/(t + 5) + 25/(t + 5)^2]$

38. $p = 1990.099 - 100,000/(t + 100)$

39. (a) $y = -60e^{-0.04t} + 60$ (b) 23%

40. $R(x) = 800\ln(x + 2) - 554.52$

41. (a) $1000 (b) $C(x) = 3x^2 + 4x + 1000$

42. 80 units, $440

43. $C(y) = \sqrt{2y + 16} + 0.6y + 4.5$

44. $C(y) = 0.8y - 0.05e^{-2y} + 7.85$ **45.** $W = CL^3$

46. (a) $\ln|P| = kt + C_1$ (b) $P = Ce^{kt}$

(c) $P = 50,000\,e^{0.1t}$ (d) The interest rate is $k = 0.10 = 10\%$.

47. ≈ 10.7 million years **48.** $x = 360(1 - e^{-t/30})$

49. $x = 600 - 500e^{-0.01t}$; ≈ 161 min

CHAPTER 12 TEST

1. $2x^3 + 4x^2 - 7x + C$ **2.** $11x - \dfrac{x^4}{2} + C$

3. $\dfrac{5x^3}{3} - 5x + C$ **4.** $4x + \frac{2}{3}x\sqrt{x} + \frac{1}{x} + C$

5. $\dfrac{(7 + 2x^3)^{10}}{10} + C$ **6.** $\dfrac{(4x^3 - 7)^{10}}{24} + C$

7. $-\frac{1}{6}(3x^2 - 6x + 1)^{-2} + C$ **8.** $e^x + 5\ln|x| - x + C$

9. $\dfrac{\ln|2s^4 - 5|}{8} + C$ **10.** $-10,000e^{-0.01x} + C$

11. $\frac{5}{8}e^{2y^4 - 1} + C$

12. $x^2 - x + \dfrac{1}{2}\ln|2x + 1| + C$

13. $6x^2 - 1 + 5e^x$ **14.** $\dfrac{1}{9}x^3 - \dfrac{5}{8}x + C$

15. $y = x^4 + x^3 + 4$ **16.** $y = \frac{1}{4}e^{4x} + \frac{7}{4}$

17. $y = \dfrac{4}{C - x^4}$ **18.** 157,498

19. $P(x) = 450x - 2x^2 - 300$

20. $C(y) = 0.78y + \sqrt{0.5y + 1} + 5.6$

21. about 332 days **22.** $x = 16 - 16e^{-t/40}$

13.1 EXERCISES

1. 7 square units   **3.** 7.25 square units
5. 3 square units   **7.** 11.25 square units
9. $S_L(10) = 4.08$; $S_R(10) = 5.28$
11. Both equal 14/3.
13. It would lie between $S_L(10)$ and $S_R(10)$. It would equal 14/3.
15. 3   **17.** 42   **19.** -5 **21.** 180   **23.** 11,315
25. $3 - \dfrac{3(n+1)}{n} + \dfrac{(n+1)(2n+1)}{2n^2} = \dfrac{2n^2 - 3n + 1}{2n^2}$
27. (a) $S = (n-1)/n$ (b) 9/10   (c) 99/100
(d) 999/1000   (e) 1
29. (a) $S = \dfrac{(n+1)(2n+1)}{6n^2}$
(b) $77/200 = 0.385$ (c) $6767/20{,}000 \approx 0.3384$
(d) $667{,}667/2{,}000{,}000 \approx 0.3338$ (e) $\frac{1}{3}$
31. $\frac{20}{3}$
33. (a) 8696 square units
(b) This represents the total per capita out-of-pocket expenses for health care between 2013 and 2021.
35. There are approximately 90 squares under the curve, each representing 1 second by 10 mph, or

$$1 \sec \times \frac{10 \text{ mi}}{1 \text{ hr}} \times \frac{1 \text{ hr}}{3600 \text{ sec}} = \frac{1}{360} \text{ mile}.$$

The area under the curve is approximately $90\left(\frac{1}{360} \text{ mile}\right) = \frac{1}{4}$ mile.

37. 1550 square feet
39. 107.734 square units. This represents the total sulphur dioxide emissions (in millions of short tons) from electricity generation from 2010 to 2015.

13.2 EXERCISES

1. 18   **3.** 2   **5.** 60   **7.** $12\sqrt[3]{25}$ **9.** 0   **11.** 98
13. $-\frac{1}{10}$ **15.** 12,960   **17.** 0   **19.** 0   **21.** $\frac{49}{3}$
23. 2   **25.** $e^3/3 - 1/3$ **27.** 4   **29.** $\frac{8}{3}(1 - e^{-8})$
31. (a) $\frac{1}{6}\ln(112/31) \approx 0.2140853$ (b) 0.2140853
33. (a) $\frac{3}{2} + 3\ln 2 \approx 3.5794415$ (b) 3.5794415
35. (a) A, C (b) B
37. $\int_0^4 (2x - \frac{1}{2}x^2)\,dx$ (b) 16/3
39. (a) $\int_{-1}^0 (x^3 + 1)\,dx$ (b) 3/4
41. $\frac{1}{6}$ **43.** $\frac{1}{2}(e^9 - e)$
45. $\int_0^a g(x)\,dx > \int_0^a f(x)\,dx$; more area under $g(x)$
47. same absolute values, opposite signs
49. -6 **51.** 0   **53.** (a) $450,000   (b) $450,000
55. (a) $5390   (b) $2450
57. $20,405.39
59. 4146 represents the total million metric tons of CO_2 emissions from 2010 to 2020.
61. 0.04 cm³   **63.** 1222 (approximately)
65. 0.1808

67. (a) 0.5934   (b) 0.1733
69. (a) $G(t) = -0.157t^2 - 0.196t + 133$
(b) 1267.9; the total amount of gasoline (1267.9 billion gallons) used by motor vehicles in the United States from 2014 to 2024.

13.3 EXERCISES

1. (a) $\int_0^2 (4 - x^2)\,dx$ (b) $\frac{16}{3}$
3. (a) $\int_1^8 [\sqrt[3]{x} - (2 - x)]\,dx$ (b) 28.75
5. (a) $\int_1^2 \left[(4 - x^2) - \left(\frac{1}{4}x^3 - 2\right)\right]\,dx$ (b) 131/48
7. (a) $(-1, 1)$, $(2, 4)$ (b) $\int_{-1}^2 [(x+2) - x^2]\,dx$
(c) 9/2
9. (a) $(0, 0)$, $\left(\frac{5}{2}, -\frac{15}{4}\right)$
(b) $\int_0^{5/2} [(x - x^2) - (x^2 - 4x)]\,dx$ (c) $\frac{125}{24}$
11. (a) $(-2, -4)$, $(0, 0)$, $(2, 4)$
(b) $\int_{-2}^0 [(x^3 - 2x) - 2x]\,dx + \int_0^2 [2x - (x^3 - 2x)]\,dx$
(c) 8
13. $\frac{28}{3}$ **15.** $\frac{1}{4}$ **17.** $\frac{16}{3}$ **19.** $\frac{1}{3}$ **21.** $\frac{37}{12}$
23. $4 - 3\ln 3$ **25.** $\frac{8}{3}$ **27.** 6   **29.** 0   **31.** $-\frac{4}{9}$
33. $11.8\overline{3}$
35. average profit $= \dfrac{1}{x_1 - x_0}\displaystyle\int_{x_0}^{x_1} [R(x) - C(x)]\,dx$
37. (a) $1402 per unit   (b) $535,333.33
39. (a) 102.5 units   (b) 100 units
41. (a) 40.05 million/year   (b) 69.93 million/year
43. 147 mg
45. Black: 0.479; Hispanic: 0.459
The income distribution for Black households is more unequal than it is for Hispanic households.
47. 2012: 0.468; 2004: 0.455
2012 shows more income distribution inequality than 2004.
49. $G = \dfrac{p - 1}{p + 1}$

13.4 EXERCISES

1. $126,205.10   **3.** $346,664 (nearest dollar)
5. $506,000 (nearest thousand)
7. $18,660 (nearest dollar)
9. $82,155 (nearest dollar)
11. $PV = \$2{,}657{,}807$ (nearest dollar), $FV = \$3{,}771{,}608$ (nearest dollar)
13. $PV = \$190{,}519$ (nearest dollar), $FV = \$347{,}147$ (nearest dollar)
15. Gift Shoppe, $151,024; Wine Boutique, $141,093. The gift shop is a better buy.
17. $83.33   **19.** $161.89   **21.** (5, 56); $83.33
23. $11.50   **25.** $204.17   **27.** $2766.67
29. $17,839.58   **31.** $133.33   **33.** $2.50
35. $103.35

13.5 EXERCISES

1. formula 5: $\frac{1}{8}\ln|(4+x)/(4-x)| + C$
3. formula 11: $\frac{1}{3}\ln[(3+\sqrt{10})/2]$
5. formula 14: $w(\ln w - 1) + C$
7. formula 12: $\frac{1}{3} + \frac{1}{4}\ln\left(\frac{3}{7}\right)$
9. formula 13: $\frac{1}{8}\ln\left|\dfrac{v}{3v+8}\right| + C$
11. formula 7: $\frac{1}{2}[7\sqrt{24} - 25\ln(7+\sqrt{24}) + 25\ln 5]$
13. formula 16: $\dfrac{(6w-5)(4w+5)^{3/2}}{60} + C$
15. formula 3: $\frac{1}{2}(5^{x^2})\log_5 e + C$
17. formula 1: $\frac{1}{3}(13^{3/2} - 8)$
19. formula 9: $-\frac{5}{2}\ln\left|\dfrac{2+\sqrt{4-9x^2}}{3x}\right| + C$
21. formula 10: $\frac{1}{3}\ln|3x + \sqrt{9x^2-4}| + C$
23. formula 15: $\frac{3}{4}\left[\ln|2x-5| - \dfrac{5}{2x-5}\right] + C$
25. formula 8: $\frac{1}{3}\ln|3x+1 + \sqrt{(3x+1)^2+1}| + C$
27. formula 6: $\frac{1}{4}[10\sqrt{109} - \sqrt{10} + 9\ln(10+\sqrt{109})$ $-9\ln(1+\sqrt{10})]$
29. formula 2: $-\frac{1}{6}\ln|7-3x^2| + C$
31. formula 8: $\frac{1}{2}\ln|2x + \sqrt{4x^2+7}| + C$
33. $2(e^{\sqrt{2}} - e) \approx 2.7899$
35. $\frac{1}{32}[\ln(9/5) - 4/9] \approx 0.004479$
37. \$3391.10
39. (a) $C = \frac{1}{2}x\sqrt{x^2+9} + \frac{9}{2}\ln|x+\sqrt{x^2+9}| + 300$ $-\frac{9}{2}\ln 3$
    (b) \$314.94
41. \$3882.9 thousand

13.6 EXERCISES

1. $\frac{1}{2}xe^{2x} - \frac{1}{4}e^{2x} + C$ 3. $\frac{1}{3}x^3\ln x - \frac{1}{9}x^3 + C$
5. $\dfrac{104\sqrt{2}}{15}$ 7. $-(1+\ln x)/x + C$ 9. 1
11. $\dfrac{x^2}{2}\ln(2x-3) - \frac{1}{4}x^2 - \frac{3}{4}x - \frac{9}{8}\ln(2x-3) + C$
13. $\frac{1}{5}(q^2-3)^{3/2}(q^2+2) + C$ 15. 282.4
17. $-e^{-x}(x^2+2x+2) + C$ 19. $(9e^4+3)/2$
21. $\frac{1}{4}x^4\ln^2 x - \frac{1}{8}x^4\ln x + \frac{1}{32}x^4 + C$
23. $\frac{2}{15}(e^x+1)^{3/2}(3e^x-2) + C$ 25. II; $\frac{1}{2}e^{x^2} + C$
27. IV; $\frac{2}{3}(e^x+1)^{3/2} + C$ 29. I; $-5e^{-4} + 1$
31. \$2794.46   33. \$34,836.73   35. 0.264
37. 166 million

13.7 EXERCISES

1. 1/5   3. 2   5. 1/e   7. diverges   9. diverges
11. 10   13. diverges   15. diverges   17. 0
19. 0   21. 0.5   23. 1/(2e)   25. $\frac{3}{2}$
27. $\int_{-\infty}^{\infty} f(x)\,dx = 1$ 29. $c=1$ 31. $c=\frac{1}{4}$

33. 20
35. area $= \frac{8}{3}$
37. $\int_0^{\infty} Ae^{-rt}\,dt = A/r$
39. \$2,400,000
41. \$700,000
43. (a) 0.368   (b) 0.018
45. 0.147
47. (a) $500\left[\dfrac{e^{-0.03b} + 0.03b - 1}{0.0009}\right]$
    (b) The amount approaches ∞.

13.8 EXERCISES

1. $h=\frac{1}{2}; x_0=0, x_1=\frac{1}{2}, x_2=1, x_3=\frac{3}{2}, x_4=2$
3. $h=\frac{1}{2}; x_0=1, x_1=\frac{3}{2}, x_2=2, x_3=\frac{5}{2}, x_4=3, x_5=\frac{7}{2},$ $x_6=4$
5. $h=1; x_0=-1, x_1=0, x_2=1, x_3=2, x_4=3, x_5=4$
7. (a) 9.13   (b) 9.00   (c) 9   (d) Simpson's
9. (a) 0.51   (b) 0.50   (c) $\frac{1}{2}$ (d) Simpson's
11. (a) 5.27   (b) 5.30   (c) 5.33   (d) Simpson's
13. (a) 3.283   (b) 3.240
15. (a) 0.743   (b) 0.747
17. (a) 7.132   (b) 7.197   19. 7.8   21. 10.3
23. 119.58 (\$119,580)   25. \$32,389.76
27. \$14,133.33   29. 1222.35 (1222 units)
31. (a)

x	0	0.2	0.4	0.6	0.8	1
$L_a - L_b$	0	0.003	0.005	0.013	0.029	0

    (b) 0.020
    (c) positive; 1990
33. (a) Yes   (b) Simpson's   (c) 1586.67 ft²

CHAPTER 13 REVIEW EXERCISES

1. 212   2. $\dfrac{3(n+1)}{2n^2}$ 3. $\frac{91}{72}$ 4. 1   5. 1
6. 14   7. $\frac{248}{5}$ 8. $-\frac{205}{4}$ 9. $\frac{825}{4}$ 10. $\frac{4}{13}$
11. -2 12. $\frac{1}{6}\ln 47 - \frac{1}{6}\ln 9$ 13. $\frac{9}{2}$
14. $\ln 4 + \frac{14}{3}$ 15. 190/3   16. $\frac{1}{2}\ln 2$
17. $(1-e^{-2})/2$ 18. $(e-1)/2$ 19. 95/2
20. 36   21. $\frac{1}{4}$ 22. $\frac{1}{2}$
23. $\frac{1}{2}x\sqrt{x^2-4} - 2\ln|x+\sqrt{x^2-4}| + C$
24. $2\log_3 e$ 25. $\frac{1}{2}x^2(\ln x^2 - 1) + C$
26. $\frac{1}{2}\ln|x| - \frac{1}{2}\ln|3x+2| + C$
27. $\frac{1}{6}x^6\ln x - \frac{1}{36}x^6 + C$
28. $-e^{-2x}(x^2/2 + x/2 + 1/4) + C$
29. $2x\sqrt{x+5} - \frac{4}{3}(x+5)^{3/2} + C$
30. 1   31. diverges   32. -100
33. $\frac{5}{3}$ 34. $-\frac{1}{2}$
35. (a) $\frac{8}{9} \approx 0.889$ (b) 1.004   (c) 0.909
36. 3.135   37. 3.9
38. (a) $n=5$ (b) $n=6$ 39. \$28,000
40. $1 - e^{-2.8} \approx 0.939$ 41. \$1297.44   42. \$76.60

43. 1969: 0.3737; 2000: 0.4264; more equally distributed in 1969

44. (a) $(7, 6)$ (b) $7.33   **45.** $24.50

46. $1,621,803   **47.** (a) $403,609   (b) $602,114

48. $217.42   **49.** $10,066 (nearest dollar)

50. $86,557.41

51. $C(x) = 3x + 30(x + 1)^2 \ln (x + 1)$
$- 15(x + 1)^2 + 2015$

52. $e^{-1.4} \approx 0.247$

53. $4000 thousand, or $4 million

54. $197,365   **55.** $480,000 hundred, or $48,000,000

CHAPTER 13 TEST

1. 3.496 (approximately)

2. (a) $5 - \dfrac{n + 1}{n}$ (b) 4

3. $\int_0^6 (12 + 4x - x^2)\, dx$; 72

4. (a) 4   (b) 3/4   (c) $\frac{5}{4} \ln 5$ (d) 7
(e) 0; limits of integration are the same
(f) $\frac{5}{6}(e^2 - 1)$

5. (a) $3xe^x - 3e^x + C$ (b) $\dfrac{x^2}{2} \ln (2x) - \dfrac{x^2}{4} + C$

6. -8

7. (a) $x[\ln (2x) - 1] + C$
(b) $\dfrac{2(9x + 14)(3x - 7)^{3/2}}{135} + C$

8. 16.089

9. (a) $4000   (b) $16,000/3

10. (a) $961.18 thousand   (b) $655.68 thousand
(c) $1062.5 thousand

11. 125/6

12.

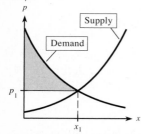

13. Before, 0.446; After, 0.19. The change decreases the difference in income.

14. (a) About 20.92 billion barrels
(b) About 2.067 billion barrels per year

15. About 2.9666   **16.** 6800 ft²

14.1 EXERCISES

1. $\{(x, y)\colon x \text{ and } y \text{ are real numbers}\}$

3. $\{(x, y)\colon x \text{ and } y \text{ are real numbers and } y \neq 0\}$

5. $\{(x, y)\colon x \text{ and } y \text{ are real numbers and } 2x - y \neq 0\}$

7. $\{(p_1, p_2)\colon p_1 \text{ and } p_2 \text{ are real numbers and } p_1 \geq 0\}$

9. -2 **11.** $\frac{5}{3}$ **13.** 2500   **15.** 36   **17.** 3

19. $\frac{1}{25} \ln (12)$ **21.** $\frac{13}{3}$

23. $6640.23; the amount that results when $2000 is invested for 20 years

25. 500; if the cost of placing an order is $200, the number of items sold per week is 625, and the weekly holding cost per item is $1, then the most economical order size is 500.

27. Max: $S \approx 112.5°F$; $A \approx 106.3°F$
Min: $S \approx 87.4°F$; $A \approx 77.6°F$

29. (a) $752.80; when $90,000 is borrowed for 20 years at 8%, the monthly payment is $752.80.
(b) $1622.82; when $160,000 is borrowed for 15 years at 9%, the monthly payment is $1622.82.

31. (a) $x = 4$ (b) $y = 2$
(c)

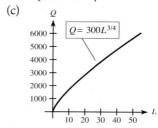

33. (a) 37,500 units
(b) $30(2K)^{1/4}(2L)^{3/4} = 30(2^{1/4})(2^{3/4})K^{1/4}L^{3/4} = 2[30K^{1/4}L^{3/4}]$
(c)

35. (a) 7200 units   (b) 5000 units   **37.** $284,000

14.2 EXERCISES

1. $\dfrac{\partial z}{\partial x} = 4x^3 - 10x + 6$ $\dfrac{\partial z}{\partial y} = 9y^2 - 5$

3. $z_x = 3x^2 + 8xy$ $z_y = 4x^2 + 12y$

5. $\dfrac{\partial f}{\partial x} = 9x^2(x^3 + 2y^2)^2$ $\dfrac{\partial f}{\partial y} = 12y(x^3 + 2y^2)^2$

7. $f_x = 2x(2x^2 - 5y^2)^{-1/2}$ $f_y = -5y(2x^2 - 5y^2)^{-1/2}$

9. $\dfrac{\partial C}{\partial x} = -4y + 20xy$ $\dfrac{\partial C}{\partial y} = -4x + 10x^2$

11. $\dfrac{\partial Q}{\partial s} = \dfrac{2(t^2 + 3st - s^2)}{(s^2 + t^2)^2}$ $\dfrac{\partial Q}{\partial t} = \dfrac{3t^2 - 4st - 3s^2}{(s^2 + t^2)^2}$

13. $z_x = 2e^{2x} + \dfrac{y}{x}$ $z_y = \ln x$

15. $\dfrac{\partial f}{\partial x} = \dfrac{y}{xy + 1}$ $\dfrac{\partial f}{\partial y} = \dfrac{x}{xy + 1}$ **17.** 2

19. 7   **21.** -19

23. (a) 0   (b) $-2xz + 4$ (c) $2y$ (d) $-x^2$

25. (a) $8x_1 + 5x_2$ (b) $5x_1 + 12x_2$ (c) 1

27. (a) 2   (b) 0   (c) 0   (d) $-30y$

29. (a) $2y$ (b) $2x - 8y$ (c) $2x - 8y$ (d) $-8x$

31. (a) $2 + y^2 e^{xy}$ (b) $xye^{xy} + e^{xy}$
(c) $xye^{xy} + e^{xy}$ (d) $x^2 e^{xy}$

33. (a) $1/x^2$ (b) 0   (c) 0   (d) $2 + 1/y^2$

35. -6 **37.** (a) $\frac{188}{4913}$ (b) $\frac{-188}{4913}$ **39.** $2 + 2e$

41. 0   **43.** (a) $24x$ (b) $24x$ (c) 0

45. (a) For a mortgage of $100,000 and an 8% interest rate, the monthly payment is $771.82.
(b) The rate of change of the payment with respect to the interest rate is $66.25. That is, if the rate goes from 8% to 9% on a $100,000 mortgage, the approximate increase in the monthly payment is $66.25.

47. (a) If the number of items sold per week changes by 1, the most economical order quantity should also increase. $\dfrac{\partial Q}{\partial M} = \sqrt{\dfrac{K}{2Mh}} > 0$
(b) If the weekly storage costs change by 1, the most economical order quantity should decrease.
$$\frac{\partial Q}{\partial h} = -\sqrt{\frac{KM}{2h^3}} < 0$$

49. (a) 23.912; If brand 2 is held constant and brand 1 is increased from 100 to 101 liters, approximately 24,000 additional insects will be killed.

51. (a) $2xy^2$ (b) $2x^2y$

53. $\dfrac{\partial Q}{\partial K} = 100$; If labor hours are held constant at 5832 and K changes by $1 (thousand) to $730,000, Q will change by about 100 units. $\dfrac{\partial Q}{\partial L} = 25$; If capital expenditures are held constant at $729,000 and L changes by 1 hour (to 5833), Q will change by about 25 units.

55. (a) $\dfrac{\partial WC}{\partial s} = 0.16s^{-0.84}(0.4275t - 35.75)$
(b) At $t = 10$, $s = 25$, $\dfrac{\partial WC}{\partial s} \approx -0.34$
This means that if wind speed changes by 1 mph (from 25 mph) while the temperature remains at 10°F, the wind chill temperature will change by about -0.34°F.

14.3 EXERCISES

1. (a) $105   (b) $C_x = 3$ means total costs would change by $3 if labor costs changed by $1 and raw material costs stayed the same.

3. (a) $2 + y/50$ (b) $4 + x/50$

5. (a) $25.78   (b) $74.80

7. (a) If y remains at 10, the expected change in cost for a 9th unit of X is about $36.
(b) If x remains at 8, the expected change in cost for an 11th unit of Y is about $19.

9. (a) $\sqrt{y^2 + 1}$ dollars per unit
(b) $xy/\sqrt{y^2 + 1}$ dollars per unit

11. (a) $1200y/(xy + 1)$ dollars per unit
(b) $1200x/(xy + 1)$ dollars per unit

13. (a) $\sqrt{y/x}$ (b) $\sqrt{x/y}$

15. (a) $\ln(y + 1)/(2\sqrt{x})$ (b) $\sqrt{x}/(y + 1)$

17. $z = 1092$ crates (approximately)

19. $z_x = 3.6$; If 500 acres are planted, the approximate change in productivity from a 301st hour of labor is 3.6 crates.

21. (a) $z_x = \dfrac{240y^{2/5}}{x^{2/5}}$ (b)

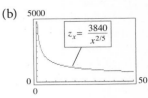

(c) $z_y = \dfrac{160x^{3/5}}{y^{3/5}}$ (d)

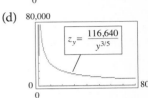

(e) Both z_x and z_y are positive, so increases in both capital investment and work-hours result in increases in productivity. However, both are decreasing, so such increases have a diminishing effect on productivity.

23. $q_1 = 188$ units; $q_2 = 270$ units

25. any values for p_1 and p_2 that satisfy $6p_2 - 3p_1 = 100$ and that make q_1 and q_2 nonnegative, such as $p_1 = 10, $p_2 = $21\frac{2}{3}$

27. (a) -3 units per dollar   (b) -2 units per dollar
(c) -6 units per dollar   (d) -5 units per dollar
(e) complementary

29. (a) -50 units per dollar
(b) $600/(p_B + 1)^2$ units per dollar
(c) $-400/(p_B + 4)^2$ units per dollar
(d) $400/(p_A + 4)^2$ units per dollar
(e) competitive

31. (a) Competitive; as the price of one type of car declines, demand for the other declines
(b) (i) $q_{NEW} = 2600 - p_{NEW}/30 + p_{USED}/15$
$q_{USED} = 750 - 0.25\, p_{USED} + 0.0125 p_{NEW}$
(ii) Since the mixed partials are both positive (1/15 and 0.0125), the products are competitive.

14.4 EXERCISES

1. max(0, 0, 9)   **3.** min(0, 0, 4)
5. saddle($-2, -3, 16$)   **7.** min($1, -2, 0$)
9. saddle($1, -3, 8$)   **11.** max(12, 24, 456)
13. min($-8, 6, -52$)
15. saddle(0, 0, 0); min($2, 2, -8$)
17. $\hat{y} = 5.7x - 1.4$
19. $x = 5000$, $y = 128$; $P = $25,409.60
21. $x = \frac{20}{3}$, $y = \frac{10}{3}$; $W \approx 1926$ lb
23. $x = 28$, $y = 100$; $P = 5987.84$ tons

25. $x = 20$ thousand, $y = 30$ thousand;
$P = \$1900$ thousand
27. length $= 100$ in., width $= 100$ in., height $= 50$ in.
29. $x = 15$ thousand, $y = 24$ thousand;
$P = \$295$ thousand
31. (a) eat-in $= 2400$; take-out $= 3800$
   (b) eat-in @ \$3.60; take-out @ \$3.10; max profit $=$
   \$12,480
   (c) Change pricing; more profitable
33. (a) $\hat{y} = 0.81x - 2400$
   (b) $m = 0.81$; means that for every \$1 that males earn, females earn about \$0.81.
   (c) The slope would probably be smaller. Equal pay for women for equal work is not yet a reality, but much progress has been made since 1965.
35. (a) $\hat{y} = 0.06254x + 6.191$, x in years past 2000, $\hat{y}$ in billions
   (b) 7.317 billion
   (c) World population is changing about 0.06254 billion persons per year past 2000.

14.5 EXERCISES

1. 18 at $(3, 3)$ **3.** 35 at $(3, 2)$ **5.** 32 at $(4, 2)$
7. -28 at $\left(3, \frac{5}{2}\right)$ **9.** 15 at $(5, 3)$
11. 3 at $(1, 1, 1)$ **13.** 1 at $(0, 1, 0)$
15. $x = 2, y = 2$
17. $x = 40, y = \frac{40}{3}$

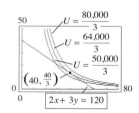

19. (a) $x = 400, y = 400$
   (b) $-\lambda = 1.6$; means that each additional dollar spent on production results in approximately 1.6 additional units produced.
   (c)

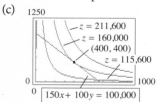

21. $x = 900, y = 300$; 900 units at plant X, 300 units at plant Y
23. $x = \$10,003.33, y = \$19,996.67$
25. length $= 100$ cm, width $= 100$ cm, height $= 50$ cm

CHAPTER 14 REVIEW EXERCISES

1. $\{(x, y): x \text{ and } y \text{ are real numbers and } y \neq 2x\}$
2. $\{(x, y): x \text{ and } y \text{ are real numbers with } y \geq 0 \text{ and } (x, y) \neq (0, 0)\}$
3. -5 **4.** 896,000
5. $15x^2 + 6y$ **6.** $24y^3 - 42x^3y^2$
7. $z_x = 8xy^3 + 1/y$; $z_y = 12x^2y^2 - x/y^2$

8. $z_x = x/\sqrt{x^2 + 2y^2}$; $z_y = 2y/\sqrt{x^2 + 2y^2}$
9. $z_x = -2y/(xy + 1)^3$; $z_y = -2x/(xy + 1)^3$
10. $z_x = 2xy^3 e^{x^2y^3}$; $z_y = 3x^2y^2 e^{x^2y^3}$
11. $z_x = ye^{xy} + y/x$; $z_y = xe^{xy} + \ln x$
12. $z_x = y$; $z_y = x$ **13.** -8 **14.** 8
15. (a) $2y$ (b) 0   (c) $2x - 3$ (d) $2x - 3$
16. (a) $18xy^4 - 2/y^2$ (b) $36x^3y^2 - 6x^2/y^4$
   (c) $36x^2y^3 + 4x/y^3$ (d) $36x^2y^3 + 4x/y^3$
17. (a) $2e^{y^2}$ (b) $4x^2y^2e^{y^2} + 2x^2e^{y^2}$
   (c) $4xye^{y^2}$ (d) $4xye^{y^2}$
18. (a) $-y^2/(xy + 1)^2$ (b) $-x^2/(xy + 1)^2$
   (c) $1/(xy + 1)^2$ (d) $1/(xy + 1)^2$
19. max$(-8, 16, 208)$
20. saddles at $(2, -3, 38)$ and $(-2, 3, -38)$; min at $(2, 3, -70)$; max at $(-2, -3, 70)$
21. 80 at $(2, 8)$
22. 11,664 at $(6, 3)$
23. (a) $x^2y = 540$ (b) 3 units
24. (a) \$46,204
   (b) When the monthly contribution is \$250 and the interest rate is 7.8%, the accumulated value is about \$143,648.
   (c) When the contribution is \$250, if the interest rate changed from 7.8% to 8.8%, the approximate change in the account would be \$17,770.
   (d) $A_R \approx 574.59$ means that with an interest rate of 7.8%, if the monthly contribution changed from \$250 to \$251, the approximate change in the accumulated value would be \$574.59.
25. (a) 8.996 thousand, or \$8996
   (b) 0.009; means that when the benefits are paid for 20 years, if the account value changes from 1000 to 1001 (thousand dollars), the monthly benefit increases by about 0.009 (thousand), or \$9.
   (c) -0.161; means that when the account value is \$1,000,000, if the duration of benefits changes from 20 to 21 years, the monthly benefit decreases by about \$161.
26. (a) If selling price is fixed, more dollars spent for advertising will increase sales.
   (b) If advertising dollars are fixed, an increase in the selling price will decrease sales.
27. (a) 280 dollars per unit of x
   (b) $2400/7$ dollars per unit of y
28. $\partial Q/\partial K = 81.92$ means that when capital expenditures increase by \$1000 (to \$626,000) and work-hours remain at 4096, output will change by about 8192 units; $\partial Q/\partial L = 37.5$ means that when labor hours change by 1 (to 4097) and capital expenditures remain at \$625,000, output will change by about 3750 units.
29. (a) -2 (b) -6 (c) complementary
30. competitive
31. $x = 20, y = 40$; $P = \$2000$
32. 200 units at plant I; 1500 units at plant II
33. $x = 10, y = 4$
34. (a) $x = 1000, y = 500$

(b) $-\lambda \approx 3.17$; means that each additional dollar spent on production results in approximately 3 additional units.

(c)

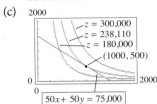

35. (a) $\hat{y} = 2375x + 39,630$ (b) $75,255
36. (a) $\hat{y} = 0.736x + 28.4$
    (b) $m = 0.736$ means for every 1000 women entering the workforce, there are about 736 men entering it.

CHAPTER 14 TEST

1. (a) all pairs (x, y) with $y < x^2$ (b) 14
2. $z_x = 5 + 10y(xy + 1)^4$ $z_y = -18y + 10x(xy + 1)^4$
    $z_{xx} = 40y^2(xy + 1)^3$ $z_{yy} = -18 + 40x^2(xy + 1)^3$
    $z_{xy} = z_{yx} = 10(5xy + 1)(xy + 1)^3$
3. $(0, 2)$, a relative minimum; $(4, -6)$ and $(-4, -6)$, saddle points
4. (a) $1625 thousand
    (b) 73.11; means that if capital investment increases from $10,000 to $11,000, the approximate change

in monthly production value will be $73.11 thousand, if labor hours remain at 1590.

(c) 0.56; means that if labor hours increase by 1 to 1591, the approximate change in monthly production value will be $0.56 thousand, if capital investment remains at $10,000.

5. (a) When $94,500 is borrowed for 25 years at 7%, the monthly payment is $667.91.
    (b) If the percent goes from 7% to 8%, the approximate change in the monthly payment is $60.28, if the loan amount remains at $94,500 for 25 years.
    (c) Negative. If the loan amount remains at $94,500 and the percent remains at 7%, increasing the time to pay off the loan will decrease the monthly payment, and vice versa.
6. $8xy\, e^{x^2y^2}(x^2y^2 + 1)$
7. Find $\dfrac{\partial q_1}{\partial p_2}$ and $\dfrac{\partial q_2}{\partial p_1}$ and compare their signs. Both positive means competitive. Both negative means complementary. These products are complementary.
8. $x = $7, y = $11; P = 5065
9. $x = 200, y = 100$
10. (a) $\hat{y} = 0.24x + 5.78$
    (b) The fit is excellent.
    (c) 16.6%

Index

Social Science